SECOND EDITION

Encyclopedia of
Cancer

VOLUME III   L - Q

SECOND EDITION

Encyclopedia of Cancer

VOLUME III   L - Q

Editor-in-Chief

Joseph R. Bertino
The Cancer Institute of New Jersey
Robert Wood Johnson Medical School
New Brunswick, New Jersey

ACADEMIC PRESS
An imprint of Elsevier Science

Amsterdam   Boston   London   New York   Oxford   Paris   San Diego   San Francisco   Singapore   Sydney   Tokyo

This book is printed on acid-free paper. ∞

Academic Press
An imprint of Elsevier Science
525 B Street, Suite 1900, San Diego, California 92101-4495, USA
http://www.academicpress.com

Academic Press
84 Theobalds Road, London WC1X 8RR, UK
http://www.academicpress.com

Library of Congress Catalog Card Number: 2002102352

International Standard Book Number: 0-12-227555-1 (set)
International Standard Book Number: 0-12-227556-X (Volume 1)
International Standard Book Number: 0-12-227557-8 (Volume 2)
International Standard Book Number: 0-12-227558-6 (Volume 3)
International Standard Book Number: 0-12-227559-4 (Volume 4)

PRINTED IN THE UNITED STATES OF AMERICA
02   03   04   05   06   07   MM   9   8   7   6   5   4   3   2   1

Contents

VOLUME I

A

VOLUME II

D

Contents by Subject Area

VIRAL CARCINOGENESIS

Contributors

Sanjiv S. Agarwala
University of Pittsburgh Cancer Institute
Melanoma: Epidemiology

Siamak Agha-Mohammadi
University of Pittsburgh
Cytokine Gene Therapy

Jaffer A. Ajani
University of Texas M. D. Anderson Cancer
Center
Gastric Cancer: Epidemiology and Therapy

Anthony P. Albino
The American Health Foundation
Multistage Carcinogenesis

Jeffry R. Alger
University of California, Los Angeles Medical
Center
Brain Cancer and Magnetic Resonance Spectroscopy

Robert Amato
Baylor College of Medicine
Testicular Cancer

Howard Amols
Memorial Sloan-Kettering Cancer Center
*Dosimetry and Treatment Planning for
Three-Dimensional Radiation Therapy*

Darrell E. Anderson
Scientific Consulting Group, Inc., Gaithersburg,
Maryland
*Cancer Risk Reduction (Diet/Smoking
Cessation/Lifestyle Changes)*

Cristina R. Antonescu
Memorial Sloan-Kettering Cancer Center
TLS-CHOP in Myxoid Liposarcoma

Wadih Arap
University of Texas M. D. Anderson Cancer Center
Vascular Targeting

Ralph B. Arlinghaus
University of Texas M. D. Anderson Cancer
Center
BCR/ABL

Georg Aue
University of Pennsylvania School of Medicine
Antisense Nucleic Acids: Clinical Applications

Nicholas R. Bachur
University of Maryland Cancer Center
Anthracyclines

Richard Barakat
Memorial Sloan-Kettering Cancer Center
Endometrial Cancer

Fred G. Barker II
Massachusetts General Hospital
*Brain Tumors: Epidemiology and Molecular and
Cellular Abnormalities*

Frederic G. Barr
University of Pennsylvania School of Medicine
*PAX3–FKHR and PAX7–FKHR Gene Fusions in
Alveolar Rhabdomyosarcoma*

Michael T. Barrett
Fred Hutchinson Cancer Research Center
*Esophageal Cancer: Risk Factors and
Somatic Genetics*

P. Leif Bergsagel
Weill Medical College of Cornell University
Multiple Myeloma

Leslie Bernstein
University of Southern California Keck School of
Medicine
*Non-Hodgkin's Lymphoma and Multiple Myeloma:
Incidence and Risk Factors*

Sandra H. Bigner
Duke University Medical Center
Genetic Alterations in Brain Tumors

R. Michael Blaese
ValiGen, Inc., Newtown, Pennsylvania
Suicide Genes

Eda T. Bloom
U.S. Food and Drug Administration
Gene Therapy Vectors, Safety Considerations

Clara D. Bloomfield
Roswell Park Cancer Institute
Chromosome Aberrations

Peter Blume-Jensen
Serono Reproductive Biology Institute
Kinase-Regulated Signal Transduction Pathways
*Signal Transduction Mechanisms Initiated by Receptor
Tyrosine Kinases*

Paolo Boffetta
International Agency for Research on Cancer,
Lyon, France
Lung, Larynx, Oral Cavity, and Pharynx

Melissa Bondy
University of Texas M. D. Anderson Cancer
Center
Brain and Central Nervous System Cancer

David Boothman
University of Wisconsin–Madison
Radiation Resistance

Ernest C. Borden
Taussig Cancer Center
*Interferons: Cellular and Molecular Biology of
Their Actions*

George J. Bosl
Memorial Sloan-Kettering Cancer Center
Germ Cell Tumors

Marc E. Bracke
Ghent University Hospital
Molecular Mechanisms of Cancer Invasion

Patrick J. Brennan
University of Pennsylvania School of Medicine
Her2/neu

Ricardo R. Brentani
Ludwig Institute for Cancer Research,
Sao Paulo
Cell–Matrix Interactions

Norman E. Breslow
University of Washington, Seattle
Wilms Tumor: Epidemiology

Ronald Breslow
Columbia University
*Differentiation and the Role of Differentiation
Inducers in Cancer Treatment*

Jacqueline F. Bromberg
Memorial Sloan-Kettering Cancer Center
STAT Proteins in Growth Control

Steven J. Burakoff
Dana-Farber Cancer Institute
T Cells and Their Effector Functions

Barbara Burtness
Yale Univesity School of Medicine
Head and Neck Cancer

Anna Butturini
Children's Hospital of Los Angeles
BCR/ABL

Blake Cady
Brown University School of Medicine
Endocrine Tumors

José Campione-Piccardo
National Laboratory for Viral Oncology, Canada
Viral Agents

Judith Campisi
Lawrence Berkeley National Laboratory
Senescence, Cellular

Eli Canaani
Kimmel Cancer Center
ALL-1

France Carrier
University of Maryland
Ataxia Telangiectasia Syndrome

JoAnn C. Castelli
University of California, San Francisco
HIV (Human Immunodeficiency Virus)

Webster K. Cavenee
University of California, San Diego
PTEN

R. S. K. Chaganti
Memorial Sloan-Kettering Cancer Center
Germ Cell Tumors

Roger Chammas
Ludwig Institute for Cancer Research,
Sao Paulo
Cell–Matrix Interactions

Paul B. Chapman
Memorial Sloan-Kettering Cancer Center
Anti-idiotypic Antibody Vaccines

Irvin S. Y. Chen
University of California, Los Angeles School of
Medicine
Human T-Cell Leukemia/Lymphotropic Virus

Seng H. Cheng
Genzyme Corporation, Framingham,
Massachusetts
Cationic Lipid-Mediated Gene Therapy

David A. Cheresh
The Scripps Research Institute
Integrin-Targeted Angiostatics

Rajas Chodankar
University of Southern California Keck School
of Medicine
Ovarian Cancer: Molecular and Cellular Abnormalities

Ting-Chao Chou
Memorial Sloan-Kettering Cancer Center
Chemotherapy: Synergism and Antagonism

Edward Chu
Yale University School of Medicine
*Resistance to Inhibitor Compounds of
Thymidylate Synthase*

John A. Cidlowski
National Institute of Environmental Health Sciences
Corticosteroids

Lena Claesson-Welsh
Uppsala University
*Anti-Vascular Endothelial Growth
Factor-Based Angiostatics*

Bayard Clarkson
Memorial Sloan-Kettering Cancer Center
*Chronic Myelogenous Leukemia: Etiology, Incidence,
and Clincal Features*
*Chronic Myelogenous Leukemia: Prognosis and
Current Status of Treatment*

Jack S. Cohen
The Hebrew University
*Magnetic Resonance Spectroscopy and Magnetic
Resonance Imaging, Introduction*

Peter Cole
Cancer Institute of New Jersey
Folate Antagonists

Susan P. C. Cole
Queen's University, Canada
Multidrug Resistance II: MRP and Related Proteins

Jerry M. Collins
U.S. Food and Drug Administration
PET Imaging and Cancer

O. Michael Colvin
Duke University
Akylating Agents

Raymond L. Comenzo
Memorial Sloan-Kettering Cancer Center
Stem Cell Transplantation

Abigail A. Conley
The Mayo Clinic
*Pancreatic Cancer: Cellular and
Molecular Mechanisms*

Louis Constine
University of Rochester Medical Center
Late Effects of Radiation Therapy

Leslie C. Costello
University of Maryland, Baltimore
*Metabolic Diagnosis of Prostate Cancer by Magnetic
Resonance Spectroscopy*

Wendy Cozen
University of Southern California Keck School of
Medicine
*Non-Hodgkin's Lymphoma and Multiple Myeloma:
Incidence and Risk Factors*

Carlo M. Croce
Kimmel Cancer Center
ALL-1

Stanley T. Crooke
Isis Pharmaceuticals, Inc.
*Antisense: Progress toward Gene-Directed
Cancer Therapy*

Lloyd A. Culp
Case Western Reserve University School
of Medicine
*Extracellular Matrix and Matrix Receptors:
Alterations during Tumor Progression*

Thomas J. Cummings
Duke University Medical Center
Genetic Alterations in Brain Tumors

David T. Curiel
University of Alabama at Birmingham
Targeted Vectors for Cancer Gene Therapy

Tom Curran
St. Jude Children's Research Hospital
fos Oncogene

George Q. Daley
Whitehead Institute
Cytokines: Hematopoietic Growth Factors

Chi V. Dang
The Johns Hopkins University School of
Medicine
c-myc Protooncogene

James E. Darnell, Jr.
Rockefeller University
STAT Proteins in Growth Control

Michael David
University of California, San Diego
Jak/STAT Pathway

Roger G. Deeley
Queen's University, Canada
*Multidrug Resistance II: MRP and
Related Proteins*

Samuel R. Denmeade
Johns Hopkins University School of Medicine
Hormone Resistance in Prostate Cancer

Christopher T. Denny
University of California, Los Angeles School
of Medicine
EWS/ETS Fusion Genes

Channing J. Der
University of North Carolina at Chapel Hill
Ras Proteins

Mark W. Dewhirst
Duke University Medical Center
Hyperthermia

Frederick A. Dick
Massachusetts General Hospital Cancer Center
Retinoblastoma Tumor Suppressor Gene

John P. Dileo
University of Pittsburgh
Liposome-Mediated Gene Therapy

Eugene P. DiMagno
The Mayo Clinic
Pancreatic Cancer: Cellular and Molecular Mechanisms

Clark W. Distelhorst
Case Western Reserve University
Steroid Hormones and Hormone Receptors

Ethan Dmitrovsky
Dartmouth Medical School
Chemoprevention, Pharmacology of

M. Eileen Dolan
University of Chicago
Resistance to DNA-Damaging Agents

Alessia Donadio
Memorial Sloan-Kettering Cancer Center
Germ Cell Tumors

Zhongyun Dong
University of Texas M. D. Anderson Cancer
Center
Macrophages

Harold O. Douglass, Jr.
Roswell Park Cancer Institute
Pancreas and Periampullary Tumors

Louis Dubeau
University of Southern California Keck School
of Medicine
*Ovarian Cancer: Molecular and
Cellular Abnormalities*

Anita K. Dunbier
University of Otago
Gastric Cancer: Inherited Predisposition

Nicholas J. Dyson
Massachusetts General Hospital Cancer Center
Retinoblastoma Tumor Suppressor Gene

Timothy J. Eberlein
Washington University School of Medicine,
St. Louis
T Cells against Tumors

Randa El-Zein
University of Texas M. D. Anderson Cancer
Center
Brain and Central Nervous System Cancer

Elaine A. Elion
Harvard Medical School
MAP Kinase Modules in Signaling

Volker Ellenreider
The Mayo Clinic
Pancreatic Cancer: Cellular and Molecular Mechanisms

Paul F. Engstrom
Fox Chase Cancer Center
Hepatocellular Carcinoma (HCC)

Zelig Eshhar
Weizmann Institute of Science
Antibodies in the Gene Therapy of Cancer

Conrad B. Falkson
McMaster University
Malignant Mesothelioma

Geoffrey Falkson
University of Pretoria
Malignant Mesothelioma

Gerold Feuer
State University of New York Upstate
Medical University
Human T-Cell Leukemia/Lymphotropic Virus

Isaiah J. Fidler
University of Texas M. D. Anderson Cancer
Center
Macrophages

Mary E. Fidler
The Mayo Foundation
Renal Cell Cancer

Richard Fishel
Thomas Jefferson University
*Hereditary Colon Cancer and DNA
Mismatch Repair*

David FitzGerald
National Cancer Institute
*Antibody–Toxin and Growth Factor–Toxin
Fusion Proteins*

Hernan Flores-Rozas
Ludwig Institute for Cancer Research
Mismatch Repair: Biochemistry and Genetics

Albert J. Fornace Jr.
National Cancer Institute
Ataxia Telangiectasia Syndrome

Ruben C. Fragoso
Dana-Farber Cancer Institute
T Cells and Their Effector Functions

Thomas S. Frank
Myriad Genetic Laboratories, Salt Lake City
*Hereditary Risk of Breast and Ovarian
Cancer: BRCA1 and BRCA2*

R. B. Franklin
University of Maryland, Baltimore
*Metabolic Diagnosis of Prostate Cancer by Magnetic
Resonance Spectroscopy*

Eric O. Freed
National Institute of Allergy and Infectious
Diseases
Retroviruses

Michael L. Freeman
Vanderbilt University School of Medicine
Hyperthermia

Krystyna Frenkel
New York University School of Medicine
*Carcinogenesis: Role of Active Oxygen and Nitrogen
Species*

Frank B. Furnari
University of California, San Diego
PTEN

Robert Peter Gale
Center for Advanced Studies in Leukemia,
Los Angeles
BCR/ABL

Susan Gapstur
Arizona Cancer Center and Southern Arizona
VA Health Care System
*Nutritional Supplements and Diet as
Chemoprevention Agents*

Lawrence B. Gardner
The Johns Hopkins University School of
Medicine
c-myc Protooncogene

Harinder Garewal
Arizona Cancer Center and Southern Arizona
VA Health Care System
*Nutritional Supplements and Diet as
Chemoprevention Agents*

James E. Gervasoni, Jr.
Robert Wood Johnson Medical School
Endocrine Tumors

Pär Gerwins
Uppsala University
*Anti-Vascular Endothelial Growth
Factor-Based Angiostatics*

Alan M. Gewirtz
University of Pennsylvania School
of Medicine
Antisense Nucleic Acids: Clinical Applications

John F. Gibbs
Roswell Park Cancer Institute
Pancreas and Periampullary Tumors

Anna Giuliano
Arizona Cancer Center and Southern Arizona
VA Health Care System
*Nutritional Supplements and Diet as
Chemoprevention Agents*

R. A. Gjerset
Sidney Kimmel Cancer Center
p53 Gene Therapy

Peter S. Goedegebuure
Washington University School of Medicine,
St. Louis
T Cells against Tumors

Jason S. Gold
Memorial Sloan-Kettering Cancer Center
Cell-Mediated Immunity to Cancer

Ashwin Gollerkeri
Yale University School of Medicine
*Resistance to Inhibitor Compounds of
Thymidylate Synthase*

Jesús Gómez-Navarro
University of Alabama at Birmingham
Targeted Vectors for Cancer Gene Therapy

Ellen L. Goode
University of Washington
Genetic Predisposition to Prostate Cancer

Richard Gorlick
Memorial Sloan-Kettering Cancer Center
Bone Tumors

Kathleen Heppner Goss
University of Cincinnati College of Medicine
*APC (Adenomatous Polyposis Coli) Tumor
Suppressor*

Michael M. Gottesman
National Cancer Institute
Multidrug Resistance I: P-Glycoprotein

Joseph P. Grande
The Mayo Foundation
*Kidney, Epidemiology
Renal Cell Cancer*

Ellen Graver
Arizona Cancer Center and Southern Arizona
VA Health Care System
*Nutritional Supplements and Diet as
Chemoprevention Agents*

F. Anthony Greco
Sarah Cannon–Minnie Pearl Cancer Center
Neoplasms of Unknown Primary Site

Mark I. Greene
University of Pennsylvania
School of Medicine
Her2/neu

Peter Greenwald
National Cancer Institute
*Cancer Risk Reduction (Diet/Smoking
Cessation/Lifestyle Changes)*

John R. Griffiths
St. George's Hospital Medical School, London
*Magnetic Resonance Spectroscopy of Cancer: Clinical
Overview*

Joanna Groden
University of Cincinnati College of Medicine
*APC (Adenomatous Polyposis Coli)
Tumor Suppressor*

Jun-Lin Guan
Cornell University College of
Veterinary Medicine
Integrin Receptor Signaling Pathways

Udayan Guha
Albert Einstein Cancer Center
Transgenic Mice in Cancer Research

Parry J. Guilford
University of Otago
Gastric Cancer: Inherited Predisposition

Anjali Gupta
University of Pennsylvania Hospital
Molecular Aspects of Radiation Biology

John D. Hainsworth
Sarah Cannon–Minnie Pearl Cancer Center
Neoplasms of Unknown Primary Site

Joshua W. Hamilton
Dartmouth Medical School
Chemical Mutagenesis and Carcinogenesis

Joyce L. Hamlin
University of Virginia School of Medicine
Drug Resistance: DNA Sequence Amplification

Kenneth R. Hande
Vanderbilt University School of Medicine
Purine Antimetabolites

J. Marie Hardwick
Johns Hopkins School of Public Health
Caspases in Programmed Cell Death

Louis B. Harrison
Beth Israel Medical Center
Brachytherapy

Lynda K. Hawkins
Genetic Therapy Institute, Gaithersburg, Maryland
Replication-Selective Viruses for Cancer Treatment

Lifeng He
Albert Einstein College of Medicine
*Taxol and Other Molecules That Interact
with Microtubules*

Stephen S. Hecht
University of Minnesota Cancer Center
Tobacco Carcinogenesis

Ingegerd Hellström
Pacific Northwest Research Institute
Tumor Antigens

Karl Erik Hellström
Pacific Northwest Research Institute
Tumor Antigens

Kurt J. Henle
University of Arkansas for Medical Sciences
Hyperthermia

Meenhard Herlyn
The Wistar Institute
Melanoma: Biology

Masao Hirose
Nagoya City University Medical School
*Antioxidants: Carcinogenic and Chemopreventive
Properties*

Dah H. Ho
University of Texas M. D. Anderson Cancer
Center
L-Asparaginase

Samuel B. Ho
University of Minnesota Medical School
Glycoproteins and Glycosylation Changes in Cancer

F. Stephen Hodi
Dana-Farber Cancer Institute
Interleukins

Kyle Holen
Memorial Sloan-Kettering Cancer Center
Colorectal Cancer: Epidemiology and Treatment

Julianne L. Holleran
Case Western Reserve University School
of Medicine
*Extracellular Matrix and Matrix Receptors:
Alterations during Tumor Progression*

Waun Ki Hong
University of Texas M. D. Anderson Cancer
Center
Chemoprevention Trials

Susan Band Horwitz
Albert Einstein College of Medicine
*Taxol and Other Molecules That Interact
with Microtubules*

Alan N. Houghton
Memorial Sloan-Kettering Cancer Center
Cell-Mediated Immunity to Cancer
DNA-Based Cancer Vaccines

Jane Houldsworth
Memorial Sloan-Kettering Cancer Center
Germ Cell Tumors

Franklyn A. Howe
St. George's Hospital Medical School,
London
*Magnetic Resonance Spectroscopy of Cancer:
Clinical Overview*

H.-J. Su Huang
University of California, San Diego
PTEN

Leaf Huang
University of Pittsburgh
Liposome-Mediated Gene Therapy

James Hulit
Albert Einstein Cancer Center
Transgenic Mice in Cancer Research

Tony Hunter
The Salk Institute
Kinase-Regulated Signal Transduction Pathways
*Signal Transduction Mechanisms Initiated by Receptor
Tyrosine Kinases*

Mark D. Hurwitz
Harvard Medical School
Bladder Cancer: Assessment and Management

David H. Ilson
Memorial Sloan-Kettering Cancer Center
Esophageal Cancer: Treatment

Katsumi Imaida
Nagoya City University Medical School
*Antioxidants: Carcinogenic and
Chemopreventive Properties*

Harry L. Ioachim
Lenox Hill Hospital
Immune Deficiency: Opportunistic Tumors

John T. Isaacs
Johns Hopkins University School of Medicine
Hormone Resistance in Prostate Cancer

Mark A. Israel
University of California, San Francisco
Brain Tumors: Epidemiology and Molecular and Cellular Abnormalities

Nobuyuki Ito
Nagoya City University Medical School
Antioxidants: Carcinogenic and Chemopreventive Properties

Helen A. James
University of East Anglia
Ribozymes and Their Applications

Gail P. Jarvik
University of Washington Medical Center
Genetic Predisposition to Prostate Cancer

Alan M. Jeffrey
Columbia University
Carcinogen–DNA Adducts

D. Joseph Jerry
University of Massachusetts, Amherst
TP53 Tumor Suppressor Gene: Structure and Function

Eric Johannsen
Harvard Medical School
Epstein–Barr Virus and Associated Malignancies

Ricky W. Johnstone
Peter MacCallum Cancer Institute, East Melbourne
P-Glycoprotein as a General Antiapoptotic Protein
Wilms Tumor Suppressor WT1

Douglas J. Jolly
Chiron Viagene, Inc., San Diego, California
Retroviral Vectors

Peter A. Jones
University of Southern California
DNA Methylation and Cancer

V. Craig Jordan
Northwestern University Medical School
Estrogens and Antiestrogens

Ellen D. Jorgensen
The American Health Foundation
Multistage Carcinogenesis

Jacqueline Jouanneau
Institut Curie
Tumor Cell Motility and Invasion

Raymond Judware
Case Western Reserve University School of Medicine
Extracellular Matrix and Matrix Receptors: Alterations during Tumor Progression

Joseph G. Jurcic
Memorial Sloan-Kettering Cancer Center
Monoclonal Antibodies: Leukemia and Lymphoma

Joanna Kaczynski
The Mayo Clinic
Pancreatic Cancer: Cellular and Molecular Mechanisms

William G. Kaelin, Jr.
Harvard Medical School
von Hippel–Lindau Disease

Dhananjaya V. Kalvakolanu
Greenebaum Cancer Center
Interferons: Cellular and Molecular Biology of Their Actions

Barton A. Kamen
Cancer Institute of New Jersey
Folate Antagonists

Mark P. Kamps
University of California, San Diego School of Medicine
Differentiation and Cancer: Basic Research

Gary D. Kao
University of Pennsylvania Hospital
Molecular Aspects of Radiation Biology

Johanne M. Kaplan
Genzyme Corporation, Framingham, Massachusetts
Cationic Lipid-Mediated Gene Therapy

Emmanuel Katsanis
University of Arizona
Neuroblastoma

Frederic J. Kaye
National Cancer Institute
Lung Cancer: Molecular and Cellular Abnormalities

Michael J. Keating
University of Texas M. D. Anderson Cancer Center
Chronic Lymphocytic Leukemia

David Kelsen
Cornell University Medical College
Esophageal Cancer: Treatment

Nancy Kemeny
Memorial Sloan-Kettering Cancer Center
Colorectal Cancer: Epidemiology and Treatment

Fadlo R. Khuri
University of Texas M. D. Anderson Cancer
Center
Chemoprevention Trials

Se Won Ki
University of California, San Diego
Cellular Responses to DNA Damage

Edward S. Kim
University of Texas M. D. Anderson Cancer
Center
Chemoprevention Trials

Young S. Kim
University of California, San Francisco
*Glycoproteins and Glycosylation Changes
in Cancer*

Sol Kimel
Sheba Medical Center, Israel
*Photodynamic Therapy: Basic Principles and
Applications to Skin Cancer*

Timothy Kinsella
University of Wisconsin–Madison
Radiation Resistance

John M. Kirkwood
University of Pittsburgh Cancer Institute
Melanoma: Epidemiology

David Kirn
Kirn Biopharmaceutical Consulting
*Replication-Selective Viruses for
Cancer Treatment*

Jan Kitajewski
Columbia University
Wnt Signaling

George Klein
Karolinska Institute
Tumor Suppressor Genes: Specific Classes

Priit Kogerman
Case Western Reserve University School
of Medicine
*Extracellular Matrix and Matrix Receptors:
Alterations during Tumor Progression*

Richard D. Kolodner
Ludwig Institute for Cancer Research
*Mismatch Repair: Biochemistry
and Genetics*

Genady Kostenich
Sheba Medical Center, Israel
*Photodynamic Therapy: Basic Principles and
Applications to Skin Cancer*

Robert J. Kreitman
National Cancer Institute
*Antibody–Toxin and Growth Factor–Toxin
Fusion Proteins*

J. Kurhanewicz
University of California, San Francisco
*Metabolic Diagnosis of Prostate Cancer by Magnetic
Resonance Spectroscopy*

Alexander E. Kuta
U.S. Food and Drug Administration
Gene Therapy Vectors, Safety Considerations

Mark Ladanyi
Memorial Sloan-Kettering Cancer Center
TLS-CHOP in Myxoid Liposarcoma

Michael M. C. Lai
University of Southern California Keck School
of Medicine
Hepatitis C Virus (HCV)

Wayne D. Lancaster
Wayne State University School of Medicine
Viral Agents

Jean-Baptiste Latouche
Memorial Sloan-Kettering Cancer Center
*Cancer Vaccines: Gene Therapy and Dendritic
Cell-Based Vaccines*

John S. Lazo
University of Pittsburgh
Bleomycin

Derek Le Roith
National Institutes of Health
Insulin-like Growth Factors

Jane S. Lebkowski
Applied Immune Sciences, Inc.,
Santa Clara, California
*Adeno-Associated Virus: A Vector for
High-Efficiency Gene Transduction*

Linda A. Lee
The Johns Hopkins University School
of Medicine
c-myc Protooncogene

Loïc Le Marchand
Cancer Research Center of Hawaii
Lung, Larynx, Oral Cavity, and Pharynx

Alexandra M. Levine
University of Southern California Keck School
of Medicine
*Neoplasms in Acquired
Immunodeficiency Syndrome*

Alexander Levitzki
The Hebrew University of Jerusalem
Protein Kinase Inhibitors

Jay A. Levy
University of California, San Francisco
HIV (Human Immunodeficiency Virus)

Runzhao Li
Medical University of South Carolina
ETS Family of Transcription Factors

Nicole T. Liberati
Duke University Medical Center
TGFβ Signaling Mechanisms

David C. Linehan
Washington University School of Medicine,
St. Louis
T Cells against Tumors

Stephen J. Lippard
Massachusetts Institute of Technology
Cisplatin and Related Drugs

Philip O. Livingston
Memorial Sloan-Kettering Cancer Center
Carbohydrate-Based Vaccines

Jay S. Loeffler
Harvard Medical School
Proton Beam Radiation Therapy

W. Thomas London
Fox Chase Cancer Center
Liver Cancer: Etiology and Prevention

Dan L. Longo
National Institute on Aging
Lymphoma, Non-Hodgkin's

Ti Li Loo
George Washington University Medical Center
L-Asparaginase

Michael T. Lotze
University of Pittsburgh
Cytokine Gene Therapy

Henry T. Lynch
Creighton University School of Medicine
*Colorectal Cancer: Molecular and
Cellular Abnormalities*

Wendy J. Mack
University of Southern California
Thyroid Cancer

Robert G. Maki
Memorial Sloan-Kettering Cancer Center
Sarcomas of Soft Tissue

David Malkin
University of Toronto School of Medicine
Li-Fraumeni Syndrome

Yael Mardor
Sheba Medical Center, Israel
*Magnetic Resonance Spectroscopy and Magnetic
Resonance Imaging, Introduction*

Marc M. Mareel
Ghent University Hospital
Molecular Mechanisms of Cancer Invasion

Paul A. Marks
Memorial Sloan-Kettering Cancer Center
*Differentiation and the Role of Differentiation
Inducers in Cancer Treatment*

Peter M. Mauch
Harvard Medical School
Lymphoma, Hodgkin's Disease

Harold M. Maurer
University of Nebraska Medical Center
Rhabdomyosarcoma, Early Onset

George Mavrothalassitis
University of Crete
ETS Family of Transcription Factors

William H. McBride
University of California, Los Angeles
Radiobiology, Principles of

Thomas S. McCormick
Case Western Reserve University
Steroid Hormones and Hormone Receptors

Charles J. McDonald
Brown University Medical School
Skin Cancer, Non-Melanoma

Sharon S. McDonald
Scientific Consulting Group, Inc.,
Gaithersburg, Maryland
*Cancer Risk Reduction (Diet/Smoking
Cessation/Lifestyle Changes)*

Clare H. McGowan
The Scripps Research Institute
Cell Cycle Checkpoints

Melissa S. McGrath
Memorial Sloan-Kettering Cancer Center
Resistance to Antibody Therapy

W. Gillies McKenna
University of Pennsylvania Hospital
Molecular Aspects of Radiation Biology

Paul M. J. McSheehy
St. George's Hospital Medical School, London
Magnetic Resonance Spectroscopy of Cancer:
  Clinical Overview

Peter W. Melera
University of Maryland School of Medicine
Resistance to Inhibitors of Dihydrofolate Reductase

Richard A. Messmann
National Cancer Institute
Targeted Toxins

Paul A. Meyers
Memorial Sloan-Kettering Cancer Center
Bone Tumors

Carson J. Miller
Case Western Reserve University School
  of Medicine
Extracellular Matrix and Matrix Receptors:
  Alterations during Tumor Progression

Amin Mirhadi
University of California, Los Angeles
Radiobiology, Principles of

Elizabeth Moran
Temple University School of Medicine
DNA Tumor Viruses: Adenovirus

Thomas Moritz
University of Essen Medical School
Transfer of Drug Resistance Genes to
  Hematopoietic Precursors

John C. Morris
National Cancer Institute
Suicide Genes

Krzysztof Mrózek
Roswell Park Cancer Institute
Chromosome Aberrations

Bijay Mukherji
University of Connecticut Health Center
Molecular Basis for Tumor Immunity

Annegret Müller
Thomas Jefferson University
Hereditary Colon Cancer and DNA
  Mismatch Repair

Karl Münger
Harvard Medical School
Papillomaviruses

Tatsuya Nakamura
Kimmel Cancer Center
ALL-1

Hector R. Nava
Roswell Park Cancer Institute
Pancreas and Periampullary Tumors

Andrea K. Ng
Harvard Medical School
Lymphoma, Hodgkin's Disease

Jac A. Nickoloff
University of New Mexico School of Medicine
Recombination: Mechanisms and Roles
  in Tumorigenesis

Garth L. Nicolson
Institute for Molecular Medicine
Autocrine and Paracrine Growth Mechanisms in
  Cancer Progression and Metastasis

John L. Nitiss
St. Jude Children's Research Hospital
Resistance to Topoisomerase-Targeting Agents

Karin C. Nitiss
St. Jude Children's Research Hospital
Resistance to Topoisomerase-Targeting Agents

Philip D. Noguchi
U.S. Food and Drug Administration
Gene Therapy Vectors, Safety Considerations

Shoichiro Ohta
University of California, San Francisco
Brain Tumors: Epidemiology and Molecular and
  Cellular Abnormalities

Arie Orenstein
Sheba Medical Center, Israel
Photodynamic Therapy: Basic Principles and
  Applications to Skin Cancer

George A. Orr
Albert Einstein College of Medicine
Taxol and Other Molecules That Interact
  with Microtubules

Keren Osman
Memorial Sloan-Kettering Cancer Center
Stem Cell Transplantation

Michelle A. Ozbun
University of New Mexico School of Medicine
TP53 Tumor Suppressor Gene: Structure
  and Function

Robert F. Ozols
Fox Chase Cancer Center
Ovarian Cancer: Epidemiology

Kevin W. Page
Applied Immune Sciences, Inc.,
Santa Clara, California
Adeno-Associated Virus: A Vector for High-Efficiency Gene Transduction

Tej Krishan Pandita
Columbia University
Telomeres and Telomerase

Renata Pasqualini
University of Texas M. D. Anderson Cancer Center
Vascular Targeting

Ira Pastan
National Cancer Institute
Antibody–Toxin and Growth Factor–Toxin Fusion Proteins

Frederica P. Perera
Mailman School of Public Health at Columbia University
Molecular Epidemiology and Cancer Risk

Richard G. Pestell
Albert Einstein Cancer Center
Transgenic Mice in Cancer Research

Anusch Peyman
Avetis Pharma Deutschland GmbH
Antisense: Medicinal Chemistry

Pieter Pil
Massachusetts Institute of Technology
Cisplatin and Related Drugs

Giuseppe Pizzorno
Yale University School of Medicine
Pyrimidine Antimetabolites

Miriam C. Poirier
National Cancer Institute
DNA Damage, DNA Repair, and Mutagenesis

Pamela M. Pollock
National Human Genome Research Institute
Melanoma: Molecular and Cellular Abnormalities

Randy Y. C. Poon
Hong Kong University of Science and Technology
Cell Cycle Control

Susan Preston-Martin
University of Southern California
Thyroid Cancer

Wendy Morse Pruitt
University of North Carolina at Chapel Hill
Ras Proteins

Amanda Psyrri
Yale University School of Medicine
Pyrimidine Antimetabolites

Harry Quon
Beth Israel Medical Center
Brachytherapy

Govindaswami Ragupathi
Memorial Sloan-Kettering Cancer Center
Carbohydrate-Based Vaccines

R. Beverly Raney
University of Texas M. D. Anderson Cancer Center
Rhabdomyosarcoma, Early Onset

Ritesh Rathore
Boston University School of Medicine
Vinca Alkaloids and Epipodophyllotoxins

Bandaru S. Reddy
American Health Foundation
Animal Models for Colon Cancer Chemoprevention

E. Premkumar Reddy
Fels Institute for Cancer Research and Molecular Biology
myb

John C. Reed
The Burnham Institute
Bcl-2 Family Proteins and the Dysregulation of Programmed Cell Death

Heinz R. Reiske
Cornell University College of Veterinary Medicine
Integrin Receptor Signaling Pathways

Victoria Richon
Memorial Sloan-Kettering Cancer Center
Differentiation and the Role of Differentiation Inducers in Cancer Treatment

Richard A. Rifkind
Memorial Sloan-Kettering Cancer Center
Differentiation and the Role of Differentiation Inducers in Cancer Treatment

Gert Rijksen
University Hospital, Utrecht, The Netherlands
Pyruvate Kinases

Paul F. Robbins
National Cancer Institute
Cancer Vaccines: Peptide- and Protein-Based Vaccines

Leslie Robinson-Bostom
Brown University Medical School
Skin Cancer, Non-Melanoma

Sara Rockwell
Yale University School of Medicine·
Hypoxia and Drug Resistance

Charles E. Rogler
Albert Einstein College of Medicine
Hepatitis B Viruses

Ronald K. Ross
University of Southern California/Norris
Comprehensive Cancer Center
Bladder Cancer: Epidemiology

Astrid A. Ruefli
Peter MacCallum Cancer Institute,
East Melbourne
P-Glycoprotein as a General Antiapoptotic Protein

N. Saadatmandi
Sidney Kimmel Cancer Center
p53 Gene Therapy

Michel Sadelain
Memorial Sloan-Kettering Cancer Center
*Cancer Vaccines: Gene Therapy and Dendritic
Cell-Based Vaccines*

Ajay Sandhu
Eastern Virginia Medical School
Late Effects of Radiation Therapy

Kapaettu Satyamoorthy
Manipal Academy of Higher Education, India
Melanoma: Biology

Edward A. Sausville
National Cancer Institute
Targeted Toxins

David A. Scheinberg
Memorial Sloan-Kettering Cancer Center
*Monoclonal Antibodies: Leukemia and Lymphoma
Resistance to Antibody Therapy*

Charles A. Schiffer
Barbara Ann Karmanos Cancer Institute
Acute Lymphoblastic Leukemia in Adults

Cornelius Schmaltz
Memorial Sloan-Kettering Cancer Center
Graft versus Leukemia and Graft versus Tumor Activity

John D. Schuetz
St. Jude Children's Research Hospital
*Genetic Basis for Quantitative and Qualitative
Changes in Drug Targets*

Nicholas T. Schulz
University of Pittsburgh School of Medicine
c-mos Protooncogene

Shelley Schwarzbaum
Weizmann Institute of Science
Antibodies in the Gene Therapy of Cancer

Andrew D. Seidman
Memorial Sloan-Kettering Cancer Center
Breast Cancer

Victor Sementchenko
Medical University of South Carolina
ETS Family of Transcription Factors

Arun Seth
University of Toronto
ETS Family of Transcription Factors

George Sgouros
Memorial Sloan-Kettering Cancer Center
Radiolabeled Antibodies, Overview

Brenda Shank
University of California, San Francisco
Total Body Irradiation

Navneet Sharda
University of Wisconsin–Madison
Radiation Resistance

Yang Shi
Harvard Medical School
Wilms Tumor Suppressor WT1

Kang Sup Shim
Thomas Jefferson University
*Hereditary Colon Cancer and DNA
Mismatch Repair*

James D. Shull
University of Nebraska Medical Center
Hormonal Carcinogenesis

William M. Siders
Genzyme Corporation, Framingham, Massachusetts
Cationic Lipid-Mediated Gene Therapy

Alfred R. Smith
Harvard Medical School
Proton Beam Radiation Therapy

Judy L. Smith
Roswell Park Cancer Institute
Pancreas and Periampullary Tumors

Thomas Smyrk
Creighton University School of Medicine
*Colorectal Cancer: Molecular and
Cellular Abnormalities*

Mark J. Smyth
Peter MacCallum Cancer Institute,
East Melbourne
P-Glycoprotein as a General Antiapoptotic Protein

Robert J. Soiffer
Dana-Farber Cancer Institute
Interleukins

Michael B. Sporn
Dartmouth Medical School
Chemoprevention, Pharmacology of

Gerard E. J. Staal
University Hospital, Utrecht, The Netherlands
Pyruvate Kinases

Patricia S. Steeg
National Cancer Institute
nm23 Metastasis Suppressor Gene

Peter G. Steinherz
Memorial Sloan-Kettering Cancer Center
Acute Lymphoblastic Leukemia in Children

M. I. Straub
Connecticut Veterans Administration
Medical Center
Carcinogen–DNA Adducts

Dwayne G. Stupack
The Scripps Research Institute
Integrin-Targeted Angiostatics

Michael Wei-Chih Su
Dana-Farber Cancer Institute
T Cells and Their Effector Functions

Hubert Szelényi
Weill Medical College of Cornell University
Multiple Myeloma

Chris H. Takimoto
University of Texas Health Science Center
Camptothecins

R. V. Tantravahi
Fels Institute for Cancer Research and Molecular
Biology
myb

Jean Paul Thiery
Institut Curie
Tumor Cell Motility and Invasion

Gian Paolo Tonini
National Institute for Cancer
Research, Genoa
Pediatric Cancers, Molecular Features

Timothy J. Triche
Keck School of Medicine at the University of
Southern California
Ewing's Sarcoma (Ewing's Family Tumors)

Donald L. Trump
University of Pittsburgh Medical Center
Prostate Cancer

Shigeki Tsuchida
Hirosaki University School of Medicine
Glutathione Transferases

Eugen Uhlmann
Aventis Pharma Deutschland GmbH
Antisense: Medicinal Chemistry

Raul Urrutia
The Mayo Clinic
*Pancreatic Cancer: Cellular and
Molecular Mechanisms*

Marcel R. M. van den Brink
Memorial Sloan-Kettering Cancer Center
*Graft versus Leukemia and Graft versus
Tumor Activity*

Catherine Van Poznak
Memorial Sloan-Kettering Cancer Center
Breast Cancer

Amelia M. Wall
St. Jude Children's Research Hospital
*Genetic Basis for Quantitative and Qualitative
Changes in Drug Targets*

Andrew D. Wallace
National Institute of Environmental Health Sciences
Corticosteroids

Fred Wang
Harvard Medical School
Epstein–Barr Virus and Associated Malignancies

Hwei-Gene Heidi Wang
Bristol Myers Squibb, Wallingford, Connecticut
DNA Tumor Viruses: Adenovirus

Jean Y. J. Wang
University of California, San Diego
Cellular Responses to DNA Damage

Xiao-Fan Wang
Duke University Medical Center
TGFβ Signaling Mechanisms

Carl F. Ware
La Jolla Institute for Allergy and Immunology
Tumor Necrosis Factors

Dennis K. Watson
Medical University of South Carolina
ETS Family of Transcription Factors

Pascal A. Oude Weernink
University Hospital, Utrecht,
   The Netherlands
Pyruvate Kinases

Alan B. Weitberg
Boston University School of Medicine
Vinca Alkaloids and Epipodophyllotoxins

Haim Werner
Tel Aviv University, Israel
Insulin-like Growth Factors

Ainsley Weston
National Institute for Occupational Safety and
   Health
DNA Damage, DNA Repair, and Mutagenesis

Luke Whitesell
University of Arizona
Neuroblastoma

Peter H. Wiernik
New York Medical College
Acute Myelocytic Leukemia

David W. Will
Avetis Pharma Deutschland GmbH
Antisense: Medicinal Chemistry

David A. Williams
Children's Hospital Medical Center
*Transfer of Drug Resistance Genes to
   Hematopoietic Precursors*

Jacqueline Williams
University of Rochester Medical Center
Late Effects of Radiation Therapy

Brian C. Wilson
Ontario Cancer Institute
Photodynamic Therapy: Clinical Applications

D. R. Wilson
Introgen Therapeutics, Inc.
p53 Gene Therapy

Jedd D. Wolchok
Memorial Sloan-Kettering Cancer Center
DNA-Based Cancer Vaccines

Margaret Wrensch
University of California, San Francisco
Brain and Central Nervous System Cancer

Yue Xiong
University of North Carolina at Chapel Hill
p16 and ARF: Crossroads of Tumorigenesis

Yoshiya Yamada
Memorial Sloan-Kettering Cancer Center
Stereotactic Radiosurgery of Intracranial Neoplasms

Chin-Rang Yang
University of Wisconsin–Madison
Radiation Resistance

Wendell G. Yarbrough
University of North Carolina at Chapel Hill
p16 and ARF: Crossroads of Tumorigenesis

James W. Young
Memorial Sloan-Kettering Cancer Center
*Cancer Vaccines: Gene Therapy and Dendritic
   Cell-Based Vaccines*

Mimi C. Yu
University of Southern California/Norris
   Comprehensive Cancer Center
Bladder Cancer: Epidemiology

Brad Zerler
Locus Discovery Inc., Blue Bell,
   Pennsylvania
DNA Tumor Viruses: Adenovirus

Dong-Er Zhang
The Scripps Research Institute
RUNX/CBF Transcription Factors

Foreword

Cancer, a most feared and morbid disease, is the second most common cause of mortality in the United States after cardiovascular disease. Clinical and research information with respect to cancer is expanding at an extraordinary rate. Keeping abreast of information relative to one's field, whether a clinician, researcher, student, or patient, is an increasing challenge. The *Encyclopedia of Cancer, Second Edition* organizes such information in a style that is highly effective and remarkably useful. The encyclopedia will be a source of great assistance to general practitioners, cancer specialists, and researchers and should be available in all institutional and private libraries. The editors and the contributors have been carefully selected for their outstanding credentials and should be congratulated for the excellence of the encyclopedia they produced.

Emil Frei
Director and Physician-in-Chief, Emeritus
Dana-Farber Cancer Institute
Professor of Medicine, Emeritus
Harvard Medical School

Preface

Since the last edition of the *Encyclopedia of Cancer*, there has been an amazing amount of new information published in the cancer research field. This second edition has attempted to capture these advances that have occurred in the etiology, prevention, and treatment of this disease. Accordingly, we have increased the coverage of topics, and the encyclopedia now requires four volumes instead of three volumes to accommodate the increase in articles.

Feedback about and reviews of the first edition have been positive, and this second edition builds on the format of the first edition. Our goal was to cover all aspects of cancer, from basic science to clinical application. A distinguished group of associate editors has provided topics to be covered, suggested authors for those topics, and reviewed the submitted manuscripts. Without them, this compendium would not have been possible. The authors chosen to write the articles are experts in their fields, and we are indebted to them for their contributions.

A major problem in organizing this effort was to avoid overlap of the material presented. While some redundancy is unavoidable, it also may be of interest to the reader to have a subject covered from more than one vantage point. We have limited references to a few key ones listed at the end of each article as a guide for further reading. The intent of the encyclopedia is not to provide a comprehensive, detailed review of each subject, but a concise exposition of the topic, directed toward the reader who would like information on topics outside of his or her expertise. Thus the encyclopedia should be especially useful as a reference for students, fellows in training, and educators.

I thank the many authors who made this second edition possible and the associate editors for their invaluable input. I also thank Craig Panner, Hilary Rowe, and Cindy Minor of Academic Press, who have been instrumental in bringing this effort to fruition.

Joseph R. Bertino

Guide to the Use of the Encyclopedia

The *Encyclopedia of Cancer, Second Edition* is a comprehensive summary of the field of cancer research. This reference work consists of four separate volumes and 220 different articles on various aspects of the disease of cancer, including its epidemiology, its treatment, and its molecular and genetic processes. Each article provides a comprehensive overview of the selected topic to inform a wide range of readers, from research professionals to students.

This *Encyclopedia of Cancer* is the second edition of an award-winning, widely used reference work first published six years ago. Dr. Joseph Bertino has served as Editor-in-Chief for both editions, and the Editorial Board has remained largely the same.

This new version provides a substantial revision of the first edition, reflecting the dynamic nature of cancer research. Of the 220 articles appearing here, more than 60% have been newly commissioned for this edition, and virtually all the others have been significantly rewritten, making this in effect more of an original work than a revision.

ORGANIZATION

The *Encyclopedia of Cancer* is organized to provide the maximum ease of use for its readers. All of the articles are arranged in a single alphabetical sequence by title. Articles whose titles begin with the letters A to Cm are in Volume 1, articles with titles from Co to K are in Volume 2, articles from L to Q to in Volume 3, and R to Z in Volume 4.

So that they can be easily located, article titles generally begin with the key word or phrase indicating the topic, with any descriptive terms following (e.g., "Radiobiology, Principles of" is the article title rather than "Principles of Radiobiology").

TABLE OF CONTENTS

A complete table of contents for the entire encyclopedia appears in the front of each volume. This list of article titles represents topics that have been carefully selected by Dr. Bertino and the members of the Editorial Board (see p. ii for a list of editors).

Following this list of articles by title is a second complete table of contents, in which the articles are listed alphabetically according to subject area. The *Encyclopedia of Cancer* provides coverage of twenty specific subject areas within the overall field of cancer, such as cell proliferation, drug resistance, gene therapy, oncogenes, tumor suppressor genes, and viral carcinogenesis.

INDEX

A subject index is located at the end of Volume 4. Consisting of more than 7,500 entries, this index is the most convenient way to locate a desired topic within the encyclopedia. The subjects in the index are listed alphabetically and indicate the volume and page number where information on this topic can be found.

ARTICLE FORMAT

Each new article in the *Encyclopedia of Cancer* begins at the top of a right-hand page so that it may be quickly located by the reader. The author's name and affiliation are displayed at the beginning of the article.

Each article in the encyclopedia is organized according to a standard format, as follows:

- Title and author
- Outline
- Glossary
- Defining paragraph
- Body of the article
- Cross-references
- Bibliography

OUTLINE

Each article begins with an outline indicating the content of the article to come. This outline provides a brief overview of the article so that the reader can get a sense of what is contained there without having to leaf through the pages. It also serves to highlight

important subtopics that will be discussed within the article (for example, risk factors in the article "Thyroid Cancer"). The outline is intended as an overview and thus it lists only the major headings of the article. In addition, extensive second-level and third-level headings will be found within the article.

GLOSSARY

The glossary contains terms that are important to an understanding of the article and that may be unfamiliar to the reader. Each term is defined in the context of the particular article in which it is used. Thus the same term may be defined in two or more articles, with the details of the definition varying slightly from one article to another. The encyclopedia includes approximately 1,700 glossary entries.

DEFINING PARAGRAPH

The text of each article begins with a single introductory paragraph that defines the topic under discussion and summarizes the content of the article. For example, the article "Camptothecins" begins with the following defining paragraph:

C amptothecin derivatives are a novel group of antitumor agents with clinical utility in the treatment of human malignancies, including colorectal, lung, and ovarian tumors. Camptothecins uniquely target topoisomerase I, an enzyme that catalyzes the relaxation of torsionally strained double-stranded DNA. Camptothecins stabilize the binding of topoisomerase I to DNA and, in the presence of ongoing DNA synthesis, can generate potentially lethal DNA damage.

CROSS-REFERENCES

Many of the articles in the encyclopedia have cross-references to other articles. These cross-references appear at the end of the article, following the article text and preceding the bibliography. The cross-references indicate related articles that can be consulted for further information on the same topic, or for other information on a related topic.

BIBLIOGRAPHY

The bibliography appears as the last element in an article. It lists recent secondary sources to aid the reader in locating more detailed or technical information. Review articles and research papers that are important to an understanding of the topic are also listed.

The bibliographies in this encyclopedia are for the benefit of the reader, to provide references for further research on the given topic. Thus they typically consist of a half-dozen to a dozen entries. They are not intended to represent a complete listing of all materials consulted by the author in preparing the article.

COMPANION WORKS

The *Encyclopedia of Cancer* is one of a series of multivolume references in the life sciences published by Academic Press/Elsevier Science. Other such works include the *Encyclopedia of Human Biology, Encyclopedia of Virology, Encyclopedia of Immunology, Encyclopedia of Microbiology, Encyclopedia of Reproduction, Encyclopedia of Stress,* and *Encyclopedia of Genetics.*

L-Asparaginase

Dah H. Ho
M. D. Anderson Cancer Center, Houston, Texas

Ti Li Loo
George Washington University Medical Center, Washington, DC

GLOSSARY:

apoptosis Programmed cell death or cell suicide. The process includes systemic degradation of DNA, chromatin condensation, cell shrinkage, and fragmentation.

anaphylaxis Hypersensitivity to drugs or foreign proteins. Anaphylaxis results in urticaria, pruritis, and angioedema, followed by vascular collapse and shock, and often leads to life-threatening respiratory distress.

half-life $t_{1/2}$ The time it takes for half the amount of a drug to leave the body.

volume of distribution A hypothetical volume of body fluid required to dissolve the total amount of drug at the same concentration as that found in the blood.

In the annals of developmental therapeutics, the story of the discovery of L-asparaginase (LAS, L-asparagine amidohydrolase, EC 3.5.1.1) and the ultimate establishment of LAS as a clinically active cancer chemotherapeutic agent make for fascinating and instructive reading. In 1953, Kidd reported that guinea pig serum caused the regression of certain transplantable rodent lymphomas. Eight years later, Broome identified LAS as the antitumor principle in the guinea pig serum. These observations were thought to represent a major breakthrough in experimental medicine: researchers believed that a magic bullet had finally been found, that a clear biochemical and metabolic difference had been demonstrated between the normal and the malignant cell that could be therapeutically exploited for cancer treatment. Unfortunately, this optimism was short-lived because further studies soon revealed that the difference between "normal" and "malignant" was essentially quantitative rather than qualitative. Nonetheless, subsequent clinical trials of LAS showed that the enzyme unquestionably had clinical activity. With its uncommon pharmacologic and therapeutic properties, LAS has therefore established itself as an important cancer chemotherapeutic agent, particularly as part of combination therapy for childhood lymphoid malignancies.

A ubiquitous naturally occurring enzyme, LAS cleaves asparagine to ammonia and aspartic acid. Another enzyme, asparagine synthetase (aspartate-ammonia ligase, EC 6.3.1.1), mediates the reverse reaction, with the amino group derived from glutamine. Both asparagine and aspartic acid are generally accepted as nonessential amino acids; in reality, however, asparagine is essential to certain lymphoid cancer cells for protein synthesis and survival. When these cells are exposed to an overwhelming supply of exogenous LAS with little or no asparagine synthetase activity, they are selectively killed through asparagine deletion. In some resistant cells, however, LAS may reactivate asparagine synthetase gene to restore the capacity of the cell to synthesize asparagine (see Section V).

For clinical applications, LAS is prepared from either *Escherichia coli (E. coli)* or *Erwinia chrysanthemi*. Further, to improve the antigenicity of LAS and to prolong its *in vivo* plasma half-life ($t_{1/2}$), the enzyme prepared from *E. coli* has been conjugated to polyethylene glycol (peg) to form pegLAS. Pharmacologically, therapeutically, and immunologically, the three LAS preparations (*E. coli*, *Erwinia*, and pegLAS) are not equivalent; hence, in cases of severe LAS allergy, an alternative preparation can be substituted with appropriate dose and schedule modifications (see Section IV).

The molecular mass of LAS ranges from 138,000 to 145,000 Da, depending on the source. The *E. coli* preparation is composed of four identical subunits, each with an active center. LAS also acts on glutamine to produce glutamic acid. However, asparagine is a far better substrate than is glutamine: the K_m value with asparagine, 10 μM, is almost 300-fold smaller than that with glutamine, 3000 μM. Nevertheless, glutamic acid and ammonia generated from glutamine hydrolysis may also contribute to the toxicity of LAS.

I. CLINICAL ASPECTS

LAS has significant activity against acute lymphocytic leukemia (ALL) and some lymphomas, but is not active against Hodgkins' lymphoma. Children respond better to treatment of LAS than adults. Used as a single agent, LAS produces impressively high response rates, but responses are transient, lasting only a few weeks. As a result, LAS is seldom given alone. When LAS is used for remission induction, consolidation, or intensification in patients with ALL, it is always used in combination with other drugs, typically prednisone and vincristine. Pediatric patients with newly diagnosed ALL treated with weekly LAS as part of intensification therapy had significantly better event-free survival than patients treated similarly but without LAS. Other advantages of LAS in combination chemotherapy are the lack of myelosuppression and absence of cross-resistance with the other component agents. LAS, especially in combination with cytarabine (ara-C), has additionally exhibited activity in treating myeloblastic leukemia in adults and children, but the response is less impressive.

The LAS dose and dosing schedule vary with the treatment protocol. With *E. coli* and *Erwinia* preparations, the LAS dose usually ranges from 10,000 to 50,000 IU/m². The typical pegLAS dose is 10 times lower. One international unit (IU) represents the amount of LAS required to generate 1 μmol of ammonia and aspartic acid from asparagine in 1 min under standard conditions. Because LAS is not absorbed intact from the gastrointestinal tract, this drug must be administered intravenously or intramuscularly. To reduce the risk of anaphylaxis, the intramuscular route is preferred.

Due to its potential to cause hypersensitivity reactions (see Section IV), LAS must be administered by experienced cancer chemotherapists in a hospital setting. Appropriate emergency measures, including those to maintain an adequate airway, should be readily at hand in case of any severe allergic response. A contact irritant, LAS must be handled carefully to avoid inhalation of the agent and contact of the agent with the skin and eyes. Freezing diminishes potency; LAS solution should be discarded after it has stood at 2 to 8° C for 8 h or if it becomes cloudy.

II. PHARMACODYNAMICS

After a single intramuscular administration of *E. coli* or *Erwinia* LAS (25,000 IU/m^2) or pegLAS (2500 IU/m^2), blood levels of asparagine become undetectable, i.e., below 1 μM, almost immediately. The duration of asparagine depletion varies with the enzyme source and ranges from 7 to 15 days with *Erwinia* LAS, from 14 to 23 days with *E. coli* LAS, and from 26 to 34 days with pegLAS. The duration of asparagine depletion also depends on the immunologic status of the patient. For example, asparagine depletion after treatment with *E. coli* LAS lasts from 7 to 10 days in enzyme-naïve patients but from 2 to 3 days in patients previously treated with the *E. coli* enzyme without hypersensitivity reactions.

LAS depletes asparagine in the plasma but also in the cerebrospinal fluid. Asparagine concentrations in the cerebrospinal fluid become undetectable, i.e., below 0.04 μM, in about 75% children who receive *E. coli* LAS 10,000 IU/m^2 intramuscularly three times weekly for six to nine doses, but asparagine returns to pretreatment levels upon discontinuing therapy. The pharmacodynamic effects of LAS are not limited to asparagine depletion. Significant changes in blood concentrations of other amino acids associated with asparagine are also evident. After *Erwinia* LAS administration, asparagine and glutamine concentrations are decreased on both days 2 and 3; in comparison, both aspartic acid and glutamic acid concentrations are increased on day 3. Concomitant blood LAS activities are no higher than 100 IU/L. The changes of these asparagine-related amino acids and the production of ammonia may play a part in LAS toxicity.

Asparagine depletion by LAS initially inhibits protein synthesis and subsequently inhibits nucleic acid synthesis. In cultures, the action of LAS is cell cycle specific and appears to arrest cells in G1 phase. DNA fragmentation finally leads to cell death by apoptosis, which was also seen in dogs with lymphoma treated with LAS.

III. PHARMACOKINETICS

Because LAS is a relatively large foreign protein molecule, it was not expected to be absorbed intact through the gastrointestinal tract, to have a long plasma $t_{1/2}$, to be distributed primarily within the intravascular space, to be cleared metabolically by some proteolytic processes, to be excreted in the urine, and to show antigenicity. All of these predictions have been born out experimentally.

A single intramuscular administration of LAS gives rise to plasma enzyme activity that peaks in 1 to 2 days for the *E. coli* preparation, in less than 1 day for the *Erwinia* preparation, and in 3 to 4 days for pegLAS; plasma enzyme activity for all three preparations is undetectable after 10 to 14 days. The average plasma $t_{1/2}$ of LAS varies from different sources: 1.2 days with the *E. coli* preparation, 0.7 day with the *Erwinia* preparation, and 5.7 days with pegLAS. In patients treated with pegLAS, but previously exhibiting hypersensitivity to the native enzyme, however, the plasma $t_{1/2}$ of LAS is significantly shortened to 1.8 days. The plasma $t_{1/2}$ of LAS is independent of the conventional dosage and the patients' age, gender, body surface area, diagnosis, disease status, and kidney and liver functions. Moreover, in patients treated with *E. coli* LAS 25,000 IU/m^2 weekly for at least 20 weeks, no difference in the plasma $t_{1/2}$ of LAS is seen among the first, middle, and last doses.

The apparent volume of distribution of LAS in children, 2.1 liter/m^2 or 53 ml/kg, is close to the volume of the plasma space, consistent with the notion that the drug is distributed within the intravascular space. In fact, after intravenous administration, LAS appears only slowly after about 3 h in the thoracic and cervical lymph, where its activity peaks at 20% of the concomitant plasma activity, and less than 1% of LAS in the cerebrospinal fluid.

Given the relatively small volume of distribution and comparatively long plasma $t_{1/2}$ of LAS, it is not surprising that LAS is cleared sluggishly and its total clearance averages 5.3 ml · h^{-1} · m^{-2} or 0.21 ml · h^{-1} · kg^{-1}. In patients hypersensitive to the *E. coli* preparation, native LAS is cleared more rapidly than pegLAS, as mentioned in the previous paragraph. Further, patients with high antibody titers to LAS clear the enzyme faster and show a higher response rate than patients with low titers. Exactly how LAS is cleared from the body is unknown. However, because it is a protein, probably LAS is primarily cleared by proteolysis and ultimately eliminated by the reticuloendothelial system. Only a very small proportion of LAS is excreted in the urine.

Because the three LAS preparations are not equivalent, close monitoring of LAS pharmacokinetics in each patient has been advocated to optimize the drug dosage and schedule in order to achieve the most favorable response.

IV. HYPERSENSITIVITY AND TOXICITY

A complex antigenic foreign protein capable of inhibiting macromolecular biosynthesis in cells that depend on asparagine for normal functioning and survival, LAS is endowed with certain immunologic and toxicologic properties unique among cancer chemotherapeutic agents. These characteristics are manifest in a variety of ways in the responses of patients to LAS therapy. Almost all patients react to LAS in some fashion sooner or later; however, pediatric patients tolerate the drug better than adults.

Although hypersensitivity to LAS occurs in fewer than 10% of treated patients, hypersensitivity reactions are serious, often immediate, and sometimes fatal. The reactions involve localized erythema, general urticaria, and pain at the injection site. Systemic allergic reactions consist of hypotension, bronchospasm, respiratory distress, and cardiac arrest—in short, frank anaphylaxis. Most of these immunologic side effects are encountered most commonly when LAS is used alone. The effects are reversible and subside upon cessation of LAS therapy. Repeated use of LAS raises the risk of sensitization. Skin and antibody tests are not helpful in predicting potential allergic reactions. Intramuscular administration is less likely to provoke antigenic attacks than the intravenous route. Fortunately, because of the lack of cross-immunoreactivity, *Erwinia* LAS is an apt substitute for *E. coli* LAS in pa-

tients with hypersensivity to the *E. coli* preparation. Finally, pegLAS is designed to be less antigenic and more slowly cleared from the body than native LAS and therefore can be substituted.

Most patients treated with LAS, especially older children and adults, experience nausea, vomiting, anorexia, fever, and chills. Unlike other anticancer agents, however, LAS has no effect on the oral mucosa, gastrointestinal tract, or hair follicles, nor does it cause serious myelosuppression. It is, therefore, a desirable component in combination chemotherapy protocols for treating lymphocytic malignancies.

Other side effects of LAS are directly or indirectly attributable to its inhibition of protein synthesis and, secondarily, nucleic acid synthesis. Diminished insulin biosynthesis is the most likely cause of the acute pancreatitis observed in some patients treated with LAS and evidenced by nausea, vomiting, abdominal pain, loss of appetite, hypoinsulinemia, hyperglycemia, and other diabetic symptoms. Hence, LAS is contraindicated in patients with a history of acute pancreatitis. Furthermore, a number of liver function tests may display abnormality, including increased alanine transaminase, aspartate transaminase, and alkaline phosphatase activities and a rise in serum bilirubin concentration. However, serum albumin, cholesterol, lipoprotein, uric acid, and fibrinogen concentrations may decrease. The last effect indicates impaired synthesis of clotting factors, which may be a prelude to serious thrombotic events.

One third of LAS-treated patients experienced central nervous system symptoms such as confusion, depression, lethargy, convulsion, and coma, reminiscent of ammonia intoxication. Reasons for these neurologic side effects remain obscure; these symptoms may be ascribable to brain depletion of asparagine or glutamine, or both.

V. DRUG RESISTANCE

Resistance to LAS therapy can occur through natural selection of a subpopulation of tumor cells with enhanced asparagine synthetase activity or through reactivation of the asparagine synthetase gene in response to a fall in intracellular asparagine activity. Another resistance mechanism is the development of antibody against LAS such that the immunologic clearance of LAS is hastened and its pharmacodynamic effects are reduced. Some patients have no overt allergic reactions even though their plasma LAS concentration is low. The phrase silent hypersensitivity has been coined to describe this phenomenon. The frequency of "silent hypersensitivity" occurrence may constitute a resistance mechanism.

VI. DRUG INTERACTIONS

Drug interactions are a serious concern with LAS because of its unusual immunologic and toxicologic characteristics. Nowadays LAS is seldom administered singly but rather is nearly always in combination with other antitumor drugs that may interact with LAS favorably or unfavorably, giving rise to synergism or antagonism. In addition, patients with cancer have complex medical problems that require the administration of multiple drugs, and LAS may interact with these drugs and create new problems. A case in point is that the concurrent use of LAS and anticoagulants such as warfarin causes coagulopathy and a heightened risk of bleeding in some patients. Anticancer agents like cyclophosphamide and dacarbazine are biotransformed by liver enzymes. Because LAS may interfere with the action of these drug-metabolizing enzymes, treatment with LAS may affect the therapeutic efficacies of cyclophosphamide and dacarbazine.

The most studied and best documented LAS interactions are those that occur with methotrexate (MTX) and ara-C. In the LAS–MTX interaction, the effect is exquisitely dependent on time and schedule; in other words, the outcome of LAS–MTX combination therapy hinges on the sequence and interval of drug administration. When LAS is given before MTX, LAS inhibits protein synthesis, impedes cell entry into the S phase of the cell cycle, and lessens cellular susceptibility to MTX. In addition, LAS pretreatment inhibits the formation of MTX polyglutamate and decreases cellular retention of this MTX metabolite. In contrast, when LAS is given after MTX, the combination is synergistic in experimental murine leukemia models. Studies with human leukemic lymphoblasts suggest that for optimal therapeutic effect, the interval between MTX and a subsequent dose of LAS

should be 24 h, and this MTX–LAS cycle should be repeated every 10 days. The key to success with the MTX–LAS regimen is escalation of the dose of MTX with successive cycles. The repeated use of this (MTX–LAS) tandem schedule permits the host to tolerate increasingly large doses of MTX. This cyclic treatment protocol has been used in the treatment of patients with relapsed ALL and is currently used as a part of therapy in the treatment of some newly diagnosed patients with ALL at a high risk.

Synergism between LAS and high-dose ara-C is likewise schedule dependent. Sequential high-dose ara-C followed by LAS has been shown to be highly effective in the reinduction of remission in adults and children with relapsed and refractory acute myeloblastic leukemia. LAS may reinforce the hyperglycemic effect of prednisone. Further, LAS in combination with vincristine may elicit cumulative neuropathy and erythropoietic dysfunction. When all three are used together to induce remission of ALL, it is advisable to administer LAS after the other two drugs because its pharmacodynamic effects last the longest.

VII. CONTRAINDICATIONS

Thus far it is clear that LAS should not be used in patients who have had a previous anaphylactic reaction to LAS or in the rare patients with acute pancreatitis or a history of pancreatitis. Use of LAS should also be avoided in patients with coagulation problems resulting from previous LAS therapy.

VIII. SUMMARY

LAS is a cancer chemotherapeutic agent particularly active against childhood ALL. LAS is usually used in combination with other agents for remission induction, consolidation, and intensification. LAS can cause serious allergic and toxic effects, and thus must be administered with great care.

Acknowledgments

Our sincere thanks to Drs. Robert L. Capizzi, Norman Jaffe, Irma Ramirez, and David Tubergen for reviewing the manuscript and their valuable comments, to Mrs. Olia Palmer for help with the literature search, and to Ms. Stephanie Deming for editing the manuscript.

See Also the Following Articles

Acute Lymphoblastic Leukemia

Bibliography

Aguayo, A., Cortes, J., Thomas, D., Pierce, S., Keating, M., and Kantarjian, H. (1999). Combination therapy with methotrexate, vincristine, polyethylene-glycol conjugated-asparaginase, and prednisone in the treatment of patients with refractory or recurrent acute lymphoblastic leukemia. *Cancer* **86,** 1203.

Asselin, B. L. (1999). The three asparaginases. Comparative pharmacology and optimal use in childhood leukemia. *Adv. Exp. Med. Biol.* **457,** 621.

Boos, J. (1997). Pharmacokinetics and drug monitoring of L-asparaginase treatment. *Int. J. Clin. Pharmacol. Ther.* **35,** 96.

Capizzi, R. L., Bertino, J. R., and Handschmacher, R. E. (1970). L-asparaginase. *Annu. Rev. Med.* **21,** 433.

Capizzi, R. L. (1981). Asparaginase-methotrexate in combination chemotherapy: Schedule-dependent differential effects on normal versus neoplastic cells. *Cancer Treat. Rep.* **65**(Suppl. 4), 115.

Cappizi, R. L. (1993). Asparaginase revisited. *Leukemia Lymphoma* **10**(Suppl.), 147.

Capizzi, R. L., Davis, R., Powell, B., Cuttner, J., Ellison, R. R., Cooper, M. R., Dillman, R., Major, W., Dupre, E., and McIntyre, O. R. (1988). Synergy between high-dose cytarabine and asparaginase in the treatment of adults with refractory and relapsed acute myelogenous leukemia: A Cancer and Leukemia group B study. *J. Clin. Oncol.* **6,** 499.

Chabner, B. A., and Loo, T. L. (1996). Enzyme therapy: L-Asparaginase. *In* "Cancer Chemotherapy Biotherapy: Principles and Practice" (B. A. Chabner and D. L. Longo, eds.), 2nd Ed., p. 485. Lippincott-Raven, Philadelphia.

Haskell, C. M., and Cannellos, G. P. (1969). L-Asparaginase resistance in human leukemia-asparagine synthetase. *Biochem. Pharmacol.* **18,** 2578.

Ho, D., Brown, N., and Yen, A. (1986). Clinical pharmacology of polyethylene glycol-L-asparaginase. *Drug Metab. Dispos.* **14,** 349.

Kurtzberg, J. (2000). "Asparaginase in Cancer Medicine" (R. C. Bast, D. W. Kufe, R. E. Pollock, R. R. Weichselbaum, J. F. Holland, and E. Frei III, eds.), p. 699, Decker, Hamilton, Ontario.

Lobel, A., O'Brien, J., McIntosh, S., Aspens, G., and Capizzi, R. L. (1979). Methotrexate and asparaginase combination chemotherapy in refractory acute lymphoblastic leukemia of childhood. *Cancer* **43,** 1089.

Maita, T., and Matsuda, G. (1980). The primary structure of L-asparaginase for *Escherichia coli. Hoppe Seyler's Z. Physiol. Chem.* **361,** 105.

Muller, H. J., and Boos, J. (1998). Use of L-asparaginase in childhood ALL. *Crit. Rev. Oncol. Hematol.* **28,** 97.

Pinheiro, J. P., Vieira, Ahlke, E., Nowak-Gottl, U., Hempel, G., Muller, H. J.,

Lumkemann, K., Schrappe, M., Rath, B., Fleischhack, G., Mann, G., and Boos, J. (1999). Pharmacokinetic dose adjustment of Erwinia asparaginase in protocol II of the paediatric ALL/NHL-BFM treatment protocols. *Br. J. Haematol.* **104,** 313.

Sallan, S. E., Hitchcock-Bryan, S., Gelber, R., Cassady, J. R., Frei, E., and Nathan, D. G. (1983). Influence of intensive asparaginase in the treatment of childhood non-T-cell acute lymphoblastic leukemia. *Cancer Res.* **43,** 5601.

Ueno, T., Ohtawa, K., Mitsui, K., Kodera, Y., Hiroto, M., Matsushimam A., Inada, Y., and Nishimura, H. (1997). Cell cycle arrest and apoptosis of leukemia cells induced by L-asparaginase. *Leukemia* **11,** 1858.

Late Effects of Radiation Therapy

Ajay Sandhu
Jacqueline Williams
Louis Constine

University of Rochester Medical Center

GLOSSARY

fibrosis The replacement of normal tissue architecture by a proliferation of fibroblasts and accumulation of extracellular matrix.

late effect syndromes Organ-specific clinical symptoms associated with radiation late effects.

normal tissue Nontumor tissue(s) that is affected during radiation therapy.

target cells The specific cell population(s) whose injury or death leads to the expression of late effects.

tolerance dose(s) Defined dose levels above which late effects increasingly occur.

The use of radiation therapy in the management of cancer must be determined, in part, through an understanding of the late effects of radiation on normal tissues. "Late effects" have their onset months or years following the cessation of treatment. This implies that therapeutic decisions intended to obviate late effects can only be based on the probability, not the certainty, that such events affect the interplay of therapy, patient, and tumor factors. Therapy factors include the total and fractional dose of irradiation, dose rate, overall treatment time, machine energy, treatment volume, dose distribution, and the use of other therapies (surgery, chemotherapy, radiosensitizers and protectors). Patient factors include the patient's developmental status, genetic predisposition, inherent tissue sensitivities and capacity for normal tissue repair, underlying disease or abnormalities (both structural and functional), and compensating mechanisms (i.e., the presence of an unirradiated second kidney). Tumor factors include direct tissue effects (such as extent of invasion), systemic effects of tumor-induced organ dysfunction or chemical secretion, and indirect mechanical effects (e.g., hydronephrosis).

I. GENERAL INTRODUCTION

Radiation late effects are produced through a combination of parenchymal cell loss and injury to the underlying vasculature. Initial tissue recovery is due mainly to parenchymal cell repopulation; the progressive component of damage is the arteriocapillary fibrosis that predominates in late irreparable injury and accentuates the cellular depletion of the parenchyma. It is the vascular changes that follow irradiation, but not chemotherapy, that partially account for the differences in late effects of the two modes of treatment. Indeed, the distribution of late radiation damage reflects primarily vascular injury and, therefore, cannot be explained simply as an indirect effect of parenchymal cell loss. Because of this vascular injury, devastating late effects of radiation, or of radiation and chemotherapy, can occur in both rapidly and slowly proliferating normal tissues without a clinically recognizable acute phase.

Advances in molecular biophysiology have provided insights into the responses of normal tissues to both chemotherapeutic and radiation injury. The classic concept of a single target cell that can explain the dynamic sequence of events leading to organ damage has been supplanted by that of interacting multiple cell systems. Moreover, the acute and late phases of adverse effects are actually manifestations of an ongoing sequence of events due to autocrine, paracrine, and endocrine messages that are initiated immediately after injury to a variety of cells: epithelial, endothelial, fibroblasts, and inflammatory. As schematized in Fig. 1, a variety of growth and inhibitory factors are released, specific cell receptors are altered, and the resulting signals received by these receptors are translated into postreceptor cytoplasmic, nuclear, and interstitial events. The importance of this pathway is that interventions are possible that can up- or downregulate cytokine responses, leading to a modulation of the toxic reaction.

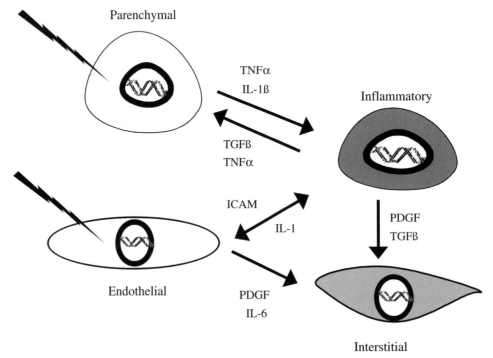

FIGURE 1 A hypothetical generalized pathway showing cell–cell interactions and the resultant cytokine and growth factor regulation of radiation damage expression.

Late effects of radiation therapy in select organ systems are summarized.

II. CENTRAL NERVOUS SYSTEM

The basic anatomies and physiologies of both brain and spinal cord are similar, as are the microscopic changes seen in these tissues following radiation therapy. However, there are fundamental differences in the observed clinical late effects following radiation injury, primarily due to the function of the volume irradiated. There is a spectrum of effects seen in the brain (Table I), ranging from neurocognitive and neuroendocrinological dysfunctions resulting from low doses to necrosis following higher doses; radiation myelopathy is the most feared complication of radiation therapy to the spine.

A. Anatomy and Pathophysiology

The primary histological division into gray and white matter is similar throughout the central nervous system (CNS), with variations in anatomical layering. At the cellular level, the targets for radiation injury have been hypothesized as being myelin-supporting glial cells (e.g., the oligodendrocytes) or the endothelial cells found in the small blood vessels. These hypotheses were concluded from the commonest observed injuries to white matter, which include demyelinization and coagulation necrosis. Astrocytes and glial cells are distributed in abundance and play a prominent role in radiation injury, and diffuse white matter changes and cerebral atrophy are commonly seen following radiation therapy. Indeed, it is the combination of white matter and vascular changes that characterizes late CNS radiation injury. However, a wide variety of vascular lesions have been described that are essentially nonspecific.

At a molecular level, the role of cytokines in mediating CNS radiation-induced toxicity is under close scrutiny. There appears to be a critical balance between proinflammatory cytokines and growth factors resulting in inflammation, tissue damage, repair, and fibrosis.

B. Clinical Features

A spectrum of clinical abnormalities can result from damage to the various target cells (Table I).

TABLE I

Evaluation of Patients for CNS Radiation Late Effects[a]

Late effect	Radiation dose	Target cells(s)	Signs and symptoms	Management/intervention
Spine				
Lhermitte's sign	Any	Myelin	Electric shock-like sensation	Self-resolving
Growth	>20 Gy	Chondro- or osteoblasts	Impaired spinal growth	Monitor for scoliosis/kyphosis
Myelitis	>45–50 Gy	Glial/vascular	Paresis, spasticity, altered sensation, loss of sphincter control	Steroids, physical therapy, occupational therapy
Brain				
Neurocognitive deficit	>18 Gy (with MTX) or >40–50 Gy	White matter	Difficulty with reading, language, memory, decreased speed of mental processing, attention deficit, decreased IQ, poor hand–eye coordination	Psychoeducational assistance
Somnolence syndrome	Any	Myelin		Self-resolving
Focal necrosis	>50 Gy (especially with >2 Gy fx)	Glial/vascular	Headaches, nausea, seizures, papilledema, hemiparesis/other focal findings, speech, learning and memory deficits	Steroid therapy, debulking of necrotic tissue
Large vessel stroke	>60 Gy	Vascular	Headache, seizures, hemiparesis, aphasia, focal neurologic findings	Determined by specific neurologic impairment
Ototoxicity	>50 Gy	Middle or inner ear	Abnormal speech development, hearing	Speech therapy, hearing aid
Blindness		Optic nerve chiasm, occipital lobe	Progressive visual loss	Visual aids

[a]Modified from Halperin *et al.* (1999).

1. Spine

Lhermitte's sign, which occurs between 2 and 6 months after irradiation, manifests as electric shock-like sensation radiating down the spine on flexion movement. This is a transient effect and resolves by itself.

Myelopathy has a latent period of 6 months. The anatomical level should correspond with the radiation field and dose delivered. The radiation dose and time to expression of injury can be influenced by various factors, such as the use of chemotherapy, preexisting vascular disease, and CNS damage from other etiologies. The conventionally described tolerance dose for this complication is 45 Gy, although cervical spine can tolerate doses up to 50 Gy. The incidence of myelopathy is 5% at doses between 57 and 61 Gy, increasing to 50% for doses between 68 and 73 Gy.

2. Brain

The acute effects are rare but include headache, seizure, changes in mental status, and exacerbation of the signs and symptoms associated with the tumor. These symptoms may reflect increased edema due to either progressive tumor or irradiation and will respond dramatically to steroids. Memory alterations, mood, and personality changes also can occur, depending on the location and volume under treatment.

Neurocognitive effects include intellectual deficits with decreases in various IQ parameters, learning disabilities (with attention deficit and impaired speed of mental processing common) and poorer academic achievement. These are more profound in children due to the immaturity of brain and incomplete formation of synapses and dendrites. Data come from prophylactic cranial irradiation used for leukemia where the toxicity from chemotherapy (particularly methotrexate and cytosine arabinoside) is a contributing factor. Adverse effects are somehow more pronounced in young females.

Somnolence syndrome occurs between 2 and 6 months and is transient.

Brain *necrosis* is a characteristic late effect and is a function of total dose, dose per fraction, and volume irradiated. At conventional dose fractionation, this complication is rarely seen below 50 Gy. The signs and symptoms can be similar to recurrence and depend on location and size.

The addition of chemotherapy may substantially lower the tolerance doses, and a high degree of caution is advocated for combining radiation therapy with high-dose systemic or intrathecal methotrexate. *Necrotizing leukoencephalopathy* is a characteristic side effect of this combination.

3. Neuroendocrine

The neuroendocrine sequelae need special emphasis largely due to their dramatic effects on the lives of pediatric cancer survivors.

The most common late effect on the hypothalamic–pituitary (H-P) axis is *growth hormone deficiency,* which has the lowest threshold compared with other hormone deficits. The effects, which can be seen at doses above 18 Gy, include stunted growth due to an inadequate growth spurt at puberty. Less commonly, precocious puberty (most commonly seen in females) can occur at similar doses, manifesting as premature sexual development.

The effects on other hormones, such as prolactin, adrenocorticotropic hormone (ACTH), thyrotropin-releasing hormone (TRH), and gonadotropin, are observed less commonly and at higher doses. Hormonal assays are used for diagnosis, and replacement therapies are instituted accordingly.

The thyroid gland may be damaged from irradiation incidental to spinal axis therapy. Primary *hypothyroidism* can be observed at doses of 20 Gy or greater and manifests itself as elevated thyroid-stimulating hormone (TSH) with decreased thyroxine (T_4). This should be distinguished from central hypothyroidism resulting from H-P axis irradiation with resultant TSH deficiency. Treatment with thyroxine reverses the symptoms, and dose adjustment is based on serum concentrations. Rarely, a hyperthyroid state can be seen from hyperfunctioning nodules in the thyroid.

The limitations of conventional imaging in differentiating recurrent disease from treatment-related changes are being overcome by the increasing capability of newer techniques. Functional imaging, which includes magnetic resonance spectroscopy and positron emission tomography, is being increasingly employed for providing biological parameters to distinguish tumor recurrence from necrosis. These modalities take advantage of the increased metabolic activity seen in cancer cells compared to necrotic cells.

C. Treatment

The acute and subacute effects are generally reversible and self-limiting. Steroids remain the standard treatment for symptom relief during the acute phase. Surgical resection may be required for a focal necrotic lesion. In addition to symptomatic treatment, physical therapy and psychotherapy may be beneficial to patients with motor and cognitive deficits, respectively.

III. LUNG

The lung is one of the most radiosensitive organs. In general, late radiation reactions can occur 1 to 3 months after either fractionated or single-dose therapy. However, when certain chemotherapeutic agents have been used, as when total body irradiation is combined with chemotherapy in bone marrow transplantation (BMT) conditioning regimens, reactions can (and do) occur with a shorter elapsed interval.

A. Anatomy and Pathophysiology

The most common acute radiation effect in the lung, radiation pneumonitis, has been classically attributed to an ablation of type II alveolar cells, resulting in early surfactant release into the alveoli. Previously believed to be a separate syndrome, vascular injury plays a role in the later, chronic syndrome of pulmonary or interstitial fibrosis. However, a number of research laboratories now have demonstrated a cascade of events in the normal tissue of the lung following radiation injury. These events are initiated and maintained through the secretion of multiple cytokines and chemokines, expressed by many of the resident cell populations in the pulmonary environment, including both type I and type II cells, endothelial cells, fibroblasts, and monocyte/macrophages, as well as cells recruited into the lung in response to the tissue injury.

B. Clinical Features

Two distinct, delayed lung injuries occur following irradiation (Table II): the *pneumonitic phase*, which occurs after 1 to 3 months, and the *fibrotic phase*, which can be seen after 2 to 4 months, but normally develops 1 to 2 years later.

Cough, pinkish sputum, congestion, chest tightness, and pleuritis are common complaints with a pneumonitic reaction. In general, there will be a geometric outline observable on chest film, limited to the radiation field, although late radiation-induced effects have been seen outside the radiation field and, very occasionally, even in the contralateral, unirradiated lung.

Chronic fibrosis leads to a decrease in pulmonary function and heart failure. Many of the patients will be asymptomatic, but there will be a gradual decrease in tidal volume and breathing rate. As the impairment progresses, dyspnea, orthopnea, cyanosis, or cor pulmonale may occur. CT and perfusion scans can be used to demonstrate these changes.

The most important factors relating to the development of radiation late effects in the lung are dose and volume. With respect to dose, it is the total dose affecting the lung normal tissue that dictates the level of late reaction, as well as the size of the daily fraction. For single doses to the whole of both lungs, the tolerance dose that will induce a response in 5% of the patients (the TD_5) is 7 Gy. With respect to the

TABLE II
Evaluation of Patients for Pulmonary Radiation Late Effects[a]

Late effect	Radiation dose	Target cells(s)	Signs and symptoms	Management/intervention
Pneumonitis	>15–20 Gy	Multicellular	Cough, pinkish sputum, congestion, chest tightness, and pleuritis	Steroid therapy
Pulmonary fibrosis	>15–20 Gy	Multicellular	Fatigue, cough, dyspnea on exertion, reduced exercise tolerance, orthopnea, cyanosis, finger clubbing, rales, cor pulmonale	Consider pulmonary evaluation, steroid therapy

[a]Modified from Halperin *et al.* (1999).

radiation volume, for fractionated doses of 1.8 to 2.0 Gy with limited volume (>30%), the TD_5 is 45 to 50 Gy; total doses of greater than 45 Gy to >75% of the organ can result in cor pulmonale and death. Of note, both laboratory and clinical studies have shown that there is a higher risk of pulmonary late effects when the radiation volume includes the lower lobes compared to the upper lobes.

Administration of some agents has been shown to reveal latent radiation damage in so-called *recall pneumonitis* or, as with bleomycin and carmustine (BCNU), has induced secondary damage via a separate injury pathway. Radiation late effects in the lung can be induced earlier, or even potentiated, when in combination with some chemotherapeutic agents, e.g., doxorubicin and actinomycin D. This has been particularly observed in some pediatric national trials; a number of the National Wilms' Tumor Study trials demonstrated an increase in pulmonary-related toxic effects using doxorubicin-based chemotherapy with whole lung irradiation.

Also, as noted earlier, this potentiation of effects has been of particular concern in BMT-conditioning regimens. Intensification of the regimens has increased morbidity and mortality without increasing overall survival, and some investigators are studying the timing of the radiation in order to decrease mortality. However, select patient prognostic indicators, e.g., performance status and gender, may have a greater impact on outcome than the parameters of irradiation. For example, investigators from Duke University have identified elevated pretreatment levels of transforming growth factor-β (TGF-β) in patients undergoing BMT that were predictive for lethal pneumonitis and hepatic venocclusive disease. Whether these pretreatment levels were indicative of a tumor effect per se or an inherent genetic predisposition is yet to be determined.

C. Treatment

As with the CNS, steroid therapy is the primary therapy for pulmonary late effects. However, a major component of preventing lung late effects is the avoidance of precipitatory events, such as smoking and infections, e.g., influenza.

IV. HEART

The variety of late effects that can occur following radiation reflects the structural complexity of the heart. In particular, the pediatric population, especially females less then 20 years of age, is at high risk for radiation-induced cardiac late effects in the form of coronary artery disease (CAD) and should be informed of the potential risks and encouraged to have a healthy life style. This same principle applies to young adults receiving mediastinal or mantle radiation.

A. Anatomy and Pathophysiology

The histologic hallmark of cardiac radiation injuries is fibrosis in the interstitium, with normal-appearing myocytes and capillary and arterial narrowing. In a now classic series of experiments, Fajardo and Stewart determined that the primary target for radiation is the endothelial cell, injury to which alters the fine vasculo-connective stroma of the myocardium. Pathologically, this is seen as fibrosis, involving a thickened collagenous pericardium and an extensive fibrinous exudate. When the myocardium is involved, diffuse interstitial fibrosis occurs, which follows the pattern of septae in the myocardium

B. Clinical Features

A classification system of radiation-induced cardiac late effects (Table III), modified from Fajardo and Stewart, includes a rare *acute pericarditis* that can occur during irradiation and is associated with juxta-pericardial cancer; *delayed pericarditis*, which can present abruptly or as a chronic pericardial effusion; *pancarditis*, including pericardial and myocardial fibrosis; *myopathy* in the absence of significant pericardial disease; *coronary artery disease*, usually involving the left anterior descending artery, although this is relatively uncommon and multifactorial; and *functional valve injury* and *conduction defects*.

Approximately 30% of patients treated with radiation for Hodgkin's disease to the entire heart with a mean midplane heart dose of 40–45 Gy will be affected by delayed acute pericarditis with an average onset of 6 months. However, with equally weighted anterior and posterior fields and the use of subcarinal blocking,

TABLE III
Evaluation of Patients for Cardiac Radiation Late Effects[a]

Late effect	Radiation dose	Target cells(s)	Signs and symptoms	Management/intervention
Cardiomyopathy	>35 Gy	Cardiomyocytes and/or endothelium	Fatigue, cough, dyspnea on exertion, peripheral edema, hypertension, tachypnea/rales, tachycardia, cardiomegaly, hepatomegaly, syncope, palpitations, arrhythmias	Diuretics, digoxin, afterload reduction, antiarrhythmics, cardiac transplant Education on risks: alcohol, anesthesia, drug use, pregnancy, smoking, obesity
Valvular damage	>40 Gy		Weakness, cough, dyspnea on exertion, new murmur, pulsating liver	Penicillin prophylaxis for surgery/dental procedures
Pericardial damage	>35 Gy		Fatigue, dyspnea on exertion, chest pain, cyanosis, ascites, peripheral edema, hypotension, friction rub, muffled heart sounds, venous distension, pulsus paradoxus	Pericardial stripping
Coronary artery disease	>30 Gy	Endothelium	Fatigue, cough, dyspnea on exertion, reduced exercise tolerance, orthopnea, cyanosis, finger clubbing, rales, cor pulmonale	Diuretics, cardiac medications, low sodium/low fat diet, conditioning regimens

[a]Modified from Halperin *et al.* (1999).

this incidence decreases to 2.5%. Pancarditis is severe but rare and requires radiation doses in excess of 60 Gy.

There has been some concern with respect to a perceived rising incidence of CAD in two populations—early breast cancer patients and Hodgkin's disease survivors—as they have become long-term survivors. Both autopsy and patient series have indicated an increased incidence in CAD after radiation doses of greater than 24 Gy. At autopsy, patients treated with anterior-weighted radiation techniques demonstrated arterial narrowing of up to 75%. Consistent with observed pathological findings, the media and adventitia were thickened or replaced by fibrosis tissue, and bizarre fibroblasts, hyalinization, intimal thickening with collagen, and histiocytes have been seen. A number of large clinical series have supported an increased relative risk for CAD among Hodgkin's survivors compared to a normal control population. A real concern, as noted earlier, is young pediatric patients, especially girls less than 20 years of age, where the highest incidence is found and the relative risk rises to 40%. However, studies from our own department have shown that treatment with adequate shielding to doses of 30 Gy demonstrate minimal to no significant abnormalities in Hodgkin's disease survivors at long-term follow-up (10 years average).

Of additional concern is the potentiation of cardiac effects due to the increasing use of combined modality treatments. These can appear as severe cardiomyopathies that are encountered as a late effect of cancer treatment, demonstrating the additive effects of both radiation and drugs through their activities on different populations of cells. For example, doxorubicin appears not to affect endothelial cells directly, but has been shown to frequently induce congestive heart failure through a direct effect on cardiac myocytes. In the absence of cardiac irradiation, doses of less than 550 mg/m^2 are well tolerated; however, when in combination with radiation (which should not exceed 25 Gy), doses of less than 300 mg/m^2 should be given. In contrast, the primary target of radiation is the endothelial cell, altering the fine vasculo-connective stroma of the myocardium leading to fibrosis.

C. Treatment

Symptomatic therapy using diuretics and antiarrhythmics may be used. Treatment of cardiac failure may be necessary, and cardiac transplantation has rarely been performed. As with the lung, education with respect to confounding factors, such as smoking and drug use, can be of profound importance.

V. GASTROINTESTINAL TRACT

The gastrointestinal (GI) tract is composed of long and diverse structures traversing through large portions of the body. Late effects may be observed in this organ as a result of treatment for a variety of cancers. The discussion in this section focuses on esophagus, stomach, and intestines, including rectum.

A. Anatomy and Pathophysiology

The entire GI tract is similar in terms of its histology, although the length and shape of each division vary markedly. The wall is composed of mucosa, submucosa, muscularis, and serosa. The GI mucosa is a rapid cell renewal system and is considered to be responsible for observed acute effects. The submucosa contains blood vessels, the lymphatic network, and the nerve plexus, and is the target for the expression of late injury. The acute effects start during the second week of radiation therapy and are a result of mucosal denudation and ulceration. The late changes are less well defined, but can be related to vascular insufficiency and muscular changes leading to fibrosis, although mucosal changes may be present as well (Table IV).

B. Clinical Features

The esophagus is typically exposed to significant doses during the mediastinal irradiation of various malignancies. The tolerance dose for the whole of the esophagus is estimated to be 50–55 Gy; however, partial lengths can receive up to 60 Gy. The classic acute symptom is painful swallowing with substernal burning. These are reversible but dose limiting and are managed conservatively. These patients are also prone to developing an underlying candidiasis infection requiring antifungal medications for the relief of symptoms. Late effects result from stricture formation causing dysphagia. This generally happens 6 months after radiation therapy, although a recurrent tumor should be ruled out. Ulceration resulting in hematemesis and fistula formation has been described in a high percentage of patients receiving intraluminal brachytherapy. Barium swallow and endoscopic examination are required when there are persistent symptoms.

Stomach irradiation can lead to a suppression of acid and enzyme secretion at relatively low doses (around 20 Gy); this is reversible with the passage of time. Serious late effects, including ulceration, bleeding, and perforation, are seen at doses above 45 Gy, and the incidence rate increases dramatically with the higher doses, particularly beyond 60 Gy.

Small and large intestines are exposed to radiation therapy during the treatment of abdominal and pelvic cancers. Acute effects are manifested as diarrhea and enteritis due to intestinal hypermotility and malabsorption. These are temporary and are managed symptomatically. The late effects can appear around 1 year after therapy. Alteration in bowel habit is a commonly reported symptom. Diarrhea and cramping are seen with small intestine injury, whereas frank blood, mucus, tenesmus, fecal urgency, and pain are symptoms of distal intestinal injury. Serious late effects in-

TABLE IV
Evaluation of Patients for Gastrointestinal Radiation Late Effects[a]

Late effect	Radiation dose	Target cells(s)	Signs and symptoms	Management/intervention
Esophagus Fibrosis (stricture)	>50–60 Gy	Vasculature	Weight loss, dysphagia, poor linear growth	Esophageal dilation, antireflux surgery
Small intestine Fibrosis	>50 Gy	Vasculature	Abdominal pain, diarrhea, weight loss, obstruction	Local/systemic analgesics, high fiber diet, resection, antidiarrheals
Large intestine Fibrosis	>50 Gy	Vasculature	Abdominal colic, rectal pain, melena, weight loss, constipation, obstruction	Local/systemic analgesics, stool softeners, high-fiber diet

[a]Modified from Halperin et al. (1999).

clude intractable diarrhea, severe bleeding, fistula formation, stricture, and stenosis leading to intestinal obstruction. Some of these require surgical intervention as part of therapeutic management. The threshold for small bowel injury is 50 Gy, and there is a steep response curve beyond this dose. The rectum can tolerate higher doses up to 70–75 Gy depending on the length and circumference irradiated.

C. Treatment

The conservative management of GI tract injury includes antiemetics, antidiarrheals, local and systemic analgesics, antacids, H2 receptor antagonists, and agents such as sucralfate for ulcer healing. Specific treatment depends on the location and severity, including dilatation for strictures and surgery for intestinal obstruction.

VI. LIVER

The development and refinement of conformal radiation techniques have not only made it possible to deliver high doses of radiation therapy to hepatic tumors, but also to quantify the effects of dose and volume on normal tissues.

A. Anatomy and Pathophysiology

The basic functional anatomic unit of the liver is the lobule, which consists of a central vein with portal triads in the periphery. Kupffer cells, which constitute the reticuloendothelial component, separate the plates of liver cells, individually termed hepatocytes. The portal area consists of a vein, an artery, and a bile duct, apart from nerve and lymphatics. The targets for radiation and chemotherapy effects are conventionally regarded to be the vasculature and the parenchymal tissue, respectively. However, venoocclusive disease has been described both for radiation-induced toxicity and following bone marrow transplants. The lesion at the microscopic level is congestion in the central portion resulting from thrombus in the central vein. In addition, radiation therapy results in injury to the Kupffer cells, thereby releasing cytokines, particularly TGF-β, which has been shown to stimulate fibrogenesis.

B. Clinical Features

Radiation-related liver disease usually occurs 1–4 months after completion of radiation in the form of *hepatic fibrosis* (Table V). The common presentations include ascites; hepatomegaly; elevated enzymes, particularly alkaline phosphatase; and later developing *jaundice*. This needs to be differentiated from the progressive neoplastic process. A hypodense area on a CT scan should correspond to the high-dose zone on isodose distribution. The clinical picture with the use of chemoradiotherapy is altered to early onset with pronounced jaundice.

The tolerance doses for whole and partial organ have been studied in detail. With the availability of the three-dimensional conformal technique, it is now possible to deliver high doses to small volumes safely. Although the whole liver tolerance has been reported below 30 Gy, significant volumes can be treated to high therapeutic doses predicated on dose volume histograms. Based on this information, partial liver volumes can be treated to doses beyond 50 Gy by keeping at least 60% of normal liver to doses below 28 Gy.

TABLE V
Evaluation of Patients for Hepatic Radiation Late Effects[a]

Late effect	Radiation dose	Target cells(s)	Signs and symptoms	Management/intervention
Hepatic fibrosis/cirrhosis	>30 Gy	Vasculature	Itching, jaundice, spider nevi, bruising Portal hypertension: esophageal varices, hemorrhoids, hematemesis	Diuretics, liver transplant, vascular shunting

[a]Modified from Halperin *et al.* (1999).

C. Treatment

Liver cells can regenerate following acute insult and recover functional capability following treatment. However, this is strictly a function of dose and volume. Definitive treatment for liver failure is transplantation, although bypass procedures, diuretics, steroids, and anticoagulants can be considered for symptomatic relief.

VII. KIDNEY

The kidneys constitute critical dose-limiting structures when using radiation therapy for abdominal malignancies, as the threshold dose for producing clinical toxicity is low compared to any other abdominal organ. A wide variety of clinical syndromes have been defined for radiation-induced damage to kidneys.

A. Anatomy and Pathophysiology

The functional unit of the kidney is the nephron, which consists of a tuft of capillaries, termed the glomerulus, found within the Bowman's capsule located in the cortex. The proximal and distal convoluted tubules are a continuation of the Bowman's capsule, connected through the loop of Henlé. The distal tubules join into collecting ducts, which empty into calyces. The kidneys perform multiple and complex tasks, primarily maintaining the environment through the removal of toxic products and, secondarily, controlling fluid and electrolyte balance, blood pressure, red blood cell formation, and regulation of active vitamin D production. The target cells for radiation damage are multiple, with a variable clinical picture

and time of onset, although vascular damage again plays an important role. Irradiation of the cortex is more likely to be detrimental in view of the location of the nephrons. The classic lesion is described as *glomerulosclerosis* with an obliteration of glomeruli. Tubular cell damage includes atrophy and necrosis of tubules. In addition, interstitial fibrosis is seen as a late effect of radiation therapy.

B. Clinical Features

There is a spectrum of clinical syndromes, the most benign being a silent reduction in the glomerular filtration rate (GFR) and asymptomatic proteinuria progressing to nephropathy. The clinical picture usually overlaps, and both nephritic and nephrotic phases have been described (Table VI).

The asymptomatic phase is usually seen up to 6 months after treatment. This is followed by *acute nephritis* presenting with dyspnea, edema, headaches, lassitude, hypertension, anemia, papilledema, and derangement of kidney functions. These findings may resolve with medical management or progress to a chronic phase. The chronic phase, which usually appears 12–18 months following treatment, can comprise of malignant hypertension, benign hypertension, or hyperreninemic hypertension and *nephrotic syndrome*. Death in the chronic phase can occur from left ventricular failure or pulmonary edema.

Based on available data, a threshold dose of 15 Gy with conventional fractionation is considered a safe limit for clinical application. However, there is a steep dose response; doses greater than 25 to 30 Gy will cause complete elimination of useful renal function. In addition, similar effects can be seen at lower doses with the addition of chemotherapy.

TABLE VI
Evaluation of Patients for Renal Radiation Late Effects[a]

Late effect	Radiation dose	Target cells(s)	Signs and symptoms	Management/intervention
Hypoplastic kidney/renal arteriosclerosis	20–30 Gy (10–15 Gy with chemotherapy)	Multicellular	Asymptomatic or fatigue, anemia, oliguria	Low protein diet, dialysis, renal transplant
Nephrotic syndrome	20–30 Gy	Cortex	Proteinuria, edema	Low salt diet, diuretics, renal transplant

[a]Modified from Halperin *et al.* (1999).

C. Treatment

Medical management comprises a low protein diet, dialysis, antihypertensives, and diuretics. Treatment with angiotensin receptor antagonists has shown promise in recent studies. Anemia needs to be treated with blood transfusions and erythropoietin. Nonetheless, transplantation remains the definitive treatment, although prevention by limiting the volume of kidneys subjected to significant radiation doses remains the most effective and best option.

VIII. OVARY AND TESTES

In adults, the concerns of cancer survivors with respect to the genital organs tend to center on their functional status and the potential for sterilization, as well as consequences on the health of their offspring. In pediatric patients, although these are still of concern, there is the additional fear of impaired development of secondary sexual characteristics.

A. Anatomy and Pathophysiology

1. Ovary

The main function of the ovary is to produce oocytes and secrete steroid hormones. Indeed, ovarian hormones have critical physiologic effects on other organs, including maturation and maintenance of the breasts and vagina, bone mineralization, integrity of the cardiovascular system, and libido.

2. Testes

In the testes, spermatogonia and Leydig cells are particularly sensitive to cytotoxic therapy. Spermatogenesis is the process of formation of spermatozoa from immature germ cells, the least differentiated of which, the spermatogonia, divide to form spermatocytes. The entire process takes place in the seminiferous epithelium within the testicular tubules and may take up to 74 days to occur. A constant supply of germ cell precursors is essential to the continuous production of spermatozoa, which are then transported through the lumen of the seminiferous tubules into the epididymis where they are stored. Leydig cells are the primary androgen-secreting cells and account for at least 75% of the total testosterone produced by the normal adult male; intact Leydig cell function is required for normal spermatogenesis.

B. Clinical Features (Table VII)

1. Ovary

The dose of radiation that will ablate ovarian function depends on the patient's age, i.e., stage of development, and whether the dose was fractionated. Some of the observed features include amenorrhea, a failure to develop secondary sexual characteristics (in prepubertal girls), early menopause, and ovarian failure. After single fractions, temporary sterility can occur with ovarian doses of 1.7–6.4 Gy and permanent sterility after 3.2–10 Gy. All patients can show elevated follicle-stimulating hormone (FSH) and low estradiol levels.

TABLE VII
Evaluation of Patients for Ovarian and Testicular Radiation Late Effects[a]

Late effect	Radiation dose	Target cells(s)	Signs and symptoms	Management/intervention
Ovary				
Ovarian failure	4–12 Gy in pediatrics; increases with age	Oocytes/follicles	Pediatrics: delayed/arrested/absent pubertal development Adults: early menopause, dyspareunia, low libido, infertility	Hormone (estrogen) replacement therapy, counseling for alternate parenting strategies
Testes				
Oligo-azoospermia	>1–6 Gy	Germ cells	Testicular atrophy, failure to impregnate	Instruction in self-exam, counseling for alternate parenting strategies
Testosterone deficiency	>24 Gy	Leydig cells	Pediatrics: delayed/arrested/absent pubertal development	Hormone (testosterone) replacement therapy

[a]Modified from Halperin *et al.* (1999).

2. Testes

The common features in patients are oligospermia and azoospermia, ultimately leading to impaired infertility and sterility. These features are due to the exquisite sensitivity of spermatogonia, such that even small doses of radiation can produce measurable damage. A depression in sperm counts is discernible at doses as low as 15 cGy and complete sterilization may occur with fractionated irradiation to a total dose of 1–2 Gy. Spermatocytes generally fail to complete maturation division at doses of 2–3 Gy and are visibly damaged after 4–6 Gy with the resulting azoospermia. At low doses, a reduced sperm count is seen 60–80 days after exposure, which is the time that maturation would otherwise be complete. Higher doses are necessary to damage spermatids when compared to the more sensitive spermatocytes; however, at the highest doses, permanent sterility is frequent.

C. Treatment

In women, hormone replacement (estrogen) therapy can be instigated, together with guidance on coping with estrogen deficiency and early menopause. Hormonal therapy may also alleviate other potential late problems, such as osteoporosis and atherosclerosis. In males, again hormone therapy can be used (testosterone), with similar guidance for hormone deficiencies. In both sexes, alternative methods of parenting should be discussed.

IX. SUMMARY

All tissues can be affected by radiation therapy, but this must not deter its use in treating cancer. Clearly, the radiation oncologist must understand both the efficacy and the morbidity of radiation in order to make optimal treatment decisions. In the new era of molecular biology and gene therapy, the potential to prevent, ameliorate, or treat radiation-induced normal tissue injury exists and, in fact, should soon be realized.

See Also the Following Articles

DOSIMETRY AND TREATMENT PLANNING FOR THREE-DIMENSIONAL RADIATION THERAPY • MOLECULAR ASPECTS OF RADIATION BIOLOGY • TOTAL BODY IRRADIATION

Bibliography

Anscher, M. S., Peters, W. P., Reisenbichler, H., Petros, W. P., and Jirtle, R. L. (1993). Transforming growth factor beta is a predictor of liver and lung fibrosis after autologous bone marrow transplantation for advanced breast cancer. *N. Engl. J. Med.* **328,** 1592.

Cassady, J. R. (1995). Clinical radiation nephropathy. *Int. J. Radiat. Oncol. Biol. Phys.* **31,** 1249.

Coia, L. R., Myerson, R. J., and Tepper, J. E. (1995). Late effects of radiation therapy on the gastrointestinal tract. *Int. J. Radiat. Oncol. Biol. Phys.* **31,** 1213.

Constine, L. S., Woolf, P. D., Cann, D., Mick, G., McCormick, K., Raubertas, R. F., and Rubin, P. (1993). Hypothalamic-pituitary dysfunction after radiation for brain tumors. *N. Engl. J. Med.* **328,** 87.

Griffin, T. W. (1980). White matter necrosis, microangiography and intellectual abilities in survivors of childhood leukemia. Association with central nervous system irradiation and methotrexate therapy. *In* "Radiation Damage to the Nervous System" (H. A. Gilbert, and A. R. Kagan, eds.). Raven Press, New York.

Grigsby, P. W., Russell, A., Bruner, D., Eifel, P., Koh, W.-J., Spanos, W., Stetz, J., Stitt, J. A., and Sullivan, J. (1995). Late injury of cancer therapy on the female reproductive tract. *Int. J. Radiat. Oncol. Biol. Phys.* **31,** 1281.

Hale, G. A., Marina, N. M., Jones-Wallace, D., Greenwald, C. A., Jenkins, J. J., Rao, B. N., Luo, X., and Hudson, M. M. (1999). Late effects of treatment for germ cell tumors during childhood and adolescence. *J. Pediat. Hematol. Oncol.* **21,** 115.

Halperin, E. C., Constine, L. C., Tarbell, N. J., and Kun, L. E. (eds.) (1999). "Pediatric Radiation Oncology," 3rd Ed. Lippincott Williams and Wilkins, Philadelphia.

Izard, M. A. (1995). Leydig cell function and radiation: A review of the literature. *Radiother. Oncol.* **34,** 1.

King, V., Constine, L. S., Clark, D., Schwartz, R. G., Muhs, A. G., Henzler, M., Hutson, A., and Rubin, P. (1996). Symptomatic coronary artery disease after mantle irradiation for Hodgkin's disease. *Int. J. Radiat. Oncol. Biol. Phys.* **36,** 881.

Kureshi, S. A., Hofman, F. M., Schneider, J. H., Chin, L. S., Apuzzo, M. L., and Hinton, D. R. (1994). Cytokine expression in radiation-induced delayed cerebral injury. *Neurosurgery* **35,** 822.

Lawrence, T. S., Robertson, J. M., Anscher, M. S., Jirtle, R. L., Ensminger, W. D., and Fajardo, L. F. (1995). Hepatic toxicity resulting from cancer therapy. *Int. J. Radiat. Oncol. Biol. Phys.* **31,** 1237.

Lushbaugh, C. C., and Casarett, G. W. (1976). The effects of gonadal irradiation in clinical radiation therapy: A review. *Cancer* **37,** 1111.

Marcus, R. B. Jr., and Million, R. R. (1990). The incidence of myelitis after irradiation of the cervical spinal cord. *Int. J. Radiat. Oncol. Biol. Phys.* **19,** 3.

McDonald, S., Rubin, P., Phillips, T. E., and Marks, L. B. (1995). Injury to the lung from cancer therapy: Clinical syndromes, measurable endpoints, and potential scoring systems. *Int. J. Radiat. Oncol. Biol. Phys.* **31,** 1187.

Relander, T., Cavallin-Stahl, E., Garwicz, S., Olsson, A. M., and Willen, M. (1995). Gonadal and sexual function in men treated for childhood cancer. *Med. Pediat. Oncol.* **35,** 52.

Rezvani, M., Hopewell, J. W., and Robbins, M. E. (1995). Initiation of non-neoplastic late effects: The role of endothelium and connective tissue. *Stem Cells* **13**(Suppl), 248.

Rubin, P., Constine L., and Williams, J. P. (1998). Late effects of cancer treatment: Radiation and drug toxicity. *In* "Principles and Practice of Radiation Oncology" (C. Perez and L. W. Brady, eds.), p. 155. Lippincott-Raven, Philadelphia.

Rubin, P., Finkelstein, J. N., and Williams, J. P. (1998). Paradigm shifts in the radiation pathophysiology of late effects in normal tissues: Molecular vs classic concepts. *In* "Current Radiation Oncology" (J. S. Tobias and P. R. M. Thomas, eds.), Vol. 3, p. 1. Arnold Press, London.

Rubin, P., Johnston, C. J., Williams, J. P., McDonald, S., and Finkelstein, J. N. (1995). A perpetual cascade of cytokines postirradiation leads to pulmonary fibrosis. *Int. J. Radiat. Oncol. Biol. Phys.* **33,** 99.

Schultheiss, T. E., Kun, L. E., Ang, K. K., and Stephens, L. C. (1995). Radiation response of the central nervous system. *Int. J. Radiat. Oncol. Biol. Phys.* **31,** 1093.

Schwartz, C. L., Hobbie, W. L., Constine, L. S., and Ruccione, K. S. (1994). "Survivors of Childhood Cancer: Assessment and Management." Mosby, St. Louis.

Sklar, C. A., and Constine, L. S. (1995). Chronic neuroendocrinological sequelae of radiation therapy. *Int. J. Radiat. Oncol. Biol. Phys.* **31,** 1113.

Stewart, J. R., Fajardo, L. F., Gillette, S. M., and Constine, L. S. (1995). Radiation injury to the heart. *Int. J. Radiat. Oncol. Biol. Phys.* **31,** 1205.

Li–Fraumeni Syndrome

David Malkin

University of Toronto School of Medicine, Canada

GLOSSARY

familial cancer A form of cancer that occurs in various members of the same family at a far higher rate than could be expected to occur by chance or that can be attributed to shared environmental conditions, e.g., Li–Fraumeni syndrome.

Li–Fraumeni syndrome (LFS) A statistically rare but highly significant familial cancer syndrome associated with a wide variety of tumors, including breast carcinomas, soft tissue sarcomas, leukemia, and brain tumors. For families at risk, the probability of developing some invasive form of cancer by age 30 is close to 50%. (Identified from studies by Frederick P. *Li* and Joseph F. *Fraumeni*. Jr.)

p53 A tumor suppressor gene whose mutation is the most frequently observed genetic event in human cancers; the inactivation of the *p53* gene and the disruption of its protein are associated with multiple cancers in Li–Fraumeni families.

***p53* (transgenic) mice** Mice that have been genetically engineered either to be devoid of functional *p53* or to express mutant alleles that inhibit wild-type *p53* function.

tumor suppressor gene A gene whose product can contribute to the malignant transformation of a normal cell to a tumor cell.

Nonrandom aggregations of cancer have been recognized to occur since the middle of the last century. Although almost every type of cancer has been reported to occur in a familial form, evidence of hereditary and familial influences exists in only a few percentages of cases. The actual fraction of human cancers that are causally associated with genetic and familial factors is not known. The Li–Fraumeni syndrome is a rare, yet important, family cancer syndrome. Our understanding of this disorder and the importance of molecular genetic events in the development of familial cancer has evolved through the evaluation of clinical observations, genetic epidemiology, and molecular biology of several of these affected kindreds. Presented in chronological order, this article discusses the original clinical observations and outlines evidence to implicate the *p53* tumor suppressor gene in development of cancer in these families. The problems of genetic heterogeneity are discussed, and the potential impact of predictive genetic testing in this syndrome is evaluated.

I. INTRODUCTION

Inherited cancer genes pose the most potent oncogenic influence on human carcinogenesis, exceeding the effects of such environmental factors as ionizing radiation, tobacco, and occupational carcinogens. Hereditary cancers have been reported to occur in autosomal dominant, recessive or X-linked inherited patterns, and for some (most notably breast and colon) at least two different hereditary forms exist, distinguished by their clinical features. Different genetic events are thought to influence the respective phenotypic associations. Some neoplasms such as acute myelogenous leukemia occur only rarely in a familial form, whereas others such as retinoblastoma occur in the heritable form almost as frequently as in the sporadic form. There tends to be a wide degree of penetrance of the susceptibility to tumors arising among family members for each particular gene.

Furthermore, the number of different types of cancer varies from family to family. For example, the only well-documented second tumor in members of retinoblastoma families is osteosarcoma. However, members of a Li–Fraumeni family are at risk for a wide spectrum of tumors, including carcinoma of the breast, soft tissue sarcomas, osteosarcoma, leukemia, brain tumors, and adrenocortical carcinoma. Studies of hereditary cancers have identified a class of genes that is critical both in carcinogenesis and in normal development. In addition, these studies have generated significant counseling issues both for families and for clinicians.

II. THE LI–FRAUMENI SYNDROME

In the late 1960s Li and Fraumeni reported the results of a survey of 280 medical records and 418 death certificates of childhood rhabdomyosarcoma patients diagnosed in the United States. In five families in whom siblings or cousins had a childhood sarcoma, a high concentration of cancers of diverse types was noted on the ancestral line of one parent. Soft tissue sarcomas and breast carcinomas, as well as acute leukemias, brain tumors, carcinomas of the lung, pancreas, and skin frequently occurred in first- and second-degree relatives, and adrenocortical carcinomas were often seen in siblings.

This family cancer syndrome came to be known as the Li–Fraumeni (LFS). A subsequent prospective analysis of more than 50 similarly affected families has defined the list of cancer phenotypes in affected members to include osteosarcoma, brain tumors, leukemias, and adrenocortical carcinomas, in addition to the originally described component tumors, namely soft tissue sarcomas and breast cancer (Fig. 1).

It was suggested in the original reports that the familial occurrence of neoplasms originating at discordant sites might represent a counterpart of the tendency for a single individual to develop multiple primary tumors. In fact, epidemiologic studies have confirmed that the neoplasms in LFS tend to develop in children and young adults, often as multiple primary cancers in affected individuals. No obvious predilection for a particular human subpopulation has been noted. Although LFS shares with other heredi-

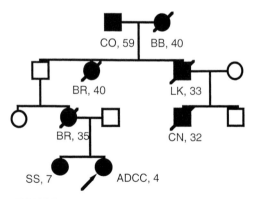

FIGURE 1   Li–Fraumeni syndrome "classic" pedigree.

tary cancer syndromes the tendency for tumors to develop at unusually early ages at multiple sites, the constellation of tumors is quite distinct.

Segregation analysis applied to LFS demonstrated that the observed cancer distribution best fit a rare autosomal dominant gene model. This model also predicts for families at risk that the probability of developing any invasive cancer (excluding skin cancer) approaches 50% by age 30. Penetrance is very high and predicts that more than 90% of gene carriers would develop cancer by age 70.

Potential ascertainment biases have developed from the preferential attention given to the dramatically affected kindreds, the possibility of chance association of cancer in rare families (phenocopies), the uncertainty of the prevalence of the syndrome in the general population, and uncertainties in defining both the spectrum of cancers in the syndrome or the penetrance of the predisposing gene(s). Nonetheless, recent prospective reports monitoring families over many years have revealed continued expression of the dominantly inherited syndrome among young family members. Excesses were most often confined over time to the six previously described cancer types.

"Classic" LFS families include one member diagnosed with a sarcoma before age 45, a first-degree relative with cancer before age 45, and another first- or second-degree relative in the same ancestral line with any cancer diagnosed under 45, or a sarcoma at any age. LFS "variants" closely fit the "classic" definition, yet may lack one major criterion. It was recognized that the identification of a defective gene or genes conferring a predisposition in carriers within these families would assist in clarification of the definition of the syndrome.

Although LFS had been characterized in both a statistical and a classical genetic manner, identification of the gene(s) that yielded this striking cancer predisposition remained elusive until early 1990. Recognition of the limitations placed on standard linkage analysis suggested that the candidate approach to isolating the responsible gene might be productive. The class of genes most strongly associated with familial neoplasms has been the tumor suppressor genes. Of those genes cloned at the time, *p53* was most likely to be linked to LFS.

III. THE *p53* TUMOR SUPPRESSOR GENE

Alterations of the *p53* gene or its encoded protein are the most frequently observed genetic events in human cancer. The human gene, located on chromosome 17p13, encodes a 53-kDa nuclear phosphoprotein. The nucleotide sequence of its 393 amino acids reveals five evolutionarily conserved domains that are essential for normal *p53* growth-suppressing functions and encompass the most frequently mutated codons. *p53* binds specific DNA consensus sequences and is a transcription factor that regulates the expression of other growth regulatory genes. Introduction of wild-type *p53* into a variety of transformed cell types inhibits their growth, most likely by blocking progression through the cell cycle at a checkpoint control site prior to G_1/S. The antiproliferative effect of *p53* may also involve cell cycle regulation at the G_2/M restriction point or as a component of a spindle checkpoint.

Although *p53* may not have a major role in the S-phase recombinational events leading to sister chromatid exchange formation, suggesting that conversion of radiation damage to chromatin lesions is independent of *p53*, the time to peak levels of chromosomal damage is shorter in *p53* null cells—consistent with kinetic differences based on specific *p53* genotype. These kinetic differences have been observed as well in *p53*-deficient LFS-derived lymphocytes. *p53* is important in maintaining the fidelity of DNA repair, particularly in response to double-stranded (ds) DNA breaks induced by ionizing radiation or certain chemotherapeutic drugs. Finally, wild-type *p53* mediates apoptosis when overexpressed in cultured cells in the absence of appropriate differentiation or proliferation signals.

Structural analysis suggests that several highly conserved amino acids actually contact the minor or major grooves of the DNA helix. *p53* function may be inactivated through sequence changes at these or other codons that alter the conformation of the protein and prevent it from forming tetramers or activating transcription. Transcriptional targets of *p53* include Mdm-2, which is involved in a negative regulatory system that terminates the response of a cell to DNA damage; cyclin G_1 of unknown function;

Bax, a promoter of apoptosis; GADD45, a DNA repair protein; and p21$^{CIP1/WAF1}$, a multifunctional regulator and the best candidate for control of cell cycle arrest. Several DNA tumor virus gene products bind *p53*. In cells that coexpress one of these viral oncoproteins, expression of *p53*-inducible reporter genes cannot be activated. *p53* interactions with tumor suppressor genes such as the Wilms tumor gene, *WT1*, in transfected cells modulates the ability of each protein to transactivate its targets; coincident mutations in *p53* and the retinoblastoma susceptibility gene *(RB1)* cooperate in the transformation of certain cell types in mice.

Models have been proposed to explain the complex *p53* functions. In a cell with normal *p53*, levels of the protein rise in response to DNA damage mediated by pRB1, and the cell arrests prior to the G_1/S transition, where genomic repair or apoptosis ensues with the mechanism being determined by the transforming oncoprotein(s). In a cell in which *p53* is inactivated, G_1 arrest does not occur and damaged DNA is replicated. During mitosis, the presence of damaged DNA results in mutation, aneuploidy, mitotic failure, and cell death. *p53* alterations are necessary, but not sufficient, for the ultimate cancer that arises from these malignant clones, as other genetic events are clearly required.

IV. *p53* AND THE LI–FRAUMENI SYNDROME

Inactivating mutations of the *p53* gene and disruptions of the p53 protein have been associated with some fraction of virtually every sporadically occurring human malignancy. Included among these are osteosarcomas, soft tissue sarcomas, rhabdomyosarcomas, leukemias, brain tumors, and carcinomas of the lung and breast. Together, these tumors account for greater than two-thirds of the cancers in selected series of Li–Fraumeni families.

Based on these observations, five LFS families were studied to determine whether *p53* played any role in the occurrence of cancer in affected family members. Base pair mutations were identified in the germline of affected members in each of the five families studied. Although the missense mutations were initially ob-

served between codons 252 and 258 in exon 7, within one highly conserved region of the gene, further analysis of one family revealed a 2-bp deletion at codon 184 in exon 5 instead of the codon 252 mutation. The wild-type allele was deleted in tumors of affected individuals. Several unaffected relatives were mutant gene carriers, suggesting that they might be at risk to develop cancer at a later date. Following this initial report, a sixth classic Li–Fraumeni family was reported with another constitutional mutation in the same region as the previously identified ones. In this family, however, one affected member was not a carrier of the mutant gene, suggesting that the mechanism of tumor formation in this individual did not involve *p53*.

Germline *p53* mutations are not reported in many LFS families, yet there is a lack of 100% concordance with the "classic" LFS phenotype. In at least one quite typical LFS kindred, although no *p53* gene mutations were identified, overexpression of wild-type *p53* was observed. Explanations for genotype–phenotype discordance include posttranslational *p53* alterations, endogenous promoter defects leading to aberrant expression of *p53* message, complete *p53* deletion, effects of modifier genes, or alterations of other genes that may influence the phenotype generated by the presence of a specific germline *p53* mutation. Nevertheless, the high frequency of germline *p53* mutations in LFS families together with the tight association of tumor formation in *p53*-deficient mice (see Section VII) do confirm a causal association of germline *p53* alterations and cancer predisposition.

V. GERMLINE *p53* MUTATIONS OUTSIDE LI–FRAUMENI SYNDROME

As DNA screening and mutation analysis techniques improved, it became possible to analyze large populations of patients for constitutional abnormalities of the *p53* gene. Several studies have demonstrated that certain groups of "high-risk" patients and their families carry germline *p53* mutations that presumably predispose them to the development of their respective malignancies.

Germline *p53* mutations may be inherited from a parent who is healthy at the time cancer is diagnosed in the child. A striking feature of LFS kindreds is the high frequency, approaching 50% of affected members who develop multiple primary neoplasms. One multi-center study demonstrate germline mutations of the *p53* tumor suppressor gene in leukocyte DNA from 4 of 59 patients (6.8%) who had survived second cancers, but did not have family histories compatible with the LFS. In addition to implicating codons outside the classically defined conserved regions of the *p53* gene, this study also demonstrated the occurrence of germline *p53* mutations in patients with cancers not commonly represented among LFS component tumors. These included non-Hodgkin's lymphoma, colon and gastric carcinoma, and neuroblastoma.

Another extensive analysis of 196 patients with malignant sarcomas was reported along with the just-described study. Eight of these 196 patients (4%) had germline *p53* mutations, and 5 of the 8 mutations were identified in patients from families with a high incidence of cancer. In addition to missense mutations, nonsense germline mutations were found in this series, all of these presumably yielding a truncated p53 protein. In these cases, as in the previously described study, the affected individual presented a history that was not entirely consistent with LFS. This study also confirmed the observation of neutral polymorphisms within the *p53* sequence that must be carefully analyzed to rule out their disease-associated potential. One of these, at codon 213 in exon 6 (a nonconserved region), has been frequently identified in sporadic tumors. Finally, this study pointed out the vagaries of the clinical definition of LFS in that one family with definitive germline inheritance of *p53* mutations had an excess of gastric carcinomas, a tumor that is thought to be rare in the operative definition of the syndrome. Other factors, both genetic and environmental, may influence the type of tumors that arise in patients who are carriers of the same *p53* germline mutations.

Although sarcomas and multiple primary cancers in affected patients constitute the most consistent characteristic features of the LFS phenotype, certain other cancers are also commonly represented. Of these, early onset breast cancer is most frequently encountered. However, the frequency of germline *p53* mutations in breast cancer patients outside families with classical LFS is exceedingly low, representing less than 2% of all such at-risk women. It is evident that other genetic events are responsible for the genesis of this familial cancer clustering. At least two genes, BRCA1 and BRCA2, have been identified and shown to be altered in a substantial subset of these patients.

De novo mutations have been reported in a child with multifocal osteosarcoma and in a few patients with multifocal glioma. Site-specific cancer is not characteristic of LFS. This observation is confirmed by the rarity of germline *p53* alterations in families with site-specific breast cancer, gliomas, and leukemia. Adrenocortical carcinoma (ADCC), osteosarcoma, and rhabdomyosarcoma (RMS) are frequently encountered pediatric tumors in LFS. In a survey of sarcoma patients, 8/196 (4%) harbored germline *p53* mutations. It has been observed that germline *p53* mutations occur in 3/6 (50%) children with sporadic ADCC, 7/235 (3.0%) with osteosarcoma, and 3/33 (9.5%) with sporadic RMS. In the latter population, it appears that the presence of a germline *p53* alteration may decrease the latency to tumor formation as compared with a wild-type *p53* genotype population. Thus, the method of ascertainment of the proband influences the carrier frequency in the study population (Table I).

More than 90% of germline and somatic *p53* mutations are missense and occur in the conserved regions of the gene (Fig. 2), with residues 175, 245, 248, and 273 being the most frequently altered codons. Nevertheless, splice mutations that yield significant disruptions of the gene product have been reported.

TABLE I

Estimated Frequency of Germiline p 53
Mutations in Specific Cancer Patients/Families

Clinical phenotype	Mutation frequency (%)
LFS and ADCC	75–100
LFS	50–85
LFS	10–30
Multisite cancer (non-LFS)	0–20
Sporadic ADCC	40–70
Sporadic rhabdomyosarcoma	5–15
Osteosarcoma	1–10
Second neoplasms	5–15
Early onset breast cancer	<1

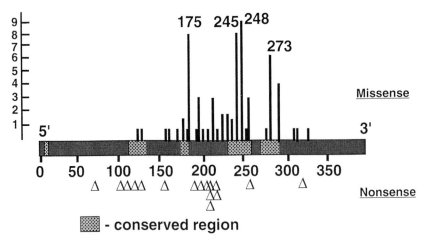

FIGURE 2 Location of human germline p53 mutations.

VI. FUNCTIONAL ANALYSES OF *p53* MUTATIONS

As both the biological and the biochemical characteristics of *p53* are elucidated, it has also been important to attempt to establish the functional significance of germline *p53* mutations and the structural features of the corresponding mutant p53 proteins. In addition, before associating a germline *p53* mutation with the development of cancer, its functional significance must be carefully determined. In one particularly extensive analysis, seven distinct *p53* mutations identified from Li–Fraumeni families were studied. Oligonucleotide-directed mutagenesis of the *p53* cDNA was performed to generate mutant clones that could then be subcloned into expression vectors for transfection assays. Six of seven missense germline mutations disrupted the growth inhibitory properties and structure of the wild-type p53 protein. One mutation, at codon 181, was not recognized by the antibody PAb 240, which recognizes an epitope specific for a mutant conformation, and did not appear to alter the ability to suppress cell growth when transfected into Saos-2 osteosarcoma cells.

Genetic analysis of this mutation demonstrated that it was not always associated with the development of cancer in the family from which it was derived. The mutation was not present in a member of the kindred who had developed two cancers, and the codon 181 mutant gene, rater than the normal allele, was somatically lost in tumor tissue from a cancer in another relative. It became apparent therefore that certain germline mutations of *p53* might change the amino acid sequence in a conserved domain yet not be associated with an increased cancer risk.

The functional significance of heterozygous germline mutations in members of LFS families has also been examined through the expression of the mutant *p53* allele in normal skin fibroblasts. It was observed that both normal and mutant *p53* RNA are expressed at low levels. In contrast to the transfection studies, the normal skin fibroblasts provide a system which both wild-type and mutant *p53* alleles are naturally expressed at similarly low levels without potentially interfering dosage effects. Based on the studies demonstrating that mutant *p53* may inactivate the transcriptional activity of wild-type protein, it has been postulated that direct analysis of the transcriptional activity of *p53* expressed in fibroblasts or lymphocytes should permit the detection of inactivating germline mutations. Using a short-term biological assay whereby *p53* cDNA was amplified from cells and cloned into a eukaryotic expression vector that was then transfected with a reporter plasmid for the transcriptional activity of *p53* into Saos-2 cells lacking *p53*, analysis of transcriptional activation could be performed. This assay could confirm the presence of both wild-type and mutant *p53* in these cells. The rapidity and apparent sensitivity of this assay suggest that it may be valuable as a functional screen. Yet another "functional" assay has been described that takes advantage of the fact that plasmids can be generated by homologous recombination *in vivo* in the yeast *Saccharomyces cerevisiae*. By this method, *p53* is tested for its ability to activate transcription from a promoter containing *p53*-binding sites in these yeast. Cotransformation of a *p53* polymerase chain reaction (PCR) product and a cut promoter-containing plasmid results in repair of the plasmid with the PCR product *in vivo* and in constitutive expression of the full-length human p53 protein in the yeast. Clones that have repaired the plasmid are selected on media lacking leucine, and subsequent screening for histidine prototrophy identifies colonies that contain transcriptionally active *p53*. This assay has the advantages of being rapid (less than 5 days) and having few steps, although it does assume that cancer-causing mutations of *p53* are defective in transactivation.

VII. ANIMAL MODELS OF LI–FRAUMENI SYNDROME

Transgenic animals carrying distinct deregulated oncogenes develop tumors that appear to be cell-type specific. To better study *p53 in vivo*, mice have been created that either lack functional *p53* or express dominant-negative mutant alleles that inhibit wild-type *p53* function.

The *p53* transgenic mice carry transgenes that encode for proteins differing from wild-type p53 either by an ^{193}Arg > Pro or by an ^{135}Ala > Val substitution. The transgenes are under transcriptional control of the endogenous promoter and the mice carry the normal wild-type *p53* complement. Thus, they weakly resemble the human LFS *p53* genotype, although neither mutation has been implicated in LFS. The transgene was expressed in a wide range of tissue, yet tumors (primarily osteosarcomas, lymphomas, and adenocarcinomas of the lung) occur in only 20% of the mice, suggesting intrinsic tissue-specific differences. This model contributed to the hypothesis that the tumor spectrum in LFS might arise from transmission of a mutant *p53* gene.

Homologous recombination has also been used in mouse embryonic stem (ES) cells to derive "null" alleles of *p53*. Two models result from the replacement of exons 2–6 with a *neo*^{r} cassette. The third comprises into exon 5, as well as a deletion of 350 nucleotides

of intron 4 and 106 nucleotides of exon 5. None of the *p53*$^{-/-}$ mice express detectable intact or truncated mRNA or protein. The mutant *p53* allele has been established in the germline of chimeric mice with a mixed inbred (C57BL/6 × 129/Sv), pure 129/Sv, or 129/O1a backgrounds. In all mice, spontaneous development of different tumor types, predominantly lymphomas and sarcomas, occurred in >75% before 6 months of age. Tumor development, primarily sarcomas, is delayed in heterozygotes (*p53*$^{+/-}$); however, by 18 months of age, 50% develop tumors. Multiple primaries were noted in ~30% of tumor-bearing *p53*$^{-/-}$ mice, while virtually none of the *p53*$^{+/+}$ mice had developed tumors by 18 months. The importance of genetic background in influencing the tumor type is exemplified by the occurrence of unusual cancers, including pineoblastomas and islet cell tumors in *p53*$^{-/-}$ mice crossed with mice heterozygous for an *RB1* mutation. The relative lack of strain-to-strain variance in the *p53* null-induced phenotype suggests that the *p53* genotype is important in dictating phenotype. Evidence with other genetic crosses further supports this premise. APC-mutated (*Min*) mice develop bowel adenomas with malignant potential that is accelerated when outbred to different genetic backgrounds, in particular carrying a modifier of *Min*, termed *Mom-1*.

Provocative studies have tested whether the tumorigenic activity of a mutant *p53* is altered by the presence or absence of wild-type *p53 in vivo*. Mice carrying the ^{135}Ala > Val mutant transgene were crossed with *p53*-deficient mice. The mutant *p53*-Tg accelerated tumor formation in *p53*$^{+/-}$, but not in *p53*$^{-/-}$ mice, suggesting that this loss-of-function mutation had a dominant-negative effect with respect to tumor incidence and cell growth rates. Although the tumor spectrum was similar in transgenic and nontransgenic mice, the transgenics showed a predisposition to lung adenocarcinomas. Thus, a given *p53* alteration may have distinct tissue specificity with respect to tumorigenic potential. It would be of interest to extend this approach to alleles that behave differently *in vivo* or *in vitro*.

The *p53*$^{-/-}$ state is compatible with normal development, although the yield of *p53*$^{-/-}$ offspring from varies from 16.6 to 23%. This apparent increase in fetal loss is corroborated by the demonstration of fetal exencephaly, although increased fetal loss is not seen in human LFS families.

$p53$-deficient mice are more sensitive to the effects of certain carcinogenic agents. $p53^{+/-}$ mice exposed to dimethylnitrosamine developed liver hemangiosarcomas more rapidly than treated $p53^{+/+}$ animals. $p53^{-/-}$ mice treated with an initiator, dimethylbenzanthracene, and a promoter, 12-O-tetradecanoyl-phorbol-13-acetate, show a more rapid rate of malignant progression of skin papillomas to carcinomas.

These studies help distinguish whether $p53$ mutations play rate-limiting or tissue-specific roles in the tumor progression pathway. $p53$-deficient and $p53$-Tg mice exposed to sublethal doses of γ-irradiation develop tumors, usually sarcomas, earlier than in untreated animals. This susceptibility is associated with a 2X increase in the accumulation of radiation-induced dsDNA breaks compared to that seen in $p53^{+/+}$ animals. These studies confirm that $p53$ prevents the accumulation of cells sustaining radiation- or chemically induced DNA damage. $p53$-deficient mice have been used to study the effects of environmental factors on tumorigenesis and development. Given the important role of $p53$ in cell cycle control, a $p53$-deficient state might be expected to deregulate differentiation and development, yielding aberrant morphogenesis and embryonic lethality. The teratogen/DNA-damaging agent benzo[a]pyrene and the anticonvulsant/teratogenic drug phenytoin induce a 2–4X increase in in utero fetal death, teratogenicity, and postpartum lethality in pregnant $p53^{+/-}$ mice, further supporting the embryoprotective role of $p53$.

VIII. ISSUES IN $p53$ PREDICTIVE GENETIC TESTING

Important issues have arisen as a result of the identification of germline mutations of the $p53$ tumor suppressor gene in rare cancer-prone families. These include such practical problems as clarification of the definition of clinical manifestations of the Li–Fraumeni syndrome, determination of the functional significance of somatic and germline $p53$ mutations in cancer patients generally, and the development of practical and accurate laboratory techniques to identify mutations. Ethical questions of predictive testing in LFS families address the selection of patients to be tested, the development of

pilot testing programs, both as research endeavors and as service needs, the means of transmission of results to test subjects, their affected and unaffected relatives and interested third parties, and the potential roles for preventive and therapeutic interventions based on testing results. This article is not meant to discuss in detail these problems, but one would be remiss to ignore their significance.

Predictive testing for germline $p53$ mutations (or any other disease-predisposing gene) must be based on theoretical principles of respect for the autonomy of the patient and freedom from coercion, benefit to the patient, universal accessibility and freedom from discrimination, and maintenance of confidentiality of results. In anticipation of the flood of disease and cancer-predisposing genes that are being made available for mutation screening, guidelines addressing the following issues must now be established using $p53$ testing as a model: (1) who is to have access to the information, (2) what safeguards are to be established to protect employees and others from discrimination, (3) at what stage in the development of these genetic tests should mass screening be advocated, and (4) when might mandatory genetic screening be acceptable practice?

For several reasons, testing cannot at present be offered to the general population. Even within the general cancer population the carrier rate is demonstrably low, the prevalence of germline $p53$ mutations likely being only a fraction of 1%. The sensitivity and specificity of screening methods to identify mutations are unknown and both false-positive and false-negative results have been encountered. The sequence-confirmed presence of a base pair alteration itself must be interpreted carefully to ensure that its protein product has significance in that in some way it inactivates normal $p53$ function.

Because the frequency and implications of germline $p53$ mutations are not known at present, it is essential to initiate multicenter research surveys to define these parameters in young patients with malignant tumors and, at least at the present time, to limit these surveys to the research setting. Similar analyses must also be carried out in potential carriers, including members of cancer-prone families not typical of LFS. Screening of unaffected individuals should be restricted initially to blood relatives of LFS families or cancer cases with documented germline $p53$ mutations. Thus, predictive testing for germline *p53* mutations in healthy individuals must be clearly distinguished from surveys among select groups of cancer patients.

Furthermore, effective ways must be developed to provide informed consent to those being screened about potential beneficial and harmful psychologic and social sequelae of participation in these screening programs. These studies should be undertaken in a research setting involving expertise in oncology, psychiatry, psychology, genetic counseling, medical ethics, and molecular and medical genetics. The incorporation of all these services precludes, at least for the present time, any screening to be performed by uninformed parties.

There is evidence to suggest that by providing cancer risk information in medical practice, it may be possible to facilitate the patients' informed decision-making about future participation in cancer prevention and surveillance programs. However, the discovery of genetic markers such as *p53* for cancer risk will require new knowledge about how to communicate risk information and how to motivate adherence to cancer prevention and early detection. For example, how much information should be disclosed to an individual if despite knowledge that their cancer risk is increased due to the presence of specific predisposing genetic factors, there is no known way of reducing that risk, of identifying the target organ, or determining the age at which the tumor will develop? Is there an obligation to inform family members of individuals who are identified as having such a genetic susceptibility? How aggressively should people at genetic risk for cancer be recruited into chemoprevention or other trials?

The issue of potential interventative measures is complex. For the most part, the component malignancies of the Li–Fraumeni syndrome are difficult to cure, with the exception of early stage breast cancer, rare germ cell tumors of the testis, and childhood acute lymphoblastic leukemia. Although the prognosis for most of the component solid tumors improves with earlier stage at diagnosis, only screening for breast cancer has been shown to potentially reduce mortality. Recognized effective screening tests are generally not available for the other cancers typically found in Li–Fraumeni syndrome. Chemoprevention may be of some value in certain cancers, but is not at present of universal benefit. Despite the many drawbacks of predictive testing, the potential to reduce the marked loss of human potential resulting from the death of a child or young adult makes pilot research efforts necessary for early intervention in *p53* mutation carriers.

See Also the Following Articles

Ataxia Telangiectasia Syndrome • Brain and Central Nervous System Cancers • Gastric Cancer: Inherited Predisposition • Hereditary Risk of Breast Cancer and Ovarian Cancer: BRCA1 and BRCA2 • Sarcomas of Soft Tissue • TP53 Tumor Suppressor Gene: Structure and Function • Transgenic Mice in Cancer Research

Bibliography

Caron de Fromentel, C., and Soussi, T. (1992). TP 53 suppressor gene: A model for investigating human mutagenesis. *Genes Chrom. Cancer* **4,** 1.

Donehower, L. A., Harvey, M., Slagle, B. L., McArthur, M. J., Montgomery, C. A., Jr., Butel, J., and Bradley, A. (1992). Mice deficient for p53 are developmentally normal but susceptible to spontaneous tumors. *Nature* **356,** 215.

Garber, J. E., Goldstein, A. M., Kantor, A. F., Dreyfus, M. G., Fraumeni, J. F., Jr., and Li, F. P. (1991). Follow-up study of twenty-four families with Li-Fraumeni syndrome. *Cancer Res.* **51,** 6094.

Harris, C. C., and Hollstein, M. (1993). Clinical implications of the *p53* tumor-suppressor gene. *N. Engl. J. Med.* **329,** 1318.

Ishioka, C., Frebourg, T., Yan, Y.-X., Vidal, M., Friend, S. H., et al. (1993). Screening patients for heterozygous p53 mutations using a functional assay in yeast. *Nature Genet.* **5,** 124.

Lane, D. P. (1992). p53, guardian of the genome. *Nature* **358,** 15–16.

Lane, D. P., and Crawford, L. V. (1979). T antigen is bound to a host protein in SV40-transformed cells. *Nature* **278,** 261.

Li, F. P., and Fraumeni, J. F., Jr. (1969). Rhabdomyosarcoma in children: Epidemiologic study and identification of a familial cancer syndrome. *J. Natl. Cancer Inst.* **43,** 1365.

Li, F. P., Garber, J. E., Friend, S. H., Strong, L. C., Patenaud, A. F., et al. (1992). Recommendations on predictive testing for germline p53 mutation among cancer-prone individuals. *J. Natl. Cancer Inst.* **84,** 1156.

Malkin, D., Li, F. P., Strong, L. C., Fraumeni, J. F., Jr., Nelson, C. E., Kim, D. H., et al. (1990). Germ line p53 mutations in a familial syndrome of breast cancer, sarcomas, and other neoplasms. *Science* **250,** 1233.

Srivastava, S., Zou, Z. Q., Pirollo, K., Blattner, W., and Chang, E. H. (1990). Gene-line transmission of a mutated p53 gene in a cancer-prone family with Li-Fraumeni syndrome. *Nature* **348,** 747.

Liposome-Mediated Gene Therapy

John P. Dileo and Leaf Huang
University of Pittsburgh

GLOSSARY

CpG motif Unmethylated dinucleotide sequence presence in bacterial or plasmid DNA. These sequences are responsible for the potent inflammatory response seen upon systemic administration of lipoplexes.

DOTAP *N*-[1-(2,3-Dioleoyloxy)propyl]-*N*,*N*-trimethylammonium methylsulfate. Cationic lipid commonly used *in vitro*.

DOTMA *N*-[1-(2,3-Dioleoyloxy)propyl]-*N*,*N*,*N*-trimethylammonium chloride. Cationic lipid commonly used *in vitro*.

DC-Chol 3-β[*N*-(*N'*,*N'*-Dimethylaminoethane carbamoyl)] cholesterol. Cationic lipid derived from cholesterol; commonly used *in vivo*.

helper lipid Lipid that aids in the formation of a liposome.

lipoplex A liposome/plasmid DNA complex.

G ene therapy approaches have been proposed for the treatment of numerous conditions, and many clinical trials of gene therapy strategies for cancer are currently in progress. Several areas of investigation have demonstrated that cancer results from the accumulation of multiple genetic alterations, some of which are inherited, whereas others are accumulated over time. While we understand a good deal about cancer formation and progression, the complete story has yet to be revealed. Despite its complexity, cancer is at heart a genetic disease, and as such it is a good candidate for intervention by gene therapy.

I. VECTORS

A. Viral

In vivo gene transfer can be accomplished by two classes of vectors: viral and nonviral. Both of these systems have distinct advantages and disadvantages, and the choice of vector used largely depends on the suggested application. Viral vectors use replication-incompetent viruses such as adenovirus to deliver genetic material to target tissues. Because these vectors are based on viruses that have evolved specifically to deliver genetic material to mammalian cells, they usually result in a high percentage of cells being transfected. Because these vectors are so efficient, approximately 85% of all current gene therapy clinical trails use viral vectors. Unfortunately, they also suffer from limitations, such as limited packaging capacity, immunogenicity, and an inability to transfect nondividing cells.

B. Nonviral

Several of these issues can be resolved by the use of completely synthetic, nonviral systems to deliver DNA. These methods of gene delivery include naked DNA injection, biobalistics (gene gun), DNA/liposome complexes, calcium phosphate precipitation, and electroporation. Nonviral systems have several advantages over viral systems. Particularly, they cause no specific immune response and can therefore be administered safely and repeatedly; there is no limit on the size of the DNA that can be delivered; they can be targeted for specific tissues; they are easier to prepare than virus-based systems; and they can easily be adapted to specific needs.

1. Naked DNA

Wolfe and colleagues were the first to observe that the injection of naked plasmid DNA (pDNA) into muscle results in the sustained expression of genes encoded on that pDNA. A modification of naked DNA injection is particle-mediated gene delivery. In this system, pDNA is precipitated onto inert microcarriers and accelerated into the target by an explosive burst of air. These two methods have been widely used in genetic vaccination protocols.

2. Liposomes

While naked DNA is suitable for intramuscular injection, it is degraded rapidly upon intravenous administration. One way to protect DNA from degradation while allowing for efficient gene delivery is by using liposomes. Because of their simplicity, liposomes are by far the most commonly used nonviral DNA delivery system. Felgner and co-workers reported the first use of liposomes as a gene delivery vehicle in 1987. Figure 1 shows the structure of some common lipids used to produce liposomes. Of these, the two most commonly used lipids for *in vitro* applications are N-[1-(2,3-dioleoyloxy)propyl]-N,N,N-trimethylam-

monium methylsulfate (DOTAP) and N-[1-(2,3-dioleoyloxy)propyl]-N,N,N-trimethylammmonium chloride (DOTMA), but many different lipids are available and the formulation can be adapted to suit the specific application. For example, helper lipids such as DOPE that facilitate the fusion of the liposomes with cellular membranes can be added to the mix. For clinical applications, the most commonly used lipid is 3-β[N-(N',N'-dimethylaminoethane carbamoyl)] cholesterol (DC-Chol).

Liposome/DNA complexes (lipoplexes) are formed by the addition of pDNA to a solution of preformed liposomes. Upon addition of the pDNA, rearrangement of the lipids occurs such that the DNA is coated with a lipid bilayer (shown in Fig. 2). Most currently used lipids contain positively charged head groups. The positive charge facilitates the association of the liposomes with the negatively charged DNA. In addition, upon systemic administration, the excess positive charge helps form an electrostatic interaction with negatively charged extracellular matrix proteins. In particular, heparin sulfate has been shown to be the receptor for lipoplexes.

Lipoplexes have been shown to be capable of delivering pDNA to a variety of cell types *in vitro* and *in vivo*. When lipoplexes come in contact with cell membranes they are endocytosed and deposit their cargo of pDNA in the cytoplasm of the target cell. Most of the pDNA is degraded but some is translocated to the nucleus where it is transiently expressed. When administered locally by intratumor injection, lipoplexes are taken up and gene expression is observed in approximately 1–10% of the tumor cells. When administered, intravenously lipoplexes interact with and become coated by serum proteins. This leads to their uptake by the RES system and may in part account for the low transfection efficiency of these vectors. However, gene expression is seen in all major organs, with the lung showing the highest level of activity in mice. Gene expression peaks at 24 h and high-level gene expression is observed for approximately 2 days. It has been shown that the systemic administration of lipoplexes results in a nonspecific immune response that is characterized by high levels of cytokine production and natural killer cell activation. It is believed that this is due to the presence of unmethylated CpG motifs present in the pDNA.

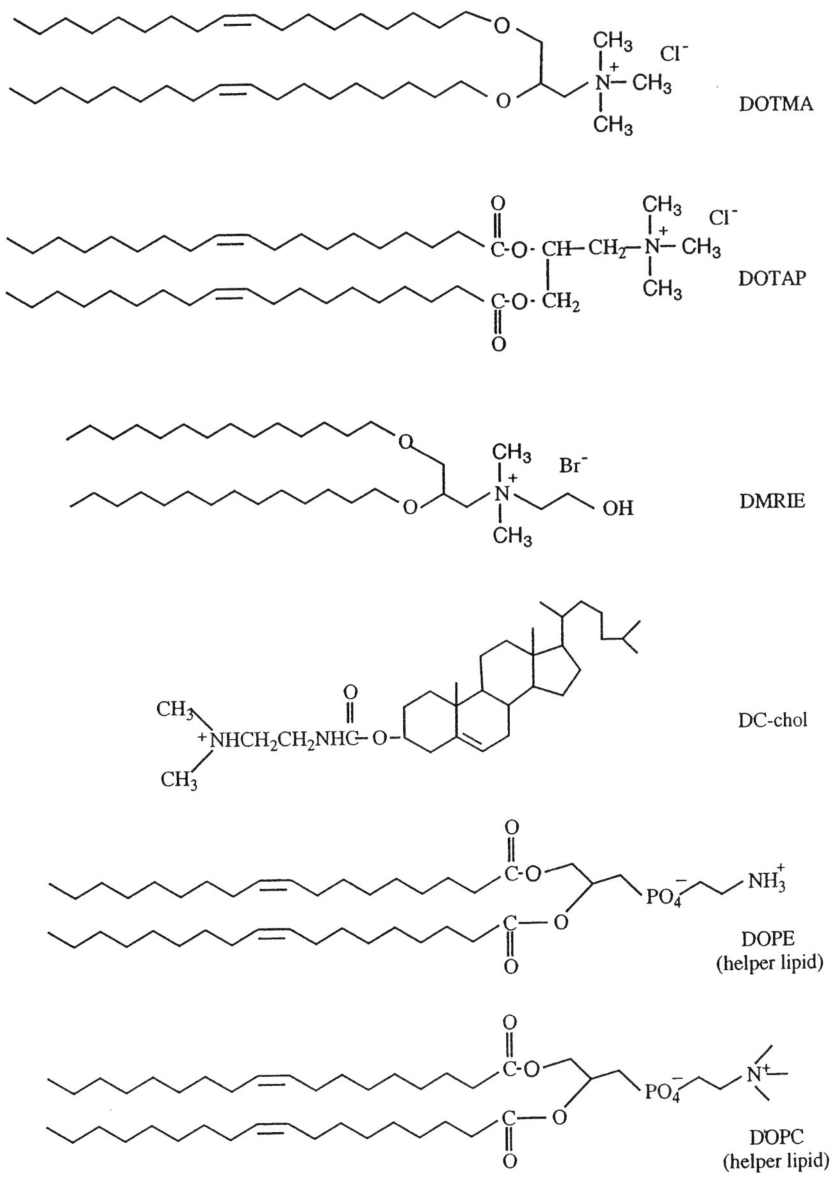

FIGURE 1 Structures of some commonly used cationic lipids and helper lipids used for gene delivery.

Lipoplexes are generally not specifically targeted but can be made specific by the addition of targeting ligands such as glycolipids that target the liver or monoclonal antibodies.

Despite the many advantages presented by the use of nonviral DNA delivery methods, there are still many significant problems that must be overcome in order to make their widespread use feasible. The most significant limitation of nonviral systems is the low transfection efficiency and resultant low-level gene expression that is observed. For many treatment regimens, prolonged, high-level expression of the therapeutic gene is desirable. Because only a small percentage of cells express the delivered gene, the high-level expression that is necessary for a therapeutic effect may not be achievable.

Another difficulty with nonviral systems is their inability to target specific tissues. Many nonviral systems,

FIGURE 2 Electron micrograph of lipid:pDNA complex (lipoplex).

such as gene gun or naked DNA injection, rely on physical methods to deliver pDNA to cells. By nature, these methods are difficult to target to specific tissues. However, much work has been done using tissue-specific promoters to limit gene expression to the target of interest.

II. STRATEGIES FOR TUMOR ERADICATION

Because cancers result from the abnormal function of normal cellular processes, it has been proposed that restoring normal cellular functions by the addition of exogenous genes can be an effective way to treat cancers. If normal function cannot be restored, then there are natural processes that can be activated that will cause the cancer cells to die or be killed by the host immune system.

Because cancers are caused by multiple genetic changes, it is impractical to attempt to correct every lesion. However, several strategies have been developed that have been shown to be effective in preclinical studies. While we do not discuss all strategies

for dealing with solid tumors, this article reviews the most common ones. These strategies include the introduction of genes that (1) directly kill tumor cells or render them susceptible to specific drugs, (2) protect normal cells from toxic side effects of traditional chemotherapy or radiation therapy (3) enhance the hosts immune response against the tumor, or (4) halt tumor growth/progression. Any one of these methods can be used in combination with nonviral delivery systems.

A. Apoptosis Induction

All cells possess a genetic program that, when activated, causes the cell to self-destruct in what is termed active cell death (ACD) or apoptosis. While many of the details of apoptosis signaling remain to be elucidated, enough is known to form a general pathway. This path can be subdivided into three phases: formation of the death signaling complex; activation of the caspase signaling pathway; and the activation of these caspases, cellular proteases that carry out the work of killing the cell. Direct tumor killing can be accomplished activating this path at any of these stages. This is typically done by delivering genes that encode for proteins involved in the apoptosis signal transduction pathway (TNF-α, etc.) to tumor cells. However, this approach is limited by the fact that there is indiscriminate killing of all cells, including normal cells surrounding the tumor, that take up and express the cytotoxic gene.

B. Enzyme/Prodrug Treatments

An alternative method is to make cancer cells susceptible to radiation or specific drugs. In this strategy, genes are delivered that encode an exogenous enzyme that converts a nontoxic prodrug into a toxic metabolite. After the tumor has been transduced, the prodrug is given systemically. The most common enzyme/prodrug combination utilizes the herpes simplex virus thymidine kinase gene (HSV-tk) combined with gancyclovir. More recently, a system combining the *Escherichia coli* cytosine deaminase gene (CD) and 5-fluorocytosine (5-FC) has been developed. In this system, CD converts 5-FC to the toxic metabolite 5-flouorouracil (5-FU). The mechanism by which these systems kill dividing cells is by producing nucleotide analogs, which inhibit DNA synthesis by being incorporated into the growing DNA strand.

These systems result in the production of a locally high concentration of the cytotoxic product with minimal systemic accumulation. This local concentration of drug creates what is termed the bystander effect in which nontransfected cells are killed. This happens when the cytotoxic agent produced in one cell is passed to a nearby cell directly through gap junctions or indirectly through local diffusion. The bystander effect can be so great that only 5–10% of tumor cells need to be transfected to produce complete tumor regression. Because only a limited amount of transfection in a local area is needed for this type of therapy, it is particularly amenable to the use of nonviral vectors.

C. Chemoprotection

Most commonly used chemotherapeutic agents in use today are designed to target rapidly dividing cells, such as tumor cells. Unfortunately, these drugs also kill cells that naturally divide at a rapid pace, such as bone marrow and gut epithelium. The multidrug resistance gene (MDR) encodes a transmembrane protein that pumps cytotoxic agents, such as taxol, adriamycin, vincristine, and actinomycin D, out of the cell. Several clinical trials are now investigating the possibility of delivering the MDR gene to bone marrow cells and reintroducing them into the patient in an attempt to limit the hematopoietic toxicity of chemotherapy regimens. Unfortunately, this type of intervention is limited by the inefficiency with which genes can be delivered into marrow cells.

D. Immunostimulation

To eradicate a tumor, all of the cells that compose it must be killed. Even the most efficient gene delivery vehicles cannot achieve 100% efficiency so ways to eradicate nontransfected tumor cells must be developed. One way to eliminate the need to deliver DNA to all cells of a tumor is to have the hosts' natural anticancer mechanisms destroy the tumor. Normal cells expose thousands of peptides in their surface MHC class I molecules, which can potentially be recognized by T cells. These peptides can be derived from self, foreign, or, in the case of tumors, mutated cellular proteins that are tumor-specific markers. Based on this, tumors can be targets for immune eradication. However, because tumors are derived from normal tissues in the first place, they are inefficiently recognized by the immune system. In addition to low immunogenicity, tumors have developed many ways to escape from the immune system. For example, many tumors downregulate immune recognition or costimulatory molecules such as the class I major histocompatability protein (MHCI) or B7.1. In addition, tumors can damp down the immune response by producing immunodepressive cytokines such as interleuken 10 (IL-10) and tumor growth factor β (TGF-β). Gene-based treatments designed to overcome each of these evasive tactics have been proposed. Despite the tumors best efforts, the immune system can be trained to recognize these "foreign" cells. It has been shown that delivering genes encoding immunostimulatory factors to tumors increases their immunogenicity. The most common class of immunostimulatory molecules are the cytokines. These naturally occurring factors enhance the ability of immune effector cells to eliminate tumors. It is believed that the addition of these genes to tumors will mimic the natural cytokine environment, promote T-cell recognition of poorly immunogenic tumors, activate NK cells, and enhance tumor antigen presentation.

The cytokine that has been most closely studied is IL-2, but the overproduction of this cytokine was associated with significant toxicity, particularly capillary leak syndrome. In addition to cytokines (IL-4, IL-12, etc.), growth factors (GM-CSF, G-CSF), inflammatory mediators (TNFα) and interferons (IFN-γ, IFN-α) have been tested and have shown good antitumor potential.

For the same reasons that enzyme/prodrug regimens are well suited to the use of nonviral vectors, immunostimulatory therapies often use nonviral vectors. There is no need to deliver the gene of interest to all tumor cells. Limited transfection within the tumor should be sufficient to initiate a systemic antitumor immune response. Instead of the toxic metabolite providing the bystander effect, it is provided by the host immune system.

E. Restoration of Tumor Suppressor Gene Function

The multistep model of cancer formation proposed by Fearon and Vogelstein in 1990 states that multiple genetic lesions are necessary for normal cells to transform into a neoplastic phenotype. Cancer comes about through the activation of protooncogenes and the inactivation of tumor suppressor genes. Tumor suppressor genes are defined as genes whose loss or inactivation contributes to tumor formation. These proteins normally act as a brake on cell growth and division and are typically involved in regulating the cell cycle or inducing programmed cell death (apoptosis). Mutation of a tumor suppressor gene can have transforming capability even if only one copy of the gene is disrupted due to the dominant-negative effect of the mutant allele. However, the activation of protooncogenes is a dominant gain-of-function mutation. These proteins signal the cell to progress through the cell cycle, and constitutive activation of these genes results in a constant signal to divide. A third class of genes that are involved in the DNA damage repair mechanism promotes genetic instability, which leads to the accumulation of mutations in tumor suppressor and protooncogenes.

In 1992, work by Goyette and co-workers showed that the correction of only one of the many mutations in a tumor may halt its progression. This observation has led to the development of strategies that aim to restore the function of mutated or missing genes by delivering a normal copy of the gene. One of the most commonly mutated genes in all cancers is the p53 tumor suppressor gene. Restoration of normal p53 function has shown to inhibit tumor growth in a wide variety of tumor models, including gliomas, head and neck cancers, and colon cancer. These encouraging preclinical studies have led to this approach being used to treat patients with several types of cancers.

F. Inhibition of Oncogene Expression

A similar strategy targeting oncogenes utilizes antisense RNA or ribozymes to reduce gene expression. In antisense-based therapies, an RNA molecule whose sequence is complementary to the messenger RNA (mRNA) sequence of the target gene is produced *in situ*. These antisense RNAs then bind to the mRNA by Watson–Crick base pairing and inhibit mRNA splicing, nuclear export, or protein translation. This approach has been successfully used for the treatment of lung cancers by inhibiting the expression of mutant K-ras. Other laboratories have used antisense-based strategies to decrease the expression of virally encoded oncogenes such as the human papiloma virus E6 and E7 proteins. Ribozymes are RNA molecules that have the ability to cleave mRNAs of specific sequences and are used similarly to antisense constructs. As an alternative to *in situ*-produced antisense RNAs or ribozymes, oligonucleotides that hybridize to the desired mRNA can be delivered to tumor masses.

Although there has been significant progress in the field of gene therapy for cancer, a single successful treatment has yet to be developed. In order to be more effective for use in cancer treatments, nonviral vectors need to be developed that have improved targeting ability, better *in vivo* transduction efficiency, and produce prolonged gene expression. Considering the current pace at which we are elucidating the mechanisms of cancer formation and vector development, we believe that successful gene-based treatment for cancer will be developed.

See Also the Following Articles

CATIONIC LIPID-MEDIATED GENE THERAPY • CYTOKINE GENE THERAPY

Bibliography

Dass, C. R., and Burton, M. A. (1999). Lipoplexes and tumors: A review. *J. Pharm. Pharmacol.* **51,** 755.

Fearon, E. R., and Vogelstein, B. (1990). A genetic model for colorectal tumorigenesis. *Cell* **60,** 397.

Felgner, P. L., Gadek, T. R., Holm, M., *et al.* (1987). Lipofection: A highly efficient, lipid mediated DNA transfection procedure. *Proc. Natl. Acad. Sci. USA* **84,** 7413.

Felgner, P. L. (1999). Progress in gene delivery research and development. *In* "Nonviral Vectors for Gene Therapy" (L. Huang, M. C. Hung, and E. Wagner, eds.), p. 26. Academic Press, San Diego.

Goyette, M. C., Cho, K., Fasching, C. L., *et al.* (1992). Progression of colorectal cancer is associated with multiple tumor suppressor gene defects but inhibition of tumorigenicity is accomplished by correction of any single defect via chromosome transfer. *Mol. Cell. Biol.* **12,** 1387.

Harrington, K. J., Lewanski, C. R., and Stewart, J. S. (2000). Liposomes as vehicles for targeted therapy of cancer. 1. Preclinical development. *Clin. Oncol.* **12,** 2.

Harrington, K. J., Lewanski, C. R., and Stewart, J. S. (2000). Liposomes as vehicles for targeted therapy of cancer. 2. Clinical development. *Clin. Oncol.* **12,** 16.

Lin, A. J., Slack, N. L., and Ahmad, A., *et al.* (2000). Structure and structure function studies of lipid/plasmid DNA complexes. *J. Drug Target* **8,** 13.

Maurer, N., Mori, A., Palmer, L., *et al.* (1999). Lipid-based systems for the intracellular delivery of genetic drugs. *Mol. Membr. Biol.* **16,** 129.

McLean, J. W., Thurston, G., and McDonald, D. M. (1999). Sites of uptake and expression of cationic liposome/DNA complexes injected intravenously. In "Nonviral Vectors for Gene Therapy" (L. Huang, M. C. Hung, and E. Wagner, eds.), p. 120. Academic Press, San Diego.

Schenborn, E. T., and Oler, J. (2000). Liposome mediate transfection of mammalian cells. *Methods Mol. Biol.* **130,** 155.

Templeton, N. S., and Lasic, D. D. (1999). New directions in liposome gene delivery. *Mol. Biotechnol.* **11,** 2.

Wolff, J. A., Malone, R. W., Williams, P., *et al.* (1990). Direct gene transfer into mouse muscle in vivo. *Science* **247,** 1465.

Liver Cancer: Etiology and Prevention

W. Thomas London

Fox Chase Cancer Center, Philadelphia, Pennsylvania

GLOSSARY

aflatoxin Cancer-causing toxin produced by fungi of the *Aspergillus* type.

aflatoxin B₁ The major cancer-causing molecule of the aflatoxins.

angiosarcoma Rare malignant liver tumor of adults.

cholangiocarcinoma Malignant liver tumor of bile duct cells.

focal nodular hyperplasia A benign liver tumor usually considered a reactive disorder.

hepatocellular carcinoma The major primary cancer of the liver.

hemangioma Benign tumor of lining cells of blood vessels.

hemochomatosis Genetic disease of increased iron absorption.

hepatic adenoma Benign liver tumor.

hepatoblastoma Malignant liver tumor of early childhood.

polyvinyl chloride A chemical widely used in the manufacture of plastics.

primary sclerosing cholangitis Inflammation and scarring of bile ducts.

vinyl chloride monomer A chemical that can cause angiosarcoma.

Cancers that originate in the liver, primary liver cancers, are often confused with cancers that begin in some other site and spread to the liver, i.e., secondary liver cancers. This article is concerned only with primary liver cancers, 85 to 90% of which are hepatocellular carcinomas (HCC). These are malignant tumors of liver parenchymal cells (hepatocytes). HCCs cause more than 500,000 deaths annually, primarily (about 80%) in the developing countries of Asia and Africa. The other primary liver cancer that occurs with a much lower, but still significant frequency in some countries is cholangiocarcinoma, a tumor of cells lining bile ducts.

I. INTRODUCTION

Eighty to 95% of HCCs are associated with chronic infection of hepatocytes with either of two viruses, hepatitis B virus (HBV) or hepatitis C virus (HCV). Of these, HBV infections account for 75 to 80% of virus-associated HCCs, with HCV responsible for 10 to 20%. HBV infection is preventable by immunization, and HCV is largely preventable by public health measures. Therefore, if the opportunities for intervention were acted upon, HCC could become a minor cause of cancer mortality in the foreseeable future (Table I).

Cholangiocarcinoma has a completely different etiology. It is associated with chronic inflammation and injury of bile duct cells (cholangitis). In southeast Asian countries, cholangitis and cholangiocarcinoma are related to infestation with liver flukes, *Clonorchis sinensis* and *Opistorchis viverinni*. In developed countries, a particular type of cholangitis, primary sclerosing cholangitis, often associated with inflammatory bowel diseases, is the leading etiological factor.

Other malignant and benign liver tumors are also discussed briefly.

II. BENIGN TUMORS

There are three common benign tumors of the liver: hemangiomas, adenomas, and focal nodular hyperplasias. They are important primarily because they are often detected on ultrasonography or other imaging procedures of the liver and must be distinguished from malignant tumors. There is no evidence that any of these benign lesions progress to malignant tumors.

Hemangioma, a tumor of cells lining blood vessels (endothelial cells), is the most common benign tumor of the liver in both children and adults. In adults, hemangiomas are usually discovered as an incidental finding of diagnostic imaging, but in infants such tumors may grow very large and can be fatal. The general view is that these are congenital lesions, but there are no studies on the epidemiology of this tumor. Studies indicate that hemangiomas are clonal outgrowths of endothelial cells.

Hepatic adenomas are well-differentiated sheets or cords of cells of hepatocyte origin that are clearly delimited from the surrounding liver. Before the advent of oral contraceptives (OCs) in the 1960s, they were extremely rare. Since then there have been many case reports and three case-control studies showing an association of OC use of greater than 5 years duration with hepatic adenoma. Nevertheless, from 1971 to 1994 fewer than 250 such cases were reported in the world literature, despite the tens of millions of women who had taken OCs. Hepatic adenomas are very rare in men. Hepatic adenomas are also associated with a rare genetic disease, glycogen storage disease type I.

Focal nodular hyperplasia (FNH), which consists of well-circumscribed, unencapsulated nodules of hepatocytes, has been classified as a benign tumor. Studies show that it is a polyclonal lesion and, therefore, not a true tumor. FNH has also been associated with OC use.

III. MALIGNANT TUMORS

A. Childhood Liver Cancer

Fortunately, primary liver cancers are rare in childhood. The most common malignant tumor of the

TABLE I
Relationship of Chronic HBV and HCV Infections to HCC

	HBV	HCV
Global HCC cases (No./year)	375–400,000	50–100,000
Highest risk regions	East Asia, sub-Saharan Africa	Japan, southern Europe, Egypt
Global number of chronically infected persons	350,000,000	170,000,000
Age at highest risk of chronic infection	0 to 5 years	All ages
Highest risk of HCC by age at infection	0 to 5 years	>40 years
Gender at higher risk of HCC	Males	Males
Time from infection to HCC diagnosis	30 to 70 years	25 to 40 years

liver in children before 3 years of age is hepatoblastoma, a tumor of embryonic or fetal hepatocytes. It is associated with very low birth weight, as well as with genetic diseases, including the Beckwith–Wiedemann syndrome, characterized by large body size, large tongue and large body organs, and familial adenomatous polyposis (FAP), an inherited predisposition to multiple colorectal tumors. About 2% of children with hepatoblastoma also have hemihypertophy, enlargement of organs in half or one region of the body. After age 3, HCC is the more common malignancy. Its risk factors are similar to those of adults and will not be discussed further here. The prognosis for hepatoblastoma with surgical resection and modern chemotherapy is excellent.

B. Primary Liver Cancers of Adults

1. Angiosarcoma

This multicentric tumor, composed of spindle-shaped cells, probably originates from the liver vasculature. Although it is a rare tumor, only 20 to 30 cases occur each year in the United States, it is important because it is causally associated with exposure to certain environmental agents. These include Thorotrast (thorium dioxide), an α particle radiation emitter used between 1935 and 1947 to image the brain; vinyl chloride monomer (VCM) used to manufacture polyvinyl chloride (PVC), which in turn is used in the production of a variety of plastic products; and arsenic compounds previously used in certain medications (Fowler's solution for treatment of psoriasis and Neosalvorsan for syphilis). Because the time of Thorotrast use was clearly demarcated, the latent period from exposure to diagnosis of angiosarcoma has been estimated more precisely than for almost any other human carcinogen. The average latent period is about 36 years.

Industrial exposures to VCM, primarily through inhalation, are associated with a significantly increased incidence of angiosarcoma. The International Agency for Research on Cancer (IARC) classified VCM in 1987 as a class 1 carcinogen to humans based on both epidemiological and experimental animal evidence.

2. Cholangiocarcinoma

Cholangiocarcinomas can occur within the liver (intrahepatic) or outside the liver (extrahepatic). Intrahepatic cholangiocarcinomas account for less than 15% of all primary liver cancers. Although precise incidence or mortality figures for cholangiocarcinoma are not available because most registries combine this tumor with HCC, 2000 to 3000 cholangiocarcinomas are estimated to occur annually in the United States. In western countries, where the incidence is low, cholangiocarcinoma occurs most often in patients with primary sclerosing cholangitis (PSC), an inflammatory disease of bile ducts. The lifetime risk for patients with PSC to develop cholangiocarcinoma is about 10%. Although the etiology of PSC is unknown, 50 to 75% of patients with this disease also have an inflammatory disease of the bowel, either ulcerative colitis or Crohn's disease. Persons exposed to Thorotrast (see earlier discussion) also have an increased risk of developing cholangiocarcinoma.

In southeast Asia, infestation with *O. viverinni* in Thailand, Laos, and Malaysia or *C. sinensis* in Korea, Japan, and Vietnam, as assayed by either antibodies to parasite antigens or liver fluke eggs in stool, is associated with a two- to fivefold increased risk of cholangiocarcinoma. Parasites in bile ducts induce DNA damage probably by eliciting formation of oxygen radicals and carcinogens. The life cycle of liver flukes involves excretion of parasite eggs in feces, ingestion of eggs by freshwater snails, transmission of larvae to freshwater crabs or crayfish, and consumption of larvae in raw crabs or crayfish by humans. Interruption of this cycle of infection would prevent cholangitis and cholangiocarcinoma, but implementation of appropriate strategies has not been energetically pursued.

3. Hepatocellular Carcinoma

HCCs are composed of moderately to well-differentiated hepatocytes, with abundant eosinophilic cytoplasm, arranged in sheets or cords. Although they can metastasize, HCCs tend to be lethal by expanding within the liver until the organ fails or into the portal vein, causing portal hypertension.

Worldwide HCC is the fifth most common cancer by incidence among men and the eighth most common among women, but overall it is the third most common cause of cancer mortality. The actual number of deaths from HCC in the world is unknown because the areas where HCC is most common, east Asia and sub-Saharan Africa, have few reliable tumor registries. Extrapolations from the available registries have yielded estimates of about 500,000 HCC deaths annually, with 300,000 in China alone. Treatment for HCC is unsatisfactory. The 5-year life expectancy after diagnosis is 5% or less.

About 80% of all HCCs are found in livers affected by cirrhosis and about 15% by chronic hepatitis. HCC may be found in a histologically normal liver, but it is unusual. Among patients with biopsy-proven cirrhosis followed prospectively in liver disease clinics, 1 to 5 % develop HCC annually. Initially, most investigators thought that both chronic liver disease and HCC were caused by the consumption of alcohol and exposure to environmental carcinogens. However, the discovery of HBV in the 1960s and HCV three decades later resulted in our current understanding of the relationship of HCC to chronic hepatitis and cirrhosis. Chronic, but not transient, infection with either of these viruses may lead to the development of chronic hepatitis, cirrhosis, and HCC.

i. HBV   The World Health Organization (WHO) estimates that there are 350 million people in the world who are chronically infected with HBV. Chronic infection is defined as the presence in serum of hepatitis B surface antigen for 6 or more months. Prospective studies of chronically infected individuals in Taiwan, China, and Japan forecast a lifetime risk of HCC of 20 to 25%. Thus, the WHO estimates that 1 million of the 350 million chronic carriers of HBV will die annually of HCC or chronic liver disease.

HBV is transmitted in three ways: by exposure to virus-contaminated blood or blood products; sexually from infected man to woman, woman to man, or man to man; and by exposure of an infant to an infected mother in the perinatal period. Less than 10% of perinatal infections are transmitted *in utero*. The great majority results from exposure of the infant to maternal blood or body fluids during or after birth. Eighty to 90% of perinatal infections become chronic. Infections in 1 to 5 year olds result in 25 to 50% chronicity, whereas less than 10% of infections acquired by older children and adults become chronic. Therefore, HBV infections of infants and young children carry the greatest risk of eventual development of HCC.

Although HBV-associated cases of HCC are seen in children, they are rare. More typically, in populations with more than 2% chronically infected individuals (chronic carriers), the incidence of HCC begins to rise in the third decade and continues to increase through the seventh decade of life. Chronically infected men are three to four times more likely than chronic carrier women to develop HCC. The reason for this gender difference is not understood. HCC may occasionally develop in a HBV carrier with a histologically normal liver.

ii. Aflatoxin and HBV   Aflatoxin is a mycotoxin produced by *Aspergillus* species. Storage of corn or peanuts in warm, humid environments may lead to overgrowth of *Aspergillus* and heavy contamination with aflatoxin. Experiments in fish, poultry, and rodents have shown that aflatoxin B_1 (AFB1) is a powerful hepatic carcinogen. Although ecological studies of AFB1 contamination of food were compatible with a role for this carcinogen in human HCC, it has been person-specific epidemiological studies performed in the last decade that have yielded the strongest evidence.

p53 is the most frequently mutated gene in human cancer. Usually, such mutations are distributed throughout the coding regions of the gene. Among HCCs, however, a mutational hot spot at the third base of codon 249 has been observed in 30 to 60% of tumors arising in persons living in environments thought to be rich in aflatoxin. A G-to-T transversion at codon 249 is postulated to result from the reaction of the 8,9-epoxide-activated form of AFB1 with the N-7 guanine in DNA.

An interaction of AFB1 exposure with chronic HBV infection was revealed in prospective studies in Shanghai, China. Urinary excretion of aflatoxin metabolites increased the risk of HCC fourfold, HBV infection increased the risk sevenfold, but individuals who both excreted AFB1 metabolites and were HBV carriers had a 60 times increased risk of HCC. The current view is that AFB1 is primarily a carcinogen in HBV carriers.

iii. HCV   In contrast to HBV, childhood infection with HCV is rare. In the United States, about one in a thousand children 6 to 11 years old has antibodies to HCV (indicator of past or current infection with HCV). However, 60 to 80% of acute HCV infections in adults become chronic. Globally, about 170 million people are or have been infected with HCV. In the United States, the Centers for Disease Control and

Prevention estimate that 3.9 million people have been infected, of whom 2.7 million are chronically infected. Chronic HCV infection is the most common cause of HCC in Japan and western countries. Also, in contrast to HBV, HCV-associated HCC is always preceded by cirrhosis. Retrospective studies from Japan imply that as many as 20% of chronically infected persons will develop HCC. Clinic-based prospective studies and cohort studies beginning from time of initial HCV infection, however, show much lower rates of HCC development ranging from 0 to 2%.

HCV is transmitted primarily by exposure to contaminated blood or blood products. Perinatal infection is uncommon; less than 5% of infected mothers infect their babies. Sexual transmission of HCV may also occur, but is much less efficient than HBV. Prior to screening of blood donations in 1992, transfusion-mediated transmission was common. Fortunately, this is now very rare. At least 60% of new infections in United States are accounted for by injection drug use.

HCV infection is usually silent in onset and throughout most of its course. The current view is that HCV causes a chronic hepatitis that is slowly progressive in about 65% of chronically infected individuals. The likelihood is that these persons will not develop cirrhosis or HCC in their lifetimes. The other 35% will develop more rapidly progressive disease and severe liver injury. About 20% of all chronic infections will progress to cirrhosis. After cirrhosis develops, 10 to 30% of patients will develop HCC over the subsequent 10 years.

iv. Alcohol, Other Cofactors, and HCV Alcohol increases the rate of progression and severity of HCV-associated liver damage, and HCV increases the risk of severe liver disease in alcoholics. HCV-infected alcohol abusers (175 g/day) have 10 times the risk of cirrhosis as HCV-infected nondrinkers. About 40 to 60% of alcoholics with cirrhosis are infected with HCV. The association of alcohol abuse with HCC is weak in the absence of HCV infection.

HCV genotypes, particularly 1a and 1b, may be associated with more severe liver disease. Host genotypes that affect immune responses, such as HLA class II DR and DQ loci, may be associated with disease progression.

Infection after age 40 is associated with more severe outcomes. Males are more likely to have pro-gressive HCV disease than females. Thus, the most favorable prognostic profile is initial HCV infection before age 40 in a nonalcohol-drinking woman. Progression to clinically significant liver disease or HCC in such women may take more than 40 years.

v. Hemochromatosis Hemochromatosis is an autosomal recessive genetic disorder of iron metabolism in which affected individuals absorb too much iron. Toxic levels of iron may accumulate in the liver, heart, pancreas, and other organs, leading to damage and dysfunction. Iron overload in the liver can result in cirrhosis, which then carries the same risk of HCC as cirrhosis of other etiologies. Hereditary hemochromatosis is the commonest genetic disorder of whites, with a prevalence of homozygosity for a mutation in the hemochromatosis gene (HFE) of 1 in 200. Studies of untreated persons homozygous for the most common mutation of HFE (C282Y) indicate a lifetime risk of cirrhosis or HCC of only 2 to 3%. Reduction of body iron to normal levels can be achieved by frequent phlebotomy, thereby decreasing or eliminating this relatively small risk.

IV. PREVENTION OF HEPATOCELLULAR CARCINOMA

A. HBV

An effective vaccine for the prevention of HBV infection has been available in the United States since 1982. Universal vaccination of newborn infants greatly reduces the incidence of chronic HBV infections. In Taiwan, where HCC is endemic and universal vaccination of newborns has been practiced since 1984, HCC incidence was reduced by 75% among vaccinated children 6 to 9 years old compared with the rate in unvaccinated children prior to 1984.

B. HCV

Although there is no vaccine available for the prevention of HCV infection, the incidence of HCV has been declining in the United States and other developed countries since 1992, primarily because of screening blood and organ donors. A further reduction in transmission can be achieved by counseling of injection drug users, provision of disposable needles followed by their destruction after use, and sterilization of reusable surgical and dental equipment. Studies in Japan show that treatment of HCV-associated chronic hepatitis with interferon-α reduces the risk of HCC.

Global institution of preventive measures for HBV and HCV would greatly reduce the incidence of HCC within 3 to 4 decades.

See Also the Following Articles

BLADDER CANCER: EPIDEMIOLOGY • HEPATITIS B VIRUSES • HEPATITIS C VIRUS • HEPATOCELLULAR CARCINOMA • KIDNEY, EPIDEMIOLOGY • PANCREATIC CANCER, CELLULAR AND MOLECULAR MECHANISMS • THYROID CANCER

Bibliography

Alter, H. J., and Seef, L. B. (2000). Recovery, persistence, and sequelae in hepatitis C infection: A perspective on long-term outcome. *Semin. Liver Dis.* **20,** 17–35.

Befeler, A. S., and DiBisceglie, A. M. (2000). Hepatitis B. *Infect. Dis. Clin. North Am.* **14,** 617–632.

Chen, P. J., and Chen, D. S. (1999). Hepatitis B virus infection and hepatocellular carcinoma: Molecular genetics and clinical perspectives. *Semin. Liver Dis.* **19,** 253–262.

London, W. T., and McGlynn, K. A. (1996). Liver cancer. *In* "Cancer Epidemiology and Prevention" (D. Schottenfeld and J. F. Fraumeni, Jr., eds), pp. 772–793. Oxford Univ. Press, New York.

Parkin, D. M., Ohshima, H., Srivatanakul, P., and Vatanasapt, V. (1993). Cholangiocarcinoma: Epidemiology, mechanisms of carcinogenesis and prevention. *Cancer Epidemiol. Biomarkers Prev.* **2,** 537–544.

Lung Cancer: Molecular and Cellular Abnormalities

Frederic J. Kaye

National Cancer Institute and National Naval Medical Center

I. Introduction
II. Clinical, Pathologic, and Biologic Features
III. Cancer Genes in Lung Cancer
IV. Conclusions

GLOSSARY

comparative genomic hybridization A molecular technique to screen chromosomes for discrete regions where the copy number of genes has either increased or decreased.
cyclin A family of proteins that bind to cyclin-dependent kinases to regulate their enzymatic activity.
cyclin-dependent kinase A family of enzymes that drive all eukaryotic cells through meiosis and mitosis by catalyzing the phosphorylation of key protein substrates.
loss of heterozygosity Molecular technique to detect usually large deletions of either the maternal or the paternal allele at a specific chromosomal locus.

Lung cancer is the leading cause of cancer death in the United States and will be a persistent health crisis worldwide over the next century due to inadequate methods to restrict teenage smoking, the increased marketing of tobacco overseas, air pollution, and the long latency period of the preneoplastic state. Epidemiologic and genetic evidence has proven that lung cancer arises from the sequential accumulation of specific gene alterations that is accelerated following chronic exposure to tobacco smoke and other environmental carcinogens. Much has been made of the initial observation that only 10% of heavy smokers develop lung cancer and that a large segment of the population, therefore, may be protected by a combination of endogenous "modifier genes" or other unknown elements. Analyses of a more recent cohort of lifelong >25 cigarettes/day abusers, however, shows that the cumulative risk for clinical lung cancer in men by age 75 is substantially higher at 24.4% and the risk for subclinical lung cancer may be even greater with the use of more sensitive imaging studies. Lung cancer, therefore, will remain a major health issue for the next century and attention needs to be focused on a global multidisciplinary approach to prevent tobacco addiction and improve air quality. Other important goals include the ability to (i) identify and remove proximate carcinogens from tobacco products, (ii) improve early detection techniques to maximize current treatment regimens, (iii) catalogue and define the cancer gene pathways that are altered by these compounds, and (iv) use this knowledge for the design of a new generation of prevention and treatment strategies. This article briefly discusses some of the genes that are either proven or suspected to play an important role in the genesis of this cancer.

I. INTRODUCTION

Over the past decade, modest improvements in outcome have been observed with the use of combined regimens of surgery, systemic chemotherapy, and radiation therapy in selected patients with lung cancer. Unfortunately, the ultimate prognosis for the vast majority of patients with lung cancer has not changed. This same period, however, has witnessed a continuing explosion of basic science information concerning the cellular and molecular basis for lung tumors. These developments have resulted in great optimism for the future of lung cancer management as (i) the increasing number of cancer genes identified have paradoxically revealed the presence of a smaller number of interconnecting cancer gene pathways that are altered during tumorigenesis and which will ultimately simplify our understanding of the events underlying lung cancer, (ii) the gene pathways targeted in lung cancer are similar to those that are altered in many other common human cancer, suggesting that advances in one field will have broad implications, and finally (iii) the ability to control tumor cell growth or induce cell death by regulating these cancer gene pathways is undergoing intensive testing in both academic and pharmaceutical laboratories.

The molecular genetics of lung cancer, however, is hindered by both the absence of clearly defined families with an inherited tumor susceptibility and the absence of a consistent chromosomal translocation breakpoint that would allow the use of powerful positional cloning methodologies to isolate genes with "gatekeeper" function. As a result, lung cancer research has relied heavily on the analysis of chromosomal gains and losses as measured in tumor samples using cytogenetics, loss of heterozygosity (LOH) analyses, or comparative genomic hybridization (CGH). These types of studies, however, have not been so useful, to date, for new gene discovery in lung cancer and have created a database of a large number of nonrandom alterations, which localize to almost every chromosomal arm. The recent mapping and sequencing of the human genome will offer an opportunity to rigorously test all candidate genes within these regions and to complete a careful catalogue of validated genes involved in the genesis of lung cancer. Even with this knowledge, new ingenuity will be required to use this information to devise effective strategies to reduce the burden of lung cancer.

II. CLINICAL, PATHOLOGIC, AND BIOLOGIC FEATURES

A. Small Cell Lung Cancer (SCLC)

SCLC is a distinct clinical and pathologic entity that represents about 20% of all cases of lung cancer and is characterized by (i) its absence in nonsmokers, (ii) widespread dissemination with frequent metastasis to the brain, adrenal gland, bone marrow, and other sites, (iii) a high response rate to initial chemotherapy or radiotherapy treatments, and (iv) a low cure rate due to the regrowth of disease refractory to subsequent treatment. Patients, therefore, are managed with systemic chemotherapy/radiotherapy and rarely undergo surgical resection. This has resulted in a relative lack of primary tumor material, which has hampered laboratory investigations. The defining biological feature of primary SCLC and its derived tumor cell lines is the expression of a wide array of neuroendocrine markers, which occasionally results in unusual symptoms at sites distal to the tumor (paraneoplastic symptoms) (Table I). While the cell of origin for this tumor has not been defined, it is hypothesized that SCLC arises from neuroendocrine cells that are scattered within the basal layers of the bronchial epithelium (formerly called APUD or Kulchitsky cells). The majority of SCLCs synthesize large amounts of enzymatically active dopa decarboxylase, neuron-specific enolase, the brain isoenzyme of creatine kinase, gastrin-releasing peptide, chromogranin,

TABLE I
Clinical and Biological Characteristics of Lung Cancer

	SCLC	Non-SCLC
Clinical		
Diagnosis	Light microscopy	Light microscopy
No. of U.S. cases in 2000	32,000	132,000
Clinical presentation	Early dissemination	Locally advanced
Primary treatment	Nonsurgical	Surgical
Paraneoplastic syndrome from ectopic peptides	Occasional	Rare (hypercalcemia from PTH-like factor)
Biological		
Tumor growth in cell culture	Large clusters of floating cells	Adherent monolayer
Neuroendocrine markers		
Neurosecretory granules		
L-Dopa decarboxylase	90–100%	10%
Neuron-specific enolase		
Creatine kinase-brain		
Chromogranin		
Other neural peptides		
ACTH		
Bombesin/gastrin		
Releasing peptide	Occasional	Rare
Atrial natiuretic factor		
Arginine vasopressin		

synatophysin, and other neural peptides; however, the functional significance of these gene products is unknown. Although an autocrine or paracrine growth positive feedback loop has been suggested for some of these peptides, a specific role *in vivo* has yet to be defined. In addition to a specific neuroendocrine phenotype, SCLC is genetically characterized predominantly by (i) the absence of *Ki-ras* mutations, (ii) mutational inactivation (>90%) of the retinoblastoma (RB) gene, which is in sharp contrast to all other human tumors, except for the rare pediatric retinoblastoma tumor, (iii) mutational inactivation (>90%) of the *p53* gene, and (iv) DNA loss (>90%) on chromosome 3p (see later).

B. Non-SCLC

Non-SCLC is a nondescriptive term that unites the large majority of malignant lung tumors in the United States and comprises several histologic subtypes, including squamous cell carcinoma, adenocarcinoma, bronchioloalveolar carcinoma, and large cell or undifferentiated carcinoma. Pulmonary carcinoid, mesothelioma, mucoepidermoid carcinoma, and other rare forms of lung tumors are considered separately from this general SCLC and non-SCLC classification. Because non-SCLC may present with locally invasive disease, these tumors are often managed with surgical resection, which has allowed the collection of primary tumor tissues for experimental studies. In contrast to SCLC, which arises within submucosal tissues that hide the cells of origin, non-SCLC tumors appear to originate from surface epithelial cells that have undergone a gradual transition through the morphologic changes of squamous metaplasia and preneoplastic dysplasia. Non-SCLC can also exhibit a wide range of cellular differentiation patterns as single biopsy samples can show markers of both squamous and glandular differentiation. In addition, approximately 10% of non-SCLC can also show focal features of neuroendocrine differentiation admixed within nonneuroendocrine, non-SCLC tumor cells. The biological significance of these mixed cell lineages is unknown. Non-SCLC tumor cells are also characterized by frequent mutational inactivation of p53 and show evidence for DNA loss on chromosome 3p. In contrast to SCLC, however, non-SCLC typically retain a wild-type *RB* sequence and demonstrate inactivation of *CDKN2A* or *p16*, an upstream regulator of RB function (see later).

III. CANCER GENES IN LUNG CANCER

A. RB/Cyclin/p16 Gene Pathway Gene

The *RB* gene (13q14) was the first tumor suppressor gene identified as a target for mutations in lung cancer and provided the first evidence for a distinct genetic etiology between SCLC and non-SCLC. RB encodes a ubiquitous nuclear phosphoprotein that (i) regulates transit through the G_1/S phase of the eukaryotic cell cycle, (ii) modulates programmed cell death (apoptosis), and (iii) regulates patterns of cellular differentiation in selected cell lineages. Hypophosphorylated RB folds into a special protein ("pocket") conformation that facilitates binding to a group of nuclear protein partners, which then serve to maintain cells in a nonproliferative state (Fig. 1). Internal or external growth signals subsequently activate cyclin-dependent kinase:cyclin (CDK:cyclin) molecules that have substrate specificity for the RB protein. Cyclin-mediated RB hyperphosphorylation disrupts RB "pocket" binding, and the release of its protein-binding partners is proposed to directly induce growth proliferation. The normal function of the p16 gene product at chromosome 9p12 helps retain RB in its active hypophosphorylated, protein-binding conformation by blocking a critical CDK:cy-

clin kinase activity. The tumor-specific inactivation of p16, therefore, is predicted to result in loss of RB growth suppressor function by constitutive RB hyperphosphorylation.

Primary SCLC tumors and their derived cell lines showed either absent or mutant protein in 90% of samples. RB was confirmed as a tumor suppressor in lung cancer by the observation that (i) each single codon mutant RB protein isolated from SCLC had lost all protein "pocket" binding function and by (ii) demonstrating that the ectopic expression of wild-type RB in RB(−) lung tumor cells suppressed tumorigenicity *in vitro* and *in vivo*. In sharp contrast, only 10% of non-SCLC show mutational inactivation of RB (Fig. 2). The remaining lung tumors that retain wild-type RB activity (10% of SCLC and 75% of non-SCLC) demonstrate inactivation of the p16 gene product, which directly deregulates RB tumor suppressor activity. While structural DNA alteration is the main mechanism for loss of RB function in lung tumors, aberrant DNA hypermethylation with mRNA gene silencing is the major mechanism for loss of p16 activity. This observation is of considerable clinical interest as exposure to DNA demethylating agents and/or histone deacetylase inhibitor agents has shown the ability to demethylate the p16 locus, reinduce p16 mRNA and protein expression, and suppress cell growth *in vitro* and *in vivo*.

Although multiple studies have been undertaken to examine whether the status of RB or p16 expression affects the clinical behavior of lung cancer, there is no evidence that these data add useful prognostic information. LOH analyses at 13q14 and 9p12 using microdissected samples from preneoplastic and lung cancer sections suggest that loss of the RB/p16 pathway is an early event in the genesis of non-SCLC tumors.

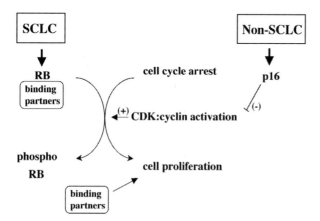

FIGURE 1 RB/CDK/p16 cancer gene pathway. Schema depicts the transition to enter DNA replication and mitosis in the eukaryotic cell cycle. Although theoretically any segment of the cell cycle might serve as a target for somatic mutations in human cancer, the RB/CDK/p16 pathway is particularly susceptible to genetic alterations. Although this pathway may also be activated or inhibited by other mechanisms as well, the loss of either RB or p16 function predominates in lung cancer.

B. p53/MDM2/ARF Gene Pathway

The p53 protein pathway serves to arrest or kill cells that are at risk for aberrant clonal expansion. For example, cells that acquire somatic alterations in the RB/p16 gene pathway undergo p53-mediated programmed cell death. Accordingly, mutational inactivation of the *p53* gene is also observed in the majority of SCLC and non-SCLC tumors and derived cell lines. Acceleration of p53 protein degradation, by aberrantly altering MDM2 (increased levels through

	gene	SCLC	non-SCLC
strong evidence	RB inactivation	90%	10%
	p16 inactivation	10%	75%
	p53 mutation	90-100%	50-70%
	K-ras mutation	0%	30%
	Telomerase activation	90-100%	75%
under investigation	Myc amplification	30%	10%
	Chr 3p allele loss	100%	70-100%
	PTEN mutation	10-20%	0-5%
	Absent FHIT protein	50%	75%
	Elevated BCL2	80%	10-30%
	ErbB1/EGFR	20-40%	20-40%
	ErbB2/neu	<5%	20-30%
	Epigenetic silencing of many Chr 3p genes of ? significance		

FIGURE 2   Genetic alterations observed in lung cancer.

gene amplification) or p14ARF (decreased levels by mutations or hypermethylation), can also mediate loss of normal p53 function in the subset of lung tumors with normal p53 nucleotide sequence. Therefore, inactivation of both the p53/MDM2/ARF pathway and the RB/CDK/p16 pathway is believed to occur in essentially 100% of all SCLC and non-SCLC lung tumors. In contrast to colon cancer where *p53* alterations occur as a late event, LOH at both *p16* and *p53* loci (17p13.1) are believed to be early events present in preneoplastic, microdissected non-SCLC tissue samples. The *p53* gene is the most potent of all cancer genes studied to date in inducing growth arrest and cell death when reintroduced into lung tumor cell lines. Clinical trials are underway to exploit this observation; however, the ability to target widely disseminated tumor cells remains a major obstacle.

C. Ras

Ras genes function as complex cytoplasmic switches that transmit and amplify external growth signals in a cascade toward the nucleus to regulate gene transcription. Acquired somatic mutations within the *Ras* gene are observed in a subset of a wide range of human cancers where it locks the protein in a conformation that aberrantly signals growth. Although there are many different members of the *Ras* gene family, the *Ki-ras* gene (at chromosome12p12.1) appears to be exclusively targeted for somatic activating mutations in lung cancer. Activating *Ki-ras* mutations were detected in approximately 30% of non-SCLC tumor samples; how-

ever, tumors with nonadenocarcinoma histology may have a lower 10–15% incidence. These mutations appear to arise as a late event, similar to colon cancer, in the genesis of non-SCLC. In addition, several studies have confirmed an inferior prognosis in patients with early stage lung tumors that have acquired activating ras mutations. Strikingly, *Ki-ras* mutations are absent in all SCLC tumors studied to date.

D. Activation of Telomerase

Activation of telomerase, mediated largely by induction of the telomerase holoenzyme, has been observed in 100% of SCLC and 85% of non-SCLC. This high frequency event occurs early in the development of lung cancer and is believed to be required in order to allow clonally expanded cells to escape replicative senescence.

E. MYC Gene

Amplification and mRNA overexpression of the c-MYC, N-myc, and L-myc oncogenes have been detected in a subset of both SCLC and non-SCLC tumor cell lines. In contrast to alterations within the RAS, RB, and p53 gene pathways, it appears that Myc amplification occurs more frequently in derived lung tumor cell lines rather than primary tumors, suggesting that it may represent a late event in tumorgenesis and/or a cell culture artifact. While clustering of somatic mutations within the transactivation domain of c-MYC has been reported in some cases of Burkitt's lymphoma, no evidence for similar types of mutations has been reported for lung cancer. Unusual intrachromosomal rearrangements of the L-myc gene have been detected in several lung cancer cell lines, which result in chimeric mRNA molecules between L-myc and two other genes of unknown function. The biological relevance of these rearrangements, however, is still unknown. In contrast to neuroblastoma tumors, where amplification of N-myc is an important negative prognostic factor, amplification of the different members of the MYC gene family appears to convey little prognostic information. While there is compelling data from animal models demonstrating the importance of MYC and Ras activation in the genesis of murine lung tumors *in vivo*, the role of these genes in human lung tumor development is still undefined.

F. Chromosome 3p Gene

A search for the candidate chromosome 3p lung cancer gene(s) has been ongoing for more than a decade. Mapping studies in all types of lung cancer have suggested consistent allelic deletions at perhaps three different loci between chromosome bands 3p12-p25, and several genes within these loci have been reported with features of tumor suppressor activity. For example, the *FHIT* gene at 3p14.2 shows frequent genomic alterations with absent protein expression in many lung cancer samples. Other interesting candidates include a retinoic acid receptor gene, several phosphatase genes, and many others of undefined function. The recent recognition that gene function may also be altered by haploinsufficiency (loss of only one allele) and by epigenetic mechanisms (such as hypermethylation) will make the process of validating each candidate tumor suppressor gene at chromosome 3p even more complex. Although the putative 3p gene has been elusive to date, it is anticipated that the role of *FHIT* and other candidate genes within this chromosome 3p region will be defined shortly.

G. Other Genes

The *PTEN* gene encodes a lipid phosphatase activity that serves to antagonize the proliferation and survival signals generated by the phosphoinositide 3-kinase/AKT pathway. Although there are conflicting reports about the frequency of somatic *PTEN* mutations in lung cancer, it appears that 20–40% of SCLC and 0–8% of non-SCLC contain inactivating mutations. In addition, hemizygous loss of *PTEN* (at 10q23.3) may occur in 50% of non-SCLC, which may be sufficient to exhibit an aberrant phenotype through gene dosage alterations (haploinsufficiency). Activation of ErbB1/EGFR, ErbB2/neu, raf1, IGF-like members, and c-Kit has been observed in a subset of lung cancer samples where they have generated considerable interest as monoclonal antibodies, and small molecule inhibitors to several of these receptor kinase genes are currently being tested in clinical trials. Finally, elevated levels of the antiapoptotic *Bcl2* gene have also been observed in 80% of SCLC and 10–30% of non-SCLC.

IV. CONCLUSIONS

Progress in defining the molecular events underlying the initiation and progression of human lung cancer is continuing at a rapid pace. It is anticipated that the nondescriptive classification of non-SCLC will soon be replaced by more informative molecular genetic subtypes, which will offer more logical algorithms for clinical management. The challenge for the future, however, will be to use this information to develop more effective strategies for the prevention and treatment of all types of lung cancer.

See Also the Following Articles

CANCER RISK REDUCTION (DIET/SMOKING CESSATION/ LIFESTYLE CHANGES) • C-MYC PROTOONCOGENE • LUNG, LARYNX, ORAL CAVITY, AND PHARYNX • P16 AND ARF • PTEN • RAS PROTEINS • RETINOBLASTOMA TUMOR SUPPRESSOR GENE • TELOMERES AND TELOMERASE • TOBACCO CARCINOGENESIS

Bibliography

Ginsberg, R. J., Vokes, E. E., and Raben, A. (1997). Non-small cell lung cancer. *In* "Principles and Practice of Oncology" (V. T. DeVita, S. Hellman, and S. A. Rosenberg, eds.), p. 858–911. Lippincott-Raven, Philadelphia.

Ihde, D. C., Glatstein, E., and Pass, H. I. (1997). Small cell lung cancer. *In* "Principles and Practice of Oncology" (V. T. DeVita, S. Hellman, and S. A. Rosenberg, eds.), pp. 911–951. Lippincott-Raven, Philadelphia.

Kohno, T., and Yokota, J. (1999). How many tumor suppressor genes are involved in human lung carcinogenesis? *Carcinogenesis* **20**, 1403–1410.

Marchioli, C. C., and Graziano, S. L. (1997). Paraneoplastic syndromes associated with small cell lung cancer. *Chest Surg. Clin. Am.* **7**, 65–80.

Peto, R., Darby, S., Deo, H., Silcocks, P., Whitley, E., and Doll, R. (2000). Smoking, smoking cessation, and lung cancer in the UK since 1950: combination of national statistics with two case-control studies. *Br. Med. J.* **321**, 323–329.

Shay, J. W., Zou, Y., Hiyama, E., and Wright, W. E. (2001). Telomerase and cancer. *Hum. Mol. Genet.* **10**, 677–685.

Sherr, C. J. (1998). Tumor surveillance via the ARF-p53 pathway. *Genes Dev.* **12**, 2984–2991.

Tuveson, D. A., and Jacks, T. (1999). Modeling human lung cancer in mice: Similarities and shortcomings. *Oncogene* **18**, 5318–5324.

Weinberg, R. (1995). The retinoblastoma protein and cell cycle control. *Cell* **81**, 323–330.

Zochbauer-Muller, S., and Minna, J. D. (2000). The biology of lung cancer including potential clinical applications. *Chest Surg. Clin. N. Am.* **10**, 691–708.

Lung, Larynx, Oral Cavity, and Pharynx

Loïc Le Marchand
Cancer Research Center of Hawaii, Honolulu

Paolo Boffetta
International Agency for Research on Cancer, Lyon, France

T his article provides an overview of the epidemiology of cancers of the lung, larynx, oral cavity, and pharynx. Changing patterns of occurrence and the role of lifestyle, occupational, environmental, and genetic factors are described for these highly preventable diseases.

I. OCCURRENCE

Lung cancer is the most common malignancy in the world. It is the leading cause of cancer death in North America and Europe, and rates are increasing rapidly in most other regions, especially in Asia and South America. Temporal trends and geographical differences track cigarette consumption patterns with a 20- to 30-year lag, as epitomized by the sharp rise in lung cancer occurrence that took place between the 1930s and 1980s in western countries as the result of a major increase in cigarette consumption starting in the 1910s. Even in areas where smoking rates have now started to fall, this disease will remain an important source of mortality due to the large number of former smokers. The most common histologic forms of lung cancer are adenocarcinoma, squamous cell carcinoma, and small cell carcinoma. The frequency of adenocarcinoma has markedly increased in North America since the 1970s, whereas that of squamous cell carcinoma has proportionally decreased, presumably as a result of changes in cigarette composition and smoking behavior. Survival from lung cancer has remained extremely poor, with a 5-year survival rate of 12–15%.

Cancer of the mouth and pharynx is the 5th and cancer of the larynx is the 14th most common cancer worldwide. These tumors are more frequent in developing countries and are usually more common in men than women. Five-year survival rates vary between 53% (oral cavity and pharynx) and 65% (larynx).

II. TOBACCO

Tobacco smoking is universally recognized as the overwhelming cause of lung cancer. In the United States, it is estimated that 90% of deaths from this disease are caused by smoking. Risk increases in relation to both intensity and duration of smoking, and a person who smoked one pack per day for 30 years is estimated to have a lung cancer risk 10- to 20-fold greater than a lifelong nonsmoker. Smoking cessation leads to a reduction in the risk of lung cancer, but not significantly before the fifth year and risk, possibly, never returns to the background level of a lifelong nonsmoker. Evidence shows that the lung cancer risk associated with smoking may differ among ethnic/racial groups and between sexes (higher risks for women and African Amer-

icans; lower risk for Japanese). Among the thousands of compounds in cigarette smoke, 55 have been evaluated as being carcinogens by the International Agency for Research on Cancer. Compounds present in mainstream cigarette smoke that have been found convincingly to induce lung tumors in animals are shown in Table I. Pipe and cigar smoking are also clearly linked to lung cancer, with risks, however, that are somewhat lower than that observed with cigarettes, possibly because the smoke from pipe and cigar is more irritating and inhaled less deeply than cigarette smoke.

Cigarette smoking is also a strong cause of cancers of the oral cavity, pharynx, and larynx. In addition, smokeless tobacco is a well-established cause of oral cancer. For example, the chewing of tobacco and betel nut has been shown to greatly contribute to the high rates of oral cancer in India. Carcinogens, such as tobacco-specific nitrosamines, have been found at relatively high levels in commercially available smokeless tobacco products.

Exposure to environmental tobacco smoke (ETS) (i.e., passive smoking) has been associated with lung

TABLE I
Pulmonary Carcinogens in Cigarette Smoke[a]

Carcinogen class	Compound	Amount in mainstream cigarette smoke (ng/cigarette)
Polycyclic aromatic hydrocarbons	Benzo[a]pyrene	20–40
	Benzo[b]fluoranthane	4–22
	Benzo[j]fluoranthane	6–21
	Benzo[k]fluoranthane	6–12
	Dibenzo[a,i]pyrene	1.7–3.2
	Indenol[1,2,3-cd]pyrene	4–20
	Dibenz[a,h]anthracene	4
	5-Methylchrysene	0.6
Azo-arenes	Dibenz[a,h]acridine	0.1
	7H-Dibenzo[c,g]carbazole	0.7
N-Nitrosamines	N-Nitrosodiethylamine	0–2.8
	4-(Methylnitrosamino)-1-(3-pyridyl)-1-butanone (NNK)	80–770
Miscellaneous organic compounds	1,3-Butadiene	$20–70 \times 10^3$
	Ethyl carbamate	20–38
	Hydrazine	24–43
Inorganic compounds	Nickel	0–510
	Chromium	0.2–500
	Cadmium	0–6670
	Polonium-210	0.03–1.0 pCi
	Arsenic	0–1400

[a]Adapted from Hecht (1999). Compounds for which there is convincing evidence of pulmonary tumorigenicity in at least one animal species.

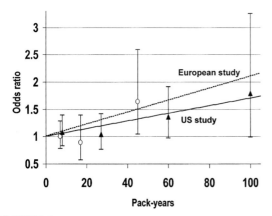

FIGURE 1 Risk of lung cancer among nonsmoking women by cumulative exposure to their husband's cigarette smoke [based on the data from Fontham *et al.* (1994) and Boffetta *et al.* (1999)].

cancer in a number of case-control and prospective studies. The excess risk has been estimated to be 20% in nonsmoking women whose husband smoked. This association does not seem to be due to confounding by active smoking, diet, and other factors or to reporting bias and is consistent with the presence of carcinogens (e.g., nitrosamines) in sidestream smoke. The evidence has led the U.S. Environmental Protection Agency to classify ETS as a known human carcinogen. Two large studies have provided information on the cumulative lung cancer risk of nonsmoking women exposed to passive smoking from their spouse. These risks expressed for increasing dose × duration levels and their linear extrapolation are presented in Fig. 1.

III. DIET

Epidemiologic studies since the 1980s have provided strong evidence that diet affects the risk of lung cancer. A recent review of the literature noted that 7 cohort and 17 case-control studies were almost entirely consistent in suggesting a protective effect of vegetables and fruits against lung cancer. Risk for subjects in the highest intake category was about 50% lower than for low consumers. The evidence was noted to be most abundant for green vegetables and carrots. This effect is unlikely to be due to residual confounding by smoking, as the protective association has also been observed among nonsmokers. Although the evidence for fruits and vegetables is quite convincing, the specific constituents of these foods that could be protective against lung cancer remain unidentified. A decreased risk has been observed for high intakes of carotenoids, tocopherols, ascorbic acid, folic acid, selenium, flavonoids, and isothiocyanates. However, the effects of these various phytochemicals are difficult to differentiate from each other and could also be attributable to other (unmeasured) components in fruits and vegetables.

Results from large intervention trials of the protective effect of β-carotene, vitamin E, or retinol supplements against lung cancer have shown no beneficial effect in well-nourished populations and, unexpectedly, have provided evidence for an adverse effect from β-carotene supplementation in people at high lung cancer risk, such as heavy smokers.

An excess in lung cancer risk has also been associated with some consistency with a diet rich in fat and cholesterol. Experimental studies showing increased tumor yield in animals fed high levels of saturated or unsaturated fat or cholesterol add credence to these findings.

Based on limited evidence available for larynx cancer and on more abundant data for oral and pharyngeal cancers, epidemiologic studies also suggest a protective effect of fruits and vegetables against these cancers. The data are particularly suggestive for a protective effect of fruits rich in vitamin C against oral and pharyngeal cancer. Small intervention studies among tobacco chewers and smokers have shown regression of precancerous lesions after supplementation with vitamin A, β-carotene, selenium and riboflavin, and zinc. However, whether these compounds have similar protective effects against oral cancer is not known.

IV. ALCOHOL

Although several epidemiologic studies have suggested that the consumption of alcoholic beverages may be associated with an increased lung cancer risk, this association has been difficult to establish or refute. Because drinking is strongly correlated with smoking in most populations, a major concern in these studies has been the possibility of incomplete adjustment for the confounding effect of smoking.

In contrast, the adverse effect of alcohol on the risk of laryngeal and oropharyngeal cancers is well established, irrespective of the type of beverage. Moreover, a synergistic effect of alcohol and tobacco has been shown for those cancers: individuals with exposure to both tobacco and alcohol appear to be at much greater risk than those exposed to either one of these factors. Mechanisms for a carcinogenic effect of alcohol include its solvent ability, which would facilitate the entry of carcinogens in the cell, and its inducting effect on carcinogen-activating enzymes. Acetaldehyde, the initial metabolite of ethanol, has also been shown to be an experimental carcinogen. Finally, alcoholic beverages may contain toxic contaminants, and chronic consumption of alcohol may compromise nutritional status in ways that may increase susceptibility to cancer.

V. OCCUPATION

Lung cancer risk has been found to be elevated among workers employed in several industries and occupations. In some cases, the agent(s) responsible for the increased risk has been identified. Evidence on the carcinogenicity of many occupational agents has been evaluated by IARC. Table II summarizes this evaluation for occupational agents classified as established (group 1) or probable (group 2A) carcinogens that have the lung as a target organ. In addition, a number of other important compounds have been classified as possible lung carcinogens (group 2B) (e.g., inorganic lead compounds, synthetic vitreous fibers).

Overall, mixtures of polycyclic aromatic hydrocarbons (PAHs), crystalline silica, and asbestos are probably the most important occupational lung carcinogens, as exposure to these agents is prevalent in many industries and often occurs at high levels. Exposure to heavy metals (arsenic, chromium, nickel, cadmium, and beryllium) and to ionizing radiation, including radon, has now been controlled in many industries, but might still represent an important hazard in some occupations (e.g., among miners). Other occupational lung carcinogens, such as bis-chloromethyl ether and chloromethyl ether, are mainly of historical interest.

Employment in a few occupations and industries (e.g., painters) appears to also result in an increased lung cancer risk. However, the responsible agent(s) has not been identified.

It has been estimated that occupational carcinogens in industrialized countries are responsible for 5–10% of all cancers, either directly or because of synergism with tobacco smoke. However, these occupational cancers, including lung cancer, are not equally distributed in the population, as they occur disproportionally more among blue collar workers. Similarly, high exposure situations are now common in developing countries and occupational cancers may be proportionally more frequent there.

Occupational exposure to mists of strong inorganic acids, particularly sulfuric acid, is an established risk factor of laryngeal cancer. An association with this disease has been suggested for other occupational exposures, including nickel, asbestos, and ionizing radiation, but data are not conclusive at present.

Several occupations have been sporadically associated with an increased risk of oral and pharyngeal cancer. The evidence is only somewhat consistent for employment as a waiter and bartender, probably reflecting an increased consumption of alcohol and tobacco.

VI. RADON

Underground uranium miners exposed to radioactive radon and its decay products have been found to be at increased lung cancer risk. The risk increased with estimated cumulative exposure and decreased with attained age, time since exposure, and time since cessation of exposure. A pooled analysis of 11 cohorts estimated a relative risk of 1.0049 (95% confidence interval: 1.002–1.010) per month of exposure, with little suggestion of departure from a linear dose–response relationship between cumulative exposure and excess risk.

However, the concern about lung cancer risk from radon and its decay products comes more from residential exposure than from occupational exposure, as radon is found in homes in many areas. A meta-analysis of the eight most informative studies aimed at directly estimating the risk of lung cancer from resi-

Occupational Agents, Groups of Agents, Mixtures, and Exposure Circumstances[a]

Agents, mixture, circumstance	Main industry, use	Evidence of carcinogenicity in humans[b]	Other target organs
Group 1: Carcinogenic to humans			
Agents, groups of agents			
Arsenic and arsenic compounds	Glass, metals, pesticides	S	Skin
Asbestos	Insulation, filters, textiles	S	Pleura
Beryllium and beryllium compounds	Aerospace	S	
Bis(chloromethyl)ether and chloromethyl methyl ether	Chemical intermediate	S	
Cadmium and cadmium compounds	Dye/pigment	S	
Chromium[VI] compounds	Metal plating, dye/pigment	S	Nose
Dioxin (TCDD)	Chemical industry	L	Many
Nickel compounds	Metallurgy, alloy, catalyst	S	Nose
α and γ radiation	Medical	S	Many
Radon and its decay products	Mining	S	
Silica, crystalline	Stone cutting, mining, glass, paper	S	
Talc-containing asbestiform fibers	Paper, paints	S	
Mixtures			
Coal-tar pitches	Construction, electrodes	S	Skin, bladder
Coal tars	Fuel	S	Skin
Soots	Pigments	S	Skin
Exposure circumstances			
Aluminum production		S	Skin
Coal gasification		S	
Coke production		S	
Hematite mining (underground) with exposure to radon		S	
Iron and steel founding		S	
Painter (occupational exposure)		S	
Group 2A—Probably carcinogenic to humans			
Agents and groups of agents			
α-Chlorinated toluenes and benzoyl chloride (combined exposure)	Chemical intermediate	L	
Nonarsenical insecticides (occupational exposures in spraying and application of)	Farming	L	
Exposure circumstances			
Art glass, glass containers, and pressed ware (manufacture of)		L	

[a]Classified by the IARC Monographs Program (Volumes 1–72) into groups 1 and 2A, which have the lung as the target organ.
[b]S, sufficient; L, limited.

dential radon exposure resulted in a pooled relative risk of 1.14 (95% confidence interval 1.0–1.3) at 150 Bq/m³, an exposure level exceeded by 6% of U.S. households.

VII. AIR POLLUTION

Detailed reviews on air pollution and lung cancer have been provided by Speizer and Samet (1994) and Katsouyanni and Pershagen (1997). The overall evidence suggests that urban air pollution is possibly a risk factor for lung cancer. Confounding by tobacco smoking or other risk factors does not seem to explain this excess risk. The results have been fairly consistent across studies independently of the way in which air pollution was assessed (e.g., residence in urban settings, residence near a major pollution emission source, cumulative exposure based on historical air monitoring data) and of the population studied. In particular, three large cohort studies have carefully assessed exposure to different pollutants and controlled the analysis for possible confounders. Their results (Table III) are fairly consistent in suggesting a small increase in risk for persons in the highest air pollution exposure categories.

In many populations, indoor air pollution is a more important source of exposure to carcinogens than outdoor air pollution. Two important indoor sources of exposure to potential lung carcinogens are the use of coal-burning heating devices without proper exhaust emission (e.g., "kang" in northeastern China) and high-temperature cooking using unrefined vegetable oils, such as rapeseed oil (common in several parts of China). Indoor levels of benzo[a]pyrene have been reported to be very high in such exposure situations. In several studies, indoor air pollution has been found to be a major cause of lung cancer in Chinese women, who, as a group, experience high lung cancer rates despite a low prevalence of smoking. A positive association between various indicators of indoor air pollution and lung cancer risk has also been reported in populations exposed to less extreme conditions (e.g., in the United States and Japan).

VIII. GENETIC SUSCEPTIBILITY

Although most lung cancers would not occur in the absence of exposure to smoking or other environmental risk factors, it has long been proposed that individuals vary in their susceptibility to these environmental insults. Investigators have reported a two- to fourfold increase risk of lung cancer among first-degree relatives of patients with the disease. A segregation analysis in a study conducted in southern Louisiana suggested a codominant inheritance pattern of a rare major susceptibility gene acting in conjunction with cigarette smoking and resulting in early age lung cancer. In addition, a familial tendency to develop chronic obstructive pulmonary disease has been reported in relatives of lung cancer patients. Thus, there is evidence for an inherited genetic component in lung cancer. However, the specific genetic factors involved have not been identified.

In searching for markers of genetic susceptibility, Kellerman and colleagues (1973) reported higher levels of aryl hydrocarbon hydroxylase activity (mediated by cytochrome P450 1A1) in the lymphocytes of lung cancer patients compared to controls. However, this finding, which suggested a genetically determined increased metabolic activation of PAHs, has been difficult to replicate. In support of Kellerman's observation, a common genetic variant (a T-to-C substitution at nucleotide 6235) in the CYP1A1 gene, apparently linked to an increase in the activity of the enzyme, has been associated with an elevated risk of lung cancer in Japanese in Japan and Hawaii. However, this association has been more inconsistent in Caucasians, a group in which this polymorphism is rare and large studies are needed to detect an association. A common genetic polymorphism at one of the glutathione S-transferase isoenzymes (GSTM1) involved in the detoxification of PAHs has also been implicated in lung cancer susceptibility, especially when combined with the CYP1A1 variant. Other genetic variations in the metabolic activation or detoxification of tobacco carcinogens have been associated

TABLE III
Results of Selected Cohort Studies on Air Pollution and Risk of Lung Cancer[a]

Study (year)	Population, follow-up	N	Exposure range	Contrast	Pollutant, RR	95% CI
Dockery (1993)	6 cities, USA, 1974–1991	8,111	FP: 11–30 µg/m^3	Highest vs lowest city	FP, 1.37	1.11–1.68
Pope (1995)	151 areas, USA, 1982–1989	552,138	FP: 9–33 µg/m^3	Highest vs lowest areas	FP, 1.03	0.80–1.33
			Sulfates: 3.6–23 µg/m^3		Sulfates, 1.36	1.11–1.66
Beeson (1998)	California, nonsmokers, 1977–1992	6,338	FP: 10–80 µg/m^3	Interquartile range[b]	FP, 5.21	1.94–13.99
			Sulfates: 0.6–11 ppb		Sulfates, 2.66	1.62–4.39
			Ozone: 4–40 ppb		Ozone, 2.23	0.79–6.34

[a]N, number of subjects; FP, fine particulate; RR, relative risk; CI, confidence interval.
[b]FP, 24 µg/m^3; sulfates, 3.7 ppb; ozone, 2.1 ppb.

with lung cancer, including polymorphisms in the *CYP2E1*, *CYP2D6*, *CYP2C9*, NAD(P)H:quinone oxidoreductase *(NQO1)*, myeloperoxidase *(MPO)*, and microsomal epoxide hydrolase *(mEPX)* genes. With the exception of *CYP2D6*, for which a meta-analysis of 18 studies suggested a weak decreased lung cancer risk for "poor metabolizers" (median odds ratio: 0.69 (95%, confidence interval: 0.52–0.90), available data for the other genes are still sparse and inconclusive. Fewer studies of genetic polymorphisms and laryngeal or oropharyngeal cancers have been published. However, a genetic variant in the alcohol dehydrogenase type 3 *(ADH3)* gene has been associated with oral and pharyngeal cancers in some studies, but data are still inconsistent.

Inherited defects in DNA repair have also been explored with regard to lung cancer risk. A mutagen sensitivity assay in which a clastogen is used to induce chromosome breakage in cultured lymphocytes has suggested lower DNA repair capacity among lung and head and neck cancer patients compared to healthy controls.

IX. PREVENTION

Worldwide, lung cancer kills about one million people each year, and oral, pharyngeal, and laryngeal cancers kill another 235,000. Unlike for many other cancers, a great deal is known about the etiology of these malignancies, making primary prevention an effective tool. Avoidance of all types of tobacco products is a clear priority in preventing these malignancies and lowering alcohol consumption is also important in preventing oral, pharyngeal, and laryngeal cancers. Public health strategies have been largely successful in gradually changing these behaviors. However, novel approaches are needed for adolescents, who, as a group, are now smoking at an increased rate, as well as for strongly addicted smokers who are unable to quit and for ex-smokers because they remain for many years at significantly increased risk.

Current progress in our understanding of the biological processes involved in nicotine addiction and lung carcinogenesis may lead to the identification of genetic susceptibility markers for smoking and/or lung cancer, as well as markers of early disease. Such new markers might allow the identification of high-risk individuals for targeted intervention. Moreover, many nutritional and pharmaceutical agents are known that can block carcinogen activation, enhance detoxification, or inhibit downstream carcinogenic events in experimental models. They may lead to nutritional or chemoprevention approaches. Further progress in controlling occupational exposures and air pollution may also contribute to lung cancer prevention. However, further tobacco control and improved cessation strategies are likely to remain the backbone of the prevention of respiratory tract cancers.

See Also the Following Articles

CANCER RISK REDUCTION (DIET/SMOKING CESSATION/LIFESTYLE CHANGES) • ESOPHAGEAL CANCER • HEAD AND NECK CANCER • LUNG CANCER: MOLECULAR AND CELLULAR ABNORMALITIES • TOBACCO CARCINOGENESIS

Bibliography

Boffetta, P., Agudo, A., Ahrens, W., Benhamou, E., Benhamou, S., Darby, S. C., Ferro, G., Fortes, C., Gonzalez, C. A., Jöckel, K. H., Krauss, M., Kreienbrock, L., Kreuzer, M., Mendes, A., Merletti, F., Nyberg, F., Pershagen, G., Pohlabeln, H., Riboli, E., Schmid, G., Simonato, L., Trédaniel, J., Whitley, E., Wichmann, H.-E., Winck, C., Zambon, P., and Saracci, R. (1998). Multicenter case-control study of exposure to environmental tobacco smoke and lung cancer in Europe. *J. Natl. Cancer Inst.* **90,** 1440–1450.

Beeson, W. L., Abbey, D. E., and Knutsen, S. F. (1998). Long-term concentrations of ambient air pollutants and incident lung cancer in California adults: Results from the AHSMOG study. Adventist Health Study on Smog. *Environ. Health Perspect.* **106,** 813–823.

Dockery, D. W., Pope, A. C., III, Xu, X., Spengler, J. D., Ware, J. H., Fay, M. E., Ferris, B. G., Jr., and Speizer, F. E. (1993). An association between air pollution and mortality in six U.S. cities. *N. Engl. J. Med.* **329,** 1753–1759.

Ferlay, J., Parkin, D. M., and Pisani, P. (1998). "GLOBOCAN 1: Cancer Incidence and Mortality Worldwide." International Agency for Research on Cancer, World Health Organization. IARC Press, Lyon.

Fontham, E. T., Correa, P., Reynolds, P., Wu-Williams, A., Buffler, P. A., Greenberg, R. S., Chen, V. W., Alterman, T., Boyd, P., Austin, D. F., and Liff, J. (1994). Environmental tobacco smoke and lung cancer in nonsmoking women: A multicenter study. *J. Am. Med. Assoc.* **271,** 1752–1759.

Hackshaw, A. K., Law, M. R., and Wald, N. J. (1997). The accumulated evidence on lung cancer and environmental tobacco smoke. *Br. Med. J.* **315,** 980–988.

Hecht, S. S. (1999). Tobacco smoke carcinogens and lung cancer. *J. Natl. Cancer Inst.* **91,** 1194–1210.

International Agency for Research on Cancer (IARC) (1972–1999). "Monographs on the Evaluation of Carcinogenic Risks to Humans," Vols. 1–74. IARC Press, Lyon.

Katsouyanni, G., and Pershagen, G. (1997). Ambient air pollution exposure and cancer. *Cancer Causes Control* **8,** 284–291.

Kawajiri, K. (1999). CYP1A1. *In* "Metabolic Polymorphisms and Susceptibility to Cancer" (P. Vineis, N. Malats, M. Lang, A. d'Erico, N. Caporaso, J. Cuzick, and P. Boffetta, eds.), IARC Scientific Publications No. 148, pp. 159–172. International Agency for Research on Cancer, Lyon.

Kellermann, G., Shaw, C. R., and Lyten-Kellermann, M. (1973). Aryl hydrocarbon hydroxylase inducibility and bronchogenic carcinoma. *N. Engl. J. Med.* **289,** 934–937.

Le Marchand, L., Sivaraman, L., Pierce, L., Seifried, A., Lum, A., Wilkens, L. R., and Lau, A. F., (1998). Associations of *CYP1A1, GSTM1,* and *CYP2E1* polymorphisms with lung cancer suggest cell type specificities to tobacco carcinogens. *Cancer Res.* **58,** 4858–4863.

Lubin, J. H., and Boice, J. D., Jr. (1997). Lung cancer risk from residential radon: Meta-analysis of eight epidemiologic studies. *J. Natl. Cancer Inst.* **89,** 49–57.

Lubin, J. H., Boice, J. D., Edling, C., Hornung, R. W., Howe, G., and Kunz, E. (1994). Radon and lung cancer risk: A joint analysis of 11 underground miners studies. NIH Publication No. 94-3644. U.S. Department of Health and Human Services.

Pope, C. A., III, Thun, M. J., Namboodiri, M. M., Dockery, D. W., Evans, J. S., Speizer, F. E., and Heath, C. W., Jr. (1995). Particulate air pollution as a predictor of mortality in a prospective study of U.S. adults. *Am. J. Respir. Crit. Care Med.* **151,** 669–674.

Ries, L. A. G., Kosary, C. L., Hankey, B. F., Clegg, L., and Edwards, B. K. (1999). "SEER Cancer Statistics Review, 1973–1986." National Cancer Institute, Bethesda, MD.

Rostami-Hodjegan, A., Lennard, M. S., Woods, H. F., and Tucker, G. T. (1998). Meta-analysis of studies of the CYP2D6 polymorphism in relation to lung cancer and Parkinson's disease. *Pharmacogenetics* **8,** 227–238.

Smith, K. R., and Liu, Y. (1994). Indoor air pollution in developing countries. *In* "Epidemiology of Lung Cancer" (J. M. Samet, ed.), Lung Biology in Health Disease, Vol. 74, pp. 151–184. Dekker, New York.

Speizer, F. E., and Samet, J .M. (1994). Air pollution and lung cancer. *In* "Epidemiology of Lung Cancer" (J. M. Samet, ed.), Lung Biology in Health Disease, Vol. 74, pp. 131–150. Dekker, New York.

World Cancer Research Fund (WCRF) and American Institute for Cancer Research (AICR) (1997). Food, Nutrition and the Prevention of Cancer: A Global Perspective. AICR, Washington, DC.

Lymphoma, Hodgkin's Disease

Andrea K. Ng
Peter M. Mauch

Harvard Medical School and Brigham and Women's Hospital

GLOSSARY

cytokines Hormone-like low molecular weight proteins, secreted by many different cell types, which regulate the intensity and duration of immune responses and are involved in cell-to-cell communication.

immunotherapy Therapeutic administration of serum or γ-globulin containing preformed antibodies; also include non-specific systemic stimulation, and use of monoclonal antibodies to attack cancerous cells directly.

mantle radiation therapy Radiation therapy targeted at nodal groups above the diaphragm, including submantel, cervical, supraclavicular, infraclavicular, mediastinum, hilar, and axillary lymph nodes; typically extends from the level of the external auditory meatus to the T10 level.

meta-analysis The process of using statistical methods to combine the results of different randomized studies to improve the power to detect small differences.

paraaortic radiation therapy Radiation therapy targeted at the paraaortic nodes, typically matched to a mantle field, and extending down to the L4 level.

Hodgkin's disease is a form of malignancy involving the lymphatic system. In the last three decades, dramatic success has been achieved in the management of the disease. Future challenges include better understanding of its biology and etiology, optimization of control rates, especially in patients with unfavorable prognosis or advanced-stage disease, modification of therapeutic approaches to reduce the risk of long-term complications, and increasing the awareness of patients and physicians of the potential late effects of treatment so that patients can receive appropriate follow-up care.

I. INTRODUCTION

Hodgkin's disease was first identified as a clinical entity in 1832, when Thomas Hodgkin reported six cases of pathologic enlargement of lymph nodes and spleen. Initially, only temporary palliation of the disease could be achieved using crude, low-energy X-ray equipment. Tremendous progress had been made over the years in the management and treatment of the disease. These include the development of modern radiation techniques and more effective combination chemotherapy regimens, advances in radiographic and surgical staging, and identification of prognostic factors that allow better tailoring of treatments. As a result, Hodgkin's disease, a previously fatal illness, has now been transformed to one of the most curable forms of malignancy. It is estimated that approximately three-quarters of all patients with Hodgkin's disease will achieve long-term cure, and among patients with early stage, favorable prognosis disease, the chance of cure is close to 90%.

II. EPIDEMIOLOGY

In the United States, an estimated 7500 new cases of Hodgkin's disease are diagnosed, and 1500 deaths occur each year. The United States Surveillance, Epidemiology, and End Results Registry data report an annual incidence of 2.6 per 100,000 and mortality rates of 0.5 per 100,000 in 1996. In developing countries, the overall incidence of Hodgkin's disease is lower, with childhood Hodgkin's disease being more common than the adult presentation. Developed countries have the highest incidence of Hodgkin's disease among 15 to 34 year olds, and a bimodal age-incidence pattern has been recognized, with the first peak at around age 25 and the second peak after age 50.

In recent years, there appears to be a slight decline in the overall incidence of Hodgkin's disease in the United States, and as a result of effective therapy, there has been a substantial improvement in the mortality rates over the years. Between 1973 and 1996, the estimated annual percentage reduction in the incidence of Hodgkin's disease is 0.3% and the annual percentage decrease in mortality is 4.2%.

III. BIOLOGY AND PATHOGENESIS

The cells that confer "malignancy" in Hodgkin's disease, known as Reed-Sternberg cells, are large, multinucleated cells that usually comprise only a minority of the cells present in the tissue sample, with the majority of the tumor consisting of a variety of inflammatory cells and fibrosis. Cytokines produced by Reed-Sternberg cells and the surrounding inflammatory cells have both local and systemic effects, contributing to the distinctive histopathologic and clinical features of Hodgkin's disease. Efforts are currently underway to identify cytokines and expression of cytokine receptors that may reflect tumor burden and may be of prognostic value. Results of these studies may allow identification of poor prognosis patients who may benefit from more aggressive treatment, facilitate detection of disease recurrence, and, finally, help in the development of potential targets for immunotherapy of Hodgkin's disease.

The pathogenesis of Hodgkin's disease is an unresolved issue. Many clinical features of the disease are suggestive of infectious causes. A number of childhood factors associated with reduced exposure to infectious agents at an early age have been linked to the development of Hodgkin's disease. Isolated clusters of the disease have been reported, but its communicability has not been proven. Studies have demonstrated an approximately threefold increased incidence of Hodgkin's disease in patients with a history of infectious mononucleosis. The role of Epstein–Barr virus (EBV), the causative agent of infectious mononucleosis, in the pathogenesis of Hodgkin's disease is currently being actively investigated.

IV. HISTOPATHOLOGIC CLASSIFICATION

The Rye classification subdivides Hodgkin's disease into four major histologic subtypes: nodular sclerosis, mixed cellularity, lymphocyte predominance, and lymphocyte depletion, each with its characteristic clinical presentation and natural history. In recent years, nodular lymphocyte predominance Hodgkin's disease has been recognized as an entity separate from classical Hodgkin's disease based on its distinctive morphologic, immunophenotypic, and clinical features. In the revised European–American classification of lymphoid neoplasms (R.E.A.L. classification), the histopathologic classification of Hodgkin's disease has been slightly modified and now consists of three main categories: classic Hodgkin's disease, nodular lymphocyte predominance Hodgkin's disease, and Hodgkin's disease unclassifiable. The four subtypes within classic Hodgkin's disease include nodular sclerosis, mixed cellularity, lymphocyte depletion, and lymphocyte-rich classical Hodgkin's disease, a new subtype that has a predominance of lymphocytes, but with Reed-Sternberg cell morphology and immunophenotype of classic Hodgkin's disease.

V. CLINICAL PRESENTATION

The typical clinical presentation of Hodgkin's disease is the development of a painless enlarged lymph node. Another common presentation is the finding of a mediastinal mass on a routine chest radiograph in an asymptomatic patient. Patients may also present with one or more of the constitutional symptoms, including B symptoms, the criteria of which include unexplained weight loss of more than 10% of the body weight 6 months prior to the diagnosis, unexplained fever with temperature above 38 °C, and recurrent drenching night sweats in the previous 1 month. Less commonly, patients with Hodgkin's disease may present with unexplained generalized pruritus, or alcohol-induced pain in areas involved by the disease. The Ann Arbor staging classification, developed in 1971 and subsequently modified and updated in 1988 in Cotswolds, England, is the current accepted staging system for Hodgkin's disease (Table I).

VI. STAGING WORK-UP

An adequate surgical biopsy for pathological assessment by an experienced hematopathologist is essential in the initial diagnosis of Hodgkin's disease. Also important is a careful history and physical examination, with special attention to the presence and duration of constitutional symptoms, and palpation of all nodal groups. Radiographic studies should include a posteroanterior and lateral chest radiograph with measurement of the tumor mass:thoracic ratio at either T5-6 or at the diaphragm, and computed tomography (CT) of the chest, abdomen, and pelvis. Gallium-67 citrate scanning is increasingly being used for both initial evaluation prior to treatment and for follow-up of disease after treatment. More recently, the role of positron emission tomography imaging in Hodgkin's disease is being investigated. Bipedal lymphangiography, although less commonly used nowadays, can be helpful in detecting disease in the paraaortic and pelvic nodes. Bone marrow biopsies are useful in patients presenting with B symptoms or advanced stage disease, but are of limited value in those with early stage and favorable prognosis disease because of its low yield of less than 1%. Staging laparotomy can help detect occult disease below the diaphragm in 20–25% of patients with clinical stage I–IIA disease and in 35% of patients with clinical stage I–II B disease. It involves a splenectomy, needle and wedge biopsy of the liver, and biopsies of the paraaortic, mesenteric, portal, celiac, and splenic hilar lymph nodes. However, its use is diminishing in many parts of the world as a result of widespread use of chemotherapy as a component of initial treatment.

VII. TREATMENT

A. Stages I and II

The mainstay of treatment in patients with early stage, favorable prognosis disease (lack of B symptoms or bulky tumor mass) has been mantle and paraaortic (MPA) radiation therapy, with inclusion of the spleen in the field if a staging laparotomy is not performed, yielding a long-term disease-free survival of approximately 80–85%. Studies have shown that carefully selected pathologically staged, early stage patients can be safely treated with a mantle radiation field alone. In clinically staged patients, mantle radiation therapy alone should be offered only to those in whom the risk of occult disease below the diaphragm is low, e.g., in young female patients with clinical stage (CS) I

TABLE I
Coltswold's Staging Classification for Hodgkin's Disease

Stage I	Involvement of a single lymph node region or lymphoid structure (e.g., spleen, thymus, Waldeyer's ring) or involvement of a single extralymphatic site (IE)
Stage II	Involvement of two or more lymph node regions on the same side of the diaphragm (hilar nodes, when involved on both sides, constitute stage II disease); localized contiguous involvement of only one extranodal organ or site and lymph node region(s) on the same side of the diaphragm (IIE) The number of anatomic regions involved should be indicated by a subscript (e.g., II_3)
Stage III	Involvement of lymph node regions on both sides of the diaphragm (III), which may also be accompanied by involvement of the spleen (IIIs) or by localized contiguous involvement of only one extranodal organ site (IIIE) or both (III SE) III_1: With or without involvement of splenic, hilar, celiac, or portal nodes III_2: With involvement of paraaortic, iliac, and mesenteric nodes
Stage IV	Diffuse or disseminated involvement of one or more extranodal organs or tissues with or without associated lymph node involvement
Designations applicable to any disease stage	
A:	No symptoms
B:	Fever (temperature >38°C), drenching night sweats, unexplained weight loss >10% of body weight within the prior 6 months
X:	Bulky disease (a widening of the mediastinum by more than one-third of the presence of a nodal mass with a maximal dimension greater than 10 cm)
E:	Involvement of a single extranodal site that is contiguous or proximal to the known nodal site
CS:	Clinical stage
PS:	Pathological stage (as determined by staging laparotomy)

disease or in male patients with CS I disease with lymphocyte predominance histology or disease limited to the upper neck.

Replacement of the combination chemotherapy regimen of mechlorethamine, oncovin, procarbazine, and prednisone (MOPP) by the less toxic and more effective regimen of adriamycin, bleomycin, procarbazine, and prednisone (ABVD) has increased the role of chemotherapy in early stage Hodgkin's disease. In addition, chemotherapy should presumably control occult abdominal disease, thus eliminating the need for staging laparotomy. A number of randomized trials have compared radiation therapy alone with combined modality therapy in patients with early stage disease.

Although an improved relapse-free survival with the addition of chemotherapy to radiation therapy has been found, no survival differences have been detected. This is likely due to the higher salvage potential after radiation therapy alone and to the increased risk of fatal treatment-related complications in patients who received combined modality therapy. However, in patients with unfavorable prognostic features such as B symptoms, bulky disease, or other factors associated with high disease burden, treatment with ra-

diation therapy alone has been found to be inadequate, and combined modality therapy should be offered to these patients. Preliminary data are available, suggesting that involved field radiation therapy may suffice when combined with chemotherapy.

Randomized studies are currently underway to determine the optimal number of cycles of chemotherapy and radiation dose. Chemotherapy alone has been advocated by some as an alternative option in early stage patients. Two randomized trials comparing MPA radiation therapy with MOPP chemotherapy in PS I–II patients yielded conflicting results. However, recurrence rates of 18–33% after MOPP alone in pathologically staged patients may be too high compared with recurrence rates with combined modality therapy of only 10–15%. More importantly, salvage of relapse after chemotherapy often requires very intensive and toxic approaches, including high-dose chemotherapy and stem cell rescue.

B. Stages III and IV

The introduction of the combination chemotherapy regimen, MOPP, in the mid-1960s substantially improved the curability of patients with advanced stage

Hodgkin's disease. The ABVD regimen was initially introduced as a form of second-line therapy in patients who had a poor response to or relapse after MOPP chemotherapy. A number of randomized studies in advanced stage patients have subsequently shown that the ABVD-containing regimen is associated with a significantly higher failure-free survival as well as overall survival. With appropriate treatment, patients with advanced stage disease have a long-term failure-free survival of 70–75%, and among patients who achieve a complete response, the failure-free survival approaches 90%. To further improve treatment results, research institutions have devised dose-intensive regimens and dose-escalated regimens with hematopoietic growth factor support for advanced Hodgkin's disease. However, only preliminary data are available, and longer follow-up time is needed to confirm their potential superiority over conventional regimens.

The role of adjuvant radiation therapy in advanced stage Hodgkin's disease is controversial. The rationale for addition of radiation therapy to combination chemotherapy in advanced stage Hodgkin's disease is based on the fact that the majority of relapses are at the site of initial disease. Reducing the risk of relapse by using aggressive up-front treatment is imperative because of the poor salvage potential and the likely need to resort to transplantation in patients failing after chemotherapy.

Randomized studies and a recent meta-analysis have demonstrated a significantly improved freedom from treatment failure rate, but did not detect any survival advantage with the addition of radiation therapy to chemotherapy in advanced stage Hodgkin's disease. Subgroup analysis showed that patients with bulky nodal involvement, NS histology, or more localized advanced stage disease are most likely to benefit from adjuvant radiation therapy.

VIII. SALVAGE THERAPY

One of the main influences on successes of salvage after a relapse is the extent of prior therapy. Patients who relapse after radiotherapy alone have an over 60% chance of achieving durable second remissions using conventional dose salvage therapy compared to patients who relapse after chemotherapy or combined modality therapy in which the chances are only 20 to 30%. The exception is in a small minority of highly selected patients with limited nodal relapses after chemotherapy in whom the chance of successful salvage with conventional dose therapy can be as high as 80%.

High-dose therapy with bone marrow or stem cell support is increasingly being employed in chemotherapy–refractory disease or after chemotherapy failure. With improvements in supportive measures, peritransplant mortality has decreased over the years, and the chance of achieving long-term second remission is as high as 50–60%. However, it is important to note that many of the studies include only selected patients with mostly favorable features at the time of transplantation.

IX. TREATMENT COMPLICATIONS

Hypothyroidism is observed in about 30% of patients after mantle radiation therapy, and localized herpes zoster is found in about 15–20% of patients. Xerostomia is another self-limited complication of radiotherapy, but may have a more prolonged effect in older patients. Radiation pneumonitis, occurring in less than 5% of patients typically 1 to 6 months after completion of mantle irradiation, is characterized by a nonproductive cough, low grade fever, and shortness of breath. After ruling out an infectious etiology, it can be treated with a course of nonsteroidal anti-inflammatory agents. Severe pneumonitis may require treatment with steroids. The addition of a bleomycin-containing chemotherapy regimen may further increase the risk of symptomatic pneumonitis, as well as long-term pulmonary fibrosis. With the diminished use of MOPP, sterility after treatment for Hodgkin's disease is no longer of prevailing concern in most patients, but will still affect those who receive alkylating chemotherapy for salvage purposes or radiation treatment to the pelvis region for infradiaphragmatic Hodgkin's disease.

The two main causes of death other than Hodgkin's disease in long-term survivors are second malignancies and, to a much less extent, cardiac complications. Leukemia, the least common form of second malignancy, is almost uniformly fatal and is related to the cumulative doses of alkylating agents received. With the replacement of MOPP by ABVD, this relatively rare complication now is even more scarce. While the risk of non-Hodgkin's lymphoma is increased after Hodgkin's disease, whether it is related to the disease itself or its treatment is not completely apparent. The development of secondary solid tumors, which typically have a latency of 10 years or more, is becoming increasingly recognized in survivors of Hodgkin's disease. Some of the treatment factors that have been implicated to influence secondary solid tumor risk include radiation dose, field size, and addition of chemotherapy to radiation therapy. Chemotherapy alone has also been found to be associated with increased risk for secondary solid tumors, especially lung cancer. Other important observations are the alarmingly high incidence of breast cancer in women irradiated at a young age and a potential positive interaction between the carcinogenic effects of smoking and radiation in lung cancer development. Such findings have important implications in terms of patient education, counseling for behavioral changes, and targeting of high-risk populations for more rigorous cancer screening.

After second malignancies, cardiac toxicity is the next most common treatment-related cause of death. Multiple studies have documented an association between mediastinal irradiation and risk of fatal cardiovascular complications, particularly acute myocardial infarctions. Improvements in radiation techniques in recent years have substantially reduced treatment-related cardiac complications and mortality. However, the long-term toxicities of chemotherapeutic agents known to have dose-related cardiotoxicity and their potential synergistic effects with radiotherapy remain unknown. Cardiac function monitoring and cardiac disease screening, as well as efforts to minimize other cardiac risk factors, may have a role in the follow-up care of long-term survivors of Hodgkin's disease.

X. SUMMARY

Despite the relative rarity of the disease and its high curability, the impact of Hodgkin's disease on society cannot be underestimated. It predominantly affects young adults, during the time when they are beginning the most productive parts of their lives. Moreover, after patients are cured of their Hodgkin's disease, they continue to face excessive mortality from other causes, primarily as a result of the late effects from management of their disease. Continued efforts are needed to further improve the treatment outcome of this already largely curable disease. These include better understanding of the etiology and pathophysiology of the disease, optimization of control rates, especially in patients with unfavorable prognosis or advanced stage disease, modification of therapeutic approaches to reduce the risk of long-term complications, and increasing the awareness of patients and physicians of the potential late effects of treatment so that patients can receive appropriate follow-up care.

See Also the Following Articles

BLEOMYCIN • CYTOKINES: HEMATOPOIETIC GROWTH FACTORS • EPSTEIN–BARR VIRUS AND ASSOCIATED MALIGNANCIES • LYMPHOMA, NON-HODGKIN'S • MONOCLONAL ANTIBODIES: LEUKEMIA AND LYMPHOMA

Bibliography

Biti, G. P., *et al.* (1992). Extended-field radiotherapy is superior to MOPP chemotherapy for the treatment of pathological-stage I-IIA Hodgkin's disease: 8-year update of an Italian prospective randomized study. *J. Clin. Oncol.* **10,** 378–382.

Canellos, G., *et al.* (1992). Chemotherapy of advanced Hodgkin's disease with MOPP, ABVD or MOPP alternating with ABVD. *N. Engl. J. Med.* **327,** 1478–1484.

Fabian, C., *et al.* (1994). Low-dose involved field radiation after chemotherapy in advanced Hodgkin's disease: A southwest oncology group randomized study. *Ann. Intern. Med.* **120,** 903–912.

Hancock, S., *et al.* (1996). Long-term complications of treatment and causes of mortality after Hodgkin's disease. *Sem. Radiat. Oncol.* **6,** 225–242.

Harris, N., *et al.* (1999). World Health Organization of neoplastic disease of the hematopoietic and lymphoid tissues: Report of the clinical advisory committee meeting-Airlie House, Virginia. *J. Clin. Oncol.* **17,** 3835–3849.

Harris, N., *et al.* (1994). A revised European-American classification of lymphoid neoplasms: A proposal from the International Lymphoma Study Group. *J. Clin. Oncol.* **84,** 1361–1392.

Jones, E., *et al.* (1996). Limited radiation therapy for selected patients with pathological stages IA and IIA Hodgkin's disease. *Sem. Radiat. Oncol.* **6,** 162–171.

Loeffler, M., *et al.* (1998). Meta-analysis of chemotherapy versus combined modality therapy trials in Hodgkin's disease. *J. Clin. Oncol.* **16,** 818–829.

Longo, D. L., *et al.* (1991). Radiation therapy versus combination chemotherapy in the treatment of early-stage Hodgkin's disease: 7-year results of a prospective randomized trial. *J. Clin. Oncol.* **9,** 906–917.

Mauch, P., *et al.* (1995). Long-term survival in Hodgkin's disease: Relative impact of mortality, secondary tumor, infection and cardiovascular disease. *Cancer J. Sci. Am.* **1,** 33–42.

Specht, L., *et al.* (1998). Influence of more extensive radiotherapy and adjuvant chemotherapy on long-term outcome of early-stage Hodgkin's disease: A meta-analysis of 23 randomized trials involving 3,888 patients. *J. Clin. Oncol.* **16,** 830–843.

Tubiana, M., *et al.* (1989). Toward comprehensive management tailored to prognostic factors of patients with clinical stages of I and II in Hodgkin's disease. The EORTC Lymphoma Group controlled clinical trials: 1964–1987. *Blood* **73,** 47–56.

Lymphoma, Non-Hodgkin's

Dan L. Longo

National Institute on Aging
National Institutes of Health

GLOSSARY

B-cell Lymphocyte derived from bone marrow in mammals and the bursa of Fabricius in chickens; these cells are specialized to produce immunoglobulin molecules that aid in host defense; 85% of human lymphomas are derived from B cells.

bcl-2 A 24-kDa protein encoded by a gene on chromosome 18q21; bcl-2 acts to prevent programmed cell death; overexpressed by translocation into the immunoglobulin heavy chain gene in follicular lymphomas, bcl-2 is thought to prevent the death of cells and conveys resistance to chemotherapeutic agents.

bcl-6 A 95-kDa protein encoded by a gene on chromosome 3q27 also known as lymphoma-associated zinc finger-3 (LAZ-3); it is a transcriptional repressor frequently mutated or rearranged in diffuse large B-cell lymphoma.

Epstein–Barr virus A herpes virus that selectively infects human B cells through CD21 (complement receptor 2);

75% of people carry the virus in latently infected B cells that are controlled by T cells; conditions associated with defective T-cell function permit the outgrowth first of polyclonal and then monoclonal populations of virus-infected cells.

lymphoid follicle Aggregates of B cells around follicular dendritic cells; the follicle is the site of immunoglobulin gene hypermutation and selection of B cells making antibodies of higher affinity for the selecting antigen; follicular center B cells give rise to follicular lymphoma.

mantle zone Cuff of lymphocytes surrounding the lymphoid follicle; unlike follicular center cells, mantle zone B cells do not undergo immunoglobulin gene hypermutation; gives rise to mantle cell lymphoma often containing a characteristic t(11;14) that results in the activation of cyclin D1.

mucosa-associated lymphatic tissue (MALT) Lymphoid cells in epithelia and lamina propria beneath the body's mucosal surfaces, particularly the gut and bronchi; lymphomas arising from MALT most commonly originate in the stomach as a consequence of *Helicobacter pylori* infection; MALT lymphomas of other sites are likely also antigen driven but the stimulating antigens are not well defined.

natural killer (NK) A lymphoid cell capable of producing a variety of cytokines and lysing certain tumor cells *in vitro* without prior activation; gives rise to a form of leukemia, large granular lymphocytic leukemia, and a form of lymphoma, nasal NK cell lymphoma.

T cell Lymphocyte derived from bone marrow precursors that mature through the thymus; they recognize antigen fragments presented on the surface of cells in the cleft of the major histocompatibility complex gene products; they have a wide range of effector functions, including generation of cytokines to promote antibody formation or cytokines to promote the lysis of target cells; 15% of human lymphomas are derived from T cells.

This article focuses on the malignancies of lymphoid cells that are classified as a group on the basis of their distinction from Hodgkin's lymphoma. The general aspects of lymphoid malignancies are explored, and features and management of specific lymphoma entities are discussed.

I. INTRODUCTION

Malignancies of lymphoid cells have generally been classified into different disease categories based on clinical criteria such as sites of involvement and natural history. Thus, lymphoid tumors that mainly involve the blood were called leukemias and were divided into acute or chronic subtypes based on the natural history. When lymphoid tumors involved lymph nodes or organs, three main categories of malignancy were named: follicular lymphomas grew in a nodular pattern and had an indolent natural history; diffuse aggressive lymphomas grew in sheets and had a natural history of about 6 months, if not effectively treated; and the third category of lymphoma was Hodgkin's disease, which had the peculiar feature of contiguous spread from one lymph node group to another and the malignant cell was a rare cell within the tumor, most of its bulk being a lymphoid/inflammatory infiltrate of apparently normal cells. The final disease of lymphoid cells was multiple myeloma, a tumor of plasma cells with disease manifestations related to bone destruction and inhibition of normal host resistance to infection. Although all of these cancers are derived from lymphocytes, until very recently, no classification scheme embraced them all. Acute leukemias were categorized based on cell morphology and genetics into a French–American–British classification. A

bewildering array of lymphoma classifications were developed based on histology, but two predominated: the Working Formulation (an updated Rappaport scheme) in North America and the Kiel Classification in Europe and Asia. Myeloma and chronic lymphoid leukemia were not subdivided into subsets based on pathologic criteria, but clinical staging systems were used to categorize patients into risk groups.

As additional sophisticated analytic tools were applied to lymphoid malignancies, it became clear that genetic, immunologic, and clinical features could add significant information to histologic classifications. Efforts to infer genetic and immunologic features based on histologic features were not routinely successful. The additional information identified heterogeneity not completely evident on histologic examination. New discrete disease entities were identified within old familiar categories.

The World Health Organization (WHO) classification of lymphoid malignancies pulls together in a single classification all of these disease entities, acute and chronic lymphoid leukemias, indolent and aggressive lymphomas, Hodgkin's disease, and myeloma (Table I). The classification includes histology, genetics, immunophenotype, and clinical information in identifying clinicopathologic disease entities. Another distinctive feature of the WHO classification is that it was arrived at by consensus of leading hematopathologists and clinicians from around the world, a distinct break from the "great man" approach that had previously dominated lymphoma classification in which a single strong-willed pathologist dictated the system to others. The number of named entities has increased, but the added complexity has permitted the development of specific management approaches that achieve a better outcome than is obtained when different diseases are treated as one.

II. GENERAL ASPECTS OF LYMPHOID MALIGNANCIES

A. Epidemiology

Non-Hodgkin's lymphomas have increased in frequency in the United States at a rate of about 4% per year since 1950. The reasons for the increase are not known. About 60,000 cases were diagnosed in 2000. The disease is more common in patients with primary

TABLE I
WHO Classification of Lymphoid Malignancies[a]

B cell	T cell	Hodgkin's disease
Precursor B-cell neoplasm	Precursor T-cell neoplasm	Nodular lymphocyte-predominant
Precursor B lymphoblastic leukemia/ lymphoma (precursor B-cell acute lymphoblastic leukemia)	**Precursor T lymphoblastic lymphoma/ leukemia (precursor T-cell acute lymphoblastic leukemia)**	Hodgkin's disease
Mature (peripheral) B-cell neoplasms	Mature (peripheral) T-cell neoplasms	Classical Hodgkin's disease
B-cell chronic lymphocytic leukemia/ small lymphocytic lymphoma	T-cell prolymphocytic leukemia	Nodular sclerosis Hodgkin's disease
B-cell prolymphocytic leukemia	T-cell granular lymphocytic leukemia	Lymphocyte-rich classical Hodgkin's disease
Lymphoplasmacytic lymphoma	Aggressive NK cell leukemia	Mixed cellularity Hodgkin's disease
Splenic marginal zone B-cell lymphoma (± villous lymphocytes)	Adult T-cell lymphoma/leukemia (HTLV-I +)	Lymphocyte depletion Hodgkin's disease
Hairy cell leukemia	Extranodal NK/T-cell lymphoma, nasal type	
Plasma cell myeloma/plasmacytoma	Enteropathy-type T-cell lymphoma	
Extranodal marginal zone B-cell lymphoma of MALT type	Hepatosplenic γ/δ T-cell lymphoma	
Mantle cell lymphoma	Subcutaneous panniculitis-like T-cell lymphoma	
Follicular lymphoma	**Mycosis fungoides/Sézary syndrome**	
Nodal marginal zone B-cell lymphoma (± monocytoid B cells)	Anaplastic large cell lymphoma, primary cutaneous type	
Diffuse large B-cell lymphoma	**Peripheral T-cell lymphoma, not otherwise specified**	
Burkitt's lymphoma/Burkitt cell leukemia	Angioimmunoblastic T-cell lymphoma	
	Anaplastic large cell lymphoma, primary systemic type	

[a]HTLV, human T-cell lymphotropic virus; MALT, mucosa-associated lymphoid tissue; NK, natural killer; WHO, World Health Organization. The more common entities are listed in bold type.

or secondary immunodeficiencies. The prevalence of particular forms of lymphoma varies geographically. T-cell lymphomas are common and follicular lymphomas are rare in Asia; the reverse is true in the West. Although the etiology of the vast majority of lymphomas is unknown, some infectious agents can cause lymphomas (Table II). Epstein–Barr virus and human herpesvirus 8 are DNA viruses associated with particular disease subsets; hepatitis C and human T lymphotropic virus I are RNA viruses associated with certain lymphoma types. *Helicobacter pylori* bacterial infection of the stomach is a prerequisite for the development of gastric mucosa-associated lymphatic tissue (MALT) lymphoma; treatment of the infection often causes the lymphoma to regress.

B. Genetics

All lymphomas are clonal malignancies (i.e., derived from a single cell) and contain genetic abnormalities, some of which are defined and associated with partic-ular types of lymphoma (Table III). The lesions may be at a variety of levels, including gross chromosomal changes (translocations, additions, or deletions), re-arrangement of specific genes that may not be apparent from cytogenetic studies, and overexpression, underexpression, or mutation of specific genes. Lymphomas often contain balanced chromosomal translocations involving the antigen receptor genes; immunoglobulin genes on chromosomes 2, 14, and 22 in B cells; and T-cell antigen receptor genes on chromosomes 7 and 14 in T cells. The fact that these gene segments must rearrange to form normal antigen receptors in normal cells creates a vulnerability to aberrant recombination during which chromosome segments from other chromosomes are juxtaposed with the antigen receptor genes. B cells are also susceptible to acquiring mutations during their maturation in germinal centers. In the germinal center, immunoglobulin genes are mutated in an effort to generate an antibody with even higher affinity for the selecting antigen. While the variable region genes are

TABLE II

Infectious Agents Associated with the Development
of Lymphoid Malignancies[a]

Infectious agent	Lymphoid malignancy
Epstein–Barr virus	Burkitt's lymphoma
	Postorgan transplant lymphoma
	Primary CNS diffuse large B-cell lymphoma
	Hodgkin's disease
	Extranodal NK/T cell lymphoma, nasal type
HTLV-I	Adult T-cell leukemia/lymphoma
HIV	Diffuse large B-cell lymphoma
	Burkitt's lymphoma
Hepatitis C virus	Lymphoplasmacytic lymphoma
Helicobacter pylori	Gastric MALT lymphoma
Human herpesvirus 8	Primary effusion lymphoma
	Multicentric Castleman's disease
	? Myeloma

[a]CNS, central nervous system; HTLV, human T-cell lymphotropic virus; MALT, mucosa-associated lymphoid tissue; NK, natural killer.

the target of this mutational process, other genes (e.g., bcl-6 on chromosome 3) may also become mutated with the result that control over cell proliferation may be lost.

The development of techniques to examine the expression of genes within tumors (e.g., cDNA microarray or other methods of assessing global gene expression) seems likely to lead to a further refinement of the lymphoma classification system as particular patterns of gene expression are identified that predict response or lack of response to particular therapeutic interventions. Early efforts to define lymphoma subtypes based on gene expression patterns have yielded promising results in diffuse large B-cell lymphoma, a type recognized as heterogeneous but not further subclassifiable on morphologic grounds.

C. Immunology

About 75% of lymphoid leukemias and 90% of lymphomas in the United States are of B-cell origin. During their development from primitive hematopoietic stem cells, T and B cells undergo a series of developmental changes that can be identified based on changes in the expression of particular cell surface proteins. While particular lymphoid malignancies retain the cell surface phenotype characteristic of lym-

phocytes at normal stages of development, this fact does not reflect any useful information about the etiology or likely course of the disease. Usually, genetic lesions begin occurring at the earliest stages of development and continue to accumulate until the normal growth control is lost. For example, among the acute leukemias derived from B cells, the most clinically aggressive form is the one with cell surface phenotypic features of mature follicular B cells (Burkitt's leukemia) rather than the ones with more immature cell features (precursor B lymphoblastic lymphoma). Similarly, the t(14;18) that is often seen in follicular lymphoma was most often generated in the malignant cell at a very early stage in its development when the immunoglobulin genes were initially rearranging. However, that genetic change is not sufficient to generate a follicular lymphoma. Additional genetic lesions occur during the cell's development such that its malignant potential is not expressed until it has acquired a mature follicular B-cell phenotype. The major value of cell surface phenotyping of lymphomas is

TABLE III

Cytogenetic Translocations and Associated Oncogenes
Often Seen in Lymphoid Malignancies

Disease[a]	Cytogenetic abnormality	Oncogene
CLL/small lymphocytic lymphoma	t(14;15)(q32;q13)	—
MALT lymphoma	t(11;18)(q21;q21)	API2/MALT1
Precursor B-cell acute lymphoid leukemia	t(9;22)(q34;q11) or variant t(4;11)(q21;q23)	BCR/ABL AF4, ALLI
Precursor acute lymphoid leukemia	t(9;22) t(1;19) t(17;19) t(5;14)	BCR, ABL E2A, PBX HLF, E2A IL3, Igμ
Mantle cell lymphoma	t(11;14)(q13;q32)	BCL-1
Follicular lymphoma	t(14;18)(q32;q21)	BCL-2
Diffuse large cell lymphoma	t(3;-)(q27;-)[b] t(17;-)(p13;-)[b]	BCL-6 P53
Burkitt's lymphoma Burkitt's leukemia	t(8;-)(q24;-)[b]	C-MYC
CD30+ anaplastic large cell lymphoma	t(2;5)(p23;q35)	ALK
Lymphoplasmacytic lymphoma	t(9;14)(p13;q32)	PAX5

[a]CLL, chronic lymphoid leukemia; MALT, mucosa-associated lymphoid tissue.
[b]Numerous sites of translocation may be involved with these genes.

to assist in the differential diagnosis of lymphoma. For example, benign follicular hyperplasia may resemble follicular lymphoma; however, the demonstration that all of the cells bear the same immunoglobulin light chain confirms the presence of a clonal malignancy rather than a polyclonal reactive process.

D. Staging

Regardless of the type of lymphoma, the initial evaluation of the patient includes a careful history and physical examination and the performance of series of laboratory and imaging tests to define the extent of disease and develop an assessment of the patient's prognosis. The components of the typical patient workup are listed in Table IV. In addition, patients with symptoms that direct attention to a particular site or organ system may have other tests to define involvement with tumor. This process of defining the extent of disease is called staging. In general, once a particular site is found to be free of lymphoma, it is not necessary to reevaluate it after therapy. However, sites involved with lymphoma must be reevaluated to assure that the disease has been cleared after therapy.

There are three major determinants of outcome in lymphoma: (1) the inherent biology of the tumor, (2) the tumor burden, and (3) the physiologic reserve of the patient. At present, the clinical assessment of

these factors is imprecise and indirect. Histologic and genetic features may reflect the tumor biology, but information on the gene expression in tumors is not currently available in a clinically useful time frame. The approach to defining tumor burden is to assess the stage of disease. However, the staging system is an anatomic based one (Table V) that often fails to define prognosis. For example, a patient with stage II diffuse large B-cell lymphoma could have small nodes in two adjacent lymph node groups and a very good prognosis or a football-size mass in the abdomen and a very poor prognosis. Additional assessments of tumor mass have been developed, including lactate dehydrogenase (LDH) levels and β_2-microglobulin, high levels of which predict a poor outcome. Among the most difficult clinical assessments is the physiologic reserve of the patient. Surrogate markers include age and performance status, but neither of these is completely accurate. An 80-year-old person who presents with an acute decline in performance status related to the tumor is different from an 80 year old with poor performance status from multisystem disease. Additional patient assessment tools are needed. However, one clinical system that has been applied to virtually all forms of lymphoma with some success is the International Prognostic Index (IPI; Table VI). Originally developed for diffuse large cell lymphoma, the five component IPI also predicts prognosis in other forms of lymphoma. The IPI is likely to be revised as we develop more information and tools to assess tumor biology and physiologic reserve.

TABLE IV
Staging Evaluation for Non-Hodgkin's Lymphoma[a]

Physical examination
Documentation of B symptoms
Laboratory evaluation
  Complete blood counts
  Liver function tests
  Uric acid
  Calcium
  Serum protein electrophoresis
  Serum β_2-microglobulin
Chest radiograph
CT scan of abdomen, pelvis, and usually chest
Bone marrow biopsy
Lumbar puncture in lymphoblastic, Burkitt's, and diffuse large B-cell lymphoma with positive marrow biopsy
Gallium scan (SPECT) in large cell lymphoma

  [a]CT, computed tomography; SPECT, single photon emission CT.

III. FEATURES AND MANAGEMENT OF SPECIFIC LYMPHOMA ENTITIES

A. Chronic Lymphoid Leukemia (CLL)/ Small Lymphocytic Lymphoma (SLL)

B-cell CLL is the most common form of leukemia in the Western world (13,000 cases/year) and small lymphocytic lymphoma accounts for about 7% of all lymphomas. The median age of patients with CLL/SLL is 65. The malignant cell in both entities is a normal-appearing small lymphocyte with surface markers of the B1 so called T-cell-independent population of B cells that generally do not mature through a germinal

TABLE V
Ann Arbor Staging System

Stage	Definition
I	Involvement of a single lymph node region or lymphoid structure (e.g., spleen, thymus, Waldeyer's ring)
II	Involvement of two or more lymph node regions on the same side of the diaphragm (the mediastinum is a single site; hilar lymph nodes should be considered "lateralized" and, when involved on both sides, constitute stage II disease)
III	Involvement of lymph node regions or lymphoid structures on both sides of the diaphragm
III$_1$	Subdiaphragmatic involvement limited to spleen, splenic hilar nodes, celiac nodes, or portal nodes
III$_2$	Subdiaphragmatic involvement includes paraaortic, iliac, or mesenteric nodes plus structures in III$_1$
IV	Involvement of extranodal site(s) beyond that designated as "E"
	More than one extranodal deposit at any location
	Any involvement of liver or bone marrow
A	No symptoms
B	Unexplained weight lost of >10% of the body weight during the 6 months before staging investigation
	Unexplained, persistent, recurrent fever with temperatures >38°C during the previous month
	Recurrent drenching night sweats during the previous month
E	Localized, solitary involvement of extralymphatic tissue, excluding liver and bone marrow

center (CD5). The diagnosis of CLL usually requires the presence of more than 4000 lymphocytes/μl of blood. SLL is diagnosed on lymph node biopsy. It is not clear what determines whether lymphadenopathy or leukemia is the dominant clinical feature in an individual patient.

Patients with CLL/SLL usually follow a slowly progressive chronic course over 15–20 years. The major threats from the disease are an increased susceptibility to bacterial infections from hypogammaglobulinemia and progressive marrow failure from replacement of normal hematopoietic elements with tumor. About 25% of patients may develop autoimmune anemia or thrombocytopenia; therefore, the mechanism of new onset anemia or thrombocytopenia must be sought. Autoimmune mechanisms are generally able to be controlled without influencing survival; myelophthisis generally signifies a survival of less than 2 years. In addition to infections and marrow failure as risks, 5% of patients undergo a histologic progression of the disease to diffuse large B-cell lymphoma (called Richter's syndrome) that is usually fatal. Two subsets of CLL patients may be defined based on whether the tumor immunoglobulin molecule is mutated (reflecting maturation through a germinal center and having a good prognosis) or contains the germline sequence (having

TABLE VI
International Prognostic Index for Non-Hodgkin's Lymphoma

Five clinical risk factors
  Age ≥60 years
  Serum lactate dehydrogenase levels elevated
  Performance status ≥2 (ECOG) or ≤70 (Karnofsky)
  Ann Arbor stage III or IV
  >1 site of extranodal involvement
Patients are assigned a number for each risk factor they have
Patients are grouped differently based on the type of lymphoma
For diffuse large B-cell lymphoma

0, 1 factor = low risk	35% of cases; 5-year survival, 73%
2 factors = low-intermediate risk	27% of cases; 5-year survival, 51%
3 factors = high-intermediate risk	22% of cases; 5-year survival, 43%
4,5 factors = high risk	16% of cases; 5-year survival, 26%

a poorer prognosis). CD38 expression may aid in distinguishing these two groups; cells with mutated immunoglobulin tend to be CD38 low. More CD38 expression may be a poor prognostic sign.

Intervention in early stages of disease is not beneficial. Treatment is usually reserved until symptoms develop from adenopathy, anemia, or thrombocytopenia. Many agents are active at killing tumor cells, including fludarabine, alkylating agents, glucocorticoids, doxorubicin, vinca alkaloids, and others. Monoclonal antibodies such as rituximab and CAMPATH-1H are active as single agents, but antitumor effects appear to be heightened by using rituximab together with chemotherapy. In late stages of disease, some investigators are employing minitransplants (preparative regimens are immunosuppressive rather than myelosuppressive) with some long-lasting remissions. No therapy has been defined as curative. Patients who recover from a serious infection may benefit from monthly gammaglobulin injections.

B. Follicular Lymphoma

Follicular lymphoma accounts for about 22% of all lymphomas worldwide and about 30% in the United States. The median age of patients is about 59 years, but the disease also affects younger people. The disease is most often widespread at the time of diagnosis. The tumor grows in a follicular or nodular pattern that resembles germinal centers in normal nodes, but the tumor is composed of two major cell types (both from the same clone): a smaller cell with a cleaved nucleus and a larger cell that resembles a proliferating centroblast. Initially the small cells are present in large predominance, but over time the large cells gradually increase in frequency. The initial follicular lymphoma nearly always becomes a diffuse large B-cell lymphoma over time at a rate of about 6–7% of cases/year. Very few patients with follicular lymphoma die with follicular lymphoma; nearly all the deaths occur after histologic transformation to diffuse large B-cell lymphoma with an attendant acceleration in the growth characteristics of the tumor. Early in the course of the disease, adenopathy may wax and wane over the course of several months in up to 25% of patients. However, the disease is generally progressive but the course of disease in individuals is highly variable.

Follicular lymphomas nearly always contain a chromosomal translocation between chromosomes 14 and 18 that causes the *bcl-2* gene on 18 to be overexpressed. This gene prevents programmed cell death (apoptosis) and permits the cell to survive to sustain other genetic lesions. When follicular lymphomas become diffuse large B-cell lymphomas, mutations are frequently found in *p53* and other genes related to cell growth. The overexpression of bcl-2 protein can also convey drug resistance on the tumor cells, as many chemotherapeutic agents kill cells by inducing apoptosis.

The treatment of patients with localized follicular lymphoma is radiation therapy, which is curative in the vast majority. However, most patients do not have localized disease. The management of advanced follicular lymphoma is controversial. It is not clear that treatment alters the natural history of the disease. Many forms of treatment may induce remissions that last 1–2 years but relapse is nearly always seen and median survival is about 10 years. Death generally follows histologic progression to diffuse large B-cell lymphoma, a form of disease that seems less responsive to treatment than *de novo* diffuse large B-cell lymphoma. When treatment is indicated to control symptoms, combination chemotherapy with fludarabine, mitoxantrone, and dexamethasone (FND) or cyclophosphamide, doxorubicin, vincristine, and prednisone (CHOP) is commonly used. The rituximab monoclonal antibody against the B-cell antigen, CD20, is effective as a single agent but may be best used in conjunction with chemotherapy. Single alkylating agents are effective at killing tumor. Vaccine and adoptive cellular therapy approaches to killing tumor cells in the minimal residual disease state are in development. The addition of interferon-α to chemotherapy may improve survival in patients with poor prognostic features.

C. Diffuse Large B-Cell Lymphoma (DLCL)

DLCL accounts for about one-third of cases of lymphoma in the United States. Median age is 64 years. Many of these tumors contain mutations in the *bcl-6* gene on chromosome 3. A subset contains t(14;18), a molecular signature for follicular lymphoma, implying perhaps a clinically silent chronic follicular lymphoma phase of growth, analogous to chronic myeloid leukemia presenting in accelerated phase or blast transformation. The tumor is composed of large cells growing in sheets. However, this group of tumors is heterogeneous and it is hoped that the analysis of gene expression patterns will further subdivide these tumors into discrete clinicopathologic entities. At least two defined histologic subsets are immunoblastic lymphomas and DLCL with extensive fibrosis. There are no apparent differences between immunoblastic and DLCL; however, DLCL with extensive fibrosis is commonly associated with a clinical syndrome of mediastinal lymphoma in young women (median age 37).

DLCL can be either a primary lymph node disease or involve extranodal sites. About one-half of patients have extranodal involvement with the gastrointestinal tract and marrow being the most common sites. The disease can involve nearly any organ, making biopsy a key component of patient evaluation. Renal and pancreatic masses of lymphoma have better prognoses than primary tumor of those organs; thus, diagnostic certainty is important for organ masses. Primary brain DLCL is increasing in frequency even in patients who are not immunosuppressed.

After careful staging, about one-half of patients have stage I or II disease and one-half have more advanced disease. Patients with stage I or II disease can be effectively managed with four cycles of CHOP chemotherapy followed by involved-field radiation therapy. More than 80% of patients are cured with this approach. Patients with advanced stage disease should receive a combination chemotherapy regimen; CHOP is most commonly used but other regimens are as effective and use less doxorubicin. The outcome of treatment is influenced greatly by the IPI (Table VI). About 40% of patients not cured by the initial course of treatment may benefit from high-dose chemotherapy plus autologous stem cell transplantation. Efforts to improve outcome by moving high-dose therapy to the front line of treatment have not been effective.

D. Mantle Cell Lymphoma

This form of lymphoma comprises about 6% of all lymphomas. It is composed of small lymphocytes with indented nuclei and a characteristic cell surface phenotype including CD5 plus B-cell markers such as CD19 and CD20. Like CLL cells, these cells usually mature outside the germinal center. Normal mantle cells are located in a cuff surrounding germinal centers in normal nodes. A characteristic chromosomal translocation associated with mantle cell lymphoma is the t(11;14) that results in overexpression of the cyclin D1 gene on chromosome 11. It remains unclear what role this aberrant expression plays in the development of the malignancy.

Patients present with adenopathy and frequently have systemic symptoms. Bone marrow is often involved. Involvement of the gastrointestinal tract can be extensive, and lymphomatous polyposis of the colon may be evident. Those with gastrointestinal involvement may also have Waldeyer's ring involvement, and vice versa.

Mantle cell lymphoma is one of the most intrinsically drug-resistant forms of lymphoma. Its natural history can range from extraordinarily aggressive to indolent. Rare patients have been observed without any treatment for several years. Aggressive combination chemotherapy is usually ineffective. Rituximab plus CHOP may be more effective. However, the 5-year survival is generally about 25%. It is not clear that high-dose therapy with autologous stem cell transplantation improves treatment outcome.

E. Extranodal Marginal Zone Lymphoma

MALT lymphomas may arise in a number of extranodal sites, including salivary and lacrimal glands, thyroid, and lung, but the most common site is the stomach. They account for about 8% of lymphomas. They are tumors of small lymphocytes. Nearly always they arise as part of an autoimmune or inflammatory response in an organ. In the stomach, gastric MALT lymphoma arises as a consequence of *H. pylori* infection. In the lacrimal and salivary glands, MALT lymphoma often occurs in the setting of a defined clinical sicca syndrome. In the thyroid, MALT lymphoma is often seen within Hashimoto's thyroiditis.

Like follicular lymphoma, gastric MALT can evolve into diffuse large B-cell lymphoma and when MALT lymphomas do this, it often signifies that their growth has become independent of the inciting antigen.

Thus, for gastric MALT lymphoma, more than one-half of the lymphomas will regress completely within a year of eradication of the *H. pylori* infection. Those that do not regress after antibiotics are able to be treated with chemotherapy, particularly alkylating agents, or radiation therapy. When histologic progression to diffuse large B-cell lymphoma occurs, these lymphomas need to be treated with aggressive combination chemotherapy regimens as if they were *de novo* diffuse large B-cell lymphomas.

F. Burkitt's Lymphoma/Leukemia

Burkitt's leukemia/lymphoma accounts for <1% of lymphoid malignancies in adults but ~30% of lymphomas in children. The cells are monotonously homogeneous in size and shape, express surface immunoglobulin, and nearly always contain a chromosomal translocation that activates the *c-myc* gene on chromosome 8 by rearranging into a transcriptionally active immunoglobulin gene (usually the heavy chain gene on 14, but less commonly a light chain gene on chromosome 2 or 22).

The disease occurs in three distinct clinical forms: endemic, sporadic, and HIV associated. Endemic and sporadic forms occur in African children and the sporadic form is seen in Western countries. Burkitt's lymphoma is unusual in that nearly 100% of the cells are in cycle. For most other malignancies, the growth fraction is less than 5%. Because of its rapid growth rate, treatment is initiated nearly emergently once the diagnosis is made.

Patients are usually treated with intensive combination chemotherapy that includes high doses of cyclophosphamide, and central nervous system prophylaxis is important to prevent recurrence. Hydration and urine alkalinization are important to prevent the consequences of the rapid tumor lysis syndrome with the enormous uric acid load presented to the kidney that accompanies massive cell death. In patients able to tolerate intensive therapy, 70–80% of patients may be cured. Patients with immunodeficiency usually are

unable to tolerate curative doses of treatment and the lymphoma progresses to kill the patient, often with concurrent systemic opportunistic infection.

G. Anaplastic Large T/Null Cell Lymphoma

This unusual form, which accounts for about 2% of all lymphomas, is composed of large cells with considerable cellular atypia that can mimic malignant histiocytosis. The tumors express CD30 on their surface (a feature they share with Reed Sternberg cells in Hodgkin's disease) and often contain a characteristic chromosome translocation, t(2;5), that results in overexpression of the anaplastic lymphoma kinase, alk. Expression of alk is a good prognostic feature. Despite the aggressive histologic appearance, response to diffuse large B-cell-type therapy is excellent, with 5-year survival exceeding 75%. The disease commonly involves skin; however, when skin alone is involved (i.e., no adenopathy), the disease tends to be more indolent and has been called cutaneous anaplastic large T/null cell lymphoma.

See Also the Following Articles

Acute Lymphoblastic Leukemia • Acute Myelocytic Leukemia • Chronic Lymphocytic Leukemia • Chronic Myelogenous Leukemia • Immune Deficiency: Opportunistic Tumors • Lymphoma, Hodgkin's Disease • Monoclonal Antibodies: Leukemia and Lymphoma

Bibliography

Armitage, J. O., Cavalli, F., and Longo, D. L. (1999). "Text Atlas of Lymphomas." Martin Dunitz, London.

Armitage, J. O., and Longo, D. L. (2001). Malignancies of lymphoid cells. *In* "Harrison's Principles of Internal Medicine" (E. Braunwald *et al.*, eds.), 15th Ed., pp. 715–727. McGraw-Hill, New York.

Harris, N. L., *et al.* (1999). World Health Organization classification of neoplastic diseases of hematopoietic and lymphoid tissues: Report of the Clinical Advisory Committee Meeting. Airlie House, Virginia, November, 1997. *J. Clin. Oncol.* **17,** 3835.

Macrophages

Zhongyun Dong
Isaiah J. Fidler
University of Texas M. D. Anderson Cancer Center

GLOSSARY

angiogenesis The development of new blood vessels.

heterogeneity Variation in biological characteristics between different neoplasms and among cells populating a single tumor.

liposomes Vesicles consisting of phospholipid bilayers containing hydrophilic or lipophilic substances.

macrophage tumoricidal activation The process by which normal noncytotoxic macrophages are rendered cytotoxic to tumor cells.

reticuloendothelial cells Fixed and free phagocytic cells found in the blood, lymph nodes, liver, spleen, etc.

$\mathbf{M}$acrophages are an essential part of homeostasis. The major function of macrophages is to regulate tissue turnover and dispose of damaged cells and invading microorganisms. Normal macrophages can become cytotoxic against tumor cells after they undergo a complex biochemical process termed activation. Macrophages are activated to become cytotoxic after contact with microorganisms or their products, such as endotoxin or cell wall skeleton, by interaction with lymphokines, or by interaction with both. Once activated, macrophages can recognize and destroy neoplastic cells both *in vitro* and *in vivo* without injuring nontumorigenic cells, discriminating between the two by a process that is independent of major histocompatibility antigens, tumor-specific antigens, cell cycle phase, or transformation phenotype. Macrophage recognition of tumorigenic cells is nonimmunologic, requiring cell-to-cell contact. Macrophages systemically activated by liposomes containing various immunomodulators have been shown to eradicate established metastases in rodents with spontaneous metastasis and in dogs with autochthonous osteogenic sarcoma. Systemic activation of macrophages has been shown to be efficacious in children with osteogenic sarcoma lung metastases resistant to conventional chemotherapy.

I. INTRODUCTION

By the time of diagnosis, and nearly always in clinically advanced lesions, malignant neoplasms contain multiple cell populations that exhibit a wide range of biological heterogeneity in, for example, cell surface features, antigenicity, immunogenicity, growth rate, karyotype, drug sensitivity, and the ability to invade normal tissue and produce distant metastasis. Biological diversity is equally prominent among cells in metastatic lesions. Metastases are produced by the nonrandom dissemination and establishment of specialized subpopulations of cells that are present in the primary tumor. Metastases can be clonal in origin, and different metastases can originate from different progenitor cells. Interlesional biologic heterogeneity is further complicated by the genetic instability of metastatic cells, which leads to the development of resistance to therapy. For these reasons, the successful treatment of metastatic disease requires the development of new strategies with a spectrum of activity that overcomes the existing cellular diversity of neoplasms and that can overcome the development of resistance. Appropriately activated macrophages have proved to be a successful treatment.

II. ROLE OF MACROPHAGES IN HOMEOSTASIS

For well over a century, detailed microscopic studies have concluded that mononuclear phagocytes are involved in processes of tissue turnover, such as tissue remodeling during embryogenesis, tissue destruction and repair subsequent to injury, and tissue renewal following the removal of damaged or senescent cells. Indeed, the macrophage, a cell remarkably well conserved in evolution, is one of the most versatile cells in multicellular organisms. One essential function of macrophages is recognition of "altered self." Macrophages are present early during embryonic development where they regulate or participate in the remodeling of tissues that undergo programmed cell death (apoptosis). Macrophages recognize and remove dead and dying cells in both embryogenesis and in invertebrates during metamorphosis. For example, *Xenopus laevis* (frog) and *Ambystoma maculatum* (salamander) undergo extensive tissue remodeling during metamorphosis, including tail regression and gill resorption through apoptosis. In both frogs and salamanders, many macrophages are always found at the site of tissue regression, where they phagocytose the apoptotic cells and, in mature animals, senescent, dying cells.

The removal of apoptotic and senescent cells by macrophages continues throughout the lifetime of an organism. One example is the removal of effete red blood cells (RBC) from the circulation, a continuous process that requires macrophages to distinguish young from old RBC and healthy from damaged cells. Macrophages also play an active role in the differentiation and maturation of certain cell populations. Macrophages participate in the differentiation of mature T cells by recognizing and eliminating certain populations of immature thymocytes. Macrophages can also regulate the differentiation of hematopoietic cells in the adult's bone marrow. Macrophages are present in the bone marrow at the center of erythropoietic and hematopoietic islands that apparently serve as the sites of erythroid proliferation and differentiation.

Macrophages are continuously involved in the controlled metabolism of lipids and iron and in host response to injury, inflammation, and tissue healing and repair. Frequently, macrophages that line body cavities provide the first line of defense against microbial infections and parasitic infestations, and they participate in the second line of defense against foreign invaders. Macrophages often regulate both afferent and efferent arms of the immune system. Furthermore, the activation of cells of the macrophage–histiocyte series to become bactericidal and/or tumoricidal also enhances host defense against cancer. This last function is the major topic of this article.

III. ROLE OF MACROPHAGES IN TUMOR ANGIOGENESIS AND PROGRESSION

The progressive growth of neoplasms and their ability to produce metastasis depend on the induction of adequate vasculature, i.e., angiogenesis. The process of angiogenesis begins with the local degradation of the basement membrane surrounding capillaries followed by invasion of the surrounding stroma by the underlying endothelial cells toward the source of angiogenic molecules. Endothelial cell migration is accompanied by cell proliferation at the leading edge of the migrating column. The capillary sprout subsequently expands and undergoes morphogenesis to yield a capillary. The vasculature of many tumors may differ from that of normal tissues, which may be reflected in the differences in cellular composition, vascular permeability, blood vessel stability, and growth regulation.

Macrophages are important effector cells in angiogenesis. For instance, vascularization in tumors from mice depleted of macrophages is significantly reduced, and macrophages isolated from tumors can induce neovascularization subsequent to injection into normal tissues. Macrophages may influence new capillary growth by several different mechanisms. First, macrophages produce factors, such as fibroblast growth factor (FGF) family members, vascular endothelial cell growth factor (VEGF) or vascular permeability factor (VPF), interleukin-8 (IL-8), angiotropin, platelet-derived growth factor (PDGF), transforming growth factor (TGF)-α, TGF-β, and tumor necrosis factor (TNF)-α, that act directly to stimulate angiogenesis-linked endothelial cell growth or functions. A second mechanism by which macrophages can modulate angiogenesis is by modifying the extracellular matrix (ECM), thereby influencing new capillary growth.

IV. TUMORICIDAL ACTIVATION OF MACROPHAGES

Constitutive or continuous functions of macrophages, e.g., removal of senescent RBC, do not require activation. In contrast, infrequent activities, such as the destruction of tumor cells, require that macrophages undergo a complex biochemical activation process that heightens their activity against microorganisms and cancer cells.

Macrophages are activated *in vivo* by two pathways. Macrophages can be activated subsequent to contact with microorganisms or their products, such as lipopolysaccharide (LPS), other endotoxins, or cell wall skeleton. Although such interactions are common, attempts to activate macrophages systemically by administering microorganisms or their products have resulted in major side effects, such as allergic reactions and granuloma formation. For this reason, progress was delayed until the discovery of muramyl dipeptide (MDP), the minimal component of the bacterial cell wall capable of activating the immune system. MDP is a water-soluble, low molecular weight (M_r 495) synthetic compound, N-acetylmuramyl-L-alanyl-D-isoglutamine. It has potent effects on many host defense cells, including macrophages. A lipophilic analog of MDP has also been synthesized: muramyl tripeptide phosphatidylethanolamine (MTP-PE). Although muramyl peptides influence macrophage function *in vitro*, comparable effects have not been observed *in vivo* because these peptides are rapidly excreted after parenteral administration.

In vivo macrophage activation can also be produced by a family of polypeptides generally referred to as lymphokines. Macrophage activation is produced by a group of lymphokines termed macrophage-activating factors (MAFs). This group includes interferon (IFN)-γ, interleukin-2 (IL-2), granulocyte macrophage colony-stimulating factor (GM-CSF), c-reactive protein, TNF, and monocytes chemotactic and activating factor (MCAF), to name a few. To activate macrophages, the lymphokines must first bind to surface receptors and then be internalized. Tumoricidal activation of macrophages frequently occurs in sequence: lymphokines prime macrophages to respond to a second triggering signal, such as LPS or MDP. It is known that protein kinase C (PKC) plays an important role in the priming of macrophages by lymphokines, such as IFN-γ. Stimulation of macrophages by LPS is mainly mediated by CD14 and the toll-like receptor-4 (TLR-4). Interaction of LPS with macrophages can lead to the activation of pertussis toxin-sensitive guanine nucleotide-binding proteins and to the activation of Ca^{2+}- and phospholipid-dependent PKC, which phosphorylates proteins on threonine and serine residues. However, the major signal transduction pathways that regulate macrophage activation for the production of cytotoxic products and antitumor activity involve the activity of protein tyrosine kinases.

Once activated, tumoricidal macrophages distinguish tumorigenic cells from nontumorigenic cells and bind only to the former. Tumor cell lysis occurs by both direct macrophage-tumor cell contact and the release of a plethora of cytotoxic molecules from the activated macrophages: superoxide anion, hydrogen peroxide, nitric oxide, monokines (IL-1 and TNF), and various degradative enzymes, e.g., collagenases. Many of the released molecules can also modulate additional activation of macrophages to maintain their tumoricidal state.

V. MACROPHAGE–TUMOR CELL INTERACTION

Macrophage killing appears to be sufficiently diverse to prevent the emergence of macrophage-resistant tumor cells. In one illustrative experiment, activated macrophages were incubated with tumor cells for 72 h. Surviving tumor cells were subjected to a second round of macrophage killing. After six cycles, the surviving tumor cells were still as susceptible to macrophage killing as the initial tumor cells, i.e., no resistant cells had been selected. In contrast, if cytotoxic T lymphocytes or natural killer cells were substituted for macrophages in the same selection protocol, resistant cell lines resulted, demonstrating the efficacy of the selection procedure.

Differential sensitivities to macrophage-mediated killing have been observed for different tumor cells. Even so, the least sensitive tumor cells are still subject to macrophage-mediated cytotoxicity. The duration of the macrophage–tumor cell incubation, the length of activation, and the agents used for activating the macrophage to a tumoricidal state all influence this interaction. Activated macrophages distinguish normal from tumor cells and only lyse the latter even under cocultivation conditions. An excellent example of this finding comes from studies where three tumorigenic human cell lines and three nontumorigenic human cell lines were labeled with either [³H]TdR or [¹⁴C]TdR. Coincubation of activated human monocytes with any combination of tumor cells and normal cells resulted in the lysis of only the tu-

morigenic cells, leaving the nontumorigenic cells untouched. These findings indicate that macrophages recognize and kill tumor cells selectively and avoid the bystander lysis common to complement antibody-mediated lysis. Because metastatic cells proliferate in close proximity to normal cells, these findings are relevant to therapeutic manipulations of macrophages.

The destruction of tumor cells by macrophages requires direct cell–cell contact. This association of macrophages with tumor cells is characterized in the initial stage by a weak binding force that is nonselective in nature: normal, nontumoricidal as well as tumoricidal macrophages exhibit initial weak binding to tumor cells. This initial contact leads to the second stage of the association, characterized by a strong binding only between tumoricidal macrophages and tumor cells, not nontumorigenic cells. The strong binding is due to a tight association of plasma membranes of the macrophage and tumor cell (Fig. 1). Several lines of experimental evidence support this concept of a two-stage process. The *in vitro* incubation of mouse peritoneal macrophages with normal or malignant lymphocytes results in tight, permanent binding between activated macrophages and lymphoma cells. In contrast, the association of macrophages with normal lymphocytes is transient, with the lymphocytes detaching unharmed after the interaction. Moreover, lymphoma cells are phagocytosed, whereas normal lymphocytes are not. Human monocytes have been shown to bind to neoplastic cells but not to normal cells. Furthermore, analysis of somatic cell hybrids of tumor and normal cells binding to monocytes revealed that, in all cases, monocytes bound tumorigenic hybrids but did not bind hybrids that were nontumorigenic.

VI. MECHANISMS FOR MACROPHAGE RECOGNITION OF TUMOR CELLS

The mechanisms by which macrophages recognize tumor cells are not clearly defined. Macrophages are capable of destroying syngeneic, allogeneic, and xenogeneic tumor cells, whereas normal, nontumorigenic cells remain unharmed, suggesting that histocompatibility and tumor-specific antigens are not involved.

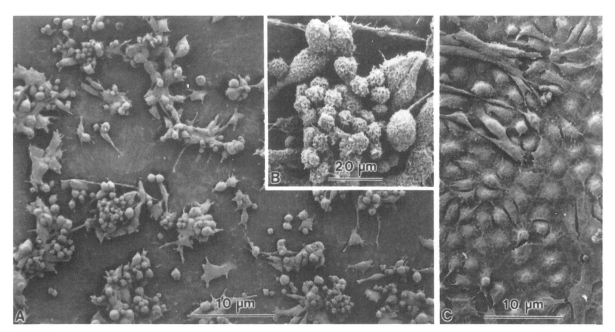

FIGURE 1 Differential binding of activated human blood monocytes to allogeneic melanoma cells (A and B) and normal keratinocytes (C). Note that monocytes do not bind to nontumorigenic, normal keratinocytes.

Cell cycle duration and replication of endogenous C-type viruses or associated fluctuations in antigen expression were ruled out as factors in macrophage recognition of tumor cells, as tumor cells with different cell cycling times and with various levels of virus expression were recognized and lysed by activated macrophages. In addition, differences in metastatic potential, chromosome number, or resistance to chemotherapeutic agents are not important factors for macrophage recognition of tumor cells.

The ubiquitous role of macrophages in homeostasis suggests that macrophages recognize numerous molecules via a wide variety of plasma membrane receptors. A number of these interactions also appear to be relevant for macrophage–tumor cell interactions. For example, macrophages are able to recognize certain sugar residues on tumor cells by specific cell surface lectins. An *N*-acetylgalactosamine/galactose (GalNAc/Gal)-specific receptor on liver macrophages mediates the attachment of desialylated cells to the liver macrophages. Various simple monosaccharides can inhibit macrophage–tumor cell binding and subsequent cytotoxicity in some systems. Mouse macrophage binding to concanavalin A-resistant Chinese hamster ovary cells is inhibited by D-mannose but not galactose or *N*-acetylglucosamine. The binding of metastatic colon carcinoma cells to rat liver macrophages is inhibited by exogenous D-mannose and *N*-acetylgalactosamine. In contrast, the binding of murine peritoneal macrophages to lymphoma cells is inhibited by *N*-acetylgalactosamine but not by D-mannose. Collectively, these results suggest that macrophages can recognize several simple sugars that vary among different tumor cells.

Macrophages can recognize complex asparagine-linked oligosaccharides on tumor cells. Treatment of mastocytoma cells with oligosaccharide-processing inhibitors 1-deoxynojirimycin or 1-deoxymannojirimycin results in glycoproteins that lack the complex structure of N-linked oligosaccharides and a decreased level of macrophage-mediated lysis. The inhibition of tumor cell–macrophage binding by saccharides suggests a role for membrane lectins on the tumor cell and macrophage cell surfaces, such as a 175-kDa mannose/fucose receptor on the macrophage membrane surface. Endogenous lectins of 14.5 and 34 kDa that recognize β-galactosides have been identified on the surface of different tumor cells and host effector cells.

Macrophages have plasma membrane receptors that interact with extracellular proteins as well as known adhesion superfamilies, such as the integrins. An inflammatory response requires the macrophage to extravasate from the circulation and enter tissue at the site of injury. It is therefore not surprising that macrophages are able to recognize laminin, a basement membrane protein. The adhesion of macrophages to laminin or fibronectin aids diapedesis into damaged tissues. The presence of fibronectin- or laminin-binding receptors on both the tumor cell and macrophages suggests that laminin can form a bridge between the two cells. Lymphocyte function-associated antigen (LFA-1), which is expressed on T lymphocytes and macrophages, is a member of the integrin superfamily noted for its role in a variety of cellular adhesion interactions. Pretreatment of some tumor cell lines or macrophages with an anti-LFA-1 antibody inhibits the interaction between tumor cells and macrophages.

Although carbohydrates and proteins have long been known to play a part in cellular adhesion, evidence suggests that phospholipids are also involved in macrophage recognition of target cells. Phospholipids are the most conserved molecules in biology. All cell membranes are composed of a phospholipid bilayer containing four major phospholipids: the choline phospholipids, phosphatidylcholine (PC) and sphingomyelin, and the amino phospholipids, phosphatidylethanolamine (PE) and phosphatidylserine (PS). The distribution of phospholipids in the bilayer membrane is asymmetric. PC and sphingomyelin are preferentially positioned in the outer leaflet, whereas PE is preferentially distributed in the inner leaflet. PS displays absolute asymmetry in its distribution: normal cells contain PS only in the inner leaflet of the cell membrane. Experimental evidence now suggests that when PS is displayed on the outer leaflet, it serves as a recognition molecule for macrophages. This conclusion is based on several lines of evidence. Inclusion of negatively charged phospholipids, such as PS, in liposomes greatly enhances their binding and endocytosis by macrophages. Liposomes containing PS are phagocytosed 5–10 times faster than identical liposomes consisting only of PC.

Invertebrate phagocytes from larvae of the moth *Heliothis virescens* were assessed for their ability to bind negatively charged membrane phospholipids. Both *H. virescens* phagocytes and macrophages bound

and endocytosed negatively charged phospholipid vesicles in preference to neutral or positively charged liposomes, suggesting that recognition of negatively charged phospholipids may be a primitive mechanism for the identification of potential targets by macrophages.

Macrophage recognition of PS in RBC was demonstrated by the insertion of fluorescent PS into the plasma membrane of RBC, which resulted in their preferential uptake by macrophages. Binding of RBC with inserted PS was fivefold higher than untreated RBC or those with inserted PC. Preincubation of macrophage monolayers with PS liposomes led to a 60% inhibition in the uptake of RBC with exogenous PS, whereas preincubation with liposomes consisting of different phospholipids did not.

The recognition of PS by macrophages is also observed *in vivo*. RBC containing a fluorescent analog of PS were injected into the circulation of syngeneic mice. These RBC were rapidly removed from the circulation relative to control RBC. Although PS is present exclusively on the inner leaflet of normal, young RBC, in the pathological condition of sickled RBC, PS is localized in both inner- and outer-membrane leaflets. Under oxygenated conditions, sickled RBC express PS only in the inner leaflet, whereas in a deoxygenated environment, sickled RBC assume the sickled morphology and present PS on the outer leaflet too. Deoxygenated sickled RBC bind to monocytes in greater numbers than oxygenated sickled RBC or normal RBC. The correlation of PS expression and monocyte binding is additional evidence that PS in the outer leaflet serves as a recognition moiety for macrophages.

Macrophage recognition of PS is also correlated with their increased binding to tumor cells. The levels of PS on the outer leaflet of murine erythroleukemia cells (MELC) and differentiated murine erythroleukemia cells (dMELC) have been measured by the prothrombinase assay, which takes advantage of the fact that immobilized membrane PS is an absolute requirement for the formation of thrombin from prothrombin in the coagulation cascade. Results demonstrated that MELC contain a greater density of PS on the outer leaflet than dMELC. As MELC differentiate to dMELC and progressively lose PS from the outer leaflet, they are less bound by macrophages.

Additional data were derived by examining the interaction of human monocytes with three human tumorigenic cell lines and one normal human epidermal keratinocyte line. The three tumor cell lines exhibited elevated levels of external leaflet PS as compared to normal cells. The PS levels directly correlated with monocyte binding to target cells as well as with monocyte-mediated cytotoxicity. All three tumor cell lines had higher external leaflet PS and cytotoxicity levels than normal cells, which were neither bound nor lysed by the human monocytes. Collectively then, the recognition of tumor cells by macrophages depends on interactions with carbohydrates, glycoproteins, and phospholipids.

VII. SUPPRESSION OF TUMOR ANGIOGENESIS BY MACROPHAGE-DERIVED FACTORS

In addition to directly killing tumor cells, activated macrophages can also inhibit tumor progression by the suppression of angiogenesis mediated by at least three different mechanisms. First, activated macrophages can secrete IFN-α and IFN-β. The progressive growth of infantile cutaneous hemangiomas correlates with the expression of endogenous IFN-β in the tumor and surrounding tissues. Indeed, systemic daily administration of low-dose IFN-α can accelerate the regression of infantile hemangiomas, hemangioendothelioma, pulmonary hemangiomatosis, and hemangiopericytoma and can improve the symptoms of Kaposi's sarcoma. Intratumoral or peritumoral injection of IFN-β or IFN-α/-β has also been shown to induce ischemic necrosis as a result of pronounced vascular endothelial cell damage. IFN-β can also directly inhibit the proliferation of endothelial cells.

The second mechanism is the generation of angiostatin, a potent antiangiogenic molecule that can inhibit endothelial cell proliferation, migration, and invasion of the ECM. Macrophages activated by GM-CSF express a high level of macrophage–metalloelastase (MME), which can cleave plasminogen to generate angiostatin. Macrophage density in tumors inversely correlates with tumorigenicity and directly correlates with expression levels of GM-CSF in tumor cells. Subcutaneous tumors producing high levels of GM-CSF have been shown to significantly suppress the growth of distant lung metastases in several mouse tumor models. The third mechanism for macrophage suppression of angiogenesis is the activation of inducible nitric oxide synthase (iNOS) that catalyzes the generation of nitric oxide, which can damage endothelial cells.

VIII. MACROPHAGE INFILTRATION INTO TUMORS

To eradicate solid tumors, macrophages must first infiltrate the lesions. The presence of inflammatory macrophages in growing tumors is maintained through the recruitment of circulating monocytes and, in certain tumors, the proliferation of mononuclear phagocytes. One mediator of monocyte recruitment to inflammatory sites and neoplasms is monocyte chemotactic and activating factor MCAF. MCAF also stimulates in monocytes an increase in cytosolic calcium level, superoxide anion production, lysosomal enzyme release, production of IL-1 and IL-6, and regulated surface expression of adhesion molecules, as well as tumoricidal activation.

The distribution pattern of host inflammatory cells in rodent tumors has been studied for many years. In regressing murine sarcomas, tumor-associated macrophages (TAM) are found throughout the tumors, whereas in progressing sarcomas, TAM are confined to the periphery of the tumor or to accompanying bands of connective tissues. The growth rate of murine tumors varies with their macrophage content: the faster-growing tumors are those with fewer infiltrating macrophages. Small tumors are infiltrated with a relatively large number of macrophages, whereas large tumors are not; perhaps because of the decreased recruitment of macrophages into larger tumors, several investigators have suggested possible mechanisms for this decrease. These large tumors and metastases may outstrip the host's ability to mount a macrophage response. Reduced macrophage responsiveness or effects of the geometry of large solid tumors may also decrease macrophage invasion into tumors. Others have demonstrated that soluble products of tumor cells from several different cell lines impair macrophage recruitment in normal animals. Several independent studies also conclude that the accumulation of macrophages in tumors does not necessarily correlate with the metastatic properties or immunogenicity of the tumors. The presence of noncytotoxic (nonactivated) macrophages in neoplasms could actually promote the growth of the tumors, given that macrophages can produce many diffusible growth factors and angiogenic factors as well as cytotoxic factors. According to the type and level of such mediators, TAM may either enhance or inhibit the growth of neoplasms.

IX. SYSTEMIC ACTIVATION OF MACROPHAGES BY LIPOSOMES CONTAINING IMMUNOMODULATORS

Because activated macrophages can destroy phenotypically diverse tumor cells, including cells resistant to killing by other host defense mechanisms and anticancer drugs, the systemic activation of macrophages is an attractive strategy for the destruction of metastatic cells. Efforts to activate the tumoricidal properties of macrophages significantly *in vivo* by the administration of lymphokines (e.g., IFN-γ) have not succeeded because lymphokines injected iv have an extremely short half-life. Even under ideal *in vitro* conditions, a minimum 8-h interaction time between human monocytes and free lymphokines is required for successful activation. Similarly, the short half-life of MDP in the blood (<30 min) does not result in significant monocyte–macrophage activation.

Advances in liposome technology have provided a means for the systemic activation of macrophages. Most attempts to target synthetic phospholipid vesicles to extracirculatory compartments have not succeeded because these vesicles are rapidly taken up by circulating and fixed phagocytic cells. However, this natural fate of liposomes can be used to advantage to target cells of the reticuloendothelial system (RES). The uptake of liposomes containing specific immunomodulators can result in the activation of phagocytic cells to the tumoricidal state. Once liposomes are phagocytosed, biological compounds are released into the cytoplasm of the cell. Such intracellular delivery avoids the problems of dilution, protein

binding, and rapid clearance; it produces a sustained release of molecules and minimizes undesirable side effects (Fig. 2).

Several conditions must be satisfied for liposomes to deliver biologically active agents effectively to mononuclear phagocytes *in situ:* (1) the liposomes must readily bind to and be phagocytosed by free and fixed phagocytes; (2) they must prevent degradation of the entrapped drug; (3) they must retain the encapsulated agent for delivery to the intracellular compartment of RES cells; and (4) they must localize to macrophages in organs with metastases. The distribution of intravenously administered liposomes is determined by the size of the inoculum and their physical size, composition, and charge. Although distribution patterns can be modified by manipulating these

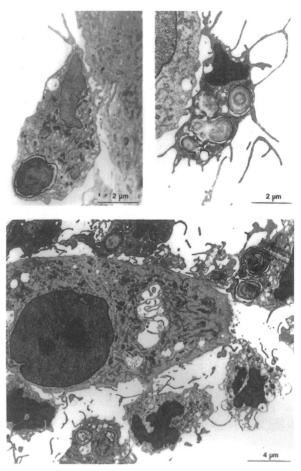

FIGURE 2 Interaction of macrophages with phospholipid liposomes.

parameters, the majority of infused liposomes are removed from the circulation mainly by free and fixed cells of the RES.

Certain classes of phospholipids are preferentially recognized by macrophages. In particular, the addition of negatively charged phospholipids, such as PS, to liposomes consisting primarily of PC greatly increases macrophage binding and phagocytosis. Rodent and human macrophages can become tumoricidal following the phagocytosis of multilamellar vesicles (MLV) consisting of PC and PS and containing lymphokines, muramyl peptides, combinations of these molecules, and many others.

The lung is a major site of metastatic disease, but it is not rich with RES activity. To localize liposomes to the lung, it is necessary to use large MLV (>0.1 μm). In addition, liposomes of the same structural class localize in the lungs more efficiently when they contain PS then when they contain only PC. The PC/PS liposomes deliver encapsulated compounds to blood monocytes, which then migrate out of the circulation to differentiate into lung macrophages.

The intravenous injection of PC/PS MLV containing MDP or MTP-PE (MLV-MTP-PE) produces *in situ* activation of mouse lung macrophages that persists for 3 to 4 days. This activation results from a direct effect on macrophages; it does not depend on an indirect action of the immunomodulators on T cells to induce a release of macrophage-activating lymphokines. This conclusion is based on data from studies in which lung macrophages from mice deficient in T cells (nude mice) were tumoricidal after a systemic administration of liposome-encapsulated MTP-PE.

X. THERAPY OF CANCER METASTASIS IN MURINE MODELS

Systemic macrophage activation with liposomes containing lymphokines, MDP, MTP-PE, or combinations of these agents results in the eradication of well-established lung and lymph node metastases produced by subcutaneous murine melanoma. Similar findings demonstrating the successful treatment of metastases by the intravenous injection of liposomes containing immunomodulators have also been reported for several murine fibrosarcomas, melanomas, lung carci-

noma, liver metastases, renal cell carcinoma, and primary skin cancers. Free or liposome-encapsulated lymphokines (IFN-γ) and bacterial products (LPS or MDP) can act synergistically to activate macrophages. Because liposomes can deliver more than one compound to macrophages *in situ*, combining IFN-γ and MDP within the same liposome has been used to produce synergistic activation of mouse lung macrophages *in vivo* and enhanced eradication of lung melanoma metastases (Fig. 3).

XI. THERAPY OF AUTOCHTHONOUS LUNG METASTASIS IN DOGS WITH OSTEOGENIC SARCOMA

The natural history of canine osteosarcoma comprises progressive growth of the primary neoplasm and death due to visceral (lung) metastasis, mirroring the disease process in humans. In another parallel, surgical removal of the primary tumor yields a median survival of 3 to 6 months, with only 10% survival after 1 year or longer. Thus, this model may be a good test of activated macrophage therapy for metastases. A randomized double-blind study of liposome-encapsulated MTP-PE for osteosarcoma metastasis in dogs has been completed. All animals in this study had histologically documented osteosarcoma and complete amputation of the primary tumor-bearing limb. Immediately after surgery, dogs were randomized to receive either MLV–MTP-PE or MLV containing saline

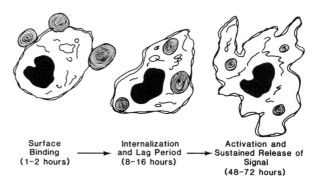

| Surface Binding (1–2 hours) | Internalization and Lag Period (8–16 hours) | Activation and Sustained Release of Signal (48–72 hours) |

FIGURE 3 Transmission electron microscopy of human monocytes containing liposome–MTP-PE. Note clustering of monocytes with target cell, tight binding, and vacuolization.

(placebo). Intravenous infusions of liposomes were given twice weekly for 8 weeks. The median survival time of dogs receiving placebo was 77 days, a figure that did not differ from that for surgical treatment alone. In contrast, the median survival of dogs treated with MLV–MTP-PE was 222 days, and several dogs were alive and free of disease 3 years after surgery. Had dogs with initially large metastatic burdens been excluded, results would likely have been even better, as a major limitation for treatment of metastases by macrophage activation is tumor burden.

XII. CLINICAL STUDIES

A. Phase I Trials

Because chemotherapy can inhibit the function of host immune cells, blood monocytes were collected from patients at the time of diagnosis during and after doxorubicin (DXR) therapy. The monocytes were incubated *in vitro* with liposomes containing MTP-PE and their ability to lyse tumorigenic targets was monitored. These data demonstrated that the monocyte function of osteosarcoma patients treated with DXR is intact and, by inference, that the systemic administration of liposome-encapsulated immunomodulators may be combined with DXR in the treatment of metastatic osteogenic sarcoma.

At the dose and schedule used in several phase I trials, liposome–MTP-PE was safe. The dose-limiting side effects were chills, fever, fatigue, nausea, and vomiting. Toxicity was not cumulative, and the maximum tolerated dose of MTP-PE (in PC/PS MLV) was 6 mg/m^2. In agreement with preclinical data, a consistent increase in absolute white blood cells and granulocytes was observed. Patients with an increased granulocyte count also exhibited a significant decrease in serum cholesterol. Significant elevations in C-reactive protein and α_2-microglobulin were observed in many patients, but whether these elevations were due to the generation of IL-6 was not clear. The iv administration of liposome–MTP-PE activated tumoricidal properties in blood monocytes of the majority of the patients in the study. The optimal dose for rendering monocytes cytotoxic to tumors was far less than the maximal tolerated dose.

The biodistribution and pharmacokinetics of MLV–MTP-PE were studied in four patients subsequent to iv infusion of ^{99m}Tc-labeled liposomes. At 6 h following injection, radioactivity was found in the liver, spleen, nasopharynx, thyroid, and, to a lesser extent, the lungs. This radioactivity partially cleared by 24 h. In two of the four patients studied, lung metastases were imaged, presumably by tumor-associated macrophages containing phagocytosed liposomes.

B. Treatment of Relapsed Osteogenic Sarcoma

The major cause of death in patients with osteogenic sarcoma is pulmonary metastasis resistant to conventional therapies. Most recurrences appear in the first year while the patient is still on chemotherapy. Although these patients can be rendered disease free by surgery, the recurrence rate is 60 to 70% within 1 year. Salvage chemotherapy has little effect on the disease-free interval in this group of patients. A phase II trial using PC/PS MLV containing MTP-PE has been completed in a group of osteosarcoma patients. Selection criteria for the patients included those with histologically proven osteosarcoma and pulmonary metastases that had developed during adjuvant chemotherapy or that were present at diagnosis and had persisted despite chemotherapy. Prior to entry into the study, each patient's primary tumor had to be resected and the patient rendered disease free by surgical resection. MLV–MTP-PE were administered iv twice weekly for 12 weeks. Because of histologic changes observed in pulmonary lesions removed from the first six patients in the study (see later), the next patients received MLV–MTP-PE twice weekly for 12 weeks and then once weekly for an additional 12 weeks. For both treatment groups, chest X rays were obtained monthly, a lung CT scan was repeated every 3 months, and a bone scan every 6 months. All patients had a physical examination monthly. Complete blood counts with differential and platelet counts were determined weekly. Values for serum chemistry, serum cholesterol, urinalysis, and clotting profile were obtained monthly.

The first 12 patients entering the phase II trial received liposome MTP-PE twice weekly for 12 weeks.

Seven of 12 patients had disease recurrence (in the lungs) within 6 months of completing liposome therapy near the sites of lung resection. The nodules were excised from 6 of these patients and submitted for pathological examination, and the histologic specimens were compared with the lesions resected immediately before liposome therapy. In the lesions resected from 5 of 6 patients, peripheral fibrosis developed around the tumors, as did inflammatory cell infiltration and neovascularization. In contrast, lesions resected following chemotherapy and immediately prior to MLV–MTP-PE therapy exhibited either central necrosis with viable tumor cells in the periphery of the metastasis and no inflammatory response or neither necrosis nor inflammatory response.

Immunohistochemistry studies confirmed that the infiltrating cells consisted mainly of histiocytes/macrophages. The implication of these results is that MLV–MTP-PE altered the host response so that inflammatory cells infiltrated the osteogenic sarcoma metastases. Further, the histological appearance of the metastases had been changed. Activated macrophages secrete cytokines such as IL-1 and TNF, which not only kill tumor cells, including osteosarcoma cells, but also produce fibrosis and granulomas. The histological changes in the osteogenic sarcoma metastases were reminiscent of the appearance of pulmonary tuberculosis lesions. Initially, the lesion is walled off and slow necrosis proceeds from the outside so that the lesion is replaced by fibrous tissue. The resolution of a tuberculosis lesion by chronic inflammation is a slow process, and viable bacilli can persist for months. Similarly, the resolution of metastasis by activated macrophages may require several months, and so prolonged administration of MLV–MTP-PE (>12 months) may be advantageous. This possibility is now under active investigation.

A phase IIb trial of combination therapy with ifosfamide (IFX) and MLV–MTP-PE in patients with relapsed osteosarcoma revealed that the antitumor effect of IFX was not abolished by MLV–MTP-PE and that the immune response to MLV–MTP-PE was not ablated by IFX. Combination therapy with IFX plus MLV–MTP-PE is tolerable and does not result in increased toxicity or reduced immune stimulation. Moreover, the addition of MLV–MTP-PE to the adjuvant regimen may increase the 2-year metastasis-free survival rate, which has remained stagnant for many years.

XIII. CONCLUSIONS

The outcome of macrophage–tumor interaction *in vivo* is regulated by the rate of tumor cell proliferation, the ratio of macrophages to target cells, and the state of activity of the macrophages. The treatment of metastases is most successful when the lesions are small and slow growing and contain a large number of tumoricidal macrophages. To achieve this *in vivo*, therapeutic regimens designed to stimulate tumoricidal macrophages must be used subsequent to or in combination with other treatment modalities used to destroy tumor cells or arrest their growth. Long, continuous tumoricidal activation of macrophages should then be used to eliminate the residual tumor cells that are resistant to conventional therapy.

Patients with a recurrence of osteosarcoma metastases who received 6 months of MLV–MTP-PE therapy had a significant prolongation in time to relapse as compared to those who received only 3 months of therapy. These data suggest that liposome–MTP-PE is an active agent in osteosarcoma and that it should be investigated in a more appropriate adjuvant setting. Data also suggest that a more prolonged administration of the drug (12 months or longer) could benefit more patients and result in even longer disease-free intervals.

Acute diseases such as infections develop rapidly and must be arrested rapidly and then eradicated. Otherwise, the patient will die. In contrast, a chronic disease, e.g., tuberculosis, is usually treated chronically. Cancer is a chronic disease whose clinical course is measured in years. Like any other chronic disease, cancer should be treated first to arrest tumor cell growth and then chronically by biological therapies such as the systemic activation of macrophages. Data summarized here support this conclusion.

See Also the Following Articles

ANGIOGENESIS AND NATURAL ANGIOSTATIC AGENTS • CASPASES IN PROGRAMMED CELL DEATH • EXTRACELLULAR

Matrix and Matrix Receptors: Alterations during Tumor Progression • Interleukins • Liposome-Mediated Gene Therapy • Tumor Necrosis Factors

Bibliography

Dong, Z., Kumar, R., Yang, X., and Fidler, I. J. (1997). Macrophage-derived metalloelastase is responsible for the generation of angiostatin in Lewis lung carcinoma. *Cell* **88,** 801–810.

Fidler, I. J. (1988). Targeting of immunomodulators to mononuclear phagocytes for therapy of cancer. *Adv. Drug Del. Rev.* **1,** 69–106.

Fidler, I. J., and Schroit, A. J. (1988). Recognition and destruction of neoplastic cells by activated macrophages: Discrimination of altered self. *Biochim. Biophys. Acta* **948,** 151–173.

Kleinerman, E. S., Gano, J. B., Johnston, D. A., Benjamin, R. S., and Jaffe, N. (1995). Efficacy of liposomal muramyl tripeptide (CGP 19835A) in the treatment of relapsed osteosarcoma. *Am. J. Clin. Oncol.* **18,** 93–99.

Kleinerman, E. S., Raymond, A. K., Bucana, C. D., Jaffe, N., Harris, M., Krakoff, I. H., Benjamin, R., and Fidler, I. J. (1992). Unique histological changes in lung metastases of osteosarcoma patients following therapy with liposomal muramyl tripeptide (CGP 19835A lipid). *Cancer Immunol. Immunother.* **34,** 211–220.

Nathan, C. F. (1987). Secretory products of macrophages. *J. Clin. Invest.* **79,** 319–326.

Poste, G., Kirsh, R., and Bugelski, P. (1984). Liposomes as a drug delivery system in cancer therapy. *In* "Novel Approaches to Cancer Chemotherapy" (P. Sunkara, ed.), pp. 165–230. Academic Press, New York.

Magnetic Resonance Spectroscopy and Magnetic Resonance Imaging, Introduction

Yael Mardor
Jack S. Cohen

Sheba Medical Center, Tel Hashomer, Israel

GLOSSARY

chemical shift The value of the frequency (often expressed in parts per million) at which a spin gives a resonance signal, which is dependent on the value of the external applied magnetic field and the local magnetic shielding/deshielding due to the electrons surrounding the spin.

contrast agent A substance used to increase the contrast in an MR image, usually a metal ion complex or chelate, e.g., GdDTPA.

diffusion weighting A method whereby a range of motion is selected to observe only the signals from molecules with a limited diffusion range; the range is determined by the delays used in a specifically designed pulse sequence.

diffusion-weighted MRI or MRS (DWMRI or DWMRS) The method of MRI or MRS that uses diffusion weighting in order to discriminate the molecules in terms of their motion and allows the observation of MR images or spectra of only slowly moving intracellular components.

fourier transform A mathematical transformation that allows information in the time domain to be inverted to information in the frequency domain.

gyromagnetic ratio The ratio between spin and magnetic properties of a given type of nucleus, with a characteristic value for that nucleus that determines its frequency of observation at a given magnetic field strength.

Larmor frequency The frequency of precession of nuclear spins.

longitudinal relaxation time The exponential rate, with rate constant designated T_1, whereby the net magnetization vector **M** for all spins in an ensemble relaxes back to its equilibrium value along the longitudinal or z axis (see also spin–lattice relaxation).

magnet Required for observation of the MR phenomenon; the magnet can be a permanent magnet, an electromagnet, or a superconducting magnet.

magnetic nuclei Atomic nuclei of a specific element that has magnetic properties due to unpaired fundamental particles in the nucleus; these properties are only manifested in the presence of an external magnetic field.

magnetic resonance imaging (MRI) The formation of a spatial image using the MR phenomenon by application of a magnetic field gradient superimposed upon the static magnetic field.

magnetic resonance spectroscopy (MRS) The phenomenon of resonance observed in a magnetic field upon application of the resonant (Larmor) frequency.

nuclear magnetic resonance (NMR) spectroscopy The correct scientific name for the phenomenon of resonance observed in a magnetic field upon application of the resonant (Larmor) frequency. Also known as MRS.

pixel A single picture element in a two-dimensional image.

precession Rotation about an axis that is not the same as the axis of spin.

pulse sequence The combination of delays and RF pulses that are used to obtain an MR signal.

radiofrequency The value of the frequency that excites the spins, which happens to be in the range of frequencies used for radio transmission.

relaxation The process of gradual return to equilibrium following excitation.

resolution The ability to separate/resolve signals that are adjacent to each other in a spectrum or image.

sensitivity The quantitative ratio of signal to noise observed in a spectrum or image.

shielding/deshielding The local magnetic field effect due to the presence of electrons in bonds in molecules.

spin–lattice relaxation The process of exchange of energy from an excited spin to the surrounding environment or lattice. The spin-lattice relaxation time is designated T_1 (see also longitudinal relaxation time).

spin–spin relaxation The process of exchange of energy between two like spins such that there is no net loss of energy to the surroundings. Spin–spin relaxation time is designated T_2 (see also transverse relaxation).

superconducting magnet A magnet in which the magnetic field is produced by the flow of electric current in a solenoid of wire constructed from a special alloy (such as niobium-tin) that remains superconducting in liquid helium; superconducting means that at that temperature (4°K), the solenoid exhibits no electrical resistance.

transverse relaxation time The exponential rate, with rate constant designated T_2, whereby the transverse (x-y) component of the net magnetization vector **M** for all spins in an ensemble relaxes back from its value after spin excitation to its equilibrium value of zero (see also spin–spin relaxation).

Since the discovery of the phenomenon known as nuclear magnetic resonance (NMR) in 1946, the technique has revolutionized several areas of science and medicine. Most notably, magnetic resonance imaging (MRI), first described by Paul Lauterbur in 1973, has become the method of choice for the clinical imaging of soft tissues. In order to understand the techniques currently being used and the many clinical applications now being described, we have included here a short primer of these methods. We should point out that these methods, while based on atomic properties, use only stable isotopes. Nevertheless, to avoid any confusion with nuclear methods that involve the use of radioactive isotopes, we will henceforth use the now general term magnetic resonance spectroscopy (MRS) in place of the more scientific term NMR spectroscopy.

I. BASIC CONCEPTS

The fundamental particles of matter possess the properties of *charge* and *spin*. These properties result in the atomic nuclei of the elements also exhibiting magnetic properties (Table I). It is the interaction of these atomic magnets with an applied external magnetic field that gives rise to the phenomenon of magnetic resonance (MR). However, all atomic nuclei do not possess magnetic properties. Generally, an even number of fundamental nuclear particles (protons and neutrons) results in no net spin (e.g., ^{12}C, ^{16}O) and a consequent lack of magnetic properties. However, there are exceptions to this rule, such as deuterium (^2H), the nuclei of which retain an overall spin and magnetic properties.

TABLE I
MR Properties of Common Biological Nuclei

Nucleus[a]	Relative gyro magnetic ratio[b] (%)	Relative sensitivity[c] (%)	Natural abundance (%)
^{1}H	100	100	99.9
^{2}H	15	1	0.016
^{13}C	25	1.6	1.1
^{15}N	10	0.1	0.4
^{19}F	94	80	100
^{23}Na	26	9	100
^{31}P	40	7	100

[a]All stable nuclei.

[b]The ratio of frequencies for observation at constant magnetic field strength.

[c]Same number of nuclei in same field.

When placed in an externally applied magnetic field, the spins of nuclear particles exhibit precession about the axis of the magnetic field as does a gyroscope in the earth's gravitational field (Fig. 1). The frequency of this precession (Larmor frequency, ν_L) is related to the magnetic property of the nucleus by a simple equation, such that the magnetic field required to bring about an excitation of the nuclear spin is directly proportional to the Larmor frequency, i.e., $B_o \, \alpha \, \nu_L$. The constant of proportionality in this case relates the field to the frequency and is called the gyromagnetic ratio, γ, literally the ratio between the spin and magnetic properties of the nucleus. The value of γ depends on the particular nucleus and is a constant for that nucleus. It is the interaction of the (nuclear) spins at the Larmor frequency with a magnetic field of the value related by γ that causes the resonance phenomenon, i.e., the production of a signal resulting from the excitation of the spins. Other resonance phenomena, for example, are the vibration of a bridge in a wind of a certain speed or of a taut string when a bow vibrates it. The Larmor frequency is in the range of frequencies known as radiofrequencies or RF (i.e., the same as FM radio). Thus, at the RF resonance frequency in the presence of the correct value of the magnetic field, nuclear spins give rise to a resonance signal.

The signal can also be considered from the point of view of the energy state of the collection of spins constituting the sample (Fig. 2). In this approach the energy of the spins is represented at a certain level in the presence of the field. When the RF frequency that produces the resonance condition is applied, the spins are excited into a higher energy state and then relax back to their equilibrium condition by exchanging energy with their surroundings through molecular motions. A correct description of the interaction of the spins with the magnetic field relies on quantum mechanics. Fortunately, all the theory necessary in order to understand the basic MR concepts can be based on a simple classical model (see later).

Relaxation is an important consequence of the fact that the MR phenomenon is a dynamic process

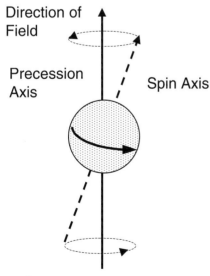

FIGURE 1   Precession of an atomic nucleus.

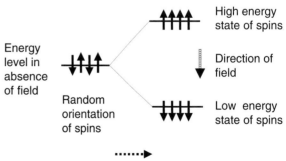

FIGURE 2   Energy levels and transitions of nuclear spins.

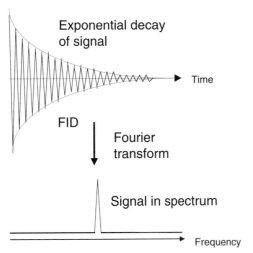

FIGURE 3 Fourier transformation of MR spectrum from the time domain into the frequency domain.

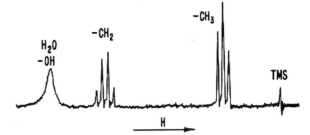

FIGURE 4 Proton MR spectrum of ethanol showing signals of the different chemical (electron shielded) environments (hydroxyl OH; methylene CH_2; methyl CH_3). Note also the fine splitting due to thru-bond magnetic interactions of the protons. Tetramethylsilane (TMS) is the internal standard.

occurring in real time. Generally the MR signal is obtained by acquiring the relaxing signal in a computer as a function of time and then subjecting it to a mathematical Fourier transformation to convert it to a signal as a function of its Larmor frequency (Fig. 3).

II. WHAT IS MAGNETIC RESONANCE SPECTROSCOPY (MRS)?

A. Obtaining an MR Spectrum

The atomic nuclei that give rise to the MR signal are not bare isolated entities, they generally exist in molecules where they are surrounded by clouds of electrons constituting the bonds between atoms. These electrons have a profound effect on the magnetic properties of the nuclei, often shielding them from the external magnetic field, thus changing the frequency at which resonance occurs, and hence in effect shifting the signal (in the frequency domain). This shift is called the *chemical shift* because it depends on the bonding pattern around the nucleus, which is related to its chemical properties. It is easier to see the meaning of the chemical shift by referring to an actual spectrum of a compound in which the different protons show different shifts as a result of differential electron shielding (Fig. 4). Note that as well as shielding an atom, electron clouds can also result in deshielding, e.g., in the case of delocalized π

electron clouds associated with benzene and other conjugated aromatic systems. Because of the chemical shift, MRS has become a major tool in the identification of chemical substances.

The area under a MR signal is proportional to the number of atoms giving rise to that signal. Although absolute intensities are difficult to measure, by using a substance with a known concentration that gives rise to a known well-resolved signal, it is possible by comparison to determine the concentration of a given substance from its MR spectrum. Similarly, the relative number of atoms in different chemical environments in a given substance is easy to determine from the relative areas of their resonances (Fig. 4).

B. Relaxation Times

As has already been explained, excited nuclear spins return to equilibrium via relaxation processes. Generally speaking, there are two such processes: one involving loss of energy with the surroundings, the so-called spin lattice, and the other in which no energy is lost, but rather energy is exchanged from one spin to another. The former is called spin–lattice relaxation, and is designated T_1, and the latter is called spin–spin relaxation, and is termed T_2. Both processes occur via dipolar exchange, but while they have different mechanisms, they are both exponential decays. Because T_1 relaxation derives from interactions of the excited spin with the lattice involving a net loss of energy, it is defined by the return to equilibrium of the main net magnetic component of the spins in the direction of the magnetic field (defined as the z direction), and otherwise known as longitudinal relaxation. Because T_2 relaxation derives from interactions where there is no net energy loss, and hence no return to equilibrium, it derives from an exchange of energy affecting the net magnetic spin component only in the transverse (x–y plane), hence it is also known as transverse relaxation. The relaxation of proton spins plays an important role in determining the intensities of signals and hence the contrast observed in MR images.

MR Primer

In the presence of a strong homogeneous magnetic field, magnetic nuclei such as protons (^{1}H) will align either parallel with the magnetic field or in the antiparallel direction. Because the parallel orientation is the lower energy state, more protons will align along the external field direction. Therefore, in the steady state, net magnetization (which we will refer to as the magnetization vector, **M**) is due to surplus protons and it is pointing in the direction of the external magnetic field, the longitudinal direction (defined as the z direction). Because the magnetization vector of the water sample in the steady state is aligned along the longitudinal direction, it is impossible to detect it. By applying a pulse of radio frequency (RF) at the Larmor frequency, the protons resonate and, as a consequence, **M** is rotated into the transverse (x–y) plane (Fig. 5). The amplitude and duration of the RF pulse determine the angle by which **M** will be rotated. A radio pulse that rotates all of the magnetization vector into the transverse plane is referred to as a 90° pulse. After applying such a pulse, **M** is precessing in the transverse direction, where it can be detected as an induced voltage in an RF coil (this could be the same coil that was used to transmit the RF pulse or a different one). Because the RF pulse is turned off after **M** reaches the transverse plane, **M** will relax back to the steady state along the longitudinal direction, causing the transverse magnetization to vanish. The amplitude of this signal is maximal when the transverse magnetization is maximal (immediately after the RF pulse in the case of a 90° pulse) and then it decays back to the steady state, where it vanishes. This initial rapidly decaying signal is called free induction decay.

The width of an MR signal (defined as the width at half-height) is related to the relaxation time of the atoms giving rise to the signal. Generally, it results from motions that affect only the transverse relaxation time, T_2. The relationship is an inverse one, such that the slower a molecule is moving, the broader is its signal. Thus, small molecules tend to have sharp signals whereas large macromolecules have broad signals. Aggregations of molecules such as membranes or substances in the solid state have very broad signals, which can be understood to result from spin–spin (transverse) relaxation being highly efficient due to the large amount of time the spins spend close to (or

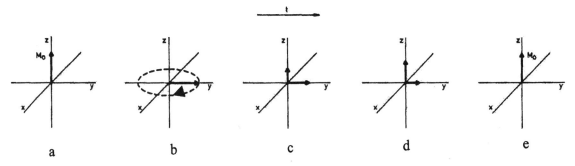

FIGURE 5 Exponential decay of the net magnetization vector (M_o) following an excitation RF pulse. (a) The system is at equilibrium with M_o in the z direction (of the applied magnetic field). (b) An RF pulse has been applied to flip M_o into the xy plane, where is precesses (for convenience, we ignore this precession for the rest of the figure). (c) and (d) The value of M in the xy plane decreases and that in the z direction concomitantly increases due to relaxation. (e) Equilibrium has been reestablished.

correlated with) each other. A broad line width lowers the signal intensity, but does not change the area under the signal.

III. WHAT IS MAGNETIC RESONANCE IMAGING (MRI)?

A. Obtaining an MR Image

The hydrogen nucleus (i.e., proton) is the most sensitive MR nucleus (Table I) and the most abundant nucleus in biological tissue. Therefore, all current MRI techniques in routine clinical use are based on MR signals originating from protons, mainly those contained in water and to a lesser extent in fat molecules. For simplicity, we shall start with an example of a tube of water placed with its long axis along the direction of the external magnetic field (the z direction). In the previous section it was explained that once the sample is placed in the magnet, the net magnetization of the spinning protons aligns along the direction of the external field. An RF excitation pulse causes the protons to resonate, producing a signal in the receiver coil. This signal is detected and transformed into an MR spectrum, which describes the intensity of the MR signals at their Larmor frequency. In the case of the water tube, only one peak is present in the spectrum and the intensity (the area under the peak) of the signal is proportional to the number of water protons in the tube. In order to create an MR image, it is necessary to add spatial information that will result in localization of the source of the MR signals.

This is achieved by applying magnetic field gradients. A magnetic field gradient is obtained by superimposing a low-intensity magnetic field, on the main magnetic field, the intensity of which depends on its spatial location. For example, a magnetic field gradient along the z axis (the longitudinal direction) is applied such that its intensity is linearly proportional to the location along the z axis, i.e., at low z values a low magnetic field is applied and at higher z values a higher magnetic field is applied. The magnetic field gradients, also referred to as imaging gradients, are supplemental to the external field. Before the imaging gradients are turned on, the water protons in the

sample tube all have identical chemical shift, therefore, they all resonate at the same frequency, regardless of location. When the imaging gradients are turned on, the resulting total magnetic field (the sum of the main and gradient magnetic fields) is weakest at one end and increases linearly along the axis of the gradient. Because the resonant frequency of a proton is directly proportional to the magnetic field to which it is exposed, the magnetic field gradient also produces a linear increase of the resonant frequency along this axis. Thus, application of the magnetic field gradient causes the Larmor frequency of protons at one end of the sample to be higher than that of the protons in the other end. If we look at the resulting MR spectrum, we will see that the application of the imaging gradient has caused the MR signal to result from a full range of Larmor frequencies and not from a single value of the frequency as before when the external magnetic field was homogeneous. Now we can translate the resonance frequency back to the z location, and the result is a "one-dimensional image," the MR signal intensity as a function of the z location. If the sample contains only water, this simple example will result in a "step function", i.e., there will be less signal from z locations where there is less water and an increased signal intensity from z locations where there is more (Fig. 6). If we will now replace the water with a more complex sample, the signal intensity from different locations will depend on the proton density and the relaxation properties of the sample, causing changes in the signal intensity in the resulting image. In order to obtain three-dimensional images, magnetic field gradients are applied in three orthogonal axes. The timing at which the gradients and the RF pulses are applied has a profound effect on the resulting image, and this effect is described in more detail in Section IV.C.

B. Effects of Relaxation on Images

In the previous section, we used the example of a tube with water. In this case, all the molecules of the sample experience the same magnetic environment and the proton density is uniform. Therefore, the only factor affecting MR signal intensity is the size of the volume of interest (VOI) chosen for sampling. The larger the VOI, the stronger the MR signal. In more

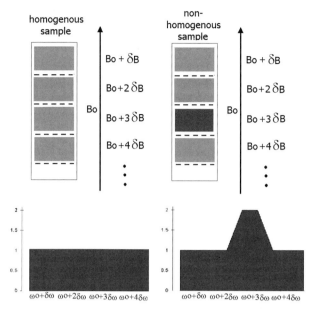

FIGURE 6 Use of a magnetic field gradient to obtain an MR image. The vertical arrow indicates the application of a magnetic field (B_o) with a gradient increasing in units of δ per unit length. The resulting frequency distribution of the signal reflects the spatial distribution of the water. The sample on the left is homogeneous, resulting in a flat frequency distribution. The sample on the right produces a stronger MR signal at a certain location. As a result, the signal intensity at the matching frequency will be increased. Translation (Fourier transform) of the frequency distribution to a spatial distribution gives a one-dimensional image.

complex samples, where the proton density varies with location, the MR signal intensity will also depend on the density of the protons in a specific location. The higher the density, the stronger the MR signal. The dependence of the signal intensity on the density of protons in a given unit of volume is also typical of other imaging modalities (such as radiography and scintigraphy). However, MR is unique in that it is also sensitive to the local magnetic environment of the protons. The contrast in an MR image is the result of three properties of the imaged sample: the proton density, the spin–lattice relaxation time, T_1, and the spin–spin relaxation time, T_2. T_1 and T_2 were defined in Section II.B.

Biological tissues are considered to consist of 60 to 80% water in which macromolecules are suspended. These water molecules are present in three compartments: free water, water molecules that are loosely bound to the surface of macromolecules, so the molecule can still rotate, and water molecules that are

strongly (irrotationally) bound. The first compartment, the free water, has the longest spin–lattice relaxation, while the strongly bound compartment has the shortest T_1. There is fast exchange among these three compartments so the signal measured in the MR image is an average. The partial time that each water molecule spends in each one of the three compartments is different from tissue to tissue and depends on factors such as the ratio between intra- and extracellular volumes and the concentration of macromolecules such as proteins and lipids. It is these factors that determine the T_1 and T_2 values of tissues.

In order to understand how the different relaxation times of different tissues affect the contrast between them, it is necessary to define the data acquisition parameters. The time between the initial excitation (the creation of transverse magnetization) and its measurement is defined as the echo time (TE). In order to obtain an image, the excitation sequence is repeated with different gradient values. The time between repetitions is defined as the repetition time (TR).

Images in which the contrast between different tissues is determined mostly by differences in T_1 relaxation times between tissues are referred to as T_1-weighted images. After each excitation the longitudinal magnetization relaxes back to its equilibrium value. If TR is chosen to be shorter than the T_1 relaxation time, the magnetization will not recover fully. After several repetitions the amount of magnetization that recovers before the next sequence repetition reaches a constant level and data acquisition begins. In a given time, tissues with short T_1 will relax more completely than tissues with long T_1. Therefore, at the time of the next sequence repetition, the short T_1 tissues will have a larger longitudinal magnetization, resulting in a larger transverse magnetization after excitation, and therefore a stronger signal intensity in the resulting MR image.

Images in which the contrast between tissues is determined mostly by differences in T_2 relaxation times between different tissues are referred to as T_2-weighted images. In order to get maximum T_2 relaxation contrast between two types of tissues, an optimal TE should be chosen so that most of the signal intensity (i.e., transverse magnetization) of the shorter T_2 tissues has decayed while most of the signal intensity of the longer T_2 tissue has remained. A long TR should be chosen in order to avoid T_1 weighting. As a result, T_2-weighted acquisition is in general longer and due to the longer TE the signal-to-noise ratio is lower than that of T_1-weighted images. For a further discussion of these effects see Section VI.A.

IV. MAGNETIC RESONANCE HARDWARE AND SOFTWARE

In order to observe the MR phenomenon, the minimum requirements are a magnet, an RF generator, and a probe containing coils to transmit the RF and receive the subsequent resonance signal from the sample. This section describes some of these essential components.

A. Magnets and Probes

There are basically three kinds of magnets: (i) permanent magnets, consisting of pieces of magnetized iron, (ii) electromagnets, in which the magnetic field is generated between two pole faces by the resistive flow of electric current in two solenoid coils, and (iii) superconducting magnets, which contain a coil of a metal alloy that when cooled to very low temperatures (a few degrees Kelvin) has no electrical resistance so that high currents can run and hence high magnetic fields can be generated. Generally, superconducting magnets are preferred for medical applications (Fig. 7) because they are much more stable and homogeneous than the other types and work at higher magnetic field strengths, thus giving higher sensitivity and resolution of signals (see later). Their drawback is that they require the constant addition of liquid helium and nitrogen in order to maintain their superconducting properties. However, some magnets now have recycling helium systems, much like very efficient refrigerators.

The RF probe is one of the most important components of the MR system, as it must detect the very weak MR signals without adding excessive noise to them. The central component of the RF coil is a piece of copper wire or foil, shaped into a loop or a combination of loops. The wire is fed by a sinusoidal electric field causing an oscillating RF field in which the magnetic component is along the geometrical axis of the loops of the coil. Following RF excitation, an MR signal is produced by the sample. The strength

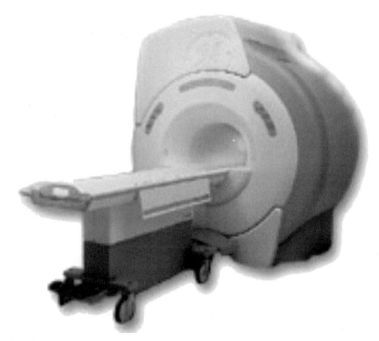

FIGURE 7 A superconducting whole body magnet (with permission of GE Medical Systems).

of the detected signal is determined by the intensity of the emitted signal, and the coil resistance is due to electrical and magnetic losses in the sample. Also, tissue closest to the coil produces the strongest signal, therefore, the coils are designed to be as close as possible to the sample tissue. The simplest coils are flat receiver coils that are placed on the surface of the sample of interest, thus called surface coils. Other coils have been designed to optimally image deep structures. This can be accomplished by completely encircling the body part of interest or even inserting a coil into the body. The larger the coil, the greater the sensitivity to signal originating from greater distances.

B. Sensitivity and Resolution

Two major parameters determine the quality of an MR spectrum: sensitivity and resolution.

Sensitivity is the minimum signal detectable in an MR machine against the background of noise (which results from the electronic noise in the system). In practice, one uses a sample containing a known quantity of a specific substance to quantitate the signal-to-noise ratio for a particular machine, which can then be compared to other machines. The sensitivity depends on several factors, including the magnetic field strength and homogeneity, the type of coil used, the magnetic properties of the sample, and the adjustments of the system for the specific sample being tested. Generally, the sensitivity increases with magnetic field strength (to the order of about $B^{3/2}$).

Spectral resolution is the ability to distinguish two signals that are adjacent to each other in an MR spectrum. The closer the signals, the more difficult it is to resolve them. The resolution is linearly proportional to the magnetic field strength (B), which is why high field strength magnets are preferred for high-resolution studies of molecules with many overlapping or broad signals. In MR images the spatial resolution is determined by the size of the pixel (picture element) used in the image. The smallest pixel size that can be obtained is determined by the maximum strength of the magnetic field gradients. However, in practice, very small pixels result in low signal to noise and longer acquisition times, thus often it is not desirable to use maximal spatial resolution.

C. Pulse Sequences

MR methods require the application of sequences of RF pulses, magnetic field gradients, and delay times between them. A combination of such elements is termed a pulse sequence. The flexibility of MR is largely due to the capability to combine such elements in different sequences to perform different functions. The most simple such sequence to obtain a spectrum would be a delay (to establish spin equilibrium) followed by a single RF pulse followed by data acquisition (Fig. 8). More complex patterns of combinations of multiple pulses, gradients, and delays are used for such purposes as measuring relaxation times, obtaining T_1- or T_2-weighted images, and for water signal suppression.

One of the main stumbling blocks in obtaining a proton spectrum of a biological sample is the huge water signal (at least three orders of magnitude larger than that of the metabolites of interest). Several methods for water suppression have been developed in high-resolution MR spectroscopy. The most common approach is chemical shift selective saturation (CHESS), where the water signal is presaturated by using a frequency selective pulse at the water frequency prior to the pulse sequence, thus causing the water signal to null at the time of data acquisition. By using more than one pulse and with correct choice of the RF pulse duration, suppression factors up to 1000 can be achieved. Other methods of water suppression exploit the differences in relaxation times between the bulk water (long T_1) and macromolecules or intracellular metabolites (short T_1).

Complex pulse sequences are usually programmed in the software that runs the MR system. Detailed

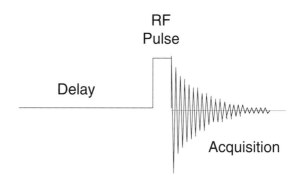

FIGURE 8 An example of a simple single pulse sequence.

descriptions of these types of pulse sequences are beyond the scope of this article, and for those interested we refer you to the bibliography.

V. MRS APPLICATIONS

MRS is a versatile technique that can be applied in many ways. This section describes the main nuclei that are observed by MRS to provide information of biomedical interest.

A. Phosphorus-31 MRS

Phosphorus-31 is the naturally occurring isotope of phosphorus and is observable by MR at 40% the frequency of protons at the same magnetic field strength. Because there are many important high-energy phosphates present in organisms, ^{31}P-MR has become a widely studied MR nucleus. One reason for the success of these studies in biological systems is that there are relatively few molecules at high enough concentration in biological systems to give resonances and ^{31}P-MRS gives generally well-resolved signals. Figure 9 shows a characteristic ^{31}P spectrum of a sample of cells grown in culture, trapped in a gel, and perfused with medium containing glucose and other nutrients. An example of how the metabolism of the phospholipid precursors can be followed with time is shown in Fig. 10 in which cells were perfused with 2 mM ethanolamine, leading to a rise in the phosphoenthanolamine peak and a concomitant decrease in the

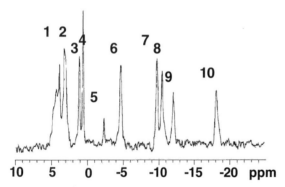

FIGURE 9 A ^{31}P-MR spectrum of cells entrapped in gel and perfused with medium. Assignments of signals are 1, phosphomonoesters (PE and PC); 2, P$_i$; 3, glycerylphosphoethanolamine (GPE); 4, glycerylphosphocholine (GPC); 5, phosphocreatine (PCr); 6, γ-ATP; 7, α-ATP; 8, UDPS and NADP; 9, UDPS; and 10, β-ATP.

phosphocholine peak, as ethanolamine is a substrate for ethanolamine kinase and is an inhibitor for choline kinase. The rates of these two reactions can then be determined *in situ*, i.e., enzyme kinetics can be studied independently in the intact cells where the kinases involved are present at the interface of the membrane and cytosol.

B. Carbon-13 MRS

Most carbon consists of carbon-12, which does not give an MR signal. However, carbon-13 is a stable isotope of carbon that exists at 1.1% natural abundance and that has magnetic properties. It can be observed in biological samples by selecting the appropriate frequency (25% that of ^{1}H at the same magnetic field strength). The main problem with ^{13}C is not only its low natural abundance, but also the fact that its intrinsic MR sensitivity is low, i.e., 10^{-2} that of ^{1}H. When these two factors are combined, it can be seen that observing ^{13}C signals is harder than for ^{1}H by a factor of about 10^3. Apart from acquiring multiple scans in order to improve the signal-to-noise ratio, it is also possible to obtain ^{13}C-enriched materials (from large-scale mass separation), up to nearly 100% ^{13}C. Thus, ^{13}C can be a tracer in metabolic studies where the method of observation is ^{13}C MRS. ^{13}C MRS is also a powerful tool in the structure determination of molecules, from simple organic compounds to large proteins.

C. Proton MRS

Initial attempts to determine the proton spectra of cell samples and biological specimens began in the 1970s, but little progress was made until recently. The main stumbling blocks were the presence of the huge water signal and the overlapping of proton metabolite signals. Currently, higher magnetic field magnets and high fidelity magnetic gradient systems enabled the development of effective water suppression techniques (see earlier discussion) and improved signal resolution (see later). Only in the 1990s did satisfactory results start to accumulate both for cell spectra and for clinically relevant samples.

In the body, the best organ for study is the brain because it has quite a large volume with little motion, whereas the heart and the abdomen are very difficult

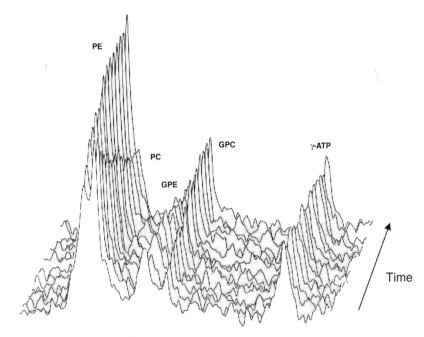

FIGURE 10 Example of ^{31}P-MRS used to follow a metabolic process in intact perfused breast cancer cells. Addition of ethanolamine (2 mM) results in an increase of the signal due to phosphoethanolamine over time due to synthesis by choline kinase and reduction of phosphocholine due to inhibition of choline kinase (each spectrum took 20 min). Note that the ATP signal remains constant as an internal control.

to study because of either motion or heterogeneity. Certain signals are well defined, particularly those of metabolites present at high enough concentration (mM) and for which the molecular mobility is fast enough to provide narrow resonances. The three substances lactate, choline, and *N*-aspartylaspartate (NAA) are most diagnostic and have been used to characterize brain tumors. Proton MRS studies of other tissues and cancers are now quite common.

Another MR technique that has had a major impact in the field of macromolecular structure determination is two-dimensional proton MRS. In this case the spectrum is spread out into two dimensions, thus giving greater inherent signal resolution and providing information about proton–proton magnetic interactions not otherwise available. However, an extensive description of these results is beyond the scope of this article.

D. Diffusion-Weighted MRS

This section presents the application of diffusion-weighted (DW) proton MRS to selectively observe only the intracellular metabolites of cancer cell. This

method, described initially by Van Zijl and colleagues, is based on differences in motional properties of the components due to the higher intracellular protein concentration and to the consequent restriction of molecular motion within cells. The apparent diffusion coefficient (ADC) of intracellular components is an order of magnitude lower than that of extracellular components and free water. In 1965, Stejskal and Tanner showed that application of a pair of pulsed magnetic field gradients sensitizes spin echo MR experiments to diffusion. Tanner subsequently showed that the stimulated echo obtained in a three 90° RF pulse experiment is useful when strong diffusion weighting is required with minimal loss of echo time. The resulting spectrum consists of signals due to slowly diffusing molecules only, i.e., intracellular molecules. The clinical application of proton MRS is an emerging field, as a noninvasive tool in evaluating various tumor systems. Several groups have shown that proton MRS could be used for differentiating benign from malignant tissues, for staging malignancies, and for providing early detection of metabolic changes as response to therapy. The clinical potential of applying DWMRS is that by observing directly the intracellular metabolite profile of the viable cancerous tissue, signals originating from nonviable matter (necrosis, edema, etc.) are avoided. This is most important in the case of malignant tissues, which are heterogeneous by nature. Avoiding averaging the signal over the extracellular nonviable matter should enhance the sensitivity of MRS, and this is being applied *in vitro* and has potential *in vivo*.

VI. MRI APPLICATIONS

A. T_1- and T_2-Weighted Images

This section describes the significant influence of the relaxation times T_1 and T_2 (defined earlier, see Sections II.B and III.B) on the contrast observed in an MR image. In Fig. 11, exponential decays for two tissues with different T_2 (water) values are shown. These curves represent the reduction in signal intensity as a function of time for each tissue. Tissue 1 in the Fig. 11 has a longer T_2 relaxation time than tissue 2. Consequently, the image acquired at a particular time, represented by the vertical dotted line, will result in tissue 1 having a higher signal intensity (brighter image) than tissue 2. This is the origin of contrast observed between tissues in T_2-weighted MR images. Thus, in T_2-weighted images, tissues with shorter T_2 values appear darker. In T_1-weighted images, however, the signal increases exponentially with time, thus tissues with shorter T_1 values appear brighter.

In order to obtain T_2 weighting it is necessary to use longer echo times (TE) than for T_1-weighted images. Consequently, the signal intensity in T_2-weighted images tends to be lower. Therefore, T_1-weighted images generally give a superior signal-to-noise ratio. However, in some cases, T_2-weighted images give better contrast between tissues compared to T_1-weighted images, e.g., between white and gray matter in the brain.

B. Contrast Agents

A contrast agent causes an increase in the contrast of an image, often between normal tissue and a pathological condition such as a tumor. Contrast agents are well known in X-ray methods, where compounds containing barium and iodine are used. In the case of MRI, a contrast agent is chosen to affect the relaxation of the water in a specific region, as relaxation is the basis of contrast in the MR image. In order to significantly affect the relaxation times, the contrast agent usually has unpaired electrons because they have more than 1000 times the dipolar relaxation effect (the process resulting in exchange of energy between spins; see Section II.B) of a proton nucleus. This effect of unpaired electrons is termed a paramagnetic effect, as opposed to a diamagnetic effect, which is produced by substances with only paired electrons. Substances that have unpaired electrons are metal ions and certain chemical substances, such as nitroxides. Usually chelates, a complex of a metal ion with a specially designed chemical substance that traps the metal ion, are used as paramagnetic contrast agents in MRI. The most widely used MRI contrast agent is gadolinium DTPA (GdDTPA), where DTPA is a chelating agent for the Gd^{3+} ion. An example of the effect of GdDTPA on an MR image is shown in Fig. 12.

C. Functional MRI

Functional MRI (fMRI) differs from standard MRI in that it reveals functional information about the system, not just anatomic images. Since its inception in the early 1990s, fMRI was used for research purposes,

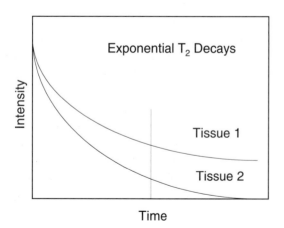

FIGURE 11 Differentiation of T_2 weighting causing contrast in an MR image. Signal intensity is plotted as a function of time for two tissues.

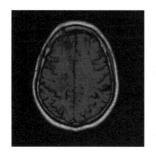 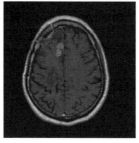

no contrast   contrast enhanced

FIGURE 12 Effect of the contrast agent GdDTPA on a brain image. T_1-weighted axial images of a glioblastoma multiformi patient pre- and postcontrast administration.

but is now used in clinical applications in the fields of neurology. A major goal of fMRI is to map the neuronal activity of the brain. Neuronal activity requires increased glucose and oxygen consumption, which generates changes in perfusion and blood oxygenation. Because the increase in perfusion is much larger than the increase in oxygen consumption, overall blood oxygenation is increased. This leads to the widely used method of blood oxygenation level-dependent fMRI, which uses the endogenous hemoglobin as a source of contrast. The red cells containing deoxyhemoglobin cause a distortion in the magnetic field, resulting in a change in the contrast of the MR image.

Clinical applications of fMRI include brain and epilepsy surgery, radiosurgery, and in the clinical evaluation of brain plasticity. fMRI results can be useful in planning surgical resection of patients and have been found to help in deciding whether to operate on a patient who had previously been considered inoperable. fMRI is reported to be a useful tool in making treatment decisions on low-grade astrocytomas or arteriovenous malformations in intact or slightly impaired patients. fMRI can be repeated in selected patients with slow-growing brain tumors or congenital lesions such as AVM to study cortical reorganization phenomena over time.

D. Diffusion MRI

Diffusion weighting enables noninvasive differentiation between intra- and extracellular water molecules by their diffusion/motion properties (see Section V.D).

DW is obtained by taking a snapshot of the spatial distribution of molecules at two different time points by applying gradients in the magnetic field. The contrast in a DWMR image is determined by the diffusion/motion of the tissue water molecules. The signal of the fast molecules is filtered out by acquiring only the signal coming from molecules that did not change their position during the interval between the two time points. Therefore, diffusion-weighted MRI (DWMRI) enables the measurement of biophysical characteristics of tissue, including the intra/extracellular volume fraction (R) and apparent diffusion coefficients (ADCs) of water.

DWMRI has proved to be of great clinical importance in the routine assessment of patients with cerebral ischemia due to its capability of imaging ischemia-induced changes in water protons within minutes after an insult. Currently, DWMRI is being applied to tumor detection, staging, and monitoring.

E. Interventional MRI

The development of open configuration magnets, together with ultrafast imaging techniques, has extended the utility of MRI from a purely diagnostic status to an imaging modality ideally suited for image guidance of a wide number of minimally invasive surgical and interventional techniques. The currently commercially available interventional MRI (iMRI) systems differ with respect to their static magnetic field strength, their gradient systems, and their patient access, but in all systems the procedures can be performed concurrent with on-line image guidance and monitoring.

While initially focused primarily on intrasurgical visualization (e.g., craniotomy), iMRI has rapidly evolved into image-guided localization for needle-based procedures, minimally invasive neurosurgical procedures, and thermal-guided ablation of tumors (see next section).

In addition, the versatility of the open design means that patients can assume physiological positions, e.g., allow dynamic joint imaging to be performed. Recent development and refinement of miniature intravascular imaging catheters and MRI-compatible guidewires, balloon catheters, and radiofrequency ablation catheters have triggered a new range of novel approaches for detecting and treating cardiovascular diseases.

MRI guidance for such invasive procedures requires unique pulse sequences and display. Instrument tracking and interactive display are used to localize, target, and monitor. Fast sequences, interventional protocols, and an in-room monitor, as well as MR-compatible (i.e., nonmagnetic) probes, cannulae, catheters, instruments, endoscopes, and auxiliary equipment, are necessary for this combined surgical MR image-guided approach.

Considering the fast progress being made in this field, there can be little doubt that interventional MRI will become a well-accepted clinical tool in the near future.

F. Temperature Mapping

A great clinical potential of MRI is in monitoring the delivery of various thermal energies. Regardless of the type of thermal therapy, the purpose is the same: to ensure that the pathological tissue is heated to a certain temperature range, usually between 50 and 80°C, for a certain period of time, while the surrounding healthy tissue is spared excess thermal treatment. Theoretical models simulating the treatment are usually not able to produce a reasonable prediction of heating, as there are many independent variables that affect the energy deposition, such as vascularity, tissue inhomogeneity, and optical and thermal tissue conductivity. Therefore, on top of good localization and targeting, MRI guidance of thermal therapy also requires quantitative spatial and temporal control of energy deposition by monitoring thermal changes and resulting tissue alterations.

Four different MR properties have been shown to be sensitive to temperature changes: spin–lattice relaxation time (T_1), water molecular diffusion coefficient (D), proton density (r), and proton resonance frequency (PRF). Some of the obstacles in MR temperature monitoring include low sensitivity, difficulties in the interpretation of signal changes in terms of temperature or tissue damage, sensitivity to motion, and the need for temperature calibrations, which is different for different organs. PRF dependence on temperature changes has been shown to be most promising, particularly because of its linear relation-

ship to temperature and its independence on tissue type. Although it can be rapidly measured, it is also very sensitive to motion. Studies in which MRI thermal monitoring was used for laser surgery, radiofrequency ablation, cryotherapy, and focused ultrasound thermal surgery have demonstrated the accuracy of MR in the monitoring and guidance of thermal therapy.

VII. RELEVANCE OF MRS AND MRI TO CANCER

Throughout the 20th century, the rate of biomedical research increased exponentially. A major part of this work involved the development of physical methods to study organisms. Concurrently, as a single subject, more money has been spent on cancer research than on any other disease. It is not surprising, therefore, that the intersection of these two fields has produced notable advances.

There are many areas where MR has been used to study, diagnose, and monitor cancer treatment.

1. MRS been used to study energy metabolism by observing ATP resonances in ^{31}P spectra and glucose consumption by labeling glucose with ^{13}C and then observing the changes in the glucose resonance using ^{13}C MRS.

2. The use of proton MRS for the detection of malignancy is an emerging field. It has been shown in several types of malignancies that the choline/creatine peak ratio is a marker for malignancy. In some malignancies, other metabolites have also been shown to relate to cancer, such as low NAA in the brain and low citrate in the prostate. High lactate has also been shown to be typical of tumors, and the necrotic areas in tumors seem to consist mainly of lactate and lipids. MRS is also useful in studying the mechanism of action of drugs by observing them directly or by observing the metabolic response to their action.

3. Contrast enhanced T_1-weighted imaging has been used to determine the anatomic location and spread of tumors. The most common application involves injecting a contrast agent (usually a gadolinium chelate) and then acquiring images. Most tumors

enhance due to the permeable blood vessels that grow around them (angiogenesis) that allow the contrast agent to leak into and accumulate in the extracellular region. Another approach is to have a more controlled injection (usually using special pumps) and then measuring the dynamics of the enhancement (by acquiring several images at predetermined intervals following the injection) and calculating from these data parameters such as blood flow and partial blood volumes.

4. The subject of studying the special features of angiogenesis of tumors is another emerging field in MR. This is usually studied by a combination of dynamic contrast enhancement, as mentioned before, and T_2^*-weighted images, in which the areas containing more capillaries appear dark. From these images it is also possible to determine the location, blood flow, and blood volume of tumors, which is used both for diagnosis and for antiangiogenesis treatment monitoring.

5. An application of fMRI in cancer patients has been to assess the brain function of patients with brain tumors.

6. Diffusion-weighted MRI has been used to determine water apparent diffusion coefficients and the intracellular fraction of tissues in the tumor. These parameters have been shown to assist in characterizing the tissue and in detecting changes in the tissue following therapy.

7. Open or interventional MRI uses a new generation of MRI machines, which enable the noninvasive monitoring and guidance of surgery, minimally invasive procedures, and thermal therapy of tumors.

MRI is one of the premier tools in radiology and has had a major impact on the noninvasive detection and diagnosis of cancer, mainly because of its ability to distinguish between soft tissues. However, it has not proved possible to characterize the nature of the lesions detected by MRI alone without recourse to invasive biopsies. In order to do this in a noninvasive manner, the method of MRS has been considered to be one of the best hopes, although so far it has not become a routine tool in clinical cancer practice.

Nevertheless, these MR techniques, which are still developing and improving, have the greatest chance in the future to allow noninvasive early diagnosis and treatment monitoring of cancer. Further, we look forward to the day when it will be possible, using tools such as high-intensity ultrasound in conjunction with MRI and MRS, to detect, characterize, and ablate cancerous tissue automatically.

See Also the Following Articles

Brain Cancer and Magnetic Resonance Spectroscopy • Magnetic Resonance Spectroscopy of Cancer: Clinical Overview • Metabolic Diagnosis of Prostate Cancer by Magnetic Resonance Spectroscopy • PET Imaging and Cancer

Bibliography

Derome, A. E. (1987). "Modern NMR Techniques for Chemistry Research." Pergamon Press, London.

Gorenstein, D. G. (ed.) (1984). "Phosphorus-31 NMR: Principles and Applications." Academic Press, New York.

Homans, S. W. (1992). "A Dictionary of Concepts in NMR." Clarendon Press, London.

Jolesz, F., and Blumenfeld, S. M. (1994). Interventional use of magnetic resonance imaging. *Magn. Reson. Quart.* **10,** 85–96.

Le Bihan, D. (1990). Magnetic resonance imaging of perfusion. *Magn. Reson. Med.* **14,** 283–292.

Macomber, R. S. (1998). "A Complete Introduction to Modern NMR Spectroscopy." Wiley, New York.

Mitchell, D. G. (1999). "MRI Principles." Saunders, New York.

Moonen, C. T. W., and van Zijl, P. C. M. (1990). Highly efficient water suppression for in vivo proton NMR spectroscopy. *J. Magn. Reson.* **88,** 28–41.

Stejskal, E. O., and Tanner, J. E. (1965). Spin diffusion: Spin echoes in the presence of a time-dependent field gradient. *J. Chem. Phys.* **42,** 288–292.

van Zijl, P. C. M., Moonen, C. T. W., Faustino, P. J., Pekar, J., Kaplan, O., and Cohen, J. S. (1990). Complete separation of intracellular, and extracellular information in NMR spectra by diffusion weighting. *Proc. Natl. Acad. Sci. USA* **88,** 3228–3232.

Vlaardingerbroek, M. T., and den Boer, J. A. (1996). "Magnetic Resonance Imaging, Theory and Practice." Springer-Verlag, Berlin.

Magnetic Resonance Spectroscopy of Cancer: Clinical Overview

Paul M. J. McSheehy
Franklyn A. Howe
John R. Griffiths
St. George's Hospital Medical School, London

Pi Inorganic phosphate.
PME Phosphomonoester.
tCr Total creatine.
tCho Total choline.

GLOSSARY

5-FU 5-Fluorouracil.
ATP Adenosine triphosphate.
FBal Fluoro-β-alanine.
FCat Catabolites including FBal and FUPA.
FNuct 5-Fluoronucleotides.
FUPA α-Fluoro-β-ureidopropanoic acid.
NAA N-Acetyl aspartate.
NTP Nucleoside triphosphate.
PC Phosphocholine.
PCr Phosphocreatine.
PDE Phosphodiester.
pH$_i$ Intracellular pH.

$\mathbf{M}$ agnetic resonance spectroscopy (MRS) is a powerful noninvasive method for studying human cancer. Although cancers in patients will inevitably be studied within the context of some treatment regimen, there is a wealth of additional information on the pathophysiology of untreated tumors obtained from *in vivo* MRS studies of animal models, *in vitro* studies of human tumor biopsies, and cell cultures that can aid in the interpretation of the results. Biochemical information obtained by MRS may be used to ask how tumor metabolism differs from normal tissue; whether spectral characteristics can provide diagnostic information on tumor type and grade; and whether changes in the tumor spectrum are prognostic for the efficacy of anticancer treatments. In addition, MRS can be used to measure the pharmacokinetics of some chemotherapeutic agents and can provide novel noninvasive end points for trials of anticancer drugs or other therapeutic modalities. Application of MRS in the clinic is increasing, and a number of formal trials are ongoing, especially on ^{1}H-MRS of brain cancer.

I. INTRODUCTION

Most clinical MRS of cancer is concerned with signals from ^{1}H or ^{31}P nuclei in endogenous metabolites or from the ^{19}F nuclei of anticancer drugs. The greatest weakness of MRS is its low sensitivity, about 10^4–10^5 lower than magnetic resonance imaging (MRI), depending on the nucleus in question. This is mainly because the biochemicals of interest are only present at millimolar concentrations, whereas the protons in tissue water that are used to produce MR images are at 90 M concentration. In addition, ^{31}P and ^{19}F nuclei, the two nuclei mainly used for MRS outside the brain, produce weaker NMR signals than the ^{1}H nucleus. In consequence, only a fairly small number of high-concentration metabolites can be detected. Fortunately, some of these metabolites, e.g., phosphocreatine and adenosine triphosphate (seen with ^{31}P-MRS), lactate, N-acetyl aspartate, choline, and creatine (seen with ^{1}H-MRS), are of great biological importance. Because of the low signal-to-noise ratio, it is usual to obtain spectra from regions of tissue (usually called voxels) that are a few cubic centimeters in size rather than the millimeter resolution obtained by MRI. Acquisition of a MR spectrum from a localized region of tissue can be achieved using a similar combination of switched magnetic field gradients and radiofrequency pulses as used for MRI. In some cases, particularly for ^{19}F pharmacokinetics and ^{31}P studies of muscle or superficial tumors, a small radiofrequency coil (called a surface coil) placed directly over the tissue being examined is all that is necessary to acquire a localized spectrum. More usually, nowadays, a localization method based on magnetic field gradients is used. Routine diagnostic MR images can be used to specify the size and position of

the spectroscopy voxel(s). The most commonly used single-voxel localization methods are point resolved spectroscopy and stimulated echo acquisition mode (STEAM) for ^{1}H-MRS and image selected in vivo spectroscopy (ISIS) for ^{31}P-MRS. It is also possible to obtain a matrix of spectra in one, two, or three dimensions by a method termed chemical shift imaging (CSI).

II. ^{31}P-MRS

Several metabolically significant phosphorus-containing compounds occur in living systems at high enough concentrations (> 0.2 mM) to be detectable. They provide a relatively low number of signals, which means that ^{31}P spectra can be simple and easy to interpret. Figure 1 shows an in vivo ^{31}P spectrum of a large B-cell lymphoma in the groin of a cancer patient demonstrating the characteristically high phosphomonoester (PME) peak that is found in tumors. The phosphomonoester (PME) peak consists primarily of phosphocholine (PC) and phosphoethanolamine (PE), and the phosphodiester peak (PDE) consists of glycerophosphocholine (GPC) and glycerophosphoethanolamine (GPE). These phospholipid metabolites are considered to reflect cell membrane

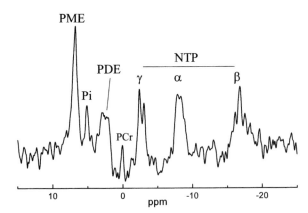

FIGURE 1 A ^{31}P spectrum ([1]H-decoupled) obtained from a large B-cell lymphoma in the groin of a patient. The PME peak is much higher compared to the other peaks in tumors than in noncancerous tissue, and PCr is generally low or nonexistent. Resonances are phosphomonoesters (PME), inorganic phosphate (P_i), phosphodiesters (PDE), phosphocreatine at 0 ppm (PCr), and γ, α, and β phosphates of NTP (predominantly ATP). The spectrum was acquired from a voxel of size $4 \times 4 \times 4$ cm^3 in 34 min.

turnover and proliferation, as both PC and PE are membrane synthesis substrates and GPC and GPE are membrane breakdown products. In rapidly proliferating tissue such as tumors, PME, and occasionally PDE, peaks dominate the spectrum as compared to spectra from normal tissue. The remaining major peaks are from inorganic phosphate (P_i), phosphocreatine (PCr), and the three resonances from the β, α, and γ phosphates of nucleoside triphosphate (NTP, which are mostly adenosine triphosphates). These three metabolites provide information on tumor energetics, although PCr is generally low or nonexistent in tumors. The chemical shift difference between the P_i peak and the α-NTP, or PCr peak, can be used to determine the mean intracellular pH (pH_i). All of these resonances may provide a means of monitoring the response to therapy. For example, decreases in PCr/P_i and NTP/P_i ratios may correlate with deterioration in the bioenergetic status, and a decrease in the PME/NTP ratio may represent decreased cell proliferation. In animal studies, administration of the exogenous nontoxic phosphate compound 3-aminopropylphosphonate (3-APP) provides the extracellular pH of the tumor, and thus calculation of the tumor plasma membrane pH gradient (ΔpH). This may prove useful in the assessment and optimization of thermo- and chemotherapy, which can be pH sensitive. Other resonances sometimes observed are uridine diphosphohexose derivatives (DPDE), which lie between β- and α-NTP peaks; both reduced and oxidized pyridine dinucleotides (NAD^+ and NADH), which appear as a shoulder on the side of the α-NTP resonance; and finally hexose-6-phosphates, and lower levels of glycerol-3-phosphate and AMP. These other resonances are most likely observed in experimental animal tumors for which the greater sensitivity of high-field (4–11 T) MR systems is more routinely available.

A. Experimental

Most animal tumors studied have a neutral or alkaline pH_i, but an acidic pH_e resulting in a negative ΔpH, i.e., $pH_i > pH_e$, the reverse of that found in normal cells. The low pH_e probably results indirectly from the high rates of glycolysis common in tumor cells, which requires that acid (lactate plus H^+) is pumped into the extracellular compartment. The presence of lactate provides an important biological marker (see later), whereas the reverse pH gradient across the cell membrane provides an opportunity for the tumor-specific uptake of anticancer drugs that behave as weak electrolytes.

In animal models, several changes are consistently seen in ^{31}P spectra during unperturbed tumor growth. These include larger P_i resonances than observed in normal tissues, high PME resonances that increase with tumor growth, decreasing PCr levels (when detectable), and a size-dependent decline in NTP relative to P_i, coupled with a decrease in tumor pH_i. The NTP/P_i ratio shows a strong positive correlation with pH_i across all tumor types. The decline in the bioenergetic status of the tumor is consistent with the tumor vasculature becoming insufficient to provide nutritive blood (including oxygen) to the rapidly proliferating tissue, leading to hypoxia.

^{31}P-MRS has been used to study changes in the energy and phospholipid metabolism of animal tumors during therapy. The response to radiotherapy has shown a common trend, with increases in PCr/P_i, NTP/P_i, and pH_i, the extent of response being dose dependent. The observed improvement in bioenergetic status is consistent with tumor reoxygenation resulting from increased tumor blood perfusion after irradiation. A variety of chemotherapeutic agents also reverse the ^{31}P trends seen during unperturbed tumor growth, i.e., they increase pH_i and the bioenergetic status. This response is accompanied by a decrease in tumor volume, yet the changes in ^{31}P spectra are detectable early after initiation of treatment before measurable changes in tumor size or histological alterations are evident. This paradoxical phenomenon is termed "tumor activation" and may be due to a reduction in ATP usage when the tumors stop growing and, at later stages, through an improvement in tumor blood supply and/or infiltration of macrophages following successful therapy. Tumor activation is not usually observed in tumors in patients.

Some drugs produce a clearly visible peak in the ^{31}P spectrum, allowing the pharmacokinetics and distribution to be monitored *in situ* in the animal. This is generally only possible when the chemotherapeutic agent is administered at high doses (>250 mg/kg) as, for example, in the case of the alkylating agent ifosfamide.

Both uptake and rates of elimination have been determined for ifosfamide and a glucosyl derivative in rat liver and tumors *in vivo*.

B. Clinical

^{31}P-MRS has been used to study human tumors *in vivo* at 1.5–2 T, which is the magnetic field strength generally available in clinical practice. Localization methods such as ISIS and CSI are commonly used, as these techniques preserve signals from metabolites that have short T2 relaxation times. Proton decoupling of the ^{31}P spectrum is possible, which provides improved spectral resolution (particularly of the PME and PDE peaks) and an increased signal-to-noise ratio (see Fig. 1). Most tumors have been found to contain very little PCr, and any that is present in the spectrum is usually considered to be a contaminating signal from surrounding muscle, which contains very high ($\approx$25 mM) concentrations.

1. Diagnosis

Similar to experimental animal tumors, human cancers are characterized by elevated PME (and sometimes PDE), an alkaline pH$_i$ (7.1–7.4), and generally, at least compared to muscle, a relatively low energetic status. Early studies showed that both non-Hodgkin's lymphomas (NHL) and soft tissue sarcomas could be metabolically characterized *in vivo* into necrotic and viable tumors, based on levels of phospholipids and NTP/P$_i$ ratios. Head and neck tumors were distinguished from normal muscle by higher PME and PDE levels, and importantly, benign and malignant sarcomas were distinguished in some cases because of a general trend toward higher levels of PME for higher grade lesions. All of these observations have been reported *in vivo*, but reports of high-field ^{31}P analysis *in vitro* of extracts of human tumor surgical specimens demonstrated that individual phospholipid components could be correlated with specific clinical and histopathological features, such as nuclear grade and lymphatic invasion.

2. Monitoring of Therapy

A review in 1992 by Negendank of 61 patients receiving chemo- or radiotherapy showed that the most frequent change was a decrease in PME. This occurred in 38 of 47 cases that eventually responded to treatment but in only 1 of the 14 nonresponders. This was in contrast to early studies on animal models for which decreases in the NTP resonance (usually detected as a decrease in the NTP/P$_i$ ratio) were most likely to correlate with response. The picture in the clinic has not changed markedly since 1992, and in studies of head and neck tumors, breast, sarcoma, and musculoskeletal tumors, a decrease in PME (expressed relative to NTP or P$_i$) has been observed prior to a significant change in tumor size. In some cases, nonresponders showed an increase in PME, PDE, or P$_i$/NTP ratios. A 5-year multicenter international trial funded by the National Cancer Institute was initiated in 1996 designed to test the hypothesis that early changes in phospholipid metabolites would predict sensitivity or resistance to treatment. The results obtained so far using ^{1}H-decoupled ^{31}P CSI of NHL and breast tumors appear to confirm the hypothesis that significant decreases in PME occur prior to a tumor response measured as a decrease in tumor volume. This study has also produced the unexpected finding that a larger PME resonance in naive NHL tumors predicted a greater response to therapy. Such a result is very promising, as a single scan prior to therapy would be easier and less expensive to arrange than scans both before and after therapy.

III. ^{1}H-MRS

Nearly every compound in living tissues contains hydrogen atoms, so, in principle, ^{1}H spectra contain a wealth of information. However, there are disadvantages associated with in vivo ^{1}H-MRS, which limit the number of biochemicals that can be routinely detected, as shown in Fig. 2, which compares a typical short echo time ^{1}H spectrum obtained from a grade III astrocytoma with normal white matter in human brain. A major obstacle is the high concentration of tissue water (ca. 45 M) and CH$_2$ lipids (ca. 1 M in muscle and 20 M in adipose tissue), which produce intense signals that must be suppressed to observe the metabolites of interest. A second limitation is the small chemical shift range of ^{1}H resonances (ca. 3.5 ppm for the main biochemicals of interest), which increases the need for a very homogeneous B$_0$ field to provide good spectral resolution and enable efficient suppression of the water signal. However, susceptibil-

A

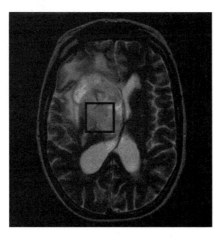

B

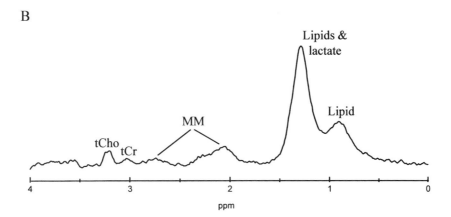

C

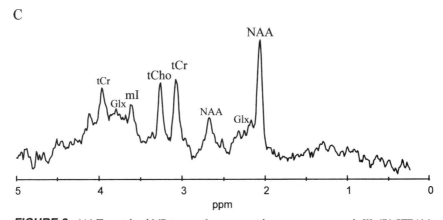

FIGURE 2 (A) T$_2$-weighted MR image of a patient with an astrocytoma grade III. (B) STEAM-localized ^{1}H-MRS spectrum acquired from the voxel indicated in A at 1.5 T with a TE of 30 ms. (C) STEAM-localized ^{1}H-MRS spectrum acquired at a TE of 30 ms from normal human brain parietal white matter. Resonances are identified for N-acetylaspartate (NAA), glutamate and glutamine (Glx), total creatines (tCr), total cholines (tCho), myo-inositol (mI), lactate and mobile lipids, and macromolecules (MM). Spectra have been processed with 1-Hz line broadening, and the residual suppressed water signal at 4.7 ppm has been removed.

ity variations due to the microscopic structure of tissue are always present so that the resonances of many biochemicals overlap and are indistinguishable (e.g., the single peak observed at 3.2 ppm comprises signals from choline, phosphocholine, and glycerophosphocholine). Local hemorrhaging within the tumor, which releases paramagnetic compounds from blood, can further degrade spectral resolution and water suppression efficiency, as can motion, a problem pertinent to most studies outside of the brain. For all of these reasons, the majority of ^{1}H-MRS in both experimental and clinical studies has been performed on brain tumors.

The techniques of *in vivo* water-suppressed ^{1}H-MRS require that spectra be acquired with an echo time delay (TE). The resonances observed depend on the TE used because of different T_2 relaxation times and whether the signal is from coupled spins. In the brain, typical resonances observed at long TE (e.g., 272 ms) may include *N*-acetyl aspartate (NAA), total creatines (tCr, comprising creatine and phosphocreatine), total cholines (tCho, comprising choline, glycerophosphocholine, phosphocholine, and glycerolcholine), alanine, and lactate. A TE of 144 ms (or sometimes 136 ms) is commonly used to distinguish lactate (which is inverted at this echo time) from mobile lipids that resonate at the same frequency. Resonances attributed to myo-inositol (mI), glutamate and glutamine (Glx), taurine, and mobile lipids may appear at short echo times (e.g., 10–50 ms), as well as a broad background signal from short T_2 macromolecules (MM). Note that in Fig. 2 the tumor spectrum has very large signals from both macromolecules and lipids.

A. Experimental

Preclinical studies of tumors *in vivo* by ^{1}H-MRS are few, and most have been limited to brain tumor models in which lipid signals are less intense and there is little motion. A handful of studies have investigated the ^{1}H spectrum of subcutaneously grown animal tumors before and after chemo- or radiotherapy. An indicator of treatment appears to be lactate, which decreases in cases of significant tumor cell kill and increases when blood flow is restricted. Lactate is the end product of glycolysis and as such may act as a

marker for solid tumors as well as an indicator of grade, as less differentiated tumors show higher glycolytic rates. A study by Hakumaki and colleagues showed that tCho in rat glioma decreased in response to successful gancyclovir treatment, which in that model was consistent with increased growth arrest and apoptosis.

B. Clinical

Conventionally, tumor diagnosis and grading are done by biopsy, followed by histological analysis. In the case of brain tumors, this invasive procedure carries with it some risk, hence clinical ^{1}H-MRS has focused on the diagnosis and grading of brain tumors as a potential replacement to biopsy. Because adult human brain tumors generally respond poorly to chemotherapy or radiotherapy, the scope for using ^{1}H-MRS to monitor the effects of treatment has been limited. However, with the advent of new chemotherapy, such as temozolomide, as well as the relatively new technique of gamma knife surgery, this is gradually changing.

1. Diagnosis

Numerous ^{1}H-MRS studies have now shown significant differences between *in vivo* spectra of human brain tumors of various type and grade and that of healthy brain tissue. NAA, which is considered to be a specific neuronal marker, is generally not found in tumors. When present in a spectrum, it is most likely to come from normal brain tissue within a tumor and so the signal will be greatly reduced compared to that in normal white matter. In contrast, tCho is usually elevated. Phosphorylcholine is a well-known substrate for membrane phospholipid synthesis, and when membranes are damaged, the visibility of lipid-bound choline groups is increased. Its elevation has also been attributed to increased cell membrane synthesis within rapidly proliferating tissue. Creatine is used as a marker of brain cell density and is considerably lower in tumor tissue. Alanine is often observed in meningiomas, suggesting that their metabolism may involve transamination pathways and partial oxidation of glutamine rather than glycolysis. Lactate is frequently observed in tumors, with greater levels generally found in higher grade tumors. However, because tumors are generally very heterogeneous, and the absolute lactate level is dependent on the balance between production rate and clearance, this correlation is weakened. Lipid resonances are also often observed in brain tumor spectra at both short and long echo times. These signals arise from mobile lipids rather than lipid bilayers in intact membranes and other macromolecules. The amount of lipid signal has been correlated with the extent of necrosis and malignancy and in cell cultures with the proliferation state of the cells. These mobile lipid resonances can obscure important metabolite peaks such as lactate and alanine, particularly in short echo time spectra (see Fig. 2).

The interpretation of *in vivo* spectra has been assisted by comparison with high-resolution ^{1}H spectra *in vitro* on both whole tumor biopsies and their extracts. The enhanced spectral quality (resolution and signal to noise) provides additional biochemical information by identifying a wider range of metabolites. Individual classification of choline-containing compounds has been achieved in addition to the assignment of phosphoethanolamine, inositol, and amino acids such as glycine, taurine, glutamate, and glutamine.

An approach to provide automated analysis and classification of brain tumor ^{1}H spectra has been to use pattern recognition techniques that allow a statistical comparison of the relative intensity of all peaks in the ^{1}H spectrum. Results have been reported using techniques such as principal component and linear discriminant analysis in which either *in vivo* or *in vitro* ^{1}H spectra could be used to classify tumors with typically 90% accuracy.

2. Monitoring of Therapy

Two clinical studies, each of which monitored 10 patients with gliomas treated with chemo- or radiotherapy, demonstrated clear decreases in tumor tCho of patients with responding or stable disease. A study of human glioma showed a strong inverse correlation between tCho and the water diffusion coefficient, which suggested that a low tCho correlated with low cellularity. Another study of 44 patients with breast carcinoma showed that the water-fat ratio was raised in tumor compared to normal tissue; in patients responding to chemotherapy, this ratio was significantly reduced.

One of the limitations of MRI in following treatment is in determining whether residual lesions that enhance after administration of a contrast agent are due to malignancy or radiation necrosis. By using a three-dimensional CSI technique to obtain ^{1}H spectra from brain tumors and surrounding tissue, Nelson and co-workers demonstrated that ^{1}H-MRS could be superior to MRI in delineating the real extent of residual active tumor regions by the elevated tCho/NAA ratio. Furthermore, their data support the argument for using such metabolic imaging to define the extent of tumor in planning to treatment.

IV. ^{19}F-MRS

The ^{19}F nucleus has several advantages for MRS, as it is 100% abundant, has a high sensitivity, 83% that of ^{1}H, and a wide chemical shift range so that resonances are well separated. The absence of endogenous fluorine compounds means there is no background signal. A number of important chemotherapeutic agents contain the ^{19}F nucleus as a key component of drug cytotoxicity or stability, allowing ^{19}F-MRS *in vivo* to be used in both preclinical and clinical oncology for monitoring pharmacokinetics or assessment of tumor biochemistry by using probe molecules. Such noninvasive monitoring may aid in the optimization of drug therapy, as it is increasingly clear that pharmacologically guided dose regimes in clinical oncology may allow the individualization of drug therapy.

A. Experimental

The fluoropyrimidines, 5-fluorouridine and 5-fluorouracil (5FU), have been the most widely studied chemotherapeutic agents by ^{19}F-MRS. 5-FU is a prodrug, which is activated in the tumor by anabolism to cytotoxic 5-fluoronucleotides (FNuct), leading to DNA- or RNA-directed cytotoxicity. It is deactivated to catabolites (FCat), which include α-fluoro-β-ureidopropanoic acid (FUPA) and fluoro-β-alanine (FBal), a process that occurs in many tissues but predominantly in the liver (see Fig. 3). Early experiments by Stevens and colleagues using mice showed that ^{19}F-MRS could be used to follow the uptake, metabolism, and elimination of 5-FU in both the liver and the tumor. Subsequent studies using rodent

A

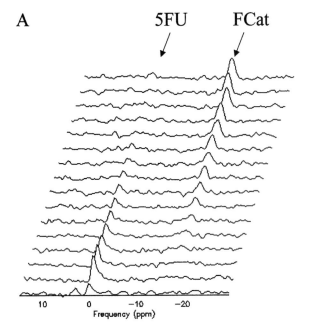

B

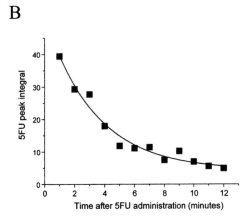

FIGURE 3 (A) ^{19}F-MRS spectra obtained from the liver of a patient with metastases from colorectal cancer over 30 min after bolus administration of 0.45 g/m^2 5-fluorouracil. Spectra were acquired in 2-min blocks with a 15 × 20-cm surface coil that conformed to the abdomen over the liver. (B) Exponential fit of the 5-FU peak area with time gives $t_{1/2}^{5FU} \approx 4$ min. 5FU, 5-fluorouracil; FCat, mostly fluoro-β-alanine but also contributions from α-fluoro-β-ureidopropanoic acid.

tumors or human xenografts grown in nude mice showed that administration of drugs that modulated 5-FU efficacy *in vivo* resulted in predicted increases or decreases in FNuct concentration. However, increased levels of FNuct did not always signify increased cytotoxicity and, in some cases, the rate of elimination of 5FU ($t_{1/2}^{5FU}$) proved to be a better correlate with tumor response. Formation of FCat in the liver has also

been correlated negatively with response, and inhibition of the initial catabolic enzyme dihydropyrimidine dehydrogenase (DPD) can increase tumor FNuct levels and markedly increase the therapeutic ratio. DPD inhibitors are becoming an important adjuvant in clinical 5FU therapy.

Prodrugs of 5FU, which require one or more enzymatic step in the liver and/or tumor to yield 5FU, have also been studied in rodent tumors, e.g., Ftorafur, Doxfluoridine, Capecitabine, and OGT719. In these cases, the rate of formation of 5FU in the tumor should be strongly indicative of tumor sensitivity to this form of chemotherapy and the techniques could be developed for application in the clinic. A number of other fluorinated anticancer drugs, including Gemcitabine and Flutamide, and antifolates such as ZD9331 have been studied in animals *in vivo* and in tumor extracts. In these cases, ^{19}F-MRS is used as a preclinical pharmacokinetic research tool to provide information about drug distribution and rates of metabolism or elimination; studies that are important in drug development.

Some fluorinated molecules act as probes of the tumor environment. For example, tumor pH, rates of metabolism of glucose, and levels of oxygen are important determinants of sensitivity to chemo- and radiotherapy. ZK150471 is a fluorinated probe of pH$_e$ and as such performs a similar function to the ^{31}P probe 3-APP, but with improved sensitivity. Perfluorocarbons have a very high affinity for O$_2$ and have been used to measure the pO$_2$ of many rodent tumors, although poor tumor uptake has precluded clinical application. In contrast, SR4554 is a fairly soluble fluorinated 2-nitroimidazole, which undergoes reduction in hypoxic cells and has proved to be an effective marker of hypoxia in tumor spheroids *in vitro* and rodent tumors *in vivo* and has begun phase I clinical trials. 2-Fluoro-2-deoxy-D-glucose (FDG) is a glucose analog that is phosphorylated to FDG-6P and retained by cells, especially tumor cells, which tend to be strongly glycolytic. Thus, the use of tracer doses of FDG in conjunction with the highly sensitive technique of positron emission tomography is well established in the clinic for the diagnosis of tumors. However, ^{19}F-MRS of mouse ascites and tumors has shown that FDG-6P is converted to other metabolites that persist for long periods at high levels and may be used for tumor detection and also correlated with tumor response.

B. Clinical

For ^{19}F-MRS performed in clinical 1.5-T whole body scanners, localization with surface coils of 3–15 cm in diameter is used for both surface and deeper tumors (e.g., liver metastases). This is necessary to maximize the signal-to-noise ratio and provide the time resolution needed for pharmacokinetic analysis (see Fig. 3). Apart from two brief reports, one on Gemcitabine and another on Doxfluoridine, all studies thus far have focused on the pharmacokinetics of 5FU *in situ*, although as with other analytical techniques such as HPLC, important information has been gleaned from the analysis of human samples *in vitro*. There are currently no reports of fluorinated drugs being administered *in vivo* as probes of tumor biochemistry.

1. Monitoring of Therapy

5FU is used predominantly for the treatment of head and neck, breast, and gastrointestinal tumors. It is found to be most effective when in combination with leucovorin, although other adjuvants are also used. About 80% of tumors fail to respond when 5FU is used as a single chemotherapeutic agent, and the aim of ^{19}F-MRS, along with other more conventional clinical methods, is early detection of nonresponders. This would minimize unnecessary toxicity and save resources, as well as perhaps allowing the optimization of scheduling for more responsive tumors. The first reported ^{19}F-MRS study of 5FU in patients was by Wolf and colleagues, who observed uptake and elimination of 5FU in liver following a bolus administration of the drug. Subsequent reports by Wolf and other groups have confirmed that the sensitivity of the method is adequate to detect 5FU itself in the tumor tissue, occasionally FNuct, and also large FCat signals, which may originate from the liver, as this is the organ where most catabolism occurs. Although all reports are nonquantitative and are generally limited therefore to a measurement of the $t_{1/2}^{5FU}$ from the tumor, this has nevertheless provided very useful information. In the early 1990s, three different clinical centers reported studies of liver metastases in which there was a strong and highly significant association between 5FU reten-

tion in the tumor and patient response, whether partial or complete. 5FU signals were observed in 78–100% of responders but in only 8–23% of nonresponders. Furthermore, there was clearly a slower elimination of 5FU from responding tumors ($t_{1/2}^{5FU}$ between 20 and 80 min) compared to nonresponders or metastatic-free livers or plasma ($t_{1/2}^{5FU}$ between 8 and 20 min). This phenomenon was termed "tumor trapping." The mechanism of this trapping is unknown, but animal studies suggest that it is related to the poor vascular supply of tumors and their reverse pH gradient across the cell membranes. A recently completed study showed that patients receiving radiotherapy for head and neck tumors had a ca. twofold greater tumor uptake of 5FU and FCat, suggesting that radiotherapy improved the tumor blood supply, as has been demonstrated in animal tumors.

Acknowledgments

Data presented in the figures of this article are from ongoing research at St. George's Hospital Medical School funded by Cancer Research Campaign Grant SP1971/0404 and by a grant from the National Cancer Institute (CA62558-04) as part of the "Co-operative Group on MRS Applications to Cancer."

See Also the Following Articles

BRAIN CANCER AND MAGNETIC RESONANCE SPECTROSCOPY • MAGNETIC RESONANCE SPECTROSCOPY AND MAGNETIC RESONANCE IMAGING, INTRODUCTION • METABOLIC DIAGNOSIS OF PROSTATE CANCER BY MAGNETIC RESONANCE SPECTROSCOPY • PET IMAGING AND CANCER

Bibliography

de Certaines, J. D., Larsen, V. A., Podo, F., Carpinelli, G., Briot, O., and Henriksen, O. (1993). *In vivo* ^{31}P MRS of experimental tumors. *NMR Biomed.* **6,** 345–365.

Gadian, D. G. (1995). "NMR and Its Applications to Living Systems," 2nd Ed. Oxford Science Publications, Oxford.

Hakumaki, J. M., Poptani, H., Sandmair, A.-M., Herttuala, S., and Kauppinen, R. A. (1999). ^{1}H-MRS detects polyunsaturated fatty acid accumulation during gene therapy of glioma: implications for the in vivo detection of apoptosis. *Nature Med.* **5,** 1323–1327.

Howe, F. A. (1998). Magnetic resonance spectroscopy in vivo. In "Principles of MRI: Selected Topics" (J. A. Markisz and J. P. Whalen, eds.), Chap. 2. Appleton & Lange, Stamford.

McSheehy, P. M. J., Lemaire, L. P., and Griffiths, J. R. (1995). Fluorine-19 MRS applications in oncology. *In* "Encyclopaedia of Nuclear Magnetic Resonance" (D. M. Grant and R. K. Harris, eds.), Vol. 3, pp. 2048–2052. John Wiley and Sons, Ltd., Chichester.

Negendank, W. G. (1992). Studies of human tumors by MRS: A review. *NMR Biomed.* **5,** 303–324.

Nelson, S. J., Vigneron, D. B., and Dillon, W. P. (1999). Serial evaluation of patients with brain tumors using volume MRI and 3D ^{1}H MRSI. *NMR Biomed.* **12,** 123–138.

Podo, F. (1999). Tumor phospholipid metabolism. *NMR Biomed.* **12,** 413–439.

Preul, M. C., Caramanos, Z., Collins, D. L., Villemure, J.-G., Leblanc, R., Olivier, A., *et al.* (1996). Accurate, noninvasive diagnosis of human brain tumors by using proton magnetic resonance spectroscopy. *Nature Med.* **2,** 323–325.

Steen, R. G. (1989). Response of solid tumors to chemotherapy monitored by *in vivo* ^{31}P nuclear magnetic resonance spectroscopy: A review. *Cancer Res.* **49,** 4075–4085.

Stevens, A. N., Morris, P. G., Iles, R. A., Sheldon, P. W., and Griffiths, J. R. (1984). 5-Fluorouracil metabolism monitored *in vivo* by ^{19}F NMR. *Br. J. Cancer* **50,** 113–117.

Wolf, W., Albright, M. J., and Silver, M. S. (1987). Fluorine-19 NMR spectroscopic studies of the metabolism of 5-fluorouracil in the liver of patients undergoing chemotherapy. *Magn. Reson. Imag.* **5,** 165–169.

Malignant Mesothelioma

Conrad B. Falkson
McMaster University

Geoffrey Falkson
University of Pretoria

GLOSSARY

adjuvant therapy A second treatment modality used after a potentially curative treatment in an attempt to cure micrometastatic disease.

asbestos A fibrous amphibole used for making fireproof articles.

chemotherapy The treatment of cancers with chemicals or drugs (may be divided into cytostatic, hormonal, and immunotherapy).

cytostatic therapy Therapy aimed at killing cells rather than just stopping their growth.

Gy (Gray) The SI unit for absorbed dose of ionizing radiation (1 Gy = 1 J/kg).

immunotherapy Utilizing biological response modifiers to change the host immune response to the cancer.

intracavitary Into a body cavity, e.g., pleural or peritoneal cavities.

mesothelioma A malignant growth arising from mesothelial cells lining the chest (pleural) and abdominal (peritoneal) cavities.

peritoneum The serous membrane lining the abdominal cavity and covering the abdominal viscera.

pleura The serous membrane, which covers the lungs and lines the inside of the thoracic (chest) cavity.

pneumonectomy Complete or partial surgical removal of lung tissue.

radiation therapy/radiotherapy The treatment of patients with ionizing radiation.

Malignant mesothelioma (MM) shows an increasing incidence due to the, until recently, widespread use of asbestos. Electron microscopy is a prerequisite for confirmation of the diagnosis. CT and MRI are essential for staging, which is prognostic. Surgery is indicated for patients with stage I disease. For patients with more advanced disease, the role of both cytostatic and radiation treatment remains to be defined.

I. HISTORY AND ETIOLOGY

Malignant pleural mesothelioma as a distinct entity, associated with asbestos exposure, was defined by Chris Wagner in 1960. Following the description of MM in mine workers and those living near the asbestos mines in South Africa, the disease was described in workers in the shipping industry in the United Kingdom and miners in Canada. Women working with asbestos in factories in the United Kingdom were subsequently shown to have a higher incidence of peritoneal mesothelioma.

In contrast to the asbestosis, associated with heavy asbestos, exposure malignant mesothelioma was shown to occur with lesser exposure and an induction period of 20 or more years. The New Jersey experience of exposure to asbestos in shipyards during World War II delineated this clearly and also showed that the wives of men working with asbestos later also had an increased risk for mesothelioma. Until recently, asbestos was used in insulation and ceilings in most large buildings, including school buildings. With the demolition of these buildings, the asbestos fiber count in the air has continued to rise in most large cities, especially in North America.

Although MM was first described following exposure to crocidilite, it was subsequently shown to follow exposure to amosite and chrysotile asbestos.

II. DIAGNOSIS

A. Clinical Presentation

The diagnosis should be suspected in people exposed to asbestos, including boilermakers and builders. In patients with pleural MM, the first symptoms are usually related to a pleural effusion, namely chest pain and shortness of breath. The radiological features of malignant pleural mesothelioma classically show pleural effusion and pleural thickening. CT and/or MRI scanning is essential for staging of the disease, especially as cardiophrenic angle and pericardial involvement are important. Primary malignant peritoneal mesothelioma can be misdiagnosed as ovarian carcinoma.

B. Staging

The staging currently in use is that of Butchart (see Table I). The International Mesothelioma Interest Group proposed a new TNM staging system in 1995 but this has not been universally accepted. Staging is necessary for treatment options and is of prognostic significance. The importance of other patient discriminants, such as performance status, age, and histological subtype, also play a role.

C. Histological Confirmation

The diagnosis of MM requires pathological confirmation. Although the radiological appearance, including asbestos plaques, is often suggestive of the diagnosis, the finite diagnosis requires enough tissue for electron microscopic confirmation. The histological pattern may be epithelial, mesenchymal, or mixed. There is some evidence that the epithelial subtype is associated with a better prognosis.

III. TREATMENT

Despite some advances in the treatment of MM, the prognosis is mainly related to the stage of the disease.

TABLE I
Butchart Staging System

Stage	Description
I	Tumor confined within the capsule of the parietal pleura, involving only ipsilateral pleura, lung, pericardium, and diaphragm
II	Tumor invading chest wall or involving mediastinal structures such as esophagus, heart, and opposite pleura
III	Tumor penetrating diaphragm to involve peritoneum; involvement of opposite pleura
	Lymph node involvement outside the chest
IV	Distant blood-borne metastases

From E. G. Butchart *et al.* (1976). *Thorax* **31**, 15, BMJ Publishing Group, with permission.

A. Surgery

Radical surgery is indicated in patients with stage I disease. The usual technique is extrapleural pneumonectomy. Long-term survival is documented in patients who successfully undergo resection with clear margins and have no nodal involvement. There is currently no evidence that patients with more advanced disease or peritoneal disease benefit from radical surgery.

Pleurectomy and decortication may be employed to give relief from symptoms of tumor mass, pain, and recurrent pleural effusions. An open technique is generally preferred to an endoscopic approach.

B. Radiation Therapy

The definitive role of irradiation is uncertain, as there have not been any prospectively randomized trials reported. The variability of the clinical course and combination with other treatment modalities make assessment of the value of radiation difficult.

External beam radiation may be used to palliate symptoms of dyspnoea and pain. Irradiation of the entire hemithorax is indicated, and this large target volume prevents the administration of tumoricidal doses, as lung, cardiac, and spinal cord tolerances are likely to be exceeded. The total dose required to achieve symptom palliation is greater than 40 Gy at 2 Gy/#. It has been suggested that fraction size >4 Gy is more effective in achieving symptom relief and that 20 Gy/5#/1 week is a feasible regimen. Treatment techniques that have been employed are anterior–posterior/posterior–anterior, rotational arcs, and photon–electron combination. Instillation of radioactive colloids (^{198}Au and ^{32}P) into the pleural cavity may help control reaccumulation of a pleural effusion. These isotopes have also been used intraperitoneally to control ascites.

C. Chemotherapy

A wide range of cytostatic agents have been investigated, mainly in phase II studies, without any consistent evidence of response rates above 20% and no evidence of increased survival time. In the few randomized trials reported, no evidence has been shown that either single agents or cytostatic combinations are of value. The intergroup randomized study

combing doxorubicin with cyclophosphamide with or without dacarbazine (DTIC) found a response rate of 7% for each arm. In a randomized study of cisplatinum plus mitomycin C versus cisplatinum plus doxorubicin, the objective response rate (13%) in patients with measurable disease was similar in both arms. It has been shown in several phase II studies (CALGB 2001, EORTC 1999) that gemcitabine and irinotecan have little if any activity.

Several phase II studies have been conducted using biological response modifiers. Mulerato and colleagues (2001) reported a series in which they treated patients with intravenous and subcutaneous recombinant interleukin-2. They concluded that the treatment was well tolerated but showed a partial response in only 2 out of 29 patients (7%), whereas 11 patients are reported to have had stable disease with a median survival of 8.6 months. The Gustave Roussy Institute (2000) reported response rates ranging from 15 to 40% when they reviewed their experience using chemoimmunotherapy (cisplatinum and interferon-α), but are currently conducting a phase II study evaluating the combination of ralitrexed and oxaliplatin, which showed a 35% partial response in their phase I study.

Intracavitary administration of various cytostatic agents and interferons, as well as substances such as formalin, have been tried during the last three decades. There is no evidence that this approach is of value except as pleurodesis for pleural effusion.

D. Combined Modality Therapy

1. Adjuvant Therapy after Surgical Resection

Until such time as randomized trials are done, no conclusions can be drawn about the value of adding adjuvant cytostatic treatment or radiation therapy following surgery.

2. Combined Chemotherapy and Radiotherapy

A small number of phase II studies have reported encouraging results. A study of procarbazine plus radiation reported in the 1970s showed an increased objective response rate. Patients treated with doxorubicin and radiation (10 Gy every 6 weeks for four courses) showed a longer than expected median survival time. Results of the intergroup study (ECOG, RTOG, SECSG, SWOG) testing the role of radiotherapy with and without subsequent doxorubicin are still outstanding.

IV. CONCLUSION

Except for an established role for surgery in stage I malignant pleural mesothelioma, the role of radiation therapy and cytostatic treatment, as well as that of combined modality therapy, remains investigational. Among patients with advanced disease who cannot be referred to an academic center, doxorubicin can be used with an expected low response rate. Palliation of short duration may be achieved with radiation.

See Also the Following Articles

CHEMICAL MUTAGENESIS AND CARCINOGENESIS • CHEMOTHERAPY: SYNERGISM AND ANTAGONISM • RADIOBIOLOGY, PRINCIPLES OF

Bibliography

Antman, K. H., Pass, H. P., and Schiff, P. B. (1997). Benign and malignant mesothelioma. *In* "Cancer: Principles and Practice of Oncology" (V. T. De Vita, S. Hellman, and S. A. Rosenberg, eds.), 5th Ed., pp. 1853–1878. Lippincott-Raven, Philadelphia.

Bissett, D., Macbeth, F. R., and Cram, I. (1991). The role of palliative radiotherapy in malignant mesothelioma. *Clin. Oncol.* 3(6), 315–317.

Chahinian, A. P. (1993). Malignant mesothelioma. *In* "Cancer Medicine" (J. F. Holland *et al.*, eds.), 3rd Ed., pp. 1337–1355. Lea & Febiger, Philadelphia.

Sugarbaker, D. J., and Body, S. C. (1994). Technique of pleural pneumonectomy in diffuse mesothelioma. *In* "General Thoracic Surgery" (T. W. Shields, ed.), 4th Ed., pp. 749–756. Lea & Febiger, Philadelphia.

Sugarbaker, D. J., Jaklitsch, M. T., Soutter, A. D., Aisner, J., and Antman, K. (1995). Multimodality therapy of malignant mesothelioma. *In* "Thoracic Oncology" (J. A. Roth, J. C. Ruckdeschel, and T. H. Weisenburger, eds.), 2nd Ed., pp. 538–555. Saunders, Philadelphia.

Watson, D. C. T. (1995). Mesothelioma. *In* "Oxford Textbook of Oncology" (M. Peckham, H. M. Pinedo, and U. Veronesi, eds.), pp. 1557–1562. Oxford Univ. Press, Oxford.

MAP Kinase Modules in Signaling

Elaine A. Elion

Harvard Medical School

GLOSSARY

adaptor proteins A protein that contains no intrinsic enzymatic activity, but does contain multiple protein–protein interaction domains.

kinase Any enzyme that transfers a phosphate group from a nucleoside triphosphate to another molecule.

mitogen-activated protein Originally identified as a protein associated with microtubules that becomes tyrosine phosphorylated upon mitogen stimulation.

signal transduction A series of ordered biochemical reactions by which a signal initiated at the cell surface is transmitted inside the cell to elicit specific cellular responses.

$\mathbf{A}$ll eukaryotic cells utilize multiple mitogen-activated protein kinase (MAPK) cascades to respond to a wide variety of external stimuli that regulate proliferation, differentiation, survival, and response to stress. MAPK cascades form the central core of larger signal transduction cascades that lead to the phosphorylation of a variety of effector proteins, including many nuclear transcription factors. MAPK cascades can function both downstream and upstream of oncoproteins and anti-oncoproteins, and the status of

MAPK cascades can have profound effects on the decision of a eukaryotic cell to either terminally differentiate or divide. This article defines the MAPK module and discusses the dictates of pathway specificity at the level of interactions between kinases with a module, MAPKs, and their substrates, as well as the role of key scaffold proteins, localization and cellular architecture, and signal strength. Finally, this article discusses links between MAPK cascades and known regulators of tumorigenesis.

I. SIGNAL TRANSDUCTION AND MITOGEN-ACTIVATED PROTEIN KINASE (MAPK) CASCADES

All eukaryotic cells utilize signal transduction networks to respond in specific ways to a plethora of stimuli from their external environment. The term transduction originates from the Latin root *duce*, which means to lead. Literally, signal transduction is the mechanism by which a cell leads an external signal through a cell, transforming it biochemically into a series of discrete entities with specific biochemical properties. The first recognized example of a signal transduction cascade was the demonstration that adrenalin/epinephrine induces the synthesis of a second messenger, cAMP, which activates protein kinase A to directly regulate the activity of enzymes involved in the generation of metabolic energy required for the fight, flight, and flee responses. Today, signal transduction is more generally defined as any situation in which a cell must respond to an external stimulus. In human cells, these external stimuli are wide-ranging and include hormones, growth factors, cytokines, nutrients, and mechanophysical changes, in addition to a wide variety of stressful stimuli, such as UV. The physiological responses to these external stimuli are equally wide-ranging and include differentiation and development, morphogenesis, alterations in the proliferative state of a cell, changes in metabolism, and apoptosis. Common features shared by many signal transduction pathways include ligand-induced activation of a cell surface receptor that is coupled directly or indirectly to a G protein, either monomeric or heterotrimeric, followed by serial activation of a set of protein kinases that directly phosphorylate target pro-

teins involved in the particular cellular response. Additional signal transduction enzymes that regulate pathway activity include G protein regulators [i.e., guanine exchange factors (GEFs) and GTPase-activating proteins (GAPs)], protein phosphatases, and a variety of adapter molecules mediate specific interactions among signal transduction components, their substrate targets, and cellular locale.

Mitogen-activated protein kinase cascades often form the central core of these signal transduction networks. MAPKs are known to participate in a diverse array of cellular responses, including proliferation, differentiation and development, morphogenesis and cell movement, apoptosis, and survival from stress. MAPKs phosphorylate many different effector proteins, including many transcription factors in the nucleus and a variety of signal transduction enzymes. The emerging theme of signal transduction through MAPK cascades is that these pathways often form higher order molecular assemblies within cells and that spacial organization may play a critical role in mediating efficient activation and specificity.

II. DEFINITION OF A MAPK MODULE

MAPKs were originally identified through biochemical searches for serine/threonine protein kinases stimulated by growth factors and in genetic screens for mutations that affect growth and differentiation in yeast, worms, and flies. The core elements of a MAPK cascade module are three sequentially activated protein kinases, named after the last kinase in the series [i.e., MAPKK kinase (MKKK) → MAPK kinase (MKK) → MAPK, Fig. 1A]. MAPK modules are conserved throughout evolution, with remarkably high conservation beween MAPK modules in humans and yeast. MAPKs and their MKK activator kinases (also termed MEKs) are quite homologous within their respective subgroups, whereas MKKKs include at least four subtypes: Raf, MEKK, mixed lineage kinases (or MLKs), and Mos. A third upstream activating kinase (a putative MKKKK) is thought to activate the uppermost kinase (the MKKK) in a number of MAPK cascades. This third upstream activating kinase includes at least two subtypes: Ste20/p21-activated ki-

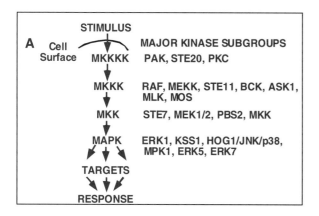

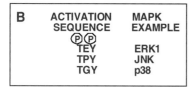

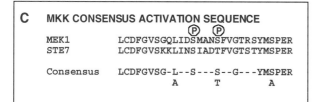

FIGURE 1 The MAPK module. (A) Features of a MAPK module. (B) MAPK signature activation sequences that are phosphorylated. (C) MKK consensus activation sequences known to be phosphorylated in MEK1 and Ste7.

nases (PAK) and protein kinase C (Figs. 1A, 2, and 3). Biochemical and genetic data support a series of direct phosphorylation events within the three-tier MAPK module, leading to serial activation of the MKK and MAPK tiers. Genetic and biochemical studies in yeast also support a direct activation mechanism for the MKKK tier.

The activation mechanism for MAPKs is highly conserved. All MAPKs are activated by the phosphorylation of both threonine and tyrosine residues within the activation (or T) loop at the catalytic cleft by the MKK, a dual specificity kinase. The threonine and tyrosine residues lie within a signature T-X-Y sequence that is characteristic for different MAPKs (Fig. 1B). MAPKs can also autophosphorylate on the tyrosine residue, but dual phosphorylation is required for full activation. Most MAPKs are thought to be tightly regulated and

activate only in the presence of an extracellular stimulus. However, there are exceptions to this rule. For example, *Saccharomyces cerevisiae* Mpk1 and Kss1 and mammalian ERK7 have basal activities in the absence of stimulus, and it is known that both Mpk1 and Kss1 perform specific cellular functions in the absence of an extracellular stimulus (Figs. 2 and 3).

Less is known about how the MKK and MKKK tiers of the MAPK cascade are activated. Work on the MKKs MEK1 and Ste7 argues that MKKs are activated by the dual phosphorylation of two serine and serine/threonine residues that fall within a conserved domain near what is predicted to be the activation loop (Fig. 1C). *In vitro* analysis suggests that phosphorylation of either site leads to some activation of the kinase; however, genetic analysis in *S. cerevisiae* suggests that both sites must be phosphorylated for function *in vivo*. MKKKs have a wide variety of signature protein interaction motifs built into their regulatory domains, including pleckstrin homology (PH) domains, proline-rich sequences for binding SH (Src homology) 3 domain, sites for binding G proteins, and dimerization domains. MKKKK Raf is thought to be activated through a complex process that involves its recruitement to Ras-GTP at the cell cortex in parallel with dimerization and association with 14-3-3 proteins. MKKK Ste11 is thought to be activated through derepression of an inhibitory N-terminal regulatory domain. Full activation of Ste11 is thought to involve both association of its N-terminal regulatory domain with a conserved protein called Ste50 and direct phosphorylation by MKKKK Ste20.

Eukaryotic cells have multiple MAPK cascades that can be activated by either one or more stimuli. In *S. cerevisiae*, seven MAPKs are known to exist, based on the sequence of the *S. cerevisiae* genome, and six of them have been placed into defined MAPK modules that form the cores of six distinct signal transduction pathways, based on functional analysis (Fig. 2). To date, 13 MAPKs have been identified in mammalian cells and they appear to fall into six families based on structural considerations (Fig. 3). Approximately 7 MKKs and 14 MKKKs have also been defined. Currently, biochemical analysis tentatively places mammalian MAPKs in a minimum of at least five pathways (Fig. 3); however, pathway definition is being further refined through functional analysis. Gene knockout studies in mice are underway to concretely

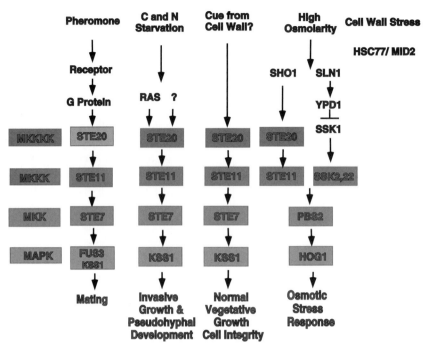

FIGURE 2 Summary of MAPK modules in S. *cerevisiae*.

define individual MAPK modules and their functions. For example, ERK1 appears to be required for thymocyte maturation in mice, whereas JNK2 is required for efficient T-cell activation and apoptosis. The phenotype of mouse MEKK1 disruption mutants is consistent with this kinase functioning upstream of both ERK and JNK kinases (Fig. 3). Functional redundancy between different MAPKs and their activators may make simple genetic analysis complex. For example, the yeast MAPK Kss1 has been shown to efficiently substitute for Fus3 during mating and to be more highly expressed in a *fus3Δ* null mutant. In addition, the potential utilization of the same MAPK cascades for embryonic development and adult tissue functions will also make functional analysis more difficult.

III. DICTATES OF SPECIFICITY IN MAPK MODULES

A major biological question is how specificity is achieved to assure that the appropriate response takes place in the presence of a particular stimulus. In *S. cerevisiae*, it is known that the individual MAPK

pathways exhibit exquisite specificity. This specificity is particularly surprising given that three of the pathways use subsets of the same kinases yet activate different effector proteins depending on the stimulus (Fig. 2). In mammalian cells, the level of complexity is even greater, with the combination of 13 MAPKs, 7 MKKs, and 14 MKKKs and evidence of functional redundancy between kinases at each tier of the module (Fig. 3). Pathway specificity appears to arise through multiple layers of control that include preferred kinase/kinase and kinase/substrate interactions, the use of scaffold or adapter-like proteins to route signals through specific MAPK modules, and cross-regulation between MAPK modules, as well as controlled localization of MAPKs and control of the strength of the activation.

A. Kinase/Kinase Interactions within the Module

Preferred interactions between different sets of kinases within a module explains one level of pathway specificity. For example, the yeast MKK Ste7 preferentially binds to and activates MAPKs Fus3 and Kss1

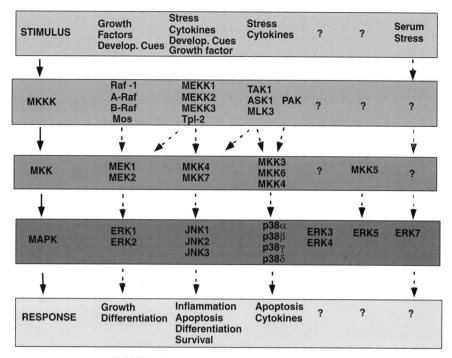

FIGURE 3   Summary of mammalian MAPK modules.

of the mating and vegetative growth and invasive growth/pseudohyphal development pathways, but does not bind to or activate MAPKs Mpk1 or Hog1 of the protein kinase C or high osmolarity growth pathways, and *ste7Δ* null mutants only have defects in mating and invasive growth/pseudohyphal development (Fig. 2). Similarly, members of the Raf family specifically bind to and activate MEK MAPKKs but not MKK MAPKKs in the stress pathway by recognizing a proline-rich sequence that is specific to the MEKs. Likewise, MKK JNKK1 makes specific interactions with MKKK MEKK1 and MAPK JNK1, and MAPK JNK2 is activated in a module that makes specific interactions between MKKK MEKK2 and MKK JNKK2. The interaction of some MAPKs with regulatory kinases is mediated by a conserved carboxyl-terminal docking site termed the CD domain that is composed of negatively charged residues.

B. MAPK/Substrate Interactions

Functional analysis in yeast demonstrates that MAPK cascade specificity is enhanced through the use of different MAPKs that preferentially recognize specific substrates. For example, the mating, invasive growth/pseudohyphal development and high osmolarity growth pathways utilize some of the same upstream MAPK module components (i.e., MKKKK Ste20, MKKK Ste11, and MKK Ste7), yet elicit very different responses through the use of different MAPKs (Fig. 2).

MAPKs are proline-dependent kinases that typically phosphorylate a serine or threonine adjacent to a proline (S/TP), often with a proline at the -2 position (PXS/TP). Nevertheless, significant selectivity is still found to occur even among S/TP or PXS/TP sites within the same substrate, and MAPKs display specific preferences to different substrates both *in vitro* and *in vivo*. Distinct sequences within individual MAPKs determine substrate preferences. For example, JNK2 binds c-Jun 25 times more efficiently than 83% identical JNK1. The structural basis for this difference maps to a small β-strand-like region near the catalytic pocket of the enzyme. In addition, effective MAPK substrates contain MAPK docking sites distinct from the phosphoacceptor site. For example, ERK and JNK kinases bind to a similar δ domain or D box, whereas p38 MAPKs recognize another D box.

ERK substrates can contain another specific docking site, called the FXFP sequence. Substrates and kinases may contain multiple docking sites that function independently or in combination, and these sites may be conserved among protein families. Finally, heterodimerization of substrates can also affect their ability to be recognized by different MAPKs. For example, poor JNK substrates such as JunD can be phosphorylated by JNK through heterodimerization with competent docking partners.

MAPKs can form stable complexes with their targets, either as active or as inactive kinases, suggesting that such complexes may play a regulatory role. For example, in nonstressed cells, catalytically inactive JNK has been shown to bind to a variety of transcription factors, including p53, c-Jun, JunB, and AFT2, and target them for destruction by a ubiquitin-dependent proteasome pathway. The functional importance of catalytically inactive MAPK/substrate complexes has been demonstrated in yeast. Genetic analysis indicates that the MAPK Kss1 of the invasive growth/pseudohyphal development pathways provides positive functions in its activated form and inhibitory functions in its catalytically inactive form with respect to activation of a Ste12/Tec1 heterodimeric transcription factor (Fig. 4A). In the absence of stimulus, inactive Kss1 binds to Ste12 and inhibits transcriptional activity of the Ste12/Tec1 dimer. In the presence of stimulus, Kss1 is phosphorylated and converted to an active form that is released from inhibitory binding and which phosphorylates and activates the Ste12/Tec1 dimer. The fact that the same MAPK provides both negative and positive functions for signaling means that a *kss1* null mutation does not block signaling, whereas catalytically inactive Kss1 derivatives do. These findings are significant in light of anticipated efforts to assign function to any MAPK and argue that it is important to analyze catalytically inactive kinase mutations in addition to null mutations.

C. Adaptor Proteins

The existence of specific kinase/kinase and kinase/substrate interactions does not explain pathway specificity in MAPK cascades that utilize shared components that respond to multiple stimuli and perform

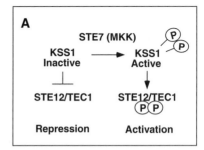

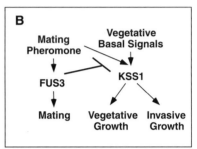

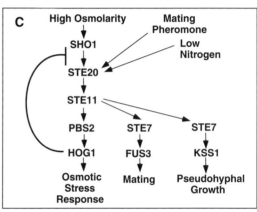

FIGURE 4 MAPKs are specificity factors. (A) Catalytically inactive Kss1 binds to and represses the Ste12/Tec1 transcription factor. (B) Fus3 blocks both pheromone-induced and basal activation of Kss1 in the vegetative growth and invasive growth pathways. Hog1 prevents misactivation of Fus3 and Kss1.

different readouts. A variety of biochemical and genetic evidence suggests that simple activation of the kinases that constitute a MAPK module may not be sufficient for function *in vivo* and that scaffold proteins play key roles in maintaining MAPK pathway function and fidelity by linking individual components to each other, to upstream activators, downstream targets, and specific cellular locales (Fig. 5).

Many of our ideas about scaffolds are based on work on the prototype MAPK scaffold Ste5 of the yeast mating pathway (Fig. 5). Criteria for assigning a scaf-

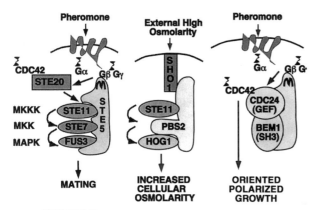

FIGURE 5 *S. cerevisiae* analogs of the Ste5 scaffold.

fold function to Ste5 included defining separable binding sites for each of the three tiers of protein kinases (i.e., Ste11, Ste7, and Fus3/Kss1), biochemical evidence for simultaneous binding of the kinases to Ste5 in a high molecular weight complex that requires the presence of Ste5 for its existence, and biochemical and genetic evidence that Ste5 promotes Ste11/Ste7 interactions and increases the specific activity of MAPK Fus3. Formation of the active complex requires oligomerization of Ste5, possibly as a dimer. Ste5 also plays a direct role in the initial activation of MKKKK Ste11 by MKKKK Ste20 (Fig. 4). Ste20 is normally associated with the Rho-type G protein Cdc42 at the cell cortex and Ste11 must be properly targeted to Ste20 for activation to take place. This function is tied to the proper recruitment of Ste5 to GβGγ dimers at the plasma membrane, which also bind to Ste20 in the presence of the signal mating pheromone. The route of Ste5 to the plasma membrane is circuitous and requires prior shuttling through the nucleus, raising the possibility that nuclear transit imparts a modification that makes Ste5 competent

to bind to Gβ, in addition to other as yet undefined functions.

A growing number of putative MAPK cascade scaffolds are being described (Figs. 5 and 6). Proteins that fall into the same category as Ste5 in terms of binding multiple kinases within a MAPK module include c-jun N-terminal kinase (JNK) interacting protein JIP-1 and structurally related family members (e.g., JIP2) and JNK/SAPK (stress-activated protein kinase) activating protein 1 (JSAP). The kinase suppressor of Ras (KSR) protein may also serve a scaffold function that links components of the Ras/Raf pathway and provides both stimulatory and inhibitory roles. MAPK kinase (MEK) partner 1 (MP1) appears to play an adapter function that links MAPKK MEK1/2 to MAPK ERK1/2 MAPK and enhances the activation of ERK1/2 by Raf. Dimeric 14-3-3 proteins may also play an adapter function to link Raf-1 to other kinases, such as MEKK1 or MEKK2. In addition, regulatory domains of MAPK cascade enzymes may also play a scaffold function in coordinating the different kinases within a MAPK module. Two candidates include Pbs2, the MAPKK of the yeast high osmolarity growth pathway, and MEKK1, which may serve a scaffold function in the JNK pathway. Whereas Ste5, Pbs2, and Ksr1 were originally defined based on genetic analysis in model organisms, all of the mammalian scaffolds have been identified as proteins that physically interact with specific MAPK cascade enzymes through two hybrid analysis.

None of the scaffolds bear homology to each other, suggesting that they have evolved independently for the individual requirements of individual subsets of kinases and upstream activating events. Given the identification of several JIP1 homologues, it is interesting to speculate that JIP1, MP1, and JSAP1 represent

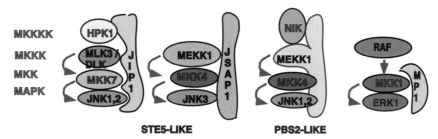

FIGURE 6 Mammalian MAPK cascade scaffolds.

founder members of families of related scaffold proteins with different functions for the same MAPK cascade in distinct cell types or different MAPK cascades within the same cell. Like Ste5, JIP1 and JIP2 oligomerize and concentrate at the cell periphery in cell projections in Rin5F insuloma cells. Moreover, one member of a family of human homologues of JIP1 has been shown to localize to the tips of neurites and to interact with p190 rhoGEF, which promotes cytoskeletal rearrangements in neuronal cells. These findings suggest that, like Ste5, JIP1 may function to specifically localize signaling complexes in differentiated cells.

Based on both theoretical and experimental analysis, it has been proposed that the multistep MAPK cascade allows for switch-like responses that are ultrasensitive. The existence of MAPK cascade scaffolds raises the important question of how they affect signal propogation. A three-tier MAPK cascade has built into it the capability of signal amplification; however, colocalization of kinases from each tier by a scaffold may prevent such amplification.

D. Localization

Specificity is also regulated by the proper localization of MAPKs. Much evidence argues that MAPKs are stably associated with the microtubule apparatus. For example, active forms of ERK1 copurify with tubulin and centromeric protein CENP-E at kinetochores, whereas JNK1 and its activator MLK2 localize to punctate structures along the microtubules. Many MAPKs translocate to the nucleus as a result of their activation in order to phosphorylate their transcription factor targets. Work on ERK1 suggests that MAPKs translocate to the nucleus through regulated processes and may be retained in the cytoplasm through interactions with a cognate MAPKK, which may also shuttle. Phosphorylation of the T-loop threonine and tyrosine has been shown to greatly enhance the nuclear translocation of ERK1 and Hog1. Work on several MAPKs (i.e., ERK2, ERK1, p38, and JNK) suggests that phosphorylation causes homodimerization and that this event may be part of the recognition process for the nuclear translocation of several MAP kinases and a property common to all MAPKs. Nuclear translocation may result in colocalization of the MAPK with inhibitory phosphatases, in addition to transcription factor targets.

E. Signal Strength/Attenuation Mechanisms

The duration and strength of activation of a given MAPK cascade may also affect the ultimate outcome of a response. For example, transient activation of the Ras/Raf/ERK pathway by the epidermal growth factor in PC12 cells causes cell proliferation, whereas sustained activation of the same pathway by the nerve growth factor causes terminal differentiation as shown by neurite outgrowth. Multiple factors can regulate the duration of activation of a MAPK cascade. MAPKs are directly downregulated by a variety of phosphatases, including a group of dual specificity Ser/Thr/Tyr phosphatases called MAP kinase phosphatases that may form stable associations with their target MAPKs. MAPKs may be downregulated through inhibitory associations with MAPKKs from different pathways. SEK1/MKK4, a MAP kinase kinase proposed to activate SAPK/JNK, is a potent inhibitor of SAPK β/JNK3. Attenuation factors such as the MPKs themselves can be induced by the MAPK. In addition, MAPKs may attenuate the activity of upstream signaling components through direct phosphorylation.

F. Signal Strength and Cellular Architecture

The strength and nature of the MAPK cascade activation process are dependent on proper cellular architecture. Regulators of the actin cytoskeleton, such as the Rho family member Cdc42 and SH3 domain morphogenesis protein Bem1, have been demonstrated to modulate the activity of the *S. cerevisiae* mating and invasive growth/pseudohyphal development MAPK cascades and the *S. pombe* mating pathway. Cytoskeletal components are required for efficient growth factor signaling, and the Rho family member Cdc42, whose activity is regulated by integrins, is thought to upreglate the activity of the ERK pathway (Fig. 7).

G. Cross-Regulation

Cross-regulatory inputs from other signal transduction cascades may affect the overall activity of a given MAPK cascade to be activated by a given stimulus. For example, cAMP may affect which Raf isoform

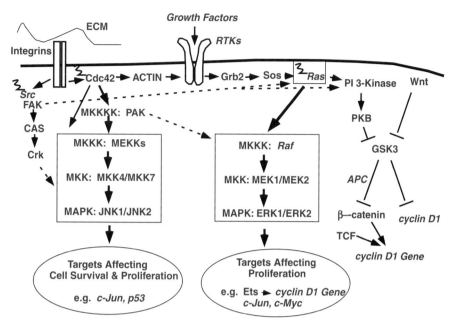

FIGURE 7 Signal transduction relationships among oncoproteins, antioncoproteins, and MAPK cascades. Oncoproteins and antioncoproteins are italicized.

can be activated by Ras. Another level of specificity is the ability of one MAPK cascade to cross-regulate another MAPK cascade in order to prevent misactivation. The mating MAPK Fus3 inhibits the activity of both the invasive growth/pseudohyphal development and vegetative growth pathways (Fig. 4B). This inhibition does not require Fus3 catalytic activity and it prevents inappropriate hyperactivation by the mating pathway stimulus. Likewise, osmoregulatory pathway MAPK Hog1 inhibits the mating MAPK cascade in both the absence and the presence of a high osmolarity stimulus (Fig. 4C). This cross-regulation requires Hog1 kinase activity and has been speculated to involve attenuation of the upstream transmembrane receptor Sho1 to prevent chronic activation of MKKK Ste11, which could lead to misactivation of MKK Ste7.

IV. CANCER AND MAPK CASCADES

Cancer is caused by stepwise mutations in protooncogenes and tumour-suppressing genes that regulate proliferation, differentiation, and cell survival. Many oncogenes have been shown to encode upstream activators of MAPK cascades as well as downstream targets of the MAPKs (Fig. 7). Oncogenes that act as direct upstream activators of MAPK cascades include growth factor receptors (such as the EGF and HER), the Ras G protein, and protein kinases Raf and Mos. Oncogenes may also indirectly affect the ability of MAPK cascades to be activated by normal stimuli, as is suggested by work on the Wnt-1 protooncogene. Direct links between oncogene-mediated activation of MAPK cascades and carcinogenesis is supported by the observation that gain-of-function point mutations in MEK-1, a direct kinase activator of a subset of MAPKs, induce cellular transformation. Cellular transformation has also been shown to be induced by gain-of-function mutations in specific MAPKs. Further support of a direct connection between MAPK cascades and oncogenesis comes from the identification of oncogene targets of MAPKs, such as the AP-1 transcription factor constituents c-Jun and c-fos, in addition to c-Myc and p53. Collectively, these findings argue strongly that MAPK cascade activation is involved in the action of many oncogenes. Thus, a detailed understanding of the players within a given MAPK cascade and the *in vivo* requirements for MAPK cascade activation, as well as the identification of *bona fide* substrates in relevant tissues, is of value in understanding cancer and providing potential routes for drug therapy. Because the role of Raf and the ERK MAP kinase cascade in Ras signaling and transformation is well established, drugs that inhibit this pathway are in preclinical development as potential anticancer therapies.

Current knowledge suggests that oncogenes and tumour-suppressing genes promote transformation through the activation of multiple signal transduction pathways that intersect and overlap in complex ways that involve direct or indirect inputs from MAPK cascades (Fig. 6). For example, Ras is known to activate multiple signal transduction pathways by binding multiple effector proteins that include PI-3-kinase, Ral GDS, and Raf, which cause widespread changes in gene expression that promote cell division and cell survival. The resulting activation of ERK1/ERK2 MAPKs by Raf leads to increases in the expression of key regulators of cell cycle progression, including p21, cyclin D1, HbEGF, and Fos, as well as genes that may affect cell motility and invasion and the amount of angiogenesis. Furthermore, the relative strength of activation of the ERK pathway can be a determinant in the decision to either proliferate or terminally differentiate.

The change to a tumorigenic state may also involve the suppression of apoptotic pathways. Some of the same genes that are upregulated by the Ras/Raf/ERK MAPK cascade appear to also be under the control of the Wnt pathway, which negatively regulates their expression through the inhibition of GSK3 and which is itself regulated by the adenomatous polyposis coli tumor suppressor (APC). Thus, the relative balance between these two counteracting events may also determine the proliferative state of a cell. Inactivation of APC causes the accumulation of β-catenin, which binds to and activates transcription factors of the T-cell factor (TCF)/lymphoid enhancer factor (LEF) family to induce the expression of a variety of genes, including cyclin D1, which is also regulated by the Raf/ERK pathway. Recently described connections between cell adhesion and MAPK cascade activation reveal additional layers of regulation that may be perturbed during carcinogenesis. This work supports a connection between integrins and G protein-coupled receptors that act upstream of MAPK cascades and raises the possibility that the normal cellular response to a mitogen may be dramatically altered by changes in cell adhesion.

Finally, entry into a tumorigenic state has been shown to correlate with genetic instability, a process that is controlled in part by the spindle checkpoint apparatus. p38 MAPKs are most closely related to the fission yeast Sty1 pathway, and work in this organism suggests a connection to cell cycle control at the G_2/M transition. Activation of p38 correlates with activation of the mammalian spindle assembly checkpoint, as well as increases in cyclin D1 expression. Connections among the JNK and p38 MAPK cascades, apoptosis, and cell cycle control raise the possibility that proper control of these pathways may also be important for determining the proliferative state of a cell.

Acknowledgments

This work was supported by a grant from the National Institutes of Health (GM46962).

See Also the Following Articles

Cell Cycle Control • c-myc Protooncogene • fos Oncogene • Ras Proteins • Signal Transduction Mechanisms Initiated by Receptor Tyrosine Kinases

Bibliography

Abe, M. K., Kuo, W. L., Hershenson, M. B., and Rosner, M. R. (1999). Extracellular signal-regulated kinase 7 (ERK7), a novel ERK with a C-terminal domain that regulates its activity, its cellular localization, and cell growth. *Mol. Cell. Biol.* **19,** 1301–1312.

Aplin, A. E., Howe, A. K., and Juliano, R. L. (1999). Cell adhesion molecules, signal transduction and cell growth. *Curr. Opin. Cell Biol.* **11,** 737–744.

Burack, W. R., and Shaw, A. S. (2000). Signal transduction: Hanging on a scaffold. *Curr. Opin. Cell Biol.* **12,** 211–216.

Caffrey, D. R., O'Neill, L. A. J., and Shields, D. C. (1999). The evolution of the MAP kinase pathways: Coduplication of interacting proteins leads to new signaling cascades. *J. Mol. Evol.* **49,** 567–582.

Cahill, D. P., Kinzler, K. W., Vogelstein, B., and Lengauer, C. (1999). Genetic instability and darwinian selection in tumors. *Trends Cell Biol.* **9,** M57–M60.

Cobb, M. H. (1999). MAP kinase pathways. *Progr. Biophys. Mol. Biol.* **71,** 479–500.

Cobb, M. H., and Goldsmith, E. J. (2000). Dimerization in MAP-kinase signaling. *Trends Biochem. Sci.* **25,** 7–9.

Elion, E. A. (1998). Routing MAP kinase cascades. *Science* **281,** 1625–1627.

Ferrell, J. E., and Machleder, E. M. (1998). The biochemical basis of an all-or-none cell fate switch in *Xenopus* oocytes. *Science* **280,** 895–898.

Garrington, T. P., and Johnson, G. L. (1999). Organization and regulation of mitogen-activated protein kinase signaling pathways. *Curr. Opin. Cell Biol.* **11,** 211–218.

Giancotti, F. G., and Ruoslahti, E. (1999). Transduction: Integrin signaling. *Science* **285,** 1028–1032.

Guan, K. L. (1994). The mitogen activated protein kinase signal transduction pathway from the cell surface to the nucleus. *Cell. Signal.* **6,** 581–589.

Gustin, M. C., Albertyn, J., Alexander, M., and Davenport, K. (1998). MAP kinase pathways in the yeast *Saccharomyces cerevisiae*. *Microbiol. Mol. Biol. Rev.* **62,** 1264–1300.

Ip, Y. T., and Davis, R. J. (1998). Signal transduction by the c-Jun N-terminal kinase (JNK)-from inflammation to development. *Curr. Opin. Cell Biol.* **10,** 205–219.

Jacobs, D., Glossip, D., Xing, H., Muslin, A. J., and Kornfeld, K. (1999). Multiple docking sites on substrate proteins form a modular system that mediates recognition by ERK MAP kinase. *Genes Dev.* **13,** 163–175.

Kallunki, T., Deng, T. L., Hibi, M., and Karin M. (1996) C-Jun can recruit JNK to phosphorylate dimerization partners via specific docking interactions. *Cell* **87,** 929–939.

Keyse, S. M. (2000). Protein phosphatases and the regulation of mitogen-activated protein kinase signalling. *Curr. Opin. Cell Biol.* **12,** 186–192.

Kieran, M. W., Katz, S., Vail, B., Zon, L. I., and Mayer B. J. (1999). Concentration-dependent positive and negative regulation of a MAP kinase by a MAP kinase kinase. *Oncogene* **18,** 6647–6657.

Lee, B. N., and Elion, E. A. (1999). The MAPKKK Ste11 regulates vegetative growth through a kinase cascade of shared signaling components. *Proc. Natl. Acad. Sci. USA* **96,** 12679–12684.

Madhani, H. D., and Fink, G. R. (1998). The riddle of MAP kinase signaling specificity. *Trends Genet.* **14,** 151–155.

Mahanty, S. K., Wang, Y., Farley, F. W., and Elion, E. A. (1999). Nuclear shuttling of yeast scaffold Ste5 is required for its recruitment to the plasma membrane and activation of the mating MAPK cascade. *Cell* **98,** 501–512.

Marshall, C. J. (1995). Specificity of receptor tyrosine kinase signaling: Transient versus sustained extracellular signal-regulated kinase activation. *Cell* **80,** 179–185.

McCormick, F. (1999). Signaling networks that cause cancer. *Trends Biochem. Sci.* **24,** M53–M56.

Meyer, D., Liu, A., and Margolis, B. (1999). Interaction of c-Jun amino-terminal kinase interacting protein-1 with p190 rhoGEF and its localization in differentiated neurons. *J. Biol. Chem.* **274,** 35113–35118.

Ono, K., and Han, J. (2000). The p38 signal transduction pathway: Activation and function. *Cell. Signal.* **12,** 1–13.

Pages, G., Guerin, S., Grall, D., Bonino, F. D., Smith, A., Anjuere, F., Auberger, P., and Pouyssegur, J. (1999). Defective thymocyte maturation in p44 MAP kinase (Erk 1) knockout mice. *Science* **286,** 1374–1377.

Pawson, T., and Scott, J. D. (1997). Signaling through scaffold, anchoring, and adaptor proteins. *Science* **278,** 2075–2080.

Sabapathy, K., Hu, Y. L. M., Kallunki, T., Schreiber, M., David, J. P., Jochum, W., Wagner, E. F., and Karin, M. (1999). JNK2 is required for efficient T-cell activation and apoptosis but not for normal lymphocyte development. *Curr. Biol.* **9,** 116–125.

Schaeffer, H. J., and Weber, M. J. (1999). Mitogen-activated protein kinases: Specific messages from ubiquitous messengers. *Mol. Cell. Biol.* **19,** 2435–2444.

Seger, R., and Krebs, E. G. (1995). The MAPK signaling cascade. *FASEB J.* **9,** 726–735.

Sprague, G. F., Jr. (1998). Control of MAP kinase signaling specificity or how not to go HOG wild. *Genes Dev.* **12,** 2817–2820.

Treisman, R. (1996). Regulation of transcription by MAP kinase cascades. *Curr. Opin. Cell Biol.* **8,** 205–215.

Tzivion, G., Luo, Z. J., and Avruch, J. (1998). A dimeric 14-3-3 protein is an essential cofactor for Raf kinase activity. *Nature* **394,** 88–92.

Widmann, C., Gibson, S., Jarpe, M. B., and Johnson, G. L. (1999). Mitogen-activated protein kinase: Conservation of a three-kinase module from yeast to human. *Physiol. Rev.* **79,** 1–35.

Xia, Y., Wu, Z., Su, B., Murray, B., and Karin, M. (1998) JNKK1 organizes a MAP kinase module through specific and sequential interactions with upstream and downstream components mediated by its amino-terminal extension. *Genes Dev.* **12,** 3369–3381.

Yasuda, J., Whitmarsh, A. J., Cavanagh, J., Sharma, M., and Davis, R. J. (1999). The JIP group of mitogen-activated protein kinase scaffold proteins. *Mol. Cell. Biol.* **19,** 7245–7254.

Melanoma: Biology

Kapaettu Satyamoorthy
Meenhard Herlyn

The Wistar Institute, Philadelphia, Pennsylvania

GLOSSARY

α helix One of the regular arrangements of amino acids in the proteins. It is a chain of 3.6 residues per turn with each carbonyl group hydrogen bonded at the C terminus to the fourth NH group of the chain.

angiogenesis The development of blood vessels in the embryo or during repair, healing, regeneration, or cancer.

autocrine Self-stimulation through the production of a factor by cells and expression of a specific receptor for it.

epigenetic Relating to or describing changes in the expression of genes due to prereplication or postreplication modification of the genome.

loss of heterozygosity The loss of one allele at a given locus in tumor cells compared to normal cells.

oncogene A gene product that can cause transformation of a normal cell to a cancer cell.

paracrine The release of an effector molecule into the intercellular space within the microenvironment of adjacent cells.

protooncogene The precursor of an oncogene caused by an alteration in the normal gene.

transcription Process by which DNA is converted to RNA.

Melanomas are found primarily in the skin and almost exclusively in white Caucasians. Tumors arise from pigment-producing melanocytes in the basal layer of the epidermis, spreading first radially and then vertically. Although the exact causes of melanoma are unknown, environment (including sunlight), immunological factors, and genetic abnormalities are implicated. A wide range of biologically relevant cellular abnormalities in melanoma are well established, such as growth factor overproduction for autocrine and paracrine stimulation, angiogenesis, adhesion, motility, and invasion. The expression of tumor-associated antigens combined with genetic heterogeneity results in extensive diversity in the malignant phenotype of melanomas.

I. INTRODUCTION

Melanocytes in the human skin represent an intriguing and intricate group of cells that impart skin color. Melanocytes are dendritic and separated from the dermis by the basement membrane. Although the number of melanocytes in various parts of the body varies, each melanocyte contacts about 20 to 30 keratinocytes through dendritic processes, thus forming the epidermal melanin unit. The dendritic processes are responsible for transferring the pigment melanin in granules to keratinocytes, thereby providing protection against damaging ultraviolet radiation. Studies of maturation, migration, and maintenance of melanocytes, which originate from the neural crest, have been the subject of considerable research in animal models. During development, melanocytes arise from pluripotent cells of the neural crest. Their survival, migration to the skin, and gradual commitment to maturation are related to the spatial and temporal expression of specific molecules, not only on the migrating cells, but also on juxtaposed other cell types and the extracellular matrix.

The worldwide incidence of melanoma is rising, with a projected 100,000 cases/year. In the United States, there are approximately 40,000 new cases reported each year, with a mortality rate of approximately 22% that accounts for 1.5% of all cancer deaths. Increasing information on cell cycle regulatory molecules has led to a gradual understanding of the mechanisms of transformation and progression to melanoma. This article outlines new findings in molecular and cellular abnormalities during melanoma progression with a special emphasis on growth-related genes.

II. GROWTH CHARACTERISTICS OF MELANOMA

Melanomas originate from melanocytes, which are highly specialized pigment-producing cells located in the basal layer of the epidermis (Fig. 1), the eye, and the inner ear. Differentiated melanocytes in the epidermis are subjected to homeostatic forces that inhibit melanocyte proliferation to maintain a constant melanocyte/keratinocyte ratio of about 1:30. Mela-

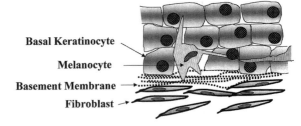

FIGURE 1   Schematic representation of human skin. Various components of human skin are shown with melanocytes situated at the basal layer of epidermis.

noma can develop in a sequence of steps from benign proliferative lesions. The lesions representing each step are common acquired nevus, dysplastic (atypical) nevus, radial growth phase primary melanoma, which does not metastasize, and vertical growth phase primary melanoma, which has metastatic competence, and metastatic melanoma. Figure 2 gives the characteristics that exemplify each step of melanoma progression.

Normal melanocytes and common acquired nevi differ in their proliferation rates and abilities to tolerate separation from keratinocytes. Common acquired nevi are clusters of pigmented cells that develop with further genetic and cytological abnormalities into dysplastic nevi or radial growth phase melanomas. Lesions that progress to the phase of vertical growth contain extensive chromosomal abnormalities and grow *in vitro* indefinitely and independently of most exogenous growth factors. To survive *in vivo* and acquire metastatic capabilities, these cells must gain the ability to degrade normal extracellular matrix proteins and to rearrange their cell surface adhesion molecules so that they can bind to their own secreted matrix proteins.

Metastases are the result of a complex process that is characterized by a sequence of steps that can be subdivided as detachment from the primary tumor followed by dermal invasion, intravasation into a vessel, circulation, stasis within a vessel, extravasation, invasion of the recipient tissue bed, and, ultimately, proliferation. In the metastatic cascade, at least three important categories of proteins are involved: growth factors, proteases, and adhesion molecules. Elucidation of the mechanisms by which these three categories of proteins regulate melanoma growth and

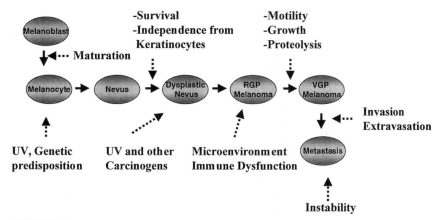

FIGURE 2 Experimental stages of human melanoma progression. Events responsible for melanoma progression are shown. Possible biological and genetic events that control melanoma progression during each step of progression are shown.

metastasis should lead to better therapeutic interventions. The outcome of metastasis depends on the interaction of metastatic cells with various host cells and factors. Organ-specific metastases to skin, lung, brain, liver, pancreas, intestine, and kidney have been demonstrated in melanoma and may even be specific to a particular site within one organ. This suggests that melanoma cells can recognize systemic and organ-specific physiologic signals.

III. BIOLOGY OF MELANOMA GROWTH FACTOR DEPENDENCE

Investigations into the roles of growth factors in tumor–stroma interactions have led to several key insights. This article focuses on three melanoma-derived growth factors that have stroma-inducing potential: basic fibroblast growth factor (bFGF), platelet-derived growth factor (PDGF), and vascular endothelial cell growth factor (EGF) (Fig. 3). bFGF and PDGF are expressed constitutively, i.e., without prior stimulation, by VGP primary and metastatic melanoma cells. bFGF, not VEGF and PDGF, is found already in nonmalignant nevi and RGP primary melanoma cells, but not in normal melanocytes. bFGF has autocrine stimulatory functions in melanoma and appears to act as a "stimulation factor" of melanocytic cells of all stages because its overexpression in normal melanocytes allows growth in serum-free media in the

absence of not only bFGF but also insulin/IGF-1. Whether melanoma-derived bFGF has paracrine functions and stimulates stromal fibroblasts and endothelial cells is unclear because the lack of a signal sequence does not allow protein secretion by conventional mechanisms. bFGF may be released from cells through alternate mechanisms, such as transport by the heparin-binding protein FGF-BP (FGF-binding protein), or it may act indirectly by activating the expression of VEGF. Thus bFGF, the "stimulation factor," appears to act in functional synergy with other melanoma-derived growth factors. The short 18-kDa isoform of bFGF that is more readily found in supernatants of cultured melanoma cells has major potential as a paracrine growth factor for stimulating fibroblasts and endothelial cells.

PDGF acts as a "maintenance and survival factor" in melanoma progression, i.e., PDGF helps the tumor to organize the stroma, including extracellular matrix (ECM) production. PDGF-B is secreted by melanoma cells only for paracrine stimulation, because unlike fibroblasts, melanoma cells lack the PDGF-β receptor. Those melanoma cells that are already tumorigenic grow more rapidly and at higher viability when overexpressing PDGF-β, but RGP melanomas cannot be induced to tumorigenicity when overexpressing it, suggesting that PDGF acts only in synergy with another growth factor(s). The ability of PDGF to induce angiogenesis on its own is limited; instead, PDGF induces VEGF, which, in turn, orchestrates angiogenesis.

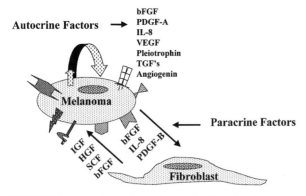

Autocrine Factors →

bFGF
PDGF-A
IL-8
VEGF
Pleiotrophin
TGF's
Angiogenin

Melanoma

← **Paracrine Factors**

IGF
HGF
SCF
bFGF

bFGF
IL-8
PDGF-B

Fibroblast

FIGURE 3 Autocrine and paracrine mechanisms of melanoma. Interaction of melanoma cells with stromal cells is shown. Cross talk between several growth factors secreted by either melanoma or fibroblasts responsible for autocrine and paracrine effect is shown.

For melanoma progression from RGP to VGP, VEGF appears important as an "expansion and invasion factor" because of its strong angiogenic properties. VEGF stimulates not only endothelial cell growth, but also their migration, invasion, and tube formation. VEGF is constitutively expressed by melanoma cells *in situ* is of advanced stages, particularly of larger lesions, whereas it plays a lesser role in small RGP melanomas, where the cells survive without a major need for new vascularization. Because VEGF expression is inducible by a variety of factors, such as PDGF, bFGF, interleukin (IL)-1, or tumor necrosis factor-α, or by hypoxic growth conditions, it is conceivable that expression during expansion of the tumor mass may be temporarily stimulated by any of these factors or combinations of factors. Thus, expression in lesions at the time of surgery may not reflect the biological significance of this growth factor

in melanoma. Because of the restrictive specificity of VEGF for endothelial cells, tumor growth cannot be sustained unless the tumor cells also attract and stimulate fibroblasts, which are the main source of extracellular matrix proteins.

Fibroblasts are a rich source of growth factors, but only after prior activation. When stimulated, e.g., by malignant cells, fibroblasts can produce several growth factors with mitogenic activity for melanoma cells, including insulin-like growth factor-1 (IGF-1). Melanoma cells apparently rely on IGF-1 secreted by fibroblasts because they do not produce it on their own. Other growth factors and cytokines produced by activated fibroblasts such as IL-6 show a gradient from growth inhibition of biologically early primary melanoma cells to growth stimulation of biologically late metastatic cells. IL-6, unlike IGF-1, is secreted by melanoma cells from advanced lesion. Activated endothelial cells also produce a variety of growth factors, but not much is known of endothelial cells as a source of melanoma stimulation. Of potential importance for melanomas are the endothelins because they are mitogenic for melanocytes but are not normally produced by these cells.

The mechanisms by which growth factors are able to induce melanoma growth, maintenance, survival, and expansion have become increasingly clear. Most of the receptors for growth factors are protein tyrosine kinases, which upon ligand binding are able to transduce signals through the cytoplasm into the nucleus (Fig. 4). Signal transduction is mediated by a number of adaptor and effector molecules through a cascade of phosphorylation reactions. Depending on the strength and duration of the signals, there is exten-

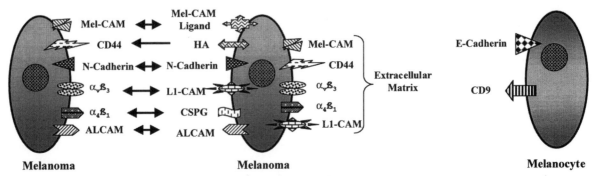

Melanoma   **Melanoma**   **Melanocyte**

Mel-CAM ⟷ Mel-CAM Ligand
CD44 ← HA
N-Cadherin ⟷ N-Cadherin
α$_v$β$_3$ ⟷ L1-CAM
α$_4$β$_1$ ⟷ CSPG
ALCAM ⟷ ALCAM

Mel-CAM
CD44
α$_v$β$_3$
α$_4$β$_1$
L1-CAM

} **Extracellular Matrix**

E-Cadherin

CD9

FIGURE 4 Schematic representation of cross talk between growth factor receptors and adhesion molecules in melanoma. Intracellular signaling responsible for growth advantage and those that mediate inhibition of apoptosis is indicated.

sive cross talk between the pathways that may decide the fate of the cell to a given stimulus.

IV. BIOLOGY OF MELANOMA CELL ADHESION MOLECULES

Expression of a number of cell surface molecules that mediate cell–cell interactions is associated with melanoma development. These molecules include members of the immunoglobulin gene superfamily proteins, such as melanocytic cell adhesion molecule (Mel-CAM) and intercellular cell adhesion molecule-1 (ICAM-1); integrins such as $\alpha_4\beta_1$ and $\alpha_v\beta_3$; and cadherins such as E-cadherin and N-cadherin. Mel-CAM is a cell–cell adhesion molecule whose expression increases during melanoma progression (Fig. 5). The β_3 integrin binds to several extracellular matrix proteins and is highly expressed in VGP and metastatic melanomas. Overexpression of the β_3 integrin in RGP melanomas can confer VGP phenotype in them, suggesting a role for this integrin in adhesion, migration, and invasion. Therefore, multiple

adhesive interactions are intertwined, rather than individual interactions, and play critical roles in modulating cell survival and growth.

Cadherins form a family of cell surface glycoproteins that function in promoting calcium-dependent cell–cell adhesion and serve as the transmembrane components of cell–cell adhesion. There are classical cadherins, such as E-, N-, and P-cadherin, and atypical cadherins, such as VE-cadherin. These are expressed in a cell-, tissue-, and development-specific manner. For example, E-cadherin is the major cadherin in polarized epithelial cells, whereas N-cadherin is expressed by nerve cells, myocytes, and fibroblasts. In vertebrates, cadherin molecules and cadherin–catenin complexes are involved during embryogenesis and morphogenesis in cell recognition, motility, tissue integrity, and homeostasis. There are strong links among cadherin-mediated cell–cell adhesion, growth factor receptor tyrosine kinases, and the WNT signaling pathway, which together form a complex network (Fig. 6). The organization of such a hierarchy of multiple components allows cadherins to function as cell adhesion machinery, as well as signaling receptors for intercellular and intracellular communication, resulting in the regulation of cell growth, differentiation, and apoptosis in both normal and malignant cells.

Loss of functional E-cadherin has been well documented from various human tumor systems. This may be due to inactivation by deletions, mutations, or silencing by methylation of the promoter. E-cadherin also plays an important role in melanoma development. Disruption of E-cadherin-mediated cell adhesion facilitates tumor invasion, whereas restoration of E-cadherin expression results in growth retardation and inhibition of the invasive and metastatic phenotype in human melanoma cells. Therefore, E-cadherin is considered a melanoma invasion suppressor gene. It has been demonstrated that E-cadherin is the major adhesion mediator between epidermal melanocytes and keratinocytes. Expression of E-cadherin itself has triggered interest in its role during melanoma progression. Melanocytes, but not nevus cells or melanoma cells, express E-cadherin. The loss of E-cadherin not only leads to loss of adhesion, but also to uncontrolled proliferation and progressive invasion. The melanocytic cells that do not express E-cadherin can now escape from neighboring

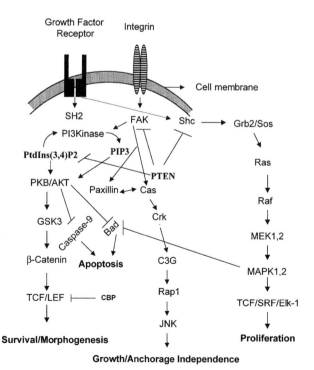

FIGURE 5   Molecules responsible for cell–cell and cell–matrix interactions in melanoma. Lack of expression of these molecules on normal melanocytes is also shown.

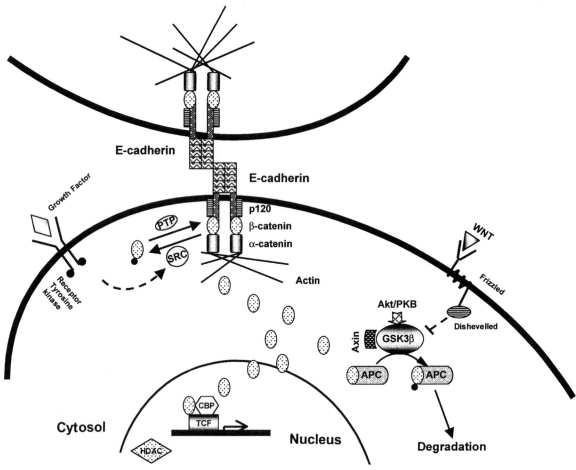

FIGURE 6 Interplay among cell–cell adhesion molecule, cadherin signaling, and Wnt signaling is shown. Wnt signaling synergizes with the cadherins to stabilize β-catenin to induce nuclear effects.

keratinocytes to invade the dermis. Our laboratory has shown that forced expression of E-cadherin by melanoma cells through gene transduction, followed by coculture with keratinocytes, has profound consequences on the phenotype of melanoma cells. E-cadherin-expressing melanoma cells can adhere to keratinocytes. After coculture with keratinocytes, the transduced melanoma cells no longer express invasion-related molecules such as $\alpha_v\beta_3$ or Mel-CAM and lose their invasive capacity. However, whether the signals between melanocytes or E-cadherin-expressing melanoma cells and keratinocytes are relayed directly through E-cadherin/E-cadherin adhesion or through other intercellular interactions such as gap junctional communication has yet to be demonstrated. It has been shown that the formation of functional gap junction communication between

two cells or cell types largely requires cadherin-mediated cell adhesion.

Despite the loss of E-cadherin expression by melanoma cells *in vitro* and *in vivo*, these cells compensate with high levels of expression of N-cadherin. This may lead to interaction with dermal fibroblasts or endothelial cells. This switch in partners may lead to an acquisition of new properties and may facilitate the development of aggressive properties.

V. CHROMOSOMAL ABNORMALITIES IN MELANOMA

Earlier studies have identified a large number of deletions, translocations, mutations, and amplifications on several chromosomes in melanoma. All chromosomal regions with gross abnormalities contain candidate oncogenes or tumor suppressor genes.

Several mutations, deletions, amplifications, and translocations involving chromosomes 1, 6, 7, 9, and 10 have been identified in melanomas. These regions may consist of genes that are necessary for the growth and survival of melanomas. Chromosome 1p may involve deletions and translocations, whereas chromosome 6q may contain rearrangements and breakpoints. Duplications of chromosome 7 have also been observed in melanomas. Chromosome 9p deletions are often found in melanoma-prone kindreds, and both cytogenetic and molecular analyses suggested the presence of a tumor suppressor locus on chromosome 9. After the initial identification of the 9p suppressor locus by Fountain and colleagues, loss of heterozygosity (LOH) at 9p21-24 was implicated in two populations of melanoma-prone families from Utah and Australia. Subsequently, several groups using markers close to the 9p21 locus showed that LOH at 9p21 is the hallmark of genetic predisposition to melanoma. Independently, Serrano and co-workers cloned a cell cycle regulator gene, now known as p16 (INK4a, MTS1, CDK4IN, CDKN2), which is located at 9p21 and is a tumor suppressor gene.

Initiation and completion of cell division are controlled by a group of molecules at specific checkpoints (Fig. 7). Cyclins are an integral part of these checkpoint molecules and are indispensable to cell cycle control. They form regulatory subunits with cyclin-dependent kinases (CDKs). A number of cyclin genes have been identified with varying expression patterns in different phases of the cell cycle. Levels of different cyclins are generally increased in proliferating cells. The homology between cyclins is often limited to a conserved domain of about 100 amino acids called the cyclin box, which is responsible for CDK binding and activation. D-type cyclins are closely linked to cell cycle progression at G_1 to S phase and remain active until mitosis. Three types of D cyclins (D1, D2, and D3) have been identified, which are products of separate genes on different chromosomes. Most cells express D3 and either D1 or D2. D cyclins can associate not only with CDKs, but also with the tumor suppressor protein Rb.

Cyclin-dependent kinases are a group of closely related molecules from 35 to 40 kDa in size with sequence homology of about 40%. Their activity is tightly controlled by additional regulatory mechanisms, but not all CDKs are involved in cell cycle regulation. CDKs are activated by binding to cyclins and by phosphorylation of a conserved threonine residue by a CDK-activating kinase. Each CDK interacts with a specific subset of cyclins, and cyclins may interact with several CDKs. For example, cyclin D1 can interact with either CDK4 or CDK6, whereas CDK2 can interact with both cyclin E and cyclin A. CDK levels are highest in proliferating cells, and CDK4 gene amplification has been observed in glioma cells. The mechanisms whereby CDKs bind to cyclins are still unclear.

Retinoblastoma protein levels are generally constant in cycling cells, but the degree of Rb phosphorylation changes dramatically during different phases of the cell cycle. Rb becomes highly phosphorylated during the G_1 to S transition, and phosphorylation decreases following mitosis as the cell return to G_1 phase (Fig. 7). In its hypophosphorylated form, Rb binds to the transcription factor E2F and activates transcription of several key DNA-synthesizing enzymes, including thymidine kinase, MYC, MYB, dihydrofolate reductase, and DNA polymerase α. Therefore, hypophosphorylated Rb inhibits cell cycle progression from G_1 to S phase by inactivating the E2F transcription factor. Rb and E2F-1 are the only known substrates for the cyclin D–CDK4 complex, and the phosphorylation of Rb is induced by the cyclin D–CDK4 complex.

p16 encodes a 16-kDa mammalian cell cycle regulator. p16 contain four ankyrin repeats, which are 32

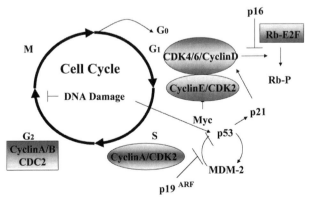

FIGURE 7 Cell cycle regulation by p53 and Rb. Various members of the RB and p53 pathway that interact with cyclin, CDKs, and CDKIs to regulate cell cycle are shown.

amino acid motifs present in a number of proteins of diverse functions, including transcription factors, enzymes, toxins, cell differentiation molecules, and structural proteins. The ankyrin repeats contain predicted central hydrophobic α helices and are functionally involved in protein–protein interactions. p16 inhibits the phosphorylation of Rb by the cyclin D–CDK4 complex by suppressing the enzymatic kinase activity of CDK4. Rb is therefore hypophosphorylated and is able to bind to the E2F transcription factor, which is thereby inhibited and unable to contribute to the cell cycle progression through G_1 to S phase. This is a potential molecular mechanism of tumor suppression. An alternative reading frame within the p16, called p14^{ARF}, has been found to interfere with p53-dependent deregulation mediated by mdm2. However, its importance in melanoma is unclear.

Analyses of cell cycle regulation have provided insight into the various mechanisms by which cells with aberrant growth characteristics survive in a hostile environment. In the context of melanomagenesis, the events that occur and are responsible for disease progression are increasingly being understood. The normal melanocyte becomes predisposed to tumor formation after undergoing various epigenetic insults (Fig. 2). Genetic predisposition is also a contributing factor, as not all individuals develop nevi. UV irradiation may represent the promoting event, either directly by damaging DNA or indirectly by inducing inflammatory responses, which in turn lead to DNA damage. Dysplastic nevi are persistent lesions. Whether p16 mutations or deletions already occur at this stage remains to be determined. Immortalization of cells is most likely associated with abnormalities in cell cycle checkpoints, either at one gene or at several. Finally, the progression of cells from the vertical growth phase, which represents tumorigenic cells, to metastasis occurs through a stepwise adaptation of cells to a different microenvironment, such as survival in blood vessels. Apparently, cells progressing from a vertical growth phase to metastatic dissemination do not require further genetic alterations.

Acknowledgment

Part of the studies were supported by Grant CA-25874 from the National Institutes of Health.

See Also the Following Articles

ANGIOGENESIS AND NATURAL ANGIOSTATIC AGENTS • AUTOCRINE AND PARACRINE GROWTH MECHANISMS IN CANCER PROGRESSION AND METASTASIS • CELL CYCLE CHECKPOINTS • MELANOMA: EPIDEMIOLOGY • PHOTODYNAMIC THERAPY: BASIC PRINCIPLES AND APPLICATIONS TO SKIN CANCER • SKIN CANCER • TUMOR ANTIGENS

Bibliography

Cannon-Albright, L. A., Goldgar, D. E., Meyer, L. J., Lewis, C. M., Anderson, D. E., Fountain, J. W., Hegi, M. E., Wiseman, R. W., Petty, E. M., Bale, A. E., Olopade, O. I., Diaz, M. O., Kwiatkowski, D. J., Peipkorn, M. W., Zone, J. J., and Skolnick, M. H. (1992). Assignment of a locus for familial melanoma, MLM, to chromosome 9p13-22. *Science* **258,** 1148.

Fountain, J. W., Karayiorgou, M., Ernstoff, M. S., Kirkwood, J. M., Vlock, D. R., Titus-Ernstoff, L., Bouchard, B., Vijayasarraadhi, S., Houghton, A. N., Lahti, J., Kidd, V. J., Housman, D. E., and Dracopoli, N. C. (1992). Homozygous deletions within human chromosome band 9p21 in Melanoma. *Proc. Natl. Acad. Sci. USA* **89,** 10557.

Herlyn, M. (1993). "Molecular Biology of Melanoma." R. G. Landes, Austin, TX.

Hsu, M.-Y., Meier, F., Nesbit, M., Hsu, J.-Y., and Herlyn, M. (2000). E-cadherin expression in melanoma cells restores keratinocyte-mediated growth control and downregulates expression of invasion-related adhesion receptors. *Am. J. Pathol.*

Hsu, M.-Y., Shih, D.-T., Meier, F. E., Van Belle, P., Hsu, J.-Y., Elder, D. E., Buck, C. A., and Herlyn, M. (1998). Adenoviral gene transfer of β3 integrin subunit induces conversion from radial to vertical growth phase in primary human melanoma. *Am. J. Pathol.* **153,** 1435.

Hunter, T., and Pines, J. (1994). Cyclins and cancer. II. Cyclin D and CDK inhibitors come of age. *Cell (Cambridge, Mass.)* **79,** 573.

Hussussian, C. J., Struewing, J. P., Goldstein, A. M., Higgins, P. A., Ally, D. S., Sheahan, M. D., Clark, W. H., Tucker, M. A., and Dracopoli, N. C. (1994). Germline p16 mutations in familial melanoma. *Nature Genet.* **8,** 15–21.

Kamb, A., Gruis, N. A., Weaver-Feldhaus, J., Liu, Q., Harshman, K., Tavtigian, S. V., Stockert, E., Day, R. S., Johnson, B. E., and Skolnick, M. H. (1994). A cell cycle regulator potentially involved in genesis of many types of cancer. *Science* **264,** 436–440.

Kamb, A., Shattuck-Eidens, D., Eles, R., Liu, Q., Gruis, N. A., Ding, D. W., Hussey, C., Tran, T., Miki, Y., Weaver-Feldhaus, J., *et al.* (1994). Analysis of the p16 gene (CDKN2) as a candidate for the chromosome 9p melanoma susceptibility locus. *Nature Genet.* **8,** 23–26.

Li, G., and Herlyn, M. (2000). Dynamics of intercellular communication during melanoma development. *Mol. Med. Today* **6,** 163.

Meier, F., Satyamoorthy, K., Nesbit, M., Hsu, M. Y., Schittek, B., Garbe, C., and Herlyn, M. (1999). Molecular events in melanoma development and progression. *Front. Biosci.* **15,** D1005.

Morgan, D. O. (1995). Principles of CDK regulation. *Nature (Lond.)* **374,** 131.

Nobori, T., Miura, K., Wu, D. J., Lois, A., Takabayashi, K., and Carson, D. A. (1994). Deletions of the cyclin-dependent kinase-4 inhibitor gene in multiple human cancers. *Nature* **368,** 753–756.

Nancarrow, D. J., Mann, G. J., Holland, E. A., Walker, G. J.,

Beaton, S. C., Walters, M. K., Luxford, C., Palmer, J. M., Donald, J. A., Weber, J. L., Fountain, J. W., Kefford, R. F., and Hayward, N. K. (1993). Confirmation of chromosome 9p linkage in familial melanoma. *Am. J. Hum. Genet.* **53,** 936.

Parmiter, A. H., and Nowell, P. C. (1993). Cytogenetics of melanocytic tumors. *J. Invest. Dermatol.* **100,** 254S.

Serrano, M., Hannon, G. J., and Beach, D. A. (1993). A new regulatory motif in cell cycle control causing specific inhibition of cyclin D/CDK4. *Nature (Lond.)* **366,** 704.

Sherr, C. J. (1994). G$_1$ phase progression: Cycling on cue. *Cell (Cambridge, Mass.)* **79,** 551.

Melanoma: Cellular and Molecular Abnormalities

Pamela M. Pollock

National Human Genome Research Institute
National Institutes of Health

GLOSSARY

extracellular matrix Composed of collagens, elastin, glycoproteins, and proteoglycans and stabilized by a variety of protein–protein and polysaccharide–protein interactions.

extravasation The process whereby tumor cells exit a blood or lymph vessel into the surrounding tissue.

intravasation The process whereby tumor cells enter the circulatory system via either the blood or lymph vessels.

loss of heterozygosity The loss of one allele at a given locus in tumor cells when compared to normal cells.

pathogenesis The origin and development of disease.

PTEN Phosphatase and tensin homologue on chromosome ten.

The incidence of melanoma is increasing in a number of countries, including the United States. Although in many cases this increase in incidence is associated with an increase in the diagnosis of early lesions, advanced melanoma still accounts for considerable morbidity and mortality. Like many cancers, a proportion of individuals (5–15%) report a family history of melanoma. It is hoped that the identification and characterization of the genes responsible for melanoma predisposition will lead to a greater understanding of the molecular events associated with sporadic melanoma. A vast inventory of cellular and molecular abnormalities associated with melanocyte transformation has been amassed and cannot be given justice in this article. The neoplastic transformation of a melanocyte to metastatic melanoma offers a valuable model for studying cell–cell and cell–matrix adhesion and communication and the importance of the extracellular matrix and stromal cells in tumorigenesis. In addition, several tumor suppressor pathways have been implicated in melanoma development. These include the p16/pRb pathway regulating entry into the cell cycle, the p14 ^{ARF}/p53 pathway detecting inappropriate oncogenic activation, and the PI3kinase/PTEN/AKT pathway regulating cell survival and proliferation. These signaling pathways play central roles in tumorigenesis in a wide range of tissues, and their continuing elucidation promises improved understanding of the molecular events underlying tumor initiation and progression.

I. INTRODUCTION

A model for melanoma progression has been proposed that involves a sequential progression from benign and dysplastic precursor lesions. It should be noted, however, that histological evidence for this linear progression of precursor lesions is only clearly observed in a subset of melanomas (Fig. 1). Although in many cases it is likely that the resultant tumor obliterates evidence of the precursor lesion, it is acknowledged that melanomas may also develop from appar-

ently normal melanocytes in apparently normal skin. Unlike some cancers, melanomas and their precursor lesions are easily removed and therefore available for study. In addition, the requirements for culturing melanocytes and melanocytic cells from all stages of tumor progression have been elucidated, enabling the phenotypic differences between these cell types to be cataloged. These phenotypic differences include differences in *in vitro* and *in vivo* growth characteristics, e.g., decreasing dependence on exogenous growth factors, increasing anchorage-independent growth in soft agar, and tumorigenicity in nude mice. In addition, there are dynamic changes in the expression of cell surface molecules, including those involved in cell–cell and cell–matrix adhesion and communication (Fig. 1).

As well as cataloguing the different "cellular" abnormalities associated with melanocytic transformation, several attempts have been made to catalog the molecular genetic aberrations associated with different stages of melanoma progression. A compilation of cytogenetic findings for >97 melanocytic lesions including a number of dysplastic nevi, has been performed. These compiled data have been corroborated in a single study reporting cytogenetic analysis of 126 regional and disseminated melanomas. A subset of the latter tumors, 49, demonstrated a near diploid karyotype, hence the alterations are thought to reflect

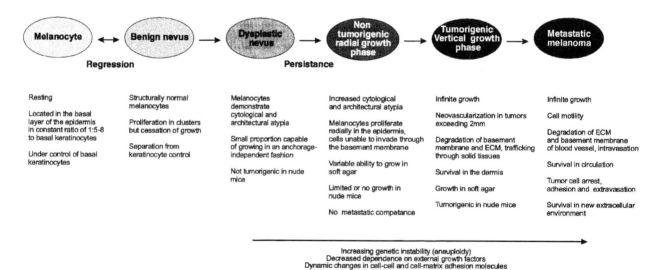

FIGURE 1   On the basis of histopathological data, five steps of melanoma pathogenesis have been proposed. A variety of phenotypic differences associated with each stage of progression are provided (adapted from data provided in Fidler, 1997; Nesbit *et al.*, 1997; Satyamoorthy *et al.*, 1997).

those that occur early in melanocyte transformation. Table I presents a summary of the five chromosomes most commonly rearranged in these latter studies. While loss of 1p, 6q, 9p, 10q, and 11q is common, aberration of chromosome 7 normally involves duplications, specifically the region 7p22-7q11.

The advent of polymorphic molecular markers has allowed genome-wide allelotype studies to identify chromosomal arms likely to encode important tumor suppressor genes (TSGs) and, more importantly, permitted the refined localization of chromosomal regions thought to harbor potential melanoma TSGs. Moreover, functional studies have confirmed that chromosomes 6, 9, and 11 carry potential melanoma TSGs. The CDKN2A gene, mapping to chromosome 9p21, has been shown to be important in melanoma susceptibility and somatic melanoma development. Approximately 50% of large multiaffected families demonstrate linkage to chromosome 9p21 and just under half of these families have been shown to carry germline mutations in CDKN2A. More recently, the PTEN gene, mapping to chromosome 10q23, has been shown to be inactivated in a subset of melanoma tumors. These genes are discussed in more detail later. It is of interest to note that strong evidence for a significant role in melanoma pathogenesis has yet to be demonstrated for any TSG or oncogene already mapped to chromosomes 1p, 6q, 7, and 11q. This article provides an overall framework of the cellular and molecular abnormalities associated with the neoplastic transformation of the melanocyte to metastatic melanoma.

II. MELANOCYTES

Cutaneous malignant melanoma results from the uncontrolled growth of melanocytes, located within the basal layer of the epidermis in the skin. Normal melanocytes are isolated from one another but are in contact with 5–8 basal keratinocytes. Each melanocyte produces melanin pigment in melanosome organelles and then transports these melanosomes through its dendritic extensions to the surrounding keratinocytes. The dendrites of one melanocyte can be in contact with as many as 32 keratinocytes, and this structure has been called the epidermal melanin unit. It is through the deposition of a light-absorbing barrier of melanin in the surrounding keratinocytes that melanocytes are thought to protect organisms from the direct DNA damage induced by ultraviolet (UV) radiation. In vitro studies have demonstrated that undifferentiated basal keratinocytes, present in the basal layer of the epidermis, can regulate various aspects of melanocyte growth, including the abundance of dendritic extensions and the expression of various cell surface molecules. When melanocytes are isolated and cultured in vitro, they assume bipolar or tripolar morphology and acquire the expression of a variety of melanoma-associated cell surface molecules (antigens). Upon coculturing with basal keratinocytes, the melanocytes assume a morphology resembling that in situ, i.e., they attach to keratinocytes via multiple dendrites and lose their expression of melanoma-associated antigens. In addition, the proliferation of melanocytes is regulated such that the ratio of

TABLE I

Frequency of the Five Most Common Cytogenetic Abnormalities and Chromosome Imbalances Reported in Melanoma Tumors

Chromosome	Structural abnormalities and imbalances $N > 97$ (Albino et al., 1993)	Chromosome	Structural abnormalities $N = 126$ (Thompson et al., 1995)	Chromosome	Chromosome imbalances $N = 49$ (Thompson et al., 1995)
1	82%	1	74%	6	63%
6	64%	6	58%	10	63%
7	61%	7	42%	1	59%
9	46%	11	33%	7	59%
11	399%	9	32%	9	59%

[a]Taken with permission from Fountain (1997).

melanocytes to keratinocytes remains constant, at the ratio in which they were originally seeded. It is the loss of this keratinocyte control that marks the transition from normal melanocyte to benign nevus cell, and coculture experiments have demonstrated that melanoma cells are refractory to keratinocyte control.

III. CELLULAR ABNORMALITIES ASSOCIATED WITH MELANOMA PROGRESSION

A. Changes in Expression of Cell Adhesion Molecules

As in all cancers, melanoma progression is characterized by changes in cell–cell and cell–matrix adhesion and cell–cell communication. This is not surprising given that the melanocytic cells must escape from their normal extracellular milieu (in the epidermis surrounded by keratinocytes), invade through the basement membrane, and proliferate ectopically in the new dermal microenvironment, composed of fibroblasts and endothelial cells. A wide variety of molecules mediate cell–cell and cell–matrix adhesion and the formation of cell–cell and cell–matrix junctions. These include the family of Ca^{2+} dependent cell–cell adhesion molecules called cadherins, members of the immunoglobulin superfamily of proteins that mediate Ca^{2+} independent cell–cell adhesion, and the family of cell–matrix adhesion molecules called integrins. A large number of changes in cell adhesion molecules have been documented in melanoma progression.

1. E-cadherin/N-cadherin

Loss of E-cadherin expression and the concomitant increase in N-cadherin expression are some of the main features of melanocytic transformation and coincide with the escape of the melanocytic cells from keratinocyte control. It has been demonstrated that ectopic expression of E-cadherin in melanoma cells results not only in cell adhesion to keratinocytes, but renders the transduced melanoma cells susceptible to keratinocyte-mediated control. Although E-cadherin transduction had no effect on the expression of cell surface molecules on melanoma cells, subsequent co-

culture of these transduced melanoma cells with keratinocytes led to the downregulation and complete loss of expression of several melanoma-associated antigens. These included Mel-CAM, a member of the immunoglobulin superfamily of cell adhesion proteins, and the β subunit of the αvβ3 vitronectin receptor. Furthermore, in a three-dimensional skin reconstruction model, the ectopic expression of E-cadherin inhibited the invasion of melanoma cells into the dermis and those that did migrate into the dermis showed signs of apoptosis. The exact mechanism whereby E-cadherin inhibits invasion is unknown. It is also unknown whether keratinocyte-mediated growth control is transduced directly through E-cadherin signaling and/or other signaling pathways, e.g., gap junctions that are dependent on E-cadherin-mediated cell–cell adhesion.

Data have emerged indicating that melanocyte transformation is associated with a change in gap junctional specificity. Gap junctions are composed of a cluster of transmembrane proteins called connexins (Cx). Six connexin subunits form a ring around a central pore to form a connexon or hemichannel. These hemichannels align and interact with another hemichannel on an adjacent cell to form a pore through which small molecules up to 1000 Da can travel. Gap junctional communication among melanocytes, melanoma cells, keratinocytes, fibroblasts, and endothelial cells has been analyzed in coculture experiments using dye transfer assays. As expected, melanocytes exhibit gap junctional communication with keratinocytes but no other cell type, whereas melanoma cells can no longer form gap junctions with keratinocytes but form gap junctions with other melanoma cells, fibroblasts, and endothelial cells. This change in gap junction forming ability was not correlated with any changes in the expression of connexin subunits; however, it could be correlated with E-cadherin expression. Ectopic expression of E-cadherin in melanoma cells led to the downregulation of N-cadherin and allowed the establishment of functional gap junctions with keratinocytes. Melanoma cells could form functional gap junctions with dermal fibroblasts, endothelial cells, and other melanoma cells that were dependent on the expression of N-cadherin.

2. αvβ3 Integrin Subunit

Integrins are cell surface molecules predominantly involved in cell–matrix adhesion and the transduction of intracellular signaling. The integrin family is composed of a large number of α and β subunits that combine to form heterodimers. Compared to benign melanocytic lesions, metastatic melanomas demonstrate loss of α6β1 expression (laminin receptor) and an increase in α4β1 and αvβ3 (vitronectin receptor) expression. Expression of α4β1 and αvβ3 in melanomas is associated with poor prognosis and a shorter disease-free interval. One of the ligands of the α4β1 integrin is the endothelial cell adhesion molecule VCAM, and expression of α4β1 is thought to be associated with an increased ability to extravasate and metastasize. Upregulation of the β3 subunit of the αvβ3 vitronectin receptor is associated with tumor thickness and the ability to invade and metastasize and correlates with the transition from radial growth phase (RGP) to vertical growth phase (VGP). Transfection of the β3 subunit into a RGP melanoma cell line results in an increase in anchorage-independent growth in soft agar and in increased invasiveness and survival in three-dimensional skin reconstruction models and enhanced tumorigenicity in nude mice.

B. Increasing Autonomy from Growth Factors

One of the key characteristics shared by all cancers is losing dependence on the extracellular environment for growth factors and cytokines. Growth regulatory pathways can be deregulated during tumor progression in a number of ways, including altered or overexpression of autocrine growth factors or growth factor receptors or resistance to inhibitory paracrine growth factors. In addition, aberration of downstream molecules involved in growth factor signaling pathways and decoupling of the cell cycle from external stimuli often occurs and is discussed in detail in Section IV. There has been considerable research in understanding the different *in vitro* requirements for exogenous growth factors required by cells from different stages of melanoma progression. Upregulation of basic fibroblast growth factor (bFGF) expression during

melanoma progression has been shown to be widespread and to have both autocrine and paracrine roles in melanoma development.

IV. MOLECULAR GENETIC ABNORMALITIES ASSOCIATED WITH MELANOMA PROGRESSION

A. Introduction

The genes in which abnormalities have been detected most frequently in melanoma samples represent the three tumor suppressor pathways most often disturbed in all malignancies. These include the p16/pRb pathway regulating entry into the cell cycle, the p14^{ARF}/p53 pathway detecting inappropriate oncogenic activation, and the PI3 kinase/PTEN/AKT pathway regulating cell survival and proliferation. One of the quandaries that has arisen in understanding the molecular genetics of melanoma is the relative importance of the two protein products encoded by the *CDKN2A* locus, namely p16 and p14^{ARF}, in melanoma pathogenesis. Although data implicating p16 in melanoma development are unambiguous, namely germline mutations in affected members of melanoma families and mutations and deletions in uncultured melanoma tumors, data implicating p14^{ARF} in melanoma development are equivocal. Despite a certain role for p14^{ARF} as a tumor suppressor and its pivotal position in tumorigenesis, no germline mutations have been found in melanoma families and no point mutations in exon 1β have been found in melanoma tumors. Given that p16 is often inactivated by homozygous deletion, which in turn often inactivates p14^{ARF}, the possibility that p14^{ARF} is important in a subset of somatic melanomas cannot be excluded.

B. CDKN2A: The p16/p14^{ARF} Locus

Identification of the *CDKN2A* gene, encoding the p16 cell cycle inhibitor, was the result of a positional cloning effort that relied on the demonstration of linkage to chromosome 9p21-22 in melanoma families, loss of heterozygosity (LOH) studies in a number of different tumor types, and finally the presence of homozygous deletions in a number of cultured cell lines. Inactivating mutations have since been reported in a large number of melanoma families, cultured cell lines, and uncultured tumors from a wide variety of tissue types, including melanoma, confirming the importance of p16 as a tumor suppressor important in many tissue types. In 1995, a second *CDKN2A* transcript was reported containing a different first exon (termed exon 1β) spliced onto exons 2 and 3 (Fig. 2). Because the initiating codon in this alternative exon is not in the same reading frame as exon 2 of p16, the protein derived from this alternative transcript is translated in a alternate reading frame (ARF) and hence does not share any amino acid homology to p16. The encoded protein has been designated p19^{ARF} in mouse and p14^{ARF} in humans in recognition of the different sizes of the encoded proteins. Data demonstrate that p14^{ARF} plays a very important role in the transmission of hyperproliferative signals to p53 to induce either senescence or apoptosis, depending on the cell type.

C. p16^{INK4A} Function

As mentioned previously, one of the characteristic features of neoplastic transformation is increasing autonomy from exogenous growth factors. Aberration of the p16/pRb pathway is the ultimate means of decoupling the cell cycle from external stimuli. For cells to pass through G$_1$ to S phase, in response to exogenous growth factor stimulation, cells must pass what is known as the late G$_1$ restriction point. For progression past this restriction point, cyclin D/CDK4 must phosphorylate the retinoblastoma protein, pRb. During G$_o$/G$_1$ the Rb protein exists in a DNA-bound protein complex, where it is bound to the transactivation domain of E2F transcription factors, preventing the transactivation of E2F target genes. The phosphorylation of pRb results in the disassociation of this protein complex and the release of E2F such that it can transactivate the necessary genes for entry into S phase. Overexpression of p16 inhibits the progression of cells through the G$_1$ phase of the cell cycle by blocking the kinase activity of the enzyme, primarily through preventing the association of CDK4 and cyclin D. Without a functional p16, pRb is hyperphosphorylated by CDK4, and the unsequestered transcription factors are perpetually activating the genes involved in entry to the cell cycle (Fig. 3). In addition to this well-characterized role at the G$_1$/S border, data have implicated an additional role for p16 at the G$_2$/M border in melanocytes in response to UV. Gabrielle and co-workers have shown that in response to UV, p16 levels accumulate and lead to a G$_2$ arrest that is dependent on the binding of p16 to CDK4. The authors postulate that inactivation of *CDKN2A* disrupts a p16-dependent G$_2$ cell cycle checkpoint, and thus cells progress through the cell cycle without repairing UV-induced damage, leading to the acquisi-

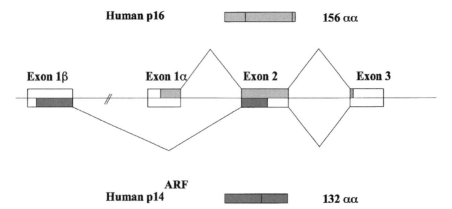

FIGURE 2 Alternative transcripts and products encoded by the *CDKN2A* locus. The exons of *CDKN2A* are shown as boxes and identified as exons 1α, 1β, 2, and 3. Alternative splicing occurs as indicated to give rise to two transcripts; exons that splice to encode p16 are shown in light gray and those that encode p14^{ARF} are shown in dark gray. Sizes of the human proteins are provided.

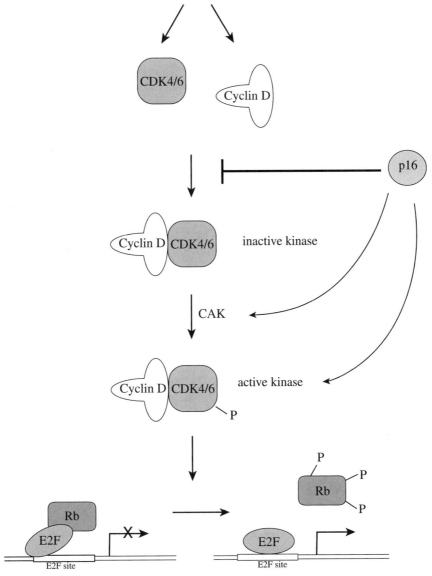

Growth factors
Mitogenic signalling cascade

CDK4/6   Cyclin D

p16

Cyclin D | CDK4/6   inactive kinase

CAK

Cyclin D | CDK4/6   active kinase
P

Rb
P

P
Rb
P

E2F
X

E2F
E2F site

E2F site

Transcription of E2F responsive genes
required for S phase eg cyclins E and A

FIGURE 3 Function of p16 at the G_1/S restriction point in the cell cycle. Through a complex system of signal transduction, mitogenic stimulation leads to the assembly of cyclin D and CDK4. This complex is then activated by the CDK-activating kinase (CAK), and cyclinD/CDK4 in turn phosphorylates the pRb protein. The phosphorylation of pRb leads to the release of transcription factors, e.g., E2F-1, which then transactivate the genes required for entry into S phase. Although p16 has been shown to inhibit this pathway by binding to the complex and inhibiting the kinase activity of CDK4 and inhibiting the CAK-dependent phosphorylation of CDK4, the principal mechanism of inhibition *in vivo* (thick black line) is through inhibiting the assembly of the cyclin D/CDK4 complex. The figure is necessarily simplistic; however, it appears that p16 may also inhibit the phosphorylation of pRb by indirectly inactivating other CDKs, e.g., CDK2, a consequence of the redistribution of other CDK inhibitors, e.g., p27 and p21.

tion of genetic defects. Although this additional function of p16 has yet to be confirmed by other laboratories, it is potentially exciting, as it may explain the tissue specificity of tumors resulting from germline mutations in *CDKN2A*, and as such it requires further corroboration by other groups.

D. Current Understanding of the Role for p16 in Melanoma

The presence of germline mutations in the exons encoding p16 that segregate with the disease in approximately 20–25% of large multicase melanoma families, together with functional data indicating that the mutations prevent/impair binding to CDK4, provides unequivocal proof for an important role for p16 in melanoma pathogenesis. Nevertheless some questions remain. One of these involves the importance of *CDKN2A*/p16 in those 20–30% of melanoma families with haplotype sharing or linkage to chromosome 9p21 but no germline mutations in *CDKN2A*. Several reasons have been proposed to account for this anomaly. It may be that these families are indeed linked to 9p21 and (1) some families carry germline mutations outside the coding region of *CDKN2A* or (2) they may carry germline mutations in an as yet unidentified predisposition locus on chromosome 9p21-22. Alternatively, it may be that the observed haplotype sharing is a chance event because (1) the affected individuals represent a cluster of sporadic cases with no hereditary component or (2) indeed the families do have a hereditary component, but are linked to an unidentified predisposition locus mapping to another chromosome.

Another polemical issue centers on whether *CDKN2A* is the only TSG involved in sporadic melanoma development mapping to 9p21-22. Although LOH surrounding chromosome 9p21-22 is observed in 40–70% of uncultured melanomas, mutations in *CDKN2A* are only found in approximately 10% of these tumors. Although not all studies have also analyzed the presence of homozygous deletions and methylation, in those studies that have, these mechanisms of inactivation together comprise another 15%, still leaving approximately half without a detectable second "hit". Considerable debate exists in the literature as to whether this reflects an inability to detect the second hit, given that homozygous deletions are notoriously hard to detect in nonmicrodis-

sected tumors, or indeed these data suggest the presence of one or more additional TSGs involved in melanoma mapping to this chromosomal region.

The remaining question involves the contribution of *CDKN2A* germline mutations to melanoma predisposition in different populations. Early mutation analyses of *CDKN2A* were performed in the large multiaffected families that were used in the initial linkage studies; however, the majority of individuals who report a family history of melanoma report only one to two affected family members. Subsequent population-based screens for germline mutations in *CDKN2A*, even in population preselected for having a higher a priori probability of carrying a germline mutation, revealed a surprisingly low frequency of mutations in most populations. Only in France and Scotland did the number of individuals with a germline mutation suggest that population screening of at-risk individuals was warranted.

Given that melanoma predisposition demonstrates genetic heterogeneity, it may be that many of these questions will be resolved upon the identification of additional genes responsible for melanoma predisposition. To this end, a genome-wide linkage study using 400 markers is underway at the National Human Genome Research Institute in concert with the International Melanoma Linkage Consortium. Each family contains at least three affected individuals available for typing, all families are mutation negative for *CDKN2A*, and, importantly, all families show no evidence of linkage-haplotype sharing to the 9p21-22 region.

E. p14^{ARF} Function

For successful tumorigenesis, neoplastic cells must deregulate growth, often through inactivation of the p16/pRb pathway. However, inappropriate proliferative stimuli such as E1A, myc, oncogenic ras, v-abl, and E2F-1 can lead to a potent induction of p53-dependent apoptosis. These observations suggest that nascent cancer cells must also evolve a means for avoiding apoptosis. In recent years it has become clear that p14^{ARF} plays a central role in transmitting this hyperproliferative signal to induce p53-dependent apoptosis, hence inactivation of any one of the proteins in this p14^{ARF}/p53 pathway provides the means for a cell to bypass apoptosis on the road to an infinite life span. In a normal cell, the murine double minute 2 (MDM2) oncogene (HDM2 in humans), a ubiquitin ligase, plays a central role in regulating p53 levels and activity. It accomplishes this by targeting p53 to ubiquitin-dependent proteosome degradation in the cytoplasm and also binding to the transactivation domain of p53 inhibiting the activity of the protein. In response to a variety of oncogenic stimuli, p14^{ARF} transcription is upregulated. The p14^{ARF} protein then stabilizes p53 by binding to HDM2 in the nucleus and preventing HDM2 targeting p53 to the cytoplasm for proteosome degradation (Fig. 4). The exact mechanism whereby p14^{ARF} interacts with HDM2 to result in p53 stabilization is still under debate and may be different in mice and humans.

Although it is clear that p14^{ARF} plays an important role in neoplastic surveillance, there is a paradoxical paucity of data to suggest that p14^{ARF} plays an impor-

tant role in melanoma pathogenesis. Missense mutations in exon 2 of *CDKN2A* had no effect on the ability of p14^{ARF} to block cell cycle progression, and complete removal of the exon 2 sequences only marginally impaired p14^{ARF} function. In addition, no germline mutations in exon 1β have been found in a large number of melanoma families, sporadic melanomas, or cell lines analyzed. It is difficult to exclude a role for p14^{ARF}, however, as p16 is often inactivated by homozygous deletion, possibly due to the advantage to the cell gained from inactivating both p16 and p14^{ARF}.

F. PTEN

The long arm of chromosome 10 has been implicated in melanoma pathogenesis by cytogenetics and LOH studies. The PTEN gene, mapping to chromosome

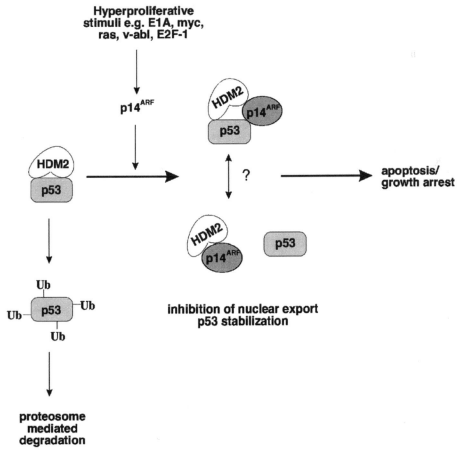

FIGURE 4 Model for p14^{ARF} function. p14^{ARF} transcription is induced in response to a variety of hyperproliferative stimuli and is believed to inhibit the export of p53 from the nucleus for cytoplasmic degradation. Whether inhibition by p14^{ARF} involves binary and/or ternary ARF–MDM2–p53 complexes is presently under debate. The stabilization of p53 in the nucleus leads to apoptosis or growth arrest.

10q23, was identified as a candidate TSG involved in many tissues through positional cloning. The gene encoded a protein that displayed homology to dual specificity phosphatases, and PTEN has been shown to possess both protein phosphatase activity and lipid phosphatase activity. Although the PTEN product has been shown to dephosphorylate the focal adhesion kinase (FAK), this could not be verified by another laboratory. The majority of data suggest that the main role of PTEN is to antagonize the function of the phosphoinositide 3-kinase (PI3K) in dephosphorylating the 3 position of phosphatidylinositol (PI) phosphates, e.g., PI-(3,4,5)-P$_3$. This signaling pathway, whereby levels of the PI-(3,4,5)-P$_3$ second messengers increase rapidly following growth factor stim-

ulation, has been well defined. Accumulation of PI-(3,4,5)-P$_3$ at the cell membrane leads to the recruitment of several proteins, including the AKT oncogene, a serine/threonine kinase that is subsequently activated by phosphorylation. Activated AKT phosphorylates a number of cellular targets that result in protection from several apoptotic stimuli in addition to increased proliferation (Fig. 5). Loss of PTEN leads to an increased concentration of PI-(3,4,5)-P$_3$ and AKT hyperactivation, leading to protection from various apoptotic stimuli. Current genetic data suggest that the PTEN/PI3-K/AKT pathway constitutes an important regulatory pathway in tumorigenesis.

The crucial role of PTEN as a tumor suppressor was confirmed by the identification of germline mutations

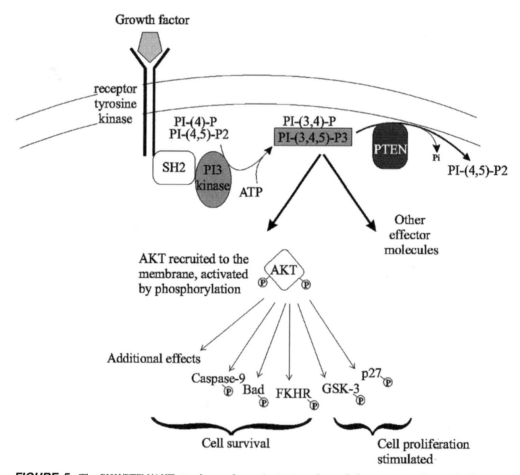

FIGURE 5 The PI3K/PTEN/AKT signaling pathway. Activation of growth factor receptor kinases leads to recruitment of the phosphoinositide 3-kinase (PI3-K) and phosphorylation of the phosphoinositide second messengers at the D-3 position. These second messengers then recruit cytosolic signaling proteins to the membrane, e.g., AKT. Subsequent activation of AKT then results in the phosphorylation of a range of downstream targets involved in cell proliferation and apoptosis.

in several familial hamartoma syndromes, including Cowden disease and Bannayan–Riley–Ruvulcaba syndrome. Inactivating mutations have been found in tumors derived from a wide variety of tissue types, including melanoma, although like p16, a higher frequency of mutations have been reported in cell lines than tumors. At this time, one study has revealed the presence of inactivating mutations in both p16 and PTEN in melanoma samples, suggesting that loss of PTEN provides an additional selective advantage over loss of the p16/pRb pathway. In addition, one study has suggested that PTEN may be inactivated by epigenetic mechanisms in melanoma tumors. Further corroboration is needed to determine the importance of PTEN in melanoma pathogenesis.

V. CONCLUSION

Much progress has been made in the previous two decades documenting the molecular and cellular abnormalities associated with melanoma progression. However, many important aspects of melanoma initiation and progression are still poorly understood. What are the initiating events in melanoma genesis? What other oncogenes and TSGs play important roles in melanoma pathogenesis? What are the crucial genetics events that govern the transition from RGP to VGP melanoma and underlie the phenotypic changes observed? Sequencing of the human genome combined with current genomic techniques, including comparative genome hybridization, cDNA microarrays, and tissue microarrays, heralds an unprecedented time of gene discovery. It also promises a more comprehensive characterization of the molecular and cellular abnormalities associated with melanoma development and correlation with clinical outcome. It is hoped that an increased understanding of the genetic and epigenetic events in melanoma pathogenesis may then result in the tailoring of treatment modalities to the specific molecular abnormalities of a particular tumor. This should, in turn, lead to a decrease in the high morbidity and mortality associated with this disease.

Acknowledgment

The author thanks Professor Jeffrey Trent for critical reading of the manuscript.

See Also the Following Articles

CELL CYCLE CHECKPOINTS • MELANOMA: EPIDEMIOLOGY • MOLECULAR MECHANISMS OF CANCER INVASION • P16 AND ARF: CROSSROADS OF TUMORIGENESIS • PTEN • SKIN CANCER

Bibliography

Albino, A. P., and Fountain, J. W. (1993). Molecular genetics of human malignant melanoma. *Cancer Treat. Res.* **65,** 201–255.

Ashcroft, M., and Vousden, K. H. (1999). Regulation of p53 stability. *Oncogene* **18,** 7637–7643.

Bonneau, D., and Longy, M. (2000). Mutations of the human PTEN gene. *Hum. Mutat.* **16,** 109–122.

Cantley, L. C., and Neel, B. G. (1999). New insights into tumor suppression: PTEN suppresses tumor formation by restraining the phosphoinositide 3-kinase/AKT pathway. *Proc. Natl. Acad. Sci. USA* **96,** 4240–4245.

Dahia, P. L. (2000). PTEN, a unique tumor suppressor gene. *Endocr. Relat. Cancer.* **7,** 115–129.

Di Cristofano, A., and Pandolfi, P. P. (2000). The multiple roles of PTEN in tumor suppression. *Cell* **100,** 387–390.

DiLiberti, J. H. (1998). Inherited macrocephaly-hamartoma syndromes. *Am. J. Med. Genet.* **79,** 284–290.

Duro, D., Bernard, O., Della Valle, V., Berger, R. and Larsen, C. J. (1995). A new type of p16INK4/MTS1 gene transcript expressed in B-cell malignancies. *Oncogene* **11,** 21–29.

Fidler, I. J. (1997). Biology of melanoma metastasis. *In* "Cutaneous Melanoma" (C. Balch, A. Houghton, A. Sober, and S. Soong, eds.), pp. 493–516. Quality Medical Publishing, St. Louis.

Foulkes, W. D., Flanders, T. Y., Pollock, P. M., and Hayward, N. K. (1997). The CDKN2A (p16) gene and human cancer. *Mol. Med.* **3,** 5–20.

Fountain, J. (1997). Genetic factors. *In* "Cutaneous Melanoma" (C. Balch, A. Houghton, A. Sober, and S. Soong, eds.), pp. 475–492. Quality Medical Publishing, St. Louis.

Gabrielli, B. G., Sarcevic, B., Sinnamon, J., Walker, G., Castellano, M., Wang, X. Q., and Ellem, K. A. (1999). A cyclin D-Cdk4 activity required for G_2 phase cell cycle progression is inhibited in ultraviolet radiation-induced G_2 phase delay. *J. Biol. Chem.* **274,** 13961–13969.

Haluska, F. G., and Hodi, F. S. (1998). Molecular genetics of familial cutaneous melanoma. *J. Clin. Oncol.* **16,** 670–682.

Hayward, N. (1998). Melanoma susceptibility: Population bases incidence of germline *CDKN2A* mutations in selected families with cutaneous melanoma. *Curr. Pract. Med.* **1.**

Herlyn, M., Berking, C., Li, G., and Satyamoorthy, K. (2000). Lessons from melanocyte development for understanding the biological events in naevus and melanoma formation. *Melanoma Res.* **10,** 303–312.

Hsu, M., Andl, T., Li, G., Meinkoth, J. L., and Herlyn, M. (2000). Cadherin repertoire determines partner-specific gap junctional communication during melanoma progression. *J. Cell Sci.* **113,** 1535–1542.

Hsu, M. Y., Meier, F. E., Nesbit, M., Hsu, J. Y., Van Belle, P., Elder, D. E., and Herlyn, M. (2000). E-cadherin expression in melanoma cells restores keratinocyte-mediated growth control and down-regulates expression of invasion-related adhesion receptors. *Am. J. Pathol.* **156,** 1515–1525.

Hsu, M. Y., Shih, D. T., Meier, F. E., Van Belle, P., Hsu, J. Y., Elder, D. E., Buck, C. A., and Herlyn, M. (1998). Adenoviral gene transfer of beta3 integrin subunit induces conversion from radial to vertical growth phase in primary human melanoma. *Am. J. Pathol.* **153,** 1435–1442.

Johnson, J. P. (1999). Cell adhesion molecules in the development and progression of malignant melanoma. *Cancer Metast. Rev.* **18,** 345–357.

Kamb, A., Gruis, N. A., Weaver-Feldhaus, J., Liu, Q., Harshman, K., Tavtigian, S. V., Stockert, E., Day, R. S., 3rd, Johnson, B. E., and Skolnick, M. H. (1994). A cell cycle regulator potentially involved in genesis of many tumor types. *Science* **264,** 436–440.

Lazar-Molnar, E., Hegyesi, H., Toth, S., and Falus, A. (2000). Autocrine and paracrine regulation by cytokines and growth factors in melanoma. *Cytokine* **12,** 547–554.

Li, G., and Herlyn, M. (2000). Dynamics of intercellular communication during melanoma development. *Mol. Med. Today.* **6,** 163–169.

Li, J., Yen, C., Liaw, D., Podsypanina, K., Bose, S., Wang, S. I., Puc, J., Miliaresis, C., Rodgers, L., McCombie, R., Bigner, S. H., Giovanella, B. C., Ittmann, M., Tycko, B., Hibshoosh, H., Wigler, M. H., and Parsons, R. (1997). PTEN, a putative protein tyrosine phosphatase gene mutated in human brain, breast, and prostate cancer. *Nat. Genet.* **15,** 356–362.

Mao, L., Merlo, A., Bedi, G., Shapiro, G. I., Edwards, C. D., Rollins, B. J., and Sidransky, D. (1995). A novel p16INK4A transcript. *Cancer Res.* **55,** 2995–2997.

Meier, F., Satyamoorthy, K., Nesbit, M., Hsu, M. Y., Schittek, B., Garbe, C., and Herlyn, M. (1998). Molecular events in melanoma development and progression. *Front. Biosci.* **3,** D1005–D1010.

Nesbit, M., Setaluri, V., and Herlyn, M. (1997). Biology of melanocytes and melanoma. *In* "Cutaneous Melanoma" (C. Balch, A. Houghton, A. Sober, and S. Soong, eds.), pp. 463–473. Quality Medical Publishing, St. Louis.

Nobori, T., Miura, K., Wu, D. J., Lois, A., Takabayashi, K., and Carson, D. A. (1994). Deletions of the cyclin-dependent kinase-4 inhibitor gene in multiple human cancers. *Nature* **368,** 753–756.

Piepkorn, M. (2000). Melanoma genetics: An update with focus on the CDKN2A(p16)/ARF tumor suppressors. *J. Am. Acad. Dermatol.* **42,** 705–722.

Pollock, P. M., and Trent, J. M. (2001). The genetics of cutaneous melanoma. *Clin. Lab. Med.*

Quelle, D. E., Cheng, M., Ashmun, R. A., and Sherr, C. J. (1997). Cancer-associated mutations at the INK4a locus cancel cell cycle arrest by p16INK4a but not by the alternative reading frame protein p19ARF. *Proc. Natl. Acad. Sci. USA* **94,** 669–673.

Quelle, D. E., Zindy, F., Ashmun, R. A., and Sherr, C. J. (1995). Alternative reading frames of the INK4a tumor suppressor gene encode two unrelated proteins capable of inducing cell cycle arrest. *Cell* **83,** 993–1000.

Ruas, M., and Peters, G. (1998). The p16INK4a/CDKN2A tumor suppressor and its relatives. *Biochim. Biophys. Acta.* **1378,** F115–F177.

Satyamoorthy, K., and Herlyn, M. (1997). Melanoma: Molecular and cellular abnormalities. *In* "Encyclopedia of Cancer" (J. Bertino, ed.), pp. 1042–1050. Academic Press, San Diego.

Seftor, R. E. (1998). Role of the beta3 integrin subunit in human primary melanoma progression: Multifunctional activities associated with alpha(v)beta3 integrin expression. *Am. J. Pathol.* **153,** 1347–1351.

Sharpless, N. E., and DePinho, R. A. (1999). The INK4A/ARF locus and its two gene products. *Curr. Opin. Genet. Dev.* **9,** 22–30.

Sherr, C. J. (1998). Tumor surveillance via the ARF-p53 pathway. *Genes Dev.* **12,** 2984–2991.

Sherr, C. J., and Roberts, J. M. (1999). CDK inhibitors: Positive and negative regulators of G1-phase progression. *Genes Dev.* **13,** 1501–1512.

Sherr, C. J., and Weber, J. D. (2000). The ARF/p53 pathway. *Curr. Opin. Genet. Dev.* **10,** 94–99.

Smith-Sorensen, B., and Hovig, E. (1996). CDKN2A (p16INK4A) somatic and germline mutations. *Hum. Mutat.* **7,** 294–303.

Steck, P. A., Pershouse, M. A., Jasser, S. A., Yung, W. K., Lin, H., Ligon, A. H., Langford, L. A., Baumgard, M. L., Hattier, T., Davis, T., Frye, C., Hu, R., Swedlund, B., Teng, D. H., and Tavtigian, S. V. (1997). Identification of a candidate tumour suppressor gene, MMAC1, at chromosome 10q23.3 that is mutated in multiple advanced cancers. *Nature Genet.* **16,** 64–67.

Stone, S., Jiang, P., Dayananth, P., Tavtigian, S. V., Katcher, H., Parry, D., Peters, G., and Kamb, A. (1995). Complex structure and regulation of the P16 (MTS1) locus. *Cancer Res.* **55,** 2988–2994.

Thompson, F. H., Emerson, J., Olson, S., Weinstein, R., Leavitt, S. A., Leong, S. P., Emerson, S., Trent, J. M., Nelson, M. A., Salmon, S. E., et al. (1995). Cytogenetics of 158 patients with regional or disseminated melanoma: Subset analysis of near-diploid and simple karyotypes. *Cancer Genet. Cytogenet.* **83,** 93–104.

Tsao, H., Zhang, X., Benoit, E., and Haluska, F. G. (1998). Identification of PTEN/MMAC1 alterations in uncultured melanomas and melanoma cell lines. *Oncogene* **16,** 3397–3402.

Zhou, X. P., Gimm, O., Hampel, H., Niemann, T., Walker, M. J., and Eng, C. (2000). Epigenetic PTEN silencing in malignant melanomas without PTEN mutation. *Am. J. Pathol.* **157,** 1123–1128.

Melanoma: Epidemiology

Sanjiv S. Agarwala
John M. Kirkwood
University of Pittsburgh Cancer Institute

GLOSSARY

adjuvant therapy Postsurgical treatment given in an effort to prevent relapse and metastasis.

biochemotherapy Combination of chemotherapy and immunotherapy drugs given in various schedules, usually administered in the hospital.

chemotherapy The use of cytotoxic pharmacologic agents to kill cancer cells.

dysplastic/atypical nevus A mole that shows atypical features on clinical inspection or pathologic evaluation.

immunotherapy/biotherapy The use of drugs that modulate the immune system to treat cancer. Examples include interferons and interleukins.

sentinel lymph node The first draining lymph node of the regional lymph node basin. This would be expected to be the first lymph node to show cancer cells in the event of metastases.

Melanoma is a lethal form of skin cancer with an increasing incidence. Clinical suspicion of melanoma is always confirmed by a pathologic evaluation, which provides important prognostic information. Current staging procedures incorporate the technique of sentinel lymph node evaluation, which has allowed accurate assessment of the regional lymph node basin. The staging for melanoma has undergone evolution since the 1980s, and the new system adopted by the American Joint Committee on Cancer Staging (AJCC) incorporates several newly recognized and important prognostic factors. Surgical therapy for primary melanoma is followed by adjuvant therapy using interferon-α for patients deemed to be at high risk for recurrence. Options for stage IV melanoma are limited, but include immunotherapy and combined chemoimmunotherapy.

I. INTRODUCTION

The incidence of cutaneous melanoma in the United States is increasing at a rate that exceeds all other neoplasms except for lung cancer in women. In 2001, an estimated 51,800 Americans will develop this cutaneous melanoma and 7800 will die. It is the potentially lethal nature of this disease that distinguishes it from other far more common types of skin cancer, such as squamous cell and basal cell carcinoma. By its location on the skin surface, melanoma provides a unique opportunity for early recognition and diagnosis at a stage when it is still curable, a luxury not provided by most other malignancies. Knowledge of risk factors for melanoma and a well-defined precursor lesion, the atypical nevus, also allow efforts at prevention, a modality that is likely to be more successful than treatment given the paucity of successful therapeutic alternatives for advanced disease.

II. EPIDEMIOLOGY

As noted earlier, the incidence of melanoma has increased rapidly among Caucasians in the United States, Europe, Australia, and New Zealand. Most recent data from the National Cancer Institute's (NCI) Surveillance, Epidemiology, and End Results (SEER) program indicate an incidence of 16 per 100,000 persons in 1996 compared to 6.4 per 100,000 in 1973, an increase of 120%. Skin pigmentation is protective, and incidence rates in African-Americans, Hispanics, and Asians are considerably lower. Mortality from this disease also increased by 40% between 1973 and 1995, and melanoma accounts for three-quarters of all deaths from skin cancer. Both incidence and mortality are higher for males than for females. Recent data may indicate a slight stabilization in incidence and mortality, perhaps reflecting the success of educational programs and surveillance.

III. RISK FACTORS

Although melanoma can afflict any age group, it is rare in children. The median age at diagnosis is 53 years. Identification of risk factors and individuals at high risk for development of melanoma allows improved efforts at primary and secondary prevention. The greatest risk for melanoma occurs in white males followed by white females. Established risk factors for cutaneous melanoma are shown in Table I.

IV. CLINICAL FEATURES AND DIAGNOSIS

Most cutaneous melanomas are solitary lesions that arise from apparently normal skin. The most common sites of occurrence are the trunk and upper back in males and the lower extremities in females. In darker skinned individuals, acral sites (plantar foot, subungual) and mucosal sites are more common.

Diagnosis of primary melanoma is fraught with difficulty and can confound the most experienced of clinicians. Less than 1% of atypical nevi develop into a melanoma, but more than 50% of cutaneous melanomas may develop from a preexisting nevus. The hallmark of melanoma is a change in a skin lesion that occurs at a moderate pace (3–12 months). A more rapid rate of growth is usually associated with an inflammatory or other nonmalignant condition. The diagnosis of melanoma is made by a pathologic evaluation of a biop-

TABLE I
Risk Factors for Development of Cutaneous Melanoma

High risk
    New mole or change in preexisting mole
    Familial melanoma and atypical nevi
Moderate risk
    Prior history of melanoma
    Congenital nevus
    Multiple atypical nevi
Low but elevated risk
    Sun sensitivity
    Multiple freckles
    History of blistering sunburn
    Immunosuppression

sied lesion. The ABCD rule and the seven-point check list outlined later serve as useful aids in recognizing suspicious lesions that may require a biopsy.

A. The ABCD Rule

The ABCD rule is shown in Table II. These four features are also often found in atypical nevi and help identify lesions that may deserve attention or follow-up. The simplicity of the ABCD rule is both its greatest strength and weakness. The diameter in particular can be particularly misleading, and nodular melanomas are often diagnosed at a size less than 6 mm. The other features of atypical nevi are shown in Table III. The most relevant feature of a preexisting nevus that warrants a biopsy is change. An alteration in clinical characteristics of an existing mole, such as change in size or color, itching or bleeding, or development of a new lesion should prompt an evaluation and biopsy. The dictum "when in doubt, take it out" is a good one for this disease.

B. The Seven-Point Checklist

This checklist was devised in England to assist the lay public in recognizing skin lesions that may need to be evaluated by a physician. It is a sensitive, but less specific screening test for melanoma and comprises three major and four minor features. The major features include change in size, change in color, and change in shape. The minor features are inflammation, bleeding or crusting, sensory change, and a lesion of 7 mm or greater in diameter.

V. SUBTYPES (GROWTH PATTERNS) OF MELANOMA

Four morphologic subtypes of melanoma can be identified, which reflect four different growth patterns of this disease.

TABLE II
ABCD Rule

A	Asymmetry
B	Border irregularity
C	Color variation
D	Diameter (>6 mm)

TABLE III
Features of Atypical (Dysplastic) Nevi

Clinical
    ABCD features (see Table II)
    Location on trunk
    Macular component
    Erythema
Histologic
    Cytologic atypia
    Nuclear hyperchromatism
    Dermal lymphocytic infiltration
    Rete ridge bridging

A. Superficial Spreading Melanoma

This represents the most common subtype in Caucasians (70%) and is the type that most commonly arises from a preexisting nevus. Most common sites include the upper posterior trunk in males and the legs in females. This tumor is thought to start in a radial growth phase and then enter into the vertical growth phase with an increased propensity to metastases. Recognition of this lesion in the radial growth phase (which can last for 1–5 years) is the key to prevention of metastatic disease. The ABCD rule is most applicable to diagnosis of this type of melanoma.

B. Nodular Melanoma

These comprise 15–30% of all cutaneous melanomas and may be darkly pigmented or amelanotic (5%). They are often of small diameter (<5 mm) and show a predominant vertical growth phase, often arising in previously normal-appearing skin. These features make early diagnosis of the lesions difficult. They are most frequently located on the trunk and head and neck and are more common in males.

C. Acral Lentiginous Melanoma

This subtype comprises 2–10% of all melanomas and is the most common type found in darker skinned individuals. Sixty to 70% of melanomas found in African-Americans are of this subtype. It is found most commonly on the palms, the soles, or the nail bed (subungual). Subungual melanomas are important in that they need to be differentiated from subungual hematomas. The poor prognosis of these lesions is an outcome of delayed diagnosis and treatment.

D. Lentigo Maligna Melanoma

These comprise about 5% of melanomas and are the subtype most consistently associated with excessive sunlight exposure. As a consequence, they often present as a change in a precursor lesion (lentigo maligna) in sun-damaged skin. They also tend to be slow-growing lesions that are more common in older individuals, indicating their relationship to cumulative sunlight exposure.

It should be noted that despite apparent differences in the appearance of these four types of melanoma, development of the vertical growth phase and eventual depth in millimeters (Breslow) of the lesion is the ultimate determinant of prognosis (see later). In other words, nodular melanomas appear to have a worse prognosis simply because they enter the vertical growth phase earlier in their evolution and achieve a greater depth and penetration into the skin.

VI. STAGING

The staging system for melanoma is based on recommendations of the AJCC and has undergone several revisions over the years. The most recent modification is based on a recent analysis of a database involving 17,600 patients and is due to be adopted in early 2002. Several basic facts regarding the current and future AJCC staging system for melanoma are worth noting.

1. It is and will remain a four-stage system, with stages I and II indicating tumors localized to the skin of increasing thickness (T1–T4) and no evidence for metastases to regional lymph nodes or distant sites.

2. The presence or absence of ulceration of the primary tumor has been incorporated into the T stage.

3. With regard to nodal staging, a clear distinction needs to be drawn between pathologic staging [based on selective or elective lymph node dissection (ELND)] and clinical staging (physical examination and radiologic imaging).

4. Within stage III (nodal) disease, the number of involved lymph nodes is important and serves as the basis for distinction among N1, N2, and N3.

5. Within the category of stage IV (distant metastatic) disease, the site(s) of metastases and the presence or absence of an elevated serum lactate dehydrogenase (LDH) level are important prognostic factors and distinguish M1a, M1b, and M1c disease.

Table IV shows the current and soon to be adopted AJCC staging system.

VII. DIAGNOSTIC EVALUATION

A. Physical Examination

This should involve a thorough and complete examination of the skin, including nail beds, interdigital areas, and the scalp. Lymph node basins (groin, axilla, neck, epitrochlear, popliteal) should be palpated.

B. Biopsy

This serves as the basis for making the diagnosis of melanoma, the initial staging, and the need for sentinel lymph node (SLN) evaluation. An excision biopsy is preferred, although a full thickness incisional (punch) biopsy will suffice for larger lesions. At the minimum, the pathology report should mention the depth in millimeters, the Clark level, the presence or absence of ulceration, and the status of the margins. Additional useful information includes the degree of lymphocytic infiltration, mitotic rate, and the presence or absence of angiolymphatic invasion.

C. Evaluation of Regional Lymph Nodes

Physical examination is often inaccurate regarding proper evaluation of the draining lymph nodes. The risk of microscopic metastases that are not clinically detectable is high for lesions greater than 1 mm and increases with increasing thickness. ELND is not recommended, as it has not been shown to improve survival in randomized trials and subjects patients to potential morbidity, when the nodes may, in fact, be negative. Furthermore, in anatomical areas with am-

TABLE IV
AJCC Revised Staging System for Melanoma

Proposed TNM classification							

T classification — Thickness (mm) — Ulceration status

T classification	Thickness (mm)	Ulceration status
T1	≤1.0	a: w/o ulceration and level II/III
		b: with ulceration or level IV/V
T2	1.01–2.0	a: w/o ulceration
		b: with ulceration
T3	2.01–4.0	a: w/o ulceration
		b: with ulceration
T4	>4.0	a: w/o ulceration
		b: with ulceration

N classification	No. of metastatic nodes	Nodal metastatic mass
N1	1 node	a: micrometastasis[a]
		b: macrometastasis[b]
N2	2–3 nodes	a: micrometastasis[a]
		b: macrometastasis[b]
		c: in transit met(s)/satellite(s) *without* metastatic nodes
N3	4 or more metastatic nodes, or matted nodes, or in transit met(s)/satellite(s) and metastatic node(s)	

M classification	Site	Serum LDH
M1	Distant skin, SQ or nodal mets	Normal
M2	Lung metastases	Normal
M3	All other visceral metastases or any distant metastasis	Normal
		Elevated

Cutaneous melanoma

Clinical staging[c]				Pathologic staging[d]			
0	Tis	N0	M0	0	Tis[e]	N0	M0
IA	T1a	N0	M0	IA	T1a	N0	M0
IB	T1b	N0	M0	IB	T1b	N0	M0
	T2a	N0	M0		T2a	N0	M0
IIA	T2b	N0	M0	IIA	T2b	N0	M0
	T3a	N0	M0		T3a	N0	M0
IIB	T3b	N0	M0	IIB	T3b	N0	M0
	T4a	N0	M0		T4a	N0	M0
IIC	T4b	N0	M0	IIC	T4b	N0	M0
IIIA	Any T	N1	M0	IIIA	T1-4a	N1a	M0
					T1-4a	N2a	M0
IIIB	Any T	N (multiple)	M0	IIIB	T1-4b	N1a	M0
					T1-4b	N2a	M0
					T1-4a	N1b	M0
					T1-4a	N2b	M0
					T1-4a/b	N2c	M0
IIIC	Any T	N satellite(s)	M0	IIIC	T1-4b	N1b	M0
					T1-4b	N2b	M0
	Any T	N in-transit(s)	M0		Any T	N3	M0
IV	Any T	Any N	Any M	IV	Any T	Any N	Any M

[a]Micrometastases are diagnosed after sentinel or elective lymphadenectomy.

[b]Macrometastases are defined as clinically detectable nodal metastases confirmed by therapeutic lymphadenectomy or when nodal metastasis exhibits gross extracapsular extension.

[c]Clinical staging includes microstaging of the primary melanoma and clinical/radiologic evaluation for metastases. By convention, it should be used after complete excision of the primary melanoma with clinical assessment for regional and distant metastases.

[d]Pathologic staging includes microstaging of the primary melanoma and pathologic information about the regional lymph nodes after partial or complete lymphadenectomy. Pathologic stage 0 or stage 1A patients are the exception, they do not need pathological evaluation of their lymph nodes.

[e]Melanoma *in situ.*

biguous drainage, such as the trunk and head/neck, selection of the lymph node basin to dissect is inaccurate. The relatively new technique of SLN evaluation and biopsy is a simple and effective solution to this problem. This procedure has been reviewed extensively elsewhere, but essentially comprises a preoperative lymphoscintigram to identify potential drainage areas followed by the injection of lymphazurin blue and a radioactive colloid into the region of the primary melanoma, with subsequent identification of the node most likely to harbor microscopic spread. This lymph node (blue node, hot node) is removed and can be examined carefully with histology and immunostaining to identify occult metastases. A positive result is followed by a therapeutic lymph node dissection that is "directed" and no longer "elective." This relatively simple and ingenious technique has revolutionized the staging for localized melanoma and has identified a group of patients that can now be offered potentially life-saving adjuvant therapy. It is currently offered to most patients with primary tumors of ≥1 mm at the majority of centers in the United States. Furthermore, identification of the SLN has allowed investigation of more elaborate molecular testing for micrometastases using polymerase chain reaction (PCR) for melanoma markers such as tyrosinase.

D. Radiologic Evaluation

The use of routine imaging studies such as computerized tomography (CT) scans and magnetic resonance imaging (MRI) for superficial melanomas has not been shown to be cost effective and is not recommended. For stage I–IIA melanomas, a chest X-ray and routine blood work, including LDH, is sufficient. For stage IIB and higher, an abdominal CT scan is often added and a brain MRI is performed when clinically indicated.

VIII. PROGNOSTIC FACTORS

These form the basis for the AJCC staging system for melanoma and can be considered under the following subheadings.

A. For Localized Melanoma

The thickness of the lesion in millimeters (Breslow) is the most important prognostic factor for cutaneous melanoma that is localized to the skin. The presence or absence of ulceration is the next most important factor, and for all thicknesses (T1–T4), an ulcerated lesion carries a worse prognosis. Curiously, ulceration appears to affect prognosis independent of regional lymph node involvement.

B. For Melanoma That Has Spread to Regional Lymph Nodes

Once spread to regional lymph nodes has occurred, the extent of lymph node involvement becomes the most important prognostic factor. The number of involved nodes and whether they are microscopically or macroscopically involved determine prognosis. The presence of clinically occult nodal metastases can be detected by SLN evaluation, and a positive SLN has emerged as the most important prognostic factor for localized melanoma in several series.

C. For Melanoma That Has Spread to Distant Sites

The sites of distant metastases and the presence or absence of an elevated LDH level determine the prognosis for metastatic melanoma. This is reflected in the M1a to M1c subclassification of the AJCC staging system.

IX. TREATMENT

A. Surgical

1. Surgical Treatment of the Primary Lesion

Definitive treatment of the primary melanoma involves surgical excision of the primary and a wide local excision (WLE). The width of the margin of normal skin around the primary that needs to be removed is based on the depth of the lesion and is shown in Table V. Of note, if a SLN evaluation is planned, this should be performed prior to the WLE whenever possible.

TABLE V
Recommended Margins for Excision of
Primary Cutaneous Melanoma[a]

Breslow depth (mm) of primary	Recommended margin (minimum)
In situ melanoma	0.5 cm
≤1 mm	1 cm
>1 but ≤4 mm	2 cm
>4 mm	2–3 cm

Recommended margins are for areas in which it is anatomically feasible to obtain them. In certain areas, such as the face, a smaller margin may suffice.

2. Surgical Treatment of the Regional Lymph Node Basin

For patients with clinically palpable regional lymph nodes, a complete regional lymphadenectomy is indicated. In the axilla, this should include a level I–III dissection, but in the groin, a deep groin inguinal node dissection is usually not necessary. Long-term complications of lymphadenectomy include lymphedema and parasthesias.

As mentioned earlier, ELND is no longer routinely recommended for patients with clinically negative nodes, and a directed lymphadenectomy is performed for patients with a positive SLN. The role of ELND has been investigated in three randomized trials with negative results. The most recent intergroup melanoma trial randomized 741 patients with melanoma 1–4 mm thick to ELND or WLE only. At a median follow-up of 9 years, no significant survival differences were noted between the two groups of patients. Although certain subsets (tumor thickness between 1 and 2 mm, nonulcerated tumors, patients < 60 years old) appeared to benefit from ELND, these results are not considered valid due to the retrospective subgroup analysis performed. This debate has largely been put to rest given the convenience and accuracy of SLN biopsy.

B. Postsurgical Adjuvant Therapy

The poor prognosis of deeper primary melanoma and melanoma with regional metastasis—coupled with the failure of all carefully tested treatments to prolong survival in the setting of distant AJCC stage IV metastatic melanoma—has spurred a search for an effective postsurgical adjuvant therapy in earlier disease that is operable. These efforts to prevent relapse and improve survival for patients considered at high risk for recurrence have turned from crude immunostimulants such as Bacillus Calmette Guerin (BCG) and Corynebacterium Parvum, chemotherapy, hormonal agents, and nonspecific pharmacologic immunostimulants such as levamisole. None of these agents have significantly improved survival in randomized trials and will not be discussed further. More recently, the use of postsurgical adjuvant immunotherapy with high-dose interferon-α (IFNα) for 1 year has shown significant improvement in relapse-free (RFS) and overall survival (OS) for patients at the highest risk for recurrence (AJCC stages IIB and III). This improved RFS and OS interval with high-dose IFNα2b is modest and must be balanced against toxicities and costs as detailed later. This, nonetheless, represents the first significant evidence of benefit from adjuvant therapy in high-risk melanoma.

1. Selection of Patients for Adjuvant Therapy

Patients most likely to benefit from postsurgical adjuvant therapy are those considered to be at the highest risk for recurrence. In addition, the toxicities likely to be associated with such therapy make it imperative that only patients with the "greatest need" are subjected to treatment. The AJCC staging system described earlier incorporates the most important prognostic factors for localized melanoma and serves as a useful guideline to select patients for adjuvant therapy trials. Based on data from randomized trials outlined later, patients with newly diagnosed stage IIB or III disease or those with primary regional lymph node recurrence that can be surgically resected (recurrent stage III) are routinely offered adjuvant therapy with IFNα2b. The role of modified regimens of this agent in earlier stage disease (AJCC stage IIA) is investigational.

2. IFNα

IFNs are a group of complex proteins first identified by Isaacs and Lindeman in the 1950s. They possess diverse functions and can be broadly divided into two types: type I (IFNα and IFNβ), and type II (IFNγ). Recombinant DNA technology has allowed the production of virtually unlimited quantities of purified IFN, which has facilitated their testing both in the laboratory and in the clinic. IFNα has been the most extensively evaluated agent, of which three subspecies exist: IFNα2a (Roferon, Roche Pharmaceuticals), IFNα2b (Intron A, Schering Plough), and IFNα2c (Boehringer Ingelheim), which differ slightly in amino acid sequence. The cytotoxic and immunomodulatory properties of IFNα make it an interesting agent for evaluation in the adjuvant setting. This, coupled with the modest 16% overall response rate observed with IFNα in collected series of patients with metastatic melanoma, has spawned a number of large trials testing the ability of this agent to influence the course of surgically resected high-risk melanoma.

Large randomized trials were designed and conducted over the past decade by the Eastern Cooperative Oncology Group (ECOG), the North Central Cancer Treatment Group (NCCTG), the World Health Organization (WHO), and the European Organization for Research and Treatment of Cancer (EORTC) and have now come to maturity. Regimens tested in these trials have utilized various dosages and schedules of IFNα, and for purposes of interpretation, it is useful to divide these regimens into the following: high-dose regimens (with and without an intravenous induction phase), intermediate-dose regimens, and low-dose regimens. These are summarized in Table VI.

TABLE VI
Summary of IFN Trials for Adjuvant Therapy of Melanoma

High-dose trials
  With induction phase
    E1684
    E1690
    E1694
  Without induction phase
    NCCTG trial
  Induction phase only
    E1697
Intermediate-dose trials
  EORTC trials
Low-dose trials
  WHO trial #16
  E1690 (low-dose arm)

3. High-Dose Regimens with an Induction Phase

This regimen has been pioneered by ECOG in three important large, randomized trials of adjuvant therapy for stage IIB and III melanoma. It comprises a 1-year (52 week) treatment with high-dose IFN-α2b (HDI) therapy in two phases: an initial "induction phase" of 20 million international units (MIU)/m^2/day intravenously (IV) for 4 weeks followed by a "maintenance phase" of 10 MIU/m^2 three times per week (TIW) administered subcutaneously (SC) for 48 weeks. The benefit of this regimen was first demonstrated in ECOG trial E1684. Patients randomized to treatment had significantly improved RFS and OS compared with observation. At a median follow-up of 7 years, the median RFS was improved by 9 months (1.72 years in the HDI arm versus 0.98 year in the observation arm; $P_1 = 0.0023$), and the median OS was improved by 1 year (3.82 years versus 2.78 years; $P_1 = 0.0237$). The estimated 5-year survival rate was 46% for the HDI arm versus 37% for observation, indicating an absolute benefit of 9%, which happens to be nearly identical to the survival benefit noted in adjuvant chemotherapy regimens for other malignancies, such as breast cancer and colon cancer. These data formed the basis of the U.S. Food and Drug Administration (FDA) approval for adjuvant HDI therapy in 1996 as the standard of care for patients with T4 primary lesions and/or positive lymph nodes. Moreover, the significant RFS and OS benefit of HDI therapy first demonstrated in the analysis of E1684 published in 1996 has been confirmed based on long-term follow-up data with a median follow-up of 12.6 years.

A second trial (intergroup trial E1690) attempted to confirm the results of E1684 in a prospective evaluation of the same high-dose regimen versus observation and to investigate the efficacy of a seemingly promising low-dose IFNα2b regimen (3 MIU TIW for 2 years) versus observation in a three-arm randomized trial. At a median follow-up of 52 months, a statistically significant benefit in terms of RFS for HDI as compared with observation was noted (44% vs 35%; $p = 0.05$). However, no OS benefit was noted for HDI therapy as compared to observation, a finding that was inconsistent with the results of E1684. Low-dose IFNα2b therapy was not associated with a statistically significant benefit for either end point. The reasons why the HDI treatment was associated with a benefit in RFS without a corresponding improvement in OS are uncertain. Eligibility criteria for this protocol were similar to that of E1684, except those patients with thick primary melanomas (T4) and clinically negative nodes were not routinely required to undergo staging lymphadenectomy. As a result, 25% of the 642 patients entered into this trial had thick primary melanomas and a surgically undefined nodal status with the potential for locoregional relapse due to undetected microscopic disease in the regional lymph nodes. Indeed, a retrospective analysis of postrelapse therapy demonstrated that IFNα–containing salvage therapy was utilized significantly more often in relapsed patients in the E1690 observation group compared with the HDI group with a corresponding improvement in survival. This differential use of IFNα-containing salvage therapy between treatment groups may have confounded the analysis of OS in this trial, a factor that was not evident in the previous E1684 trial.

The most recent results addressing the role of adjuvant HDI therapy have emerged from intergroup trial E1694. In this study, 880 patients with resected stage IIB and III melanoma were randomized to HDI therapy for 1 year or the ganglioside GMK vaccine for 2 years. The GMK vaccine comprises the antigen GM2, a ganglioside constituent of melanoma cells, conjugated with keyhole limpit hemocyanin and the QS-21 adjuvant, and is more immunogenic than the GM2 vaccine, which had previously shown promising results in studies conducted at Memorial Sloan-Kettering Cancer Center for patients with AJCC stage III melanoma. The primary objective of this trial was to determine if GMK was superior to HDI therapy with respect to RFS and OS, and the trial was designed with early stopping rules in the event that IFNα2b was superior. The trial was closed in June 2000 at the recommendation of the Data Safety Monitoring Committee based on an interim analysis demonstrating a highly significant RFS and OS benefit for patients treated with IFNα2b over patients who had been assigned to the GMK vaccine. Among eligible patients ($n = 774$), HDI therapy provided a statistically significant RFS benefit (hazard ratio = 1.47, $P = 0.0015$) and OS benefit (hazard ratio =

1.52, $P = 0.009$) compared with GMK, suggesting an approximately 33% decrease in the hazard of relapse and death for patients treated with IFNα2b. No observation arm was included in this trial, which was designed after FDA approval of HDI, but concerns that the GMK vaccine may have produced deleterious effects upon survival have not been substantiated, based on the overlap in the survival curves between the GMK treatment arm of E1694 and the observation arm of the previous trial, E1690. Furthermore, analysis of the outcome for patients who developed higher antibody titers to the GMK vaccine showed a trend to improved RFS survival ($P = 0.06$), consonant with earlier studies of the GM2 vaccine.

4. HDI Therapy without an Intravenous Induction Phase

NCCTG evaluated a regimen of IFNα given at a dose of 20 MU/m^2 TIW administered intramuscularly (IM) for 3 months in 262 patients with resected stage AJCC stage II and III melanoma. Major differences between this regimen and the ECOG HDI regimen are the lack of the intravenous induction phase, the shortened course (3 months), and the route of administration (IM). No benefit in either RFS or OS was noted for patients treated with IFN; however, a trend to a benefit in RFS was noted for the subset of patients with lymph node-positive disease that did not achieve statistical significance.

5. Low-Dose IFNα

The high-dose regimen devised by ECOG is associated with substantial toxicity, including flu-like symptoms (fever, myalgia, anorexia), depression, and other neuropsychiatric manifestations, neutropenia, and hepatotoxicity. In general, these are manageable and completely reversible, but nevertheless lead to dose reduction and/or discontinuation in up to two-thirds of patients treated. This has been the impetus behind the development of low-dose IFN trials for adjuvant therapy that have been pioneered mainly in Europe. The WHO trial 16 tested a regimen of IFNα at a dose of 3 MIU TIW for 3 years compared with observation for surgically resected AJCC stage III melanoma. No benefit in terms of RFS or OS was noted. The E1690 trial described earlier included a low-dose arm (3 MIU TIW SC for 2 years), and once again no benefit was demonstrable in terms of RFS or OS. A similar low-dose regimen has been investigated for patients with earlier stage (AJCC stage II) melanoma in an Austrian multicenter trial and a French cooperative group trial. While preliminary evidence for an improved RFS was noted, no benefit in terms of OS has emerged from these studies. Based on these studies, the use of low-dose IFNα in the adjuvant therapy of melanoma cannot be recommended.

6. Intermediate-Dose Regimens of IFN

Given the lack of efficacy of low-dose IFN and the toxicity associated with higher doses, an intermediate-dose regimen has been sought as a potential "happy medium." This approach has been investigated by the European groups, particularly EORTC. Trials of hybrid regimens of SC-administered IFNα with and without a SC induction phase have either been completed or are ongoing. At the present time, no conclusions regarding the use of intermediate-dose regimens of IFN can be made.

7. Vaccines in Adjuvant Therapy for Melanoma

A multitude of vaccine approaches are being investigated as adjuvant therapy for intermediate- and high-risk melanoma. The various melanoma vaccines may be considered under the following subheadings: those that employ whole tumor cells, cell lysates, or shed antigens and those that employ chemically defined or synthetic antigens of tumor cells.

8. Whole Cells, Shed Antigens, and Tumor Lysate Vaccines

Immunization with whole tumor cells, either cultured or noncultured, has been conducted with a variety of immunological adjuvants. The immunologic adjuvants employed have included microbial preparations ranging from Old Tuberculin/Freund's and BCG, an attenuated tubercle bacillus of bovine origin, to the more recent use of lipid-A derivatives such as Detox (monophosphoryl lipid-A, Ribi Immunochemicals), which is a component of the mycobacterial immunostimulants. Current vaccines under development include Cvax, a vaccine created from three allogeneic melanoma cell lines with BCG as an adjuvant; AVAX, an hapten-modified autologous tu-

mor cell vaccine; and Melacine, a vaccine from lysates of two allogeneic melanoma cell lines with Detox as an adjuvant. Another vaccine from shed antigens of allogeneic melanoma cell lines is referred to as the Bystryn vaccine.

Most vaccine trials that claim a benefit in survival do so based on phase II trials with historical controls and, with few exceptions, randomized phase III data are lacking. The exception is the Melacine vaccine, which, in a recently reported randomized phase III trial for stage II melanoma patients conducted by the South West Oncology Group (SWOG), showed a potential benefit in RFS for the vaccine as compared to observation at an early analysis. A more recent analysis has revealed that the most significant benefit appears to be restricted to certain HLA types, and the hypothesis that this vaccine may be active in only certain phase III randomized trials of the AVAX vaccine and Cvax is currently being evaluated in high-risk stage III melanoma.

9. Vaccines Composed of Chemically Defined Antigens

The chemically defined tumor cell vaccines are directed against two major categories of antigen: gangliosides and peptides/proteins. Gangliosides comprise a series of glycolipids termed according to their carbohydrate moiety (mono-M; di-D-sialylated). GM1, GM2, GM3, and GD2, GD3 induce antibody responses, the most important of which is GM2. This antigen, in the form of the vaccine GMK, was tested head to head against IFNα in the E1694 trial described earlier with negative results.

An increasing range of immunogenic proteins and their component peptides recognized by host T cells have been defined, which fall into two major categories: the first are killer CD8 T cell-recognized epitopes in the context of the major histocompatibility antigen complex (class I MHC-HLA-A1, HLA -A2, etc.). These antigens, recognized by killer CD8[+] T cells, have represented the investigation of the peptide vaccines to date. The second major category of peptide vaccine is that recognized by the helper CD4[+] T cell, and these are recognized in the context of the MHC class II complex known as HLA, DR, DP, and DQ. The first of these trials has just been initiated at the University of Pittsburgh Cancer Institute

Melanoma Center and the NCI. Combining these vaccines with IFNα2b and cytokines, such as interleukin-2 (IL-2), IL-12, and granulocyte–macrophage colony-stimulating factor (GM-CSF), represents another promising approach that is being tested in phase II and III trials.

10. Future Directions in Adjuvant Therapy for Melanoma

Current strategies for trials in the adjuvant therapy for melanoma include (a) the use of new techniques for better definition of risk groups with sentinel node mapping and early detection of micrometastases by immunologic and molecular markers; (b) building upon the significant advance of HDI with incorporation of more specific approaches with peptide vaccines and more aggressive IL-2-based regimens; (c) analysis of the contribution of the intravenous induction component of the 1-year HDI regimen is to identify whether it is the critical component of the regimen; and (d) analysis of the actual immunologic basis of the benefit from HDI and other new therapies to better select those who benefit most.

C. Therapy for Stage IV (Metastatic) Melanoma

Metastatic melanoma of AJCC stage IV remains a dismal disease with a median survival of 6 to 9 months and a 2-year survival of less than 13%. Chemotherapy alone has proved to be ineffective in altering these statistics. The ample evidence that host immunologic factors are important to the outcome of this disease has led to the evaluation of cytokines and other immunotherapy with and without chemotherapy for this setting of disease.

1. Chemotherapy

The use of cytotoxic chemotherapy for metastatic melanoma may be considered under two headings: single-agent chemotherapy and combination chemotherapy.

2. Single-Agent Chemotherapy

Drugs with demonstrated activity in MM include alkylating agents [dacarbazine (DTIC), temozolomide], nitrosureas (carmustine, lomustine), platinum analogs (cisplatin, carboplatin), and microtubule toxins (vincristine, vinblastine, paclitaxel). The lack of efficacy of these agents is highlighted by the fact that the "gold standard" among these agents remains DTIC with a response rate of 12–20%, which after three decades of research is still the only chemotherapy drug approved by the FDA for this disease. Long-term responses with single-agent DTIC or other agents are exceedingly rare and these drugs primarily have a palliative role in malignant melanoma.

3. Combination Chemotherapy

The rationale behind combining chemotherapy drugs is obvious: to obtain additive or synergistic effects with nonoverlapping toxicity. Unfortunately, this strategy has been largely unsuccessful in metastatic melanoma. An example of a widely used combination chemotherapy regimen is the "Dartmouth regimen," a combination of DTIC, cisplatin, carmustine, and tamoxifen. Early phase II data suggested a superior response rate of up to 50% for this combination and the notion that tamoxifen was in some manner critical to this regimen. Randomized phase III trials of chemotherapy with and without tamoxifen have not borne out this hypothesis. Furthermore, an important randomized phase III trial of the Dartmouth regimen compared to single-agent DTIC failed to demonstrate a statistically significant advantage for the combination in terms of response rate, time to progression, or survival. Based on this and other data, there is no role for combination chemotherapy for treatment of metastatic melanoma outside of a clinical trial.

The combination of chemotherapy with immunotherapy is known as biochemotherapy or chemoimmunotherapy. This is a promising approach and is discussed later.

D. Immunotherapy

1. IFNα

This was the first cytokine to be evaluated clinically in metastatic melanoma. The aggregate response rate with this agent in phase II studies is about 16% (one-third complete). In general, intermediate, prolonged schedules were found to be more effective than short course interrupted regimens, but durable responses were rare, with a median response duration of about

4 months. As with chemotherapy, responses tend to be restricted to skin and soft tissue disease and visceral responses are unusual. A large, randomized phase III trial conducted by ECOG failed to demonstrate a benefit of this agent in combination with DTIC as compared to DTIC alone, but a recent meta-analysis of more than 1000 patients reported a higher response rate for IFN-containing regimens, suggesting a continuing role for this agent in metastatic melanoma in combination with other agents. At the present time, although this agent is rarely used alone in metastatic melanoma, it is a component of most biochemotherapy regimens (see later).

2. IL-2

Perhaps the most therapeutically important cytokine in metastatic melanoma, IL-2 was identified in 1976 as a growth factor for T cells. Isolation of the cDNA clone in 1983 allowed unlimited quantities to be produced by recombinant DNA technology and has facilitated the testing of this agent in the laboratory and the clinic. As with IFNα, this agent has been tested using a variety of schedules, doses, and routes of administration.

3. High-Dose IL-2

This schedule of high-dose bolus intravenous administration was devised at the NCI Surgery Branch based on preclinical animal models, indicating a dose–response relationship. The dose administered is either 600,000 or 720,000 IU/kg once every 8 h in a cycle that comprises a maximum of 14 doses. Following a 1-week rest, the cycle is repeated, with two cycles comprising one course of therapy. Using such a schedule, a response rate of 16% was observed in 270 patients treated at several institutions in a pooled analysis. The important distinguishing feature of these data was the median response duration (8.9 months) and the durability of the responses among the complete responders. At a minimum follow-up of 6 years, 47% of all responders remain alive, suggesting a low but real "cure" rate. The U.S. FDA approved this dose and schedule for metastatic melanoma in 1998, but the high toxicity (cardiac, renal, pulmonary) and expense associated with this treatment have not allowed the widespread adoption of this regimen. This regimen has never formally been tested in a phase III

multicenter trial, and its use is mainly restricted to specialized centers with facilities for intensive monitoring and supportive care.

4. Intermediate-Dose IL-2

Administration of IL-2 by continuous intravenous infusion (CIV) at a lower dose was introduced in an attempt to enhance the immune effects and lower toxicity. When given as a single agent by this route at a dose of 9–18 MU/m^2, overall response rates have been comparable to the high-dose bolus regimen described earlier, but durable complete responses have not been as frequent, lessening the enthusiasm for CIV IL-2 as a stand-alone modality. The main advantage of CIV IL-2 is the possibility of combining it with other agents in biochemotherapy regimens (see later).

5. Low-Dose IL-2

The obvious advantages of low-dose IL-2 (2–9 MU/m^2)-administered SC are lower toxicity and the potential for outpatient administration. However, low-dose IL-2 as a single agent has not proved to be effective in melanoma, and a 1% response rate has been reported in a large phase III trial. The potential ability of histamine to enhance the effects of SC IL-2, particularly in patients with liver metastases from melanoma, is intriguing and under investigation. At the present time, outside of a clinical trial, low-dose SC IL-2 cannot be recommended as a therapeutic modality in metastatic melanoma.

6. Biochemotherapy (Chemoimmunotherapy)

This is a strategy that seeks to capitalize on the potential benefits of both chemotherapy and immunotherapy. This approach has been investigated at several institutions, including the MD Anderson Cancer Center (MDACC), where various schedules of a combination of three chemotherapy drugs (cisplatin, vinblastine, DTIC; CVD) and two immunotherapy agents (IL-2 and IFNα) were tested. Sequential treatment involves the administration of chemotherapy first followed by biotherapy (bio), whereas concurrent administration implies the simultaneous administration of all drugs over a 4- to 5-day period. The MDACC reported the preliminary results of a sequential biochemotherapy (CVD-bio) regimen as compared to CVD alone. Response rates and time to progression were almost doubled for the CVD-bio arm, but the survival difference was borderline and toxicity was prohibitive.

The concurrent administration of the CVD-bio regimen has been found to be safe and effective with manageable toxicity, with a response rate of over 50% and a durable response rate of about 10%. A high-priority phase III intergroup trial of this concurrent combination versus CVD alone for previously un-treated metastatic melanoma is currently ongoing. It should be noted that this aggressive regimen is also the focus of an ongoing randomized trial for the ad-juvant therapy of a subset of stage III melanoma (two or more positive lymph nodes). This biochemother-apy regimen is administered in the inpatient setting, and various outpatient variations have been tested, but have shown lower and less durable response rates.

D. Other Immunotherapeutic Approaches

1. Vaccines

Vaccines have been alluded to already under the dis-cussion of adjuvant therapy. It should be noted that most vaccine strategies are based on preliminary work in patients with advanced stage IV melanoma. Vaccine-based therapy has to date not given classical "response rates" (complete response and partial re-sponse) that are in the range of chemotherapy, but they have substantially lower toxicity and offer the hope for more sustained responses and induction of immunity. This has made the search for surrogate markers of immune response critical to advancement in the vaccine therapy field. The approaches to de-velopment of vaccines are similar to those described in Section IX,B and will likely ultimately have their greatest impact in early (adjuvant) treatment. Impor-tant antigens targeted for vaccines include a cancer-restricted family of MAGE-1, MAGE-3, and ESO-1 and a lineage marker family: Melan-A/MART-1, gp100, and tyrosinase. Derivative peptide epitopes have also been identified, which are more immuno-genic than the native peptides. Clinical trials com-bining these MHC-restricted vaccines and cytokines/IFNs/growth factors that may improve response through antigen-processing cells (dendritic cells) are ongoing.

2. Monoclonal Antibodies (mAbs)

Target antigens for mAbs are mainly the gangliosides present on melanoma cells, especially GD2 and GD3. mAbs are either unconjugated or conjugated to other agents such as cytokines and radionuclides. R24 (anti-GD3) is an example of an unconjugated mAb that has shown occasional responses in clinical trials. The difficulty with this approach lies in the early difficulty due to the origin of these antibodies, from the mouse, resulting in the development of human antimouse an-tibodies (HAMA). Humanized antibodies (chimeric antibodies) are now available conjugated with ricin A as a toxin. Once again, although toxicity has been tolerable, responses have been infrequent.

3. Adoptive Immunotherapy

This technique combines cytokine therapy (IL-2) with specialized lymphocytes selected for their en-hanced immunogenicity. Lymphokine-activated killer cells (LAK) and tumor-infiltrating lymphocytes (TIL) are cells considered to possess greater immune effects than unprimed lymphocytes. Unfortunately, isolation of these cells is difficult and expensive and no data exist that suggest the superiority of this approach over IL-2 alone. The main utility of TIL at the present time is their use in identifying melanoma-associated antigens necessary to devise vaccines.

4. Radiation Therapy (RT) for Melanoma

Melanoma is a radio-resistant tumor, and the use of RT is mainly restricted to the palliation of brain metastases, spinal cord compression, and painful bony lesions. More recently, the use of stereotactic radio-surgery or "gamma knife" for isolated brain metastases has shown promise in terms of disease control. Cur-rently, there is no established role of RT in the adju-vant therapy of melanoma.

X. SUMMARY

Melanoma is a fascinating neoplasm with a prognosis that varies from virtually 100% curable to 100% in-curable. Advances in staging and prognostic evalua-tion now permit accurate assessment of risk for recur-rence and appropriate interventions in terms of adjuvant therapy. The close relationship of this disease to the immune system has allowed immunotherapy to become an integral component of treatment, both for high risk for recurrence disease and for more advanced metastatic melanoma.

See Also the Following Articles

CYTOKINES • MELANOMA: MOLECULAR AND CELLULAR ABNORMALITIES • SKIN CANCER

Bibliography

Agarwala, S. S., and Kirkwood, J. M. (1999). Adjuvant interferon treatment for melanoma. *Hematol./Oncol. Clin. North Am.* **12,** 823–833.

Agarwala, S. S., and Kirkwood, J. M. (1999). Melanoma: Immunotherapeutic approaches. *BioDrugs* **12**(3), 193–208.

Balch, C. M., Buzaid, A. C., Kirkwood, J. M., *et al.* (2001). Final version of the American Joint Committee on Cancer Staging System for Cutaneous Melanoma (Original Reports: Melanoma). *J. Clin. Oncol.* **19**(16), 3635–3648.

Balch, C., Houghton, A. N., Sober, A. J., and Soong, S-J (eds.) (1998). "Cutaneous Melanoma," 3rd Ed. Quality Medical Publishing, St. Louis, MO.

Kirkwood, J. M., and Agarwala, S. (1993). Systemic cytotoxic and biologic therapy melanoma. *In* "Cancer Principles and Practice of Oncology," pp. 1–16.

Lotze, M. T., Dallal, R. M., Kirkwood, J. M., and Flickinger, J. C. (2001). Cutaneous melanoma. *In* "Cancer Principles and Practices of Oncology" (V. T. Devita, S. Hellman, and S. A. Rosenberg, eds.), 6th Ed., p. 2012. Lippincott-Raven, Philadelphia.

Metabolic Diagnosis of Prostate Cancer by Magnetic Resonance Spectroscopy

Leslie C. Costello
R. B. Franklin
University of Maryland, Baltimore

J. Kurhanewicz
University of California, San Francisco

GLOSSARY

central gland The region of the human prostate that consists of the central zone, transition zone, and periurethral tissue; the site for the development of benign prostatic hyperplasia.

1-H magnetic resonance spectroscopy (MRS) Like MRI, MRS uses a strong magnetic field and radiowaves to obtain a noninvasive chemical assessment of soft tissue based on the relative concentrations of cellular chemicals (metabolites). In this scenario, the much larger water signal must be suppressed in order to see the signals from metabolites that have much lower concentrations. 1-H (proton) MRS analysis relies on the positioning of the hydrogen atom component of the metabolite. The result is a frequency line plot, known as a spectrum, in which the protons appear as peaks at specific frequencies and the area under the peaks is related to the concentration of protons present. This provides an analysis of levels of cell metabolites such as citrate and choline.

magnetic resonance imaging (MRI) MRI uses a strong magnetic field and radiofrequency waves to noninvasively obtain anatomic pictures (images) based on tissue water. The images can be contrasted so that the cancer appears different from healthy tissue based on changes in the structure of the tissue, as water molecules in different chemical environments have different physical properties.

mitochondrial aconitase The enzyme that catalyzes the first reaction leading to the oxidation of citrate in cellular metabolism.

peripheral zone The largest region of the human prostate gland; responsible for the specialized function of citrate production and secretion; the major site for the development of malignancy.

one-, two-, and three-dimensional phase encoding An MR technique that allows for the encoding of spatial information through the application of magnetic field gradients. Phase encoding in one dimension yields information about a column or 1-D array of MR data, in two dimensions yields a single slice image or 2-D array of MR information, and in three dimensions yields a volume image or 3-D array of MR data.

single voxel 1-H MRS Acquires a single spectrum that provides a metabolic assessment of a three-dimensional cube of tissue whose location is typically identified based on an anatomic (MRI) image.

three-dimenional magnetic resonance spectroscopic imaging Combines the chemical information provided by 1-H MRS with the spatial information provided by three-dimensional phase encoding. This is accomplished by selecting a large volume of interest using a proton single voxel MRS technique and then dividing that volume into a three-dimensional array of higher spatial resolution volumes (multiple voxels) using phase encoding techniques. Proton MRS spectra acquired from this array of volumes provide a chemical map of the entire selected volume that can be correlated directly with MRI anatomic maps collected in the same examination using the same equipment.

T he detection of prostate cancer (Pca) and the identification of malignant loci within the prostate gland are important issues in the diagnosis and treatment of this disease. The development and employment of noninvasive techniques are especially important. Imaging technology has been and continues to be developed to address these issues. 1-H magnetic resonance spectroscopy (1-H MRS) imaging has been applied to the identification of prostate malignancy. By 1-H MRS determination of citrate and related metabolites *in situ*, a noninvasive procedure that identifies malignant loci within the prostate now exists. The procedure is more accurate, specific, and sensitive than other imaging procedures. In combination with magnetic resonance imaging (MRI), 1-H MRS provides a metabolic map of the prostate gland that can identify malignant tissue and regional differences within the prostate. This permits follow-up examinations to determine the progression or regression of malignancy during watchful waiting or pursuant to treatment. The advantages of combined 1-H MRS/MRI and its further development should make this noninvasive technology a principal tool in the diagnosis of PCa and in the detection and localization of malignancy in the prostate gland.

I. INTRODUCTION

A major current problem involved in prostate cancer is the absence of sensitive, accurate, and preferably noninvasive procedures for the diagnosis of PCa. Moreover, procedures are needed that will permit the early detection, staging, location, and estimation of the volume of the malignancy and preferably a mapping of the prostate for follow-up of progression and regression of the malignancy. The unique citrate metabolism relationships of the prostate, coupled with recent developments and technological advancements in 1-H MRS for the *in situ* determination of citrate levels, provide an excellent diagnostic procedure, which can achieve all these goals. There now exist strong, compelling basic and clinical studies in support of the employment of 1-H MRS measurements of citrate and other associated metabolites in the diagnosis of PCa and in the *in situ* visualization of malignant loci. This article provides the background leading to the current status of MRS citrate analysis, summarizes data from clinical trials, and describes the applications of the procedure for the diagnosis and treatment of PCa and follow-up of patients. The use of MRS studies in defining the functional, as well as pathological, relationships of the prostate is also discussed.

II. CITRATE RELATIONSHIPS IN PROSTATE

The human prostate gland is a complex organ composed of anatomically, functionally, and metabolically discrete regions. Major components include the peripheral zone, central zone, and transition zone. It has become common to refer to the prostate components as the peripheral zone and the central gland; the latter includes the central zone, transition zone, and periurethral tissue. The major function of the prostate gland is the production and secretion of prostatic fluid. Moreover, the major component of prostatic fluid is citrate. The peripheral zone, which comprises about 70% of the prostate gland of males under 40 years of age, is responsible for this function.

The normal prostate gland and prostatic fluid contain enormously high levels of citrate, as represented in Table I. The secretory epithelial cells of the peripheral zone are responsible for the production, accumulation, and secretion of citrate, which is referred to as "net citrate production." The metabolic pathway of net citrate production is presented in Fig. 1. In these cells, citrate is synthesized and accumulates because of a uniquely limiting mitochondrial (m-)aconitase. Citrate oxidation is minimal, and the Krebs cycle is aborted at the first step of citrate oxidation. Citrate is an end product of metabolism in these prostate cells.

Normal mammalian cell metabolism, function, and survival are highly dependent on citrate oxidation via a fully operational Krebs cycle. Citrate oxidation occupies a central role in the intermediary metabolism of cells, and its inhibition has serious consequences on cellular bioenergetics (coupled ATP production) and on biosynthetic pathways that are dependent on a functional Krebs cycle. To ensure that the operation of the Krebs cycle is not limited in normal mammalian cells, m-aconitase activity is in excess and is not a regulatory enzyme of metabolism. Consequently, citrate-producing prostate epithelial cells (e.g., normal peripheral secretory epithelial cells) exhibit unique metabolic relationships that are not associated with any other normal mammalian cells.

Like normal prostate, benign prostatic hyperplasia (BPH) tissue also exhibits extraordinarily high citrate levels (Table I). However, PCa tissue samples (biopsy, transurethral resection, prostatectomy samples) consistently exhibit low citrate levels (Table I). Moreover, the decrease in citrate occurs early in malignancy, even preceding the histopathological changes and identification of malignancy. Most importantly, malignant prostate tissue virtually never exhibits the high citrate levels that characterize the high citrate content of normal and BPH prostate. Consequently, the decrease in citrate level is presently the most consistent and persistent characteristic that distinguishes prostate PCa from normal prostate and/or BPH. Because of these relationships, it had been suggested that citrate might be a valuable marker for the diagnosis of PCa, especially in the early stages of the disease.

III. 1-H MRS ANALYSIS OF PROSTATE CITRATE

Although the analysis of resected tissue (biopsy samples) could provide an effective procedure for the identification of PCa, a method that would permit the noninvasive detection of prostate citrate levels *in situ* was more preferable and advantageous as a diagnostic tool. The application of 1-H magnetic resonance spectroscopy has proved to be highly reliable, sensitive, and specific for the quantitation of citrate levels in prostate tissues. The development of endorectal coils permitted the determination of MRS spectra of the intact prostate, thereby providing a noninvasive procedure for the determination of prostate citrate levels (Fig. 2).

With 1-H MRS, one observes specific resonances (peaks) for citrate, choline, and creatine at distinct frequencies or positions in the MRS spectrum (Fig. 2). The area under these peaks is related to the concentration of these metabolites. The normal human prostate exhibits regional differences in the absolute levels of citrate and in the relative levels of

TABLE I
Representative Citrate Levels
in the Human Prostate[a]

Normal central zone	5,000
Normal peripheral zone	13,000
BPH (mixed tissue)	8,000–15,000
BPH (glandular tissue)	20,000–50,000
PCa (mixed tissue)	1,000–3,000
Malignant tissue	<500
Stromal tissue	150–300
Other soft tissues	150–450
Blood plasma	90–110
Prostatic fluid	40,000–160,000

[a]All values are nanomoles per gram wet weight.

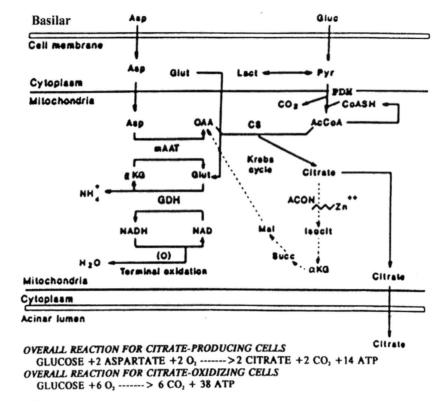

OVERALL REACTION FOR CITRATE-PRODUCING CELLS
    GLUCOSE +2 ASPARTATE +2 O₂ -------> 2 CITRATE +2 CO₂ +14 ATP
OVERALL REACTION FOR CITRATE-OXIDIZING CELLS
    GLUCOSE +6 O₂ -------> 6 CO₂ + 38 ATP

FIGURE 1 The metabolic pathway of net citrate production by normal prostate peripheral zone epithelial cells. The pathway reveals that citrate oxidation is inhibited at mitochondrial aconitase by high levels of zinc that accumulate in the mitochondria. In PCa, the malignant cells have lost the ability to accumulate zinc so that aconitase is no longer inhibited and citrate oxidation occurs. This is the basis for the low citrate levels that differentiate malignant tissue from normal peripheral zone tissue. ACON, aconitase; PDH, pyruvate dehydrogenase; mAAT, aspartate aminotransferase; CS, citrate synthase; GDH, glutamic dehydrogenase.

choline+creatine versus citrate (Fig. 3). The normal peripheral zone exhibits a strong citrate signal, particularly in relation to choline+creatine. Changes in these concentrations can be used to identify cancer (Fig. 3). Specifically, 1-H MRS reveals that peripheral zone citrate levels are dramatically decreased at malignant loci versus the pronounced citrate peak in healthy peripheral zone tissue.

1-H MRS spectroscopy techniques are now available for obtaining either a single spectrum from a specific region (single voxel of the prostate) (Fig. 2) or a multidimensional array of spectra from multiple voxels of the entire prostate (Fig. 3). The acquisition and analysis of single voxel 1H-MRS spectra from the prostate are easier to implement than multivoxel techniques. However, in the study of cancer, single voxel

techniques are limited to studying clearly defined homogeneous lesions or diseases that affect all regions uniformly. Additionally, single voxel 1H-MRS cannot provide information on the spatial extent and heterogeneity of cancer and relies on a priori information about the location of the cancer that is often poorly provided by MRI. The complexity of normal prostate zonal anatomy and the often small, infiltrative, and multifocal nature of prostate cancer require a multivoxel approach. This will provide information concerning prostate metabolite levels throughout the entire gland to be of clinical utility.

The MRS metabolic profile of the prostate also revealed that the choline peak (consisting of a conglomerate of choline derivatives) increases in prostate cancer (Fig. 2). As in other human cancers, the ele-

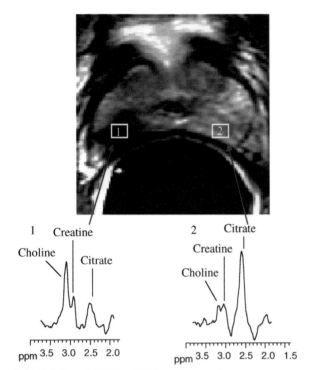

FIGURE 2 1-H MRS and MRI localization of prostate cancer in a 58-year-old man. (Top) MRI revealing a tumor focus [1] in the right lobe of the peripheral zone as compared to the normal left lobe [2]. (Bottom) 1-H spectra obtained from the malignant area [1] and the corresponding normal area [2] of the peripheral zone. The normal area is characterized by a strong citrate peak and low choline+creatine peaks. In contrast, the malignant locus exhibits a markedly diminished citrate signal and an elevated choline peak.

vation of the choline peak is associated with changes in cell membrane synthesis and degradation that occur with the evolution of cancer. The (choline+creatine)/citrate ratio takes advantage of the opposite nature of the changes in citrate and choline observed in cancer, which enhance the differentiation of malignant loci from normal tissue. Alterations in choline and citrate levels are likely metabolically linked. Malignancy requires increased lipogenesis and membraneogenesis. Citrate is the source of acetyl-CoA in lipogenesis. Therefore, a decrease in citrate should be associated with an increase in choline derivatives required for membraneogenesis.

In situ MRS studies confirm an important concept regarding the pathogenesis of prostate malignancy (Fig. 2). The origin of PCa occurs mainly in the peripheral zone. The pathogenesis of PCa involves the metabolic transformation of normal citrate-producing secretory epithelial cells (i.e., cells that do not readily oxidize citrate) to citrate-oxidizing malignant cells. Moreover, the underlying cause of this metabolic transformation has been established. Normal peripheral zone secretory epithelial cells accumulate high zinc levels that inhibit m-aconitase activity (Fig. 1). The malignant prostate cells have lost the ability to accumulate zinc, which eliminates its inhibitory effect on citrate oxidation.

The *in situ* determination of citrate reveals other important relationships. It is now evident that, as proposed by Costello and Franklin, the peripheral zone and not the central gland is the specific region of the prostate that is responsible for the function of citrate production and secretion (Fig. 3). MRS studies also reveal that glandular BPH involves the proliferation of citrate-producing secretory epithelial cells, presumably from the transition zone, into the central zone (Fig. 4).

IV. CLINICAL APPLICATIONS OF 1-H MRS

Figure 5 is a composite of studies from three different laboratories that employed 1-H MRS examination of patient populations. The results reflect the striking consistency of the significant decrease in peripheral zone citrate levels of PCa versus normal or BPH prostate. It is also clearly evident that cancerous tissue never retains the high citrate levels characteristic of normal and BPH prostate. It is striking that none of the PCa subjects from the three separate studies exhibited a high peripheral zone citrate in the range of the normal peripheral zone. One would expect that some voxels in some cancer subjects would include various combinations of malignant and histologically normal glandular tissue and would contain early, highly differentiated cancer. Under such conditions, citrate should range from relatively high levels to very low levels, which is not the case. Similarly, the determination of citrate in resected prostate tissue also reveals a consistently low citrate level even when the histologically identifiable malignancy represents a small percentage of the glandular component. The

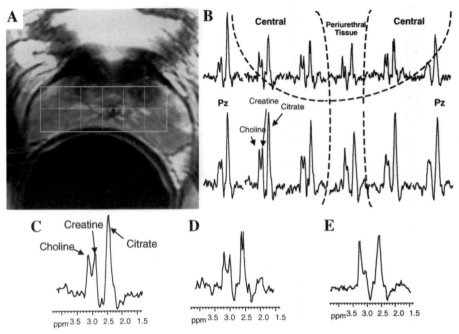

FIGURE 3 The combined MRI/1-H MRS metabolic profile of the normal prostate of a volunteer, age 35. (A) MRI with the grid identifying voxels targeted for the MRS metabolic profile. (B) MRS metabolic spectra of voxels demonstrating citrate and choline relationships in the different anatomic regions of the prostate gland. There are three distinct metabolic patterns exhibited by the peripheral zone (PZ), central zone, and periurethral tissue. (C) The metabolic pattern associated with normal peripheral zone tissue has high levels of citrate and intermediate levels of choline and creatine. (D) In the central gland, there is a 57% reduction of citrate and similar levels of choline and creatine as in the peripheral zone. (E) In periurethral tissue, there is a 67% reduction of citrate and an 11% increase in choline. Adapted from Kurhanewicz *et al.* (1996).

most plausible explanation for this relationship is that a large population of histologically normal glandular epithelial cells in proximity to the malignant loci become citrate-oxidizing cells and represent a premalignant stage. This indicates that the metabolic transformation of the neoplastic cell is an important step in the development of PCa. Thus, MRS determination of peripheral zone citrate levels could serve as an early indicator of likely development or progression of overt malignancy.

A major roadblock to improving the outcome of patients with prostate cancer is a current absence of a procedure to determine accurately the local extent of the malignancy and the risk of progression. Without this information, it is difficult to make an informed decision about what type of treatment is most appropriate or whether any treatment is needed at all. Currently available imaging tests used for the local evaluation of prostate cancer include (1) transrectal ultrasound (TRUS), a tool routinely used in clinical practice for biopsy guidance and local staging; (2) endorectal MRI, a rapidly maturing technology that shows potential for local staging; and (3) endorectal 1-H MRS, a promising technique that, as described earlier, detects metabolic patterns of prostate tissue. 1-H MRS analysis is significantly enhanced when a spatial continuum of the metabolite characteristics throughout the prostate is obtained, producing a metabolic image of the prostate (MRSI) (Figs. 3 and 4). The MRSI metabolic image can then be coupled with the anatomic image provided by MRI. This combination (MRSI/MRI) provides the anatomic information necessary for the interpretation of the metabolic pattern obtained by MRSI. The result is the production of a permanent record of the metabolic–anatomic mapping of the prostate. The determination of citrate and choline provided by MRSI, in combination with the anatomic information provided by high-resolution

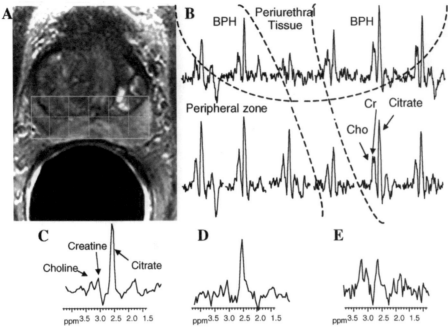

FIGURE 4 1-H MRS analysis of the prostate gland of a BPH patient, age 68. (A) MRI of the prostate gland with the grid of voxels for MRS targeting. (B) Corresponding MRS spectra. The normal peripheral zone exhibits the typical high citrate level and low choline level similar to the normal prostate of younger subjects (Fig. 3). Normal periurethral tissue exhibits the typical low citrate level. MRI of the central zone exhibits signal intensities representative of BPH and exhibits metabolic patterns different from the normal prostate (Fig. 3). (C) Metabolic profile from a region of glandular BPH in the central zone. Note the high citrate level and lower choline level, which is similar to the normal peripheral zone. In contrast, the normal central zone exhibits a low citrate signal (Fig. 3). (D) Metabolic profile of a central zone region of mixed stromal and glandular BPH. The citrate level is decreased due to the presence of extensive stromal tissue, which does not produce citrate. (E) Metabolic profile of a region of predominately stromal BPH with minimal glandular tissue. The citrate peak is markedly decreased in relation to the choline peak. Adapted from Kurhanewicz *et al.* (1996).

MRI, has significantly improved the discrimination of cancer from surrounding healthy tissue and necrosis in the prostate.

MRI uses a strong magnetic field and radio frequency waves to noninvasively obtain morphologic pictures (images) based on tissue water. MRI provides more soft tissue contrast than other radiologic techniques, with prostate cancer having low signal intensity as compared to surrounding regions of healthy tissue (Fig. 2). This decrease in signal intensity is due to differences in structure between cancerous and normal prostate tissue. Unfortunately, these morphologic assessments often do not accurately reflect the presence and spatial extent of active tumor. MRI alone has a good sensitivity (79%) but low specificity (55%) in determining tumor location and spatial extent within the prostate due to a large number of false pos-

itives. These false positives are due to factors other than cancer (postbiopsy hemorrhage, chronic prostatitis, BPH, intraglandular dysplasia, trauma, and therapy) yielding the same low signal intensity as cancer. The additional metabolic information (citrate and choline signals) provided by MRSI establishes the presence of a malignant locus (Figs. 2 and 6). The metabolic profile eliminates most of the factors that contribute to the false positives obtained with MRI alone.

V. IMPROVED LOCALIZATION OF CANCER WITHIN THE PROSTATE

The metabolic data provided by MRSI can improve the MRI identification of cancer and thereby improve

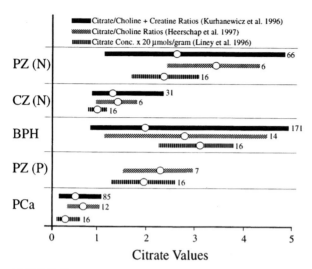

FIGURE 5 Composite results from three different laboratories of the detection of prostate cancer by 1-H MRS analysis of citrate. Data are the range of values and the mean value for each population of subjects. The number of subjects is presented at the end of each bar. PZ(N), peripheral zone of normal subjects; CZ (N), normal central zone; BPH, benign prostatic hyperplasia; PZ (P), normal peripheral zone cancer patients; PCa, cancer loci in peripheral zone. Ratio data from Kurhanewicz and colleagues have been inverted for comparison with the other studies. Adapted from Costello *et al.* (1999).

the localization of cancer within the prostate. Examples of equivocal assessment of cancer extent by MRI alone and the added information provided by MRSI are shown in Figs. 6 and 7. With MRI, diffuse low-signal intensity regions are intermingled with high-signal intensity regions on both sides of the peripheral zone. This appearance could lead a radiologist to either overcall the extent of the disease or miss the cancer altogether, as no clear-cut MRI abnormality is observed. However, MRSI data clearly show very elevated citrate and low choline and creatine levels consistent with healthy peripheral zone tissue. In contrast, malignant loci in the gland demonstrate very elevated choline levels and dramatically reduced citrate levels consistent with prostate cancer. Combining the specificity of MRSI with the sensitivity of MRI significantly increases (*p*<0.001) the accuracy of cancer localization within the prostate. High specificity (up to 91%) and high sensitivity (up to 95%) are obtained for the positive identification and localization of cancer.

Several areas of prostate cancer management benefit from improved localization of cancer within the

prostate: (1) Targeting TRUS-guided biopsies for patients with prostatic-specific antigen (PSA) levels indicative of cancer but negative previous biopsies; (2) better stratification of patients in clinical trials; (3) monitoring the progress of patients who select "watchful waiting" or other minimally aggressive cancer management options; or (4) guiding and assessing emerging "focal" prostate cancer therapies.

The addition of MRSI to MRI has also been shown to be useful in assessing the spread of cancer outside the prostate. This information is critical for choosing an appropriate therapy, as patients with cancer that is localized within the prostate or has spread minimally beyond the capsule are candidates for local therapy, whereas those with greater cancer spread require systemic therapy or a combination of systemic and local therapy. Because prior histopathologic studies have demonstrated that prostate cancer volume is a significant predictor of cancer spread outside the prostate, tumor volume estimates based on MRSI findings have been used in conjunction with high specificity MRI criteria to diagnose cancer spread. The estimation of tumor volume by MRSI improves the accuracy of MRI in the diagnosis of the early spread of cancer outside of the prostate.

VI. 1-H MRS ASSESSMENT OF THERAPEUTIC EFFICACY

It is important to track the progression or regression of malignancy in patients following treatment. Serum PSA levels are often used in assessing the success or failure of the treatment procedure. However, PSA levels are subject to change independent of the cancer status of elderly males. The accuracy of conventional radiologic techniques for detecting residual/recurrent cancer is poor because most therapies induce tissue changes that mimic cancer. Histological analysis of ultrasound guided biopsy samples is currently the procedure of choice for posttreatment assessment. However, the procedure is subject to large sampling errors, and concerns associated with invasive biopsy sampling exist. All these problems are virtually eliminated with the use of MRSI/MRI. A permanent map of the prostate with the identification of malignant loci can be obtained prior to treatment and serves as

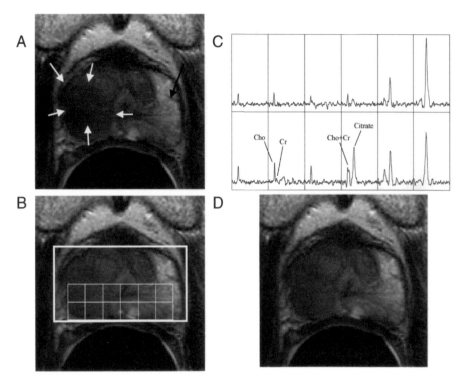

FIGURE 6 Three-dimensional MRSI enhancement of malignant locus in the prostate. (A) MRI of the midgland of a prostate cancer patient. Prostate cancer is anatomically identified as a region of low signal intensity in the right peripheral zone (white arrows) as compared to the high-signal intensity of the left peripheral zone (black arrow). (B) Same image as in A superimposed with the grid for MRS analysis (6x6 voxels). (C) Spectra (0.24 cc) associated with the region of the prostate indicated by the grid in B. Prostate cancer can be metabolically identified as a region of elevated choline and reduced citrate as compared to healthy tissue (low choline and high citrate) in the peripheral zone. (D) A (choline+creatine)/citrate ratio image (red) overlaid on the corresponding MRI. The (choline+creatine)/citrate peak area ratio has been thresholded such that all intensities below 3 SD of the mean healthy peripheral zone value are translucent, whereas those above the threshold demonstrate increasing intensities of red.

a reference record. Following treatment, the prostate can again be mapped, and the regions of previous malignancy or new malignancy can be compared with the pretreatment reference map. Because the MRSI procedure is noninvasive, it can be repeated as necessary without the problems associated with biopsy sampling.

Treatments such as cryosurgery and targeted radiotherapy often result in necrosis. Follow-up examination of the prostate becomes important in determining the effectiveness of the treatment. The conventional use of radiological examination is not effective in discriminating necrotic tissue from malignant tissue. 1-H MRS examination reveals that necrotic tissue does not exhibit any detectable citrate

or choline, which is a different metabolic profile from normal, BPH, or malignant tissue (Fig. 8). The detection of residual cancer at an early stage following treatment would allow earlier intervention with additional therapy and provide a more quantitative assessment of therapeutic efficacy.

VII. SUMMARY

The dramatic decrease in prostate tissue (peripheral zone) citrate levels is the most consistent and persistent characteristic that differentiates PCa from normal prostate and BPH. Prostate malignancy requires the metabolic transformation of nonmalignant

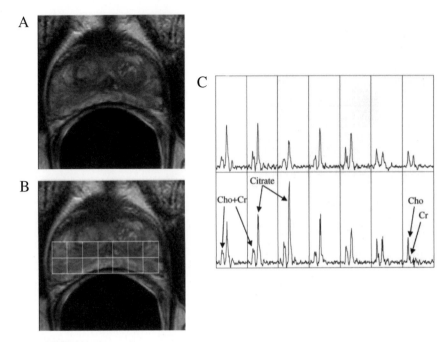

FIGURE 7 Positive identification of malignancy by 3D MRSI in a 67 year old. (A) It was not possible to identify prostate cancer by MRI alone, as diffuse low-signal intensity regions are intermingled with high-signal intensity regions on both sides of the peripheral zone. (B and C) Three-dimensional MRSI clearly showed very elevated citrate and low choline and creatine levels on the right side of the gland (left) consistent with healthy peripheral zone tissue, whereas the left side of the gland (right) demonstrates very elevated choline levels and dramatically reduced citrate levels consistent with prostate cancer.

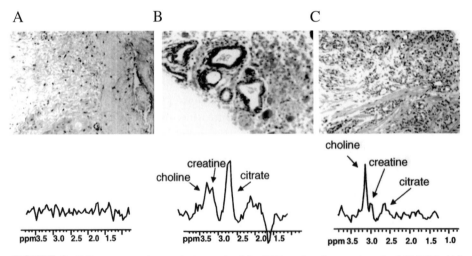

FIGURE 8 Differentiation of necrotic tissue, glandular BPH, and malignant tissue by 1-H MRS. (A) Representative spectrum of necrosis and corresponding histologic slide of necrotic biopsy tissue. (B) Representative spectrum of BPH and corresponding histologic slide of BPH biopsy tissue. (C) Representative spectrum of prostate cancer and corresponding histologic slide of malignant biopsy tissue. Data from Kurhanewicz et al. (1996). See color insert in Volume 1.

citrate-producing epithelial cells to citrate-oxidizing malignant cells. Citrate analysis of prostatic tissue provides a highly reliable, specific, and sensitive assay for the diagnosis of PCa. 1-H MRS permits the noninvasive *in situ* detection of prostate citrate and related metabolites for the accurate detection of early and advanced malignant loci. The combination of MRSI and MRI results in a metabolic–anatomic visualization (i.e., a metabolic map) of the prostate. This provides an accurate and specific localization of malignant loci along with estimates of the volume of the malignancy. Metabolic mapping allows for the follow-up of malignant progression and regression pursuant to treatment and/or watchful waiting. MRSI/MRI-guided radiotherapy and chemical seeding enhance the targeting of treatment at the malignant loci. Finally, 1-H MRS technology for citrate and related metabolites levels provides a most promising noninvasive tool for screening and diagnosing PCa and for following the progression of malignancy.

Acknowledgments

The studies of L.C.C. and R.B.F. presented in this article were supported in part by NIH grants DK42839, DK28015, CA71207, and CA79903. The studies of J.K. were supported by NIH grants CA88214, CA59897, CA79980, CA64667; by ACS grant RPG-96-146-03; and by a grant from CaPCure.

See Also the Following Articles

Brain Cancer and Magnetic Resonance Spectroscopy • Genetic Predisposition to Prostate Cancer • Magnetic Resonance Spectroscopy and Magnetic Resonance Imaging, Introduction • Magnetic Resonance Spectroscopy of Cancer: Clinical Overview • PET Imaging and Cancer • Prostate Cancer

Bibliography

Costello, L. C., and Franklin, R. B. (1991). Concepts of citrate production and secretion by prostate. 2. Hormonal relationships in normal and neoplastic prostate. *Prostate* **19,** 181–205.

Costello, L. C., and Franklin, R. B. (1997). Citrate metabolism in normal and malignant prostate epithelial cells. *Urology* **50,** 3–12.

Costello, L. C., and Franklin, R. B. (1998). The novel role of zinc in the intermediary metabolism of prostate epithelial cells and its implications in prostate malignancy. *Prostate* **35,** 285–296.

Costello, L. C., and Franklin, R. B. (2000). The intermediary metabolism of the prostate: A key to understanding the pathogenesis and progression of prostate malignancy. *Oncology* **59,** 269–282.

Costello, L. C., Franklin, R. B., and Narayan, P. (1999). Citrate in the diagnosis of prostate cancer. *Prostate* **38,** 237.

Heerschap, J., Jager, G. J., Van Der Graff, M., Barentsz, J. O., De La Rosette, J., Oosterhof, G. O. N., Ruijter, E. T. G., and Ruijs, S. H. J. (1997). In vivo proton MR spectroscopy reveals altered metabolite content in malignant prostate tissue. *Anticancer Res.* **17,** 1455–1460.

Hricak, H., White, S., Vigneron, D., Kurhanewicz, J., Kosco, A., Levin, D., Weiss, J., Narayan, P., and Carroll, P. R. (1994). Carcinoma of the prostate gland: MR imaging with pelvic phased-array coils versus integrated endorectal—pelvic phased-array coils. *Radiology* **193,** 703–709.

Kurhanewicz, J., Hricak, H., and Vigneron, D. B. (1996). Prostate cancer: Metabolic response to cryosurgery as detected with 3D H-1 MR spectroscopic imaging. *Radiology* **200,** 489–496.

Kurhanewicz, J., Vigneron, D. B., Hricak, H., Narayan, P., Carroll, P., and Nelson, S. J. (1996). Three-dimensional H-1 MR spectroscopic imaging of the *in situ* human prostate with high (0.24-0.7-cm3) spatial resolution. *Radiology* **198,** 795–805.

Kurhanewicz, J., Vigneron, D. B., Males, R. G., Swanson, M. G., Yu, K. K., and Hricak, H. (2000). The prostate: MR imaging and spectroscopy. Present and future. *Radiol. Clin. North Am.* **38,** 115–138.

Liney, G. P., Turnbull, L. W., Lowry, M., Turnbull, L. S., Knowles, A. J., and Horsman, A. (1997). In vivo quantification of citrate concentration and water T2 relaxation time of the pathologic prostate gland using 1H MRS and MRI. *Magn. Reson. Imag.* **15,** 1177–1186.

Yu, K. K., Scheidler, J., Hricak, H., Vigneron, D. B., Zaloudek, C. J., Males, R. G., Nelson, S. J., Carroll, P. R., and Kurhanewicz, J. (1999). Prostate cancer: Prediction of extracapsular extension with endorectal MR imaging and three-dimensional proton MR spectroscopic imaging. *Radiology* **213,** 481–485.

Mismatch Repair: Biochemistry and Genetics

Richard D. Kolodner
Hernan Flores-Rozas
Ludwig Institute for Cancer Research

GLOSSARY

base substitution mutation The class of mutations that result when an incorrect base is substituted for the correct base that is present in the DNA.

DNA polymerase The class of enzymes that synthesize DNA using one DNA strand as a template to direct DNA synthesis.

DNA replication The process by which cells make an exact copy of their DNA.

exonuclease The class of enzymes that degrade DNA molecules starting from the ends of DNA or breaks in DNA strands.

frameshift mutation Type of mutation that results from either insertion or deletion of one or a small number of extra bases in DNA.

germline mutation Mutation that is transmitted through the germline (e.g., inherited mutation).

heterodimer Complex of two proteins where each protein is a different protein.

immunohistochemistry Use of antibodies to stain tissue slices to detect the presence of the antigen (protein or other molecule to which the antibody binds).

microsatellite instability Accumulation of frameshift mutations within the simple repeat sequences found ubiquitously in most eukaryotic chromosomal DNA.

mispaired base An incorrectly paired base in DNA, e.g., an A paired with a C instead of a T or an extra base inserted into DNA so that it is not paired with any base.

mutation Change in the normal sequence of a DNA molecule.

MutL (bacterial MutL protein or gene) Mut is an abbreviation for "mutator" because inactivation of a mutator gene results in increased rates of accumulating mutations. MutL is the protein that interacts with the MutS protein during bacterial MMR.

MutS [bacterial MutS protein or gene (see MutL)] MutS is the protein that recognizes mispaired bases in DNA during bacterial MMR.

oncogene A gene whose increased or altered activity promotes the development of tumors. Oncogenes often accumulate activating mutations or are amplified during tumor development.

proliferating cell nuclear antigen (PCNA) A protein that forms a ring around DNA and functions to keep proteins such as DNA polymerases attached to the DNA.

redundancy Two genes or proteins are redundant when they can substitute for each other.

replication Factor C Protein complex required to load PCNA onto DNA.

replication protein A Sometimes called replication factor A and abbreviated RPA or RFA. Protein complex that binds to single strand DNA, allowing it to be a better template for DNA polymerases.

somatic mutation Mutation that occurs in a somatic cell. Such mutations are not inherited.

tumor suppressor gene Gene whose product prevents the development of a tumor. Tumor suppressor genes accumulate inactivating mutations during tumor development.

Mispaired bases arise in DNA by a number of mechanisms. One of the most important sources of such mispaired bases is misincorporation errors that are made during DNA replication (Fig. 1). If such errors are not repaired prior to the next round of DNA replication, they will be fixed in the DNA as mutations. These misincorporation errors are normally corrected by a process called DNA mismatch repair (MMR). MMR recognizes the resulting mispaired base in DNA and directs the selective degradation of the newly synthesized DNA strand where the error resides. The misincorporated base is thus removed and the degraded DNA strand is then resynthesized.

Because of the critical role of MMR in suppressing DNA replication errors, defects in MMR increase the rate at which cells accumulate mutations. Such mutations can activate oncogenes or inactivate tumor suppressor genes and contribute to the process of carcinogenesis. That increased rates of mutation accumulation can play a role in the development of cancer has been demonstrated by the discovery that (1) hereditary nonpolyposis colorectal carcinoma (HNPCC) is caused by inherited mutations in some genes encoding MMR proteins and (2) somatically acquired MMR defects underlie some sporadic cancers. This article briefly reviews our understanding of MMR.

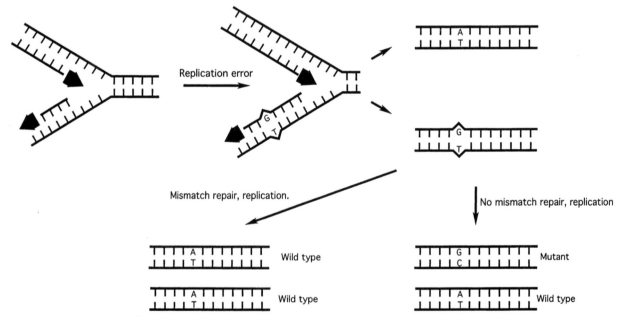

FIGURE 1 The origin of mutations as a result of errors during DNA replication. A DNA molecule in the process of being copied by DNA polymerases (large arrows) (upper left). Such structures are often called "replication forks." After an error occurs in which a G is misincorporated opposite a T (upper center), replication completes and yields one correctly paired DNA and one mispaired DNA (upper right). If the mispaired DNA is then replicated before it is repaired, a mutant and a wild-type DNA result (lower right). If mismatch repair occurs prior to DNA replication, then two wild-type DNAs result (lower left).

I. PROTEINS INVOLVED IN MISMATCH REPAIR

A. MutS Homologue Proteins Involved in Mismatch Repair

Genetic and biochemical studies have led to the proposal of a model for eukaryotic MMR in which mispaired bases in DNA are recognized by heterodimeric complexes of proteins that are homologues of the bacterial MutS protein (Fig. 2). MutS is the bacterial MMR protein that recognizes mispaired bases in DNA ("Mut" is an abbreviation for "mutator" because mutations in the *mutS* gene cause high mutation rates or a mutator phenotype). Three different MutS homologues, called MSH proteins, function in MMR. These three different MSH proteins (MSH2, MSH3 and MSH6) form two different heterodimeric complexes—MSH2–MSH6 (MutSα) and MSH2–MSH3 (MutSβ)—each of which contains a common subunit, MSH2, and a unique subunit, MSH3 or MSH6 (see Fig. 2). Extensive genetic studies indicate that the MSH2–MSH6 complex is responsible for the repair of base:base mispairs, that the MSH2–MSH6 and MSH2–MSH3 complexes are redundant for the repair of single base insertion/deletion mispairs, and that the MSH2–MSH3 complex is primarily responsible for the repair of larger insertion/deletion mispairs.

The MSH2–MSH6 (MutSα) and MSH2–MSH3 (MutSβ) complexes have been purified and extensively studied. Consistent with genetic studies, MSH2–MSH6 (MutSα) is able to support the repair of both base:base mispairs and insertion/deletion mispairs in *in vitro* MMR reactions, whereas MSH2–MSH3 (MutSβ) is only able to support the repair of insertion/deletion mispairs. The MSH2–MSH6 (MutSα) and MSH2–MSH3 (MutSβ) complexes have also been shown to preferentially bind to mispaired bases in DNA. The MSH2–MSH6 (MutSα) complex binds to both base:base mispairs and insertion/deletion mispairs, whereas the MSH2–MSH3 (MutSβ) complex appears to only bind insertion/deletion mispairs.

One of the key properties of the MSH protein complexes [MSH2–MSH6 (MutSα) and MSH2–MSH3

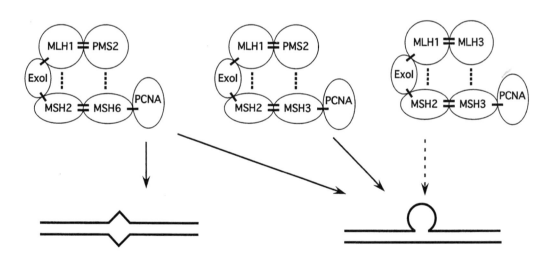

Base:Base mispair

Insertion/deletion mispair

FIGURE 2   Illustration of the protein complexes that function in mismatch repair. Circles and ovals represent MSH2, MSH3, MSH6, MLH1, MLH3, PMS2, exonuclease I, and PCNA proteins as indicated. Double solid connecting lines indicate known stable protein–protein interactions, Single solid connecting lines indicate known, less stable protein–protein interactions, and dashed connecting lines indicate interactions between protein assemblies where the exact protein contacts are not yet known. Below these illustrated protein complexes are the mispaired base-containing DNAs they interact with during mismatch repair. Solid connecting arrows indicate major repair reactions, and the dashed connecting arrow indicates a minor repair pathway.

(MutSβ)] is that they are partially redundant. This is relevant to the observation that defects in MMR can cause cancer, as will be discussed later. Because MSH2 is the only protein present in both complexes, defects in the MSH2 gene will completely inactivate MMR (see Fig. 2). As a consequence, MSH2 defects result in increased rates of accumulating both base substitution and frameshift mutations. Interestingly, short mononucleotide repeat sequences are often found within genes, and frameshift errors that occur by the copying of such sequences during replication are the most frequent misincorporation errors made by DNA polymerases. Thus, in MSH2-defective cells, frameshift mutations in mononucleotide repeats are 5 to 10 times more frequent than base substitution mutations. MSH6 and MSH3 gene defects only inactivate either MSH2–MSH6 (MutSα) or MSH2–MSH3 (MutSβ) complexes, respectively. Because of the overlapping mispair recognition specificity of each complex, defects in MSH6 only cause increased rates of accumulating base substitution mutations and defects in MSH3 have very little effect on mutation rates except for frameshift mutations in repeating sequences where the repeat unit length is two bases and larger. Dinucleotide and larger repeats are found less frequently in sequences encoding genes than short mononucleotide repeats, indicating that MSH3 defects should have little effect on the accumulation of mutations within the majority of genes.

B. MutL Homologue Proteins Involved in Mismatch Repair

MutL is a bacterial protein required for MMR and is known to interact with MutS during MMR. There are three MutL homologues, called MLH proteins, MLH1, PMS2 (called PMS1 in yeast), and MLH3, that function in MMR in eukaryotes. These proteins form two different heterodimeric complexes, MLH1–PMS2 (MutLα) and MLH1–MLH3 (see Fig. 2). Biochemical experiments have shown that the MLH1–PMS2 (MutLα) complex forms a higher order complex with both MSH2–MSH6 (MutSα) and MSH2–MSH3 (MutSβ) when these two MSH complexes interact with mispaired bases in DNA. Little is yet known about the biochemical properties of the MLH1–MLH3 complex. A fourth MutL-related pro-

tein, human PMS1, was initially suggested to function in MMR; however, all biochemical studies performed to date have been unsuccessful in demonstrating that human PMS1 has an activity that functions in MMR.

Genetic studies have shown that the MLH1–PMS2 (MutLα) complex is the major MutL-related complex that functions in MMR. The MLH1–MLH3 complex appears to only play a minor role in MMR. Like the situation with the two different MSH complexes discussed earlier, the observation that two different MutL-related protein complexes function in MMR indicates that defects in each of the three MutL-related genes may cause different MMR defects. Because MLH1 is the only protein present in both MutL-related complexes, it is only defects in the MLH1 gene that completely inactivate MMR (see Fig. 2). Because the MLH1–PMS2 (MutLα) complex is the major complex that functions in MMR, defects in the PMS2 gene cause almost as strong a defect in MMR as defects in the MLH1 gene. In contrast, because the MLH1–MLH3 complex plays a minor role in MMR, defects in the MLH3 gene only cause a partial defect in MMR, which only causes a small increase in the rate of accumulating frameshift mutations in mutant cells.

C. Other Proteins Implicated in Mismatch Repair

One of the important problems in the study of eukaryotic MMR is the identification of other proteins required for MMR. Some progress has been made in this area. Unfortunately, little is known about how MMR initiates and how the newly synthesized DNA strand is recognized nor has eukaryotic MMR been reconstituted from purified proteins.

DNA polymerase δ is required for the DNA synthesis step of MMR, as are its accessory factors proliferating cell nuclear antigen (PCNA), replication protein A (RPA/RFA), and replication factor C (RFC). PCNA is also involved in MMR at an early step; presumably by virtue of its specific interaction with MSH6 and MSH3, PCNA is required for the activity of the MSH2–MSH6 (MutSα) and MSH2–MSH3 (MutSβ) complexes. In considering the possibility that defects in genes encoding DNA polymerase δ,

PCNA, RPA, and RFC might play a role in cancer susceptibility, it is important to note that each of these genes is likely to be an essential gene, which would preclude complete loss of function defects.

In bacteria, at least four exonucleases have been shown to be able to function in the degradation step of MMR and each can substitute for all of the others. This redundancy of exonucleases appears to occur in eukaryotic MMR. Exonuclease 1 is a 5′ to 3′ double strand DNA-specific exonuclease encoded by the EXO1 gene that is thought to be one of a number of redundant exonucleases that function in eukaryotic MMR. EXO1 physically interacts with both MSH2 and MLH1, and EXO1 defects only cause small defects in MMR. Other exonucleases that have been suggested to function in MMR are the endo/exonuclease FEN1/RAD27 and the 3′ to 5′ editing exonuclease functions of DNA polymerases δ and ε. However, the exact role that these latter three exonucleases play in MMR has been difficult to determine because these exonucleases all function in other critical aspects of DNA synthesis.

II. DEFECTS IN MISMATCH REPAIR CAUSE INCREASED CANCER SUSCEPTIBILITY

HNPCC is a common cancer susceptibility syndrome characterized by a dominant mode of transmission, high penetrance, significantly earlier age of onset than sporadic cancers, multiple primary tumors, and a high proportion of colorectal cancer. Until relatively recently, clinical identification of HNPCC kindreds depended on the Amsterdam criteria (see Table I), which identify kindreds based on clustering of colorectal cancer and an early age of onset. More recently, a number of less restrictive clinical criteria have been proposed for the identification of HNPCC. Linkage analysis of HNPCC families showed that almost all of HNPCC could be accounted for two genes: one on chromosome 2p and one on chromosome 3p. Furthermore, analysis of DNA from HNPCC tumors showed a high frequency of accumulation of frameshift mutations, a phenotype called microsatellite instability (MSI) that is diagnostic for the MMR defect caused by HNPCC.

Most of the so-called Amsterdam criteria HNPCC showing tumor microsatellite instability can be accounted for by inherited defects in the MSH2 gene on chromosome 2p or the MLH1 gene on chromosome 3p. These two genes are the only known MMR genes in which defects cause a complete loss of MMR function. Most of the inherited mutations observed in these two genes are frameshift and nonsense mutations (protein truncating mutations), as well as missense mutations (protein sequence changes). Deletion mutations, as well as uncharacterized defects that result in loss of expression of either MSH2 or MLH1 have also been detected. There are no routine molecular diagnostic methods for diagnosing HNPCC-causing mutations. However, in combination with an appropriate family history of cancer, complete MSH2 and MLH1 gene sequencing along with testing of HNPCC tumors for microsatellite instability (sometimes called "MSI analysis") using a standard set of microsatellite markers and analysis of tumors for loss of MSH2 or MLH1 protein expression using immunohistochemistry (sometimes called "IHC analysis") have proven to be useful in detecting MMR defects in suspected HNPCC families. It should be noted that the less restrictive clinical criteria for HNPCC (see Table I) identify many more patients suspected of having HNPCC compared to the Amsterdam criteria, but a smaller proportion of these patients ultimately prove to have inherited MMR defects.

Defects in the MSH6 gene cause a partial loss of MMR due to the partial redundancy between MSH6 and MSH3. This results in a large increase in the rate of accumulation of base substitution mutations but causes little effect on the rate of accumulating frameshift mutations. HNPCC families have been screened for the presence of germline MSH6 mutations, but only a small proportion of HNPCC families, on the order of 1 to 3%, can be accounted for by germline MSH6 defects. These MSH6 mutant kindreds had a higher proportion of endometrial cancer than MSH2 or MLH1 detective HNPCC families. In contrast, approximately 8% of familial, non-HNPCC colorectal cancer cases were found to have germline MSH6 defects. Such familial colorectal cancer cases constitute a much larger number of total colorectal cancer cases than HNPCC, indicating that germline defects in MSH6 could be almost as prevalent in the population as germline MSH2 and MLH1 defects.

TABLE I
Clinical Criteria for HNPCC[a]

Name	Criteria
Amsterdam[b]	Three relatives with colorectal cancer (CRC), one of which must be a first-degree relative of the other two; CRC involving at least two generations of the family; one or more CRC cases diagnosed before age 50
Modified Amsterdam[c]	1. Small pedigrees, which cannot be further extended, can be considered as HNPCC if they contain CRCs in first-degree relatives; CRC must involve at least two generations and one or more CRC cases must be diagnosed before age 55 2. In pedigrees where CRC is found in two first-degree relatives, a third relative with an unusually early onset cancer, or endometrial cancer is sufficient
Young age of onset	A CRC case diagnosed at less than 40 years of age, without a family history fulfilling Amsterdam or modified Amsterdam criteria
HNPCC variant	A family history of cancer suggestive of HNPCC, but not fulfilling Amsterdam, modified Amsterdam, or young age of onset criteria
Bethesda[c]	1. Individuals in families that fulfill Amsterdam criteria 2. Individuals with two HNPCC-related cancers, including synchronous and metachronous CRCs or associated extracolonic cancers 3. Individuals with CRC who have a first-degree relative with CRC and/or a HNPCC-related extracolonic cancer and/or colorectal adenoma; one of the cancers diagnosed before age 24 and adenoma diagnosed before age 40 4. Individuals with CRC or endometrial cancer diagnosed before age 45 5. Individual with right-sided CRC with an undifferentiated pattern (solid/cribform) on histopathology diagnosed before age 45 6. Individuals with signet ring cell type CRC diagnosed before age 45 7. Individuals with adenomas diagnosed before age 40

[a]Adapted from Syngal *et al.* (1999).
[b]All criteria must be met.
[c]Meeting all features under a given-numbered criteria is sufficient.

Compared to MSH2 or MLH1 defective HNPCC kindreds, MSH6 defective kindreds had a less striking family history and later age of onset of cancer. While more work on MSH6 is needed, it appears that germline MSH6 defects cause an attenuated form of HNPCC. It is important to note that MSH6 defects do not cause a consistent effect on tumor microsatellite instability like defects in MSH2 or MLH1.

A number of other MMR genes have been identified, including MSH3, PMS2, MLH3, EXO1, and possibly PMS1. It is conceivable that defects in these genes could cause cancer susceptibility. Germline mutations in PMS2 appear to only be a rare cause of HNPCC. Little work on the possibility that defects in the MSH3, MLH3, and EXO1 genes can cause cancer susceptibility has been reported to date. Following an initial report of a germline PMS1 mutation, no other mutation reports have appeared. This apparent lack of reported germline defects in PMS1 might not be surprising given that biochemical studies have failed to demonstrate a role for PMS1 in MMR.

A variable proportion of sporadic cancers of many types have been observed to show tumor microsatellite instability indicative on a MMR defect. For example, in the case of sporadic colorectal cancer, the reported proportion of microsatellite unstable tumors (note that microsatellite instability indicated a MMR defect) ranges up to about 25%. Most tumors exhibiting microsatellite instability have been shown to lose expression of either MSH2 or MLH1, although the majority of cases show the loss of MLH1 expression. Most cases showing loss of MLH1 expression are due to somatic silencing of both copies of the MLH1 gene by hypermethylation of the MLH1 promoter. Only a small number of sporadic cases have been attributed to somatic mutations in MMR genes. These results indicate that there are both inherited and sporadic forms of MMR-defective cancers, although the etiology of the two different types of cases is quite different.

How do MMR defects actually cause the development of cancer? Loss of MMR results in increased rates of accumulating mutations. This would be expected to increase the rate of accumulation of mutations that inactivate tumor suppressor genes and activate protooncogenes and consequently increase the rate of tumorigenesis. Considerable data exist that support this view. In addition, MMR-defective cells are resistant to killing by DNA-damaging agents, suggesting that MMR defects also cause a defect in apotosis that may also contribute to tumorigenesis. Because of this resistance to killing by DNA-damaging agents, MMR-defective tumors may also not be as responsive to some chemotherapeutic agents as non-MMR-defective tumors.

III. SUMMARY

MMR requires two different heterodimeric complexes of MutS-related proteins, MSH2–MSH3 and MSH2–MSH6, that recognize mispaired bases in DNA. Two different heterodimeric complexes of MutL-related proteins, MLH1–PMS2 (yeast PMS1) and MLH1–MLH3, also function in MMR and appear to interact with other MMR proteins, including MSH complexes and replication factors. Additional proteins have been implicated in MMR, including DNA polymerase δ, RPA, PCNA, RFC, exonuclease 1, FEN1/RAD27, and the DNA polymerase δ and ε associated exonucleases. Loss of function of three of these genes, MSH2, MSH6, and MLH1, has been shown to be the cause of both hereditary cancer susceptibility syndromes and sporadic cancers.

Acknowledgments

Work performed in the laboratory of R.D.K. was supported by NIH Grants GM26017 and GM50006, as well as by the Ludwig Institute for Cancer Research. H.F.-R. was a recipient of a Jane Coffin Childs Postdoctoral Fellowship.

See Also the Following Articles

CELLULAR RESPONSES TO DNA DAMAGE • DNA METHYLATION AND CANCER • HEREDITARY COLON CANCER AND DNA MISMATCH REPAIR • RESISTANCE TO DNA DAMAGING AGENTS

Bibliography

Flores-Rozas, H., and Kolodner, R. D. (1998). The *Saccharomyces cerevisiae* MLH3 gene functions in MSH3-dependent suppression of frameshift mutations. *Proc. Natl. Acad. Sci. USA* **95,** 12404–12409.

Harfe, B. D., and Jinks-Robertson, S. (2000). DNA mismatch repair and genetic instability. *Annu. Rev. Genet.* **34,** 359–399.

Jiricny, J., and Nystron-Lahti, M. (2000). Mismatch repair defects in cancer. *Curr. Opin. Genet. Dev.* **10,** 157–161.

Kolodner, R. (1996). Biochemistry and genetics of eukaryotic mismatch repair. *Genes Dev.* **10,** 1433–1442.

Kolodner, R. D. (2000). Guarding against mutation. *Nature* **407,** 687–689.

Kolodner, R. D., and Marsischky, G. T. (1999). Eukaryotic DNA mismatch repair. *Curr. Opin. Genet. Dev.* **9,** 89–96.

Kolodner, R. D., Tytell, J. D., Schmeits, J., Kane, M. F., Das Gupta, R., Weger, J., Wahlberg, S., Fox, E. A., Peel, D. J., Ziogas, A., *et al.* (1999). Germline msh6 mutations in colorectal cancer families, *Cancer Res.* **59,** 5068–5074.

Li, G.-M. (1999). The role of mismatch repair in DNA damage-induced apotosis. *Oncol. Res.* **11,** 393–400.

Loeb, L. A. (2001). A mutator phenotype in cancer. *Cancer Res.* **61,** 3230–3239.

Lynch, H. T., and de la Chapelle, A. (1999). Genetic susceptibility to non-polyposis colorectal cancer. *J. Med. Genet.* 801–818.

Marsischky, G. T., Filosi, N., Kane, M. F., and Kolodner, R. (1996). Redundancy of *Saccharomyces cerevisiae* MSH3 and MSH6 in MSH2-dependent mismatch repair. *Genes Dev.* **10,** 407–420.

Modrich, P. (1997). Strand-specific mismatch repair in mammalian cells. *J. Biol. Chem.* **272,** 24727–24730.

Modrich, P., and Lahue, R. (1996). Mismatch repair in replication fidelity, genetic recombination, and cancer biology. *Annu. Rev. Biochem.* **65,** 101–133.

Nakagawa, T., Datta, A., and Kolodner, R. D. (1999). Multiple functions of MutS- and MutL-related heterocomplexes. *Proc. Natl. Acad. Sci. USA* **95,** 14186–14188.

Peltomaki, P. (2001). Deficient DNA mismatch repair: A common etiologic factor for colon cancer. *Hum. Mol. Genet.* **10,** 735–740.

Peltomaki, P. (2001). DNA mismatch repair and cancer. *Mutat. Res.* **488,** 77–85.

Peltomaki, P., and Vasen, H. F. (1997). Mutations predisposing to hereditary nonpolyposis colorectal cancer: Database and results of a collaborative study. *Gastroenterology* **113,** 1146–1158.

Sia, E. A., Kokoska, R. J., Dominska, M., Greenwell, P., and Petes, T. D. (1997). Microsatellite instability in yeast: dependence on repeat unit size and DNA mismatch repair genes. *Mol. Cell. Biol.* **17,** 2851–2858.

Syngal, S., Fox, E. A., Li, C., Dovido, M., Eng, C., Kolodner, R. D., and Garber, J. E. (1999). Interpretation of genetic test results for hereditary nonpolyposis colorectal cancer. *JAMA* **282,** 247–253.

Wheeler, J. M. D., Bodmer, W. F., and McC Mortensen, N. J. (2000). DNA mismatch repair genes and colorectal cancer. *Gut* **47,** 148–153.

Molecular Aspects
of Radiation Biology

Gary D. Kao
Anjali Gupta
W. Gillies McKenna
Hospital of the University of Pennsylvania

I. Radiation-Induced Cell Cycle Checkpoints
II. Signal Transduction and Radiation Resistance
III. Repair Protein Pathways
IV. Summary

GLOSSARY

checkpoint A mechanism to ensure that each stage of the cell cycle is properly completed before the next stage is initiated.

DNA repair pathways A collective term for the general mechanisms for removing endogenous and exogenous DNA damage from the genome.

signal transduction A series of ordered biochemical reactions by which a signal initiated at the cell surface is transmitted inside the cell to elicit specific cellular responses.

T he molecular mechanism of radiation resistance is probably best described at the present time as a story that is quickly evolving but remains incomplete. In recent years, investigators have used modern techniques of molecular biology, cell biology, and biochemistry to dissect cellular and physiological events that occur after exposure to DNA damage and which likely influence radiosensitivity. Broad themes have emerged, but many important details remain to be completed before an integrated understanding of the basis of radioresistance is possible. This article focuses on three main topics involving the cellular response to ionizing radiation damage that have gained prominence in recent years: (1) cell cycle checkpoints (2) signal transduction pathways (including ras and ATM), and (3) DNA repair protein pathways (including those thought to mediate homologous recombination and nonhomologous end-joining modes of repair). Other factors that may impact radioresistance include angiogenesis, hypoxia, and induction pathways of apoptosis, but will be addressed elsewhere in this encyclopedia.

I. RADIATION-INDUCED CELL CYCLE CHECKPOINTS

All mammalian cells manifest conspicuous cell cycle delays, i.e., "checkpoints," after exposure to ionizing radiation damage, especially at either G_1/S or G_2/M transitions. A prominent S phase delay usually occurs only at very high doses of ionizing radiation (>10 Gy) or after exposure to UV or certain drugs, such as hydroxyurea. The main determinant of whether the G_1 or G_2 checkpoint predominates after DNA damage in a given cell depends on the status of the p53 protein. Normal cells, having wild-type p53 function, block at G_1. Many, if not most, tumor cells lack wild-type p53 function and do not show a G_1 block after irradiation, but instead block at G_2.

DNA damaged-induced checkpoints are brought about by alterations in the cyclins and cyclin-dependent kinases (cdk) that normally drive the cell cycle in proliferating cells (Fig. 1). Binding of each cyclin to its respective cdk partner appears necessary to form active kinase complexes. Why does the cell need so many cyclins and cdks? It has been speculated, but not conclusively proven, that the multiplicity of cyclins and cdks enables the cell to finely tune and have redundant controls to ensure that uncontrolled proliferation does not occur. There is some overlap in the ability of a specific cyclin to bind to each cdk, the precise reason for which also remains not entirely clear. For example, D cyclins interacts with cdk2, 4, 5, and 6, while cyclin E also interacts with cdk2. Cyclin B appears to interact exclusively with p34cdc2 (also known as cdk1). In contrast, cyclin A interacts with both cdk2 and p34cdc2.

Why do cells have cell cycle checkpoints after DNA damage? Two possible "purposes" are (1) to prevent cells from dividing with damaged DNA, which could then perpetuate mutations or aneuploidy, and therefore give rise to tumorigenesis or (2) to allow cells additional time to repair the DNA damage. The role of the G_1 checkpoint in limiting the formation of new cancers seems highly irrefutable, as alterations or mutations in many components of the protein pathways that mediate this transition have now been linked to

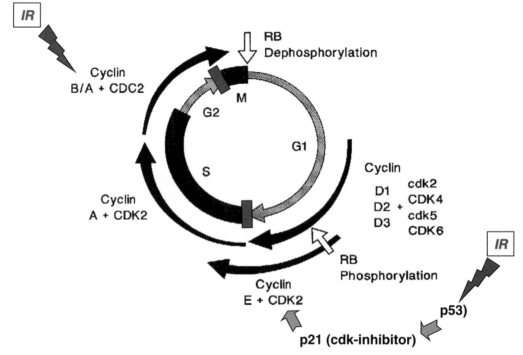

FIGURE 1 Cyclins and Cdks drive the cell cycle specific to each phase. Radiation induces cell cycle checkpoints primarily at G_1 and G_2. In cells with intact p53, p21 is induced, which inhibits cdk2 and blocks cells in G_1. In the absence of p53, the G_2 checkpoint is induced by a variety mechanisms that act on cyclin B and cdc2 (also known as cdk1).

specific tumors. Mutations that are linked to tumorigenesis now include RB, cyclin D, cyclin E, cdks, and, of course, p53 itself. It is less clear whether DNA damage repair occurs during this checkpoint. In contrast to the G_1 checkpoint, the protein components of the G_2 checkpoint conspicuously have not yet been clearly linked to carcinogenesis, while unambiguous evidence of DNA repair during the damage-induced G_2 checkpoint has been found. While it is tempting to speculate that the G_1 and G_2 checkpoints serve different functions for any given cell, there remains much to be clarified. For example, it is not known how exactly the cell senses the presence of damaged DNA and how that signal then causes alterations in the cyclins and cdks to "put the brake on."

A. Molecular Mechanisms

Radiation induces the G_1 checkpoint via two interrelated ways: stabilization of the p53 protein and the induction by p53 of the cdk inhibitor p21 [the protein was independently cloned by several groups and known by several names, including CIP1 (cdk-interacting protein 1), WAF1 (wild-type p53-activated fragment), and sdi1 (senescent cell-derived inhibitor 1)]. Because p53 is constantly synthesized and rapidly degraded, protein levels are generally low. DNA damage causes downregulation of the degradation, resulting in increased p53 concentrations. The stabilized p53 is localized mainly in the nucleus, where in addition to its effects on the cell cycle, it may affect other pathways as well, such as the induction of apoptosis. p53 stimulates the production of p21, which in turn inhibits cdk2, a kinase that is key to the efforts of the cell to initiate DNA replication (i.e., S phase), resulting in the cell being blocked in G_1.

When p53 and the G_1 block are inactivated, an irradiated cell blocks at G_2 through redundant mechanisms. These include repression of cyclin B mRNA and protein, phosphorylation (and inactivation) of p34cdc2, and exclusion of cyclin B1 and its associated kinase activity from the nucleus. The downregulation of cyclin B1 expression occurs via decreased transcription, as well as decreased stability of cyclin B1 mRNA. The effects on cyclin B mRNA and protein are not due to a general consequence of radiation depressing protein or RNA synthesis. The expression of

a wide variety of genes is induced after irradiation, but cyclin B mRNA is one of the few that specifically have been reported to be depressed at doses approximating that used clinically. Phosphorylation of p34cdc2 is accomplished by the wee1 and mik1 kinases, as well as by inactivation of the cdc25C phosphatase that would otherwise dephosphorylate and activate the p34cdc2. Both p34cdc2 and cyclin B undergo translocation from the cytoplasm to nucleus, which appears to confer an additional level of control. DNA damage results in export of cyclin B and p34cdc2 and its kinase activity from the nucleus. It can be demonstrated that this export from the nucleus is dependent on specific sequences and phosphorylation sites on cyclin B. However, in contrast to p34cdc2, the specific kinases and other regulatory proteins that act on cyclin B have yet to be identified.

B. Cell Cycle Checkpoints and Radiation Resistance

Substantial circumstantial evidence links radioresistance and cell cycle checkpoints. It has been recognized that hypoxic cells tend to be radioresistant and remain in the S/G_1 phases. This presumably allows additional time for repair, while limiting progression with unrepaired chromatin damage that would result in mitotic death. Cells lacking the G_1 checkpoint are, in general, not more radiosensitive, probably because repair occurs in the following S and G_2 phases. In S phase, it is difficult to distinguish DNA repair from processes that occur during the replication of DNA. However, a number of observations suggest that DNA repair does occur during S phase. In certain cell lines, cells irradiated in G_1 or early S have shown greater survival than those irradiated in late S or G_2. BRCA1 and Rad51 foci (discussed in more detail in following sections) have been reported in S phase cells. It has been hypothesized that DNA repair by nonhomologous end joining predominates in G_1–early S phase cells, whereas recombinational repair is preferentially used in late S–G_2 cells.

The relationship between radioresistance and the G_2 checkpoint is more established. In the HeLa human cervical cancer cell line (which lacks p53 function as the G_1 checkpoint), the length of the G_2 delay is proportional to the dose delivered. Irradiation of synchronized Hela cells at different phases of the cell cycle results in a G_2 delay regardless of whether the cells were in G_1, S, or G_2 phases at the time of irradiation. Cells can be demonstrated to incorporate nucleotides at discrete nuclear foci after irradiation of G_2 cells. Treatment with caffeine or okadaic acid prevents this G_2-specific activity, as well as abrogating the G_2 checkpoint, and results in increased cell killing. Rat embryo cells transfected with the *ras* oncogene (discussed in more detail later) show greater G_2 delay as well as radioresistance. Despite the weight of this circumstantial evidence, specific agents that specifically target the G_2 checkpoint are still lacking. Caffeine and okadaic acid have myriad effects on diverse intracellular pathways beyond G_2, and concentration levels sufficient to demonstrate clear effects in the laboratory would be lethal in the organism.

II. SIGNAL TRANSDUCTION AND RADIATION RESISTANCE

Considerable evidence has linked radioresistance with alterations in the signal transduction pathways by which cells respond to changes in their microenvironment. Outside signals are detected by receptors on the cell surface, which then trigger a cascade of events culminating in alteration in gene expression (a schematic of a simplified pathway is depicted in Fig. 2). Signal transduction pathways often demonstrate cross talk and redundancy, precluding simple interpretations of the mechanisms by which radioresistance is conferred. Nonetheless, the ideal would be to find final common pathways that converge in the induction of radioresistance. This section outlines data linking specific signal transduction pathways and radioresistance.

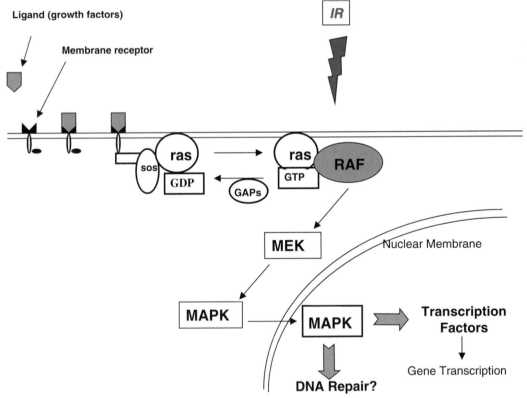

FIGURE 2 Signal transduction. Many oncogenes and tumor suppressor genes are members of the signal transduction pathway. In this model, a growth factor in the extracellular environment interacts with its receptor. This event is signaled to the nucleus via a G protein (Ras), which leads to alterations in kinase activity. The activation of the kinase cascade results in the binding of a transcription factor to the regulatory sequence of a gene, which may induce mRNA transcription or induce repair activity.

A. Growth Factors and Receptors

This family of kinases consists of protein tyrosine kinases that catalyze the transfer of γ-phosphate of ATP to tyrosine residues of protein substrates at the cell membrane. These kinases can be divided into two large families: receptor tyrosine kinases (RTKs) and nonreceptor tyrosine kinases (NRTKs). NRTKs, which include Src, Abl, FAK, and JAKs, contain no extracellular or transmembrane portion, but possess modular domains that are responsible for subcellular targeting and regulation of catalytic activity. Aberrant activity of almost all of these tyrosine kinases has been implicated in cancer. RTKs span the plasma membrane and contain an extracellular portion, which binds ligand, and an intracellular portion, which possesses catalytic activity and regulatory sequences. The RTK family includes the insulin receptor and the receptor for many growth factors, such as epidermal (EGF or ERB B), platelet-derived (PDGF), fibroblast (FGF), and nerve growth factors.

The ERB B gene family of RTKs has been to date most linked to radioresistance. The ERB B gene family consists of four closely related growth factor receptors, including EGFR or HER-1 (erb-B1); HER-2 (erb-B2); HER-3 (erb-B3); and HER-4 (erb-B4). EGFR (erb-B1) is recognized by EGF, transforming growth factor-β (TGF-β), and amphiregulins. Heregulins and neuregulins recognize erb-B3 and erb-B4. The last member of the family erb-B2 (HER-2 or p185^{neu}) does not directly bind any known ligand. Instead, it heterodimerizes with the three other family members and enhances ligand-binding affinity and reduces the rate of dissociation. These heterodimers also amplify the elicited signal through activation of the erb-B2 intracellular kinase domain and auto-cross phosphorylation. EGF stimulation has increased radioresistance in experimental systems. An association between EGFR and clinical radioresistance has been reported in patients with head and neck cancers and astrocytic gliomas. Overexpression of the HER-2/neu oncogene has also been associated with a poorer outcome following radiation therapy in breast cancer. The mechanism(s) by which RTK confers radioresistance remains unclear, but may at least in part be mediated by stimulation of PI3K (see following sections).

B. Ras

There are three forms of ras: H-ras (homologous to the Harvey murine sarcoma virus oncogene), K-ras (homologous to the Kirsten murine sarcoma virus oncogene), and N-ras (initially isolated from a neuroblastoma cell line). Activating mutations of Ras can be seen in up to 30% of all human tumors. In addition, Ras activity is upregulated in many cancers by overexpression in the absence of activating mutations. ras genes code for 21-kDa proteins that are known as G proteins because they bind GDP or GTP. G proteins are members of signal transduction pathways that transmit signals from the extracellular environment of the cell to the machinery that controls gene expression (Fig. 1). Signaling is initiated by growth factor binding to an extracellular receptor domain. This leads to guanine nucleotide exchange factor (GEF) recruitment to promote the formation of the active GTP-bound form of Ras. GTPase-activating proteins (GAPs) accelerate the intrinsic GTP hydrolytic activity of Ras to promote the formation of the inactive, GDP-bound form of Ras. Activated Ras interacts with several downstream signal transduction pathways, such as Raf, Rac/Rho, and PI3 kinase, thereby causing the signal to move to the nucleus. Mutations in Ras at amino acids 12, 13, or 61 turn Ras constituitively active and unresponsive to GAPs. This in turn causes a sustained signal to be transmitted through Ras to downstream effectors.

Evidence that activated ras can confer increased radioresistance comes from a number of independent lines of experimentation. First, overexpression or transformation of rodent or human cells by Ras has been shown in many cases to result in cell lines that are substantially more resistant to radiation than the parental cells. Second, inhibition of Ras activation has resulted in radiosensitization both in rodent cells transfected with Ras and in human tumor cell lines bearing endogenous mutations in Ras. These studies have exploited independent methods to block Ras activation. Both lovostatin and farnesyltransferase inhibitors that block the processing of Ras result in radiosensitization. Similarly, transfection of cells expressing Ras with an adenoviral vector encoding an anti-Ras antibody fragment leads to radiosensitization through inhibition of Ras action. Finally, tumor cells with endogenous Ras activation are more resistant to radiation than their counterparts in which the mutant *ras* oncogene has been eliminated by homologous recombination. Taken together, these data offer a compelling case that mutant *ras* can increase the resistance of tumor cells to killing by ionizing radiation.

C. Targets Downstream of Ras

1. Raf-MAPK

Activation of Ras, either by mutation or through signaling from the cell surface receptors, triggers downstream a series of cascading activations of cytoplasmic kinases. These downstream signaling pathways consist of at least three sequential kinase cascades that include (1) the Ras-Raf-MEK (also known as ERK) pathway, (2) the stress-activated SAPK/JNK pathway, and (3) the p38 pathway. Of these, the Ras-Raf-MAPK pathway has been implicated in radiosensitivity. Inhibition of MEK radiosensitized DU145 cells, a cell line with wild-type *ras*. In separate reports, transfection of a truncated and constituitively active Raf gene into a human squamous cell carcinoma cell line led to increased survival after radiation, whereas downregulation of Raf via antisense reduced radioresistance. In addition, it has been found that radiation itself induced Raf activation by colocalization of Ras and Raf to the inner cell membrane in cells with wild-type *ras*, although the physiological consequence of that induction has not yet been explored. As in experiments that involved overexpressed Ras, the precise mechanism(s) that confers resistance to DNA damage remains unclear. The relationship between the Ras-Raf-MEK pathway and radiosensitivity, however, is likely to be complex and perhaps cell line dependent. For example, the inhibition of MAPK using the MEK inhibitor PD98059 failed to radiosensitize T24 bladder carcinoma cells with activated Ras.

2. PI3 Kinase

In addition to the stimulation of downstream signal cascades, Ras has been found to also directly bind to and activate the catalytic p110 unit of phosphoinositide-3-kinase (PI3K). Ras activation is thus frequently associated with active PI3K. PI3K phosphorylates and converts phosphatidylinositol diphosphate [PI(4,5)P2] to the triphosphate form [PI(3,4,5)P3], which then serves as a lipid second messenger that activates a diverse range of targets that include p70S6K, Rac, and GEFs (guanine nucleotide exchange factors) and the phosphoinositide-dependent kinases PDK-1 and PDK-2 [which in turn activate Akt (also known as protein kinase B (PKB)]. PI3K activity has been implicated in a diverse range of intracellular activities that include mitogenic signaling, inhibition of apoptosis, intracellular vesicle trafficking, and secretion and regulation of actin and integrin functions.

Data have implicated PI3K as an important mediator of Ras-induced radiation resistance. The specific PI3K inhibitor LY294002 was found to radiosensitize cell lines with active PI3K and activating *ras* mutations, but not cells with wild-type *ras* and inactive PI3K. Furthermore, expression of constituitively active PI3K in cell lines with wild-type *ras* increased radiation resistance. Blocking PI3K activity with LY294002 again reversed the induced radioresistance.

The PI3K pathway may be affected independently of Ras, such as via stimulation by EGF signaling. The overexpression of EGFR frequently seen in cancers may therefore lead to increased PI3K activity and resistance to treatment. PI3K activity is reversed in normal cells via the phosphatase PTEN, which converts the active product PI(3,4,5)P3 back to PI(4,5)P2. Mutations causing PTEN to be functionally inactive are frequently found in many human cancers. Therefore, inactivation of PTEN may provide tumor cells with an alternative mechanism to increase PI3K activity and increase radioresistance. It has in fact been shown that PTEN gene transfer in human malignant gliomas sensitized cells to radiation (although this may in part be due to the growth suppression that PTEN also conferred).

D. ATM

The precise role of ATM, the protein deficient in individuals with ataxia telangiectasia, in conferring radiosensitivity remains somewhat of an enigma. The ATM protein is a member of the phosphatidylinositol 3-kinase family that functions in a variety of cell signaling pathways, including activation of p53 and cdc25C. Cells lacking ATM are radiosensitive and have been found to manifest a wide range of defects that include deficient cell cycle checkpoints, increased induction of apoptosis, decreased DNA repair, and increased mutagenesis. The increased radiosensitivity of ATM cells is possibly due to a multiplicity of mechanisms. Deficient cell cycle checkpoints may possibly allow less time for DNA repair. ATM-deficient cells do not appear to lack homologous repair, but may be disregulated. The lack of PI3K activity may function in as yet undefined pathways to further influence radiosensitivity.

III. REPAIR PROTEIN PATHWAYS

A comprehensive elucidation of what is all that is known about DNA repair pathways and damage inflicted by radiation is beyond the scope of this article. Therefore, the next sections will highlight select aspects that will hopefully serve as an introduction to the current state of knowledge.

It is commonly accepted that the central lethal event inflicted by radiation is the formation of unrepaired double strand DNA (dsDNA) breaks. It is thought that such unrepaired or misrepaired damage prevents proper progression through mitosis and so cells die in attempting to undergo cell division ("mitotic death"). Cells that are able to divide with damaged DNA often do so with missegregation of chromosomes and are doomed to die in subsequent divisions. It is also possible that unrepaired DNA damage interferes with housekeeping functions vital for the cell or may initiate apoptotic pathways leading to the death of the damaged cell prior to mitosis ("interphase death"). Different cell types and organ systems have divergent radiosensitivities, which could be due to different intrinsic repair capacities, systems inducing cell death, or both. For example, after irradiation, lymphocytes readily undergo apoptosis and are more radiosensitive than fibroblasts. However, radiosensitive cells do not consistently display greater degrees of apoptosis and instead may be lacking in repair proficiency.

The two most well-characterized repair pathways utilized by cells to repair dsDNA breaks are homologous recombination (HR)—in which the repair is accomplished by genetic exchange with a homologous chromosome—and nonhomologous end joining (NHEJ)—in which the two broken ends are simply joined back together (see Fig. 3). These will be described in greater detail in the next section. However, it appears that these repair pathways serve redundant functions, such that knocking out one or the other may not result in a dramatic increase in radiosensitivity. In addition to this redundancy, there are also overlapping mechanisms that share features or are upstream of both. A number of other proteins have been implicated in the DNA damage-induced response yet whose specific functions remain unclear (described in more detail later). Furthermore, the phase of the cell cycle will likely influence which specific repair function(s) predominates. All these considerations imply that it would be difficult to attribute the relative radioresistance of a given tumor to proficiency in a specific DNA repair function.

A. Homologous Recombination

Homologous recombination provides an accurate mechanism to repair dsDNA breaks in mammalian cells. In this form of repair, a homologous stretch of DNA serves as a template with which to regenerate nucleotides sufficient to accomplish repair of the dsDNA break. The source of the homologous template can be either from the sister chromatid (in S or G_2 phase cells) or the homologous chromosome in diploid cells. Pivotal proteins necessary in this form of repair include Rad50, Rad51, and Rad52. Rad50 forms a complex with Mre11 and xrs (also known as nibrin or NBS1) that has both nuclease and exonuclease properties. This complex appears to be involved in both HR and NHEJ, but its precise function remains unclear. Rad52 binds to single strand DNA (ssDNA) and Rad51, the latter of which also binds to ssDNA. A model of how these proteins interact has been proposed. At the ends of a dsDNA break, the Rad50 complex may participate in the formation of a small stretch of ssDNA that is then recognized and bound by Rad52. Rad52 then recruits molecules of Rad51 to "coat" the ssDNA, which then facilitates strand exchange with homologous dsDNA to accomplish the repair. The binding of the free end of a dsDNA break by Rad52 is reminiscent of the Ku proteins (described in the next paragraph); competition between Rad52 and Ku proteins for a free dsDNA end may help determine whether the repair of a given dsDNA break is accomplished by HR or NHEJ. A

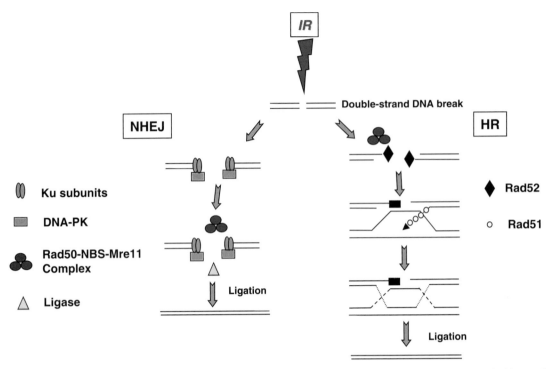

FIGURE 3 Pathways of DNA double strand break repair. The lethal event caused by radiation is thought to be double strand breaks. Two prominent pathways of repair of double strand DNA breaks in mammalian cells are nonhomologous end joining (NHEJ) and homologous recombination (HR). In NHEJ, DNA-PK and Ku subunits are recruited to the broken DNA ends. NHEJ repair appears to be facilitated in an undefined way by the Mre11-NBS-Rad50 complex, a complex which also figures in HR. In HR, Rad52 binds to free DNA ends. ssDNA is formed during the course of HR, which may be stabilized by a coating of Rad51. Final ligation in both instances is accomplished by ligase.

number of other proteins have been found to participate in HR, including Rad54, Rad55, and Rad57. At the present time, the roles these proteins play in HR remain undefined.

B. Nonhomologous End-Joining

Mammalian cells in G_1 and early S phase have only begun to replicate DNA and therefore lack sister chromatids to provide homologous sequences used in repair by homologous recombination. Consequently, at this point of the cell cycle, repair by NHEJ predominates. Seven proteins are known to be required for this process—Ku70 and Ku80, DNA ligase IV, the associated XRCC4 protein, and Mre11, Rad50, and Xrs2/p95—and these same proteins are also implicated in the end-joining processes of V(D)J recombination in the immune system. Ku proteins are thought to bind to and partially protect the free DNA ends

from digestion by 5′ to 3′ exonucleases, whereas the DNA ligase IV probably is instrumental in the final event ligating the broken ends together. Both yeast and mammalian cell lines with mutations affecting any of these components can be demonstrated to have increased radiosensitivity. NHEJ can be prone to mutations, which arise from joining of inappropriate DNA ends (such as when there are multiple DSBs) or from deletions of sequences from the cut ends. During the course of NHEJ, single strand DNA are apparently often formed, either by nucleotide insertions or by deletions, resulting in regions of 1 to 5 bp of homology (sometimes referred to as "microhomology") between the two broken ends to be joined. Because such few base pairings would be expected to be highly unstable, it has been suggested that additional proteins or complexes may confer the additional stability needed to complete repair, but which remain largely uncharacterized. The complex formed by Mre11,

Rad50, and xrs/p95 plays an early role in initiating NHEJ, possibly by generating small sequences of ssDNA that permit microhomology.

C. Other Pathways/Participants?

Irradiation of mammalian cells in culture conspicuously results in the formation of foci of Rad51, Rad52, and the Rad50/Mre11/nbs complex. These foci must represent the aggregation of many thousands of molecules to be visible on conventional microscopy. These foci presumably are involved in the repair process. Mutants that abolish formation of these foci also result in radiosensitization. Beyond such observations, it is presently unknown why these foci form. Furthermore, irradiation also results in the formation of foci of a number of other proteins, including BRCA1, BRCA2, 53BP1, and histone H2AX. It remains unclear what roles these proteins play in the sensing of DNA damage or what mode of DNA repair they are a part of.

IV. SUMMARY

This article suggests the multiplicity and complexity of mechanisms that may enable tumor cells to become more radioresistant. It is likely that different pathways come into play in different cell lines, and profound differences may exist even within the cells of a given tumor in a patient. Nonetheless, it remains a mystery how tumor cells become resistant to radiation and other forms of treatment. Are pathways induced that enable increased repair of DNA damage or avoidance of treatment-induced death (e.g., apoptosis)? The challenge lies in fully clarifying all possible mechanisms that confer such resistance to treatment and developing strategies to counteract each.

See Also the Following Articles

Angiogenesis and Natural Angiostatic Agents • Cell Cycle Checkpoints • Hyperthermia • Hypoxia and Drug Resistance • MAP Kinase Modules in Signaling • Mismatch Repair: Biochemistry and Genetics • Ras Proteins • Radiobiology, Principles of • Signal Transduction Mechanisms Initiated by Receptor Tyrosine Kinases

Bibliography

Bernhard, E. J., et al. (1998). Inhibiting Ras prenylation increases radiosensitivity of human tumor cell lines with activating mutations of Ras oncogenes. Cancer Res. **58,** 1754–1761.

Khanna, K. K., and Jackson, S. P. (2001). DNA double-strand breaks: Signaling, repair, and the cancer connection. Nature Gene. **27,** 247–254.

Levitzki, A., and Gazit, A. (1995). Tyrosine kinase inhibition: An approach to drug development. Science **267,** 1782–1788.

Sherr, C. J. (2000). The Pezcoller lecture: Cancer cell cycle revisited. Cancer Res. **60,** 3689–3695.

Shields, J. M., Pruitt, K., McFall, A., Shaub, A., and Der, C. J. (2000). Understanding Ras: "It ain't over 'til it's over." Trends Cell Biol. **10,** 147–154.

Molecular Basis for Tumor Immunity

Bijay Mukherji

The University of Connecticut School of Medicine

GLOSSARY

adoptive transfer Introduction of immunocompetent cells.

cognate Recognition based on a particular specificity.

cytolytic T lymphocyte A class of T cells that can kill another cell.

epitope The part of the antigen that is recognized by antibody and T cells.

major histocompatibility complex A cluster of genes whose products determine tissue compatibility.

SEREX Serological identification of antigens by recombinant expression cloning.

serology Study of antibody-mediated immune response.

T-cell receptors T-cell surface molecules through which T cells recognize antigens.

transfection A technique often used for introducing a gene into a cell.

The purpose of this article is to examine the molecular basis of the host immune response against cancer. Despite years of controversy about the concept of immune surveillance against cancer, the collective work on the topic has now affirmed that whether surveillance against developing cancer works or not, once cancer has developed, the host can mount a response against it. The response is mediated by both the cellular and the serologic arms of the immune system and the responses are directed against tumor cell-associated antigens with considerable specificity. The molecular basis by which the specificity of the interaction between the immunocompetent cells or a given antibody and the target antigens is mediated, therefore, constitutes a crucial aspect of our understanding of tumor immunity.

I. INTRODUCTION

Nearly a century ago, in a talk delivered to the students of the University of Amsterdam, Paul Ehrlich articulated the concept of "tumor immunity" that still permeates our thoughts and guides our work in the field. He was convinced of a need for "protective properties of the organism" against potential outgrowths of carcinomas arising from the "derailment of germ cells" going through the "complicated steps of fetal and postfetal growth." Although others had spoken of natural tumor immunity, his own belief that natural immunity against cancer exists was based partly on theoretical reasoning and partly from the results of transplantation experiments. Summarizing his transplantation experiments in mice with spontaneously grown tumors, he went on to describe three types of tumor immunity: "naturliche immunitat," "erworbene immunitat," and "athreptische immunitat." He observed that the transplantability of tumors and the rate of growth of transplanted tumors varied and attributed this variability to two dynamic processes: the resistance of the host animals and the virulence of the tumors. The idea that immunity against cancer can be acquired (erworbene immunitat), however, evolved from his seminal discovery of the protective power of a single preinoculation with hemorrhagic primary tumors on subsequent transplants of the same highly virulent tumors. Fifty percent of his animals were protected "often with a single preinoculation," and, at times, "absolute" levels of protection could be achieved with multiple preinoculations. Although Ehrlich could not provide a satisfactory explanation of the nature of the immune response, he speculated that the immunity was likely to be mediated by cells and not by antibody. However, as we shall see later, the immune response to cancer cells involves both cells and antibodies.

These initial ideas later underwent substantial conceptual reformulation, first by Thomas and then by Burnet. Ehrlich's vision of existence of natural immunity was rephrased by Thomas as "immunosurveillance," and Burnet added more theoretical elegance to the idea and elaborated on the cardinal tenets on which the subject of tumor immunology was to rest for some time to come. Following the same experimentalist's path (i.e., transplantation biology) laid down by Ehrlich, a number of more recent investigators—notably, Foley, Prehn and Main, and Klein and colleagues—amply confirmed that, indeed, certain animal tumors are rejected following a single immunization with a nontumorigenic dose of the same tumor in the murine system and showed that there is remarkable specificity in the process. Because the phenomenon was demonstrated by transplantation techniques, this form of immunity was referred to as tumor-specific transplantation immunity, and the putative antigen that conferred such immunity was referred to as tumor-specific transplantation antigen (TSTA). Unfortunately, neither Ehrlich nor his followers were able to elucidate a cogent molecular basis for the immune interaction. Ehrlich simply did not have the tools. Similarly, his followers, while they also succeeded in providing confirmation of the phenomenon, could neither furnish good evidence of immunosurveillance against spontaneously arising cancers nor could they define the nature of the tumor antigen that was recognized by the host. Understandably, the concepts of tumor immunity, in general, and natural immunity, in particular, came under much criticism.

As all dogmas must go through careful reexamination, the concept of immunosurveillance against cancer, and the entire subject of tumor immunology for that matter, received a healthy measure of scrutiny. Schwartz and Mellief questioned the veracity of the idea with a long inquiry on the subject. Stutman similarly found flaws in the logic of surveillance with studies of immunosuppressed mice that, contrary to the prediction, were found not to be unusually susceptible to the development of cancers. Finally, Hewitt could not find any evidence of host immunity in mice bearing spontaneous cancers. Skepticism mounted as the field desperately needed firmer evidence of an immune response against spontaneously arising tumors and needed a clear identification of the nature of the tumor antigen. Fortunately, evidence of a host immune response against autologous cancer cells and the molecular identity of the tumor antigen finally emerged, but only recently, as the tools of investigation became sharper.

At this juncture, it will be useful to provide a brief scenario of the processes involved in the cognate recognition of the tumor cells by the immune system that leads to their eventual elimination. The immune system, as we know it now, has evolved from a primitive form of immunity to its present complexity. It should be understood that the main reason for evolution grafting a complex immune system in multicellular organisms has been, and remains, for the overwhelming need to provide defense against foreign invaders, be it by a bacterium, by a parasite, or by a virion. In this schema of things, it is fairly safe to conclude that evolution could not possibly have envisioned the need for a defense against altruistic grafts of alien tissues or organs. Despite the fact that mother nature did not envision a confrontation with allograft-mediated invasion, the increasingly hostile environment required her to empower the host with a fairly sophisticated mechanism of cognate immunologic processes that could distinguish nonself from self. In the case of immune response against a cancer cell, that has arisen from within, it became necessary therefore to view the cancer cells essentially as "nonself" by endowing them with a type of foreignness, or aberrant trait, acquired from the abnormal process of malignant transformation. Indeed, the general idea behind tumor immunity has been that, upon transformation, cancer cells are likely to acquire a unique tumor antigen. The host accordingly could view the unique antigen as foreign and respond through its immunological arsenal. As we shall see later, this view turned out to be only partly correct. For it is now amply clear that the immune system can surely recognize an unaltered and perfectly normal moiety on a tumor cell as an antigenic epitope and respond to it. Simply stated, the antigenic determinant on a cancer cell does not have to be either alien or unique to evoke an immune response.

In addition, a brief description of the diversity of the immune system itself and the molecular interactions that determine fine discrimination, known as specificity in immunologic parlance, will also be useful. It should be mentioned that while the immunologic apparatus consists of diverse elements of effector responses mediated serologically, or through the participation of a number of immunocompetent cells, fine discrimination (specificity) can be only mediated either through antibodies or through T cells. T cells recognize antigen only in the form of short peptides displayed on the groove of a relevant major histocompatibility complex (MHC) molecule. The helper T cells bearing the CD4 phenotype recognize peptide displayed by the class II MHC molecules, whereas cytolytic T lymphocytes (CTL) recognize peptide displayed on class I MHC molecules. Further, T helper cells usually recognize external antigen (picked up from outside by the cell as opposed by being synthesized from within), processed and displayed on the MHC class II molecules of specialized antigen-presenting cells (APC). CTL, however, recognize internal antigen (synthesized within the cell) processed and presented on the MHC class I molecules. Finally, it should be mentioned that binding of the T-cell receptor (TCR) to the peptide–MHC complex alone does not necessarily lead to the activation of T cells. Besides signals received through engagement of TCR, T cells require an additional signal(s) for full activation. These other signals are usually referred to as costimulatory signals, which can be delivered through ligations of a number of other receptors. Once activated, a T cell can proliferate and carry out its effector functions, be it cytolysis, cytokine secretion, or both. While CTL can themselves eliminate a target cell by killing it, a noncytolytic T cell, including a noncytolytic CD8$^+$ T cell, can secrete cytokines, which can, in turn, recruit and activate other types of effector cells in the immune response, although these effector cells may not exhibit fine discrimination.

An antibody—an immunoglobulin with a unique antigen-binding structure resulting from rearrangement and mutation of the immunoglobulin heavy chain and light chain genes of a given B cell—however, can bind both cell surface bound antigen or free antigen. In order to be recognized by a given antibody, the antigens do not, however, have to be processed and presented on any restricting MHC molecules. The elimination of antigen-bearing cells bound by antibodies results from lysis either through the fixation of complement or with the help of killer cells engaged in and activated to action by signaling through the Fc receptors of the killer cells engaged by the free Fc end of the bound antibody (antibody-dependent cell-mediated cytotoxicity or ADCC).

II. EVIDENCE OF T-CELL-MEDIATED IMMUNE RESPONSE AGAINST ANIMAL TUMOR MODEL

Chemically induced tumors have served as an extremely useful model in studies of tumor immunity.

Indeed, the compelling evidence of an immunogenic nature of tumors was established first in transplantation protection experiments using methylcholanthrene (MCA)-induced tumors in the murine system. The TSTA associated with these MCA-induced tumors elicited exquisite specificity. For example, not only were individual sarcomas derived from different syngeneic mice antigenically different, two sarcomas induced in the same mouse, with the same carcinogen, did not cross-react immunogenically. Table I shows an example of a classical transplantation experiment in which the immunogenic uniqueness of chemically induced sarcomas can be demonstrated. As can be seen, transplantation protection can only be achieved by preimmunization with the same tumor. The TSTA associated with these types of chemically induced sarcomas are so unique that two different sarcomas induced in the same animal, with the same carcinogen, can not cross-immunize against each other. It has been shown by adoptive transfer of the relevant immune T cells that this type of immunity is primarily mediated through T cells. Although the molecular identity of the TSTA remains quite elusive, interesting information has emerged from work of two groups of investigators. Working with an MCA-induced murine tumor, Meth A, Appella and Law demonstrated that an 84-kDa and another 86-kDa protein isolated from the Meth A sarcoma could confer specific transplantation immunity. When the genes encoding these proteins were cloned, a remarkable homology with the gene encoding the heat shock protein (HSP) was discovered. Almost simultaneously, Srivastava and Old, also working with the Meth

A sarcoma and another MCA-induced tumor, CMS 5, found a 96-kDa protein, isolated from both tumors and exhibiting similar homology with the HSP, that was capable of conferring protective immunity with a remarkable degree of fine specificity for the individual tumors. The molecular basis of this paradox (same protein antigens isolated from two different chemically transformed tumors conferring specific protective immunity) is difficult to comprehend, particularly in view of repeated demonstrations of the restricted nature of individual TSTA. It has been suggested that although preimmunization with the 96-kDa protein itself is all that is needed to induce immune rejections for both types of tumors, the protein itself might not serve as the true antigenic epitope. Instead, it might act as a chaperone. Indeed, Srivastava's group has shown that antigen-presenting cells capture and represent antigens (a processes that is referred to as cross-presentation) through HSP molecules. Although data on HSP in transplantation immunity in a tumor model are quite impressive, the molecular basis of protective transplantation immunity elicitable with the HSP is yet to be fully understood.

A. Molecular Basis of Immune Response in the Murine Plasmacytoma System

In contrast, the chemically induced murine plasmacytoma system, P815, in the DBA/2 mouse, turned out to be a remarkably more rewarding model for obtaining the molecular identity of tumor-specific antigens. Indeed, the molecular nature of the "tumor antigen" and the identity of the gene that codes for that "tumor

TABLE I

Unique Specificity of Antigens Associated with Chemically Induced Sarcomas in Mice

		Protection can be achieved only when preimmunized				
	Immunized with	Tumor 1	Tumor 2	Tumor 3	Tumor 4A[a]	Tumor 4B[a]
Mouse A	Tumor 1	+	−	−	−	−
Mouse B	Tumor 2	−	+	−	−	−
Mouse C	Tumor 3	−	−	+	−	−
Mouse D	Tumor 4A	−	−	−	+	−
Mouse E	Tumor 4B	−	−	−	−	+
Mouse F	Tumors 4A and 4B	−	−	−	+	+

[a]Induced by methylcholanthrene in the same syngeneic mouse.

antigen" emerged, for the first time, with studies of mutagen-induced variant murine plasmacytoma lines that, ironically, did not produce tumor in syngeneic animals but could immunize them from grafts of nonmutagenized, otherwise tumorigenic plasmacytoma cells. Because the variant lines did not produce tumors, they were referred to as tum− ("tumor negative") as opposed to the original tum+ cells that developed progressive tumors in syngeneic animals. Evidently, the tum− mutant cells expressed transplantation antigens that were not found in the tum+ cells. The antigens associated with these tum− variants (tum− antigens) were found to be remarkably diverse, as each tum− line carried a separate antigen(s) with them. As the advent of T-cell growth factor (later renamed interleukin-2) made it possible to grow T cell lines, or clones, in long-term culture. Working with a series of these tum− lines, Boon's group established a set of tum− antigen-specific CTL clones exhibiting fine specificities for the corresponding tum− tumor cells. These CTL, bearing restricted specificities for a given tum− line, therefore defined a number of tum− antigens.

Subsequently, Boon's group adopted a novel strategy for identifying the structure of the gene(s) that coded for these CTL-determined tum− antigens. This was based on two critical steps: The first step was to transfect an antigen-negative variant tumor cell line with DNA from the antigen-positive line. The second step involved detecting the antigen-expressing transfectants by their ability to stimulate the specific CTL clone. A highly transfectable P815 cell line was developed, and these tum− antigen-negative cells were transfected with a cosmid library of the DNA derived from a tum− line that expressed a tum− antigen called P91A. Soon, stable transfectants expressing the tum− antigen P91A were identified. Thereafter, the gene that transferred the P91A antigenicity was cloned and named the tum− gene. Structural analysis of the tum− gene, coding for the antigen P91A, revealed the gene to be composed of 12 exons encoding a 60-kDa protein without a typical N-terminal signal sequence. The open reading frame resided in exon 4 (Fig. 1). Interestingly, when the sequence of the smallest fragment that was capable of transferring immunogenicity (a 0.8-kb PstI–PvuII fragment) was compared with its normal homologue, a single point mutation, from G to A, was discovered at position 274. The peptide derived from the product of this gene that was presented by the target cell on the Ld molecule for recognition by the CTL clone was later identified. This peptide, when pulsed to appropriate syngeneic cells, made the cells sensitive to lysis by the corresponding CTL. Subsequently, this group identified the structures of a number of other tum− genes by a similar approach. All of these genes turned out to be completely unrelated and they exhibited no homology with any previously recorded gene in the data bank. Interestingly, like the tum− gene coding for the antigen P91A, these genes were also found to exhibit single point mutations at different exons.

Understandably, the tum− antigen may not be viewed as a true tumor antigen, as its antigenicity

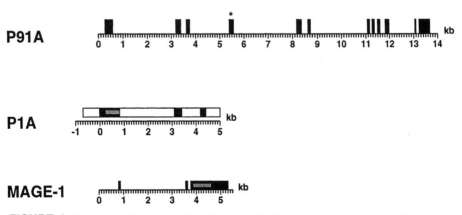

FIGURE 1 Structures of genes encoding P91A and the P1A antigens in the mouse plasmacytoma model and the human melanoma antigen MAGE-1. Black bars represent exons and the asterisk indicates the site of the point mutation. The hatched bar represents the open reading frame.

resulted from deliberate mutagenesis. The discovery of mutagen-induced tum− antigen systems, however, served the field of tumor immunology exceedingly well. These studies provided us with the first glimpse of the structure of a gene that codes for a CTL-determined antigen that operationally acts as a tumor antigen (i.e., when immunized with it, protective immunity against the wild-type tumor line can be achieved). These studies showed that mutational events can give rise to antigenic peptides and paved the path for discoveries of other antigens that might be construed as "true" tumor antigens. Before we leave the field of tum− antigens, it should be briefly mentioned that thus far a large number of tum− antigens have been identified in CTL stimulation assays. These antigens show remarkable diversity. For example, 15 out of 15 tum− antigens do not cross-react among themselves. This is reminiscent of similar diversity within the TSTA of chemically induced murine sarcomas and suggests that the enormous diversity of TSTA associated with the chemically induced animal sarcomas might some day also very well be explained on the basis of mutations. Unfortunately, despite the formidable advances in technology that have given us the structural definitions of "tumor antigens," in animals and in humans, the genetic identity of the TSTA remains remarkably elusive.

Interestingly, the structural definition of another set of tumor antigens also soon emerged from studies of the P815 plasmacytoma system. As mentioned earlier, the plasmacytoma tumor P815 is a chemically induced tumor in DBA/2 mice. These tumors express antigens that are recognized by CTL. Working with a panel of anti-P815 CTL clones, Boon's group isolated a number of antigen loss variants in immunoselection (selecting a cytolytically nonsusceptible P815 variant after subjecting the wild-type P815 cells to lysis by the CTL for several rounds). An antigen loss variant, however, remained sensitive to lysis by a different CTL clone(s). This way, they defined a number of P815 antigens that were recognized by specific CTL clones. Of these, the antigens P815A and P815B were of considerable interest. The antigens P815A and P815B appeared to be linked, as immunoselection with anti-A CTL always resulted in the development of simultaneous resistance to anti-B CTL. Although these two antigens were defined in CTL assays with two corresponding CTL clones (clone A and B), when the gene coding for the expression of these antigens was cloned by the same approach (transfection of antigen-negative variant with cDNA from a given antigen-positive line followed by identification of the gene expression in CTL assay), both antigens were found to be coded by a single gene. This gene was named P1A. Interestingly, transfection experiments with an antigen loss variant, A−B− (derived from *in vivo* escape), yielded a P815A transfectant that was found to be equally susceptible to lysis by the P815A and B CTL, again suggesting a close identity between P815A and P815B antigens.

The P1A gene, similar to tum− genes, was not homologous to any recorded gene in the data bank. It was approximately 5 kb long and consisted of three exons with an open reading frame coding for a putative protein of 224 residues starting in exon 1 and ending in exon 2. The fragment of 900 bases that transferred the expression of antigens A and B residing in exon 1 (Fig. 1) shows the basic structures of the tum− gene coding for the antigen P91A and P1A gene in the mouse plasmacytoma system. Most intriguingly, when the sequence of the gene derived from the tumor cells was compared with the sequence of the same gene from normal cells of the same strain, no structural alteration was found. Thus, unlike the tum− antigen, P91A, the antigenicity of the product of the P1A gene was not associated with any point mutation. Indeed, the P1A gene derived from normal cells also transferred antigenicity. The immunogenicity of the product coded by this gene seemed to have resulted from the expression of the gene in tumor cells, as the gene is not usually expressed in normal cells. The P1A gene was either only minimally expressed or not expressed at all in the normal cells, suggesting, therefore, that activation of the P1A gene could have resulted from the transformation process. Accordingly, its expression might have been viewed as "foreign" from an operational viewpoint. Interestingly, the gene coding for the antigen loss variant line, P815A−B+, was found to have a point mutation in exon 1. As the peptides synthesized corresponding to the normal sequence surrounding the mutation site were tested for their capacity to sensitize cells bearing the restricting element (Ld), one peptide was found capable of sensitizing the appropriate target for lysis by the CTL. The same peptide also sensitized syngeneic cells bearing the Ld molecule for lysis by anti-P815A CTL. It appears, then, that anti-P815A and anti-P815B CTL recognize two different epitopes on the same peptide.

Thus, just as a single point mutation can lead to the formation of an immunogenic peptide (as with the tum− antigens), a peptide fragment derived from the product of a perfectly normal gene sequence can also be processed and presented on the appropriate MHC restriction element as an antigenic determinant for CTL recognition.

B. Immunity against Virally Induced Cancers in Animals

In keeping with the immunogenic nature of chemically induced tumors, tumors induced by DNA viruses have been found to be highly immunogenic. For example, polyoma is a ubiquitous virus in mice and this virus can induce a large variety of tumors only when newborn mice, that have not yet been immunized by mothers milk, are inoculated with it, or it can also produce tumors in mice with impaired immune systems. Further, mice can be made resistant to transplants of polyoma virus-transformed tumor after immunization with the virus itself.

The structures of a number of antigenic molecules have been defined with both DNA viruses and retroviruses. Cytolytic T cells have been found to recognize epitopes clustering around the amino-terminal of the SV40 T antigen. Similarly, it has been shown that retroviral antigens are recognized by CTL and can induce a rejection response *in vivo*. For example, CD8$^+$ CTL and CD4$^+$ helper T cells have been shown capable of recognizing antigens coded by the gag gene and the env gene of the Friend leukemia virus on MHC class I and MHC class II molecules, respectively. It has been possible to eradicate adenovirus E1-induced tumors by E1-specific CTL.

As can be seen, the immunity to virally induced animal tumors is essentially dictated by the immune response to the viral determinants themselves.

III. T-CELL-MEDIATED IMMUNE RESPONSE AGAINST AUTOLOGOUS HUMAN CANCER

The clearest evidence in support of the existence of autologous tumor-specific T cells in cancer patients emerged almost simultaneously with the observations in the P815 system, as interleukin-2 became available, making the isolation of T-cell clones in *in vitro* culture possible. The search for autologous tumor-specific CTL clones began in several laboratories in a human melanoma model. The laboratory of the author, and Knuth and Old, independently, isolated bona fide CTL lines exhibiting exquisite specificity that were capable of recognizing autologous melanoma cells. The CTL also conformed strictly to the principles guiding the T-cell recognition of antigen, i.e., these T cells recognized antigen only in the context of a certain MHC class I molecule. Figure 2 shows an example of the cytolytic properties of two CTL lines in two separate autologous melanoma systems.

In both systems, CTL lines kill the respective autologous target and allogeneic target cells in the context of certain HLA molecules. In the RM system (Fig. 2A), the CTL kill the autologous as well as an allogeneic melanoma cell line, which share two characteristics: they express both HLA-A1 and the gene MAGE-1. In addition, in this case, the CTL kill the HLA A1-positive but MAGE-1 gene-negative target MZ 2.2 only when the target cells are pulsed with the synthetic nonapeptide EADPTGHSY. We shall see later that this nonapeptide constitutes the fragment of the protein product of the gene MAGE-1 that serves as the epitope for the MAGE-1 antigen-specific CTL. In the GL system (Fig. 2B), the CTL similarly kills the autologous and an allogeneic cell line, both of which express HLA-A2 molecules and express the tyrosinase gene. It seems, therefore, that the GL CTL line might recognize a common antigenic determinant, perhaps coded by the tyrosinase genes, presented on the HLA-A2 molecule. We shall see later that indeed the gene tyrosinase codes for several CTL-determined peptide epitopes. The nature of the antigens and their peptides recognized by these types of CTL lines will be discussed at some length in the following section. Meanwhile, it should be pointed

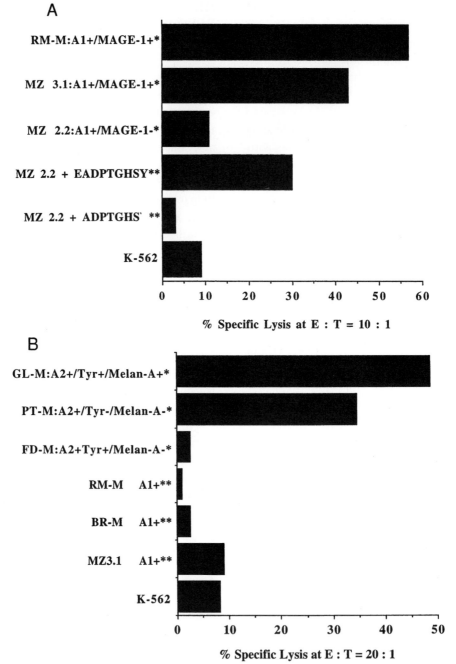

FIGURE 2 (A) Cytolytic properties (measured in a 4-h chromium 51 release microcytotoxicity assay) of a CD8[+] CTL line isolated from tumor-infiltrating lymphocytes derived from a melanoma patient from whom the autologous melanoma cell line RM-M was established. The target cell lines, MZ 3.1 and MZ 2.2, are allogeneic melanoma cell lines that were derived from a HLA A1-positive melanoma patient. The cell line MZ 3.1 expresses MAGE-1 mRNA. The cell line MZ 2.2 was derived by immunoselection as a MAGE-1 negative variant. Both lines were gifts of Thierry Boon, Ludwig Institute for Cancer research, Brussels, Belgium. The target line K-562 is the NK cell-sensitive prototype target. A single asterisk indicates HLA phenotype and the status of the expression (tested by PCR analysis) of the MAGE-1 mRNA by the respective target cell lines. A double asterisk indicates the target cell being pulsed with the respective synthetic peptide. (B) Cytolytic properties (measured in a 4-h chromium 51 release microcytotoxicity assay) of another CD8[+] CTL line isolated from the tumor-involved lymph node from a melanoma patient from whom the melanoma line GL-M was established. RM-M, BR-M, and MZ 3.1, allogeneic melanoma cell lines. K-562, NK cell-sensitive target cell line. A single asterisk indicates HLA phenotype and the status of the expression (tested by PCR analysis) of the mRNA of the gene tyrosinase (Tyr) and the gene Melan-A by the respective target cell lines. A double asterisk indicates the HLA phenotype (HLA-A1 in this case) of the respective target cell lines.

out that tumor-specific T-cell clones can be isolated from peripheral blood, from regional lymph nodes, and from the lymphocytes that infiltrate tumors. Further, it should be noted that human melanoma is not the only type of spontaneously arising tumor against which the evidence of tumor-specific T-cell-mediated immune response can be demonstrated. The evidence of similar types of cytolytic T-cell responses against autologous cancers has also been found in breast cancer, ovarian cancer, pancreatic cancer, cancer of the head and neck, sarcoma, and others.

A. Molecular Identity of the Melanoma Antigen Recognized by CTL

In the late 1980s, Boon's group generated a panel of autologous CTL clones that exhibited specific cytolysis, in context of the HLA A1 molecule, against the respective autologous human melanoma cell line, MZ 2 Mel (shown in Fig. 2A as MZ 3.1 and MZ 2.2). Boon and colleagues isolated antigen-negative variants by an immunoselection technique and identified six different antigens that were recognized by the CTL in this system. Working with one of these six antigen systems, referred to as MZ2-E, and employing the same strategy that led to the discovery of the P1A gene (i.e., transfection of the antigen-negative variant with a cosmid library derived from the cDNA of the antigen-positive variant and CTL stimulation assay), they obtained a cosmid preparation that transferred the expression of antigen E. They then deciphered the structure of the gene encoding the expression of the antigen E associated with the melanoma cell line MZ 3.1 that was recognized by the relevant CTL clone. cDNA recovered from this cosmid was composed of a 2.4-kb fragment consisting of two exons. Another exon located upstream was found by sequencing the segment of the cosmid in front of the 2.4-kb fragment. The gene, therefore, consisted of three exons, although two of the three exons corresponding to segments of the 2.4-kb fragment could transfer expression of the CTL epitope (Fig. 1). This was the first molecular definition of a human melanoma (or, for that matter, of a human tumor) associated T-cell-determined antigen. The gene was named MAGE (melanoma antigen)-1. Interestingly, the sequence of the MAGE-1 gene in melanoma cells and in normal tissue showed no structural difference.

The MAGE-1 gene is expressed by approximately 40% of all melanoma cells and by a number of other types of tumors as well, but it is not expressed by any other normal tissues, except by some unidentified cells in the testis. MAGE-1 appears to be a differentiation antigen. The MAGE-1 gene belongs to a family consisting of about 15 different genes, of which 6 (MAGE-1–6) have been found to be expressed in melanomas. CTL have been found for a number of peptides coded by these genes (MAGE-1, 2, 3, 4, etc.). In addition to the MAGE family-encoded antigens, several other genes (MAGE, BAGE, GAGE, and RAGE) with similar characteristics (i.e., expressed by melanoma cells and testis) have also been discovered with the same technique of transfection and CTL assay using different CTL clones. Interestingly, none of these genes exhibits any mutation or any other type of structural alteration. See Fig. 1 for the basic structure of the MAGE-1 gene segment that transfers the MZ-E antigen. The peptide epitope of the MAGE-1 gene that was recognized by the MZ CTL proved, as one would have expected, to be a short peptide. It consisted of nine residues bearing the sequence EADPTGHSY (see Fig. 2A).

As studies of CTL response at clonal levels against human tumors continued in various laboratories, several important points became evident. First, it was found that the existence of tumor-specific CTL in patients was not that rare. A number of investigators were able to isolate CTL lines reactive against several different types of autologous tumors. Second, considerably more about specificity was learned. It became clear that CTL lines isolated from one patient can recognize antigen(s) on tumor cells of the same and different histology derived from other patients (see Figs. 2A and 2B). Finally, it also became clear that, in some situations, such as in melanoma, the melanoma-reactive CTL clone recognized cultured autologous normal melanocytes. Most important, it became abundantly clear that whereas there is cross-reactivity, the CTL recognize a shared determinant only in the context of a particular class I MHC molecule with a given system and specificity. Thus, while the MAGE epitopes are presented on HLA A1 molecules, a number of other antigenic determinants derived from the products of other genes, as we shall soon see, are presented on the HLA A2 molecules.

Subsequent to the discovery of the MAGE-1 gene coding for the expression of the MZ-E antigen on the HLA-A1 molecule, the molecular identity of several other genes coding for distinctly different antigens emerged from continued studies with antigen-specific CTL clones in the human melanoma system. As mentioned earlier, CTL lines, established from HLA-A2 melanoma patients in different laboratories, often exhibited broad reactivities against a number of HLA-A2-positive tumor cell lines. Studying a number of HLA A2-restricted CTL lines, Knuth and colleagues and Wölfel and colleagues isolated antigen loss variants and defined the existence of several distinct antigens associated with two melanoma cell lines (SK29-MEL and LB24-MEL) that were recognized by a panel of CTL clones derived from the respective patients. Employing a slightly different strategy (transfecting an expression library in COS cells and CTL assay) the gene that encoded one of these HLA-A2-restricted antigens (antigen Ab associated with the melanoma line SK29-MEL and LB24-MEL), Brichard and coworkers from Boon's group identified the gene that directed the expression of an HLA-A2-restricted expression of the Ab antigen recognized by two CTL lines derived from the respective patients. The gene coding for the Ab antigen turned out to be the same gene that codes for the enzyme tyrosinase.

Tyrosinase is an enzyme that catalyzes dihydroxyphenylalanine (DOPA) in the pathway of melanin synthesis and is expressed by cells of melanocytic lineage. It is expressed in melanocytes, nearly in all melanoma tissues, and in a large number of cultured melanoma cell lines. A panel of nonmelanocytic tissues and nonmelanoma tumors were found not to express the tyrosinase gene. Although the sequence of the gene tyrosinase coding for the expression of the melanoma antigen Ab differed at a number of points with that of the gene tyrosinase sequenced by other investigators, the differences were thought to be a reflection of polymorphism. The sequence of the gene tyrosinase encoding the melanoma antigen Ab was found to be identical to the sequence of the gene tyrosinase derived from other cells of the same patient. Two peptides (MLLAVLYCL and YMNGTMSQV) derived from the product of the gene tyrosinase were identified as the peptide epitopes presented on the HLA-A2 molecule for CTL

recognition. Tyrosinase was also later found to code for a HLA-A24 epitope. It is of considerable interest that Topalian and colleagues from Rosenberg's group found that the gene tyrosinase also codes for an MHC class II-restricted peptide that is recognized by CD4$^+$ T cells. Thus, the tyrosinase gene codes for at least three peptides for several class I molecules for CTL recognition and another epitope for a class II MHC molecule.

Shortly after the discovery of tyrosinase-encoded HLA A2-restricted melanoma antigens, a number of genes coding for epitopes for HLA-A2, as well as other class I and class II restriction elements, were defined in melanoma. Coulie and co-worker from Boon's group described a previously unknown gene named Melan-A, and Kawakami and colleagues from Rosenberg's group described several melanoma-associated antigens (gp100 and MART-1, TRP-1, TRP-2) encoding peptide epitopes for wider MHC class molecules. The Melan-A and the MART-1 genes turned out to be identical. The gp100, MART-1/Melan-A, and TRP-1 and 2 genes are expressed by 90–100% of all melanoma cells. Again, the sequences of these genes derived from melanoma cells or from autologous normal cells showed no alteration. Further, although human melanoma dominated the field, soon CTL-determined antigens and their MHC-restricted epitopes were found in a large variety of human tumors (breast cancer, pancreatic cancer, colon cancer, renal cancer, prostate cancer, lung cancer, ovarian cancer, etc.). Some of these antigens had been previously identified as enzymes (such as PSA, CEA, myeloid tissue-restricted proteinase 3), as secretory proteins (such as mucin), or as proteins involved in some sort of differentiation process. The function of others remains unclear. For example, the real function of the Melan-A/MART-1 gene is not precisely known, although it is believed that it most likely has a role in differentiation. This leaves us with the intriguing question of why these types of differentiation proteins are processed and presented to be recognized by CTL.

Two important points seem to emerge from all these observations. First, it is now amply clear that peptides, derived from a number of proteins with no change in their sequences, can be processed and presented on certain MHC molecules for T-cell recognition. In this process, certain peptides might act as immunodominant peptides, perhaps by virtue of "high binding affinity" for a given MHC molecule exhibiting a given peptide-binding motif. Second, CTL precursors against a number of these peptides can be found in normal healthy individuals. Third, CTL precursors, capable of recognizing these normal "self" peptides, have not been eliminated from the T-cell repertoire. They exist in a tolerant state. The subject of peptide-binding motifs of MHC molecules and the mechanism(s) by which T-cell tolerance to such potentially "immunogenic" as well as "immunodominant" peptides is established—whether as a result of ignorance, anergy, or suppression—remains a subject of intense curiosity.

B. Elution of CTL-Determined Natural Peptide from Melanoma Cells

As shown in the preceding section, the molecular identity of CTL-determined peptide antigens in the previous studies was indirectly derived, with the help of peptides synthesized after establishing the sequence of the protein product of the relevant gene that could transfer the antigenicity. Several investigators have attempted to elute CTL-determined naturally presented peptides from the melanoma cell surface. A dramatic success of this approach has been reported by Storkus and co-workers and by Cox and colleagues who were able to isolate (by affinity chromatography and HPLC fractionation) at least nine natural peptides that were recognized by melanoma-specific CTL. Cox and colleagues sequenced one of these eluted peptides by mass spectrometry. The peptide was found to be a nonamer bearing the sequence YLEPGPVTA. When the sequence was compared with those in the data bank, the peptide turned out to be a part of the protein P mel 17, which is expressed by normal melanocytes and by melanoma cells. The synthetic counterpart could be shown to bind to HLA-A2, and the peptide/MHC was recognized by CTL clones derived from five different melanoma patients. Another natural peptide from a melanoma cell line bearing the sequence YMDGTMSQV, which was also recognized by CTL, was isolated from a melanoma patient. The data bank identified its homologous sequence in the tyrosinase molecule recorded as YMNGTMSQV.

Thus, this peptide turned out to be another CTL-determined epitope derived from the product of the gene tyrosinase. Of further interest, the naturally processed peptide was found not to be one of the abundant peptides extractable from the cell surface and was found to exhibit a relatively low affinity for the HLA-A2 molecule.

A number of other naturally processed peptides that are presented on the HLA-A2 molecule for CTL recognition have been isolated. One of these, having the deduced sequence of XXTVXXGVX (X = I or L), is derived from the product of the gene MART-1. The peptide, ILTVILGVL, binds to HLA-A2-positive T2 cells and makes them sensitive to lysis by CTL derived from four or more melanoma patients who are HLA-A2 positive. Like the other naturally processed peptides, this peptide also is not one of the predominant peptides bound to melanoma cell surface. It binds to the HLA-A2 molecule with an intermediate to low affinity.

Regardless of being one of the "minor" constituents of melanoma cell surface peptides and regardless of their binding affinity, available data on the peptide elution approach have clearly shown that antigenic peptides can be eluted from MHC molecules of the melanoma cell surface and that CTL clones exhibiting specificity for such naturally processed peptides can be isolated from a number of melanoma patients. This strongly suggests biological relevance of finding this type of processed self-peptide from the groove of the MHC molecule of spontaneously grown tumor cells and for finding, from melanoma patients, T cells capable of recognizing such peptides on the given HLA molecule.

C. Epithelial Mucin as a Potential Human Tumor Antigen

Among the many observations of the T-cell-mediated immune response in human tumors other than melanoma, studies by Finn's group, with mucin as a potential antigen that can be recognized by CTL in breast cancer patients, have generated considerable interest. Finn and colleagues have shown that CD8[+] CTL clones derived from patients with breast cancer and pancreatic cancer can specifically recognize, albeit in an unconventional way, an epitope of the molecule mucin without the requirement of it being presented on an MHC molecule. It has been suggested that part of the mucin molecule is expressed on the cell surface and a segment of the molecule itself can bind to the specific CTL. The portion of the mucin molecule that is believed to bind to the T-cell receptor has been identified as one-, two-, or three-tandem repeats of 20 long residues that are not glycosylated. This form of unconventional T-cell response to antigen (i.e., recognition of determinants by T cells without their being presented on an HLA molecule) has generated interest as well as controversy. Presently, the precise molecular basis of this type of nonconventional binding of TCR to nominal antigen remains unclear. Of interest, Finn's group has shown that the Epstein–Barr virus-transformed B-cell line transfected with epithelial mucin cDNA becomes sensitive to lysis by a mucin-specific CTL clone.

D. Immune Response to Products of Oncogenes

Oncogenes are often modified by point mutations or translocations or their expression is amplified in a number of tumors. Hence, the products of such modified oncogenes can serve as candidate targets for immune response, particularly for the CTL response. Indeed, evidence is beginning to emerge to suggest that some of these oncogene products may be processed and presented for T-cell recognition. The best example of a T-cell-mediated immune response to oncogene-derived peptides has emerged from a limited number of studies of certain oncogenes or suppressor oncogenes. For example, it has been reported that T cells can respond to both normal and mutated p53 peptides, K-ras, or to peptides derived from the products of the HER-2/neu oncogene (c erbB-2). While in the case of a mutated peptide the expectation is that the candidate peptide antigen will encompass the site of mutation, or that an immunodominant peptide derived from an amplified oncogene may serve as a T-cell determinant, much more work has to be done in this area to get a clear idea of the immunogenicity of oncogene products and on the molecular basis for such immunogenicity.

E. Immunity to Virally Induced Human Tumors

In general, the rule that dictates the immune response to virally induced tumors in animals also applies to immunity to virally induced cancer in humans. The best evidence for a CTL-mediated immune response to virally induced human neoplasia can be obtained in the case of HTLV-induced human leukemia. In this situation, evidence of a T-cell-mediated immune response to antigen coded by the retroviral genes has been found. Interestingly, Epstein–Barr virus is the most highly transforming human DNA virus and, although it is associated with a number of human neoplasms, there is no evidence of antitumor immunity developing based on the immune response to one or another virally coded antigens. However, a number of antigens coded by genes such as EBNA and LMP are immunogenic in humans, as the CTL response against these antigens can be shown in individuals who exhibit positive EBV serology. In the case of human tumors associated with EBV, the virus seems to persist in a sort of "equilibrium" with the host immune response. For example, Burkitt's lymphoma, which carries EBV, does not evoke an antitumor immune response on the basis of an anti-EBV CTL response. This is evidently due to the fact that antigenic viral proteins are not expressed by Burkitt's lymphoma! This is a beautiful example of a clever way of avoiding immune response. Other examples of a virus-encoded protein(s) that can serve as tumor antigens can be found in hepatomas (hepatitis B virus) and in cervical cancers (human papilloma virus). Interestingly, although the expression of the viral gene product in hepatoma is quite variable, prophylactic vaccination against the hepatitis B virus appears to have decreased the incidence of hepatomas in vaccinated individuals in Taiwan. Nearly 90% of cervical cancers express several HPV-encoded antigens (such as E6 and E7), and the CTL response can be easily generated from epitopes encoded by HPV E7. Because human cervical cancer is causatively related to human papilloma virus (HPV), and as HPV E7 is immunogenic, considerable interest has now been generated in developing a HPV-E7-based vaccine for cervical cancer.

IV. T-CELL RECEPTOR USAGE IN RECOGNITION OF HUMAN TUMOR ANTIGEN

As has been outlined earlier, a combination of clever strategy and innovative technology provided us with clear insights into the molecular nature of the tumor antigens that T cells respond to. In contrast, questions on the usage of T-cell receptors in the recognition of the tumor antigen remain somewhat confusing. From what we know about antigen binding by TCR, it can be fairly safely said that the hypervariable CDR3-like loops, encoded by the VDJ junctional regions of the TCR, play the most crucial role in the binding of a given peptide displayed on the groove of the MHC molecule. Hence, in recognition of a given melanoma peptide epitope, the question of how the VDJ segments (and especially the V segment) are selected is important. Unfortunately, the question of how the receptor repertoire is selected in response to a tumor antigen remains unresolved. In fact, conflicting information has been reported in this area. For example, preferential expressions of certain TCR gene segments (Vα7, for example, in patients with uveal melanomas or preferential expression of other V regions in different melanoma-specific CTL lines) have been found in some studies. Other studies have, however, failed to find such restricted usage of TCR gene segments in response to melanoma antigen. For it has been shown that the CTL response to melanoma antigen in a given patient is polyclonal and that different CTL clones derived from the same patient may have similar antigenic specificity, but have different TCR structures. Using synthetic peptide-conjugated HLA tetramers as a tool to isolate particular peptide-specific T cells, Romero and colleagues have confirmed that a large and diverse repertoire of T cells bearing different TCR V segments recognize a single CTL epitope derived from the melanoma antigen Melan A. However, it seems that the expression of a given antigen (presumably, the given peptide presentation) may influence the recruitment of a T-cell clone recognizing that antigen. Indeed, in support of this view, evidence of restricted clonality in T-cell recruitment within the tumor tissues, evidence for progressive and selective accumulation of certain types of T cells at the site of tumor, and evidence for the enrichment of a given clonal T-cell population in patients before, during, and after receiving immunotherapy and in spontaneously regressing melanoma *in situ* have emerged.

V. SEROLOGIC RESPONSE TO TUMOR ANTIGENS

Although Ehrlich did not envision a role of antibody in tumor immunity, solid evidence of circulating antibodies that could bind tumor cells with a fair amount of precision and specificity, however, did emerge in mice and humans as soon as reliable serologic assays became available. One can find a remarkable example of a serologic response to a tumor-associated antigen in the murine thymus leukemia system. While working in this system in the 1960s, Old, Boyse, and colleagues found that thymus leukemia (TL) cells, whether originating in TL-positive or TL-negative strain of mice, express the TL antigen on the cell surface! More surprisingly, when TL leukemia cells expressing TL antigen were transplanted into TL-negative mouse, the mouse made antibody against TL but the leukemia cells continued to grow *in vivo*! When these leukemia cells were harvested, these investigators found that they no longer expressed the TL antigen on the surface. Interestingly, after *in vitro* culture for several generations, the TL antigen reappeared on the leukemic cell surface and the same phenomenon (repression of TL expression *in vivo* upon encountering anti-TL antibody and reexpression of TL antigen in an *in vitro* culture in the absence of the antibody) could be reproduced in another round of identical experiments. This phenomenon was called "modulation" and it represented a form of adaptive repression of a gene expression under selective pressure. This article will not allow an extended discussion of similar phenomenon in the human system. Nonetheless, it should be mentioned that evidence of such selective pressure leading to the repression of a particular tumor antigen or of a single or multiple restricting MHC alleles (i.e., emergence of antigen loss variants) has also emerged in human, providing perhaps the most compelling proof that a host can indeed generate an immune response to a given epitope and tumor cells can escape the consequence by engineering an eclipse of the epitope! Returning to our present story, it should be pointed out that while serologic analyses did show that cancer patients also produce antibodies toward their tumor cells, the molecular identity of the tumor antigen remained elusive until Koprowski and colleagues and then Lloyd and Hellstrom and colleagues, independently, showed that gangliosides can serve as antigens for a monoclonal antibody raised against tumor cells. Shortly thereafter, Irie and colleagues and Old and colleagues confirmed that indeed in the sera of patients with melanoma, antibodies against a number of tumor-associated gangliosides antigens can be detected. Understandably, these carbohydrate antigens soon moved to clinical trials as potential cancer vaccines.

Eventually, Pfreundschuh and colleagues and others utilized a more sophisticated serological identifi-cation tool (recombinant expression cloning or SEREX) and deciphered the molecular identity of the antigens that are recognized by cancer patients' sera. In this technique, tumor-derived expression libraries are screened for detection by IgG antibodies in the sera of cancer patients. The SEREX technique has now defined nearly 2000 genes coding for antigens associated with various different types of human tumors that are recognized by IgG antibody derived from cancer patients. Interestingly, many of these antigens discovered by this technique have turned out to be antigens that also code for CTL and Th cell epitopes! More remarkably, SEREX-based analyses have also led to the identification of several T-cell-determined antigens. In keeping with the diversity in the nature of the antigens that are recognized by T cells, SEREX-defined antigens also fall into quite a diverse category (differentiation antigen, cancer/testis antigens, over-expressed gene products, unique antigen, shared anti-

TABLE II

Examples of Tumor Antigen-Associated Peptide
Epitopes Recognized by CTL

Encoding gene	Presenting molecule	Amino acid sequence
MAGE-1	HLA-A1	EADPTGHSY
MAGE-3	HLA-A1	EVDPIGHLY
MAGE-3	HLA-A2	FLWGPRALV
MAGE-3	HLA-DR 13	LLKYRAREPVTKAE
Tyrosinase	HLA-A2	MLLAVLYCL
Tyrosinase	HLA-A2	YMNGTMSQV[a]
Tyrosinase	HLA-B44	SEIWRDID
MART-1/Melan-A	HLA-A2	AAGIGILTV
MART-1/Melan-A	HLA-A2	ILTVILGVL[a]
MART-1/Melan-A	HLA-DR-4	RNGYRALMDKSLHVGTQCALTRR
gp 100	HLA-A2	LLDGTATLRL
gp 100	HLA-A2	YLEPGPVTA[a]
HER2/neu	HLA-A2	IISAVVGIL
HER2/neu	HLA-A2	KIFGSLAFL
NY-ESO-1	HLA-A2	SLLMWITQC
NY-ESO-1	HLA-CW3	ARGPESRLL
NY-ESO-1	HLA-DR-4	PLPVPGV-LLKEFTVSGNI
NY-ESO-1	HLA-DR-4	VLLKEFTVSGNI-LTIRLT
NY-ESO-1	HLA-DR-4	AADHRQLQLSISSCL-QQL
PSA	HLA-A2	FLTPKKLQCV

[a]These peptides have been eluded from melanoma cells as naturally presented CTL-determined peptide epitopes.

TABLE III
Examples of Tumor Antigens Recognized
by Antibody Identified by SEREX

Designation	Category	Major tumor association
MAGE-3	Cancer/testis	Melanoma
NY-ESO-1	Cancer/testis	Melanoma
HER2/neu	Oncogene	Breast/ovarian
NY COL-2	p53	Colorectal
NY BR 62, 75, 82, etc.	?	Breast
Tumor protein D 52	?	Breast
HOM-RCC-1.14	Virus (HERV-K-10)	Renal cancer
TGFβ1	Cytokine	Breast
Tyrosinase	Enzyme	Melanoma
HOX A7	Transcription factor	Ovarian cancer

gens, viral antigens, etc.). Again, while some of these genes that encode for serologic epitopes have already been assigned with function, many are of unknown function. Most interestingly, some of these genes seem to be associated with the carcinogenesis process itself.

The discussions in the previous sections dealing with antigens and epitopes recognized by T cells and antibody clearly show that these antigens are derived from a wide variety of gene products with known and unknown function. In an attempt to classify them, these antigens can be grouped into several broad classes. These include groups such as cancer testis antigens (MAGE, GAGE, BAGE, RAGE, NY-ESO, SSX-2, etc.); melanocyte differentiation antigens (tyrosinase, Melan-A/MART-1, go 100, TRP-1, TRP-2, etc.); tumor specific [CDK-4. MUM-1, caspases-8, NY-Col-38 (p53), etc.], viral antigens (HPVE7, HERV-K10, etc.), overexpressed antigens (HER-2/neu, HOM-RCC-3, etc.), and carbohydrate antigens (GD2, GD3, GM2, etc.). Tables II and III show representative examples of some of these antigens. Understandably, the search for other antigens in human cancers will be intensely pursued by many. One can be reasonably certain that the compendium of tumor-associated antigens with precise molecular identity will continue to swell with time. While this is given, the relevance of these T-cell-determined antigens and of the thousands of SEREX-defined antigens to tumor immunobiology remains to be established.

VI. CONCLUSION

The observations outlined earlier, when taken together, allow one to conclude that the lingering doubt on the very existence of tumor immunity can be finally put to rest. The molecular basis for an immune response against spontaneous cancer is now firmly established. The structural identities of the elusive tumor antigens have finally been unveiled in precise details. T cells capable of selectively responding to peptide epitopes derived from such tumor antigens have been isolated from a large number of cancer patients, and naturally processed peptides, recognized by CTL, have been recovered from human tumor cell surfaces. IgG antibodies to a variety of antigens, including some of the same antigens that are recognized by T cells, have also been found in cancer patients. These developments have now formed a foundation from which to launch vigorous investigations of how cancer cells then escape immune responses as well as have provided a solid basis for renewed explorations of treatment strategies with some of these very molecules.

See Also the Following Articles

CELL-MEDIATED IMMUNITY TO CANCER • HIV • IMMUNE DEFICIENCY: OPPORTUNISTIC TUMORS • T CELLS AGAINST TUMORS • T CELLS, FUNCTION OF • TUMOR ANTIGENS • TUMOR CELL MOTILITY AND INVASION

Bibliography

Boon, T. (1992). Genetic analysis of tumor rejection antigens. *Adv. Cancer Res.* **58,** 177–210.

Brichard, V., Van Pel, A., Wölfel, T., Wölfel, C., De Plaen, E., Lethé, B., Coulie, P., and Boon, T. (1993). The tyrosinase gene codes for an antigen recognized by autologous cytolytic T lymphocytes on HLA-A1 melanomas. *J. Exp. Med.* **178,** 489–495.

Coulie, P., Brichard, V., Van Pel, A., Wölfel, T., Schneider, J., Traversari, C., Mattei, S., De Plaen, E., Lurquin, C., Szikora, J.-P., Renauld, J.-C., and Boon, T. (1994). A new gene coding for a differentiation antigen recognized by autologous cytolytic T lymphocytes on HLA-A2 melanomas. *J. Exp. Med.* **180,** 35–52.

Ehrlich, P. (1909). Nederlandsch Tijdschrift voor Geneeskunde: Ueber den Jetzigne Stand Der Karzinomforschung. *Weekblad Jaargang Eerst. Helft* **5,** 273–290.

Kawakami, Y., Eliyahu, S., Delgado, C. H., Robbins, P. F., Rivoltini, L., Topalian, S. L., Miki, T., and Rosenberg, S. A. (1994). Cloning of the gene coding for a shared human melanoma antigen recognized by autologous T cells infiltrating into tumor. *Proc. Natl. Acad. Sci. USA* **91,** 3515–3519.

Kawakami, Y., Eliyahu, S., Delgado, C. H., Robbins, P. F., Sakaguchi, K., Appella, E., Yannelli, J. R., Adema, G. J., Miki, T., and Rosenberg, S. A. (1994). Identification of a human melanoma antigen recognized by tumor-infiltrating lymphocytes associated with in vivo tumor rejection. *Proc. Natl. Acad. Sci. USA* **91,** 6458–6462.

Lloyd, K. O. (1991). Humoral immune responses to tumor-associated carbohydrate antigens. *Semin. Cancer Biol.* **2,** 421–431.

Mackensen, A., Carcelain, G., Viels, S., Rayanal, M.-C., Michalaki, H., Triebel, F., Bosq, J., and Hercend, T. (1994). Direct evidence to support the immunosurveillance concept in a regressing melanoma. *J. Clin. Invest.* **93,** 1397–1402.

Pfreundschuh, M. (2000). Exploitation of the B cell repertoire for the identification of human tumor antigens. *Cancer Chemother. Pharmacol.* **46,** S3–S7.

Sahin, U., Turechi, O., Smitt, H., Cochlovius, B., Johannes, T., Schmits, R., Luo, G., Schobert, I., and Pfreundschuh, M. (1995). Human neoplasma elicit multiple specific immune responsesin the autologous host. *Proc. Natl. Acad. Sci. USA* **2,** 11810–11813.

Sensi, M., Salvi, S., Castelli, C., Maccalli, C., Mazzocchi, A., Mortarini, R., Nicolini, G., Herlyn, M., Parmiani, G., and Anichini, A. (1993). T cell receptor (TCR) structure of autologous melanoma-reactive cytotoxic T lymphocyte (CTL) clones: Tumor-infiltrating lymphocytes overexpress in vivo the TCR β chain sequence used by an HLA-A2-restricted and melanocyte-lineage-specific CTL clone. *J. Exp. Med.* **178,** 1231–1246.

Shilyansky, J., Nishimura, M., Yannelli, J., Kawakami, Y., Jaknin, L., Charmley, P., and Rosenberg, S. (1994). T-cell receptor usage by melanoma-specific clonal and highly oligoclonal tumor-infiltrating lymphocyte lines. *Proc. Natl. Acad. Sci. USA* **91,** 2829–2833.

Srivastava, P. K., Menoret, A., Basu, S., Binder, R. J., and McQuade, K. L. (1998). Heat shock protein come of age: Primitive functions acquire new roles in the adaptive world. *Immunity* **8,** 657–665.

Valmori, D., Dutoit, V., Leinard, D., Lejeune, F., Speiser, D., Rimoldi, D., Cerundolo, V., Dietrich, P.-Y., Cerottini, J.-C., and Romero, P. (2000). Tetramer guided analysis of TCR β-chain usage reveals a large repertoire of Melan-A specific CD8$^+$ T cells in melanoma patients. *J. Immunol.* **165,** 533–538.

Van Der Bruggen, Traversari, C., Chomez, P., Lurquin, C., De Plaen, E., Van Den Eynde, B., Knuth, A., and Boon, T. (1991). A gene encoding an antigen recognized by cytolytic T lymphocytes on a human melanoma. *Science* **254,** 1643–1647.

Molecular Epidemiology and Cancer Risk

Frederica P. Perera

Mailman School of Public Health at Columbia University

GLOSSARY

biomarkers Any of various biological indicators that serve to detect exposure to carcinogenic processes or to predict carcinogenic disposition.

hepatocellular carcinoma (HCC) A malignant tumor arising clonally in the liver from a hepatocyte.

molecular epidemiology The technique or process of establishing the risk factors for a given disease based on molecular biological data.

Cancer prevention through a better understanding of risk is the stated goal of molecular cancer epidemiology. Progress toward that goal can be evaluated by using as examples well studied environmental exposures—tobacco smoke, polycyclic aromatic hydrocarbons (PAHs), aflatoxin B_1 (AFB1), benzene, and hepatitis B virus (HBV)—and their roles in lung, breast, and liver cancer and leukemia. In these examples, the contributions of molecular epidemiology include providing evidence that environmental agents

This article is adapted from Perera, F. P., (2000). Molecular epidemiology: On the path to prevention? *JNCI* **92**(8), 602–612, with permission.

pose carcinogenic risks, helping establish the causal roles of environmental factors in cancer, identifying environment–susceptibility interactions and populations at greatest risk, and developing new intervention strategies. An incentive to make the necessary investment is the recognition that prevention of only 20% of cancer in the United States would result in 200,000 fewer new cases diagnosed each year and an annual savings of $21.4 billion in financial costs alone.

I. INTRODUCTION

Although it stands on the shoulders of seroepidemiology and genetic epidemiology, molecular cancer epidemiology as a recognized discipline is quite new, having been formalized only in the 1980s. In 1982, "molecular cancer epidemiology" was defined as an approach in which advanced laboratory methods are used in combination with analytic epidemiology to identify at the biochemical or molecular level specific exogenous and/or host factors that play a role in human cancer causation. Four categories of biomarkers were described: internal dose, biologically effective dose, response, and susceptibility. The hope was that, by introducing biomarkers into epidemiology, researchers "should be able to predict human risks more precisely than hitherto possible." Molecular cancer epidemiology has evolved rapidly since the mid-1980s, and many schools of public health and research institutes now have programs in molecular epidemiology.

The stated goal of molecular cancer epidemiology is the prevention of cancer, a disease that claims over half a million lives annually in the United States, with more than 1 million new cases diagnosed each year and attendant annual financial costs of $107 billion. This article traces the progress of this relatively new, still-developing field toward prevention.

The cancers used as examples here—lung, breast, and liver cancer and leukemia—exact a terrible toll worldwide. Many lines of evidence indicate, even more clearly than in 1982, that the great majority of these and other cancers are, in principle, preventable because the factors that determine their incidence are largely exogenous or environmental. These include exposures related to lifestyle and occupation and pollutants in air, water, and the food supply. Genetic factors are important in terms of influencing individual susceptibility to carcinogens; in some rare forms of human cancer, hereditary factors play a decisive role. There is, however, increasing recognition that controlling external factors presents the greatest opportunity for primary cancer prevention and its immediate benefits. This awareness has lent greater urgency to the search for more powerful tools in the form of early-warning systems to identify causal environmental agents and flag risks well before the carcinogenic process has begun. In this article, research on causal roles of specific environmental exposures—tobacco smoke, PAHs, AFB1, benzene, and HBV—in the cancers cited earlier will provide illustrations of the part molecular epidemiology can play in identifying and reducing cancer risk.

II. CONTRIBUTIONS OF MOLECULAR EPIDEMIOLOGY: EVIDENCE THAT ENVIRONMENTAL AGENTS POSE CARCINOGENIC RISKS

A. Lung Cancer

Tobacco smoke was identified in 1949 as a potent human lung carcinogen and still ranks at the very top of the list of environmental carcinogens. It contains 55 known carcinogens, including PAHs such as benzo[a]pyrene (BaP). PAHs are also found in outdoor air from automobile exhaust and emissions from power plants and other industrial sources; in indoor air from tobacco smoking, cooking, and heating; and in the diet. It has long been known from experimental research that many carcinogens, including PAHs, exert their effects by binding to DNA and forming adducts that may lead to mutation and, ultimately, to cancer. Thus, using adducts as biomarkers has the theoretical advantage that they reflect chemical-specific genetic damage that is mechanistically relevant to carcinogenesis.

In 1982, PAH–DNA adducts were first detected in human subjects *in vivo*, specifically in white blood cells (WBCs) and lung tissue from lung cancer patients, most of whom were smokers. Subsequent studies in healthy exposed populations have found increased concentrations of PAH–DNA adduct levels in blood and other tissues, with no apparent threshold for DNA binding. Most studies of PAH–DNA adduct levels in human subjects have observed substantial interindividual variability among persons with similar exposure. These findings were consistent with traditional epidemiologic data showing an elevated risk of lung cancer in PAH-exposed populations.

Although not all studies have been positive, since 1982 more evidence has been developed that PAH–DNA adducts in WBC or lung tissue may be risk markers for lung cancer. In one study, higher PAH–DNA adduct levels were found in WBCs from case subjects (compared with control subjects) after adjusting for amount of smoking, dietary PAH exposure, and other potential confounders. The finding was consistent with evidence that some individuals are predisposed to genetic damage from PAHs and, thereby, to lung cancer.

Supporting molecular evidence that PAHs play an important role in lung cancer comes from the observations that the p53 tumor suppressor gene is mutated in 40–50% of lung tumors and that the pattern of mutations is consistent with the types of DNA adducts and mutations induced experimentally by BaP.

B. Breast Cancer

There is conflicting but suggestive epidemiologic evidence that active and passive tobacco smoking contributes to the incidence of breast cancer. Like other constituents of tobacco smoke, such as 4-ABP and some heterocyclic amines, a number of PAHs are potent breast carcinogens in bioassays.

Aromatic carcinogen–DNA adducts were initially detected in breast tumor and nontumor tissue from a small number of breast cancer patients and control subjects. A subsequent study found case subjects to have significantly higher adduct levels than control subjects. Neither study controlled for potential confounding variables. A case-control study of breast cancer patients and control subjects with benign breast disease, all from the same source population, measured PAH–DNA adduct levels in breast tissue. After controlling for known risk factors for breast cancer and PAH exposure via tobacco smoking and dietary sources,

elevated levels of PAH–DNA adducts in breast tissue were positively associated with an increased risk of breast cancer. Because PAH–DNA adduct levels in breast tissue reflect both PAH exposure and individual susceptibility to PAH-induced genetic damage, this finding suggests that individual variations in metabolic pathways and DNA repair mechanisms play an important role in breast cancer risk.

As in lung cancer, the pattern of p53 mutations in breast tumors is consistent with a role of PAHs; they are predominantly G→T transversions, which are induced experimentally by BaP. PAHs are, however, but one of a number of environmental carcinogens suspected of playing a role in breast cancer.

C. Conclusion

Molecular epidemiologic research on lung cancer confirmed what was already known about tobacco smoking and lung cancer, so it provided no new data on causality. Rather, the research provided valuable insights into the mechanisms by which tobacco smoke constituents exert their effects. However, while molecular epidemiologic studies have not proved that PAHs and other aromatic compounds cause human lung and breast cancer, they have provided new evidence supporting that hypothesis.

III. PROVIDING DEFINITIVE EVIDENCE OF CAUSALITY IN A PROSPECTIVE COHORT OR NESTED CONTROL DESIGN

A. Biomarkers Related to PAH and Lung Cancer and AFB1 and Liver Cancer

Prospective studies or case-control studies nested within them are able to establish the predictive value of biomarkers by avoiding the temporal problem posed by retrospective studies: that the marker may reflect the disease rather than the risk factor(s). However, because of their considerable cost and because the biologic samples collected therein are so precious and limited in number and quantity, few biomarkers have been definitively established as predictors of cancer. Biomarkers that have been prospectively associated with the cancers addressed in this article include PAH and other aromatic–DNA adducts and lung cancer, metabolites of AFB1 and AFB1 adducts, which have been studied in conjunction with liver cancer, and chromosomal aberrations (CAs), which are biomarkers for many cancers, including leukemia, where they may be indicative of exposure to benzene.

In a nested case-control study of lung cancer within the Physicians' Health Study, PAH/aromatic adducts in white blood cells collected at enrollment from healthy smokers were predictors of subsequent lung cancer.

The food-borne mutagen AFB1 is a human hepatocarcinogen, acting synergistically with HBV. Nested case-control studies have indicated that a number of biomarkers of the internal or biologically effective dose of AFB1 (AFB1 metabolites, AFB1–protein and –DNA adducts) and HBV surface antigen seropositivity are risk markers for liver cancer. There was a strong interaction between the serologic marker of HBV infection and the AFB1 markers. The implication for prevention is that both reduction in dietary levels of AFB1 and wide-scale HBV vaccination are needed, as the benefits of the latter will not be manifest for many years.

The molecular evidence of a causal role for AFB1 is strengthened by other molecular data. A correlation has been observed between dietary AFB1 exposure and a characteristic mutation in the p53 tumor suppressor gene in HCCs worldwide.

B. Chromosomal Aberrations and Various Cancers

Unlike carcinogen–DNA adducts, CAs are a nonchemical-specific marker. Combined analyses of data from Nordic and Italian prospective cohort studies involving 3541 subjects found that chromosomal aberrations were predictors of cancer. CAs could theoretically be useful as biomarkers to identify individuals within high-risk populations (e.g., chemical industry workers) who could benefit from greater surveillance or chemoprevention. They do not, however, provide clues as to the specific exposure(s) responsible for an increased risk of cancer.

One remedy to the lack of exposure specificity of CAs is the analysis of exposure-specific patterns of the aberrations. For example, benzene is a model chemical leukemogen. Specific CAs have been observed in both preleukemia and leukemia patients exposed to benzene as well as in otherwise healthy benzene-exposed workers.

C. Conclusion

While it is likely that many biomarkers shown to be promising in cross-sectional or case-control studies will not survive the test of predictivity within a prospective study, those that do should have great utility in identifying at-risk populations and individuals and in serving as outcome markers in interventions, substituting for clinical manifestations of overt disease. Similarly, validated risk biomarkers will be useful as end point markers in risk assessments of environmental carcinogens, allowing regulatory and educational interventions in a more timely manner than is possible when tumor incidence or mortality is the sole outcome.

Of all the biomarkers related to environmental exposures and their biologic effects, CAs are the best validated as predictors of risk. PAH/ aromatic adducts and AFB1 metabolites, AFB1–albumin, and AFB1–DNA adducts have also been shown to be biomarkers of cancer risk in case-control studies nested within prospective studies.

IV. DOCUMENTING ENVIRONMENT– SUSCEPTIBILITY INTERACTIONS AND IDENTIFYING POPULATIONS AT GREATEST RISK

A goal of prevention research is to understand exposure–susceptibility interactions while adhering to sound ethical principles both in the conduct of research and in the communication of results and conclusions in such a way as to discourage their inadvertent or intentional misuse. The categories of susceptibility factors that can modulate environmental risks—genetic predisposition, ethnicity, age, gender, and health and nutritional impairment—have been reviewed in detail elsewhere.

With respect to the cancers and exposures discussed in this article, molecular epidemiologic studies have reported a number of interactions between exposures to tobacco smoke, PAH, AFB1, or benzene and various susceptibility factors. These include relatively common polymorphisms in genes (such as P450s, glutathione transferases, N-acetyltransferase genes) that control metabolism and detoxification of carcinogens as well as genes that control DNA repair. Molecular epidemiologic studies have also reported molecular evidence that the fetus, young child, and adolescent, certain ethnic groups, and women may be more affected by exposures to carcinogens. They have also reported complex interactions between environmental carcinogens and multiple genetic and nongenetic susceptibility factors. While susceptibility of the young has been clearly demonstrated for a number of carcinogens, in most cases, available data must be confirmed before they can be translated into specific risk assessment and prevention measures. The preliminary nature of much of the available data challenges the research community to delineate further the multiple complex interactions that determine individual cancer risk.

Molecular epidemiology has provided valuable new data on the existence of complex interactions between environmental exposures and susceptibility factors and has spurred researchers to investigate further differences in susceptibility among subsets of the population. Neither experimental nor conventional epidemiologic research alone could have done this. Although considerably more research is needed before risk assessors can routinely develop quantitative estimates of the risks to sensitive subsets posed by specific environmental agents, the information already obtained has general relevance to risk assessment and prevention. For example, government agencies are already beginning to require that regulatory policies explicitly protect children as a susceptible group.

V. PRIMARY PREVENTION: REDUCTION OR ELIMINATION OF EXPOSURES CAUSALLY RELATED TO CANCER

Primary prevention encompasses a spectrum of measures that include avoidance of exposure, prevention of carcinogen activation after it has entered the body,

blocking interactions with the genome, and suppressing the propagation of premalignant changes. Examples of molecular epidemiologic studies that have documented the benefits of reduction of exposure include a study of smokers enrolled in a smoking cessation program. Similarly, following a reduction in air concentrations of PAHs in a Finnish iron foundry, both PAH–DNA and aromatic–DNA adduct levels in workers' blood samples declined significantly.

Primary prevention measures for AFB1-related liver cancer include the reduction of mold growth in harvested crops and the modulation of the metabolism of AFB1 to enhance detoxification. Randomized intervention trials in the People's Republic of China have used biomarkers to assess whether the drug oltipraz can reduce the risk of liver cancer.

Based in part on data supporting a role of antioxidants in genetic damage in smokers, a randomized clinical trial of vitamins C and E is measuring PAH–DNA adduct levels as an intermediate marker of the efficacy of chemoprevention. Similarly, the role of retinoids in the chemoprevention of lung cancer is being tested by the use of intermediate end point markers.

In addition, biomarker assessment may be useful in primary prevention by providing motivational feedback to persons contemplating or enrolled in smoking cessation programs or undergoing lifestyle changes such as dietary modification. Biomarkers can also be used to monitor the benefits of regulations and other policies aimed at reducing the exposure of workers and the general population to pollutants.

Research demonstrates that biomarkers can measure the efficacy of exposure reduction and that clinical trials using biomarker levels as end points have the potential for making big gains in terms of immediate prevention. Both types of efficacy monitoring are more efficient and provide more immediate results than conventional approaches that rely solely on clinical endpoints such as a diagnosis of cancer.

VI. SUMMARY

Molecular epidemiology has advanced prevention research by identifying carcinogenic hazards, providing definitive etiologic data, furthering our understanding of individual susceptibility to environmental carcinogens, and facilitating clinical trials. Molecular epidemiology has not yet led to broad public health policy changes to prevent or to reduce exposure to carcinogens, but it has pointed the way. What is now needed is timely translation of existing data into risk assessment and public health policy, as well as focused research to fill gaps in scientific knowledge.

Acknowledgments

This research was supported by National Institutes of Health, Grant 5RO1 CA53772; Cancer Center Core Grant 5 P30 CA13696-23; National Institute of Environmental Health Science, Grant NCI 5RO1 CA69094, 1RO1 ES06722; U.S. Army, Grant DAMD17-94-J-4251; Department of Energy, Grant DE-FG02-93 ER61719; NIH/EPA: 1P50ES09600-01; NIH-1P30 ES09089-01; NIEHS Grant 1 RO1 ES08977-01; and awards from the Gladys and Roland Harriman Foundation, the Bauman Family Foundation, the Robert Wood Johnson Foundation, the W. Alton Jones Foundation, New York Community Trust, and the Irving A. Hansen Memorial Foundation.

See Also the Following Articles

BREAST CANCER • CANCER RISK REDUCTION • CARCINOGEN–DNA ADDUCTS • CHEMICAL MUTAGENESIS AND CARCINOGENESIS • CHEMOPREVENTION, PRINCIPLES OF • HEPATITIS B VIRUSES • HEPATOCELLULAR CARCINOMA • LIVER CANCER • LUNG CANCER • MULTISTAGE CARCINOGENESIS • TOBACCO CARCINOGENESIS

Bibliography

Ambrosone, C., Freudenheim, J., Graham, S., Marshall, J., Vena, J., Brasure, J., Michalek, A., Laughlin, R., Nemoto, T., Gillenwater, K., *et al.* (1996). Cigarette smoking, N-acetyltransferase 2 genetic polymorphisms, and breast cancer risk. JAMA **276**, 1494–1501.

Ambrosone, C., and Kadlubar, F. (1997). Toward an integrated approach to molecular epidemiology. *Am. J. Epidemiol.* **146**(11), 912–918.

Bartsch, H., Rojas, M., Alexandrov, K., and Risch, A. (1998). Impact of adduct determination on the assessment of cancer susceptibility. *Cancer Res.* **154**, 86–96.

Binková, B., Lewtas, J., Misková, I., Rössner, P., Cerna, M., Mrácková, G., Peterková, K., Mumford, J., Meyer, S., and Srám, R. (1996). Biomarker studies in the Northern Bohemia. *Environ. Health Perspect.* **104**(Suppl. 3), 591–597.

Bonassi, S., Abbondandolo, A., Camurri, L., Dal Pra, L., De Ferrari, M., Degrassi, F., Forni, A., Lamberti, L., Lando, C., and Padovani, P. (1995). Are chromosome aberrations in circulating lymphocytes predictive of future cancer onset in humans? Preliminary results of an Italian cohort study. *Cancer Genet. Cytogenet.* **79**, 133–135.

Boone, C., and Kelloff, G. (1997). Biomarker end-points in cancer chemoprevention trials. *IARC Sci. Publ.* **142**, 273–280.

Caporaso, N., and Goldstein, A. (1997). Issues involving biomarkers in the study of the genetics of human cancer. *IARC Sci. Publ.* **142**, 237–250.

Denissenko, M., Pao, A., Tang, M., and Pfiefer, G. (1996). Preferential formation of benzo[a]pyrene adducts at lung cancer mutational hotspots in p53. *Science* **274**, 430–432.

Dickey, C., Santella, R., Hattis, D., Tang, D., Hsu, Y., Cooper, T., Young, T., and Perera, F. (1997). Variability in PAH-DNA adduct measurements in peripheral mononuclear cells: Implications for quantitative cancer risk assessment. *Risk Analysis* **17**, 649–655.

El-Bayoumy, K. (1992). Environmental carcinogens that may be involved in human breast cancer etiology. *Chem. Res. Toxicol.* **5**, 585–570.

Garte, S., Zocchetti, C., and Taioli, E. (1997). Gene-environment interactions in the application of biomarkers of cancer susceptibility in epidemiology. *In* "Application of Biomarkers in Cancer Epidemiology" (P. Toniolo, P. Boffetta, D. E. G. Shuker, *et al.*, eds.), p. 251. IARC Scientific Publications, Lyon, France.

Greenblatt, M. S., Bennett, W. P., Hollstein, M., and Harris, C. C. (1994). Mutations in the p53 tumor suppressor gene: Clues to cancer etiology and molecular pathogenesis. *Cancer Res.* **55**, 4855–4878.

Grinberg Funes, R. A., Singh, V. N., Perera, F. P., Bell, D. A., Young, T. L., Dickey, C., Wang, L. W., and Santella, R. M. (1994). Polycyclic aromatic hydrocarbon-DNA adducts in smokers and their relationship to micronutrient levels and glutathione-S-transferase M1 genotype. *Carcinogenesis* **15**, 2449–2454.

Gritz, E. R. (1992). Paving the road from basic research to policy: Cigarette smoking as a prototype issue for cancer control science. *Cancer Epidemiol. Biomark. Prev.* **1**, 427–434.

Groopman, J., and Kensler, T. (1999). The light at the end of the tunnel for chemical-specific biomarkers: Daylight or headlight? *Carcinogenesis* **20**, 1–11.

Guinee, D. G., Jr., Travis, W. D., Trivers, G. E., DeBenedetti, V. M. G., Cawley, H., Welsh, J. A., Bennett, W. P., Jett, J., Colby, T. V., Tazelaar, H., *et al.* (1995). Gender comparisons in human lung cancer: Analysis of p53 mutations, anti-p53 serum antibodies and C-34bB-2 expression. *Carcinogenesis* **16**, 993–1002.

Hagmar, L., Bonassi, S., Stromberg, U., Brogger, A., Knudsen, L., Norppa, H., and Reuterwall, C. (1998). Chromosomal aberrations in lymphocytes predict human cancer: A report from the European Study Group on Cytogenetic Biomarkers and Health (EDCH). *Cancer Res.* **58**, 4117–4121.

Harris, C. (1991). Chemical and physical carcinogenesis: Advances and perspectives for the 1990s. *Cancer Res.* **51**, 5023S–5044S.

Hiatt, H., Watson, J. D., and Winsten, J. A. (1977). "Origins of Human Cancer." Cold Spring Harbor Laboratories, Cold Spring Harbor, NY.

Hulka, B. S. (1991). Epidemiological studies using biological markers: Issues for epidemiologists. *Cancer Epidemiol. Biomark. Prev.* **1,** 13–19.

Hussain, S., and Harris, C. (1998). Molecular epidemiology of human cancer. *Toxicol. Lett.* **102–103,** 219–225.

Kellerman, G., Shaw, C. R., and Kellermann, M. L. (1973). Aryl hydrocarbon hydroxylase inducibility and bronchogenic carcinoma. *N. Engl. J. Med.* **289,** 934–937.

Khoury, M. J. (1996). Genetics Working Group. From genes to public health: The applications of genetic technology in disease prevention. *Am. J. Public Health* **86,** 1717–1722.

Khuri, F., Kurie, J., and Hong, W. (1997). Chemoprevention of respiratory tract cancer. *Hematol. Oncol. Clin. North Am.* **11**(3), 387–408.

Kriek, E., van Schooten, F. J., Hillebrand, M. J. X., van Leeuwen, F. E., denEngelse, L., de Looff, A. J. A., and Dijkmans, A. P. G. (1993). DNA adducts as a measure of lung cancer risk in humans exposed to polycyclic aromatic hydrocarbons. *Environ. Health Perspect.* **99,** 71–75.

Li, D., Wang, M., Dhingra, K., and Hittelman, W. (1996). Aromatic DNA adducts in adjacent tissues of breast cancer patients: Clues to breast cancer etiology. *Cancer Res.* **56,** 287–293.

Lichenstein, P., Holm, N., Verkasalo, P., Iliadou, A., Kaprio, J., Koskenvuo, M., Pukkala, E., Skytthe, A., and Hemminki, K. (2000). Environmental and heritable factors in the Causation of cancer: Analyses of cohorts of twins from Sweden, Denmark, and Finland. *N. Engl. J. Med.* **343,** 78–85.

Mooney, L. A., Bell, D. A., Santella, R. M., Van Bennekum, A. M., Ottman, R., Paik, M., Blaner, W. S., Lucier, G. W., Covey, L., Young, T. L., *et al.* (1997). Contribution of genetic and nutritional factors to DNA damage in heavy smokers. *Carcinogenesis* **18,** 503–509.

Mooney, L. A., and Perera, F. P. (1996). Application of molecular epidemiology to lung cancer prevention. *J. Cell Biochem.* **25,** 63–68.

Mooney, L. A., Santella, R. M., Covey, L., Jeffrey, A. M., Bigbee, W., Randall, M. C., Cooper, T. B., Ottman, R., Tsai, W. Y., Wazneh, L., *et al.* (1995). Decline in DNA damage and other biomarkers in peripheral blood following smoking cessation. *Cancer Epidemiol. Biomark. Prev.* **4,** 627–634.

Moore, C. J., Tricomi, W. A., and Gould, M. N. (1986). Interspecies comparison of polycyclic aromatic hydrocarbon metabolism in human and rat mammary epithelial cells. *Cancer Res.* **46,** 4946–4952.

Morabia, A., Bernstein, M., Heritier, S., and Khatchatrian, N. (1996). Relation of breast cancer with passive and active exposure to tobacco smoke. *Am. J. Epidemiol.* **143,** 918–928.

Mumford, J., Lee, X., Lewtas, J., Young, T., and Santella, R. (1993). DNA adducts as biomarkers for assessing exposure to polycyclic aromatic hydrocarbons in tissues from Xuan Wei women with high exposure to coal combustion emissions and high lung cancer mortality. *Environ. Health Perspect.* **99,** 83–87.

Palmer, J., and Rosenburg, L. (1993). Cigarette smoking and the risk of breast cancer. *Epidemiol. Rev.* **15,** 145–156.

Perera, F. P. (1987). Molecular cancer epidemiology: A new tool in cancer prevention. *J. Natl. Cancer Inst.* **78,** 887–898.

Perera, F. (2000). Molecular epidemiology: On the path to prevention? *JNCI* **92,** 602–612.

Perera, F. P., Estabrook, A., Hewer, A., Channing, K. M., Rundle, A., Mooney, L. A., Whyatt, R., and Phillips, D. H. (1995). Carcinogen-DNA adducts in human breast tissue. *Cancer Epidemiol. Biomark. Prev.* **4,** 233–238.

Perera, F. P., Dickey, C., Santella, R., O'Neill, J. P., Albertini, R. J., Ottman, R., Tsai, W. Y., Mooney, L. A., Savela, K., and Hemminki, K. (1994). Carcinogen-DNA adducts and gene mutation in foundary workers with low level exposure to polycyclic aromatic hydrocarbons. *Carcinogenesis* **15,** 2905–2910.

Perera, F. P., Hemminki, K., Grzybowska, E., Motykiewicz, G., Michalska, J., Santella, R. M., Young, T. L., Dickey, C., Brandt-Rauf, P., DeVivo, I., *et al.* (1992). Molecular and genetic damage from environmental polution in Poland. *Nature* **360,** 256–258.

Perera, F. P., and Mooney, L. A. (1993). The role of molecular epidemiology in cancer prevention. "Cancer Prevention" (V. T. DeVita, S. Hellman, and S. A. Rosenberg, eds.), pp. 1–15. Lippincott, Philadelphia.

Perera, F. P., Poirier, M. C., Yuspa, S. H., Nakayama, J., Jaretzki, A., Curren, M. M., Knowles, D. M., and Weinstein, I. B. (1982). A pilot project in molecular cancer epidemiology: Determination of benzo[a]pyrene adducts in animal and human tissues by immunoassay. *Carcinogenesis* **3,** 1405–1410.

Perera, F. P., Santella, R. M., Brenner, D., Poirier, M. C., Munshi, A. A., Fischman, H. K., and Van Ryzin, J. (1987). DNA adducts, protein adducts and sister chromatid exchange in cigarette smokers and nonsmokers. *J. Natl. Cancer Inst.* **79,** 449–456.

Perera, F. P., and Weinstein, I. B. (1982). Molecular epidemiology and carcinogen-DNA adduct detection: New approaches to studies of human cancer causation. *J. Chron. Dis.* **35,** 581–600.

Qian, G., Ross, R., Yu, M., Yuan, J., Gao, Y., Henderson, B., Wogan, G., and Groopman, J. A. (1994). Follow-up study of urinary markers of aflatoxin exposure and liver cancer risk in Shanghai, People's Republic of China. *Cancer Epidemiol. Biomark. Prev.* **3,** 3–10.

Ross, R., Yuan, J., Yu, M., Wogan, G., Qian, G., Tu, J., Groopman, J., Gao, Y., and Henderson, B. (1992). Urinary aflatoxin biomarkers and risk of hepatocellular carcinoma. *Lancet* **339**(8799), 943–946.

Schulte, P.A., Hunter, D., and Rothman, N. (1997). Ethical and social issues in the use of biomarkers in epidemiological studies. *In* "Application of Biomarkers in Cancer Epidemiology" (P. Toniolo, P. Boffetta, D. E. G. Shuker *et al.,* eds), p. 313. IARC Scientific Publications, Lyon, France.

Schulte, P. A., and Perera, F. P. (1993). "Molecular Epidemiology: Principles and Practices." Academic Press, New York.

Smith, M., and Zhang, L. (1998). Biomarkers of leukemia risk: Benzene as a model. *Environ. Health Perspect.* **106,** 937–946.

Tang, D., Santella, R. M., Blackwood, A., Young, T. L., Mayer, J., Jaretzki, A., Grantham, S., Carberry, D., Steinglass, K. M., Tsai, W. Y., *et al.* (1995). A case-control molecular epidemiologic study of lung cancer. *Cancer Epidemiol. Biomark. Prev.* **4,** 341–346.

Tomatis, L., Aitio, A., Wilbourn, J., and Shukar, L. (1987). Human carcinogens so far identified. *Jpn. J. Cancer Res.* **78,** 887–898.

Wang, L., Hatch, M., Chen, C., Levin, B., You, S., Lu, S., Wu, M., Wu, W., Wang, L., Wang, Q., *et al.* (1996). Aflatoxin exposure and risk of hepatocellular carcinoma in Taiwan. *Int. J. Cancer* **67**(5), 620–625.

Wang, J., Shen, X., He, X., Zhu, Y., Zhang, B., Wang, J., Qian, S., Kuang, S., Zarba, A., Egner, P., *et al.* (1999). Protective alterations in phase 1 and 2 metabolism of aflatoxin B1 by oltipraz in residents of Qidong, People's Republic of China. *J. Natl. Cancer Inst.* **91**(4), 347–354.

Weinstein, I. B., Santella, R. M., and Perera, F. P. (1993). The molecular biology and molecular epidemiology of cancer. *In* The Science and Practice of Cancer Prevention and Control" (P. Greenwald, B. S. Kramer, and D. L. Weed, eds.). Marcel-Dekker, New York.

Yu, M., Lien, J., Chiu, Y., Santella, R., Liaw, Y., and Chen, C. (1997). Effect of aflatoxin metabolism and DNA adduct formation on hepatocellular carcinoma among chronic hepatitis B carriers in Taiwan. *J. Hepatol.* **2,** 320–330.

Zhang, B., Zhu, Y., Wang, J., Zhang, Q., Qian, G., Kuang, S., Li, Y., Fang, X., Yu, L. Y. D. S., Jacobson, L., *et al.* (1997). Oltipraz chemoprevention trial in Qidong, Jiangsu Province, People's Republic of China. *J. Cell Biochem. Suppl.* **28–29,** 166–167.

Molecular Mechanisms
of Cancer Invasion

Marc M. Mareel
Marc E. Bracke
Ghent University Hospital, Belgium

GLOSSARY

genotype The particular set of alleles present in each cell; alleles are genes that occupy the same relative position on homologous chromosomes, each of which originates from one of the parents.

host An entire organism, or a derivative therefrom, in which a neoplastic cell population has developed or into which such a population has been introduced.

invasion The spread of cells from a primary tumor or from a metastasis into the surrounding tissues. This term also applies to the spread of normal cells from their site of origin and to microorganisms (parasites or bacteria) penetrating either into the body or spreading inside the body.

knock out An organism into which a gene is suppressed either in all cells or in selected tissues.

master molecule A molecule that controls a complex event for which it is necessary but not sufficient.

metastasis Spread of a tumor to other parts of the body, usually including transport of tumor cells by the lymph or blood circulation.

microecosystem A community of cells and nonliving elements constituting a dynamic structural and functional unit within a tissue or an organ.

phenotype Molecular, morphological, and behavioral characteristics manifested by a cell, a tissue, or an organism as the result of gene activity and environmental influences.

promoter gene A gene whose activity promotes the expression of a given phenotype.

suppressor gene A gene whose activity suppresses the expression of a given phenotype.

transgenic An organism into which a foreign gene is introduced and successfully expressed either in all cells or in selected tissues.

Invasion is the hallmark of malignancy in all tumors. When a cell population expands within the limits of its own tissue domain, a benign tumor is formed. When cells leave their tissue domain, the tumor becomes malignant as it spreads locally and produces metastases in regional lymph nodes and in distant organs. Expression of the invasive or the noninvasive phenotype occurs within a dynamic microecosystem, which is built up by the proper neoplastic cells, by a variety of host cells, and by the extracellular matrix produced by both. During cancer development, expression of the invasive phenotypes is acquired by the accumulation of genetic changes modulating the neoplastic cells' sensitivity to invasion stimulators and invasion inhibitors. The genes implicated in the regulation of the invasive and the noninvasive phenotypes are supposed to encode master molecules regulating those cellular activities that can shift the balance between both phenotypes. Invasion-related activities that received most attention include homotypic cell–cell adhesion, cell–substrate adhesion, breakdown of extracellular matrix, cell migration, and heterotypic cell–cell adhesion. All these activities are crucial for the cross-talk between the neoplastic cells and the host.

I. INTRODUCTION

Invasion is responsible for the malignant character of tumors. It permits neoplastic cell spread locally without metastasis, locoregionally with metastasis to the lymph nodes, or systemically with metastases to distant organs. Cancer cells initiate microecosystems at which different elements of the host do participate. Within such microecosystems, there is continuous molecular cross-talk between all the elements. Metastasis results from a multistep invasion process with different microecosystems established at each step. The acquisition of the conditional or constitutive invasive phenotype results from inactivation of invasion–suppressor and activation of invasion–promoter genes. Such genetic alterations are, however, not specific for invasion, as they may be implicated also in earlier steps of cancer development and may, therefore, be classified as oncogenes or as tumor suppressor genes as well. These genes encode molecules that act as "masters" for the multiple interactions between molecules that are implicated in invasion, namely: homotypic adhesion molecules (between cells of the same type); heterotypic adhesion

molecules (between cells of a different type); elements of the extracellular matrix and their cellular receptors; lytic enzymes, their inhibitors, and the receptors for both; motility factors; and motility factor receptors. These molecules may also change the invasive phenotype upon posttranscriptional or posttranslational regulation. Invasion is not unique for cancer cells. It is also observed with embryonic cells, with leukocytes, and with parasites, all of which use molecular pathways that are similar to those used by invasive cancer cells. One of the goals of cellular and molecular invasion research is the development of new strategies for the treatment of cancer.

II. CLINICAL ASPECTS OF CANCER INVASION

Cancers are malignant because they invade locally, spread to locoregional lymph nodes, and produce metastases. Malignancy concerns not only the natural course of the disease, but also implicates resistance to treatment. A primary cancer of the breast that has not yet metastasized to the lymph nodes or to other organs is cured by surgery and radiotherapy in close to 100% of the cases. However, breast cancer becomes more difficult to cure when metastases have formed in the lymph nodes and it is virtually incurable upon metastasis to distant organs such as the liver, the lung, the brain, and the bone. Incurability does not mean that metastatic cancer does not necessitate optimal systemic (hormonal therapy, chemotherapy) and local (radiotherapy, surgery) treatment.

In the example of breast cancer, patients with metastases in the bone can survive for several years as they are presenting with a series of symptoms that respond very well to appropriate treatment. Development of cancer proceeds from bad to worse. The development of cancer may be described as a series of genetic alterations that each lead to altered microecosystems, recognizable through histological lesions such as hyperplasia, hyperplasia with atypia, carcinoma *in situ*, and invasive cancer (Fig. 1).

Uncontrolled growth is the common feature of benign, i.e., noninvasive, and malignant, i.e., invasive tumors. The step in the aforementioned sequence that is critical for malignancy is the transition from

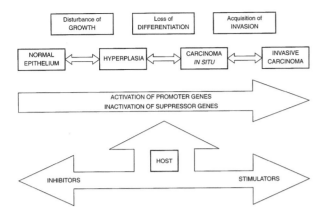

FIGURE 1 Schematic representation of cancer development with alterations in growth, differentiation, and tissue integrity (upper row) leading to phenotypes characteristic for pathological stages of the disease (second row). Multiple genetic alterations with loss of suppressor genes and activation of promoter genes underlay cancer development; these alterations change cancer cells' sensitivity and response to inhibitory and stimulatory host factors (lower row).

carcinoma *in situ* to invasive cancer. Invasion brings the cancer cells beyond the constraints of the normal tissue in which they have originated and permits them to enter into the circulation from where they can reach distant organs. The clinical course of invasive tumors covers a spectrum of malignancy from almost benign to extremely aggressive. Basal cell carcinomas of the skin are invasive but rarely form metastases; they have a good prognosis provided the lesion is completely removed.

Primary tumors of the brain also show a low frequency of metastasis; complete removal is, however, difficult and some of these tumors have an extremely bad prognosis with 2-year survival rates of less than 5%. Tumors from the mucosa of the upper respiratory and alimentary tract, usually categorized as head and neck tumors, are known to kill by locoregional extension, including metastasis to the regional lymph nodes. Head and neck cancers display a remarkable site dependence of metastasis to distant organs with frequencies of about 5% when the primary cancer is located at the vocal cords and about 30% when it is located in the nasopharynx. Melanomas are highly metastatic and have a poor prognosis. The frequency of metastasis from melanoma critically depends on the depth of invasion and/or on the thickness of the primary lesion. This also holds for the majority of the

other cancers so that early detection and immediate treatment are mandatory. Staging of malignant tumors is needed for all clinical studies because the stage of the primary tumor at diagnosis is the major index of prognosis. Invasion and metastasis are the predominant staging factors. For example, in the TNM system, propagated by the International Union against Cancer and used widely in Europe, tumors are staged following the volume and depth of invasion of the primary tumor (T), the number and the volume of invaded lymph nodes, as well as invasion through their capsula (N), and the presence and location of distant metastases (M).

III. BIOLOGICAL CONCEPTS OF CANCER INVASION

Multistep invasion eventually leads to the formation of distant metastases. The steps are (Fig. 2) invasion from the tissue in which the tumor has originated into the surrounding tissues; entry into the blood circulation either directly or via the lymphatics; transport through the circulation; exit from the circulation at the site of the putative metastasis; and invasion by the disseminated cancer cells, as metastases may be invasive tumors like primary tumors. Indeed, metastases may put cells into a new round of multistep invasion and lead to the formation of metastases from metastases, a process that has been called metastatic cascade. Microecosystems are created at each of the steps of metastasis as cancer cells interact with elements of the host, namely extracellular matrix, fibroblasts, endothelial cells, tumor-infiltrated lymphocytes (usually indicated as TILs), and possibly a number of other cell types. Cancer cells may cause transdifferentiation of host cells, e.g., fibroblasts into myofibroblasts. The type of elements participating at these microecosystems is somewhat different for each of the invasive steps. Little doubt exists that the cancer cells, in which the original genetic changes responsible for cancerogenesis have occurred, are responsible for the creation of at least the initial microecosystem of the primary tumor. A characteristic of an ecosystem is that alteration of a single element may dramatically change the entire system. The transistion from the noninvasive, i.e., maintenance of

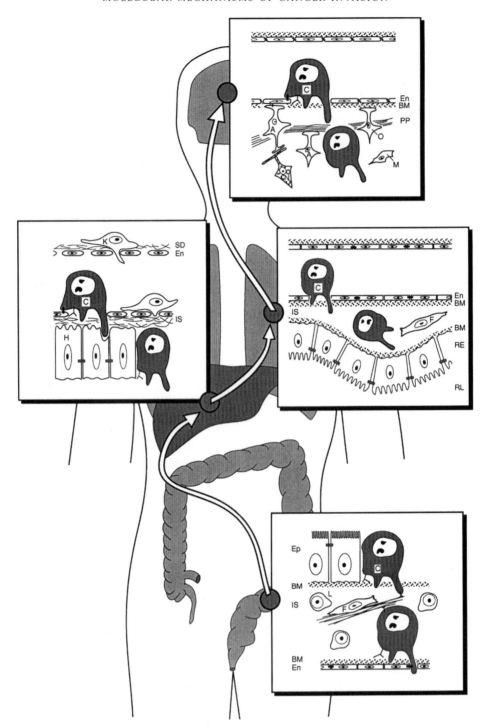

FIGURE 2 Schematic representation of metastasis from a primary cancer in the colon. The box at the level of the colon shows primary invasion and intravasation of a cancer cell (C); boxes at the level of the liver, the lungs, and the brain show extravasation and establishment of the cancer cell at the site of metastasis. Growth of these cancer cells will result in clinically overt metastases. Ep, epithelium; BM, basement membrane; IS, interstitial stroma; L, leukocyte; F, fibroblast; En, endothelium; K, Kupffer cell; SD, space of Disse; H, hepatocytes; PP, pia perivascularis; A, astrocyte; O, oligodendrocyte; N, nerve cell; M, macrophage. [Reproduced with permission from Mareel, M., Vermeulen, S., and Bracke, M. (1997). Moleculaire mechanismen van kankeruitzaaiiing: adhesie moleculen en netwerken van signaaltransductie, Verh. K. Acad. Geneeskd. Belg., LIX nr. 4, 327-351.]

normal tissue architecture or absence of invasion, to an invasive phenotype within the microecosystem represents such a dramatic change that may equally depend on alterations either in elements of the host or in the proper cancer cells.

Growth and invasion are considered to be tumor activities that may take place separately and that can be regulated independently. Experimental evidence in favor of the "growth-separate-from-invasion" concept was obtained through the use of agents that either inhibited invasion and permitted growth or inhibited growth and permitted invasion. Clinical data also exist to support the concept. In the example presented in Fig. 1, uncontrolled growth leading to the formation of a tumor is acquired before the cells become invasive. This sequence is probably reversed in the "cancer with unknown primary syndrome" where metastases grow, whereas the primary tumor is undetectable because it does not grow. Late metastases, i.e., the formation of metastases many years after removal of a primary tumor, are regularly observed for liver metastases originating from melanoma of the eye and for bone metastases originating from breast cancer. This phenomenon can be explained either by a delayed activation or inactivation of, respectively, oncogenes and tumor suppressor genes in the metastatic cancer cell or by alterations of the host, causing the production of growth factors. In view of this concept, organ specificity of metastasis is understood as organ-specific extravasation or organ-specific growth of circulating cancer cells. Transient rather than continuous invasion at the various steps of metastasis has been suggested by histological and immunohistochemical heterogeneity of primary tumors, as well as of metastases, and by conditional expression of invasiveness in experimental systems *in vitro* and *in vivo*. In view of the latter concept, a metastatic tumor is defined as a tumor in which at least part of the cell population is able to express at least temporarily the invasive phenotype at each of the steps of metastasis.

IV. INVASION IN NATURAL AND IN EXPERIMENTAL MICROECOSYSTEMS

Natural tumors present probably the only situation in which genuine invasion and metastasis do occur. Nevertheless, experimental assays *in vivo* and *in vitro* have been developed because they allow more manipulation and because they are generally easier to analyze. Assays for invasion aim at mimicking the whole process or defined invasion-related cellular activities within artificial microecosystems that resemble one or more steps of metastasis (Fig. 3). A positive correlation between invasiveness or noninvasiveness in various assays *in vitro*, as well as *in vivo*, indicates that the expression of the invasive phenotype is relatively insensitive to host factors. This is, however, not the rule for human cancer cell lines of epithelial origin. For example, human colon cancer cells fail to invade into collagen type 1 unless myofibroblasts or other stimulators of invasion are added; some types of such cancer cells do invade into embryonic tissues in organ culture, whereas closely related ones fail to do so. It is, therefore, advisable to use *in vitro* assays to examine the participation of certain molecules or molecular complexes at invasion and to unravel their signaling pathways. In the nude mouse, the expression of the invasive phenotype critically depends on the site of implantation, being positive in the wall of the colon (orthotopic) and negative in the subcutis (heterotopic). Assays for metastasis differ from one another by the route and the site of inoculation of the cells. When cells are introduced directly into the circulation, the literature uses the term "experimental" or "artificial" metastasis. When cells are introduced into a solid tissue, e.g., by subcutaneous injection, the term "spontaneous" metastasis is used. Cells injected into the tail vein first encounter the capillary bed of the lungs and, therefore, frequently, although not uniquely, give rise to artificial lung metastases. In order to obtain artificial liver metastases, cells are injected into the portal vein. In assays for spontaneous metastasis, extensive growth of the primary tumor may kill the animal before metastases appear. To overcome this problem, cells are injected at sites that are easily amputated, such as the tail or the footpad.

Transgenic and knockout mice are powerful tools for the analysis of the molecular mechanisms of invasion and metastasis. Mice with a high incidence of noninvasive tumors through activation of an oncogene at a given site are crossed with mice in which a putative invasion suppressor gene is neutralized at the same site. The high incidence of invasive and

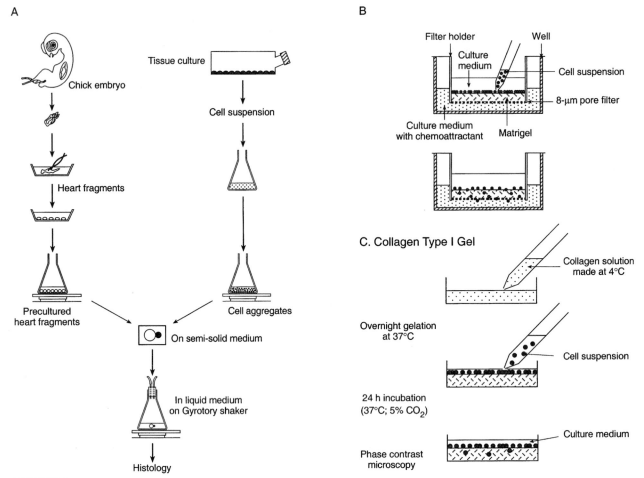

FIGURE 3   Schematic representation of frequently used *in vitro* assays for invasion. The putative invader is confronted with living normal embryonic tissue (A) or with extracellular matrix (B and C). Invasion is scored on histological sections (A) as the number of cells at the underside of the filter after nuclear staining (B) or as the number of cells inside the gel over the total number of cells under the phase contrast microscope (C). Not drawn to scale. [Details of the methods are described in Bracke, M. E., Boterberg, T. and Mareel, M. M. Chick heart invasion assay. In: "Metastasis Methods and Protocols", pp. 91–102 (S. Brooks and U. Schumacher, Eds.). Humana Press, Totowa, (2001), and in Bracke, M. E., Boterberg, T., Bruyneel, E. A. and Mareel, M.M. Collagen invasion assay. In "Metastasis Methods and Protocols," pp. 81–89 (S. Brooks and U. Schumacher, Eds.). Humana Press, Totowa (2001).]

eventually metastatic cancers in succesfully crossed offspring is considered proof for the causal relationship between the gene loss and the expression of the invasive phenotype.

V. MOLECULAR ASPECTS OF INVASION

Oncogenes or tumor promoter genes and tumor suppressor genes are implicated in the earlier stages of cancer development (see Fig. 1). The products of these genes are presumed to be implicated in growth regulation, and for most of these genes this function has been clearly demonstrated. We can, therefore, easily understand that the activation of tumor suppressor genes leads to uncontrolled cell proliferation, resulting in hyperplasia or other forms of benign tumors. Because only a minority of such benign lesions transform *in vivo* into invasive cancers, it is hard to believe that activation of such oncogenes or inactivation of such tumor suppressor genes is also responsible for the acquisition of the invasive capabilities. To acquire the invasive phenotype, alterations have to occur in other genes encoding proteins that participate either at the maintenance of the normal tissue architecture or at the stimulation of invasion. Such genes are termed invasion promoter and invasion suppressor genes. The latter do not necessarily present a separate set of genes because the same genes may act quite differently in different tumors. Moreover, single products of such genes may act differently depending on the molecular complex with which they associate. In a similar way, genes that either maintain or suppress differentiation can be defined, but, so far, less attention has been paid to such genes.

Multiple molecular interactions have been associated with the expression of the invasive phenotypes (Fig. 4). We want to emphasize that most interactions may be regulated by each of two or more molecular partners. For example, a cell may become motile through the activation of a motility factor receptor. It is presumed that the products of invasion genes are master molecules. We consider that such master molecules are responsible for initiation, continuation, or branching of molecular cascades. The question is which of these molecules are invasion gene products inasmuch as their expression or modulation can shift the invasion balance from positive to negative and vice versa.

The following tests have been used to identify invasion genes and their products: (i) The expression of the gene product correlates with the relevant invasive phenotype in cell populations derived from a single parental population; this does not imply that the presence of this molecule is sufficient, as other synchronous or metachronous events might be necessary as well. Neither does it mean that this gene product is necessary for invasiveness of other cell populations. (ii) Neutralizing antibodies specific for the presumptive invasion gene product change the invasive phenotype. (iii) Introduction and expression of the gene or its antisense construct into a cell population with a defined invasive phenotype change this phenotype. (iv) The invasive phenotype can be manipulated by environmental factors or by drugs that act on the invasion gene product. It is important to locate the activity of the invasion gene within the proper microecosystem of invasion (see Fig. 4), as it is not excluded that the products of such genes serve the expression of the invasive phenotype at one step and the expression of the noninvasive phenotype at another step.

A. The E-Cadherin/Catenin Complex

E-cadherin is a member of the type I subfamily of cadherins comprising calcium-dependent homophilic cell–cell adhesion molecules. It is a 120-kDa transmembrane glycoprotein with its intracellular domain being linked to the actin cytoskeleton through a group of proteins termed catenins. The latter linkage suggests that E-cadherin is integrated in signal/response circuits. Thus, its cell–cell adhesion function should not be interpreted solely in a mechanical way. E-cadherin is expressed from early embryogenesis on, and embryologists consider E-cadherin as a master molecule for the organization of epithelial junctional complexes. It remains present in most adult epithelia. The invasion suppressor role of E-cadherin was inferred first from *in vitro* invasion experiments with epithelial cells that were genetically manipulated to express E-cadherin or not. The causal relationship between downregulation of E-cadherin and acquisition of the invasive phenotype was demonstrated by the progression of pancreatic β-cell tumors from less invasive and nonmetastatic toward more invasive and metastatic in transgenic mice expressing dominant-negative E-cadherin under a constitutive insulin promoter. The clinical relevance of these experimental findings is corroborated by the observation that in most, if not all, invasive human cancers, as well as in melanomas, the E-cadherin/catenin complex is disturbed. Disturbances observed so far in experimental and clinical cancer comprise inactivating mutations, e.g., in diffuse gastric cancer; promoter (CpG island) methylation; repression of E-cadherin expression, e.g., by the transcription factor Snail ; transcriptional stimulation of other cadherins, e.g., N(eural)-cadherin; phosphorylation/dephosphorylation of one of the proteins of the complex, e.g., tyrosine phosphorylation of β-catenin; sterical hinderance of the extracellular part of E-cadherin, e.g., by large cell surface-exposed proteoglycans; proteolysis; and endocytosis of the whole complex. Taking into consideration the multiple levels of regulation and the multiple connections of the E-cadherin/catenin complex with other signal-transducing protein complexes, it is not surprising that more and more factors are found that influence the structure and function of this complex. E-cadherin acts also as a typical tumor suppressor, meeting Knudsen's criteria. Indeed, E-cadherin

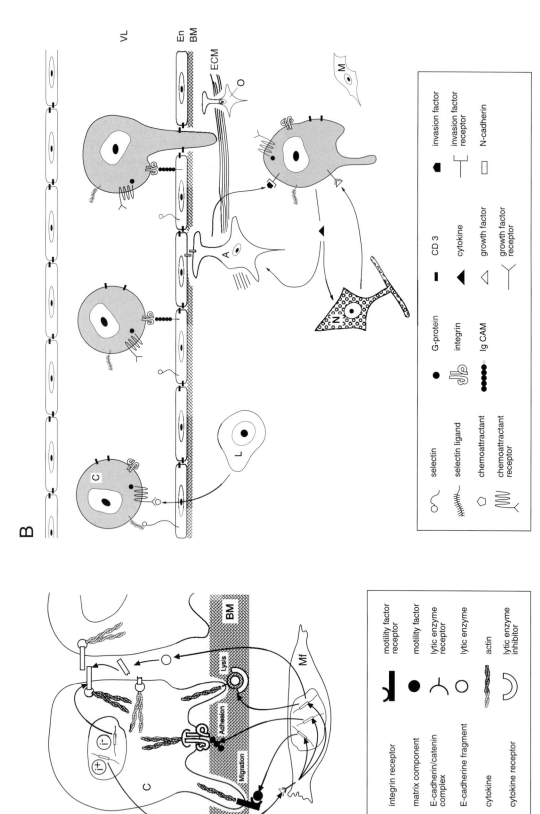

FIGURE 4 Microecosystems of invasion at the site of the primary tumor (A) and at the site of a brain metastasis (B). C, cancer cell; BM, basement membrane; MF, myofibroblast; En, endothelium; VL, vascular lumen; ECM, extracellular matrix; L, leukocyte; A, astrocyte; O, oligodendrocyte; N, neuron; M, macrophage. [Modified from Mareel, M., Van Roy, F. and De Baetselier, P. (1990). The invasive phenotypes, Cancer Metastasis Rev. **9**, 45–62, and from Mareel, M., Leroy, A. and Bracke, M. (1997). Metastasis to the brain: Cellular and molecular mechanisms. In "Handbook of Clinical Neurology, Vol. 25 (69): Neuro-Oncology, Part III," pp. 105–122 (P.J. Vinken and G.W. Bruyn, Eds.). Elsevier.]

mutations in lobular breast cancer are associated with loss of heterozygosity of the other allele. Moreover, in sporadic forms of this type of breast cancer, mutations are found in the *in situ* stage of the disease, i.e., before acquisition of invasiveness. Finally, in families with diffuse gastric cancer, germline mutations were detected. β-catenin links E-cadherin to the actin cytoskeleton via α-catenin and as such is essential for invasion–suppression. β-catenin is, however, also oncogenic. It interacts with the adenomatous polyposis coli (APC) multiprotein complex situated on the Wnt signaling pathway where it is serine/threonine phosphorylated and directed to the ubiquitine pathway for degradation. Mutation of APC or of β-catenin, hampering phosphorylation, leads to retention of β-catenin in the nucleus where it acts as a transcription factor for the *myc* oncogene and the gene encoding the invasion-related protease MMP-7 (matrix metalloproteinase-7; matrilysin).

B. Motility Factors and Their Receptors

Motility factors and their receptors serve as candidate invasion–promoter molecules. They stimulate and guide cells, which possess the machinery to translocate, along the paths of normal invasion during morphogenesis and of pathological invasion during cancer progression. Such motile cells also possess receptors that regulate their adhesion and deadhesion to and from the extracellular matrix in a way that is versatile enough to permit movement. GTPases of the Rho family are frequently implicated in motility factor-induced invasion. Autocrine motility factor (AMF) stimulates the directed movement of highly metastatic human melanoma cells in an autocrine way. It binds to a specific receptor that becomes phosphorylated and transduces the signal via G proteins. Finally, the ligand–receptor complex is internalized and transported to the leading edge of the cells activated to motility. Scatter factor (SF) and hepatocyte growth factor (HGF) have been described separately but were later shown to be identical and termed plasminogen related growth factor-1 (PRGF-1). This fact reminds us that the same molecule may serve different functions depending on the cell type. PRGF-1 is a ligand of the *c-met* protooncogene product, a member of a family of tyrosine kinase receptors. These re-

ceptors have unique signaling properties through the multifunctional docking sites of their cytoplasmic domain binding several intracellular signal transducers. The detection of PRGF-1 as a paracrine motility factor started with the observation that conditioned medium from cultures of human fibroblasts caused scattering of epithelial and endothelial cells. Evidence in favor of its role in invasion came from experiments with human carcinoma cells seeded on top of collagen type I gels. When human osteosarcoma cell lines acquire a mutated *c-met* oncogene, they become invasive and metastatic, suggesting that this oncogene might function as an invasion–promoter gene. In experimental systems, PRGF-1 downregulates the E-cadherin/catenin invasion–suppressor complex through tyrosine phosphorylation of β-catenin. PRGF-1 has characteristics of a molecule suitable for functioning in microecosystems because it is active at picomolar concentrations and because it acts in a paracrine way, thus bringing two types of cells into cross-talk. The affinity of PRGF-1 for heparin opens possibilities for regulation via retention in the glycosaminoglycan-containing extracellular matrix. Hydrolases produced by invasive cells may release and activate such sequestered motility factors.

C. Integrins, Extracellular Matrix, and IgCAMs

Integrins are heterodimeric transmembrane molecules that are linked to the actin cytoskeleton via cytoplasmic proteins, including members of tyrosine kinase families. Like cadherins they serve not only adhesion but also mutual cell-to-cell and cell-to-matrix signaling. With regard to invasion, the cross-talk between integrins and extracellular matrix has a dual function, as it arrests cells in the matrix and assists migration as well. Molecular scenarios for this dual function implicate clustering of integrin receptors anchoring the cell to the matrix and sending signals to the nucleus for stimulation of their proteases. The latter resolve the matrix, release integrins from their anchor, and so permit the cell to move. As heterotypic cell–cell adhesion molecules, they initiate intravasation. Circulating cancer cells adhere to the vascular endothelium; the endothelial cells retract and the cancer cells now interact with the endothelial basement membrane; degradation of the latter permits the cells to migrate into the underlying tissues. Alternatively, cancer cells may adhere directly to the extracellular matrix at sites of endothelial damage. This implicates that the site of tumor metastasis may be determined by preexisting damage of the vascular endothelium and that organ specificty of metastasis has to be searched for in interactions of the circulating cells with the subendothelial matrix rather than with the endothelial cells. In these scenarios of extravasation, the emphasis is on the invasive phenotype rather than on growth stimulation. Another scenario of extravasation that emphasizes growth rather than invasion is conceivable as well. Here, cancer cells form a thrombus, grow within the vascular lumen, and damage the endothelium. Later, the endothelium is activated and endothelial cells cover the tumor. Regardless of the scenario, extravasation implies multiple interactions of the cancer cells with various elements of the host, resulting in a highly dynamic microecosystem of invasion at the wall of the capillary cell (see Fig. 4).

D. Hydrolases, Their Inhibitors, and Their Receptors

Lytic enzymes are necessary for invasion because cancer cells have to penetrate through the extracellular matrix after leaving their tissue of origin. Because the activity of lytic enzymes is sensitive to regulation at multiple levels, they may be of crucial importance in temporary shifts from the noninvasive to the invasive phenotype. Transcriptional activation or repression of lytic enzymes has led to, respectively, an increased and a decreased metastatic capability of cells. Most lytic enzymes are secreted as inactive zymogens. Therefore, activators of the conversion of zymogens into active hydrolases are candidate invasion–promoter molecules. Well-documented examples of such zymogens are plasminogen, procathepsin, procollagenases, and prostromelysin.

Focalization is a way to regulate the activity of the lytic enzymes that are implicated in tumor invasion. Some proteases, such as MT-MMPs, are expressed at the cell surface. Others, such as uPA, bind to a receptor (uPAR), which is linked to the plasma membrane, and this uPA/uPAR complex remains enzy-

matically active, focalizing protease activity at the leading edge of invading cells. Several invasion-related proteases are expressed by the stromal cells that participate at the establishment of the tumor microecosystem. In colon cancer, uPA is secreted by the myofibroblasts and binds to uPAR expressed by colon cancer cells; this focalizes the enzymatic activity not only at the plasma membrane of the cancer cells, but also at the front of invasion. A remarkable regulatory loop has been demonstrated for renal cancer cells and kidney fibroblasts. *In vitro*, the cancer cells stimulated fibroblasts to produce interleukin-1, which in turn enhanced the production of type IV collagenase by the cancer cells. Interestingly, this collaboration seemed to be specific for kidney fibroblasts, thus providing a molecular explanation for site-specific invasion and metastasis of these cancer cells. This example also reminds us that the secretion of lytic enzymes may be modulated by cytokines as well as by a large variety of other environmental factors. The role of proteases in invasion is not limited to the breakdown of extracellular matrix. Proteases such as MMP7 and stromelysin-1 cleave the ectodomain of transmembrane receptors such as E-cadherin and so produce soluble parts of the receptors that modulate invasion.

Inhibitors of proteinases, such as tissue inhibitors of matrix metalloproteinases (TIMPs) and plasminogen activator inhibitors (PAIs), are putative invasion–suppressor molecules, as they serve as natural inhibitors of the lytic enzymes that were discussed earlier as invasion promoters.

TIMPs and PAIs are other examples of putative invasion–suppressor molecules. A negative correlation has been found between levels of TIMP or PAI and the metastatic capability of cancer cell variants. Genetic manipulation via transfections with specific sense and antisense DNA constructs has confirmed the invasion–suppressor function of these enzyme inhibitors. A surprising result was obtained with PAI-1 knockout mice in which skin cancer cells failed to invade unless the expression of PAI-1 was restored. With regard to the microecosystem concept, it is important that both inhibitors can act in a paracrine (between different cells) as well as an autocrine (between the same cells) manner and that they are susceptible to regulation at multiple levels as discussed already for the components of the E-cadherin/catenin complex. The balance concept is well illustrated by the relationship between lytic enzymes and their inhibitors. Here also, several levels of fine-tuning need consideration. For example, induction and endogenous activation of collagenase IV may be accompanied by the suppression of *Timp* gene transcription; sequestration of PAI into the extracellular matrix protects PAI against the loss of activity.

VI. INVASION IN NONCANCER CONDITIONS

Embryogenesis is characterized by the displacement of cells from one tissue domain into another, a phenomenon that closely resembles cancer invasion. For example, the ingression of mesoblast through the primitive streak implicates focal disappearance of the epithelial basement membrane, transformation of epithelial into fibroblastic cells, and migration of cells into the subepithelial tissue domain. Whereas embryogenic invasion is a frequent event, cells seldom enter the circulation so that the embryonic counterpart of cancer metastasis hardly exists. The primary gonocytes in the chick embryo are exceptional, as they enter the vessels of the endophyllic wall; they circulate, extravasate, and home in the germinal ridge. Similar to cancer, cell–cell adhesion molecules such as E-cadherin (called L-CAM in the chick) may act as invasion–suppressor molecules. An invasion–promoter role may be played by motility factors such as stem cell factor (SCF) recognizing the *c-kit* tyrosine kinase on melanoblasts. During embryogenesis, SCF shows a specific spatiotemporal localization that is associated with the stromal cells lining the melanoblast migratory pathway.

Leukocytes meet most, if not all, of the criteria of metastatic cells. They leave their tissue of origin in the bone marrow, enter the circulation, and home at specific sites. Circulating leukocytes have a number of heterotypic cell–cell adhesion molecules present that recognize countermolecules on the endothelium. These molecules are sensitive to modulation by elements of the microecosystem of extravasation. Affinity (strength of binding) and avidity (speed of reaction) are believed to determine which of these molecules will initiate extravasation. Carbohydrate–

selectin binding is more rapid, although weaker; it is followed by stronger interactions involving cell–cell adhesion molecules of the integrin and of the immunoglobulin-like family. It is important to understand that adhesion molecules should keep the cells together long enough for the initiation of the following steps of extravasation, yet the cells need to be released when extravasation has to be completed (see Fig. 4).

Parasites have to enter their host through lining epithelia such as the skin or the gastrointestinal mucosa. Therefore, they have to cover one more step of invasion than cancer cells do in order to metastasize. For example, *Entamoeba histolytica* trophozoites attach to and invade into the colon mucosa before reaching the position of preinvasive colon cancer cells. From that moment on, trophozoites behave much like colon cancer cells that metastasize to the liver and to the brain. The molecules presumed to be implicated in both types of metastases belong to the same functional categories, namely cell–cell adhesins, receptors for extracellular matrix molecules, hydrolases, and motility factor receptors. In some parasites the invasive phenotype is expressed during defined periods of the life cycle and shows a distinct morphotype, greatly facilitating the analysis of cellular and molecular events specifically implicated in invasion. For example, during the life cycle of *Schistosoma mansoni*, the cercaria leaves the snail, its intermediary host, and swims in the water to meet with and to invade the human host through the skin. Shortly before the parasite leaves the snail, a gene encoding a proelastase is switched on and production of the proenzyme starts. Because this enzyme is activated on contact with a specific skin lipid, the potent elastase is active only at the site of invasion. Once the cercaria has crossed the skin, the proelastase gene is switched off. This interaction between the host and the invader is a striking illustration of enzyme activation through focalization within a defined microecosystem of invasion.

VII. THERAPEUTIC ASPECTS OF INVASION

Anticancer agents aim at selective killing of cancer cells, arresting proliferation, or inducing apoptosis.

Because of the multiplicity of molecular interactions involved, one may consider the multistep invasion process of metastasis being an ideal target for therapy. Many attempts have been made to exploit this idea and at least one has led to a remarkable therapeutic success. Microtubule inhibitors, e.g., vinca-alkaloids, taxol, and estramustin, are inhibitors of invasion because they interfere with cytoplasmic microtubule complex-mediated migration. At invasion–inhibitory concentrations these agents also affect the mitotic spindle so that they have all the disadvantages of cytotoxic and cytostatic agents. The use of classical hydrolase inhibitors has been limited so far to experimental systems. Inhibitors of matrix metalloproteinases (MMPs) have been used for clinical trials. Synthetic peptides with a laminin-specific sequence such as YIGSR (tyrosine-isoleucine-glycine-serine-arginine) and a fibronectin-specific sequence RGD (arginine-glycine-aspartic acid) inhibit metastasis because they block, respectively, cancer cell–basement membrane and cancer cell–stroma interactions. Flavonoids, acting on the extracellular matrix, also interfere with invasion. For restoration of E-cadherin-mediated cell–cell adhesion functions, new possibilities are found with the family of insulin-like growth factors. Today, much attention is paid to agents affecting signal transduction; examples are alkyllysophospholipids, protein kinase, and farnesyltransferase inhibitors, agents such as pertussis toxin acting on G proteins, and synthetic substitutes of imidazoles and triazoles. Most of these treatment strategies have not been tested clinically or failed. There is, however, a remarkable exception that supports further investigation of invasion as a target for therapy. Understanding of the cellular and molecular interaction in the microecosystem of bone metastasis, particularly the dominant role of osteoclasts in this pathological form of bone destruction, has led to a new treatment. Biphosphonates interfere with osteoclast activity through one or more of the following mechanisms: prevention of the transition of mononuclear precursors to multinucleated mature osteoclasts; inhibition of osteoclast attachment to the surface of the bone; disturbance of the osteoclast function at the cellular level; or making bone matrix resistant toward osteoclastic attack. Bone metastases occur in cancer patients who survive for a relatively long period; they are painful and invalidating. A substantial contribution has been paid to the treatment of this metastatic disease by biphosphonates and their congeners. Bisphosphonates were also used in the adjuvant treatment of breast cancer. As expected, such treatment reduced the incidence of bone metastases. It, however, also reduced visceral metastasis, presumably through the inhibition of osteoclast-mediated release of growth factors from the bone marrow.

See Also the Following Articles

AUTOCRINE AND PARACRINE GROWTH MECHANISMS IN CANCER PROGRESSION AND METASTASIS • DIFFERENTIATION AND CANCER: BASIC RESEARCH • EXTRACELLULAR MATRIX AND MATRIX RECEPTORS • INTEGRIN RECEPTOR SIGNALING PATHWAYS • MOLECULAR BASIS OF TUMOR IMMUNITY • MULTISTAGE CARCINOGENESIS • TUMOR CELL MOTILITY AND INVASION • TUMOR SUPPRESSOR GENES: SPECIFIC CLASSES • VASCULAR TARGETING

Bibliography

Berx, G., Becker, K.-F., Höfler, H., and van Roy, F. (1998). Mutations of the human E-cadherin (CDH1) gene. Hum. Mutat. 12, 226–237.

Bracke, M. E., Van Roy, F. M., and Mareel, M. M. (1996). The E-cadherin/catenin complex in invasion and metastasis. In "Attempts to Understand Metastasis Formation I" (U. Günthert and W. Birchmeier, eds.), pp. 123–161. Springer, Berlin.

Fidler, I. J. (1991). Orthotopic implantation of human colon carcinomas into nude mice provides a valuable model for the biology and therapy of metastasis. Cancer Metast. Rev. 10, 229–243.

Hanahan, D., and Weinberg, R. A. (2000). The hallmarks of cancer. Cell 100, 57–70.

Lauwaet, T., Oliveira, M. J., Mareel, M., and Leroy, A. (2000). Molecular mechanisms of invasion by cancer cells, leukocytes and microorganisms. Microbes Infect. 2, 923–931.

Liotta, L. A., Steeg, P. S., and Stetler-Stevenson, W. G. (1991). Cancer metastasis and angiogenesis: An imbalance of positive and negative regulation. Cell 64, 327–336.

Mareel, M., Leroy, A., and Bracke, M. (1997a). Metastasis to the brain: Cellular and Molecular mechanisms. In "Handbook of Clinical Neurology" (P. J. Vinken and G. W. Bruyn, eds.), Vol. 25, pp. 105–122. Elsevier.

Mareel, M., Van Roy, F., and De Baetselier, P. (1990). The invasive phenotypes. Cancer Metast. Rev. 9, 45–62.

Mareel, M., Vermeulen, S., and Bracke, M. (1997b). Moleculaire mechanismen van kankeruitzaaiing: Adhesie moleculen en netwerken van signaaltransductie. Verh. K. Acad. Geneeskd. Belg. LIX(4), 327–351.

Mareel, M. M., De Baetselier, P., and Van Roy, F. M. (1991). "Mechanisms of Invasion and Metastasis." CRC Press, Boca Raton, FL.

Mundy, G. R. (1997). Mechanisms of bone metastasis. *Cancer* **80,** 1546–1556.

Nicolson, G. L. (1991). Tumor and host molecules important in the organ preference of metastasis. *Semin. Cancer Biol.* **2,** 143–154.

Noël, A., Gilles, C., Bajou, K., Devy, L., Kebers, F., Lewalle, J. M., Maquoi, E., Munaut, C., Remacle, A., and Foidart, J. M. (1997). Emerging roles for proteinases in cancer. *Invasion Metast.* **17,** 221–239.

Sparks, A. B., Morin, P. J., Vogelstein, B., and Kinzler, K. W. (1998). Mutational analysis of the APC/β-catenin/ Tcf pathway in colorectal cancer. *Cancer Res.* **58,** 1130–1134.

Sander, E. E., and Collard, J. G. (1999). Rho-like GTPases: Their role in epithelial cell–cell adhesion and invasion. *Eur. J. Cancer* **35,** 1302–1308.

Van Hoorde, L., Van Aken, E., and Mareel, M. (2000). Collagen type I: A substrate and a signal for invasion. *In* "Progress in Molecular and Subcellular Biology" (A. Macieira-Coelho, ed.), Vol. 25, pp. 105–134. Springer Verlag, Berlin.

Monoclonal Antibodies: Leukemia and Lymphoma

Joseph G. Jurcic
David A. Scheinberg

Memorial Sloan-Kettering Cancer Center and
Weill Medical College of Cornell University

GLOSSARY

α particle A helium nucleus consisting of two protons and two neutrons.

antigen modulation The downregulation of antigen expression due to the internalization of antigen after antibody binding.

anti-idiotypic antibody An antibody directed against the idiotype (unique binding site) of another antibody.

β particle A charged particle emitted from the nucleus of an atom whose mass and charge are equal to those of an electron.

chimeric antibody An antibody derived from amino acid sequences of two different animal sources, such as human and mouse.

complementaritity-determining region (CDR) A portion of the variable region of an antibody responsible for binding to a specific antigen.

humanized antibody An antibody whose framework is composed of human immunoglobulin but whose CDRs are from another animal source.

idiotope An antigenic marker of the CDR of an immunoglobulin molecule.

idiotype The set of idiotopes (unique binding sites) on an immunoglobulin molecule.

opsonization The process of binding a target, e.g., bacterium, virus, or cancer cell, to an immune cell, usually followed by engulfment.

single-chain antigen-binding protein A genetically engineered protein composed of the variable domains of the immunoglobulin heavy and light chains linked by a protein.

$\mathbf{M}$onoclonal antibodies (mAbs) have become part of the standard treatment of cancer. Nonetheless, the optimistic view of the early 1980s that mAbs were "magic bullets" has now been replaced by a more realistic understanding of their therapeutic potential.

Some of the most encouraging results using mAb-based treatments have been seen in hematologic cancers. These diseases are ideally suited to mAb therapy because of the accessibility of malignant cells in the blood, bone marrow, lymph nodes, and spleen. Moreover, the well-defined immunophenotypes of the various lineages and stages of hematopoietic differentiation have allowed antigenic targets to be identified. Advances in immunology and molecular biology have allowed many obstacles to the effective use of mAbs to be surmounted. Genetically engineered chimeric and humanized antibodies have been constructed to overcome the lack of intrinsic antitumor activity of many murine mAbs. Because host effector mechanisms are not required for tumor cell killing, radioimmunotherapy and antibody–drug conjugates have become promising approaches.

I. ANTIBODY STRUCTURE

Immunoglobulins are separated into five classes or isotypes based on structure and biologic properties. IgM is the primordial antibody whose expression by B cells represents the commitment of that cell to a particular recognition space that later narrows during maturation induced by antigen interactions. IgD is normally coexpressed with IgM on B cells. IgE, IgA, and IgG are mature immunoglobulins that are expressed after maturation of response and class switch. IgE participates in immediate-type hypersensitivity reactions and parasite immunity; IgA, in mucosal immunity, and IgG, in humoral immunity. IgG is further divided into four subclasses, and IgA into two subclasses. Most mAbs used clinically belong to the IgG isotype.

The basic structural elements of all antibodies are heavy chains of 55 to 75 kDa and light chains of 22 kDa. Heavy chains are μ, δ, γ, ϵ, and α, corresponding to IgM, IgD, IgG, IgE, and IgA. Light chains are either κ or λ. The amino-terminal domain of each chain is the variable (V_H or V_L) region that mediates antigen recognition. The remaining domains are constant regions designated C_L for light chain and C_H1, C_H2, and C_H3 for heavy chain (and C_H4 for μ and ϵ). The smallest stable unit consists of two pairs of heavy and light chains, $(HL)_2$. IgE and IgG are composed of a single $(HL)_2$ unit, but IgM exists as a pentamer of $(HL)_2$ units joined by disulfide bonds with a third J chain component. IgA exists mainly as a monomer in serum, whereas secretions are primarily a dimer plus trimer.

The variable region is composed of subdomains consisting of framework regions interdigitated with complementarity-determining regions (CDRs), or hypervariable regions, that make primary contact with antigens. Each heavy and light chain has three CDRs that may participate in antigen binding.

The IgG antibody has been defined in terms of susceptibility to proteases that cleave in the exposed, unfolded regions of the antibody (Fig. 1). The Fab contains the V region and the first constant domain of the heavy chain and the entire light chain. Fab′ also includes a portion of the H chain hinge region and one or more free cysteines. $(Fab')_2$ is a dimer of Fab′ linked by a disulfide bond. Fv is a fragment including one V_H and V_L. A single chain Fv (scFv) is an Fv with a peptide linker joining the C terminus of one chain to the N terminus of the other.

II. APPROACHES TO MONOCLONAL ANTIBODY THERAPY

A. Unconjugated Serotherapy

mAbs can be used to focus an inflammatory response against a tumor cell (Table I). The binding of mAbs to a target cell can result in complement activation, thereby initiating a number of biologically important effects. C5a can induce chemotaxis for phagocytic cells, and cell-bound C3b and C4b can lead to a rapid clearance of target cells. A late consequence of complement activation is the production of the membrane attack complex that disrupts the integrity of the cell membrane. Human immunoglobulin M (IgM), IgG1, and IgG3 isotypes are most efficient in activating complement. Cells with antibody and complement on their surfaces may also be engulfed, or opsonized, by macrophages.

Another important mechanism for tumor cell killing is antibody-dependent cell-mediated cytotoxicity

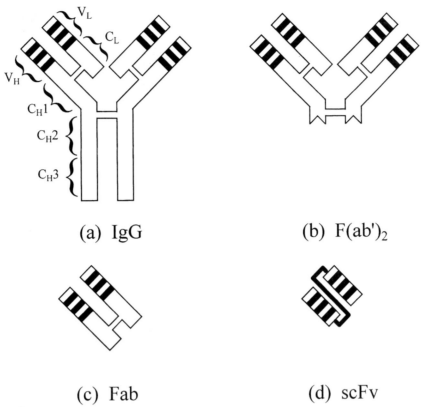

FIGURE 1 Structure of antibody fragments. (a) The immunoglobulin G (IgG) molecule consists of four polypeptide chains, two heavy chains (V_H, C_H1, C_H2, and C_H3) and two light chains (V_L and C_L). Hypervariable sequences, shown in black, are found with the V_H and V_L regions and are responsible for antigen binding. The Fc portion within the constant regions C_H1, C_H2, C_H3, and C_L, shown in white, mediates effector functions. (b) The F(ab')$_2$ fragment contains both Fab' domains linked by a disulfide bond. (c) The Fab contains V_H and C_H1 along with the entire light chain. (d) V_H and V_L domains can be joined by a synthetic peptide linker to make a single-chain antibody fragment.

(ADCC), in which an effector cell expressing an Fc receptor binds to a cell-bound mAb and is triggered to kill the target cell. Monocytes, macrophages, natural killer cells, neutrophils, and platelets can affect ADCC. For human antibodies, binding to macrophages is restricted to IgG1 and IgG3 isotypes.

Chimeric and humanized antibodies have been constructed to overcome the weak antitumor activity and immunogenicity of many murine mAbs. These antibodies retain the binding specificity of the original rodent antibody determined by the variable region but can potentially activate the human immune system through their human constant region. Nevertheless, mechanisms of resistance to complement-mediated

cytotoxicity (CMC), related to intracellular pH and expression of p-glycoprotein, have been described.

B. Anti-idiotypic Antibodies

Recognizing unique idiotypic structure in the variable region of immunoglobulin molecules, anti-idiotypic mAbs were first used in the treatment of follicular lymphomas, with the goal of targeting the idiotype expressed by the transformed B-cell clone. Several mechanisms of action have been postulated, including CMC, ADCC, downregulation of the malignant clone through the idiotypic network, inhibition of cell proliferation, and induction of apoptosis. In

TABLE I
Approaches to Monoclonal Antibody Therapy

Approach	Mechanisms of action
Unconjugated serotherapy	Complement-mediated cytotoxicity Antibody-dependent cell-mediated cytotoxicity Opsonization
Anti-idiotypic antibodies	Complement-mediated cytotoxicity Antibody-dependent cell-mediated cytotoxicity Downregulation of malignant clone Inhibition of proliferation Apoptosis Vaccines
Interference with growth and regulation	Blocking growth factors Blocking growth factor receptors Apoptosis
Delivery of cytotoxic agents	Conjugation to radioisotopes Conjugation to chemotherapeutic agents Conjugation to toxins
Bone marrow purging	Complement-mediated cytotoxicity Immunomagnetic beads Immunoadsorption columns Immunotoxins

another approach, "mirror-image" anti-idiotypic mAbs that structurally resemble the antigen recognized by the original immunoglobulin can be used as surrogate immunogens to induce protective immunity against various malignancies.

C. Interference with Growth and Regulation

mAbs can exert cytostatic or cytotoxic effects by binding to growth factors or cellular receptors needed for tumor survival. Antibodies directed against cytokines, such as interleukin-2 (IL-2) and IL-6, and growth factor receptors, such as the IL-2 receptor, have been studied. The most clinically useful mAbs may operate by several mechanisms. In addition to mediating cytotoxic effects by complement and cellular mechanisms, rituximab, a chimeric mAb targeting the B-cell surface antigen CD20, can directly induce apoptosis *in vitro* in a lymphoma cell line.

D. Delivery of Cytotoxic Agents

Because of the lack of potency of many unconjugated mAbs, investigators have used mAbs as delivery vehicles for radioisotopes, chemotherapeutic agents, and toxins. Because radioisotopes emit particles capable of inducing lethal DNA damage to cells lying within a fixed range, radioimmunoconjugates may allow the killing of antigen-negative tumor variants or tumor cells not reached by mAbs. This approach has produced significant responses in B-cell lymphomas and demonstrated the ability to ablate marrow before bone marrow transplantation (BMT) in leukemia. Chemotherapeutic agents such as doxorubicin, calicheamicin, methotrexate, and vinca alkaloids have been conjugated to various mAbs. Toxins used clinically have been either bacterial products, such as diphtheria toxin and *Pseudomonas* exotoxin A, or plant products, such as ricin, gelonin, pokeweed antiviral protein, and saponin.

E. Bone Marrow Purging

The use of mAbs *ex vivo* to eliminate residual cancer cells or to isolate early hematopoietic progenitors from marrow or blood of patients undergoing high-dose therapy with stem cell rescue has become a promising application of mAb therapy. Immunological purging methods using complement-mediated lysis, immunomagnetic bead depletion, and immunotoxins have been most widely studied. The addition of complement to mAb-coated cells has generally resulted in two to three logs of tumor cell lysis in most studies. Typically, combinations of mAbs are used to avoid problems of antigen heterogeneity on target cells. Purging with immunomagnetic beads has been performed with magnetic microspheres coated with affinity-purified sheep antimouse antibodies directed against the Fc portion of the mAb. Subsequently, particles directly attached to the primary mAb have allowed for more rapid and simple purging procedures. Whether these purging techniques decrease the relapse rate following high-dose therapy remains unanswered.

III. ANTIGENIC TARGETS

Immunophenotypic characterization of the various stages and lineages found during hematopoietic differentiation provides the rationale for the selection of mAbs that bind selectively to neoplastic cells while sparing normal tissues (Table II). Leukemia- and lymphoma-associated antigens, however, are not tumor specific, nor are they always stage or lineage specific. CD10, found on B-cell acute lymphoblastic leukemia (ALL), is also expressed by mature B-cell lymphomas and T-cell ALL. CD33, found on most acute myelogenous leukemia (AML) cells, is also expressed by normal myeloid precursors.

Nearly all neoplasms of B-cell origin express CD19 and HLA-DR. ALLs of B-cell lineage are derived from the earliest stages of B-cell differentiation. Most express CD10 and CD34, and a small proportion express CD20. B-cell non-Hodgkin's lymphomas are the malignant counterparts of cells corresponding to later stages of B-cell differentiation and express CD20, CD22, and CD23. Most follicular lymphomas express surface immunoglobulin, CD10, CD21, and the B-cell activation antigen B5. CD5 and CD11c/18 are found on small lymphocytic lymphoma (SLL) and chronic lymphocytic leukemia (CLL). Diffuse large cell lymphomas are more heterogeneous in surface antigen expression, but the activation antigens B5 and B7 are usually found.

Most T-cell ALL and lymphoblastic lymphoma are the malignant counterpart of the earliest T cells that

TABLE II
Target Antigens for Immunotherapy
of Leukemia and Lymphoma

Antigen	Disease[a]	Antibody
CD5	ALL, CLL	T101, Tp67
CD7	ALL	Tp41
CD14	AML	AML2-23
CD15	AML	PM81
CD19	NHL, ALL, CLL	Anti-B4
CD20	NHL, CLL	Tositumomab, rituximab, 2B8, 1F5
CD21	NHL	OKB7
CD22	NHL	LL2, huLL2
CD25	ATL	Anti-Tac
CD33	AML-CML	MY9, p67, M195, HuM195
CD45	AML, MDS, ALL	BC8
CD52	CLL, NHL	CAMPATH-1H
HLA-DR	NHL, CLL	Lym-1
Idiotype	NHL	Patient specific

[a]ALL, acute lymphoblastic leukemia; CLL, chronic lymphocytic leukemia; AML, acute myelogenous leukemia; NHL, non-Hodgkin's lymphoma, ATL, adult, T-cell leukemia; CML, chronic myelogenous leukemia; MDS, myelodysplastic syndrome.

express CD2, CD5, CD7, and CD10. Both diffuse small and large cell T-cell lymphomas resemble mature T cells and express CD2, CD3, CD4, CD5, and CD7; a minority express CD8.

The earliest myeloid progenitors express CD34; more committed progenitors acquire CD33 and HLA-DR. Most AML cells express CD33, CD13, and CD15. HLA-DR is found on all subtypes except acute promyelocytic leukemia (APL). Monocytic leukemias express antigens associated with more mature granulocytes and monocytes, including CD11a/18, CD11c, CD14, and CD15. Cell surface antigen expression in early phase chronic myelogenous leukemia (CML) resembles that of mature granulocytes but is heterogeneous in blast crisis.

IV. ANTIBODY PHARMACOKINETICS

A. Tumor Characteristics

Various physical and biological factors can prevent delivery of mAbs to tumor. Because of their large size and high molecular mass (typically 150–180 kDa), mAbs may have difficulty diffusing to sites of bulky disease. In early lymphoma trials, impaired tumor targeting was reported in patients with bulky adenopathy or massive splenomegaly. Additionally, variations in tumor vasculature can limit the distribution of mAbs to only well-perfused areas of tumor. Endothelial integrity and interstitial back-pressure can also interfere with mAb delivery. The use of antibody fragments potentially offers improved tumor penetration because of their smaller size and lower molecular weight. The utility of these constructs, however, may be limited by rapid serum clearance, decreased binding avidity, and decreased molecular stability and activity when conjugated to radioisotopes.

B. Antigen Characteristics

The number of available antigen sites will alter antibody pharmacokinetics and biodistribution. In a dose-escalation trial of trace-labeled ^{131}I-anti-CD33 mAb M195 for myeloid leukemias, superior targeting to sites of disease as determined by γ camera imaging

was seen with a comparatively small dose. This may be explained in part by the relatively low number of binding sites (approximately 10,000–20,000) on each leukemia cell. Circulating antigenic targets can also prevent the delivery of mAbs to the tumor. Preinfusions of unlabeled antibodies have been used to saturate circulating target cells and to increase the delivery of therapeutically radiolabeled mAbs to tumors in several systems, including ^{131}I-p67 (anti-CD33) for AML and ^{131}I-tositumomab (anti-CD20) for lymphoma.

Heterogeneous antigen expression can provide a mechanism of resistance to the cytotoxic effects of mAbs and account for toxicities associated with therapy. If the targeted antigen is lacking from a subset of tumor cells, residual tumor will remain following antibody therapy. Target antigen expression on normal tissues, including hematopoietic cells, can result in myelosuppression and other significant side effects. Radioimmunotherapy offers a potential solution to this problem, as radiation can kill cells within a given range regardless of whether they express the target antigen.

The influence of antigenic modulation on mAb-based treatments relates to specific therapeutic applications. Differences in the rates of endocytosis, intracellular degradation, and cell surface shedding can affect the selection of mAbs for therapy. Tumors in which antigen–antibody complexes remain on the cell surface may be better suited to treatments dependent on immune-mediated cytotoxicity or delivery of radioisotopes with long-ranged emissions, such as ^{131}I. Internalization of the antigen–antibody complex after binding can optimize the delivery of some radioisotopes, such as short-ranged α particle emitters, chemotherapeutic agents, and toxins. Antigen modulation can shorten the retention time of some ^{131}I-labeled mAbs due to catabolism of the radioconjugate.

C. Antibody Characteristics

The specificity of mAbs remains crucial in the development of effective immunotherapy. All of the antigenic targets discussed in Section III are seen on normal hematopoietic cells, and many are found on other normal tissues. CD34, for example, is found on most AML and ALL cells but is also expressed on endothelial cells and hematopoietic stem cells. CD13 and CD15 are widely expressed on AML but are also seen on normal tissues, especially in the gastrointestinal tract and epithelium.

The optimal binding avidity of therapeutic mAbs remains controversial, but most studies indicate that high-avidity mAbs confer a therapeutic advantage, particularly for small tumors. In contrast, others have found that binding of mAbs within antigen-rich areas of tumor could reduce the number of free antibodies available to diffuse deeper into the tumor and prevent uniform distribution.

Because most mAbs used clinically are derived from mice, they can generate a human antimouse antibody (HAMA) response. HAMA has been implicated in poor therapeutic results by neutralizing mAb on repeated doses and enhancing clearance of mAb. Usually, no additional toxicities are seen; however, with large mAb doses, circulating immune complexes can lead to serum sickness. The use of immunosuppressive agents to prevent the development of HAMA has met with variable results. The use of chimeric and humanized mAbs remains the most promising strategy to avoid HAMA responses. For some humanized mAbs, however, a prolonged biological half-life may result in nonspecific dose deposition and toxicity when used to deliver radioisotopes or chemotherapeutic agents.

V. UNCONJUGATED MONOCLONAL ANTIBODIES

A. Recent Clinical Trials for Lymphoma

Rituximab is a chimeric mAb directed against the B-cell surface antigen CD20. In a pivotal trial conducted in patients with relapsed or refractory low-grade lymphoma, rituximab infused weekly for 4 weeks produced an overall response rate of 48%. Subsequent studies have explored alternative dosing strategies and combinations with chemotherapy. When rituximab was given weekly for 8 weeks, responses were seen in patients with relapsed or refractory intermediate or high-grade lymphoma. The ability of rituximab to sensitize drug-resistant cells to cytotoxic drugs led to the development of several clinical trials using rituximab with chemotherapy. All 35 patients with low-grade lymphoma treated with rituximab and CHOP (cyclophosphamide, doxorubicin, vincristine, and prednisone) responded, including several patients in whom bcl-2 rearrangements were no longer detectable by polymerase chain reaction (PCR) following therapy. Additional trials will better define the role of rituximab when combined with various chemotherapeutic agents in the treatment of non-Hodgkin's lymphoma. Epratuzumab, a humanized anti-CD22 mAb, has also produced responses in patients with both indolent and aggressive lymphomas.

B. Recent Clinical Trials for Lymphocytic Leukemia

In initial studies with rituximab, patients with SLL, the nodal equivalent of CLL, had a lower response rate and lower serum levels of rituximab. The poorer responses were attributed to a decreased expression of CD20 on SLL and to higher numbers of circulating malignant cells. Weekly treatment with higher doses of rituximab or treatment with more frequent infusions has overcome these pharmacologic disadvantages and produced responses in patients with relapsed CLL. Another humanized mAb, CAMPATH-1H, directed against CD52, has produced encouraging results in patients with CLL. Responses were seen in one-third of patients with fludarabine-refractory disease. These responses, however, were less likely in patients with significant lymphadenopathy or splenomegaly, suggesting that the antibody did not penetrate sites of bulky disease. Because CD52 is found on normal T and B cells, severe lymphopenia and a high incidence of infectious complications were observed.

C. Recent Clinical Trials for Myeloid Leukemia

HuM195, a humanized monoclonal antibody against CD33, can rapidly target leukemia cells in patients without significant immunogenicity. When supersaturating doses were given to patients with advanced AML and CML, reductions in marrow blasts were seen, including complete remissions in three patients, all of whom had less than 30% bone marrow blasts at the start of therapy. Because in vitro studies showed enhanced ADCC when effector cells were incubated with low concentrations of IL-2, patients with advanced AML and myelodysplastic syndrome (MDS) were treated with a combination of IL-2 and HuM195. Although responses were seen, significant toxicity occurred, largely related to IL-2. HuM195 has demonstrated significant activity against minimal residual disease in APL, where the effect of therapy can be monitored using a PCR assay for the PML/RAR-α rearrangement. Of 22 patients with newly diagnosed APL who were evaluable for conversion of positive PCR assays, 11 became negative after receiving HuM195 without additional therapy. Twenty-five of the 27 patients treated with sequential all-*trans* retinoic acid, HuM195, and consolidation chemotherapy remain in complete remission with a median follow-up duration of 30 months. These studies suggest that although native HuM195 has antileukemic activity, it may be best suited for treatment of cytoreduced or minimal residual disease.

VI. RADIOIMMUNOTHERAPY

A. Isotope Selection

Targeted radiotherapy offers a promising strategy to increase the potency of mAbs and overcome tumor antigen heterogeneity. The choice of an appropriate isotope depends on many factors, including the physical half-life of the radionuclide, its emission characteristics, the labeling efficiency of the isotope to the mAb, and the sta-

bility of the radioimmunoconjugate (Table III). Most clinical studies have used ^{131}I, a long-lived β particle emitter. Because of their long range, β particles can destroy target cells without antigen internalization as well as surrounding antigen-negative tumor cells, but they may also kill normal bystander cells. The γ emissions from ^{131}I allow dosimetry studies to be performed easily, but treatment at high doses requires patient isolation and can result in significant radiation exposure to hospital staff. Radiolabeling with ^{131}I can cause loss of biological function, particularly at high specific activities. This decrease in immunoreactivity is directly related to the number of tyrosine residues in the hypervariable region of the mAb to which radioiodine attaches.

^{90}Y is a pure β emitter; its lack of γ emissions allows outpatient administration of relatively high doses. If the targeted antigen undergoes modulation, the ^{90}Y radiometal is more likely to be retained intracellularly than ^{131}I. Therapy with ^{90}Y, however, poses several difficulties: (1) Dissociation of ^{90}Y from the mAb complex *in vivo* can result in deposition of the isotope in bone. (2) Unlike ^{131}I, ^{90}Y must be linked to the antibody by a chemical chelator, such as DOTA (1, 4, 7, 10-tetraazacyclododecane-1, 4, 7, 10-tetraacetic acid) or DTPA (diethylenetriamine pentaacetic acid). (3) Because of the absence of γ emissions, biodistribution and dosimetry studies require administration of mAb trace labeled with a second isotope, typically ^{111}In, whose biodistribution is not identical to ^{90}Y. Studies comparing the biodistribution of ^{111}In- and ^{90}Y-labeled anti-CD25 mAb in

TABLE III
Characteristics of Selected Radioisotopes for Therapy

Isotope	Half-life	Particulate energy (KeV)	Mean range of emission (mm)
β emitters			
Iodine-131	8.1 days	182	0.8
Yttrium-90	2.5 days	934	2.7
Copper-67	2.6 days	142	0.9
Rhenium-186	3.8 days	1100	1.1
Rhenium-188	17 h	2100	2.4
α-emitters			
Bismuth-212	1 h	6100	0.04–0.10
Bismuth-213	46 min	8400	0.05–0.08
Astatine-211	7.2 days	5900	0.04–0.10
Actinium-225	10 days	6000–8400	0.05–0.08

patients with adult T-cell leukemia showed that radiation doses delivered to the bone marrow were underestimated by using [111]In. The use of positron emission tomography following the administration of [86]Y-labeled mAb may permit more accurate absorbed radiation dose estimates for [90]Y.

Individual clinical situations play an important role in isotope selection. Therapy with long-ranged β emitters may be better for eliminating bulky disease, whereas shorter ranged (50–80 μm) α particle-emitting isotopes, such as [212]Bi, [213]Bi, and [211]At, could potentially reduce nonspecific cytotoxicity and result in more efficient single cell killing. Because of their high linear energy transfer, as few as one to two α particles can destroy a target cell. The potential for specific antitumor effects makes targeted α particle therapy an attractive approach for the treatment of micrometastatic disease or minimal residual disease.

B. Dosimetry

Dosimetric studies are performed routinely in radioimmunotherapy trials. Most techniques are based on the medical internal radiation dose model and use serial γ camera imaging along with measurements of plasma, urine, bone marrow, and, occasionally, biopsied tumor to estimate radiation doses to tumor, marrow, and other normal tissues. The validity of these predictions, however, is limited by the accuracy in measuring activity using γ camera imaging and by the inability to visualize all sites of disease in patients. Single-photon emission-computed tomography may increase the accuracy of planar scintigraphy, especially when used in conjunction with computed tomography. Nevertheless, the quantitative value of single-photon emission-computed tomography remains unknown. Models based on dosimetric data may provide information about radiation doses delivered to tissues not directly sampled and may also be used to estimate total tumor burden and tumor burden in individual organs.

C. Clinical Trials for Lymphoma

The ^{131}I-labeled murine anti-CD20 mAb tositumomab has produced encouraging results in patients with B-cell lymphomas. In initial studies, patients were treated with escalating doses of trace-labeled mAb to determine an optimal dose for tumor targeting before receiving therapeutically labeled mAbs. Therapeutic doses of ^{131}I were escalated based on estimated whole body radiation dose. Twenty-two of 28 patients who received therapeutic doses of ^{131}I-tositumomab responded. In a larger, multicenter trial conducted in patients with relapsed low-grade or transformed lymphoma, 67% of the patients responded after ^{131}I-tositumomab, compared to only 28% of these patients who responded after their last chemotherapy regimen. ^{131}I-tositumomab has also produced high complete remission rates when used as first-line therapy for follicular lymphoma.

High doses of ^{131}I-tositumomab have also been used in a myeloablative approach. Patients were eligible for a therapeutic infusion of ^{131}I-tositumomab followed by autologous stem cell rescue if biodistribution studies using trace-labeled mAb showed that tumor sites received greater radiation doses than normal tissues. Among 29 patients treated at the maximum tolerated dose of ^{131}I-tositumomab in phase I and II trials, 25 patients had major responses, including 23 complete remissions. Studies combining high-dose ^{131}I-tositumomab with chemotherapy followed by autologous stem cell transplantation are underway.

Encouraging results have also been seen with other radiolabeled mAbs in lymphoma. Y2B8, composed of the parental murine mAb of rituximab labeled with ^{90}Y, produced responses in 34 of 58 patients in a dose-escalation trial. Responses were seen in patients with bulky disease and in patients refractory to rituximab. The use of a fractionated dose schedule enabled high doses of ^{131}I-labeled Lym-1, a mAb that targets HLA-DR, to be administered without stem cell rescue. Eleven of 21 patients with relapsed low- or intermediate-grade lymphoma responded. High tumor to normal tissue ratios and tumor regressions were demonstrated in patients treated with Lym-1 labeled to [67]Cu. These results indicate the therapeutic potential of [67]Cu, as its 62-h half-life is comparable to the uptake and residence time of many mAbs, and, unlike other radiometals, [67]Cu is not deposited in bone or marrow after catabolism of the immunoconjugate. A humanized anti-CD22 mAb hLL2 has also produced responses in patients with relapsed lymphoma when labeled with either ^{131}I or [90]Y.

D. Clinical Trials for Leukemia

Several mAbs have been studied to intensify the antileukemic effects of the conditioning regimen before BMT. Trials using ^{131}I-labeled p67, reactive with the myeloid surface antigen CD33, and BC8, which targets the pan-leukocyte antigen CD45, were conducted. Thirty-four patients received myeloablative doses of ^{131}I-BC8 with cyclophosphamide and total body irradiation (TBI), followed by matched related allogeneic or autologous transplant. Among 25 patients with advanced AML or MDS, 12 patients remain disease free with a median follow-up of 52 months. Of the 9 patients treated for ALL, 3 are disease free 10, 45, and 57 months posttransplant. Durable remissions were also seen when ^{131}I-BC8 was combined with busulfan and cyclophosphamide before matched related BMT in patients with AML in first remission.

Encouraging results in the treatment of myeloid leukemias have also been seen with the radiolabeled anti-CD33 constructs. A phase I trial showed that ^{131}I-M195 could eliminate large leukemic burdens in patients with relapsed or refractory myeloid leukemias. Subsequently, myeloablative doses of ^{131}I-labeled M195 or HuM195 were combined with busulfan and cyclophosphamide before allogeneic BMT. Engraftment was not delayed, and few toxicities could be attributed to radioimmunotherapy. Twenty-seven of 30 patients with advanced AML or CML achieved complete remission, and 3 patients with AML remain in unmaintained remission 56, 64, and 76 months after transplant.

Myeloablative therapy with ^{131}I-anti-CD33 constructs, however, has several limitations. Because labeling at high specific activities reduces the immunoreactivity of the mAb, multiple infusions are needed to deliver adequate radiation doses to the marrow for ablation. Additionally, the long half-life of ^{131}I delays the time from treatment to stem cell reinfusion. Consequently, a phase I trial of ^{90}Y-HuM195 was undertaken. Among 17 patients with relapsed or refractory AML, 12 had reductions in bone marrow blasts, including 1 patient who achieved a complete remission. This study suggested that ^{90}Y-HuM195 will be useful for myeloablation as part of a pretransplant regimen. ^{90}Y-labeled anti-Tac mAb, directed against the high-affinity IL-2 receptor CD25, has also produced responses in 9 of 16 evaluable patients with adult T-cell leukemia.

In an effort to increase the antileukemic effect of HuM195, yet avoid the nonspecific cytotoxicity of β-emitting radionuclides, 18 patients with advanced AML or MDS were treated with [213]Bi-HuM195. The absorbed dose ratios between marrow, liver, and spleen and the whole body for [213]Bi-HuM195 were 1000–10,000 times greater than those seen with β-emitting nuclides such as ^{131}I or [90]Y. Thirteen patients had decreases in bone marrow blasts. This study provides the rationale for the investigation of targeted α particle therapy in patients with minimal residual disease or reduced disease.

VII. ANTIBODY–DRUG CONJUGATES

CMA-676 consists of a humanized anti-CD33 antibody linked to the cytotoxic drug calicheamicin. In a dose escalation trial, 5 of 40 patients with relapsed or refractory AML achieved complete remission after treatment with CMA-676. In a phase II trial, 59 patients with relapsed AML, whose first remission duration was at least 6 months, were treated with two doses of CMA-676 given 2 weeks apart. Twenty patients responded, achieving less than 5% marrow blasts, granulocyte counts greater than 1500/μl, and platelet transfusion independence. Of the 5 patients who did not go on to receive BMT, 2 are leukemia free after 5+ and 6+ months.

In a similar approach, the immunotoxin LMB-2, composed of the Fv portion of the anti-Tac (anti-CD25) mAb fused to a truncated form of *Pseudomonas* exotoxin A, produced responses in 4 patients with hairy cell leukemia refractory to 2-chlorodeoxyadenosine and interferon-α. One patient treated with a second course achieved complete remission. Additionally, a CD19-directed tyrosine kinase inhibitor, B43-genistein, also produced responses in 3 of 15 patients with relapsed or refractory ALL, including one durable complete remission.

VIII. CONCLUSIONS

After nearly 20 years of investigation, mAbs have taken their place along with other treatment modalities for cancer. Encouraging results in the treatment of leukemia and lymphoma have been seen with native antibodies, radioimmunotherapy, and targeted chemotherapy when used as single agents. The most promising results to date, however, have been seen when antibody-based therapies were combined with other treatments. Myeloablative doses of radiolabeled mAbs have shown significant activity when used in transplant preparative regimens for leukemia and lymphoma. Comparative trials that definitively answer whether radioimmunotherapy improves patient outcomes in this setting will be needed. Because of the difficulties in targeting large volume disease, the elimination of minimal residual disease may be a more suitable use of some mAbs. For this application, the use of immunologically active and less immunogenic chimeric or humanized antibodies, conjugates with short-ranged α particle emitters, and drug conjugates may provide more specific leukemia cell kill and avoid the nonspecific effects of β-emitting radioimmunoconjugates.

See Also the Following Articles

Bibliography

Appelbaum, F. R. (1999). Antibody-targeted therapy for myeloid leukemia. *Semin. Hematol.* **36,** 2.

DeNardo, S. J., Kroger, L. A., and DeNardo, G. L. (1999). A new era for radiolabeled antibodies in cancer? *Curr. Opin. Immunol.* **11,** 563.

Jurcic, J. G. (2000). Antibody immunotherapy of leukemia. *Curr. Oncol. Rep.* **2,** 114.

Jurcic, J. G., Cathcart, K., Pinilla-Ibarz, J., and Scheinberg D. A. (2000). Advances in immunotherapy of hematologic malignancies: Cellular and humoral approaches. *Curr. Opin. Hematol.* **7,** 247.

Jurcic, J. G., and Scheinberg, D. A. (1999). Radionuclides as conditioning before stem cell transplantation. *Curr. Opin. Hematol.* **6,** 371.

Jurcic, J. G., Scheinberg, D. A., and Houghton, A. N. (1997). Monoclonal antibody therapy of cancer. *In* "Cancer Chemotherapy and Biological Response Modifiers Annual 16" (H. M. Pinedo, D. L. Longo, and B. A. Chabner, eds.), p. 195. Elsevier Science, Amsterdam.

McDevitt, M. R., Sgouros, G., Finn, R. D., Humm, J. L., Jurcic, J. G., Larson, S. M., and Scheinberg, D. A. (1998). Radioimmunotherapy with alpha-emitting nuclides. *Eur. J. Nuclear Med.* **25,** 1341.

White, C. A. (1999). Rituximab immunotherapy for non-Hodgkin's lymphoma. *Cancer Biother. Radiopharm.* **14,** 241.

Multidrug Resistance I: P-Glycoprotein

Michael M. Gottesman
National Cancer Institute

GLOSSARY

apoptosis A process of programmed cell death stimulated by natural factors or anticancer drugs.

ATP-binding cassette A protein sequence found in a related family of proteins, which allows the cellular source of energy, ATP, to bind to these proteins and be utilized for various transport processes.

extracellular space The space between cells in a tissue, or outside of a cell growing in tissue culture, from which drugs are taken up by a cell.

hydrophobic Of or relating to a property of molecules that prevents them from dissolving in water and enables their solution in cell membranes.

induction A form of regulation of gene expression in which an environmental alteration (frequently the presence of a specific chemical) leads to the expression of a gene. In the case of drug resistance, the cytotoxic compound may turn on expression of a protective detoxifying mechanism. Induction is contrasted with mutations that are permanent, inherited changes in genes, which may result in drug resistance.

lipid bilayer The collection of lipids that makes up the plasma (outer) membrane of cells. Phospholipids are arranged in two layers so that their polar water-soluble heads are exposed to either the inner (cytoplasmic) or the outer (extracellular) surface.

multidrug resistance The development of cross-resistance to many different drugs as the result of a single biochemical change or a single genetic alteration. In its strictest sense, cross-resistance should refer to resistance to drugs with different structural features and different cytotoxic targets.

multifactorial multidrug resistance Resistance resulting from a change in many different resistance mechanisms, not a single mechanism, as is the case in classical multidrug resistance.

natural product A pharmacological agent that comes from the natural environment and is not synthesized *de novo* in the laboratory.

P-glycoprotein An energy-dependent plasma membrane pump responsible for multidrug resistance to many natural product drugs and their derivatives. In the human, P-glycoprotein is the 1280 amino acid product of the *MDR1* gene.

pharmacogenomics A new term coined to indicate the study of those inherited changes in proteins and in the factors that regulate their expression, which account for inherited differences in metabolism, uptake, distribution, and excretion of drugs.

photoaffinity labeling The use of chemical compounds that can be activated by light so as to form chemical linkages with other macromolecules to which they are bound. When such photoaffinity labels are radioactive, they can be used to identify such binding macromolecules.

plasma membrane The lipid bilayer and associated proteins and other molecules that make up the outer surface of cells.

substrate A molecule that is acted upon by a macromolecule so as to change its chemical composition or to transport it within, into, across, or out of cells.

transgenic mice Mice whose genes have been altered in the laboratory to enable the study of the function of a specific gene or genes. Transgenic mice may carry new genes, or have altered genes, including alterations that totally knock out the expression of specific genes.

transmembrane domains Those parts of proteins inserted into the lipid bilayer of cell membranes.

xenobiotics Chemical materials, usually natural products, that are toxic to cells. Some of these are present in food and microorganisms and are ingested inadvertently, whereas others are used in the treatment of cancer and other diseases.

Multidrug resistance is the phenomenon by which cancer cells display simultaneous resistance to many different anticancer drugs that are chemically dissimilar and that do not have the same cytotoxic target within the cancer cell. It is now known that multidrug resistance can have many different causes, including failure of cancer cells to accumulate drugs, to metabolize them to toxic products, and to activate cell death pathways, but for many years this phenomenon of broad drug resistance was mysterious to investigators who studied resistance to anticancer drugs.

I. ROLE OF THE MULTIDRUG EFFLUX PUMP, P-GLYCOPROTEIN, IN MULTIDRUG RESISTANCE IN CANCER CELLS

The first big breakthrough in this field was made in 1985 when three groups published the sequence of an energy-dependent plasma membrane transporter, or P-glycoprotein, the product of the *MDR1* gene. P-glycoprotein could detect many different lipid-soluble anticancer drugs and pump them out of the cell so as to prevent accumulation to toxic levels (see Fig. 1). The relative lack of specificity of this transport pump, and the fact that many anticancer drugs are lipid-soluble natural products, accounted for its ability to confer multidrug resistance on cancer cells. Table I summarizes some of the known substrates for the P-glycoprotein pump, which include not only anticancer drugs, but also many other important pharmacologic agents in common use in the clinic. Subsequently, other energy-dependent drug efflux pumps were discovered, including the *MRP* family of transporters.

Once antibodies and molecular probes were available for detection of P-glycoprotein in cancer cells, it was possible to ask whether cancers from patients, with or without exposure to anticancer drugs, expressed this efflux pump. It was known by the late 1980s that many different kinds of cancers express

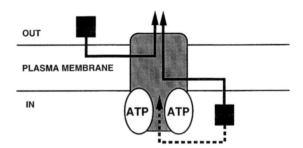

FIGURE 1 Diagram illustrating the potential mechanism of action of P-glycoprotein as it removes drugs (solid squares) from the lipid bilayer, either as they are entering the cell or once they have accumulated intracellularly. Solid lines represent likely pathways of drugs through the transporter. The dotted line is another possible pathway in which drugs are pumped directly out of the cytoplasm. [From Gottesman, M. M., and Pastan, I. (1996). "Drug resistance: alterations in drug uptake or extrusion." *In* "Encyclopedia of Cancer," Vol. I, A–F (J. R. Bertino, Ed.), p. 555. Academic Press, San Diego, CA.]

TABLE I

Selected Substrates of P-glycoprotein

Anticancer drugs
  Vinca alkaloids (vincristine, vinblastine)
  Anthracyclines (doxorubicin, daunorubicin, epirubicin)
  Epipodophyllotoxins (etoposide, teniposide)
  Paclitaxel (taxol)
  Actinomycin D
  Topotecan
  Mithramycin
  Mitomycin C
Other cytotoxic agents
  Colchicine
  Emetine
  Ethidium bromide
  Puromycin
Cyclic and linear peptides
  Gramicidin D
  Valinomycin
  N-Acetyl-leucyl-leucyl-norleucine
  Yeast a-factor pheromone
HIV protease inhibitors
  Ritonavir
  Indinavir
  Saquinavir
Other compounds
  Hoechst 33342
  Rhodamine 123
  Calcein-AM

P-glycoprotein at levels high enough to confer resistance to anticancer drugs and that the presence of P-glycoprotein frequently correlated with resistance to drugs known to be substrates for transport by P-glycoprotein. For example, epithelial cancers of the colon, small intestine, pancreas, adrenal, and kidney, derived from tissues that normally express P-glycoprotein, usually expressed high levels of this transporter. Although P-glycoprotein pump activity is not the only reason for the multidrug resistance of these epithelial tumors, expression of P-glycoprotein does appear to be a barrier to effective therapy in these cancers with many different standard anticancer drugs.

Some cancers, which did not express high levels of P-glycoprotein initially, began to express high levels after many cycles of selection in anticancer drugs. Examples include leukemias, lymphomas, myelomas, and ovarian cancer. In these cases, it is presumed that the toxic drug kills most of the sensitive cells in the original population, and only those cells that express higher levels of P-glycoprotein, as a result of a mutation in the cancer cell affecting regulation of expression of this pump, are able to survive and multiply. Evidence suggests that, to some extent, cytotoxic drugs can directly turn on the expression of P-glycoprotein and that this phenomenon might contribute to clinical multidrug resistance in some cases. However, in cultured cells, the survivors of drug selection appear to express P-glycoprotein in a stable manner, thereby arguing in favor of selection of a preexisting mutant cancer cell rather than an induction mechanism that would not result in stable, long-term expression of P-glycoprotein.

Finally, it appears that the malignant transformation process itself can result in turning on expression of the *MDR1* gene. Examples include some leukemias (especially the blast transformation of cells, which occurs in chronic myelogenous leukemia) and neuroblastomas in children. It is not known why this occurs, but presumably the malignantly transformed state itself results in induction of the P-glycoprotein gene, and the resulting tumor cells are multidrug resistant. Another possibility is that expression of P-glycoprotein enhances the malignant phenotype. There is preliminary evidence in some model systems that expression of P-glycoprotein has an antiapoptotic effect. These observations are consistent with the idea that P-glycoprotein may facilitate cell survival in tumors.

An important unanswered question is whether inhibiting the function of P-glycoprotein in tumor cells that express it will result in better responses to chemotherapy, i.e., is P-glycoprotein ever limiting in determining the response to chemotherapy? Despite many clinical trials that have addressed this issue, the answer is not yet available. Until there are potent, specific inhibitors of P-glycoprotein available, and these are tested in cancers known to express P-glycoprotein, we will not have this answer. Preliminary studies for some leukemias and myelomas suggest that improved response is possible when P-glycoprotein is inhibited, but the response in epithelial tumors seems minimal. Presumably this is because intrinsic multidrug resistance in epithelial cells is multifactorial, whereas resistance that occurs in cancers selected with anticancer drugs is more likely to be due to a single cause. However, despite the fact that inhibiting P-glycoprotein in epithelial cancers does not sensitize these cancers to natural product anticancer drugs, it will be necessary in designing new drugs to keep in mind the presence of this drug efflux pump because drugs that do not accumulate in cells cannot kill them.

II. STRUCTURE AND MECHANISM OF ACTION OF P-GLYCOPROTEIN

The discovery of a pump that can recognize and extrude many different anticancer drugs led naturally to the question of how so many different substrates could be recognized by one protein and how the energy of ATP was harnessed to the pump process. The first step was to create a model of P-glycoprotein based on its known amino acid sequence. In the human, P-glycoprotein is encoded by 1280 amino acids. A total of 12 segments consist mostly of water-insoluble amino acids, which would be expected to cross the plasma membrane of the cell; 6 of these are in the amino-terminal half of the pump and 6 are in the carboxyl half. In addition, two regions are very similar to ATP-binding regions of other proteins, and in particular appear to have some sequence characteristics seen in a large family of proteins (approximately 50 are encoded in the human genome) involved in energy-dependent transport across cellular membranes. This family is known as the ATP-binding cassette (ABC) family of proteins. A hypothetical structure of P-glycoprotein based simply on the amino acid sequence and supported by data using specific antisera is shown in Fig. 2.

Based on photoaffinity-labeling studies using analogs of know substrates for P-glycoprotein and on mutational analyses in which individual amino acids in the transmembrane domains of P-glycoprotein are mutated,

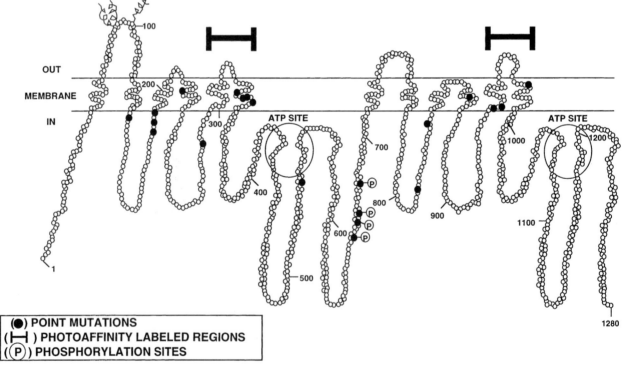

FIGURE 2 A hypothetical two-dimensional model of human P-glycoprotein based on hydropathy analysis of the amino acid sequence and its functional domains. In this schematic diagram, each circle represents an amino acid residue, with solid circles showing the positions of mutations that alter the substrate specificity of P-gp (for clarity, not all known mutations are shown). N-linked glycosylation sites are indicated by squiggly lines, and phosphorylation sites are shown as a circled P. Bars above the model show regions labeled with photoaffinity analogs. [Adapted from Gottesman, M. M., and Pastan, I. (1988). The multidrug transporter as a double-edged sword. *J. Biol. Chem.* **263**, 12163.]

it appears that the major drug interaction sites on P-glycoprotein are in the transmembrane segments. This information, plus the knowledge that P-glycoprotein is able to decrease the rate of influx of drugs as well as increase their rate of efflux, and some studies showing a direct interaction of drugs dissolved in the plasma membrane with P-glycoprotein, has led to a model of P-glycoprotein as a "hydrophobic vacuum cleaner." In other words, P-glycoprotein detects and ejects drugs while they are still in the lipid bilayer (see Fig. 1). The specific drug interaction sites on P-glycoprotein appear to be quite complex and consist of a series of overlapping hydrophobic sites within the parts of the protein that transit the plasma membrane. This model explains the rather broad substrate specificity of P-glycoprotein, as the important interactions are hydrophobic and not ionic. The general finding that recognition of drugs depends more on hydrophobicity and size and shape rather than specific chemistry is also consistent with this hypothesis.

The presence of two ATP-binding/utilization sites on P-glycoprotein has also been puzzling. Data suggest that ABC cassette proteins require hydrolysis of two molecules of ATP to transport a single molecule of substrate, and data based on the transport of vinblastine by P-glycoprotein are consistent with this generalization. Why two molecules of ATP? Hydrolysis of one molecule of ATP appears to be sufficient to reduce the affinity of P-glycoprotein for its substrates, which probably corresponds to the change in shape that the pump undergoes as it extrudes drug from the lipid bilayer into the extracellular space. Very recent evidence points to the need for hydrolysis of a second molecule of ATP so that the pump can return to its initial high-affinity binding state and begin the pumping cycle all over again. Additional experimental evidence points to the need for two functional ATP sites (inactivation of one site results in loss of pump function), asymmetry of the two sites, and the alternating action of these two sites so that ATP hydrolysis cannot occur at both sites at the same time.

III. NORMAL CELLULAR FUNCTION OF P-GLYCOPROTEIN

The discovery of P-glycoprotein and its ability to recognize dozens, and perhaps hundreds of structurally dissimilar compounds, raised questions not only about its mechanism of action, but about how it had evolved and what its normal function might be. The finding that all living organisms so far studied, from bacteria to humans, have pumps similar to P-glycoprotein suggested that free living cells could not survive without a broad-spectrum pump for hydrophobic compounds. Whether this reflects the ubiquitous presence of toxic xenobiotics in the environment (most of which are themselves the products of life forms and may be part of the armaments of battle used as organisms strive to gain a selective advantage in their biological niches) or an intrinsic requirement for *MDR* genes to maintain cellular integrity is still not known with certainty. However, genetically engineered organisms such as transgenic mice lacking *mdr1* genes (in the mouse, there are two *mdr1* genes, called *mdr1a* and *mdr1b* or *mdr1* and *mdr3*), and other mammalian cells lacking *MDR1* expression, survive with normal life spans, suggesting that there is no absolute requirements for *MDR1* expression in cells. Moreover, mice without functioning *mdr1* genes are exquisitely sensitive to certain xenobiotics, but carry on other cellular functions with reasonable efficiency. Because many transport functions of P-glycoprotein in mammals are redundant with other ABC transporters, especially the *MRP* system, it is still possible that every living cell needs one or another member of this class of transporters to survive.

What sort of evidence exists suggesting cellular functions for P-glycoprotein other than to protect cells from toxic effects of xenobiotics? In general, overexpression of P-glycoprotein after gene transfer into various cell types or after selection in cytotoxic drugs has been used to study the effect of P-glycoprotein on cellular processes. Under these conditions, it is possible to show a reduction in sensitivity to apoptosis in lymphoid cells, resistance to certain enveloped viruses, including HIV, and altered plasma membrane lipid composition. Early studies of P-glycoprotein-expressing cells suggested a correlation with the metastatic potential of cancer cells. Use of inhibitors of P-glycoprotein results in altered cellular functions, but there are probably no totally specific P-glycoprotein inhibitors that can give definitive results about the function of P-glycoprotein alone. Use of ribozymes and antisense technologies to eliminate P-glycoprotein expression have so far not totally eliminated the expression of P-glycoprotein, although some reductions in P-glycoprotein levels have been possible using this approach.

Once again, the use of mice lacking functioning *mdr1* genes has proved useful in determining the normal function of P-glycoprotein. As noted earlier, *mdr1* knockout mice live normal life spans and are sensitive to xenobiotics. More detailed studies of the function of individual tissues that normally express P-glycoprotein suggest subtle alterations in immune system function, not yet clearly defined, and relatively normal function of epithelial tissues of the gastrointestinal tract, liver, kidney, and pancreas.

IV. ROLE OF P-GLYCOPROTEIN IN DRUG PHARMACOKINETICS

The use of inhibitors of P-glycoprotein and the study of *mdr1* knockout mice have confirmed suspicions from the initial histochemical localization studies that *MDR1* played a major role in uptake, distribution, and excretion of toxic xenobiotics in mice and humans. Lack of expression of functional P-glycoprotein in the gastrointestinal tract dramatically enhances the absorption of several different drugs, including anticancer drugs such as taxol, the cardiac glycoside digoxin, and the antihistamine fexofenadine. This is manifested as much higher blood levels of these compounds after oral dosing. Furthermore, distribution of such drugs in the body is altered in the absence of function P-glycoprotein, manifested as increased brain levels of compounds such as the antihelminthic ivermectin, the anticancer drug vinblastine, and the antidiarrheal narcotic analog loperamide. This is attributed to the abrogation of the blood–brain barrier for these compounds due to the absence of P-glycoprotein in capillary endothelial cells in the brain. Similar effects of loss of P-glycoprotein at the placental barrier would be expected to result in increased teratogenicity of certain compounds, which are P-glycoprotein substrates, and perhaps toxic and/or mutagenic effects on germ cells in the testis and ovary.

Circulating cells, such as T cells and macrophages, which normally express P-glycoprotein, might become sensitized to drugs and xenobiotics if their P-glycoprotein levels are altered. Because the HIV protease inhibitors are P-glycoprotein substrates, this phenomenon has led to the suggestion that the cellular availability of drugs such as this could be manipulated by altering levels of functional P-glycoprotein. Conversely, resistance to certain drugs could occur at the cellular level because of variations in expression of P-glycoprotein that might be genetically determined (see later).

Finally, excretion by the liver (in bile) and kidney (in urine) of P-glycoprotein substrates is substantially reduced for many drugs in mice lacking P-glycoprotein. This results in a decreased rate of clearance for drugs and increased accumulation of drugs in the bloodstream and tissues. Thus, use of inhibitors of P-glycoprotein, or alterations in levels of functional P-glycoprotein that might be genetically determined, could have fairly profound effects on the blood and tissue levels of many different drugs by increasing absorption, decreasing excretion, and altering distribution into tissues protected by P-glycoprotein barriers or into cells expressing P-glycoprotein. These effects of P-glycoprotein are summarized in Fig. 3.

Evidence is beginning to be published suggesting that levels of P-glycoprotein in the gastrointestinal tract may vary considerably from individual to individual, perhaps accounting for differences in absorption of drugs that are primarily P-glycoprotein substrates. One study suggests genetic linkage with a single nucleotide polymorphism that does not change the sequence of P-glycoprotein, but is presumably linked to an alteration in a regulatory region that controls levels of P-glycoprotein in the gastrointestinal tract. Several different coding polymorphisms of P-glycoprotein have been described, but none to date have been shown to alter the ability of P-glycoprotein to pump drugs. Much more work is needed in this important area of pharmacogenomics.

V. IMPLICATIONS OF STUDIES ON P-GLYCOPROTEIN FOR TREATMENT OF CANCER

As we assemble a more complete picture of the biochemistry, pharmacology, and physiology of P-glycoprotein function, we can begin to make better guesses as to the role that manipulation of the *MDR1*

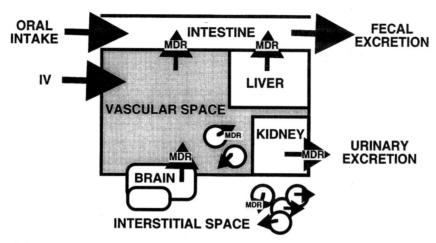

FIGURE 3   The effect of P-glycoprotein on pharmacokinetics and drug distribution is illustrated schematically. The multidrug transporter affects drug distribution throughout the body.

gene is likely to have in the future treatment of cancer. Some conclusions seem quite firm, whereas other are still speculative. First, it seems clear the P-glycoprotein is capable of conferring resistance to many anticancer drugs on cancer cells. Thus, as new drugs are developed, it will be necessary to determine whether cellular sensitivity to these drugs is affected by the presence of P-glycoprotein. If, as seems likely for the foreseeable future, we continue to be dependent for the treatment of cancer on the existing hydrophobic natural products, and new drugs that are also P-glycoprotein substrates, then we will have to learn to inhibit P-glycoprotein, and its many molecular analogs, as we try to cure and palliate cancer.

Second, despite earlier concerns, it seems likely that more potent, more specific inhibitors of P-glycoprotein, or inhibitors of related ABC transporters, can be developed and that their toxicity would be relatively limited and manageable. This conclusion comes from the studies with transgenic mice lacking P-glycoprotein, which have normal life spans under controlled laboratory conditions. These inhibitors will play a role not only in sensitizing P-glycoprotein-expressing cancers to anticancer drugs, but also in altering uptake, excretion, and cellular distribution of many different drugs. Using P-glycoprotein inhibitors it may be possible to give drugs orally that previously required intravenous administration or to deliver drugs to the brain that previously were only active outside of the central nervous system.

Third, it appears that alterations in the levels of ex-

pression of P-glycoprotein in different tissues, which may result from environmental exposures or from inherited alterations in pathways that regulate expression of the MDR1 gene, or inherited polymorphisms within the coding region of the MDR1 gene could account for variations among individuals in the way they respond to drugs. Such changes could have substantial effects on drug uptake, distribution, and excretion. It will become necessary in the future to catalog these variations in the MDR1 gene and other genes, which affect metabolism, absorption, and excretion of drugs, in order to predict individual responses to different drugs.

Finally, cloning of the MDR1 cDNA encoding P-glycoprotein has made it possible to transfer this gene into drug-sensitive cells, thereby conferring multidrug resistance on all recipient cells. Because the toxicity of anticancer drugs to sensitive tissues, such as epithelia and bone marrow, is a major dose-limiting problem in cancer chemotherapy, the ability to protect normal cells from this toxicity using transferred multidrug resistance genes has been the subject of much laboratory and clinical investigation. Although such gene transfer studies are limited by the low efficiency of existing vector systems and the safety of gene transfer of multidrug resistance genes is yet to be established, it is conceivable that multidrug resistance genes, such as MDR1, may prove useful in protecting normal tissues from cytotoxic effects of anticancer treatment.

See Also the Following Articles

Extracellular Matrix and Matrix Receptors • Multidrug Resistance II: MRP and Related Proteins • P-Glycoprotein as a General Antiapoptotic Protein

Bibliography

Ambudkar, S. V. (1995). Purification and reconstitution of functional human P-glycoprotein. *J. Bioenerg. Biomembr.* **27**, 23–29.

Ambudkar, S. V., Dey, S., Hrycyna, C. A., *et al.* (1999). Biochemical, cellular, and pharmacological aspects of the multidrug transporter. *Annu. Rev. Pharmacol. Toxicol.* **39**, 361–391.

Gottesman, M. M., Fojo, T., and Bates, S. E. (2002). Multidrug resistance in cancer: Role of ATP-dependent transporters. *Nat. Rev. Cancer* **2**, 48–58.

Gottesman, M. M., Hrycyna, C. A., Schoenlein, P. V., *et al.* (1995). Genetic analysis of the multidrug transporter. *Annu. Rev. Genet.* **29**, 607–649.

Ling, V. (1997). Multidrug resistance: Molecular mechanisms and clinical relevance. *Cancer Chemother. Pharmacol.* **40**, S3–S8.

Schinkel, A. H. (1997). The physiological function of drug-transporting P-glycoproteins. *Semin. Cancer Biol.* **8**, 161–170.

Senior, A.. E., and Gadsby, D. C. (1997). ATP hydrolysis cycles and mechanism in P-glycoprotein and CFTR. *Semin. Cancer Biol.* **8**, 143–150.

Multidrug Resistance II: MRP and Related Proteins

Susan P.C. Cole
Roger G. Deeley
Queen's University, Kingston, Ontario, Canada

GLOSSARY

ATP-binding cassette A marker for a superfamily of proteins that bind ATP and transport many different substrates across the cell surface and interior membranes.

multidrug resistance The ability of a tumor cell to survive exposure to many different drugs as the result of a biochemical change or genetic alteration.

multidrug resistance protein A member of the ATP-binding cassette protein family that causes multidrug resistance in tumor cells.

Multidrug resistance, often abbreviated MDR, is a term used to describe simultaneous resistance to multiple, structurally and chemically unrelated drugs that exert their toxic effects on cancer cells by different molecular mechanisms. MDR can be an intrinsic property in the primary tumor in a patient who has never been exposed to anticancer drugs or it may be acquired following initial chemotherapy and become apparent only upon subsequent courses of treatment. Whether intrinsic or acquired, MDR frequently limits the effectiveness of many conventional therapeutic agents.

Clinically, MDR encompasses a wide range of drugs. These may include drugs derived from natural sources (e.g., plants, microorganisms) that interfere with DNA replication, chromosome segregation, and microtubule assembly or disassembly; drugs that cause DNA damage such as alkylating agents and platinum-containing compounds; drugs that resemble normal cellular molecules ("antimetabolites") that target enzymes involved in folic acid metabolism and nucleotide synthesis; and nucleoside/nucleotide analogs that ultimately interfere with the ability of the tumor cell to synthesize DNA and/or RNA.

It is generally believed that multiple mechanisms contribute to clinical drug resistance, and no single protein has been identified that is capable of conferring resistance to all drugs in the clinical MDR spectrum. However, laboratory-based studies using tumor cells selected for resistance to any of a number of different drugs have led to the identification of several proteins that can cause resistance to many different drugs in widespread clinical use. These proteins belong to the large superfamily of ATP-binding cassette (ABC) transmembrane transport proteins. ABC transporters use the energy of ATP hydrolysis to transport their substances across cellular membranes. In the case of ABC proteins that cause MDR, these substrates include many types of chemotherapeutic agents.

The first ABC transporter shown to be associated with MDR in mammalian cells was P-glycoprotein, originally described in 1976 by Ling and colleagues during studies of colchicine-selected, multidrug-resistant hamster ovarian tumor cells. Subsequent clinical studies established that the human ortholog or counterpart of the hamster protein (encoded by the *MDR1* gene) can be an important contributor to the MDR of some tumor types. For almost a decade after its discovery, P-glycoprotein (MDR1) remained the only known human MDR protein. However, by the mid- to late-1980s, several drug selected cell lines had been obtained with MDR phenotypes very similar to cells expressing increased levels of P-glycoprotein but with no increase in P-glycoprotein detectable. Clinical studies also indicated that P-glycoprotein expression was low or absent in some of the more common tumors that displayed acquired or intrinsic MDR, such as small and nonsmall cell lung cancer. These two lines of evidence clearly predicted the existence of other multidrug resistance proteins. This prediction was confirmed in the early 1990s with the cloning and characterization of a second human ABC protein, multidrug resistance protein (MRP)1, by the group of Cole and Deeley.

I. INTRODUCTION

P-glycoprotein and MRP1 are both ABC transporters but the two proteins share only 15% overall amino acid sequence identity. They belong to different branches of the ABC superfamily that likely diverged before the evolution of lower eukaryotes. Since the discovery of MRP1 in 1992, six additional ABC transporters have been identified by virtue of their similarity to MRP1 and thus are grouped together in the MRP subfamily known as ABCC. Like MRP1 (ABCC1), four of the MRP-related proteins, MRP2–5 (ABCC2, C3, C4, and C5), have been shown by gene transfer studies to cause some form of drug resistance *in vitro*. However, the five proteins exhibit some important differences in their substrate specificity. Thus, while some MRPs confer resistance to natural product type drugs, others increase resistance to antimetabolites, platinum compounds, and nucleoside/nucleotide analogs. The physiological, pharmacological, and biochemical properties of MRPs and their possible involvement in clinical MDR are described in more detail.

II. BIOLOGY OF MULTIDRUG RESISTANCE PROTEINS

A. MRP1

The MRP1 cDNA was cloned from a multidrug-resistant human small cell lung cancer cell line using a strategy designed to identify mRNA species that were overexpressed following selection in the presence of doxorubicin. The *MRP1* gene, which is located on chromosome 16p13.1, was subsequently found to be frequently amplified in drug-selected cell lines that express high levels of the MRP1 protein. Organization of the *MRP1* gene, combined with some conserved structural features of MRP1, indicates that the protein evolved from a common ancestor shared with the cystic fibrosis transmembrane conductance regulator, mutations in which cause cystic fibrosis.

MRP1 is a 190-kDa, glycosylated phosphoprotein of 1531 amino acids. The major structural feature that distinguishes MRP1, and several of its more recently identified related proteins from other ABC transporters, is the presence of an additional NH_2-terminal membrane-spanning domain with 5 transmembrane segments and an extracellular NH_2 terminus. Thus MRP1 is predicted to have three membrane-spanning domains with a total of up to 17 transmembrane segments, as well as the two nucleotide-binding domains typical of other ABC transporters (Fig. 1).

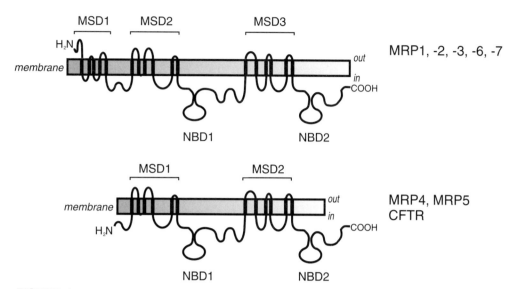

FIGURE 1 Topological models of MRP-related proteins. NBD, nucleotide-binding domain; MSD, membrane spanning domain.

Cultured tumor cells overexpressing MRP1, either as a result of drug selection or gene transfection, have a drug resistance profile similar to cells that overexpress P-glycoprotein. They are resistant to natural product drugs such as vincristine, doxorubicin, daunorubicin, and VP-16 (etoposide), as well as short-term exposure to the folic acid antimetabolite, methotrexate. However, MRP1 also causes resistance to certain antimonial and arsenical oxyanions, a property not associated with increased levels of P-glycoprotein. Thus, although the drug resistance profiles of these two proteins are similar, they are not identical. MRP1-mediated resistance is typically associated with an ATP-dependent reduced cellular accumulation of drug accompanied by increased drug efflux.

In vitro assays using inside-out membrane vesicles prepared from cells expressing MRP1 have been used extensively to characterize the substrate specificity and transport mechanism of this protein. In this way, MRP1 has been shown to be a primary ATP-dependent transporter of structurally diverse GSH-, glucuronate-, and sulfate-conjugated organic anions normally formed in the body, such as the proinflammatory cysteinyl leukotriene C_4 (LTC$_4$), the cholestatic conjugated estrogen, 17β-estradiol 17-(β-D-glucuronide) (E$_2$17βG), and the sulfated estrogen, estrone-3-sulfate (Fig. 2). Although MRP1 has also been shown to transport

chemically synthesized glucuronide and GSH conjugates of certain anticancer drugs, most of the agents to which MRP1 confers resistance are not conjugated to a significant extent *in vivo*. Instead, it appears that MRP1 transports at least some of them via a cotransport mechanism with reduced glutathione (GSH). Precisely how GSH facilitates the transport of certain substrates is not yet known.

In addition to its frequent elevated expression in drug-resistant tumour cells, MRP1 is widely expressed at variable levels in normal tissues with relatively high levels being present in lung, muscle, and testes. MRP1 is usually located in basolateral plasma membranes of normal cells, although it may also be found in apical membranes or intracellular membranes in some cells and under certain growth conditions (Fig. 3). Because of its localization primarily in the basolateral membrane of polarized epithelial cells (Fig. 3), MRP1 pumps its xenobiotic and physiological substrates into the interstitial space between cells or into the systemic circulation rather than excreting them into the bile, urine, or gut.

To gain insight into the physiological and pharmacological functions of MRP1, MRP1-deficient *mrp1*$^{(-/-)}$ "knockout" mice have been generated by two groups of investigators. These mice are viable and fertile with no obvious pathologic phenotype, indicating that mrp1 is

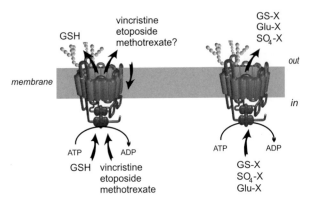

FIGURE 2 MRP1-mediated transport of its substrates across a membrane is driven by the hydrolysis of ATP. Glutathione (GS-X)-, glucuronide (Glu-X)-, and sulfate (SO_4-X)-conjugated organic anions are transported as are unconjugated chemotherapeutic drugs. Reduced glutathione (GSH) is important for the efficient transport of the latter drugs.

dispensable for normal development in these animals. However, *mrp1* knockout mice display an impaired inflammatory response, which has been attributed to decreased LTC_4 secretion from mast cells. These same knockout mice were also hypersensitive to the anticancer drug etoposide. More detailed characterization of $mrp1^{(-/-)}$ mice treated with etoposide-phosphate revealed increased damage to the mucosa of the oropharyngeal cavity, increased frequency of aberrant mitotic events in spermatogenic cells, and polyuria

(indicative of damage to kidney urinary-collecting duct tubules). Mucositis occurs commonly in patients undergoing high-dose chemotherapy and is often the dose-limiting toxicity. Thus toxicity observed in the absence of mrp1 suggests that use of MRP1 inhibitors during chemotherapy may be associated with an increased risk of certain side effects. In addition to its protective role in the oropharyngeal cavity, the kidney, and testis, mrp1 contributes to protection of the colon, as well as the central nervous system by virtue of its presence in choroid plexus epithelium where it contributes to the permeability barrier between the blood and cerebral spinal fluid (CSF).

In addition to cotransporting GSH with some unmodified xenobiotics, MRP1 displays a low rate of basal GSH transport in the absence of other substrates. The protein also transports GSSG with relatively low affinity but high capacity and it has been suggested that this may be a physiologically important role of MRP1 in the erythrocyte. *In vitro* studies indicate that GSH transport by MRP1 can be markedly stimulated by compounds such as the calcium channel blocker verapamil or dietary flavonoids. An elevated expression of MRP1 in drug-selected or -transfected cells has also been associated with a decrease in the levels of intracellular GSH and in $mrp1^{(-/-)}$ mice; increased GSH levels were detected in breast,

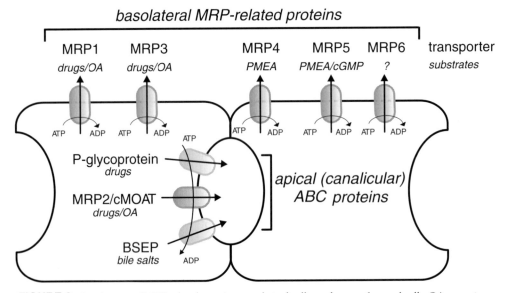

FIGURE 3 Localization of MRP-related proteins on polarized cell membranes of normal cells. OA, organic anions; BSEP, bile salt export pump; PMEA, 9-(2-phosphonylmethoxyethyl)adenine.

lung, heart, kidney, muscle, colon, testes, bone marrow cells, blood mononuclear leukocytes, and blood erythrocytes. Thus MRP1 has the potential to influence intracellular concentrations of both reduced and oxidized glutathione. Its ability to transport GSSG may serve to offset the depletion of intracellular GSH during exposure to agents that form GS conjugates effluxed by the protein or which MRP1 cotransports together with GSH (Fig. 4).

Based on the relatively high expression of the protein in normal lung epithelium and in hyperplastic type II pneumocytes, a protective role has been suggested for MRP1 in this organ. *In vitro* vesicle transport studies have served to identify several MRP1 substrates of potential toxicological relevance in the lung. One of these is aflatoxin B_1 (AFB$_1$), a mycotoxin produced by certain *Aspergillus* species that has been extensively characterized as a hepatocarcinogen and, to a lesser extent, as a pulmonary carcinogen. MRP1 transports GS conjugates of activated AFB$_1$ with high affinity and will transport the parent compound in the presence of GSH. Another substrate of MRP1 is the O-glucuronide metabolite of the tobacco-specific pulmonary carcinogen, 4-(methylnitrosamino)-1-(3-pyridyl)-1-butanol (NNAL). Al-

though a glucuronide conjugate, the transport of this metabolite is also GSH dependent.

B. MRP2

The complete MRP2 cDNA was first cloned from rat liver in 1996 using strategies that took advantage of its structural relationship to MRP1, and the human ortholog was cloned shortly thereafter. Human MRP2 is a 1541 amino acid polypeptide that is 49% identical to MRP1 and has a similar predicted membrane topology. The *MRP2* gene is located at chromosome 10q23-24 and displays clear conservation of intron/exon organization with the *MRP1* gene, consistent with the common evolutionary ancestry of the two proteins.

Although MRP2 was the second MRP-related protein to be cloned, its functional characteristics were known for a number of years prior to the cloning of MRP1. This knowledge came from studies of three naturally occurring strains of rats with congenital biliary transport defects. Transport defective TR-, Groningen Yellow (GY), and Esai hyperbilirubinemic (EHBR) mutant rats all have defects in the same gene, resulting in impaired biliary efflux of a wide range of nonbile salt-conjugated organic anions and some heavy metals. The transporter functionally defective in TR⁻/GY/EHBR rats was named the canalicular multispecific organic anion transporter (cMOAT) and is now known to be encoded by the *mrp2* gene. Certain mutations in human cMOAT/MRP2 result in a rare autosomal recessive disorder, Dubin Johnson syndrome, which is characterized by chronic conjugated hyperbilirubinemia.

MRP2 is unique among the MRP-related proteins in that it is located exclusively on apical plasma membranes in polarized cells (Fig. 3). In addition to hepatocanalicular membranes, MRP2 is present in apical membranes of the kidney proximal tubule and is also expressed in the duodenum and the ilium. When expressed by gene transfer in polarized cultured cells, such as canine or porcine kidney cells, MRP2 can be detected only in the apical membrane. Although expression of MRP2 has been achieved in nonpolarized cells, trafficking of the protein to the plasma membrane is relatively inefficient, resulting in considerable accumulation of MRP2 in intracellular membranes.

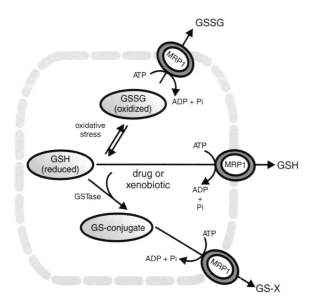

FIGURE 4 MRP1 expression modulates intracellular levels of reduced and oxidized gluatatione. GSH, reduced glutathione; GSSG, oxidized glutathione; GSTase, GSH S-transferase; GS-X, glutathione-conjugated organic anion.

Despite the relatively low primary structure identity between MRP1 and MRP2, qualitatively, the substrate specificity of the two proteins is surprisingly similar in that both are capable of transporting GSH and glucuronide organic anion conjugates. However, the affinities of the two proteins for their substrates can vary significantly. In addition, earlier analyses of the bile composition of *mrp2* mutant rats suggest a much broader range of physiological substrates for this protein, including, in addition to cysteinyl leukotrienes and estrogen glucuronides, conjugated bilirubin, conjugated bile salts, and copropoprhyrin I. These studies also implicated mrp2 in biliary GSH and GSSG excretion and impaired GSH-dependent excretion of heavy metals, including zinc, cadmium, and mercury.

The earliest evidence that MRP2, like MRP1, was capable of conferring drug resistance was provided by the cDNA cloning of a mRNA that was overexpressed in three human cisplatin-resistant cell lines. Gene transfer studies using both polarized and nonpolarized cells confirmed that human and rat MRP2 conferred resistance to certain vinca alkaloids, epipodophyllotoxins (etoposide), cisplatin, and anthracyclines. To date, there is no evidence that MRP1 causes cisplatin resistance, indicating a potentially important functional difference between the two proteins. *In vitro*, MRP2, like MRP1, has also been shown to confer resistance to short-term exposure to methotrexate.

In addition to increasing sensitivity to certain drugs, antisense suppression of MRP2 levels in HepG2 cells also elevates the intracellular GSH concentration. This observation, together with earlier studies demonstrating that biliary GSH is markedly decreased in mrp2-deficient rats, suggested that MRP2 was capable of effluxing GSH, either alone or together with other substrates. GSH alone appears to be a relatively low-affinity substrate for MRP2, but a reciprocal stimulation of GSH and drug transport has been observed similar to that described for MRP1.

C. MRP3

The partial cDNA sequence of human MRP3 (ABCC3), the chromosomal localization, and the tissue distribution of *MRP3* mRNA were first described by Borst and colleagues. Shortly thereafter the complete coding sequence of *MRP3* was reported by several groups. The *MRP3* gene is located on chromosome 17q21.3 and encodes a five domain protein (three MSDs and two NBDs), similar to MRP1 and MRP2. The 1527 amino acid MRP3 protein exhibits 58% identity with MRP1 and 48% identity with MRP2. Despite this primary sequence similarity, like the other MRP-related proteins, MRP3 has its own distinctive pattern of tissue expression and substrate specificity. It is expressed in a more limited number of tissues than MRP1 with the highest levels found in liver, colon, small intestine, and pancreas, whereas lower levels are found in kidney and prostate. MRP3 is also found in the cholangiocytes (intrahepatic bile duct epithelial cells) and, in all polarized cells examined to date, MRP3, like MRP1, has been localized to basolateral membranes (Fig. 2). In certain cell types (e.g., HepG2 human hepatoma cells), *MRP3* mRNA may be induced in response to a number of stimuli, including drugs and chemical toxins (e.g., phenobarbital and 2-acetylaminofluorene). In addition, it has been suggested that MRP3 may mediate the efflux of organic anions from the liver into the blood when secretion into the bile is blocked.

Although less well characterized than MRP1 and MRP2, MRP3 is capable of transporting a range of conjugated and unconjugated organic anions, as well as the folic acid antimetabolite drug methotrexate. The substrate specificity of MRP3 differs from MRP1 and MRP2 in several respects, most notably in that it has markedly greater affinity for glucuronidated anions compared to GSH-conjugated organic anions. Overall, MRP3 appears to have a generally lower (approximately 10-fold) affinity than MRP1 and MRP2 for the organic anion substrates that are transported by all three proteins. Interestingly, unlike MRP1 and MRP2, MRP3 does not appear to transport GSH. The structural basis for this difference from MRP1 and MRP2 is unknown but may be related to the relatively poor ability of MRP3 to transport GSH compared to glucuronide-conjugated molecules.

As is the case for MRP2, isolation of transfected, nonpolarized cells expressing high levels of MRP3 has been difficult. Consequently, the drug resistance profile conferred by elevated expression of this protein is not yet completely clear. Moderate levels of resistance to VP-16 and low-level resistance to vincristine and methotrexate have been reported in cells expressing elevated levels of MRP3. Resistance to other types of antineoplastic agents (including anthracycline antibiotics, vinca alkaloids, mitoxantrone, paclitaxel, and cisplatin) has not been observed nor were MRP3-transfected cells resistant to cadmium or to antimonial or arsenical oxyanions. Thus the spectrum of anticancer drugs to which MRP3 confers resistance appears more limited than that of MRP1 or MRP2. Whether this is related to the apparent inability of MRP3 to transport GSH (which, in the case of MRP1 and MRP2, is required for the transport of some unconjugated substrates) is not known.

D. MRP4

The partial cDNA sequence and localization of the MRP4 gene to chromosome 13 were reported in 1997, followed by the full-length cDNA sequence in 1998. The 1325 amino acid protein encoded by MRP4 is significantly smaller than MRP1, MRP2, and MRP3 because it does not contain an NH_2-terminal hydrophobic extension that is present in the latter three proteins (Fig. 1). MRP4 mRNA is expressed most abundantly in the prostate and at low levels in several other normal tissues, including the lung. Immunohistochemical studies have localized the protein to the basolateral membrane of tubuloacinar cells, which are basal cells of the prostatic glandular epithelium. The physiological function of MRP4 in the prostate is not known, but it has been suggested that it may protect the composition of prostatic fluid by pumping potentially harmful compounds out into the stroma. However, at present, little is known about the substrate specificity and transport properties of MRP4.

Multiple copies of the MRP4 gene and markedly increased levels of the protein were found in a T-cell leukemia cell line selected for resistance to 9-(2-phosphonylmethoxyethyl)adenine (PMEA), an acyclic dideoxynucleoside that is a potent inhibitor of HIV reverse transcriptase and other viral DNA polymerases. Like drug-selected leukemia cells, MRP4-transfected cells were also resistant to PMEA. However, cells expressing elevated levels of MRP4 are not cross-resistant to any of the natural products drugs that are substrates of MRP1, MRP2, or P-glycoprotein. However, like MRP1, MRP2, and MRP3, MRP4-expressing cells are cross-resistant to short-term ex-

posure of the antifolate drug methotrexate. Thus these four MRP-related proteins apparently all share the ability to cause methotrexate resistance, although their affinities for this drug vary considerably.

E. MRP5

Like MRP3 and MRP4, human MRP5 (ABCC5) was identified by screening databases of human-expressed sequence tags. Its partial cDNA sequence, chromosomal localization, and human tissue expression profile were first described in 1997, quickly followed by reports from several groups of the complete coding sequence. The MRP5 gene is located on chromosome 3q27 and encodes a protein with a four domain structure arranged in the same manner as MRP4 and P-glycoprotein (Fig. 1). MRP5 differs somewhat from MRP4 and P-glycoprotein because it contains an NH_2-terminal hydrophilic extension of approximately 90 amino acids. The 1437 amino acid MRP5 protein exhibits 33–37% amino acid identity with the other MRPs. The pattern of expression of MRP5 in human tissues is similar in some respects to that of MRP1. Thus, like MRP1, MRP5 mRNA is widely expressed in many tissues, with the highest levels found in skeletal muscle, heart, and various segments of the brain.

Studies of the substrate specificity of MRP5 have been hampered technically because, like MRP3 and MRP2, it has been difficult to establish stable MRP5-transfected cell lines for reasons that are poorly understood. In polarized cells, MRP5 localizes to the basolateral membrane as do MRP1 and MRP3, but the drug resistance profiles reported for nonpolarized cell lines stably transfected with MRP5 are somewhat inconsistent. In one study, MRP5-expressing cells were not resistant to any of more than a dozen anticancer drugs tested, including anthracycline antibiotics, vinca alkaloids, mitoxantrone, paclitaxel, and cisplatin. However, the cells were resistant to cadmium chloride and potassium antimonyl tartrate. A second MRP5-expressing cell line was also not resistant to a very broad range of anticancer drugs or heavy metals. Instead, these cells exhibited low-level resistance to the thiopurine antimetabolite anticancer drugs, 6-mercaptopurine and thioguanine. They were also resistant to PMEA, which is used in the treatment of patients with HIV infections. The reason for the different resistance profiles of the two MRP5-transfected HEK cell lines is not clear. However, it may be relevant that in the first study, MRP5 was localized to the plasma membrane, whereas in the second study, most of the MRP5 was expressed intracellularly with only a relatively small proportion of the expressed protein localized to the plasma membrane.

Membrane vesicles enriched in MRP5 showed that MRP5 is a relatively high-affinity transporter of the naturally occurring cyclic purine nucleotide, cyclic GMP (cGMP) (K_m 2.1 μM). cGMP has a wide range of biological activities, as it mediates most of the effects of the signaling molecule nitric oxide. Thus cGMP plays an important role in smooth muscle relaxation, inhibition of platelet aggregation, and neutrophil degranulation. MRP5-mediated export of cGMP from the cell has the potential to modulate these processes, but whether it actually does so remains to be determined. Interestingly, despite significant differences in their primary structures, MRP5, like MRP1 and MRP2, appears to transport GSH, although GSSG is not a substrate. Whether MRP5 transports GSH or glucuronide conjugated organic anions is not yet clear, but if it does, it does so much less efficiently than MRP1, MRP2, or MRP3. Taken together, these studies clearly indicate that the transport properties and drug resistance conferring properties of MRP5 are significantly different from those of the five domain containing MRP-related proteins, MRP1, MRP2, and MRP3.

III. CLINICAL RELEVANCE OF MULTIDRUG RESISTANCE PROTEINS

A. MRP1

1. MRP1 in Solid Tumors

As mentioned previously, MRP1 is present at variable levels in many normal tissues, although within an individual tissue, it may only be expressed in specific cell types. Consistent with its broad tissue distribution, MRP1 protein or mRNA has been detected in many types of solid tumors (lung, gastrointestinal and urothelial carcinomas, neuroblastoma, mesothelioma, glioma, retinoblastoma, melanoma, and cancers of the breast, endometrium, ovary, prostate, and thyroid).

The presence of MRP1 in normal tissues, sometimes only in specific cells, complicates the interpretation of bulk analyses, using techniques such as reverse transcriptase–polymerase chain reaction (RT-PCR), to evaluate its expression in clinical tumor samples. Nevertheless, analyses of this type, supported in some cases by immunohistology with MRP1-specific monoclonal antibodies, indicate that the levels of MRP1 are markedly elevated in some multidrug-resistant tumors and, as summarized later, that the levels of MRP1 or its mRNA are negatively correlated with outcome in some tumor types.

Several studies indicate that MRP1 protein or mRNA is frequently expressed at elevated levels in breast cancer relative to normal breast tissue. Expression of MRP1 has also been positively correlated with tumor stage, with increased levels of protein being present in T3 and T4 tumors and in tumors accompanied by distant metastases. A more recent study of 27 patients with stage II disease who received adjuvant chemoendocrine therapy postoperatively found elevated levels of *MRP1* mRNA in the 10 of 27 patients who relapsed during the subsequent 10 years.

MRP1 has been identified as a strong negative prognostic indicator with respect to time to relapse in breast cancer patients with small tumors, as well as in node-negative and node-positive patients who received adjuvant chemotherapy. Interpretation of the latter observation was initially complicated by the fact that none of the drugs used (cyclophosphamide, methotrexate, and 5-fluorouracil) were thought to be included in the MRP1 drug resistance spectrum. However, MRP1 is now known to be able to increase methotrexate resistance *in vitro*, which adds more credence to the possibility that the protein contributes to drug resistance in these tumors rather than being simply a correlate of more aggressive disease. MRP1 expression is also frequent in untreated prostate cancer (Fig. 5). Levels of expression have been positively correlated with progression from prostate carcinoma *in situ* to a more disseminated state and with both Gleason and surgical grade, as well as p53 status.

Among common tumors, high and frequent expression of MRP1 has been documented most extensively in lung cancer, particularly nonsmall cell lung cancer (NSCLC). An immunohistological study of more than 100 archival specimens from untreated

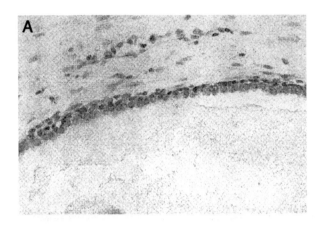

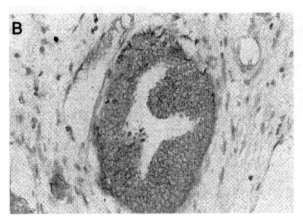
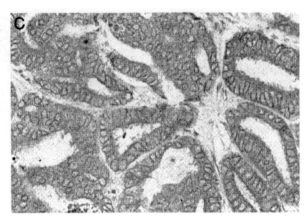

FIGURE 5 Expression of MRP1 in normal and malignant prostate. Tissues were fixed in formalin, and the protein was detected with the MRP1-specific monoclonal antibody QCRL-1. (A) normal prostate tissue, (B) prostatic intraepithelial neoplasia, and (C) adenocarcinoma of the prostate.

NSCLC patients detected MRP1 in more than 80% of cases analyzed. MRP1 levels have also been positively correlated with the differentiation status of adenocarcinomas and squamous cell carcinomas. In the latter form of NSCLC, MRP1 has been proposed to be a negative prognostic indicator of patient survival. Elevated levels of MRP1 in carcinoma *in situ* and in hyperplastic type II pneumocytes, the possible progenitor cells of adenocarcinoma of the lung, have also been detected. Overall, these observations strongly suggest that increased expression of MRP1 may be a very early event in NSCLC and might precede development of a fully malignant phenotype.

The expression of MRP1 in SCLC has been less extensively documented. An immunohistological study of archival samples from untreated patients detected some levels of MRP1 in 56% of tumor samples, but un-like NSCLC, expression was generally confined to small foci of positive cells. The less frequent expression of MRP1 in SCLC, coupled with its restriction to foci of positive cells, is consistent with the higher initial response rate of this form of the disease to chemotherapy, as well as with the possible contribution of MRP1-positive cells to the high frequency of acquired resistance that occurs at relapse. In a small study of patients with SCLC in which tumor samples were obtained at diagnosis and relapse, MRP1, together with several other drug resistance markers, was found to increase following treatment. However, large longitudinal studies that include comparable data on MRP1 expression following relapse have not been reported and remain technically difficult for ethical reasons.

There have been very few reports of the correlation of MRP1 expression with other potential prognostic markers in lung cancer. One study of 107 NSCLC patients found that those with MRP1-positive tumors who received postoperative chemotherapy with vindesine and etoposide had significantly poorer prognoses than patients with MRP1-negative tumors. A positive correlation was also found between MRP1 overexpression and the presence of mutant p53. *In vitro* studies are also beginning to lend support to the possibility that MRP1 expression is increased in cells containing mutant p53, although it remains to be established whether direct or indirect mechanisms are involved.

2. MRP1 in Pediatric Tumors

MRP1 has been implicated in the intrinsic MDR of both neuroblastoma and retinoblastoma. In a study of 60 samples from primary untreated neuroblastoma, MRP1 levels correlated positively with amplification of the N-Myc oncogene (*MYCN*) and were a strong independent negative prognostic indicator of survival and event-free survival. A similar correlation between *MYCN* amplification and MRP1 expression was also observed in an independent analysis of 40 tumors. However, as in the case of p53, it has not been possible to demonstrate direct regulation of *MRP1* expression by MYCN, and the precise mechanism involved remains to be established.

In a study of MRP1 expression in retinoblastoma, MRP1 was detected in three of three patients that failed to respond to chemotherapy alone or to chemotherapy that included cyclosporine as a P-glycoprotein-reversing agent. P-glycoprotein was not detectable in these tumors. In contrast, MRP1 was detected in only 1 of 18 nonmetastatic retinoblastomas nucleated prior to treatment. Both MRP1 and P-glycoprotein were found in other tumors that failed to respond either to chemotherapy alone or to chemotherapy in combination with cyclosporine.

3. MRP1 in Hematological Tumors

An extensive analysis of *MRP1* mRNA in normal hematopoietic cells by RT-PCR detected similar levels of expression in all peripheral blood cells, regardless of lineage. MRP1 mRNA or protein has also been detected in a number of hematological malignancies, but conclusions about the clinical significance of its expression have been discrepant. One of the confounding factors in the interpretation of these studies is that in some leukemias, MRP1 may be expressed

together with another ABC transporter, such as P-glycoprotein and possibly other members of the MRP family or the novel half-transporter, BCRP (ABCG2). This has been shown to be the case in acute myeloid leukemia, in which MRP1 expression has been studied most extensively. A more consistent relationship between expression of drug efflux pumps and disease outcome is beginning to emerge from studies that have used functional assays rather than simply determining the level of mRNA or protein for a particular transporter. These assays are based on flow cytometric analysis of the level of accumulation or rate of efflux of fluorescent dyes from leukemic blasts in the presence and absence of compounds that preferentially inhibit MRP1 (and 2) or P-glycoprotein. Studies of this type have revealed a wide range of efflux pump activities in clinical samples, with very low complete response rates being found in patients whose tumor cells show high efflux activity attributed to the presence of P-glycoprotein and MRP1 (6% complete response rate). The highest response rates were obtained in patients whose cells expressed low levels of efflux activity attributed to both protein pumps (73% complete response rate). Importantly, the combined activity of MRP1 and P-glycoprotein is a far stronger predictor of response than activity of either transporter alone. The combined activity of P-glycoprotein and MRP1 has also been strongly correlated with the *in vitro* resistance of leukemic cells to daunorubicin and etoposide, whereas no correlation was found with the activity of each protein alone. In the same study, a high level of combined P-glycoprotein and MRP1 activity was also predictive of a poor outcome. One of the remaining caveats from these studies relates to the lack of absolute specificity of the MRP1 and P-glycoprotein inhibitors used and the possibility that other transporters may contribute to the efflux activity being measured.

B. MRP2–5

Only a few studies have attempted to analyze expression of the MRP-related proteins MRP2–5 in clinical samples.

1. MRP2

Analyses of MRP2 mRNA expression in a well-characterized panel of nonsmall cell and small cell human lung cancer cell lines established directly from patients without being subjected to drug selection failed to find a correlation between mRNA levels and resistance to any of several natural product drugs or to cisplatin. One study of autopsy samples from lung cancer patients who had received platinum-based chemotherapy for their disease found a correlation between exposure to drug and increased levels of γ-glutamylcysteine synthetase mRNA, which was correlated with increases in MRP1 but not MRP2 mRNA. These data appear inconsistent with *in vitro* studies in which MRP1 has not been found to confer resistance to cisplatin, while there is at least one report of cells transfected with MRP2 cDNA displaying increased resistance to the drug. A potential confounding factor for mRNA-based analyses is that MRP2 normally traffics to the apical membrane and there may not be a consistent correlation between mRNA and protein levels in nonpolarized cells. MRP2 mRNA and/or protein has been detected in clinical samples of renal cell and ovarian carcinomas, but as yet, no correlation with response to initial treatment, disease progression, or outcome has been reported for these tumor types. In contrast, a study of MRP2 expression in colorectal carcinomas found that MRP2 mRNA levels were elevated in tumor relative to normal tissue. Tumor levels of MRP2 mRNA also correlated with resistance to cisplatin, but not to other drugs that had been used during treatment, including doxorubicin, etoposide/VP-16, and a camptothecin derivative.

2. MRP3

The clinical relevance of MRP3 in drug resistance has not yet been widely investigated and *in vitro* studies are relatively preliminary. *MRP3* mRNA levels were reported to be elevated in several cisplatin-resistant cell lines in one study but not in another. A third analysis of a collection of lung cancer cell lines showed a strong correlation of *MRP3* mRNA levels and resistance to doxorubicin and a lesser but significant association with resistance to vincristine, VP-16, and cisplatin. However, it is not clear how these studies of established cell lines relate to clinical resistance or to the resistance patterns observed in transfected cells and substrate specificities defined by *in vitro* transport assays with inside-out membrane vesicles. The availability of MRP3-specific monoclonal antibodies

should facilitate further investigations of this protein in clinical samples.

3. MRP4 and MRP5

As with MRP3, almost nothing is known of the clinical relevance of MRP4 and MRP5 in the drug resistance of malignant diseases. Increased levels of *MRP5* mRNA have been reported in both lung cancer cell lines and peripheral mononuclear cells after exposure to platinum drugs and in normal lung and lung cancer tissue specimens. Again, it is not clear precisely how studies of established cell lines relate to clinical resistance or to the resistance patterns observed in transfected cells and substrate specificities identified by *in vitro* transport assays with inside-out membrane vesicles. The development of MRP5-specific monoclonal antibodies should facilitate further investigations of this protein in clinical samples.

See Also the Following Articles

Bibliography

Bader, P., Schilling, F., Schlaud, M., Girgert, R., Handgretinger, R., Klingebiel, T., Treuner, J., Liu, C., Niethammer, D. and Beck, J. F. (1999). Expression analysis of multidrug resistance associated genes in neuroblastomas. *Oncol. Rep.* **6,** 1143–1146.

Borst, P., Evers, R., Kool, M., and Wijnholds, J. (2000). A family of drug transporters: the multidrug resistance-associated proteins. *J. Natl. Cancer Inst.* **92,** 1295–1302.

Chan, H. S. L., Lu, Y., Grogan, T. M., Haddad, G., Hipfner, D. R., Cole, S. P. C., Deeley, R. G., Ling, V., and Gallie, B. L. (1997). Multidrug resistance protein (MRP) expression in retinoblastoma correlates with rare failure of chemotherapy despite cyclosporine for reversal of P-glycoprotein. *Cancer Res.* **57,** 2325–2330.

Cole, S. P. C., Bhardwaj, G., Gerlach, J. H., Mackie, J. E., Grant, C. E., Almquist, K. C., Stewart, A. J., Kurz, E. U., Duncan, A. M. V., and Deeley, R. G. (1992). Overexpression of a transporter gene in a multidrug-resistant human lung cancer cell line. *Science* **258,** 1650–1654.

Cole, S. P. C., and Deeley, R. G. (1998). Multidrug resistance mediated by the ATP-binding cassette transporter protein, MRP. *BioEssays* **20,** 931–940.

Doyle, L. A., Yang, W., Abruzzo, L. V., Krogamann, T., Gao, Y., Rishi, A. K., and Ross, D. D. (1998). A multidrug resistance transporter from human MCF-7 breast cancer cells. *Proc. Natl. Acad. Sci. USA* **95**, 15665–15670.

Filipits, M., Suchomel, R. W., Dekan, G., Haider, K., Valdimarsson, G., Depisch, D., and Pirker, R. (1996). MRP and MDR1 gene expression in primary breast carcinoma. *Clin. Cancer Res.* **2**, 1231–1237.

Hinoshita, E., Uchiumi, T., Taguchi, K., Kinukawa, N., Tsuneyoshi, M., Maehara, Y., Sugimachi, K., and Kuwano, M. (2000). Increased expression of an ATP-binding cassette superfamily transporter, multidrug resistance protein 2, in human colorectoral carcinomas. *Clin. Cancer Res.* **6**, 2401–2407.

Hipfner, D. R., Deeley, R. G., and Cole, S. P. C. (1999). Structural, mechanistic and clinical aspects of MRP1. *Biochim. Biophys. Acta* **1461**, 359–276.

Hooijberg, J. H., Broxterman, H. J., Kool, M., Assaraf, Y. G., Peters, G. J., Scheper, R. J., Borst, P., Pinedo, H. M., and Jansen, G. (1999). Antifolate resistance mediated by the multidrug resistance proteins MRP1 and MRP2. *Cancer Res.* **59**, 2532–2535.

Ito, K., Fujimori, M., Nakata, S., Hama, Y., Shingu, K., Kobayashi, S., Tsuchiya, S., Kohno, K., Kuwano, M., and Amano, J. (1998). Clinical significance of the increased multidrug resistance-associated protein (MRP) gene expression in patients with primary breast cancer. *Oncol. Res.* **10**, 99–109.

Jedlitschky, G., Burchell, B., and Keppler, D. (2000). The multidrug resistance protein 5 functions as an ATP-dependent export pump for cyclic nucleotides. *J. Biol. Chem.* **275**, 30069–30074.

Juliano, R. L., and Ling, V. (1976). A surface glycoprotein modulating drug permeability in Chinese hamster ovary cell mutants. *Biochim. Biophys. Acta* **455**, 152–162.

Konig, J., Nies, A. T., Cui, Y., Leier, I., and Keppler, D. (1999). Conjugate export pumps of the multidrug resistance protein (MRP) family: Localization, substrate specificity and MRP2-mediated drug resistance. *Biochim. Biophys. Acta* **1461**, 377–394.

Kool, M., De Haas, M., Scheffer, G. L., Scheper, R. J., Van Eijk, M. J. T., Juijn, J. A., Baas, F., and Borst, P. (1997). Analysis of expression of cMOAT (MRP2), MRP3, MRP4, and MRP5, homologues of the multidrug resistance-associated protein gene (MRP1), in human cancer cell lines. *Cancer Res.* **57**, 3537–3547.

Kriesholt, J., Sorensen, M., Jensen, P. B., Nielsen, B. E., Andersen, C. B., and Sehested, M. (1998). Immunohistochemical detection of DNA topoisomerase IIa, P-glycoprotein and multidrug resistance protein (MRP) in small cell and non-small cell lung cancer. *Br. J. Cancer* **77**, 1469–1473.

Lee, K., Klein-Szanto, A. J. P., and Kruh, G. D. (2000). Analysis of the MRP4 drug resistance profile in transfected NIH3T3 cells. *J. Natl. Cancer Inst.* **92**, 1934–1940.

Legrand, O., Simonin, G., Beauchamp-Nicoud, A., Zittoun, R., and Marie, J.-P. (1999). Simultaneous activity of MRP1 and P-glycoprotein is associated with *in vitro* resistance to daunorubicin and with *in vivo* resistance in adult acute myeloid leukemia. *Blood* **94**, 1999.

Loe, D. W., Deeley, R. G., and Cole, S. P. C. (1998). Characterization of vincristine transport by the 190 kDa multidrug resistance protein, MRP: Evidence for co-transport with reduced glutathione. *Cancer Res.* **58**, 5130–5136.

Loe, D. W., Stewart, R. K., Massey, T. E., Deeley, R. G., and Cole, S. P. C. (1997). ATP-dependent transport of aflatoxin B_1 and its glutathione conjugates by the product of the MRP gene. *Mol. Pharmacol.* **51**, 1034–1041.

Nakamura, M., Abe, Y., Katoh, Y., Echuca, Y., Hatanaka, H., Tsuchida, T., Yamazaki, H., Kijima, H., Inoue, H., and Ueyama, Y. (2000). A case of pulmonary adenocarcinoma with overexpression of multidrug resistance-associated protein and p53 aberration. *Anticancer Res.* **20**, 1921–1925.

Nooter, K., Bosman, F. T., Burger, H., Van Wingerden, K. E., Flens, M. J., Scheper, R. J., Oostrum, R. G., Boersma, A. W. M., Van Der Gaast, A., and Stoter, G. (1996). Expression of the multidrug resistance-associated protein (MRP) gene in primary non-small-cell lung cancer. *Ann. Oncol.* **7**, 75–81.

Nooter, K., Brutel De La Riviere, G., Klijn, J. G. M., Stoter, G., and Foekens, J. A. (1997). Multidrug resistance protein in recurrent breast cancer. *Lancet* **349**, 1885–1886.

Nooter, K., Brutel De La Riviere, G., Look, M. P., Van Wingerden, K. E., Henzen-Logmans, S. C., Scheper, R. J., Flens, M. J., Klijn, J. G. M., Stoter, G., and Foekens, J. A. (1997). The prognostic significance of expression of the multidrug resistance-associated protein (MRP) in primary breast cancer. *Br. J. Cancer* **76**, 486–493.

Norris, M. D., Bordow, S. B., Marshall, G. M., Haber, P. S., Cohn, S. L., and Haber, M. (1996). Expression of the gene for multidrug-resistance-associated protein and outcome in patients with neuroblastoma. *N. Engl. J. Med.* **334**, 231–238.

Ogrui, T., Fujiwara, Y., Isobe, T., Katoh, O., Watanabe, H., and Yamakido, M. (1998). Expression of gamma-glutamylcysteine snthetase (gamma-GCS) and multidrug resistance-associated protein (MRP), but not human canalicular multispecific organic anion transporter (cMOAT), genes correlates with exposure of human lung cancers to platinum drugs. *Br. J. Cancer* **77**, 1089–1096.

Oguri, T., Isobe, T., Suzuki, T., Nishio, K., Fujiwara, Y., Katoh, O., and Yamakido, M. (2000). Increased expression of the MRP5 gene is associated with exposure to platinum drugs in lung cancer. *Int. J. Cancer* **86**, 95–100.

Oshika, Y., Nakamura, M., Tokunaga, T., Fukushima, Y., Abe, Y., Ozeki, Y., Yamazaki, H., Tamaoki, N., and Ueyama, Y. (1998). Multidrug resistance-associated protein and mutant p53 protein expression in non-small cell lung cancer. *Mod. Pathol.* **11**, 1059–1063.

Ota, E., Abe, Y., Oshika, Y., Ozeki, Y., Iwasaki, M., Inoue, H., Yamazaki, H., Ueyama, Y., Takagi, K., Ogata, T., Tamaoki, N., and Nakamura, M. (1995). Expression of the multidrug resistance-associated protein (MRP) gene in non-small-cell lung cancer. *Br. J. Cancer* **72**, 550–554.

Paulusma, C. C., Bssma, P. J., Zaman, G. J. R., Bakker, C. T. M., Otter, M., Schieffer, G. L., Scheper, R. J., Borst, P., and Oude Elferink, R. P. J. (1996). Congenital jaundice in rats with a mutation in a multidrug resistance-associated protein gene. *Science* **271,** 1126–1128.

Paulusma, C. C., and Oude Elferink, R. P. J. (1997). The canalicular multispecific organic anion transporter and conjugated hyperbilirubinemia in rat and man. *J. Mol. Med.* **75,** 420–428.

Qian, Y.-M., Song, W.-C., Cui, H., Cole, S. P. C., and Deeley, R. G. (2001). Glutathione stimulates sulfated estrogen transport by multidrug resistance protein 1. *J. Biol. Chem.* **276,** 6404–6411.

Rappa, G., Finch, R. A., Sartorelli, A. C., and Lorico, A. (1999). New insights into the biology and pharmacology of the multidrug resistance protein (MRP) from gene knockout models. *Biochem. Pharmacol.* **58,** 557–562.

Scheffer, G. L., Kool, M., Heijn, M., De Haas, M., Pijnenborg, A. C. L. M., Wijnholds, J., Van Helvoort, A., De Jong, M. C., Hooijberg, J. H., Mol, C. A. A. M., Van Der Linden, M., De Vree, J. M. L., Van Der Valk, P., Oude Elferink, R. P. J., Borst, P., and Scheper, R. J. (2000). Specific detection of multidrug resistance proteins MRP1, MRP2, MRP3, MRP5 and MDR3 P-glycoprotein with a panel of monoclonal antibodies. *Cancer Res.* **60,** 5269–5277.

Schuetz, J. D., Connelly, M. C., Sun, D., Paibir, S. G., Flynn, P. M., Srinivas, R. V., Kumar, A., and Fridland, A. (1999). MRP4: A previously unidentified factor in resistance to nucleoside-based antiviral drugs. *Nature Med.* **5,** 1048–1051.

Sullivan, G. F., Amenta, P. S., Villanueva, J. D., Alvarez, C. J., Yang, J., and Hait, W. N. (1998). The expression of drug resistance gene products during the progression of human prostate cancer. *Clin. Cancer Res.* **4,** 1393–1403.

Suzuki, H., and Sugiyama, Y. (1998). Excretion of GSSG and glutathione conjugates mediated by MRP1 and cMOAT/MRP2. *Sem. Liver Dis.* 18, 359–376.

Van Der Kolk, D. M., De Vries, E. G. E., Van Putten, W. J., Verdonck, L. F., Ossenkoppele, G. J., Verhoef, G. E., and Vellenga, E. (2000). P-glycoprotein and multidrug resistance protein activities in relation to treatment outcome in acute myeloid leukemia. *Clin. Cancer Res.* **6,** 3205–3214.

Wijnholds, J., De Lange, E. C. M., Scheffer, G. L., Van Den Berg, D.-J., Mol, C. A. A. M., Van Der Valk, M., Schinkel, A. H., Scheper, R. J., Breimer, D. D., and Borst, P. (2000). Multidrug resistance protein 1 protects the choroid plexus epithelium and contributes to the blood-cerebrospinal fluid barrier. *J. Clin. Invest.* **105,** 279–285.

Wijnholds, J., Evers, R., Van Leusden, M. R., Mol, C. A. A. M., Zaman, G. J. R., Mayer, U., Beijnen, J. H., Van Der Valk, M., Krimpenfort, P., and Borst, P. (1997). Increased sensitivity to anticancer drugs and decreased inflammatory response in mice lacking the multidrug resistance-associated protein. *Nature Med.* **3,** 1275–1279.

Wright, S. R., Boag, A. H., Campling, B. G., Valdimarsson, G., Hifpner, D. R., Cole, S. P. C., and Deeley, R. G. (1998). Immunohistochemical detection of multidrug resistance protein (MRP) in human lung cancer and normal lung. *Clin. Cancer Res.* **4,** 2279–2289.

Young, L. C., Campling, B. G., Voskoglou-Nomikos, T., Cole, S. P. C., Deeley, R. G., and Gerlach, J. H. (1999). Expression of MRP-related genes in lung cancer: Correlation with drug response. *Clin. Cancer Res.* **5,** 673–680.

Multiple Myeloma

P. Leif Bergsagel
Hubert Szelényi
Weill Medical College of Cornell University

I. Epidemiology
II. Biology
III. Diagnosis
IV. Prognostic Factors
V. Clinical Manifestations
VI. Management
VII. Future Outlook

GLOSSARY

bisphosphonates A class of drugs indicated to treat hypercalcemia and to prevent skeletal complications of metastatic breast cancer and myeloma.

high-dose chemotherapy with autologous stem cell support Most effective treatment proven to prolong survival in multiple myeloma.

immunoglobulin switch translocation Translocation into the imunoglobulin heavy chain switch region, occurring in multiple myeloma and other B-cell neoplasias.

interleukin-6 Major growth factor in multiple myeloma.

multiple myeloma A malignancy of postgerminal center plasma cells.

osteoclast-activating factor Growth factors involved in the pathogenesis of bone lesion in multiple myeloma.

thalidomide Effective drug in multiple myeloma and other malignancies; mechanisms of action discussed are antiangiogenic, anti-TNFα, and immune modulation.

Multiple myeloma (MM) is a malignant neoplasm of plasma cells that secrete a monoclonal immunoglobulin (Ig), accumulate in the bone marrow, and lead to marrow compromise and bone destruction. It is among the most common hematological malignancies and accounts for 1% of all cancers and 2% of cancer deaths. It is frequently preceded by monoclonal gammopathy of undetermined significance (MGUS), a benign plasma cell neoplasm characterized by a low level of monoclonal Ig, a marrow plasmacytosis of less than 10%, and the absence of the malignant features of myeloma. Most patients with MGUS remain asymptomatic, but because about 1% per year progress to multiple

Copyright 2002, Elsevier Science (USA).
All rights reserved.

myeloma, their prognosis is uncertain and they must be followed carefully.

I. EPIDEMIOLOGY

The incidence of MM according to SEER data is 4 per 100,000. The incidence seems to be increasing since the 1950s. This may be in part attributed to an increasing availability of diagnostic tools such as serum electrophoresis. African-Americans have a two- to threefold increase in incidence compared to Caucasians, whereas people of Chinese and Japanese descent have a lower incidence. Men have a slightly higher risk than women, varying from 1.1–1.5 to 1. MM is characteristically a disease of late middle age and the elderly. It is rarely seen under age 35. The age-specific incidence rises from 1/100,000 below 40 years to more than 40/100,000 at 80 years or older. The median age is 65 (hospital series) to 72–74 (community-based studies) years.

II. BIOLOGY

As with all B-cell malignancies, MM cells are distinguished by an idiotypic rearrangement of the Ig genes. Analysis of Ig genes reveals that they have (1) successfully undergone V(D)J recombination to produce a functional Ig, (2) been subjected to extensive somatic mutation indicating previous interaction with antigen in the context of a germinal center, (3) ceased to undergo somatic mutation, indicating no further interaction with antigen, and (4) undergone Ig isotype switch recombination. Isotype switch recombination is a hallmark of MM: IgM is exceedingly rare, 55% secrete IgG, 25% secrete IgA, 16% secrete only light chains, 2% secrete IgD, and 2% do not secrete detectable Ig. Chromosome translocations into switch regions of the IgH locus at 14q32 are a hallmark of multiple myeloma, seen in up to 75% of patients. There are several recurrent partner loci (and oncogenes) involved: 15% 4p16 (FGFR3 and MMSET), 25% 11q13 (cyclin D1), 5% 6p21 (cyclin D3), 10% 16q23 (c-*maf*), 5% 20q11 (mafB), and 15% unidentified.

III. DIAGNOSIS

The diagnosis of multiple myeloma is based on the detection of a monoclonal Ig (M protein) in the serum or urine, the presence of marrow plasmacytosis >10%, and bone lesions. The percentage of plasma cells on bone marrow aspirates is highly variable; a trephine biopsy is warranted. An M protein level associated with 10–30% marrow plasmacytosis and none of the malignant features of MM fulfils the diagnostic criteria for smoldering MM. Smaller M spikes (IgG <3.5 g/dl, IgA <2.0 g/dl, B–J <1.0 g/day) associated with <10% marrow plasmacytosis and without the malignant features of myeloma are diagnostic of MGUS.

IV. PROGNOSTIC FACTORS

There is a significant variation in the survival of patients with MM. Prognostic factors help identify patients with different survival rates and hopefully in the future will help to determine therapy. The Durie–Salmon staging system (Table I) is a helpful prognostic tool. However, patient age, as well as performance status, has an influence on the outcome of patients with MM. The median survival with conventional chemotherapy is about 5 years for those with stage IA disease and less than 15 months for those with stage IIIB disease. Several important prognostic factors identify patients with poor outcomes: the M-protein level as the best marker of the total body myeloma cell mass; serum β_2 microglobulin being more closely related to myeloma cell turnover; the acute-phase protein CRP as a surrogate marker for IL-6 levels; and plasma cell-labeling index as a measurement of the proportion of proliferating myeloma cells. Finally, plasmablastic morphology of the myeloma cell and cytogenetic abnormalities, especially on chromosome 13, appear to be unfavorable. Prognostic markers under investigation are soluble interleukin-6 receptor, markers of angiogenesis, circulating myeloma cells and specific chromosomal abnormalities. Because most prognostic factors are interrelated, combinations of independent prognostic factors may provide more information than any one factor alone. Every prognostic marker is not available

TABLE I
Durie–Salmon Staging System

Stage I All of the following	Stage II Neither stage I or stage III	Stage III One or more of the following	Renal involvement
Hemoglobin >10 g/dl		Hemoglobin <8.5 g/dl	A: Creatinine <2.0 g/dl
Calcium <12 g/dl		Calcium >12 g/dl	
One bone lesion		>3 bone lesions	B: Creatinine >2.0 g/dl
Low M component		High M component	
IgG <5 g/dl		IgG >7 g/dl	
IgA <3 g/dl		IgA >5 g/dl	
Bence–Jones <4 g/day		Bence–Jones >12 g/day	
<0.6	0.6–1.2	>1.2 myeloma cells $\times$ 10^{12}/m^2	

everywhere; some, like cytogenetics and the myeloma cell labeling index, may be done only at research institutions. At the present time there is no consensus on the ideal combination of factors that is best suited for widespread clinical use.

V. CLINICAL MANIFESTATIONS

The clinical course of MM is characterized by the infiltration of neoplastic plasma cells into the bone marrow cavity and the production of a monoclonal Ig.

A. Bone Disease

The major clinical manifestations of MM are related to enhanced bone destruction, resulting in osteolytic lesions, osteoporosis, and pathologic fractures in most patients, as well as hypercalcemia and spinal cord compression in many individuals. One of the most common features of MM is bone pain. Myeloma cells home to the bone marrow cavity, infiltrating and replacing the normal bone structure. In addition, an imbalance between osteoclasts and -blasts favoring osteoclasts is seen. Osteoclasts in MM patients show enhanced activity probably due to cytokines secreted by the myeloma cells (e.g., RANKL, interleukin-1β, MIP1-α). Typically, myeloma cells present as multiple localized tumors in the marrow (hence the name multiple myeloma) and showing the typical punched-out radiological appearance of lytic lesions. This growth pattern renders the bone mechanically unstable, and pathological fractures of extremities, ribs, or vertebrae are often the first manifestation of MM. Clinically vertebral fractures lead to a loss in body height. The increased resorption of calcium from bone may lead to severe hypercalcemia. Around 50–60% of patients present with lytic lesion on conventional X rays, whereas nearly every patient shows signs of bone marrow infiltration using MRI.

B. Anemia

Progression of bone marrow infiltration impairs normal hematopoiesis, most commonly manifested as anemia. Weakness and fatigue are common symptoms in patients with MM. This is very closely correlated to hemoglobin levels. The anemia is usually the normochromic, normocytic anemia associated with chronic disease. Other factors, such as cytokines secreted by myeloma cells, may also contribute to the anemia.

C. Renal Involvement

Renal impairment in MM is mostly due to the excretion of light chains (Bence Jones protein). These cause casts in tubules, leading to atrophy and finally to kidney failure. Deposition of light chain or amyloid in the glomerulus leads to the nephrotic syndrome. However, the pathophysiology of renal involvement in MM is still not clear. Clinical presentations range from minimal clinical syndromes with a small Bence

Jones proteinuria or albuminuria only (50–80% of patients) to acute renal failure as a presenting feature (30%). The latter can be reversed with chemotherapy and renal replacement therapy. A significant proportion of MM patients will eventually end up with chronic renal failure requiring dialysis therapy. Care must be taken to maintain good hydration and to avoid nephrotoxic agents (e.g., radiologic intravenous contrast dye).

D. Infection

Hypogammaglobulinemia due to the excessive production of a nonfunctional Ig in combination with the pancytopenia caused by the plasma cell marrow infiltration renders the patient more susceptible to infection and fever. Chemotherapy and treatment of chronic renal failure add further infectious risks.

E. Others

Sudden alteration in mental status should always lead to an exclusion of a hypercalcemic crisis due to rapid bone turnover, an infection, or the rare hyperviscosity syndrome. Other clinical presentations may be bleeding disorders, cardiac failure, or thrombotic events.

VI. MANAGEMENT

A. When to Treat?

Chemotherapy (CT), both conventional- and high-dose regimens, provides symptomatic relief and prolongs survival. However, CT has significant side effects. Randomized clinical trials have shown that starting treatment as soon as the M protein is discovered, before any symptoms have developed, while the disease is stable, does not result in an improved response rate, longer remissions, or improved survival as compared to delaying treatment until clear signs and symptoms signal the onset of progression to symptomatic myeloma. Treating an asymptomatic patient or slightly abnormal laboratory values are of no benefit in terms of survival and place the patients at unnecessary risk. However, a relentless sustained rise in the

M protein by at least 25% over the baseline for that patient is an indication to consider starting treatment before symptoms develop.

B. Evaluating the Response to Treatment

The serum and/or urine M protein is the best marker for evaluating the response to treatment. Bone marrow evaluation is only necessary to confirm a complete remission. On first presentation, a radiological survey of the skeletal system should be done. Usually, conventional radiographs are sufficient, as the value of MRI is unclear. A complete laboratory workup, including markers of tumor mass, hematopoesis, immunology, and renal function, as well as prognostic factors as discussed earlier, should be done on first presentation. Follow-up should include measurement of the serum and urinary M protein, size of plasmacytomas, serum calcium, creatinine, and hematology values. Radiographs should be repeated when clinically indicated.

C. Radiation Therapy

Radiation therapy (RT) is the treatment of choice for localized disease, i.e., single bone lesions or localized extramedullary sites. RT is also favored to quickly relieve bone pain and promote the healing of lytic lesions and pathological fractures.

D. Chemotherapy

1. Standard-Dose Therapy

Since melphalan/prednisone (MP) was introduced in the 1960s, it has been shown to prolong the survival of patients. A plethora of multidrug regimens (e.g., vincristine, adriamycin, dexamethasone VAD) has been proposed, but has not been proven to be better than MP in terms of survival. MP is favored, unless the patient is suitable for high-dose CT and autologous hemopoietic stem cell rescue.

However, the response rate to MP is about 40–50% and the maximum effect is seen after some weeks. In patients with renal involvement or thrombocytopenia, cyclophosphamide (C weekly) is preferred, as the pharmacokinetics are not altered and it is relatively sparing to the bone marrow. In patients with hyperviscosity syndrome or other emergencies where rapid elimination of the M protein is required, VAD or other high-dose dexamethasone containing protocols show a more rapid response

2. High-Dose Chemotherapy with Autologous Stem Cell Support

The introduction of high-dose chemotherapy with autologous hematopoietic stem cell support (HDT) has been proven in a French study (IMF90) to result in a higher rate of complete remission and to prolong median overall survival from 4 years with conventional therapy to 5 years with HDT. This benefit was primarily observed in patients under 60 who were enrolled in this study. Currently, HDT is considered the treatment of choice for symptomatic younger patients who are in good shape. However, there are severe side effects, preventing the elderly or patients with a low-performance status from this treatment. The mortality is still between 1 and 5%. High-dose therapy with melphalan alone (200 mg/m^2) is as effective as a lower dose melphalan (140 mg/m^2) combined with total body irradiation and is favored because it is less toxic. There is no survival difference whether HDT is administered early, immediately after remission-induction CT, or later, when patients first progress or relapse after standard-dose CT. It is not appropriate as a "last-ditch" salvage effort in heavily pretreated patients.

E. Thalidomide

Thalidomide in combination with dexamethasone has proven to be very effective in the initial treatment of myeloma, as well as for those with refractory disease. The mechanism of action is still unclear; antiangiogenesis or immunological phenomena are discussed. However, not everyone can tolerate the side effects (drowsiness, rash, constipation, neuropathy, hypercoagulability). Newer analogs (IMID) are currently under investigation.

F. Immunotherapy

1. Allogeneic Transplantation

Allogeneic transplantation is curative for a substantial fraction of patients. It is postulated that this is due to the immune-mediated elimination of residual tumor cells termed graft versus myeloma effect. However, this therapy is very toxic in MM, having a mortality rate of more than 40%. Furthermore, the majority of MM patients are too old (>55 years) for this treatment. The advent of nonmyeloablative transplantation with its lower rate of side effects is currently a focus of research to implement this potential curative therapy into a feasible therapeutic option.

2. Vaccines

In myeloma, the monoclonal immunoglobulin represents a unique antigen entity known as idiotype that may serve as a specific tumor associated antigen (TAA). Peripheral blood lymphocytes with cytotoxicity against autologous tumor cells and the induction of antitumor immune response have been demonstrated. Currently, trials are under way to test the value of vaccination against idiotype or other TAA.

3. Cytokines

Although interleukin-6 (IL-6) seems to be one of the key growth factors for myeloma, the results of monoclonal antibodies against IL-6 have so far been disappointing. Maintenance therapy with interferon-α has not shown to have a consistent survival benefit for patients.

G. Supportive Therapy

1. Hydration

Myeloma patients should increase their fluid intake to about 3000 ml/day in order to excrete the increased volume of urine required to clear their blood of urea, calcium, and light chains.

2. Infection

Infections are common and the most common cause of death in myeloma patients. A fever in a myeloma patient must be treated as an emergency, with prompt investigation and appropriate antibiotics. Good studies on the value of prophylactic antibiotic or immunoglobulin therapy have not been reported.

3. Bone Disease

Bisphosphonates have been shown to slow the progression of bone loss and bony lesions, decrease bone pain, pathological fractures, new osteolytic lesions, and the number and severity of hypercalcemic events. Furthermore, bisphosphonates may also inhibit the growth of myeloma cells. Patients with myeloma should therefore be treated with bisphosphonates to prevent a progression of bony disease. Pathological fractures should be surgically stabilized if necessary.

4. Anemia

Anemia is an important clinical manifestation of myeloma. Anemia should be corrected in the short term by transfusion or more chronically by the weekly administration of erythropoetin.

5. Emergencies

Hypercalcemia and hyperviscosity are emergencies and indications for antimyeloma treatment. Hypercalcemia responds quickly to treatment with bisphosphonates. The efficiency of plasmapheresis on hyperviscosity is only temporary and should bridge the time until the onset of the chemotherapy effect.

VII. FUTURE OUTLOOK

MM is still an incurable disease. In terms of survival, there has been no significant improvement since the advent of HDT. However, HDT is not feasible for everyone and still has major side effects. Currently, many therapeutic options are under investigation. The most promising seem to be novel drugs (thalidomide, proteasome inhibitors, etc.), nonmyeloablative bone marrow transplantation, vaccination, and monoclonal antibodies. Every patient with MM should be considered a candidate for a clinical trial testing an improved approach to the treatment of this disease. Furthermore, new insights into the interaction between myeloma cells and the tumor environment and into the immunology of myeloma and molecular pathogenesis (e.g., translocation of FGFR3) promise to translate basic science into useful clinical application.

See Also the Following Article

INTERLEUKINS

Bibliography

Alexanian, R., and Dimopoulos, M. (1994). Treatment of multiple myeloma. *N. Engl. J. Med.* **330,** 484–489.

Attal, M., Harousseau, J. L., Stoppa, A. M., Sotto, J. J., Fuzibet, J. G., Rossi, J. F., Casassus, P., Maisonneuve, H., Facon, T., Ifrah, N., Payen, C., and Bataille, R. (1996). Prospective, randomized trial of autologous bone marrow transplantation and chemotherapy in multiple myeloma. *N. Engl. J. Med.* **335,** 917.

Bataille, R., and Harousseau, J. L. (1997). Multiple myeloma. *N. Engl. J. Med.* **336,** 1657.

Berenson, J. R., Lichtenstein, A., Porter, L., Dimopoulos, M. A., Bordoni, R., George, S., Lipton, A., Keller, A., Ballester, O., Kovacs, M. J., Blacklock, H. A., Bell, R., Simeone, J., Reitsma, D. J., Heffernan, M., Seaman, J., and Knight, R. D. (1996). Efficacy of pamidronate in reducing skeletal events in patients with advanced multiple myeloma. *N. Engl. J. Med.* **334,** 488–493.

Hallek, M., Bergsagel, P. L., and Anderson, K. C. (1998). Multiple myeloma: Increasing evidence for a multistep transformation process. *Blood* **91,** 3–21.

Myeloma Trialists' Collaborative Group (1998). Combination chemotherapy versus melphalan plus prednisone as treatment for multiple myeloma: An overview of 6,633 patients from 27 randomized trials. *J. Clin. Oncol.* **16,** 3832–3842.

Singhal, S., Mehta, J., Desikan, R., Ayers, D., Roberson, P., Eddlemon, P., Munshi, N., Anaissie, E., Wilson, C., Dhodapkar, M., Zeldis, J., and Barlogie, B. (1999). Antitumor activity of thalidomide in refractory multiple myeloma. *N. Engl. J. Med.* **341,** 1565–1571.

Multistage Carcinogenesis

Anthony P. Albino
Ellen D. Jorgensen
The American Health Foundation, Valhalla, New York

GLOSSARY

apoptosis Programmed cell death via biochemical circuits responding to aberrations or defects in the cell. A normal defense against the propagation of mutant or damaged cells.

carcinogenesis The process of tumor development in an organism.

clonal expansion The selective replication of a mutated cell within a population resulting in the eventual genetic homogeneity of the cell population.

initiation The first step in the three-step model of multistage carcinogenesis in which an irreversible genetic alteration occurs, sensitizing the cell to promoting agents.

kryotypic instability The inability to maintain genomic integrity, as evidenced by chromosome rearrangement, truncation, and loss.

oncogene Implicated in cancer development when its expression is upregulated, activated, or deranged.

progression Third step in the three-step model of multistage carcinogenesis in which accumulated genetic alterations result in the ability of affected cells to invade local tissues or to metastasize to distant sites.

promotion Second step in the three-step model of multistage carcinogenesis in which initiated cells are stimulated to proliferate by promoting agents.

protooncogene Normal cellular homologue of an oncogene.

transformation Process by which normal cells become neoplastic.

tumor suppressor Gene implicated in cancer development when its expression is turned off, downregulated, or disrupted.

A hallmark of carcinogenesis, the process of tumor development in an organism, is a long latent period with no clinical evidence of disease. The age-dependent incidence of diagnosed cancers in humans suggests that carcinogenesis commonly proceeds via four to seven independent rate-limiting steps. Both animal carcinogenesis models and the analysis of human clinical samples support this stepwise progression of tumorigenesis. The genetic and biochemical defects that occur during this period to transform gradually a normal cell that maintains strict control over both intracellular and intercellular events to a cell mass with abnormal growth potential and an ability to invade adjacent tissues remain incompletely understood. Determining the temporal sequence of specific etiologically relevant events in tumorigenesis has been greatly aided by clinical and histopathological identification of a range of distinct stages in the progression of malignancies, i.e., from precursor lesion to metastasis. This recognizable biological progression must reflect a molecular progression within the genetic complement of the cell, which normally maintains multiple independent barriers to each stage of the malignant conversion process. During the past two decades, it has become clear that breaching these barriers depends on the gradual accumulation of irreversible alterations in an unknown number of genes. The molecular functions of these genes are broadly categorized as either inhibiting or promoting tumor development, i.e., tumor suppressor genes, whose functional activity is switched off or downregulated; or dominant-acting oncogenes, whose functional activity is switched on, upregulated, or otherwise deranged. Genes from both functional groups are normally involved in the homeostatic regulation of various cell processes and in coordinating communication and compatibility with neighboring cells. Current models of malignant transformation in specific tumor types are focusing on the identification of the precise genetic perturbations at each stage and elucidating the impact these molecular defects have on proliferation, differentiation, and intercellular relationships of the tumor population. Exploitation of this knowledge should result in more effective strategies for the diagnosis and treatment of the cancer patient and in the development of more specific preventive measures for the individual at high risk for developing a neoplasm.

I. EARLY OBSERVATIONS

The search for a relevant animal model of human carcinogenesis led to a series of classical experiments in the 1940s that defined how the process would be viewed for many years to come. It was observed that benign papillomas and malignant carcinomas could be induced in the skin of mice by application of a single subcarcinogenic dose of polycyclic hydrocarbons followed by a secondary treatment consisting of repeated wounding or application of an irritant such as croton oil. Neither treatment alone resulted in carcinogenesis, and reversing the order of application eliminated the effect. Surprisingly, tumor formation occurred when the secondary treatment was applied up to 1 year following the initial exposure to a carcinogen. Rous and Kidd pioneered the understanding of this latency phenomenon by conceptually dividing the process of carcinogenesis in the mouse skin model into two distinct stages: initiation and promotion. They defined initiation, a rapid process producing no apparent morphological change, as a priming event involving DNA damage resulting in irreversible genetic alterations that confer upon cells the ability to form tumors when subsequently exposed to a promoting agent. Promotion, characterized by clonal expansion of the initiated cells and dramatic morphological and biochemical changes, was considered to be an epigenetic phenomenon due to the finding that it could be reversed in the absence of continued treatment. Besides the application of chemical promoters such as phorbol esters, many diverse stimuli were found to have tumor-promoting effects, including UV irradiation and repeated physical abrasion. A common theme of promoting events appeared to be skin irritation.

In 1964 Foulds described initiation and promotion as part of a larger continuous carcinogenesis process of "progression." Later investigators redefined progression as the third stage of carcinogenesis, following promotion and characterized by a higher degree of malignancy as evidenced by an increased ability to proliferate and invade local tissues and a propensity to metastasize to distant sites. The progression stage also correlates with severe genetic damage, including visible karyotypic alterations in the majority of cells. Although it was unclear whether this phenomenon was a cause or an effect of neoplastic transformation, it had clinical importance; i.e., in many tumor types, DNA aneuploidy is a poor prognostic factor. By the mid-1970s the observation that all cells in many primary tumors exhibited the same abnormal karyotype or similarities in the karyotype of marker chromosomes prompted the idea that most neoplasms arise from a single cell of origin and that genetic instability acquired during the process of neoplasia results in genetic variability within the original clone, allowing for subsequent selection of more aggressive sublines. As described earlier, the multiple barriers a cell must overcome to become fully malignant may explain why cancer is a relatively rare event. However, it was quickly realized that based on known mutation rates for nongermline cells ($\sim 10^{-7}$ per gene/cell division), the combination of four to six genetic events necessary for the neoplastic transformation of a cell would be mathematically so rare as to virtually preclude any spontaneous tumor development during an average human lifetime. Cancer development must therefore be a self-accelerating process in which the first mutational event or events caused genetic instability, leading to an increased mutation rate. The identification of critical genomic lesions in human carcinogenesis is complicated by the background of diverse genetic defects, including not only point mutations but also deletions, amplifications, and rearrangements of genes and chromosomes present in most biopsied tumors. Although the three-stage mouse skin model of carcinogenesis was useful, it was recognized that a more precise understanding of the molecular events in carcinogenesis was needed.

II. IDENTIFYING THE MOLECULAR EVENTS IN MULTISTAGE CARCINOGENESIS

A. Oncogenes

The study of oncogenic viruses such as the Rous sarcoma virus led to the discovery of specific viral genes that were responsible for cell transformation. At the same time, investigators found that DNA isolated from human carcinomas and other tumors was able to induce neoplastic transformation at high efficiencies when transfected into transformation-sensitive "normal" mouse NIHT3 cells. In the 1970s, a group of cellular transforming genes, termed "oncogenes," was identified by homology to the transforming genes of retroviruses and by the biological activity of tumor cell DNA in transfection assays. Transfection of NIHT3 cells with *mos* (the normal cellular homo-

logue of the transforming gene of the Moloney sarcoma virus) or with H-*ras* (the normal cellular homologue of the transforming gene of the Harvey sarcoma virus) under the control of viral transcriptional regulatory sequences resulted in cellular transformation. These findings suggested that oncogenesis was the result of dominant genetic alterations in which the functional activity of these genes was upregulated or expressed in an abnormal form. Protooncogenes (normal cellular homologues of transforming genes) were found to be (1) highly conserved in vertebrate evolution, (2) expressed in a highly regulated manner, and (3) key players in the growth control mechanisms of normal cells. It seemed logical that the derangement or overexpression of one or a combination of cell growth-related genes could transform cells in a "growth gone wrong" scenario. Revisiting the chemical carcinogenesis in mouse skin model, it was found that introducing the *ras* oncogene into keratinocytes via transducing retroviruses was tantamount to chemical initiation: subsequent application of promoting agents to infected cells resulted in papilloma formation. In addition, point mutations in the H-*ras* oncogene were invariably found in methylnitrosourea-induced breast tumors in rats. It appeared as if a critical lesion in carcinogenesis had at last been identified.

An important caveat in the oncogene theory of cancer was that cell transformation by transfection of a single oncogene was only observed under certain limited experimental conditions. The established rodent cell lines (such as NIHT3) used in the original transfection experiments were already phenotypically immortal and therefore partially transformed. Additionally, the results could not be duplicated in human cell lines, cautioning against oversimplification of the carcinogenic process in humans. As the number of oncogenes associated with human cancers increased, researchers were frustrated by the inability to associate a specific genetic lesion with a particular tumor type to a degree that indicated causality. Analysis of human tumors confirmed that there was no one particular oncogene that was necessary, let alone sufficient, for any given type of cancer. With the advent of transgenic mice bearing oncogenes, it was conclusively demonstrated that simply harboring oncogene mutations in a particular cell lineage is insufficient for tumor development.

B. Lessons from the *Rb* Gene

The examination of hereditary cancers by Knudson revealed a new paradigm important to the pathogenesis of cancer. If the stages of carcinogenesis were defined by genetic events, could a person with a hereditary disposition to cancer be already "initiated" by virtue of an inherited genetic lesion? In the case of retinoblastoma, the defective gene was localized to a band on the long arm of chromosome 13. Knudson's analysis suggested that, in contrast to oncogenes, this "antioncogene" acts in a recessive manner, with one normal allele being adequate to protect against tumorigenesis. Thus, two separate mutational events were needed for retinoblastoma formation, one to inactivate each copy of an antioncogene. In 1989 Weinberg refined Knudson's hypothesis by providing a more sophisticated molecular model for the process. Weinberg based his model on the insights following the molecular cloning and analysis of the retinoblastoma gene *Rb*. At the time, little was known about the precise function of protooncogenes in normal cells or about their regulation. When primary cell cultures (as opposed to partially transformed immortal lines such as NIHT3) are transfected with *ras*, only small numbers of cells acquire the oncogene and they do not proliferate to form visible foci. If, however, the transfection includes acquisition of neomycin resistance, subsequent selection results in a pure population of transformed cells whose growth proceeds in an uncontrolled manner. It had also been observed that while implantation of cells transformed by an oncogenic virus (e.g., Harvey sarcoma virus) onto the back of a mouse resulted in rapidly growing squamous carcinomas, cell proliferation resulting in tumor formation could be nearly completely prevented by implanting the transformed cells together with a fourfold excess of normal fibroblasts. Weinberg proposed that these observations could be explained if neighboring normal cells exert a constant inhibitory effect on the growth of transformed cells. Therefore, a critical event in carcinogenesis is when cells gain the ability to overcome the limiting effect of their normal tissue environment by ignoring or neutralizing the effect of inhibitory growth signals. He suggested that a number of key genes in growth regulatory pathways could contribute to carcinogenesis by suffering mutations resulting in their *inactivation* or *downregulation*. He

termed this class of antioncogenes "tumor suppressor" genes.

Weinberg and colleagues identified the *Rb* antioncogene, central to the development of retinoblastomas, as a putative tumor suppressor. Knudson's analysis of normal tissues and retinoblastomas from the same patients had suggested that inactivation of both alleles was the critical event in tumorigenesis. It was known that the viral E1A oncoprotein from human adenovirus type 5 formed complexes with the *Rb*-encoded protein and that the region of E1A responsible for its ability to bind to the *Rb* gene product was crucial to the tumorigenic properties of E1A. The idea that loss of the *Rb* gene product enabled deregulation of cell growth was supported by experiments showing that introducing a cloned copy of the *Rb* gene into retinoblastoma cells restored normal growth control. Subsequent work has validated the *Rb* gene product as an important regulator of cell growth; it is part of a cellular pathway responding to extracellular antigrowth factors such as transforming growth factor β (TGF-β) and it controls the activity of the EF2 transcription factors responsible for activation of the genes essential for progression from G_1 into S phase. The pRb pathway has proved to be central to the cellular antigrowth signaling circuit and is disrupted in some manner in the majority of human cancers.

The appealing notion that loss of regulation of a gene that in some manner controls cellular growth through genetic or epigenetic mechanisms was essential for cell transformation allowed carcinogenesis to be described as the net result of the combination of at least two molecular events: activation of an oncogene and inactivation of a tumor suppressor gene. This was consistent with the multistage nature of animal models of carcinogenesis. Disruption of one cellular pathway triggered proliferation, and a complimentary disruption conferred upon transformed cells the ability to overcome inhibitory effects of their normal neighbors. Tumorigenesis would be the result of sustained, uncontrolled growth that rendered the cell population susceptible to other mutagenic events.

C. The Colorectal Carcinogenesis Paradigm

Colorectal cancer was the first human tumor type in which the oncogene activation/tumor suppressor gene inactivation model was conclusively validated. In 1990, Fearon and Vogelstein published an elegant model for the development of colorectal cancer that could be broadly applied to the entire field of carcinogenesis research (Fig. 1). This tumor type was uniquely suited for the study of multistep carcinogenesis because of the availability of tissue samples representing all clinical stages of the disease (i.e., from very small adenomas to large metastatic carcinomas). During the past decade, this model has not only proven its relevance but has stimulated a wide range of important advances in the study of tumor progression.

In order to gain understanding of the different clinical stages of the disease at a molecular level, Fearon and Vogelstein analyzed data from a wide range of molecular pathological studies of colorectal cancers. By correlating the clinical stages with observed genetic derangements, they identified four key sites: *ras* gene mutations and deletions of chromosomes 5q, 17p, and 18q. Mutations in the *ras* gene were found in about half of all colorectal carcinomas and adenomas greater than 1 cm in size. Familial adenomatous polyposis, an inherited disease that predisposes patients to colorectal tumor formation, was linked to a site (now known to be the locus of the *APC* gene) on chromosome 5q. Allelic losses of chromosome 5q were evident in 20–50% of colorectal carcinomas. The functional inactivation of the p53 protein is seen in more than half of all human cancers studied. The *p53* tumor suppressor gene maps to the common region of loss on chromosome 17p found in colorectal tumors. Consistent with findings in other adult tumors, Fearon

and Vogelstein found that more than 75% of colorectal carcinomas exhibit the loss of a large portion of chromosome 17p. Finally, they noted that chromosome 18q was lost in more than 70% of these carcinomas and almost half of late adenomas. The *DCC* gene maps to the common region of loss, and DCC was recognized as a cell adhesion molecule.

The nature of the prevalent genetic defects in colorectal carcinogenesis reiterated the requirement for mutational activation of an oncogene and mutational inactivation of a tumor suppressor in carcinogenesis. Indeed, this study supported the concept that genetic losses appear to be more important genetic gains during carcinogenesis. Consistent with the estimated four- to six-step mechanism of human carcinogenesis, a correlation between the number of genetic aberrations and the stage of the tumor was observed. While disruptions of at least four to five genes (all of the aforementioned key sites plus one additional allelic loss) appeared in colorectal carcinomas, most early adenomas contained an average of only two. They also confirmed that different, specific sets of genes were *likely* to be involved (but not *necessarily* involved) at different stages of colorectal tumorigenesis; however, they found exceptions from each stage that suggested that the process was more complex than could be explained by a particular set of genetic lesions. This led them to conclude that the total accumulation of changes is more important than their temporal order.

Fearon and Vogelstein noted that in some cases a mutation in the *p53* gene appeared to dominate the

Stage	Event	Result
Normal epithelium	Mutation/loss of *APC*, Loss/derangement of 5q	Hyperproliferative epithelium
Early adenoma	Mutation of *k-RAS*, derangement of 12q	Intermediate adenoma
Intermediate adenoma	Mutation/loss of *DCC*, loss/derangement of 18q	Late adenoma
Late adenoma	Mutation/loss of *p53*, Loss/derangement of 17p	Carcinoma
Carcinoma	Other events	Metastasis

FIGURE 1 Adaptation of Fearon and Vogelstein's pivotal model of colorectal carcinogenesis.

wild-type allele through oligomerization of the mutant protein with the wild-type protein, resulting in inactivation of normal p53 function. This demonstrates that a mutation in one allele of a tumor suppressor gene sometimes exerted its effect in a dominant manner. We now know that the protein encoded by the *p53* gene is a central component in the biochemical circuits controlling cell proliferation and programmed cell death (apoptosis). Removal of p53 might confer a selective growth advantage via growth deregulation and insensitivity to apoptotic signals, with a concomitant increase in the mutation rate and/or chromosomal instability leading to the eventual loss of the corresponding wild-type allele through localized mutation, mitotic recombination, or chromosomal loss. This would statistically account for the formation of sporadic tumors, which would be difficult to explain using the recessive model for tumor suppressors in which two unrelated mutational events are required, one to inactivate each allele.

D. The Cutaneous Malignant Melanoma Paradigm

The colorectal model is useful for gaining a deeper understanding of neoplastic development in virtually all types of tissues. For example, the same type of analysis can be used to examine the development of cutaneous malignant melanoma in terms of successive genetic changes. Molecular analysis of the clinically evident biological phases in melanoma development shown in Fig. 2, i.e., the development of nevi displaying architectural disorder and cytologic atypia (i.e., atypical or dysplastic nevi), the unregulated proliferation of melanocytes within the epidermis in melanoma *in situ*, the acquired competence to invade and proliferate within the dermis in primary invasive melanoma, and the development of metastatic capacity, has proven invaluable in our present understanding of this disease.

It appears that one of the earliest events in the malignant transformation of the melanocyte is the disruption of genetic integrity and the triggering of dynamic genetic instability. During this stage of melanoma development, DNA aneuploidy can be used to distinguish melanomas *in situ* from nonmalignant atypical nevi (which do not normally exhibit aneuploidy). Early melanoma cell populations with near-diploid chromosome complements are not uncommon; however, upon analysis, they can be shown to bear subtle genetic abnormalities, most probably in genes involved in maintaining genetic stability (e.g., genes critical to DNA repair, replication, cell cycle, chromosome maintenance, and mitosis).

Melanocytes acquire genetic disruptions via two major routes: (i) spontaneous endogenous damage due to deamination of pyrimidines, the generation of

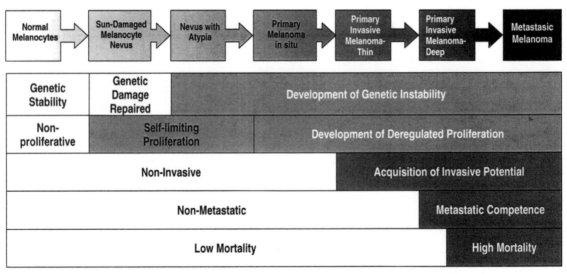

FIGURE 2   Biological stages of development for cutaneous malignant melanoma.

oxidative free radicals, infidelity in DNA replication, defects in DNA repair, and metabolism of toxic or mutagenic substances and (ii) exogenous damage by ultraviolet radiation (UVR). A number of efficient repair enzymes continually monitor DNA before, during, and after replication for a range of accumulated defects. Derangement of genes associated with repair of DNA damage is typically found in many types of cancer. DNA repair genes map to chromosomes that are often perturbed in melanomas, e.g., 3p and 7, possibly implicating these genes in the observed genetic instability of these lesions.

Deregulated cell proliferation is a phase critical to the propagation of genomic disturbances. Because epidermal melanocytes rarely divide in adult skin, damage to DNA probably contributes less to the process of melanoma development than to tumorigenesis in other tissues. However, exposure of melanocytes to UVR results in a transient and limited number of cell divisions that accelerate the development of a protective skin tanning by increasing the mean density of epidermal melanocytes. Concomitantly, UVR inflicts DNA damage by provoking an increase in lipid peroxidation and free radical formation and by inducing single strand breaks and pyrimidine dimers in DNA. Thus, following sun exposure, the melanocyte is faced with two conflicting signals: (i) cease replication of DNA and repair of UVR-induced damage or (ii) proceed with UVR-initiated cell division. Normally, melanocytes will respond by arresting the cell at G_1, activating DNA repair systems, and allow the cell to divide only when repairs are completed. If the damage is severe enough, the melanocyte may be driven into apoptosis and eliminated. However, in some instances, the intrinsic differences in repair efficiencies for a particular DNA defect or premature resumption of DNA synthesis on a damaged template results in the melanocyte repairing most, but not all, of the UVR-induced damage. One possible outcome of this incomplete repair is the formation of a premalignant melanocyte harboring a critical but biologically inert genetic lesion, which may become the first step in carcinogenesis if it is followed by a complementary lesion produced via a subsequent error in normal cell division.

The development of deregulated proliferation of melanocytes within the epidermis is a key clinical feature that differentiates melanoma *in situ* from normal and atypical nevi. As *in situ* melanomas continue to proliferate, they can accumulate additional genetic defects. The connection between abnormal proliferation and malignant progression is underscored by the observation that any melanocytic lesion (e.g., atypical nevus, primary, or metastatic melanoma) with a disproportionately high number of cells traversing the S phase has a worse prognosis than lesions in which the S-phase fraction is similar to normal tissue. Linking genetic instability with a loss of G_1/S transition control is evident from data showing that euploid melanomas have a lower percentage of cycling cells in S phase than aneuploid tumors, and this feature correlates with longer survival. How transition from the normal G_0 state of the melanocyte to G_1 and S phase is accomplished in a deregulated manner appears to involve the evolution of a subpopulation of cells that have lost control of the G_1/S phase transition due in part to gene defects in cell cycle regulatory proteins (e.g., $p16^{INK4A}$, $p15^{INK4B}$, and PITSLRE proteins) and to loss of genes regulating cell senescence (several of which have been mapped to chromosomes 1,6,7,9, and 11).

Sometime during progression, *in situ* melanoma cells that are restricted to growth in the epidermis spontaneously acquire an invasive phenotype and penetrate the underlying dermal layer. The clinical relevance of this new propensity is that it shows a strong positive correlation with the development of widespread metastases and increasing mortality rates. How a melanoma *in situ* progresses to an invasive melanoma is unknown, but it is clear from model systems that unrestrained growth of the cells alone is insufficient. Current evidence suggests that the development of melanoma cell invasion is driven by the evolution of specific biological traits, e.g., (i) melanoma-directed dysregulation of the surrounding normal tissue interactions and architecture allowing physical invasion, (ii) the ability of melanoma cells to abrogate or attenuate inhibitory growth and motility signals from the normal tissue promoting invasion, and (iii) the production by melanoma cells of paracrine and autocrine growth factors and cytokines (and their receptors) allowing altered growth and motility.

In order for physical invasion to occur, the melanoma cell must disrupt the extracellular matrix of the dermis prior to metastatic spread. More than a simple static barrier, the extracellular matrix plays a complex role in maintaining normal homeostasis of the skin by providing structural integrity and by generating biochemical signals that control cell adhesion, growth, differentiation, and migration. Invasive tumor cells must neutralize both of these barriers to affect tissue invasion. Several mechanisms have been identified in melanoma. Derangements in the expression and/or activation of proteolytic enzymes have been found that can disrupt the physical integrity of the extracellular matrix. Melanoma cells promote changes in the expression and assembly of major matrix components. Additionally, the expression and/or function of cell surface integrins and other molecules important to cell–cell communication has been found to be altered or disrupted. Contact with the extracellular matrix during the invasive stage of tumor progression alters the expression of a wide range of genes in many cell types, including melanomas. This interaction is complex, and a fuller understanding of it is necessary for the elucidation of the molecular basis of invasiveness.

Melanoma cells must also breach the biochemical barriers to invasion. The ability of melanoma cells to acquire invasive potential correlates with the acquisition of resistance to inhibitory factors produced by dermal fibroblasts and possibly infiltrating inflammatory cells. The mechanisms by which invasive melanoma cells become resistant to the inhibitory effect of cytokines and interleukins such as interleukin-6 (IL-6), tumor necrosis factor α (TNF-α), and TGF-β are unknown. It may involve alterations in the receptors for these molecules and/or in other genes that comprise a signal-transducing pathway that engages these molecules. Many of the growth factors, integrins, and inhibitory proteins that are perturbed in melanoma transduce signals to various cellular compartments via protein phosphorylation. Emerging data suggest a connection between defects in members of the protein tyrosine kinase family of genes and altered signal transduction in the pathogenesis of melanoma. Melanoma cells have been shown to express and secrete growth factors, providing autocrine stimulation of melanoma proliferation. In addition, the expression of a number of such factors is inducible in epidermal cells by UVR, including IL-1, IL-6, IL-8, and

TNF-α. In this manner, "normal" cells within the immediate tissue environment can play a major role in the growth deregulation of transformed cells. We are beginning to appreciate that tumors are not merely collections of transformed cells. They are complex tissues in which heterogeneous mixtures of normal cells such as fibroblasts, endothelial cells, and immune cells interact continuously with cancer cells. The use of heterotypic organ culture systems may ultimately prove more fruitful than a traditional cell culture for elucidating the mechanisms of neoplasia and for screening potential therapeutic agents.

The final stage of neoplasia, i.e., the development of metastatic competence and migration of tumor cells from the primary site to specific distant organs, is the most poorly understood in terms of relevant molecular defects. Many critical aspects are required for the cell to acquire metastatic competence, including the expression and/or dysfunction of numerous biologic pathways involved in the ability of the cell to invade tissue, survive, and proliferate within the invaded tissue, migrate through the tissue, inhibit immune defenses, orchestrate the development of new blood vessels, escape into the bloodstream, and reemerge in a distant organ. Studies are beginning to establish dominant roles for specific families of genes such as the cadherins in the metastatic process. In melanoma cells, switching cadherin expression from E-cadherin to N-cadherin results in the loss of keratinocyte control over these cells and establishment of communication with fibroblasts and endothelial cells. Disruption of growth factor signaling pathways, notably endothelin-3 and stem cell factor and their receptors, is also associated with the development of metastatic potential in melanomas.

In addition to a series of intrinsic molecular defects within the tumor cell, the study of melanoma has also provided evidence for another critical factor that may either suppress or aid tumor development in an as yet unpredictable manner: i.e., host immune competence and responsiveness. The potentially important role of this phenomenon in tumor growth is evidenced by spontaneous tumor regression in melanoma patients, and the observation that UVR in animal model systems can have a profound stimulatory effect on the outgrowth of tumor cells by transiently suppressing host immunological defense mechanisms. At present, relatively little is known about the interplay between immune suppression and specific genetic defects in tumor cells and how this interchange impacts upon the growth and spread of tumor cells. Presumably, through a separate series of genetic defects, the tumor cell may also develop the ability to resist or abrogate host immunity.

III. REFINING THE MODEL

A. Simplifying Complexity

The two tumor models discussed earlier clearly show that the evolution of genetic instability, deregulated proliferation, and invasive and metastatic competence are complicated events developing, not as the result of a single genetic defect, but driven by an accumulation of molecular alterations in an overlapping succession of cell subpopulations. This disruption of the cellular genome results in defects in numerous regulatory mechanisms that control normal cell homeostasis, and because these mechanisms are complex, it is not surprising that an impressive diversity of cancer genotypes and phenotypes exists. Since the 1980s, more than 100 oncogenes and tumor suppressor genes have been identified, including representatives from virtually all of the major regulatory circuits of the cell. Components of the pathways regulating the cell cycle (e.g., Rb, E2Fs, p21^{INK4A}, p15^{INK4B}), apoptosis (e.g., p53, Bax, Bcl-2), inflammatory response (cyclooxygenase-2), cell communication (e.g., integrins, cadherins), and genetic stability (e.g., mismatch repair-associated proteins, telomerase) are disrupted, damaged, or abnormally regulated in neoplasia.

Nonnuclear genetic defects may also play a role in carcinogenesis. The occurrence of somatic mutations of the mitochondrial genome in human colorectal cancer has been examined. Mutations of this type have the potential to interfere with normal oxidative phosphorylation, a disruption possibly accompanied by an increase in the level of cellular reactive oxygen species (which are known to affect DNA damage leading to mutations). Due to the nature of mitochondrial replication, it is conceivable that the entire mitochondrial population within a clonal cell population may become homogeneous if the end result of the mutated mitochondrial genome is to confer a selective growth advantage.

The carcinogenic effects of epigenetic events further complicate the picture, such as the binding of chemical promoters of carcinogenesis to cellular receptors to regulate certain gene products. Cancer cells display a variety of epigenetic mechanisms by which they circumvent normal barriers to neoplasia, e.g., the disruption of the FAS death signal pathway by upregulation of a nonsignaling decoy receptor that titrates signals away from the apoptosis pathway. Hypermethylation of the promoter regions of cancer-associated genes is another important epigenetic mechanism of carcinogenesis. Methylation of CpG islands in the promoter region of a gene can block its expression; aberrant hypermethylation of cancer-related gene promoters has been observed in several types of cancers.

There have been frequent attempts to simplify and codify this apparent diversity of mechanisms through categorization. The most recent and intellectually satisfying systems group cancer-associated genes into categories representing their functional activities. Classical tumor suppressor genes such as *p53*, *Rb*, and *APC*, which prevent cancer through direct control of growth have been termed "gatekeepers." Genes that suppress neoplasia in an indirect manner by maintaining the fidelity of the genome, including DNA mismatch repair genes, spindle checkpoint genes such as *BUB1* and *MAD1*, or DNA damage checkpoint genes that include *ATM*, *Brca1*, and *Brca2*, have been called "caretakers." A third pathway to cancer (carcinogenesis via "landscaper" defects) has been proposed based on the observation that, under certain conditions, normal cells proximal to a rapidly proliferating defective cell population are at an increased risk of neoplastic transformation due to the biochemical factors present in their abnormal microenvironment.

Although these classification systems have proven useful, they fail to address the cancer problem in a manner that connects them in a meaningful way to cell phenotype and biological behavior and that would lead to a unified understanding of the malignant process. Such an understanding is crucial to the eventual development of comprehensive therapeutic or preventive strategies. We have been fortunate in having available for study the colorectal cancer and malignant melanoma paradigms, which are amenable to analysis at multiple clinical stages, in the pursuit of a molecular mechanism of multistage carcinogenesis. Both these models focus on the genetic and biological characteristics a cell must acquire to overcome cellular and tissue barriers to oncogenesis. This theme is reflected in current models of carcinogenesis. During the next few years, aided in part by the sequencing of the human genome and recent technical advances in sophisticated and sensitive analysis of global expression of genes and proteins, such models will be greatly refined as we continue to link the phenotype and biological behavior of a tumor cell with specific genes and signaling circuits.

B. Current Models

Recent models of tumorigenesis have attempted to synthesize our understanding of the molecular events underlying the stages of neoplasia with our increasing knowledge of the central molecular circuitry of the cell. Examination of tissues from various types of can-cers has shown that when cells progress from a pre-neoplastic state through advanced malignancy, they acquire a set of characteristics that are the hallmarks of cancer. In a current model proposed by Hanahan and Weinberg, carcinogenesis can be viewed as a process in which disruption of each key cellular circuit results in the acquisition by the cell of a new capability, enabling the cell to successfully breach one of the anticancer defense mechanisms of the organism. Malignancy is thus achieved through genetic and epigenetic disruptions, resulting in the acquisition of a set of six acquired capabilities essential for fully malignant neoplastic transformation (Table 1). They argue that virtually all genetic and epigenetic disruptions that contribute to carcinogenesis result in the acquisition of one or more of these capabilities and they reiterate Fearon and Vogelstein's observation that the precise order and nature of genetic and epigenetic derangements may not always be important for carcinogenesis.

The expansion of our understanding of the molecular circuitry of the cell has facilitated an in-depth

TABLE I
Hanahan and Weinberg's Model of Multistage Carcinogenesis

Acquired capability[a]	Common mechanisms	Specific examples
Self-sufficiency in growth signals	Deregulation of growth signal pathways via disruption of extracellular signals, signal transducers, and corresponding intracellular circuits	Production of PDGF, bFGF, or TGFα (autocrine stimulation), upregulation or truncation of EGF-R/erbB, upregulation of HER2/neu, SOS-Ras-Raf-MAP kinase mitogenic cascade mutants, defects in herterotypic signaling
Insensitivity to antigrowth signals	Derangement of the pathways that recognize and respond to the antigrowth signals that normally force proliferating cells into the G_0 stage or direct them to terminally differentiate and lose their proliferative, capacity	Rb gene mutation or pRb sequestration. Other disruptions of the pRb signaling circuit, including downregulation and/or mutation of TGFβ receptors, p16^{INK4A}, p15^{INK4B} and CDK4. Overexpression of c-myc, erbA
Evading apoptosis	Defects in sensors directing apoptosis or effectors carrying it out	p53 tumor suppressor gene abnormalities, upregulation of bcl-2, disruption of FAS death-signaling, IGF-2 gene expression
Limitless replicative potential	Circumvention of telomere shortening	Upregulation of telomerase expression, induction of alternate mechanisms of telomere maintenance
Sustained angiogenesis	Disregulation of angiogenic factors, altered expression, or proteolytic modification of pro- and anti-angiogenic signaling factors	Activation of ras, upregulation of VEGF, FGF1/2, downregulation of thrombospondin-1, β-interferon
Tissue invasion and metastasis	Changes in expression of cell–cell adhesion molecules, integrins, growth factors, and extracellular proteases	Switch in expression from E-cadherin to N-cadherin, preferential expression of α3β1 and and αVβ3 integrins, downregulation of endothelin-3

[a]The process is viewed as the gradual acquisition of six key capabilities.

exploration of how different mutational and epigenetic routes can be followed that lead to the same end and how phenotypically identical cancers can have very different genotypes. We now recognize that knowledge of the unique molecular signature of a given tumor, rather than its histological identity, may prove to be the pivotal factor in designing the most effective therapeutic regimen. It has also become clear why some mutations are more oncogenic than others. The study of multifunctional proteins such as p53 and pRb indicates that it is because the gene product involved is central to more than one circuit, hence deregulation at one key point allows the cell to breach multiple barriers to neoplasia simultaneously.

IV. IMPLICATIONS FOR CANCER PREVENTION AND THERAPY

The recent refinements of the carcinogenesis model should result in superior prognostic and diagnostic modeling as well as improved clinical management of the patient with cancer. By focusing on biological characteristics common to most forms of neoplasms, new therapies can be developed that target the acquisition of these cancer-associated biological phenomena and the underlying genetic abnormalities. Antiangiogenic therapies, for example, hold the promise of being applicable to a wide variety of cancers. Through definition and elucidation of the specific molecular pathways that can lead to cancer and understanding how a cell interconnects and organizes signaling pathways in a hierarchical system to control the behavior of a cell, we may be able to identify pharmacological targets that mitigate or attenuate those circuits that often become permuted and/or rerouted during cancer development. The great strides made in large-scale gene expression analyses of cells and tissues should materially and quickly provide targets for novel therapies. The ongoing genetic mapping studies of polymorphisms in putative cancer susceptibility genes will further allow exciting opportunities to not only tailor cancer treatment, but also to identify those who may be at increased risk for a primary or secondary cancer. These individuals are potential candidates for cancer chemoprevention clinical trials.

See Also the Following Articles

Animal Models for Colon Cancer Chemoprevention • Chemoprevention Trials • Colorectal Cancer: Molecular and Cellular Abnormalities • Melanoma: Biology • Molecular Epidemiology and Cancer Risk • Retinoblastoma Tumor Suppressor Gene

Bibliography

Albino, A. P., Reed, J. A., and Fountain, J. W. (1998). Melanoma: Molecular biology. *In* "Cutaneous Oncology" (S. J. Miller and M. E. Mahoney, eds.). Blackwell Science, Oxford.

Cooper, G. M. (1982). Cellular transforming genes. *Science* **218,** 801–806.

Fearon, E. R., and Vogelstein, B. (1990). A genetic model for colorectal carcinogenesis. *Cell* **61,** 759–767.

Foulds, L. (1964). Tumour progression and neoplastic development. *In* "Cellular Control Mechanisms and Cancer" (P. Emmelot and O. Mühlbock, eds.), pp. 242–258. Elsevier, Amsterdam.

Hanahan, D., and Weinberg, R. (2000). The hallmarks of cancer. *Cell* **100,** 57–70.

Herlyn, M., Berking, C., Li, G., and Satyamoorthy, K. (2000). Lessons from melanocyte development for understanding the biological events in naevus and melanoma formation. *Melanoma Res.* **10,** 303–312.

Kinsler, K. W., and Vogelstein, B. (1996). Lessons from hereditary colorectal cancer. *Cell* **87,** 159–170.

Kinsler, K. W., and Vogelstein, B. (1997). Gatekeepers and caretakers. *Nature* **386,** 761–763.

Kinsler, K. W., and Vogelstein, B. (1998). Landscaping the cancer terrain. *Science* **280,** 1036–1037.

Knudson, A. G., Jr. (1985). Hereditary cancer, oncogenes, and antioncogenes. *Cancer Res.* **45,** 1437–1443.

Loeb, L. (1991). Mutator phenotype may be required for multistage carcinogenesis. *Cancer Res.* **51,** 3075–3079.

Nowell, P. (1976). The clonal evolution of tumor cell populations. *Science* **194,** 23–28.

Renan, M. J. (1993). How many mutations are required for tumorigenesis? Implications from human data. *Mol. Carcinogen.* **7,** 139–146.

Rous, P., and Kidd, J.G. (1941). Conditional neoplasms and subthreshold neoplastic states. *J. Exp. Med.* **73,** 365–390.

Weinberg, R. (1989). Oncogenes, antioncogenes, and the molecular bases of multistep carcinogenesis. *Cancer Res.* **49,** 3713–3721.

myb

R. V. Tantravahi
E. Premkumar Reddy

*Fels Institute for Cancer Research and
Molecular Biology, Philadelphia, Pennsylvania*

GLOSSARY

avian myeloblastosis virus A virus found to induce myelobastic leukemia in chickens *in vivo* and to transform chicken yolk sac cells *in vitro*.

c-*myb* A protooncogene that is the normal cellular homlogue of the avian myeloblastosis virus-tranforming genes v-*myb*.

***myb* oncogene** Transforming gene of avian myeloblastosis virus.

The *myb* oncogene is the transforming gene of avian myeloblastosis virus (AMV), which was isolated originally by Hall and colleagues in 1941. AMV was found to induce myeloblastic leukemia in chickens *in vivo* and to transform chicken yolk sac cells *in vitro*. Isolation of purified virus particles and molecular cloning and sequencing of the viral genome led to the identification of the transforming sequence.

Cellular gene sequences encoding either structural or functional domains with homology to v-*myb* have been found in nearly every metazoan species thus far examined. The mammalian c-*myb* proto-oncogene (the cellular counterpart of v-*myb*) encodes a transcription factor that binds to DNA in a sequence-specific manner and is localized in the nucleus. MYB proteins act to regulate the genes that control proliferation and differentiation of cells, the most important of which are of the hematopoietic lineage. The pattern of c-*myb* gene expression in cultured cell lines indicates that MYB proteins function by maintaining cells in an immature state of differentiation and in a highly active state of proliferation. *In vivo*, expression of c-*myb* is indispensably important to embryonic development, as transgenic mice nullizygous at the c-*myb* locus die *in utero* due to lack of fetal hepatic hematopoiesis.

This article attempts to describe the structure and function of the c-*myb* gene and of its protein product.

The description begins with a discussion of the first viral *myb* isolates characterized in avian systems. It also discusses the role of c-*myb* in hematopoietic cell growth control as it has been described in a variety of experimental model systems, including transgenic animals.

I. HISTORY, VIROLOGY, AND EARLY *IN VIVO* TRANSFORMATION DATA

A. v-*myb* Retroviruses

In 1941, Hall identified two week-old chickens with neurolymphomatosis. One of the chickens showed lymphoid hyperplasia of the bone marrow, while the other showed lymphocytosis of the peripheral blood. Filtered homogenate from the affected tissues was injected into newborn Rhode Island Red chicks and into adult White Leghorn chickens. Systematic passaging of the diseased tissue homogenate into unaffected animals led to the isolation of a stock of virus that could induce hemocytoblastosis at a frequency of 100% with an average latency of 19 days. This transforming principle was a novel avian acute transforming retrovirus, AMV, the avian myeloblastosis virus.

Infection of chickens with purified AMV leads invariably to myeloblastic leukemia.

In 1964, Ivanov and co-workers, working in Bulgaria, isolated a novel transforming principle from quail. The purified retrovirus isolated from these quail, avian erythroblastosis virus E26, induces myeloblastic and erythroblastic leukemias in chickens. Molecular genetic analyses in the form of cloning, restriction mapping, and heteroduplex analysis of AMV and E26 helped identify the *myb* oncogene in both viral genomes.

B. Viral *myb* Gene Structure

An examination of integrated proviruses revealed the structure of both AMV and E26. These genomic structures are shown in Fig. 1. The v-*myb* allele arose by recombination between the replication-competent myeloblastosis-associated virus type 1 (MAV-1) and cellular DNA sequences from chicken. The resulting acute transforming retrovirus, AMV, contains cellular *myb* sequences at the 3′ end of the viral genome. The AMV genome contains intact viral *gag* and nearly intact *pol* genes. The *myb* gene sequences replace 26 carboxy-terminal codons of the viral *polymerase* gene

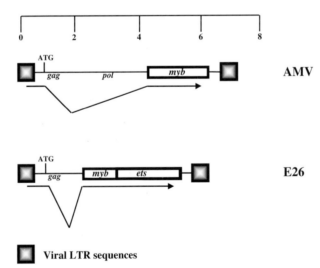

FIGURE 1 Schematic diagram of the viral genomes of avian myeloblastosis virus (AMV), and E26 avian erythroblastosis virus (E26). Sequences of the viral *gag* (group antigen glycoprotein) and *pol* (reverse transcriptase) genes are indicated. The transduced *myb* and *ets* sequences are indicated by boxes. Below each viral genome, the structure of the v-*myb* mRNA is shown by an arrow. Transcription initiates at the viral long terminal repeat (LTR) sequences, and the message is spliced to produce an mRNA containing an initiator methionine derived from *gag*.

and nearly the entire viral envelope (*env*) gene, thus rendering the virus replication defective. The v-*myb* protein of AMV is derived from a spliced mRNA containing viral *gag* sequences at the 5' end and 11 amino acids of the 3' end sequence derived from the viral *env* gene. The v-*myb* protein from AMV is 382 amino acids in length and has an M_r on SDS–PAGE of 48 kDa. The E26 v-*myb* transcript contains coding sequences from three distinct genes: the viral *gag* gene, the c-*myb* gene and the cellular *ets-1* gene. The E26 v-*myb* gene encodes a 669 amino acid tripartite fusion protein (GAG-MYB-ETS) with an M_r on SDS–PAGE of 135 kDa.

C. Discovery of a Cellular Homologue

The cellular homologue of the viral *myb* gene was isolated from chicken thymus mRNA. The chicken c-*myb* gene has an open reading frame of 2148 nucleotides and encodes a primary translation product of 639 amino acids, with an M_r on SDS–PAGE of 77 kDa. Comparison of the viral and cellular *myb* gene sequences revealed that v-*myb* alleles contain truncations of sequence at both the 5' and the 3' ends. The predicted sequence of the chicken c-*myb* cDNA contains 203 amino acids of 3' coding sequence not present in the AMV-derived v-*myb* gene. Additionally, sequence analysis of the 5' end of the AMV v-*myb* allele revealed loss of sequences found in chicken c-*myb* as well as 10 sites of nucleotide point changes, which lead to changes in the amino acid sequence of the translated protein. Comparison of the E26 v-*myb* sequence with the chicken c-*myb* sequence revealed the loss of 72 amino terminal and 272 carboxy terminal amino acids. E26^{v-myb} contains a single point mutation at the 5' end that does not appear in AMV^{v-myb}. Acquisition of oncogenic potential by MYB proteins has been associated with amino and carboxy terminus truncation since these sorts of truncations in v-MYB were first observed.

II. MYB GENE FAMILY

Following the discovery and molecular cloning of the v-*myb* oncogene, it has been possible to examine the role of the cellular counterpart of v-*myb* in cell growth, differentiation, and development. These studies have revealed that the c-*myb* gene is highly conserved through evolution and is present in all vertebrates and even in some invertebrate species. Proteins translated from viral as well as cellular *myb* genes are located in the nucleus, exhibit sequence-specific DNA binding activity, and appear to function as regulators of transcription.

A. Cellular *myb* Genes

c-*myb* cDNAs have been cloned and sequenced from chicken, human, and mouse. These cDNA clones have enabled the isolation of genomic DNA segments. The exon/intron organization of the murine c-*myb* gene is shown in Fig. 2. The c-*myb* gene is encoded on an approximately 40-kb stretch of DNA on mouse chromosome 10 and human chromosome 6. The protein-coding sequence is contained on 15 exons that are present in the major translation product, p75^{c-myb}. During the course of analysis of tumor-derived *myb* mRNA species, an additional coding exon was identified and designated exon 9A. This internal stretch of sequence is present only in a larger and less abundant transcript that encodes p89^{c-myb}.

c-myb Gene Expression Patterns

Both chicken and mouse c-*myb* genes are expressed highly in tissues associated with hematopoiesis, both during development and in the adult organism. Chicken, mouse, and human c-*myb* genes encode 3.8- to 4.0-kb mRNAs, which are abundant in the thymus, bursa, fetal liver, and yolk sac in chicken and in the thymus, bone marrow, and fetal liver in mouse. c-*myb* is expressed at high levels in immature hematopoietic cells and its expression levels change dramatically during cytokine or chemical-induced differentiation of cultured cell lines. Consequently, differentiation of t hematopoietic cells *in vivo* leads to a decrease in levels of c-*myb* mRNA. Similarly, cultured cell lines that are arrested at different stages of differentiation, such as the pre B lymphocyte 70Z/3B and the mature B lymphocyte A20 2J, differ in their c-*myb* expression levels depending on their differentiation states. Chemical induction of the myelomonocytic cell line HL-60 with dimethyl sulfoxide (DMSO) leads to differentiation of the cells, with a concomitant decrease in

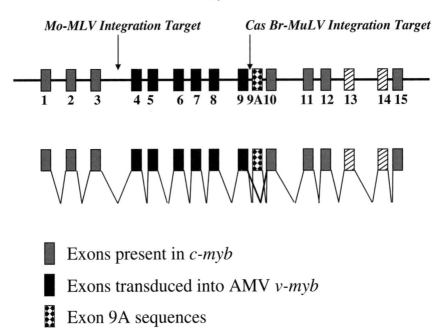

Exons present in *c-myb*

Exons transduced into AMV *v-myb*

Exon 9A sequences

Exons deleted in ABPL-4 *myb*

FIGURE 2 Schematic diagram of the c-myb locus. The human c-myb gene is located on chromosome 6q. The murine homologue is present on chromosome 10. Each box represents an exon that contains amino acid coding sequence. The key (bottom) indicates exons present in p75 and p89^{c-myb}, exons transduced in v-myb, and exons deleted in the mouse myeloid tumor cell line ABPL-4. Below the diagram of the *myb* locus, is a representation of the c-myb mRNA is shown. The alternative splicing patterns which generate p75 and p89^{c-myb} are shown by the overlapping lines beneath the exons. Arrows above the gene structure diagram indicate the positions of virus integrations by the Moloney murine leukemia virus (Mo-MLV) and the Cas Br murine leukemia virus (Cas Br MuLV).

cellular *myb* mRNA levels. Friend virus-induced murine erythroleukemia cells (F-MEL) differetiate *in vitro* in the presence of DMSO. This process is abrogated in F-MEL, which express a *myb* transgene. 32D cl3, a normal promyelocytic cell line, proliferates rapidly in the presence of interleukin-3 (IL-3). 32D cl3 cells cultured in IL-3-containing medium are also maintained in the immature (myeloblast) state of differentiation. Treatment of 32D cl3 cells with granulocyte–colony-stimulating factor (G-CSF) leads to cell cycle exit, followed by terminal differentiation into mature granulocytes. Terminal differentiation of 32D cl3 cells is accompanied by dramatic decreases in c-myb expression levels.

Persistent expression of *myb* alleles in cultured hematopoietic cell lines can lead to alterations in the growth rates of cells and to alterations in their differentiation programs. 32D/v-myb cells, for example, retain a high rate of cell proliferation in the presence of G-CSF and also are refractory to the G-CSF differentiation signal. The cells retain a myeloblastic morphology, indicating that MYB proteins cause these cells to remain in an immature state of differentiation. This direct effect of MYB proteins is also clearly observed in transformed cells of hematopoietic origin, whose high rates of proliferation are consistent with high levels of *myb* gene expression.

B. Deregulated *myb* Gene Expression and Neoplastic Transformation

Activation events that underlie neoplastic transformation include mutagenesis of the *myb* gene. These mutagenic events assume three principal forms: retroviral transduction of *myb* gene sequences into acute transforming retroviruses, alteration of the *myb* locus in human tumors, and retroviral insertional mutagenesis of the *myb* locus in murine and avian tumors.

1. Activation of myb Gene Sequences in Human Tumors

The human c-*myb* gene is located on chromosome 6q bands 22-24. Abnormalities in this region of 6q have been observed in hematological malignancies, such as acute myelogenous leukemia (AML) and T-cell leukemias. Similar abnormalities have been observed in nonhematological malignancies, such as colon carcinoma and melanoma. Amplification of the *myb* locus has been observed in a majority of these cancers. This gene amplification has been accompanied by increases in *myb* gene transcription. Although gross rearrangements of the *myb* locus have not been observed in these instances, little is known about the structure or the activity of MYB proteins produced from the amplified loci.

myb gene rearrangements have also been observed in one human melanoma cell line with a chromosomal translocation within the 6q region. Analysis of the *myb* allele in this translocation cell line indicates that the gene rearrangement falls within the 3′ region of the c-*myb*. Similar 3′ end truncations have been observed in the transduction of c-*myb* into acute transforming retroviruses and in myeloid tumors isolated from mice that have been infected with acute transforming retroviruses.

2. Activation of myb Gene Sequences by Retroviral Integration in Murine Tumors

Isolation of acute transforming retroviruses in murine and avian systems led to experimentation with those viruses *in vivo* in unaffected animals. Infection of BALB/c mice with the Abelson murine leukemia virus (A-MuLV), for example, invariably leads to the development of three distinct forms of neoplastic disease. Two of these cancers are lymphoid in origin and depend on the expression of the transforming gene of A-MuLV, v-*abl*. These lymphoid tumors were, thus, named Abelson virus induced lymphosarcoma (ABLS) and Ableson virus induced plasmacytoma (ABPC). The third type of transformed cell derived from A-MuLV infection was slow developing, less aggressive, and of the myeloid lineage. These tumor cells were named Abelson virus-induced plasmacytoid lymphsarcomas (ABPL). ABPL tumors do not express the v-*abl* protein. Molecular analysis of the proviral genome from ABPL tumor cells indicated that the activation event was an insertional mutagenesis of the *myb* locus by the A-MuLV helper virus, Moloney murine leukemia virus, Mo-MLV. It was later shown that Mo-MLV infection of BALB/c mice led to the development of identical myeloid tumor cell lines.

ABPL tumors contain a truncated Mo-MLV genome integrated between exons 3 and 4 of the murine c-*myb* gene. The ABPL mRNA is transcribed from the viral LTR sequence, and the initiator methionine is derived from the viral *gag* gene. Secondary mutagenic events to viral integration have been observed in ABPL tumors both within the proviral genome and within the cellular *myb*-coding sequences.

Retroviral insertional mutagenesis of the *myb* locus has also been observed after infection of chicken cells with avian leukosis virus (ALV). In the case of ALV-induced neoplasms, the amount of structural change to the chicken c-*myb* gene is actually quite minor. The major difference in this case is the change of promoter sequence. It can thus be argued fairly that the induction of MYB-mediated neoplasms by Mo-MLV and ALV has at least as much to do with the deregulation of *myb* gene transcription as it does with the change in the structure of the MYB protein product.

III. MYB GENE PRODUCTS

A. MYB Topology

Structure/function analysis of the murine c-*myb* cDNA took the form of *in vitro* mutagenesis of the cloned cDNA followed by transcriptional transactivation studies with a c-*myb* responsive promoter sequence. Three domains of the MYB protein were characterized by this method: the DNA-binding domain, the transcription activation domain, and the negative regulatory domain.

1. DNA-Binding Domain

The study of MYB/DNA interactions began with the use of purified v-MYB proteins in *in vitro*-binding studies. The consensus DNA sequence for MYB protein recognition was determined to be 5′ PyAACG/TG 3′. This consensus sequence has been observed in viral (SV40) transcription control sequences, as well as in cellular gene promoters, such as that of the *mim-1* gene. MYB DNA binding is mediated by the N-terminal DNA-binding domain, a structure that has been characterized by three 50 amino acid repeats. Protein secondary structure features further characterize each of the repeats (Fig. 3).

The repetitive structure of the MYB DNA-binding domain is highly conserved through evolution, and sequences corresponding to this domain have been observed in chicken, mouse, and human c-*myb*, as well as in the *Drosophila melanogaster* MYB protein. *Zea mays* transcription factor c1 and *Saccharomyces cerevisae* transcription factor BAS-1 also contain MYB repeat structure-based DNA-binding domains. Deletion analysis of the three repeats showed that the first repeat 1 (R1) is dispensable for specific DNA binding. Although R2 and R3 are required for MYB/DNA association, R1 is thought to play a role in the stabilization of the complex. Amino acid sequence analysis of the R2R3 region revealed repeated helix–turn–helix (HLH) motifs with unconventional turns. Additionally, MYB DNA-binding repeat sequences contain a periodic occurrence of tryptophan residues that are spaced 18 amino acids apart. These tryptophans are very highly conserved through evolution. Mutagenesis of either the amino acid residues of the HLH domains or of the tryptophans abolishes

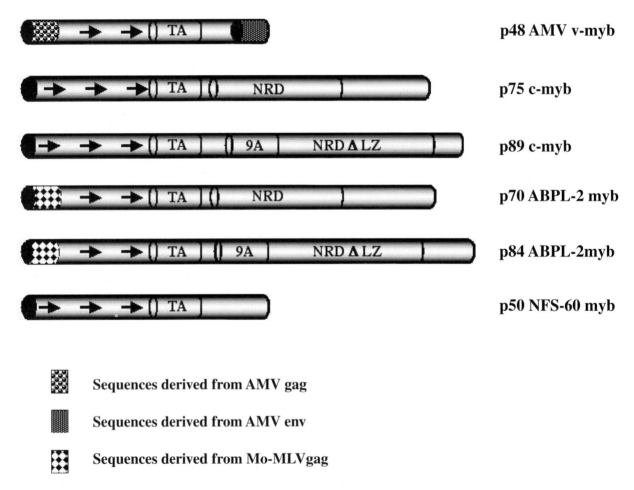

FIGURE 3 Topologies for MYB isoforms derived from c-MYB and from Myb isoforms isolated from virus-induced tumors. A key (below) denotes the origin of viral protein sequences derived from AMV or from Mo-MLV. The DNA binding domain is denoted by consecutive arrows, each representing a 50 amino acid repeat motif. TA = Transactivation domain; NRD = negative regulator domain; LZ = leucine zipper motif within the negative regulatory domain; LZΔ = disrupted leucine zipper domain; 9A = exon 9A sequences present in p89^(c-myb), which appear downstream of the transactivation domain.

MYB DNA binding. Interestingly, replacement of the tryptophans with other aromatic amino acid residues does not have an effect on DNA binding. This has led many into thinking that the HLH residues mediate contact with specific DNA sequences, while the tryptophan residues provide a hydrophobic scaffold upon which the HLH motif can contact DNA.

2. Transactivation Domain

Deletion and linker insertional analyses of c-*myb* and v-*myb* genes revealed a transcriptional activation domain downstream of the DNA-binding domain. The transactivation domain stretches 52 amino acids in length in human c-MYB (275–327) and 85 amino acids (241–325) in murine c-MYB. MYB transactivation domains contain clusters of acidic amino acids similar to those described for other transcription activators. Deletion analysis of the transactivation domain indicated that the overall negative charge of the domain might not be the sole determinant of activation activity. Deletion of 11 amino acids of the transactivation domain that do not affect the overall charge of the domain completely abrogate the transactivation activity of c-MYB. These results suggest that the transactivation domain may mediate protein–protein interactions, which require multiple subdomains within its structure.

3. Negative Regulatory Domain

The observation that viral *myb* alleles lack sequences found at the 5′ and 3′ ends of c-*myb* indicated to investigators that the deleted regions contained regulatory sequences capable of suppressing MYB biochemical function. Indeed, 3′ end deletion mutant cDNA clones were shown to possess increased transactivation activity in reporter gene assays. Increases in DNA-binding activity have also been reported for C terminus truncated MYB protein isoforms.

Analysis of the sequences contained within the negative regulatory domain indicates the presence of a leucine zipper motif containing three leucine and one isoleucine residue. The leucines are spaced to produce an α helical structure that permits intermolecular interactions at this domain. It is unclear how precisely the leucine zipper domain of c-*myb* is employed in negative regulation. Mutagenesis of the leucine residues to alanine disrupts the helical structure of the leucine zipper and results in a mutated c-MYB protein with increased transactivation activity.

This indicates that the leucine zipper may mediate MYB oligomerization, resulting in a complex unable to bind DNA and to transactivate target genes. Alternatively, a *trans* regulator of MYB encoded on a different gene may bind to and inactivate MYB proteins through interactions at the leucine zipper. Candidate *trans* regulators have been cloned, but these proteins have not demonstrated a high degree of specificity in their interaction with c-MYB.

Additional studies have suggested that the leucine zipper structure may not play as important a role as had been originally suggested. Deletion of regions within the 3′ end of c-*myb*, which lie outside of the leucine zipper structure, have been shown to increase the transactivation properties of c-MYB, indicating that these regions may mediate negative regulation either separately or in concert with the leucine zipper structure.

B. p89$^{\text{c-}myb}$

Examination of the structure of *myb* mRNAs produced by virus-induced myeloid leukemic cell lines revealed structural anomalies in the splicing patterns at the 5′ end of the gene. Initiation of the mRNA at the viral LTR sequences and inclusion of viral *gag* sequences caused these anomalies of structure. Additional structural anomalies distal to the integration site were observed also. These took the form of in-frame insertions of sequence between exons 9 and 10. The original ABPL-2 cDNA clone encodes a protein that contains 363 bp of sequence not present in p75$^{\text{c-}myb}$. Examination of *myb* cDNA sequences from nonvirus-infected sources showed that the in-frame insertion represents a novel *myb* gene transcript produced in nontransformed cells. Analysis of metabolically labeled cells with anti-MYB antisera specific for p75$^{\text{c-}myb}$ and for the sequences encoded by the insertion indicated that the inserted sequences are part of a novel MYB protein isoform, p89$^{\text{c-}myb}$. The insertion sequence was named exon 9A. Both nontransformed and tumor cells with active *myb* loci, produce exon 9A-containing MYB isoforms.

Exon 9A occupies a position within the *myb* gene that changes the configuration of the protein at the site of the C-terminal negative regulatory domain. The exon 9A region disrupts the sequence encoding the leucine zipper structure present at the C terminus. Consequently, p89$^{\text{c-}myb}$ was shown to possess higher intrinsic transactivation activity than p75$^{\text{c-}myb}$.

C. MYB Proteins and Development

A great many studies on *myb* gene structure and MYB protein function have been performed in cultured cell lines, in cell free systems, and with purified DNA from tumor cell lines and clinical samples. All of these studies have contributed greatly to our understanding of the structure of the gene and of its biochemical activity.

All of these studies also possess limitations in that they cannot shed light on the role of MYB *in vivo* either in development or in the adult hematopoietic system. These aspects of MYB biology were addressed to some degree by the generation of a transgenic mouse nullizygous at the *myb* locus. Embryonic stem (ES) cells containing wild-type murine c-*myb* alleles were transfected with a construct containing a neomycin resistance gene flanked extensively by *myb* gene sequences. Cultured ES cells that acquired resistance to neomycin were tested for recombinational inactivation of the *myb* locus, and candidate cell lines were used to generate chimeric mice lacking one *myb* allele. Germline chimeric mice were mated to produce offspring that would contain null mutant alleles of *myb* on both chromosomes.

c-*myb* "knockout" mice do not survive to term. The knockout phenotype is incompatible with live birth. Examination of aborted fetuses indicates that the mice die *in utero* due to lack of fetal hepatic hematopoiesis. Bone marrow hematopoiesis does not appear to be affected, but the critical generation of stem cells produced in the liver during development seems to be dependent on *myb* gene expression.

IV. CONCLUSIONS

The c-*myb* gene is a master control gene in the hematopoietic system. Expression of c-*myb* is indispensably important during fetal development and for the proliferation of hematopoietic cells in the adult organism. Ectopic expression of MYB proteins leads to a constellation of hematological and nonhematological malignancies in humans, which occurs often as a consequence of genetic alterations, such as chromosomal translocation, or gene amplification. Experimental induction of cancer via infection with acute transforming viruses has given us insight into structure/function relationships in the MYB protein, as we

now have some idea of the content and position of the various domains of this protein. Much of what is know about posttranslational modification, and regulation in *trans* of the MYB protein, and of MYB gene targets has not been discussed in this article due to spatial constraints. However, despite this impressive collection of experimental data, the precise role of this protein in the control of proliferation, differentiation, and development of the hematopoietic system remains to be determined fully. The development of new *in vitro* techniques with which to study protein–protein interactions and new *in vivo* models in which the expression of *myb* during development can be manipulated more exactly will aid investigators in resolving these issues. We await those and other developments.

See Also the Following Articles

Bcl-2 Family Proteins and the Dysregulation of Programmed Cell Death • c-mos Protooncogene • fos Oncogene • Ras Proteins • Retinoblastoma Tumor Suppressor Gene • *TP53* Tumor Suppressor Gene • Wnt Signaling

Bibliography

Alitalo, K., Winqvist, R., Lin, C. C., et al. (1984). Aberrant expression of an amplified c-*myb* oncogene in two cell lines from a colon carcinoma. *Proc. Natl. Acad. Sci. USA* **81,** 4534–4548.

Baluda, M. A., and Reddy, E. P. (1994). Anatomy of an integrated avian myeloblastosis provirus: Structure and function. *Oncogene* **9,** 2761–2774.

Barletta, C., Pelicci, P. G., Kenyon, L. C., et al. (1987). Relationship between the c-*myb* locus and the 6q-chromosomal aberration in leukemias and lymphomas. *Science* **235,** 1064–1067.

Bender, T. P., and Kuehl, W. M. (1986). Murine *myb* protooncogene mRNA: cDNA sequence and evidence for 5' heterogeneity. *Proc. Natl. Acad. Sci. USA* **83,** 3204–3208.

Bender, T. P., Thompson, C. B., Kuehl, W. M. (1987). Differential expression of c-*myb* mRNA in murine B lymphomas by a block to transcription elongation. *Science* **237,** 1473–1476.

Biedenkapp, H., Borgmeyer, U., Sippel, A. E., *et al.* (1988). Viral *myb* oncogene encodes a sequence-specific DNA-binding activity. *Nature* **335,** 835–837.

Clarke, M. F., Kukowska-Latallo, J. F., Westin, E., *et al.* (1988). Constitutive expression of a c-*myb* cDNA blocks Friend murine erythroleukemia cell differentiation. *Mol. Cell Biol.* **8,** 884–892.

Dasgupta, P., and Reddy, E.P. (1989). Identification of alternatively spliced transcripts for human c-myb: Molecular cloning and sequence analysis of human c-*myb* exon 9A sequences. *Oncogene* **4,** 1419–1423.

Dasgupta, P., Linnenbach, A. J., Giaccia, A. J., *et al.* (1989). Molecular cloning of the breakpoint region on chromosome 6 in cutaneous malignant melanoma: Evidence for deletion in the c-myb locus and translocation of a segment of chromosome 12. *Oncogene* **4,** 1201–1205.

Dalla-Favera, R., Franchini, G., Martinotti, S., *et al.* (1982). Chromosomal assignment of the human homologues of feline sarcoma virus and avian myeloblastosis virus onc genes. *Proc. Natl. Acad. Sci USA* **79,** 4714–4717.

Dubendorff, J. W., Whittaker, L. J., Eltman, J.T., *et al.* (1992). Carboxy-terminal elements of c-Myb negatively regulate transcriptional activation in *cis* and in *trans*. *Genes Dev.* **6,** 2524–2535.

Dudek, H., and Reddy, E.P. (1989). Identification of two translational products for c-*myb*. *Oncogene* **4,** 1061–1066.

Dudek, H., and Reddy, E.P. (1989). Murine myeloid leukemias with aberrant *myb* loci show heterogeneous expression of novel MYB proteins. *Oncogene* **4,** 1489–1495.

Favier, D., and Gonda, T.J. (1994). Detection of proteins that bind to the leucine zipper motif of c-Myb. *Oncogene* **9,** 305–311.

Gonda, T.J., and Metcalf, D. (1984). Expression of *myb*, *myc* and *fos* proto-oncogenes during the differentiation of a murine myeloid leukemia. *Nature* **310,** 249–251.

Grasser, F. A., Graf, T., and Lipsick, J. S. (1991). Protein truncation is required for the activation of the c-*myb* proto-oncogene. *Mol. Cell Biol.* **11,** 3987–3996.

Hall, W. J., Bean, C. W., and Pollard, M. (1941). Transmission of fowl leukosis through chick embryos and adult chicks. *Am. J. Vet. Res.* **2,** 272–279.

Hesketh (ed.) (1997). "The Oncogene and Tumor Suppressor Factsbook," 2nd Ed., pp. 276-286. Academic Press, London.

Ivanov, X., Mladnov, Z., Nedyalkov, S., *et al.* (1964). Experimental investigations into avian leukosis. V. Transmission, hematology and morphology of avian myelocytomatosis. *Bull. Inst. Pathol. Comp. Animaux Domest. (Sophia)* **10,** 5-38.

Jiang, W., Kanter, M. R., Dunkel, I., *et al.* (1997). Minimal truncation of the c-*myb* gene product in rapid-onset B-cell lymphoma. *J. Virol.* **71,** 6526–6533.

Kanei-Ishii, C., MacMillan, E. M., Nomura, T., *et al.* (1992). Transactivation and transformation by Myb are negatively regulated by a leucine-zipper structure. *Proc. Natl. Acad. Sci USA* **89,** 3088–3092.

Katzen, A. L., Kornberg, T. B., and Bishop, J.M. (1985). Isolation of the proto-oncogene c-myb from *D. melanogaster*. *Cell* **41,** 449–456.

Klempnauer, K. H., Symonds, G., Evan, G. I., *et al.* (1984). Subcellular localization of proteins encoded by oncogenes of avian myeloblastosis virus and avian leukemia virus E26 and by chicken c-*myb* gene *Cell* **37,** 537–547.

Lavu, S., and Reddy, E. P. (1986). Structural organization and nucleotide sequence of mouse c-*myb* oncogene: Activation in ABPL tumors is due to viral integration in an intron which results in the deletion of the 5' coding sequences. *Nucleic Acids Res.* **14,** 5309–5320.

Lipsick, J. S. (1996). One billion years of Myb. *Oncogene* **13,** 223–235.

Majello, B., Kenyon, L. C., and Dalla-Favera, R. (1986). Human c-*myb* protooncogene: Nucleotide sequence of cDNA and organization of the genomic locus. *Proc. Natl. Acad. Sci. USA* **83,** 9636–9640.

Mucenski, M.L., McLain, K., Kier, A. B., *et al.* (1991). A functional c-*myb* gene is required for normal murine fetal hepatic hematopoiesis. *Cell* **65,** 677-689.

Mushinski, J. F., Potter, M., Bauer, S.R., et al. (1983). DNA rearrangement and altered RNA expression of the c-*myb* oncogene in mouse plasmacytoid lymphosarcomas. *Science* **220,** 795–798.

Nakagoshi, H., Nagase, T., Kanei-Ishii, C., *et al.* (1990). Binding of the c-*myb* proto-oncogene product to the simian virus 40 enhancer stimulates transcription. *J. Biol. Chem.* **265,** 3479–3483.

Nomura, T., Sakai, N., Sarai, A., *et al.* (1993). Negative autoregulation of c-Myb activity by homodimer formation through the leucine zipper. *J. Biol. Chem.* **268,** 21914–21923.

Oh, I. H., and Reddy, E. P. (1999). The *myb* gene family in cell growth, differentiation and apoptosis. *Oncogene* **18,** 3017-3033.

Patel, G., Kreider, B., Rovera, G., *et al.* (1993). v-myb blocks granulocyte colony-stimulating factor-induced myeloid cell differentiation but not proliferation. *Mol. Cell Biol.* **13,** 2269–2276.

Patel, G., Tantravahi, R., Oh, I. H., *et al.* (1996). Transcriptional activation potential of normal and tumor-associated *myb* isoforms does not correlate with their ability to block GCSF-induced terminal differentiation of murine myeloid precursor cells. *Oncogene* **13,** 1197–1208.

Paz-Ares, J., Ghosal, D., Wienand, U., *et al.* (1987). The regulatory c1 locus of Zea mays encodes a protein with homology to myb proto-oncogene products and with structural similarities to transcriptional activators. *EMBO J.* **6,** 3553–3558.

Reddy, E. P., Skalka, A. M., and Curran, T. (eds.). (1988). "The Oncogene Handbook," pp. 327-340. Elsevier, Amsterdam.

Rosson, D., and Reddy, E. P. (1986). Nucleotide sequence of chicken c-*myb* complementary DNA and implications for myb oncogene activation. *Nature* **319,** 604–606.

Rosson, D., Dugan, D., and Reddy, E. P. (1987). Aberrant splicing events that are induced by proviral integration: implications for *myb* oncogene activation. *Proc. Natl. Acad. Sci. USA* **84,** 3171–3175.

Saikumar, P., Murali, R., Reddy, E. P. (1990). Role of tryptophan repeats and flanking amino acids in Myb-DNA interactions. *Proc. Natl. Acad. Sci USA* **87,** 8452–8456.

Sakaguchi, A.Y., Lalley, P. A., Zabel, B. U., Ellis, R. W., Scolnick, E. M., and Naylor, S. L. (1984). Chromosome assignments of four mouse cellular homologs of sarcoma and leukemia virus oncogenes. *Proc. Natl. Acad. Sci. USA* **81,** 525–529.

Sakura, H., Kanei-Ishii, C., Nagase, T., *et al.* (1989). Delineation of three functional domains of the transcriptional activator encoded by the c-*myb* protooncogene. *Proc. Natl. Acad. Sci. USA* **86,** 5758-5762.

Shen-Ong, G. L., and Wolff, L. (1987). Moloney murine leukemia virus-induced myeloid tumors in adult BALB/c mice: Requirement of c-*myb* activation but lack of v-*abl* involvement. *J. Virol.* **61,** 3721–3725.

Shen-Ong, G. L., Potter, M., Mushinski, J. F. *et al.* (1984). Activation of the c-*myb* locus by viral insertional mutagenesis in plasmacytoid lymphosarcomas. *Science* **226,** 1077–1080.

Shen-Ong, G. L., Luscher, B., and Eisenman, R. N. (1989). A second c-*myb* protein is translated from an alternatively spliced mRNA expressed from normal and 5'-disrupted myb loci. *Mol. Cell Biol.* **9,** 5456–5463.

Tantravahi, R., Dudek, H., Patel, G., *et al.* (1996). Murine myeloid leukemic cells with disrupted myb loci show splicing anomalies that account for heterogeneous sizes in MYB proteins. Oncogene. 1996 **13,** 1187–1196.

Tavner, F. J., Simpson, R., Tashiro, S., *et al.* (1988). Molecular cloning reveals that the p160 Myb-binding protein is a novel, predominantly nucleolar protein which may play a role in transactivation by Myb. *Mol. Cell Biol.* **18,** 989–1002.

Tice-Baldwin, K., Fink, G. R., and Arndt, K. T. (1989). BAS1 has a Myb motif and activates HIS4 transcription only in combination with BAS2. *Science* **246,** 931–935.

Valtieri, M., Tweardy, D. J., Caracciolo, D., *et al.* (1987). Cytokine-dependent granulocytic differentiation. Regulation of proliferative and differentiative responses in a murine progenitor cell line. *J. Immunol.* **138,** 3829-3835.

Westin, E. H., Gallo, R. C., Arya, S. K., Eva, A., Souza, L. M., Baluda, M. A., Aaronson, S. A., and Wong-Staal, F. (1982). Differential expression of the *amv* gene in human hematopoietic cells. *Proc. Natl. Acad. Sci. USA* **79,** 2194–2198.

Weston, K., and Bishop, J. M. (1989). Transcriptional activation by the v-*myb* oncogene and its cellular progenitor, c-*myb*. *Cell* **58,** 85-93.

Woo, C. H., Sopchak, L., and Lipsick, J. S. (1998). Overexpression of an alternatively spliced form of c-Myb results in increases in transactivation and transforms avian myelomonoblasts. *J. Virol.* **72,** 6813-6821.

Zabel, B. U., Naylor, S. L., Grzeschik, K. H., *et al.* (1984). Regional assignment of human protooncogene c-*myb* to 6q21-qter. *Somat. Cell Mol. Genet.* **10,** 105–108.

Neoplasms in Acquired Immunodeficiency Syndrome

Alexandra M. Levine
University of Southern California Keck School of Medicine

GLOSSARY

AIDS Clinical Trials Group A large, multi-institutional group sponsored by the National Institutes of Health, which performs prospective therapeutic trials in an attempt to define optimal therapies for HIV and the opportunistic illnesses with which it is associated.

AIDS-defining illness Certain clinical diseases that have been associated with underlying infection by HIV and which are considered to constitute a diagnosis of AIDS, requiring reporting to the Centers for Disease Control and Prevention. These include opportunistic infections, wasting syndrome, AIDS dementia complex, pulmonary TB, recurrent bacterial pneumonia, Kaposi's sarcoma, intermediate- or high-grade B-cell lymphoma, and invasive cervical carcinoma.

CD4$^+$ lymphocytes CD4 cells are T cells of the helper/inducer subset, which are responsible for a myriad of functions involved in the normal immune response and its regulation. In HIV-infected individuals, the CD4 count drops as a consequence of infection, resulting in the immune deficiency that is characteristics of AIDS. When the CD4 count drops to levels below 200/mm^3, serious opportunistic infections and malignancies are expected. In the absence of a clinical AIDS-defining illness, a CD4 count <200/mm^3 is considered "immunologic AIDS."

human immunodeficiency virus, type 1 (HIV-1) An RNA lentivirus, which is the etiologic agent in AIDS. The virus infects CD4 positive lymphocytes, establishing a latent infection after insertion into the DNA, or may also cause a direct cytopathic effect, destroying these CD4 positive lymphocytes. HIV-1 also infects monocytes/macrophages, Langerhans cells of the cervix, and glial cells in the brain, among others.

highly active antiretroviral therapy Consists of combinations of drugs with activity against the human immunodeficiency virus. These combinations usually consist of drugs from each of three major classes: nucleoside reverse transcriptase inhibitors, nonnucleoside reverse transcriptase inhibitors, and protease inhibitors.

T hree malignancies are statistically increased in HIV-infected individuals and, if present, constitute AIDS-defining conditions. These include Kaposi's sarcoma (KS), intermediate- or high-grade B cell non-Hodgkin's lymphoma (NHL), and squamous cell carcinoma of the cervix. Each of these malignancies has been associated with an underlying viral infection, including Kaposi's sarcoma associated herpes virus (KSHV)/human herpesvirus type 8 (HHV8) in the case of KS, Epstein–Barr virus in 30–100% of cases with NHL, and human papillomavirus (HPV) in women with invasive cervical cancer (ICC). In each case, the viral infection, along with the immune dysregulation induced by HIV, has created a mileau that is conducive to the development of malignancy. The epidemiologic features, therapeutic approaches, and ultimate prognosis of these malignancies vary with the state of the underlying HIV induced immunosuppression and have changed over the years, as more effective antiretroviral therapies have become available. Thus, the recent advent and widespread use of highly active antiretroviral therapy (HAART) has resulted in a significant decline in the incidence of AIDS-related KS, whereas characteristics of NHL and ICC appear to have changed as well. Novel approaches to therapy have been developed, which seek to target those factors critical to the pathogenesis of disease. The ultimate prevention of these malignancies will require long-term suppression of HIV, allowing a return to more normal immune regulation.

I. KAPOSI'S SARCOMA

A. Etiology and Pathogenesis

The etiology and pathogenesis of KS are complex, only recently elucidated, and still not fully understood. Underlying immunosuppression clearly increases the risk of KS. Thus, the incidence of KS in organ transplant recipients receiving immunosuppressive therapy is 400 to 500 times higher than that seen in the general population. Genetic factors may also play a role.

In addition to these factors, the epidemiology of AIDS-related KS has always suggested the possibility that another sexually transmitted organism might be involved in the pathogenesis of disease, as the disorder is statistically more likely to occur in homosexual/bisexual men, as opposed to other population groups infected by HIV. The concept of KS as a sex-

ually transmitted disease, independent of HIV infection, is also derived from studies of KS in young, sexually active, HIV-negative homosexual men in the United States.

The identification of a newly described human herpesvirus, termed KS-associated herpesvirus (KSHV) or human herpesvirus type 8 (HHV-8), provided the anticipated link between this tumor and another presumably sexually transmitted virus. Genomic material from HHV-8 was subsequently found within almost all KS tissues from virtually all types of KS, including AIDS-KS, classic Mediterranean KS, endemic KS from Africa, and transplantation-associated KS.

Subsequent work confirmed that seroconversion to HHV-8 occurred prior to the development of clinical KS and that the likelihood of infection by the virus increased with increasing numbers of homosexual contacts. Indeed, independent epidemics of HHV-8 and of HIV were confirmed among homosexual men living in New York City and Washington, DC, both beginning in the early 1980s. While presumably transmitted by sexual contact, the actual means by which HHV8 is transmitted remains speculative at this time. However, the rather consistent presence of HHV8 in saliva among infected individuals suggests the possibility of transmission via this route as well.

A number of HHV-8-encoded gene products have been identified, which have the capability to induce the multiple aberrations found within KS tissues. Nonetheless, while the virus appears necessary for the development of KS, it is not sufficient, in itself, to cause the disease. The further addition of immunosuppression, and an environment conducive to inflammatory and angiogenic signals, is apparently also required.

Aside from inducing the necessary immunosuppression, the HIV *tat* gene product is also operative in the pathogenesis of disease. Thus, *tat* protein has been shown to increase the proliferation of KS derived spindle cells. *Tat* also activates the expression of tumor necrosis factor-α (TNF-α), IL-6, and various adhesion molecules. The *tat* protein also synergizes with other inflammatory cytokines induced by HIV that stimulate endothelial cells and the invasion of KS spindle cells.

The full pathogenesis of AIDS-KS is thus complex, and the very designation of the tumor as a true malignancy remains under question. Nonetheless, it is apparent that the full expression of disease requires several components. These include HIV-1 itself, as well as the *tat* gene product, and a mileau of inflammatory cytokines and angiogenic factors. HHV-8 may induce the initial transforming event, as well as a myriad of gene products that contribute to the cascade of angiogenic and inflammatory cytokines that induce further growth of the lesion. Conceptually, then, the KS lesion is driven by factors that induce the three components that are integral to the disease: cell proliferation, inflammation, and angiogenesis. These concepts have formed the basis for the development of new modalities of therapy aimed specifically at blocking the pathogenesis of disease.

B. Changing Epidemiology of KS in the Era of Highly Active Antiretroviral Therapy (HAART)

The widespread use of HAART in resource-rich areas of the world has been associated with a significant decrease in the incidence of both KS and opportunistic infections in HIV-infected patients. In the Multicenter AIDS Cohort Study of homosexual/bisexual men, rates of KS fell by 66% between 1989–1994 and 1996–1997, coincident with the period in which HAART use increased substantially. In the Swiss HIV Cohort Study, consisting of the majority of people with advanced HIV infection in Switzerland, Ledergerber and colleagues demonstrated a substantial reduction in incident cases of KS, with a relative risk of 0.08 when comparing data from July 1997 to June 1998, after the introduction of HAART. These epidemiologic changes further attest to the importance of underlying immune suppression and the cascade of HIV-1 induced cytokines and angiogenic factors that are critical to the pathogenesis of AIDS-KS.

C. Presentation of AIDS-Related KS

KS most frequently presents as cutaneous lesions, which have a predeliction for the head and neck regions, upper torso, or extremities. The lesions are pigmented, ranging from pink to purple or brown to brownish-black. KS lesions can be flat, plaque-like, or nodular and are often symmetric, occurring in skin lines or creases. The oral cavity is commonly involved, with purple or brownish plaques on the soft palate or gingiva, which are usually asymptomatic. Involvement of the oral cavity has been associated with KS elsewhere in the gastrointestinal (GI) tract. Visceral involvement occurs in over 50% of cases, most of whom have no symptoms. Although any organ may be involved, the GI tract is the most common site of extracutaneous KS. When symptomatic, patients present with abdominal pain, weight loss, or diarrhea, which may be bloody. Pulmonary KS is the second most common site of visceral disease and is the most life-threatening form of the tumor. Patients often present with dyspnea or cough. Radiographic findings are variable and nonspecific. The diagnosis of pulmonary KS is usually made at the time of bronchoscopy.

D. Therapy of AIDS-Related KS

1. HAART

Anecdotal reports have noted the efficacy of HAART in treating KS, although formal trials have not yet been accomplished. Nonetheless, the use of effective therapy aimed at suppressing HIV-1 is a logical first step in the treatment of individuals with AIDS-related KS. Further, when HAART is used at the conclusion of other therapy for KS, a prolongation of the time to KS treatment failure has been described.

2. Therapy for Localized Disease

Multiple types of local therapy are effective in the treatment of KS lesions. However, KS is a systemic disease, even though apparently localized at the time of diagnosis. Thus, while local therapy may be efficacious in eradicating individual lesions, systemic relapse is expected. Various modes of effective local therapy include surgical excision, cryotherapy with liquid nitrogen, laser therapy, intralesional injections of vincristine (0.1 mg) or vinblastine (0.1 to 0.2 mg), or radiation. Alitretinoin topical gel (0.1%) has been licensed for use in patients with AIDS-KS, associated with a 35–50% response rate.

3. Interferon-α (IFN-α)

IFN-α has immunomodulatory, antiviral, antiproliferative, and antiangiogenic effects. When used in conjunction with antiretroviral therapy, doses ranging from 1 to 10 million units daily have been associated with response rates in the range of 50%.

4. Cytotoxic Chemotherapy

In two independent phase III studies, liposomal daunorubicin (40 mg/m^2 iv every 2 weeks) and liposomal doxorubicin (20 mg/m^2 iv every 2 weeks) as single agents had activity equivalent or superior to combinations of ABV (adriamycin, 10 or 20 mg/m^2; bleomycin, 10 U/m^2; vincristine, 1 or 2 mg) or BV, with a similar duration of response, overall survival, and decreased toxicity. Based on these large randomized studies, the liposomal agents are now considered first-line therapy in the treatment of patients with advanced AIDS-KS. Paclitaxel (135 mg/m^2 every 3 weeks by a 3-h infusion or 100 mg/m^2 every 2 weeks by a 3-h infusion) has shown response rates of 60–70% in patients with relapsed KS, with duration of response in the range of 1 year. Paclitaxel is now considered the therapy of choice in patients who have failed first line systemic therapy.

5. Antiangiogenesis Approaches

Several drugs have shown early promise of efficacy by targeting the angiogenesis that is essential for the pathogenesis of KS. These include IM-862, a dipeptide identified from soluble fractions of the thymus and administered as a nasal spray; thalidomide, at doses from 200 to 1000 mg/day; and others that aim at the inhibition of vascular endothelial growth factor (VEGF) and basic fibroblast growth factor (bFGF).

6. Retinoids

Retinoic acids mediate numerous biologic activities by regulating cellular genes, including mediators of the immune response, such as IL-6, which is a growth factor for KS *in vitro*. Oral 9-*cis* retinoic acid has been associated with major responses in approximately 30 to 40% of patients, whereas all-*trans* retinoic acid (ATRA) has shown some activity as well, especially in its liposomal form. Topical 9-*cis*-retinoic acid cream has been approved for use in localized KS lesions.

7. Antiviral Approaches Targeting HHV-8

In vitro drug sensitivity studies have shown that HHV-8 is very sensitive to cidofovir, moderately sensitive to ganciclovir and foscarnet, and insensitive to acyclovir.

Thus far, no study has yet been completed that evaluates the clinical efficacy of this approach in patients with AIDS-KS. However, a recent prospective randomized trial by Martin and colleagues found that patients randomized to receive systemic ganciclovir as maintenance therapy for cytomegalovirus induced retinitis had a statistically decreased risk of developing KS over time. These approaches are of great interest, and future trials are expected in patients with known AIDS-related KS.

II. AIDS-RELATED LYMPHOMA

A. Epidemiology

Lymphoma is a relatively late manifestation of HIV infection, accounting for approximately 3–4% of all initial AIDS defining conditions, but as many as 20% of all AIDS related deaths. The risk of ARL is as high as 650 times greater than expected in individuals who have already been diagnosed with an AIDS defining condition. All population groups at risk for HIV are at equal risk for developing ARL. While some decrease in the incidence of ARL has occurred with the widespread use of HAART, this decrease has been relatively minor.

B. Etiology and Pathogenesis

HIV-1 induces polyclonal B cell proliferation and activation and chronic antigenic stimulation. Additionally, the inflammatory cytokines (IL-6 and IL-10) released as a consequence of HIV infection may provide a mileau conducive to the ongoing proliferation of B lymphocytes. In time, this polyclonal B cell response to HIV-1 may provide the opportunity for a genetic aberration, leading to a selective growth advantage of one clone and the development of a monoclonal B cell lymphoma. The transformation from polyclonal response to monoclonal malignancy may be mediated through LMP-1 of the Epstein–Barr virus, present within ARL tissues in approximately 30–60% of systemic cases and in 100% of primary central nervous system (CNS) lymphomas associated with AIDS. EBV-driven ARLs consist primarily of diffuse large cell or immunoblastic pathologic types. Overexpression of c-*myc* is operative in the Burkitt's lymphomas associated with AIDS, whereas *bcl*-6 overexpression has been described in AIDS-related diffuse large cell lymphomas. p53 abnormalities have also been described.

C. Clinical and Prognostic Considerations

High-grade ARLs are unusual in their presentation and behavior. The majority (80–90%) are extra nodal at presentation, with the more common sites of disease including brain, GI tract, and bone marrow. However, literally any site may be affected. Approximately 80% present with systemic "B" symptoms, including fever, drenching night sweats, and/or weight loss. Prognostic features associated with short survival include a history of AIDS prior to the ARL; a poor performance status; a CD4 lymphocyte count less than $100/mm^3$; and stage III or IV disease. Additionally, an elevated LDH, older age (>35 years), and use of illicit injection drugs are also poor prognostic factors. The international prognostic index for lymphomas is valid in ARL as well.

D. Treatment

Low-dose m-BACOD is associated with a complete remission rate of 46%, with similar results in terms of CR, duration of response, and duration of survival when compared with standard dose m-BACOD. The low-dose regimen is associated with significantly reduced hematologic toxicity, as reported in a prospective randomized trial performed by the AIDS Clinical Trials Group (ACTG). Response rates to standard dose and low dose CHOP appear similar. Overall, however, median survival times have been short, ranging from approximately 6 to 8 months. Concomitant use of HAART has been associated with a prolongation in survival and a decrease in the occurrence of opportunistic infections. While zidovudine is associated with significant additive myelotoxicity, other antiretroviral agents (including protease inhibitors) appear safe when used in conjunction with combination chemotherapy, and accepted practice now includes the combined use of chemotherapy with HAART. A dose-adjusted EPOCH regimen has been used in a limited number of patients studied at the National Cancer Institute, with excellent preliminary results,

including a failure of any relapse so far. Another infusional regimen, termed CDE (cyclophosphamide, doxorubicin, etoposide), has resulted in a complete remission rate of 46% when studied in a large national trial.

Approximately 20% of asymptomatic patients with ARL may have malignant cells within the cerebrospinal fluid, mandating routine lumbar puncture as part of the staging evaluation of all patients. Routine CNS prophylaxis with intrathecal cytosine arabinoside or methotrexate is commonly employed and should certainly be used in patients with bone marrow involvement in whom the likelihood of CNS relapse is statistically increased.

IV. INVASIVE CERVICAL CANCER

A. Prevalence of HPV in HIV-Infected Women

Palefsky and colleagues have reported results from 2015 HIV-infected women and 577 HIV negative controls studied as part of the Women's Interagency HIV Study (WIHS) in whom HPV was assessed within cervico-vaginal lavage fluids, employing polymerase chain reaction. Evidence of HPV was found in 58% of HIV seropositives versus 26% of the HIV-negative controls. As the CD4 lymphocyte count declined, a greater percentage of HIV-infected women were found to have HPV, with 70% of women with CD4 cells $<200/mm^3$ demonstrating HPV infection. These data would be consistent with a high prevalence of initial infection and subsequent reactivation coinciding with a decline in immunity due to HIV. Other studies have demonstrated infection by HPV 16 or 18 in as many as 50% of HIV-infected women with less than $200/mm^3$ CD4 cells.

B. Prevalence of Abnormal Cervical Cytology in HIV-Infected Women

Data from the WIHS study demonstrated a 40% prevalence of abnormal pap smears in 2054 HIV-infected women compared with 17% among HIV-negative controls. While these abnormal pap results included cases of atypical squamous cells of undetermined significance, actual squamous intraepithelial lesions (SIL) were found at baseline in 30% of the HIV positives and 7% of controls.

C. Therapy of SIL in HIV-Infected Women

In HIV-negative women with CIN II or III, the risk of persistent or recurrent CIN occurring 1 year after specific therapy is approximately 5–10%. However, the recurrence rate in HIV-infected women approaches 40–50% within 1 year, indicating that constant surveillance of these women will be required to prevent the development of ICC. A recent ACTG study mandated usual therapy (LEEP, cone biopsy) for CIN II or III in HIV infected women, followed by a randomization between use of a 5% 5-fluorouracil (5FU) cream versus no further intervention. The use of 5FU topical cream, at a dose of 1 g every 2 weeks for 6 months, was associated with a statistically significant reduction in recurrence, occurring in 28% of treated women versus 47% of women assigned to observation.

D. Invasive Cervical Cancer in HIV-Infected Women

Maiman and colleagues described the characteristics of ICC in 16 HIV-infected women and 68 HIV-negative women treated over the same time period. High-grade (2 or 3) ICC was present in 100% of the HIV positives and 70% had stage III or IV disease at presentation, compared to only 28% of the HIV negatives. Metastasis to nodes was present in 63% of HIV-positive and 35% of HIV-negative women. After definitive therapy, 100% of the HIV-infected women experienced relapse, occurring at an interval of only 2.3 months. Mean survival was 9 months compared with 25 months in the seronegatives. It is thus clear that HIV-infected women must be carefully managed in terms of early diagnosis and therapy of cervical precursor lesions in an attempt to prevent ICC and its associated poor outcome.

See Also the Following Articles

HIV (HUMAN IMMUNODEFICIENCY VIRUS) • LYMPHOMA, HODGKIN'S DISEASE • NEOPLASMS OF UNKNOWN PRIMARY SITE • T CELLS, FUNCTION OF

Bibliography

Cannon, M., and Cesarman, E. (2000). Kaposi's sarcoma associated herpesvirus and acquired immunodeficiency syndrome related malignancy. In "Acquired Immunodeficiency Syndrome Malignancies: Seminars in Oncology" (A.M. Levine, ed.), Vol. 27, pp. 409–419. Saunders, Philadelphia.

Dezube, B. J. (2000). The role of human immunodeficiency virus-1 in the pathogenesis of acquired immunodeficiency syndrome-related Kaposi's sarcoma: The importance of an inflammatory and angiogenic milieu. In "Acquired Immunodeficiency Syndrome Malignancies: Seminars in Oncology" (A. M. Levine, ed.), Vol. 27, pp. 420–423. Saunders, Philadelphia.

Gaidano, G., Capello, D., Carbone, A, (2000). The molecular basis of acquired immunodeficiency syndrome-related lymphogenesis. In "Acquired Immunodeficiency Syndrome Malignancies: Seminars in Oncology" (A. M. Levine, ed.), Vol. 27, pp. 431–441. Saunders, Philadelphia.

Goedert, J. J. (2000). The epidemiology of acquired immunodeficiency syndrome malignancies. In "Acquired Immunodeficiency Syndrome Malignancies: Seminars in Oncology" (A. M. Levine, ed.), Vol. 27, pp. 390–401. Saunders, Philadelphia.

Kaplan, L. D., Straus, D. J., Testa, M. A. et al. (1997). Low dose compared with standard dose m-BACOD chemotherapy for non-Hodgkin's lymphoma associated with HIV. N. Engl. J. Med. 336, 1641–1648.

Krown, S. E. (2000). Diagnosis and treatment of AIDS associated Kaposi's sarcoma. In "AIDS Related Cancers and Their Treatment" (E. G. Feigal, A. M. Levine, and R. J. Biggar, eds.), pp. 59–96. Dekker, New York.

Ledergerber, B., Telenti, A., and Effer, M. (1999). Risk of HIV-related Kaposi's sarcoma and non-Hodgkin's lymphoma with potent antiretroviral therapy: Prospective cohort study. Br. Med. J. 319, 23–24.

Levine, A. M. (2000). Acquired immunodeficiency syndrome-related lymphoma: Clinical aspects. In "Acquired Immunodeficiency Syndrome Malignancies: Seminars in Oncology" (A. M. Levine, ed.), Vol. 27, pp. 442–453. Saunders, Philadelphia.

Little, R. F., and Yarchoan, R. (2000). Considerations in the management of HIV-infection in patients undergoing antineoplastic chemotherapy. In "AIDS Related Cancers and Their Treatment" (E. G. Feigal, A. M. Levine, and R. J. Biggar, eds.), pp. 281–330. Dekker, New York.

Maiman, M., Fruchter, R. G., Guy, L. et al. (1993). HIV-infection and invasive cervical carcinoma. Cancer 71, 402–406.

Martin, J. N., Ganem, D. E., Osmond, D. H. et al. (1998). Sexual transmission and the natural history of human herpesvirus 8 infection. N. Engl. J. Med. 338, 948–954.

Miles, S. A. (2000). Cytokines, viruses, angiogenesis: New therapies for Kaposi's sarcoma. In "AIDS Related Cancers and Their Treatment" (E. G. Feigal, A. M. Levine, and R. J. Biggar, eds.), pp. 169–194. Dekker, New York.

Robinson, W., III. (2000). Invasive and pre-invasive cervical neoplasia in human immunodeficiency virus infected women. In "Acquired Immunodeficiency Syndrome Malignancies: Seminars in Oncology" (A. M. Levine, ed.), Vol. 27, pp. 463–470. Saunders, Philadelphia.

Neoplasms of Unknown Primary Site

F. Anthony Greco
John D. Hainsworth
Sarah Cannon–Minnie Pearl Cancer Center, Nashville, Tennessee

GLOSSARY

adenocarcinoma A neoplasm that is derived from epithelial cells, that grows essentially in a glandular fashion, and that is malignant, i.e., it invades into surrounding tissues and disseminates to form metastases.

carcinoma A malignancy of the epithelial cells, constituting one of the four basic types of human cancer and the one most statistically prevalent.

neoplasm An abnormal growth of cells; a tumor; i.e., a mass of tissue exhibiting the general characteristics of uncontrolled proliferation of cells, an accelerated rate of growth, an abnormal structural organization, and a lack of coordination with the surrounding tissue.

squamous carcinoma An epithelial malignancy usually arising from altered cells from several organs, often attaining features similar to a form of skin cancer.

P atients with cancer of unknown primary site are common. The incidence is about 6% of all invasive cancers in the United States per year or about 80,000–90,000 patients. Extreme heterogeneity in clinical presentations, histologic appearances, and natural histories has made systematic evaluation of these patients difficult, and an established base of knowledge has developed slowly.

Management of these patients requires an understanding of several clinicopathologic features that help to identify more responsive tumors. Patients typically develop symptoms or signs at a metastatic site, and the diagnosis is made by biopsy of a metastatic lesion. History, physical examination, and additional evaluation fail to identify the primary site. Routine light microscopic histology establishes the neoplastic process and provides a practical system on which the patient can be evaluated and managed. There are four major light microscopic diagnoses: (1) poorly differentiated neoplasm, (2) well-differentiated and moderately well differentiated adenocarcinoma, (3) squamous cell carcinoma, and (4) poorly differentiated carcinoma (with or without features of adenocarcinoma).

The clinical characteristics, recommended diagnostic evaluation, treatment, and prognosis vary to some degree. Following clinical and pathological evaluation, the approximate size of the various groups and subsets of patients are illustrated in Fig. 1.

I. POORLY DIFFERENTIATED NEOPLASMS OF UNKNOWN PRIMARY SITE

In these patients, a general category of neoplasm (e.g., carcinoma, lymphoma, melanoma, sarcoma) cannot be determined from the biopsy by routine light mi-

croscopy. A precise diagnosis is necessary because many of these patients have responsive tumors. About 35 to 65% of poorly differentiated neoplasms are found to be lymphomas after further pathologic study, while most others are carcinomas, and a smaller group is melanoma and sarcoma. In a landmark report in 1989, Horning, Carrier, and others used a common leukocyte antigen (CLA) to identify anaplastic lymphoma patients among undifferentiated neoplasms. In 35 patients with equivocal histology and positive CLA staining, treatment with a variety of standard lymphoma regimens resulted in an actuarial disease-free survival of 45% at 30 months, an outcome similar to a group of concurrently treated patients who had non-Hodgkin's lymphomas with typical histology.

Poorly differentiated neoplasms require specialized pathologic studies (immunoperoxidase tumor staining, electron microscopy, and genetic analysis).

A. Immunoperoxidase Tumor Staining

Immunoperoxidase staining is a specialized technique helpful in the classification of neoplasms. Diagnoses usually cannot be made on the basis of staining alone because none of these reagents are directed at tumor-specific antigens, and results must be interpreted in

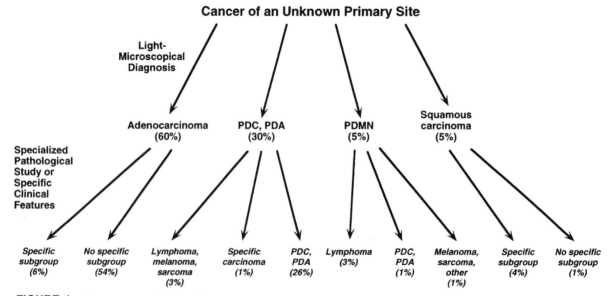

FIGURE 1 Relative size of clinical and histologic subgroups of patients as determined by optimal clinical and pathologic evaluation. PDC, poorly differentiated carcinoma, PDA, poorly differentiated adenocarcinoma; PDMN, poorly differentiated malignant neoplasm. Reprinted with permission from Hainsworth, J. D., and Greco, F. A. (1993). *N. Engl. J. Med.*, **329**, 257–263.

conjunction with the light microscopic appearance and the clinical picture. Some immunoperoxidase staining patterns useful in the differential diagnosis are outlined in Table I.

B. Electron Microscopy

Electron microscopy is not widely available, requires special tissue fixation, is relatively expensive, and should be reserved for the study of neoplasms with an unclear lineage after routine light microscopy and im-

TABLE I
Immunoperoxidase Tumor Staining Patterns
Useful in Poorly Differentiated Neoplasms

Tumor type	Immunoperoxidase staining[a]
Carcinoma	Epithelial stains (e.g., cytokeratin, EMA; +)
	CLA, S-100, vimentin (−)
Lymphoma	CLA (+), rare false (−)
	EMA occasionally (+)
	All other stains (−)
Melanoma	S-100, vimentin, HMB-45 (+)
	NSE often (+)
	Synaptophysin (−)
	Epithelial stains (−)
Sarcoma	
Mesenchymal	Vimentin (+)
	Epithelial stains usually (−)
Rhabdomyosarcoma	Desmin (+)
Angiosarcoma	Factor VIII antigen (+)
Neuroendocrine tumor	NSE, chromogranin, synaptophysin (+)
	Epithelial stains (+)
Breast cancer	ER, PR (+)
	Gross cystic fluid protein 15 (+)
	Epithelial stains (+)
Prostate cancer	PSA (+), rare false (−), and (+)
	Epithelial stains (+)
Thyroid	
Follicular	Thyroglobulin (+)
Medullary	Calcitonin (+)
Germ cell tumor	HCG, AFP (+)
	Placental alkaline phosphatase (+)
	Epithelial stains (+)

[a]+, positive result; −, negative result; AFP, α-fetoprotein; CLA, common leukocyte antigen; EMA, epithelial membrane antigen; ER, estrogen receptor; HCG, human chorionic gonadotropin; NSE, neuron-specific enolase; PR, progestrone receptor; PSA, prostate-specific antigen. Modified with permission from Greco, F. A., and Hainsworth, J. D. (2001). Cancer of Unknown Primary Site. *In* "Cancer: Principles and Practice of Oncology," 6th Ed. pp. 2537-2560. Lippincott Williams & Wilkins, Philadelphia.

munoperoxidase staining. Electron microscopy is reliable in differentiating lymphoma from carcinoma and superior to immunoperoxidase staining for the identification of poorly differentiated sarcoma. Ultrastructural features such as neurosecretory granules (neuroendocrine tumors) or premelanosomes (melanoma) can suggest a particular tumor. Some neoplasms cannot be further classified despite specialized pathologic study.

C. Genetic Analysis

The use of tumor-specific chromosomal abnormalities in diagnosis is still limited, but it is likely that future research will identify many additional specific genetic abnormalities. In 1999, Golub and co-workers reported DNA microarrays in acute leukemias, and this technique holds promise as a method to classify neoplasms based on gene expression monitoring, perhaps identifying specific genetic patterns or fingerprints independent of previous histologic and biological knowledge.

Most B-cell non-Hodgkin's lymphomas are associated with tumor-specific immunoglobulin gene rearrangements, and typical chromosomal changes have been identified in some B-cell and T-cell lymphomas [t(14:18); t(8:14); t(11:14)]. A few other nonrandom chromosomal rearrangements associated with non-lymphoid tumors have been identified [t(11:22) in neuroepithelioma and Ewing's tumor; (i12p) in germ cell tumors; t(2:13) in alveolar rhabdomyosarcoma; 3p deletion in small cell lung cancer; 1p deletion in neuroblastoma; t(X:18) in synovial sarcoma; and 11p deletion in Wilm's tumors]. These findings can occasionally make more precise diagnoses.

II. ADENOCARCINOMA OF UNKNOWN PRIMARY SITE

A. Clinical Characteristics

Typically, patients are elderly and have multiple metastatic sites. The dominant metastasis frequently determines the clinical presentation and course; metastatic sites commonly include lymph nodes, liver, lung, and bone.

The primary site becomes obvious in only 15 to 20% of patients during life. At autopsy, however, 70 to 80% of patients have a primary site detected, most commonly in the lung and pancreas, although many other sites are encountered. Adenocarcinomas of the breast, prostate, and ovary are uncommon.

These patients historically have a very poor prognosis with a median survival of only 4 months. It is an error to stereotype all patients because within this large group are subsets of patients with more favorable prognoses, as discussed later. In addition, chemotherapy has improved considerably, and many patients now have a reasonable expectation of clinical benefit and improved survival.

B. Pathology

The diagnosis is based on the formation of glandular structures by neoplastic cells. No feature is specific enough to be used as definitive evidence of the primary site. Immunoperoxidase stains and electron microscopy are of limited value in identifying the site of origin. The stain for prostate-specific antigen (PSA) is relatively specific for prostate cancer and should be used in men with suggestive clinical findings. Staining for estrogen or progesterone receptors suggests metastatic breast cancer. Neuroendocrine stains (e.g., neuron specific enolase, chromogranin, synaptophysin) can occasionally identify an unsuspected neuroendocrine neoplasm.

C. Diagnostic Evaluation

An exhaustive search for the primary site is not indicated. The evaluation should be performed to evaluate any suspicious clinical symptoms or signs and to determine the extent of metastatic disease. Initially patients need a thorough history and physicial examination, standard laboratory screening tests (i.e., complete blood count, liver function tests, serum creatinine, urinalysis), and chest radiography. All men should have a serum PSA determination, and all women mammography. A computed tomographic (CT) scan of the abdomen can identify a primary site in about 30% of patients and is often useful in identifying additional sites of metastatic disease. Additional symptoms, signs, or abnormal physical and laboratory findings should be evaluated with appropriate diagnostic studies.

D. Treatment

There are several clinically defined subgroups for which useful therapy can be given, as discussed later. Chemotherapy can also be useful for some patients who are not a part of one of these subgroups, as empiric chemotherapy has improved.

1. Peritoneal Carcinomatosis in Women

Several women have been described with diffuse peritoneal carcinomatosis without a primary site found in the ovaries or elsewhere in the abdomen at the time of laparotomy. These patients frequently had histologic features typical of ovarian carcinoma, such as papillary configuration or psammoma bodies. This syndrome has been termed "multifocal extraovarian serous carcinoma" or "peritoneal papillary serous carcinoma." These patients are now known to have a primary peritoneal carcinoma. Like ovarian carcinoma, the incidence of primary peritoneal carcinoma is increased in women with BRCA1 mutations.

Table II summarizes seven series of patients as previously reviewed in 1997 by Greco and Hainsworth. The clinical features are similar to ovarian carcinoma or abdominal carcinomatosis. Many patients have elevated serum levels of CA-125 antigen. An occasional patient will present with pleural effusion only. Optimal management of these patients includes aggressive surgical cytoreduction followed by chemotherapy considered optimal for the treatment of advanced ovarian cancer.

2. Women with Axillary Lymph Node Metastases

Breast cancer should be suspected in women who have axillary lymph node involvement with adenocarcinoma. Occasionally the histology is poorly differentiated carcinoma. The presence of estrogen and/or progesterone receptors provides strong evidence for the diagnosis of breast cancer. Modified radical mastectomy should be considered, even when physical examination and mammography are normal, but primary radiation therapy is also acceptable. An occult breast primary has been identified after mastectomy in about 60% of patients. Prognosis after local and systemic therapy is similar to that of other patients with stage II breast cancer.

TABLE II
Peritoneal Adenocarcinomatosis of Unknown Primary Site in Women

Year reported	No. of patients	Therapy	Complete response rate (%)	Median survival (months)	Long-term survival (%)
1988	23	Surgical cytoreduction and cisplatin-based chemotherapy	22	19	26
1989	18	Surgical cytoreduction and cisplatin-based chemotherapy	39	23	17
1989	31	Surgical cytoreduction and cisplatin-based or chlorambucil chemotherapy	10	11	6
1990	33	Surgical cytoreduction and cisplatin-based chemotherapy	13	17	9
1990	74	Surgical cytoreduction, cisplatin alone, or in combination or melphalan alone	20	24	25
1993	33	Surgical cytoreduction, cisplatin-based chemotherapy	35	20	15
1997	46	Surgical cytoreduction, cisplatin-based chemotherapy, paclitaxel-based chemotherapy	40	19	Too early
Total	258		22	18	16

Modified with permission from Greco, F. A., and Hainsworth, J. D. (2001). Cancer of Unknown Primary Site. In "Cancer: Principles and Practice of Oncology," 6th Ed. pp. 2537-2560. Lippincott Williams & Wilkins, Philadelphia.

3. Men with Possible Prostate Carcinoma

Prostate-specific antigen concentrations should be measured in men. These tumors can also be stained for PSA. Even when clinical features (i.e., metastatic pattern) do not suggest prostate cancer, a positive PSA (serum or tumor stain) is reason for a trial of hormonal therapy. Osteoblastic bone metastases are also an indication for an empiric hormone trial, regardless of the PSA findings.

4. Chemotherapy for Metastatic Adenocarcinoma of Unknown Primary Site

About 90% of patients are not in one of the several clinical subgroups just outlined. In the past, chemotherapy of various types has produced low response rates, very few complete responses, and even fewer long-term survivals. In one study of over 1000 patients treated with various types of chemotherapy, response rates varied from 8 to 39% (mean 20%), complete responders less than 1%, median survival 4–15 months (mean 6 months), survival beyond 2 years unusual, and survival beyond 3 years very rare (<1%).

Several clinical and pathologic features are associated with a more favorable response to empiric chemotherapy. Some of these features include tumor location solely in lymph nodes, female sex, and poorly differentiated histology. Patients with liver or bone involvement have a poor prognosis.

Chemotherapy for patients with adenocarcinoma and poorly differentiated carcinoma who do not fit into a specific "treatable" subset has improved considerably. The introduction of several new drugs with rather broad spectrum antineoplastic activity is changing the standard treatment for patients with several common epithelial cancers. These drugs include taxanes, gemcitabine, vinorelbine, and the topoisomerase I inhibitors. Several phase II trials incorporating paclitaxel and docetaxel into first-line therapy have been completed. The initial trial included 55 patients followed by long-term results of 71 patients. The chemotherapy regimen, patient characteristics, and treatment results are summarized in Table III. Patients with tumors of any histology who were not part of a previously defined treatable subset, with the exception of poorly differentiated neuroendocrine carcinoma, were eligible for this trial. The response rate was 48% with 10 (15%) complete responses. The toxicity was moderate, primarily myelosuppression, but with only 12 hospitalizations for fever/neutropenia and no treatment-related deaths. Long-term follow-up on these 71 patients (minumum follow-up 34 months) is of interest; the median survival was 11 months and the 1-, 2-, and 3-year survivals were 48, 20, and 14%, respectively.

Subsequently, Greco and colleagues used docetaxel and performed two sequential phase II trials in the same patient population with either cisplatin or carboplatin

TABLE III

TABLE III

Paclitaxel, Carboplatin, and Extended Schedule Oral
Etoposide for Unknown Primary Carcinoma

	Number of Patients (%)
Patient characteristics ($N = 71$)	
Age, years	
Median	71
Range	31–82
Gender (male/female)	35/36
Histology	
Adenocarcinoma (well differentiated)	34 (48%)
PDC or PDA[a]	30 (42%)
Neuroendocrine carcinoma (poorly differentiated)	6 (9%)
Squamous carcinoma	1 (1%)
Regimen	
Paclitaxel 200 mg/m^2, 1-h iv infusion, day 1	
Carboplatin AUC = 6.0 iv, day 1	
Etoposide 50 mg/100 mg po alternating, days 1–10	
Repeated at 21-day intervals for four to six courses	

		Survival (%)		
Results	Response rate	1 year	2 years	3 years
PDC and PDA	50%	49	20	14
Adenocarcinoma	46%	47	21	13
Entire group	48% (15% complete)	48	20	14

[a]PDC, poorly differentiated carcinoma; PDA, poorly differentiated adenocarcinoma.
Modified with permission from Greco, F. A., and Hainsworth, J. D. (2001). Cancer of
Unknown Primary Site. *In* "Cancer: Principles and Practice of Oncology," 6th Ed. pp.
2537-2560. Lippincott Williams & Wilkins, Philadelphia.

in 73 patients. More than 20% of all patients responded to these regimens. The follow-up is shorter than the paclitaxel-based trial, but the 1- and 2-year survivals are similar. By combining these taxane-based chemotherapy trials, a total of 144 patients (71 on paclitaxel regimen, 73 on docetaxel regimens) have been treated and followed. The median follow-up is 25 months, and median survival is 10 months with actuarial survival at 1, 2, 3, and 4 years of 42, 22, 17, and 17%, respectively. There was no difference in survival for adenocarcinoma versus poorly differentiated carcinomas. Women survived significantly longer than men, and those with performance status 0, 1 (ECOG scale) lived longer than those with performance status 2. The progression-free survival of these 144 patients reveals that a small number of patients remain alive without progressive cancer (1 year, 16%; 2 year, 9%; and 3 year, 9%). A subsequent trial in 72 patients confirmed the activity of paclitaxel and carboplatin with a 41% response rate.

The more common patients who do not fit into any previously defined "treatable" subset can now often attain clinical benefit from taxane-based combination chemotherapy. Despite the fact that randomized trials are still lacking, the 1-, 2-, and 3-year survival results are superior to the results seen in the past and are now comparable to the survivals of several other groups of advanced carcinoma patients receiving various types of chemotherapy, including extensive stage small cell lung cancer and advanced non-small cell lung cancer. Basic and clinical research remains a priority in order to further improve the therapy for these patients.

III. SQUAMOUS CARCINOMA OF UNKNOWN PRIMARY SITE

Squamous carcinoma at a metastatic site represents about 5% of all patients with unknown primary carcinomas, and effective treatment is available for patients with isolated cervical, supraclavicular, and inguinal lymph nodes.

When cervical lymph nodes are involved, a primary tumor in the head and neck region should be suspected, whereas the lung is more common with supraclavicular nodes; and genital or anorectal primaries should be considered for inguinal node involvement.

When no primary site is identified, local treatment should be given to the involved site. Results in more than 1400 patients with cervical and supraclavicular nodes revealed that about 30–40% of patients achieved long-term, disease-free survival after local treatment modalities. Local therapy for inguinal presentation produces about one-half as many cures. Results obtained using radical node dissection, high-dose radiation therapy, or a combination of these modalities have been similar. These patients should also be considered for neoadjuvant or adjuvant chemotherapy.

IV. POORLY DIFFERENTIATED CARCINOMA (WITH OR WITHOUT FEATURES OF ADENOCARCINOMA) OF UNKNOWN PRIMARY SITE

Many of these patients represent distinctive subgroups with specific therapeutic implications and account for about 30% of all unknown primary carcinomas. Chemotherapy trials in the past assumed that all patients were similar and often included these patients along with the more common patients with well-differentiated adenocarcinoma. They experienced a poor response (less than 10%) to 5-FU-based chemotherapy and a short survival. Some patients with poorly differentiated carcinomas have responsive neoplasms, and some are curable with cisplatin-based combination chemotherapy.

A. Clinical Characteristics

The clinical characteristics appear to differ, with some overlap, from the characteristics of patients with well-differentiated adenocarcinoma. The median age of this patient group is younger, although both groups have a wide age range. Patients with poorly differentiated carcinoma often give a history of rapid progression of symptoms (often <30 days) and have objective evidence of rapid tumor growth. The location of metastases often differs, and the predominant sites of involvement are frequently lymph nodes, mediastinum,

and retroperitoneum, occurring much more commonly than in well-differentiated adenocarcinoma.

B. Pathologic Evaluation

These tumors should routinely undergo additional pathologic study with immunoperoxidase staining; in selected tumors, electron microscopy and genetic analysis are also appropriate.

Immunoperoxidase staining should be used in the evaluation of poorly differentiated carcinomas to do the following: confirm the diagnosis of carcinoma; identify a primary site of a recognized carcinoma (e.g., prostate); identify patients who may have other neoplasms, such as lymphoma, sarcoma, or melanoma (although therapeutic recommendations for neoplasms other than lymphoma identified in this manner remain to be established); and identify a group of patients in whom electron microscopy may provide important additional information.

Chromosomal or genetic analysis is becoming an increasingly important method of diagnosis and can be helpful in some patients. Genetic analysis were performed on tumors in 40 patients with midline carcinomas of unknown primary. Motzer and colleagues documented abnormalities of chromosome 12 (e.g., i[12p]; del [12p]; multiple copies of 12p) diagnostic of germ cell tumor in 12 of 40 patients. Other specific abnormalities were diagnostic of melanoma (2 patients), lymphoma (1 patient), peripheral neuroepithelioma (1 patient), and desmoplastic small cell tumor (1 patient). Of the germ cell tumors diagnosed on basis of the genetic analysis, 5 of 12 achieved a complete response to cisplatin-based chemotherapy. This confirmed the previously formulated hypothesis that some of these patients have histologically atypical germ cell tumors.

C. Diagnostic Evaluation

The clinical evaluation of these patients is similar to that described for patients with well-differentiated adenocarcinoma, except that CT scans of the chest and abdomen should be performed in all patients due to the frequency of mediastinal and retroperitoneal involvement. Serum levels of human chorionic gonadotropin (HCG) and α-fetoprotein (AFP) should be measured because substantial elevations suggest the diagnosis of germ cell tumor.

D. Treatment

Patients with elevated serum levels of HCG or AFP and clinical features suggestive of extragonadal germ cell tumor (e.g., mediastinal or retroperitoneal mass) should be treated as if they have germ cell tumors, even when pathologic examination is not diagnostic.

Most patients have multiple metastases and no other clue of their true nature, despite additional pathologic study. The first report showing that some of these patients (a small subset) have highly responsive tumors appeared in the late 1970s through the work of Richardson, Greco, and others. Most were young men with mediastinal tumors, and serum levels of HCG or AFP were frequently elevated. Although several other tumor linages have subsequently been identified in these patients (i.e., thymoma, neuroendocrine tumors, sarcomas, melanoma lymphomas), most still defy precise classification.

Further evidence for the responsiveness of many other tumors in patients with poorly differentiated carcinoma has accumulated since the early 1980s. In a series of reports, a high overall response rate and long-term, disease-free survival in a minority of these patients have been documented.

Long-term follow-up on 220 patients treated with cisplatin-based chemotherapy shows the following: 12% (26 patients) of the entire group have remained alive and free of tumor at a minimum follow-up of 6 years with a range of 6–17 years (median 11 years). Of the 58 patients (26%) with complete response, the median survival was about 3 years. Median survival for all 220 patients was 20 months. Twenty-two of 58 complete responders remain alive and relapse free (38%), representing 10% of the entire group of 220. These results in a large series of patients support the notion that these poorly differentiated histologic types, as a whole, represent more sensitive tumors than well-differentiated adenocarcinoma, and substantial prolongation of life is possible for some of these patients with the expectation of cure for a small minority.

In patients treated with carboplatin and etoposide, with or without a taxane (paclitaxel or docetaxel), either as initial therapy or after first relapse, the response rate appears similar to cisplatin-based regimens. Furthermore, paclitaxel-based and docetaxel-based chemotherapy has been explored for both poorly differentiated and well-differentiated groups, and these regimens have been found to be useful. The authors are currently attempting to confirm that taxane-based chemotherapy is superior to other chemotherapy regimens.

At present, the treatment for most patients is controversial, but the authors think they should be treated initially with a regimen containing paclitaxel, carboplatin, and oral etoposide. There is less follow-up with docetaxel-based therapy, but early results support a similar survival rate. Treatment after relapse from primary therapy is difficult, but some new drugs, including gemcitabine, occasionally produce clinical benefit. In those patients with features highly suggestive of an extragonadal germ cell tumor, the authors continue to recommend cisplatin and etoposide.

Other investigators have also demonstrated the responsiveness of these poorly differentiated tumors. Complete remissions are seen in a minority (10–20%) of these patients, as is a small cohort (5 to 10%) of long-term, disease-free survivors. These results were usually seen with combination chemotherapy: cisplatin-based or carboplatin-based often with etoposide with or without bleomycin. More recently, taxane-based combination chemotherapy has broadened the usefulness of therapy for many of these patients. A therapeutic trial of two courses should be given. Responders should complete a total of at least four treatment courses. In patients with residual palpable or radiographic abnormalities, surgical resection or radiation therapy should be contemplated.

Although these results represent a marked improvement when compared with the dismal historical results, this group of patients is heterogeneous, and there are many patients with unresponsive tumors.

V. NEUROENDOCRINE CARCINOMA OF UNKNOWN PRIMARY SITE

Improved methods for diagnosing neuroendocrine tumors have resulted in the recent recognition of a wider spectrum of these neoplasms. Most of the well-described adult neuroendocrine tumors have distinctive histology and a known primary site of origin.

Well-differentiated or low-grade neuroendocrine tumors (typical carcinoid, islet cell tumors, and others) occasionally present without a recognizable primary site and usually possess an indolent biologic behavior. These patients are best managed as metastatic carcinoid tumors. A second group of neuroendocrine tumors are poorly differentiated by light microscopy, but have neuroendocrine features (typical small cell, atypical carcinoid, or poorly differentiated neuroendocrine carcinoma) and act aggressively. A third group of neuroendocrine tumors, recently recognized, have high-grade biology and no distinctive neuroendocrine features by standard light microscopy. The diagnosis in this group is usually poorly differentiated carcinoma, and neuroendocrine features are only recognized when immunoperoxidase staining (neuron-specific enolase, chromogranin, synaptophysin) or, more definitively, if electron microscopy is performed.

Poorly differentiated tumors are initially chemotherapy sensitive, and a major palliative benefit can be derived from treatment. An occasional patient will enjoy long-term benefit. In the rare instance when the tumor appears at a single metastatic site, the addition of radiation therapy and/or resection to combination chemotherapy should be considered.

Although the origin(s) of these poorly differentiated neuroendocrine tumors remains undefined, they are a highly treatable subgroup. A summary of 51 patients has been reviewed as illustrated in Table IV. Patients should be treated with a trial of combination chemotherapy and, in selected patients, surgery and/or radiotherapy.

VI. OTHER ISSUES IN CARCINOMA OF UNKNOWN PRIMARY SITE

A. Carcinoma of Unknown Primary Site as a Distinct Clinicopathologic Entity

A reasonable clinical and pathologic evaluation of these patients and their tumors is indicated, being aware of possible primary sites, and their clinical relevance. However, once these evaluations are complete and there is no additional helpful information, as often is the case, one should stop, discuss the issue with the patient/family, and accept the clinicopatholgic diagnosis as an unknown primary. Most of these patients have unknown primary cancer; primaries only occasionally surface during life. Patients will be better served and physicians will feel more comfortable and therefore manage their patients more effectively once they understand and accept this diagnosis as a distinct clinicopathologic entity.

B. Extragonadal Germ Cell Cancer Syndrome

Selected patients with poorly differentiated carcinoma almost certainly have germ cell tumors, although the histologic features are atypical. Chromosomal analysis may provide a definitive diagnosis in some of these patients if their tumor cells contain specific chromosome 12 abnormalities. Young people who have mediastinal or retroperitoneal masses or multiple lung nodules with or without elevated serum levels of HCG or AFP should be suspected of harboring a germ cell tumor. These patients who may have atypical germ cell tumors should be treated with cisplatin-based therapy.

TABLE IV

Treatment of Patients with Poorly Differentiated Neuroendocrine Tumors of Unknown Primary Site

	No. of patients
Female/male	17/34
Smoking (>10 pack-years)	25
Dominant tumor site	
Retroperitoneum	13
Peripheral lymph nodes	7
Mediastinum	6
Bone	6
Liver	6
Multiple sites without dominant site	6
Other	8
Treatment	
Cisplatin-based combinations	38
Cyclophosphamide, doxorubicin, vincristine, etoposide	8
Radiation therapy only (one small site of involvement)	2
Surgical excision only (one small site of involvement)	3
Response to therapy	
Complete response	13 (26%)
Partial response	20
No response or inevaluable	10
Continuously disease free	8 (15%)

Modified with permission from Greco, F. A., and Hainsworth, J. D. (2001). Cancer of Unknown Primary Site. *In* "Cancer: Principles and Practice of Oncology," 6th Ed. pp. 2537-2560. Lippincott Williams & Wilkins, Philadelphia.

C. A Single Site of Neoplasm

In the situation where only one site of neoplasm is identified (e.g., one node group or one large mass), the possibility of an unusual primary tumor mimicking metastatic disease should be considered. Patients with one site of involvement usually have metastatic carcinoma, and many other sites are present but are not detectable. In the absence of known metastatic disease, these patients should be treated with resection, or radiation therapy, or both and also be considered for chemotherapy. A minority will enjoy long-term, disease-free survival.

D. Unsuspected Gestational Choriocarcinoma

In young women with poorly differentiated carcinoma or anaplastic neoplasms, particularly with lung nodules, there is the possibility of metastatic gestational choriocarcinoma. The history of recent pregnancy, spontaneous abortion, or missed menstrual periods should suggest the possibility. In this group of patients, serum HCG levels are invariably elevated, and many of these patients are curable with methotrexate.

E. Evolving Role of Prognostic Factors: Therapeutic Implications

Both pathologic and clinical factors can now define several patients with a better prognosis, as illustrated in Table V. Although there are likely other unrecognized favorable features, it appears that the prognosis of patients who do not fit into a favorable subset have a particularly poor prognosis, regardless of their initial light microscopic diagnosis (well-differentiated adenocarcinoma or poorly differentiated carcinoma). This group of patients has been treated with taxane-based chemotherapy and it appears to improve the response rate (with some complete responses) and survival of these otherwise historically very poor prognostic groups of patients. The degree of response seen in poorly differentiated neuroendocrine carcinoma is also noteworthy.

VII. CONCLUSION

The recognition of subsets (pathological and clinical) of responsive tumors in patients with cancers of unknown primary site represents an improvement in their management. Nearly one-half of all patients fall

TABLE V
Favorable Prognostic Factors[a]

Definite
1. Poorly differentiated malignant neoplasm (otherwise not classified) (60% lymphomas)
2. Extragonadal germ cell syndrome (PDA or PDC)
3. Retroperitoneal and/or peripheral lymph node involvement (PDA, PDC, WDA)
4. Squamous cell carcinomas (head/neck or inguinal area)
5. Isolated axillary adenopathy: women, ? men (WDA, PDC, PDA)
6. Peritoneal carcinoma: women, ? men (WDA, PDC, PDA)
7. Single site of metastasis (WDA, PDC, PDA)
8. Blastic bone mets or increase PSA in serum or tumor: men (WDA, PDA, PDC)
9. Neuroendocrine carcinoma: low grade or well differentiated (carcinoid/islet cell type)
10. Neuroendocrine carcinoma: high grade or poorly differentiated (small cell and others)

Probable
1. Performance status 0, 1
2. Women
3. Estrogen and/or progesterone receptor-positive tumor
4. Nonsmoker
5. Normal LDH, CEA

[a]WDA, well-differentiated adenocarcinoma; PDA, poorly differentiated adenocarcinoma; PDC, poorly differentiated carcinoma; LDH, lactic dehydrogenase; PSA, prostate-specific antigen; CEA, carcinoembryonic antigen. Modified with permission from Greco, F. A., and Hainsworth, J. D. (2001). Cancer of Unknown Primary Site. *In* "Cancer: Principles and Practice of Oncology," 6th Ed. pp. 2537-2560. Lippincott Williams & Wilkins, Philadelphia.

TABLE VI
Summary of Evaluation and Therapy of Responsive Subsets

	Clinical evaluation	Special pathologic studies	Subsets	Therapy	Prognosis
Squamous carcinoma	Cervical node presentation Panendoscopy		Cervical adenopathy	Radiation therapy ± neck dissection ± chemotherapy	25–50% 5-year survival
	Supraclavicular presentation Bronchoscopy		Supraclavicular	Radiation therapy ± chemotherapy	5–15% 5-year survival
	Inguinal presentation Pelvic, rectal exams, anoscopy		Inguinal adenopathy	Inguinal node dissection ± radiation therapy ± chemotherapy	15–20% 5-year survival
Adenocarcinoma (well-differentiated or moderately differentiated)	Abdominal CT scan Men: Serum PSA Women: Mammogram Serum CA 15-3 Serum CA 125 Additional studies to evaluate symptoms, signs	Men: PSA stain Women: ER, PR	1. Women, axillary node involvement 2. Women, peritoneal carcinomatosis 3. Men, blastic bone metastases, high serum PSA, or PSA tumor staining 4. Single metastatic site	Treat as primary breast cancer Surgical cytoreduction + chemotherapy as in ovarian cancer Hormonal therapy for prostate cancer Lymph node dissection ± radiotherapy	Poor for entire group but improving Better for subsets
Poorly differentiated carcinoma, differentiated adenocarcinoma	Chest, abdominal CT scans, serum HCG, AFP; additional studies to evaluate symptoms, signs	Immunoperoxidase staining Electron microscopy Genetic analysis	1. Atypical germ cell tumors (identified by chromosomal abnormalities only) 2. Predominant tumor location in retroperitoneum, peripheral nodes	Treatment for germ cell tumor Cisplatin/etoposide	40–50% cure rate Prolongation of survival; 10–20% cured
Neuroendocrine carcinoma	CT abdomen, chest	Immunoperoxidase staining Electron microscopy	1. Low grade 2. Small cell carcinoma 3. Poorly differentiated	Treat as advanced carcinoid Paclitaxel/carboplatin/ etoposide or platinum/etoposide	Indolent biology High response rate prolongation of survival; rarely cured

AFP, α-fetoprotein; ER, estrogen receptor; HCG, human chorionic gonadotropin; PR, progesterone receptor; PSA, prostate-specific antigen. Modified with permission from Greco, F. A., and Hainsworth, J. D. (2001). Cancer of Unknown Primary Site. *In* "Cancer: Principles and Practice of Oncology," 6th Ed. pp. 2537-2560. Lippincott Williams & Wilkins, Philadelphia.

within a defined subset with important treatment implications. A summary of several subsets and an outline of the evaluation necessary for their identification are given in Table VI. Taxane-based combination chemotherapy has been shown to be useful for many of these patients. A therapeutic trial is the only absolute method to determine if a patient has a responsive tumor. Even for most responsive carcinomas, the tumor origin, biology, and precise lineage usually continue to be an enigma. Improved therapy for these patients are likely to mirror advances in the treatment of non-small cell lung cancer, pancreatic cancer, and the other gastrointestinal cancers because most in-sensitive carcinomas probably arise from these occult primary sites.

See Also the Following Articles

CHEMOPREVENTION TRIALS • HEPATOCELLULAR CARCINOMA • NEOPLASMS IN ACQUIRED IMMUNODEFICIENCY SYNDROME

Bibliography

Briasoulis, E., Txavaris, N., Fountzilas, G., *et al.* (1998). Combination regimen with carboplatin, epirubicin and etoposide in metastatic carcinomas of unknown primary site: A

Hellenic Cooperative Oncology Group phase II trial. *Oncology* **55**, 426–430.

Falkson, C. I., and Cohen, G. L. (1998). Mitomycin C, epirubicin and cisplatin versus mitomycin C alone as therapy for carcinoma of unknown primary origin. *Oncology* **55**, 116–121.

Fox, R. M., Woods, R. L., and Tattersall, M. H. N. (1979). Undifferentiated carcinoma in young men: The atypical teratoma syndrome. *Lancet* **1**, 1316–1318.

Golub, T. R., Slovim, D. K., Tamayo, P., *et al.* (1999). Molecular classification of cancer: Class discovery and class prediction by gene expression monitoring. *Science* **286**, 531–537.

Greco, F. A., Erland, J. B, Morrissey, L. H., *et al.* (2000). Carcinoma of unknown primary site: Phase II trials with docetaxel plus cisplatin or carboplatin. *Ann. Oncol.* **11**, 211–215.

Greco, F. A., and Hainsworth, J. D. (1997). Cancer of unknown primary site. *In* "Cancer Principle and Practice of Oncology," 5th Ed., pp. 2423–2444. Lippincott-Raven, Phildelphia.

Greco, F. A., Vaughn, W. K., and Hainsworth, J. D. (1986). Advanced poorly differentiated carcinoma of unknown primary site: Recognition of a treatable syndrome. *Ann. Intern. Med.* **104**, 547–556.

Hainsworth, J. D., Erland, J. B., Kalman, L. A., *et al.* (1997). Carcinoma of unknown primary: Treatment with 1-hour paclitaxel, carboplatin, and extended schedule etoposide. *J. Clin. Oncol.* **15**, 2385–2393.

Hainsworth, J. D., and Greco, F. A. (1993). Treatment of patients with cancer of an unknown primary site. *N. Engl. J. Med.* **329**, 257–263.

Hainsworth, J. D., Johnson, D. H., and Greco, F. A. (1988). Poorly differentiated neuroendocrine carcinoma of unknown primary site: A newly recognized clinicopathologic entity. *Ann. Interen. Med.* **109**, 364–371.

Hainsworth, J. D., Wright, E. P., Gray, G. F., Jr, and Greco, F. A. (1987). Poorly differentiated carcinoma of unknown primary site: Correlation of light microscopic findings with response to cisplatin-based combination chemotherapy. *J. Clin. Oncol.* **5**, 1272–1280.

Horning, S. J., Carrier, E. K., Rouse, R. V., *et al.* (1989). Lymphomas presenting as histologically unclassified neoplasms: Characteristics and response to treament. *J. Clin. Oncol.* **7**, 1281–1287.

Motzer, R. J., Rodriquez, E., Reuter, V. E., et al. (1995). Molecular and cytogenic studies in the diagnosis of patients with midline carcinomas of unknown primary site. *J. Clin. Oncol.* **13**, 274–283.

Pavlidis, N., Kalofonos, H., Bafaloukos, D., et al. (1992). Cisplatin/taxol combination chemotherapy in 72 patients with metastatic cancer of unknown primary site: A phase II trial of the Hellenic Cooperative Oncology Group. *Proc. Am. Soc. Clin. Oncol.* **18**, 195a. [Abstract]

Pavlidis, N., Kosmidis, P., Skaros, D., et al. (1992). Subsets of tumors responsive to cisplatin or combinations in patients with carcinoma of unknown primary site. *Ann. Oncol.* 236–241.

Raber, M. N., Faintuch, J., Abbruzzese, J., et al. (1991). Continuous infusion 5-fluorouracil, etoposide and cis-diamminedichloroplatinum in patients with metastatic carcinoma of unknown primary site. *Ann. Oncol.* **2**, 519.

Richardson, R. L., Greco, F. A., Wolff, S., et al. (1979). Extragonadal germ cell malignancy: Value of tumor markers in metastatic carcinoma of young males. *Proc. Am. Assoc. Cancer Res.* **20**, 204. [Abstract]

Richardson, R. L., Schoumacher, R. A., Fer, M. F., et al. (1981). The unrecognized extragonadal germ cell cancer syndrome. *Ann. Intern. Med.* **94**, 181–186.

van der Gaast, A., Verweij, J., Henzen-Logmans, S. C., Rodenburg, C. J., and Stoter, G. (1990). Carcinoma of unknown primary; identification of a treatable subset. *Ann. Oncol.* **1**, 119–121.

Zarba, J., Izzo, J., Hahjoubi, R., et al. (1991). Treatment of unknown primary adenocarcinoma with fluorouracil, mitomycin, epirubicin and platinum. *Eur. J. Cancer* **27**(Suppl. 2), 1350. [Abstract]

Neuroblastoma

Emmanuel Katsanis
Luke Whitesell
University of Arizona, Tucson

I. Molecular and Cellular Biology
II. Clinical Presentation
III. Treatment
IV. Prognosis

GLOSSARY

double minutes Extrachromosomal cytogenetic manifestion of gene amplification.

ganglioside G$_{D2}$ Sialic acid-containing surface membrane glycosphingolipid expressed at high levels on > 85% of neuroblastomas.

homogeneously staining region Chromosomally integrated cytogenetic manifestation of gene amplification.

MYCN Protooncogene amplified in about 25% of neuroblastomas associated with advanced staged disease and poor prognosis.

vanillylmandelic acid and homovanillic acid Catecholamine metabolites elevated in >80% of patients with neuroblastoma.

$\mathbf{N}$ euroblastoma is the most common extracranial pediatric solid tumor, accounting for 7.5% of all childhood cancers, with a prevalence of about 1 case per 7500 live births. About one quarter of malignancies in the first year of life are neuroblastomas, making it the most frequent cancer of infancy.

I. MOLECULAR AND CELLULAR BIOLOGY

Neuroblastoma arises from primitive neural crest-derived sympathoblasts destined to become adrenal medullary chromaffin tissue or neurons within ganglia of the peripheral nervous system. In an effort to understand the marked variation in clinical outcomes associated with the pathologic diagnosis of neuroblastoma, much effort has been directed at defining the significance of specific biochemical, molecular biologic, and genetic abnormalities characteristic of this problematic tumor. Clinical studies have been able to demonstrate prognostic significance for many of these abnormalities and have led some investigators to propose that the histopathologic entity neuroblastoma may consist of distinct biologic entities which can be

Encyclopedia of Cancer, Second Edition
Volume 3

distinguished on the basis of their clinical presentation and molecular marker profile.

A. Pathology

Peripheral neuroblastic tumors can present problems diagnostically due to their primitive, embryonal nature. In particular, neuroblastoma must be distinguished from the other small round blue cell tumors of childhood such as Ewing's sarcoma, neuroepithelioma, rhabdomyosarcoma, and lymphoma. Whenever possible, tissue should be obtained from multiple areas of a suspected neuroblastoma for evaluation by ancillary techniques such as electron microscopy, immunocytochemistry, special stains, and cytogenetic/molecular genetic analysis. At the level of light microscopy, neuroblastoma tumors can demonstrate a broad spectrum of morphologic differentiation. In their most primitive form, tumors are very cellular with characteristic Homer–Wright pseudorosettes of tumor cells around a core of amorphous eosinophilic material and scattered areas of hemorrhage and necrosis. In more differentiated tumors (ganglioneuroblastoma), there may be focal or diffuse areas with increased stromal content and more mature, ganglion-like cells. At the most mature, benign end of the spectrum (ganglioneuroma), well-differentiated ganglion cells, Schwann cells and nerve fiber bundles can be seen. A staging system based on tumor histology and patient age was first described by Shimada and colleagues that involves evaluation of tumor specimens for the amount of stromal content, the degree of neuroblastic maturation, and the mitosis–karyorrhexis index of the neuroblasts. The strong prognostic significance of this classification methodology has been confirmed in multiple studies, and with minor modification, it forms the basis of the current International Neuroblastoma Pathology Classification system. This type of analysis, however, requires adequate biopsy material from a primary tumor resected before therapy is instituted. Attempts to apply the Shimada classification to material from needle biopsy specimens, previously treated primaries, or metastatic sites may be misleading due to the inherent heterogeneity of neuroblastoma tumors and the potential of therapeutic agents to induce varying degrees of morphologic differentiation.

B. Biologic Markers

Urinary excretion of the catecholamine metabolites vanillylmandelic acid (VMA) and homovanillic acid (HVA) is elevated in >80% of patients with neuroblastoma. While the absolute magnitude of the elevation is not correlated with disease outcome, the ratio of VMA to HVA in patients with disseminated disease may carry prognostic significance. The uptake of catecholamine precursors by most neuroblastomas has made possible both the detection and the treatment of disease using radiolabeled preparations of the amine precursor meta-iodobenzylguanidine (MIBG). The role of MIBG-based techniques in patient management continues to be defined in clinical studies. In addition to catecholamines, other neuroendocrine markers such as neuropeptide Y and chromogranin A have been proposed as sensitive and specific aids in the diagnosis of neuroblastoma and may be useful measures of disease status during treatment. Although less specific, several other serum proteins have been identified that correlate with poor prognosis in neuroblastoma, including ferritin, neuron-specific enolase, and lactate dehydrogenase. Neuroblastoma cells express an immature pattern of sialic acid-containing surface membrane glycosphingolipids (gangliosides). The biologic significance of this finding is unclear, but multiple studies have shown that the ganglioside G_{D2} is selectively expressed at high levels on >85% of tumors. It is also shed into the systemic circulation where it can be quantitated. High affinity anti-G_{D2} monoclonal antibodies are under evaluation as both potential diagnostic and therapeutic reagents.

C. Molecular Genetics

The genetic abnormalities characteristic of neuroblastoma have been studied both as prognostic indicators of clinical outcome and as an approach to understanding the biology of the cancer itself. Abnormalities are observed at the level of whole tumor cells, individual chromosomes, and discrete genes. At the cellular level, a hyperdiploid tumor DNA content (greater than the normal amount of DNA found in somatic cells) is strongly associated with a favorable prognosis in infants, perhaps because hyperdiploid tumors in this age group have few structural rearrangements. At the chromosomal level, karyotyping of tumors has revealed both nonrandom deletions or gains of certain chromosomal regions and the presence of anomalous, nonbanding chromosomal material in the form of homogeneously staining regions (HSRs) and double minute chromosomes (DMs). These anomalies are most commonly found in tumors from patients with advanced stage disease and often contain multiple copies of genes thought to contribute to the malignant phenotype of poor prognosis disease such as MYCN (see later). The best studied chromosomal deletions found in neuroblastoma involve chromosomes lp, 14q, and 11q. The significance of 14q and 11q deletions is not clear, although loss in 11q has been reported in tumors other than neuroblastoma, suggesting that a tumor suppressor gene may be located in this region. The most frequent chromosomal deletion observed in neuroblastoma involves the short arm of chromosome 1 and is associated with advanced stage disease and poor treatment outcome. Although the extent of deleted material varies widely among individual tumors, the use of region specific probes has identified the 1p36.1-2 region as deleted in more than 90% of stage III and IV tumors. Gene transfer experiments have suggested that loss of a critical neuroblastoma tumor suppressor or activation of a tumor susceptibility gene may be associated with allelic loss at 1p. More recently, gain of genetic material from chromosome arm 17q, most often as a result of unbalanced translocations, has been reported to be the most common cytogenetic abnormality in neuroblastoma. In multivariate analysis, this gain was found to be the most powerful prognostic factor, followed by the presence of disseminated disease at diagnosis and deletion of 1p. The molecular mechanism by which gain of 17q material contributes to the malignant behavior of neuroblastoma is unknown, but may involve overexpression of genes regulating cell survival.

Tissue-specific activation of certain cellular genes (protooncogenes) has been associated with the development of many human cancers. The correlation of MYCN gene amplification with poor prognosis in neuroblastoma was one of the first examples of the clinical utility of molecular biologic analysis in clinical oncology. Although MYCN overexpression is probably not the usual initiating event in the development of neuroblastoma, recent work has demonstrated that targeted overexpression of this gene within cells of the developing sympathetic nervous system can induce the spontaneous development of tumors in transgenic mice with many of the biologic and genetic abnormalities characteristic of the human disease. In addition to shedding light on the molecular genetics of neuroblastoma tumorigenesis, these animals provide a particularly useful preclinical model in which to explore the activity of new molecularly targeted therapeutics. Following the first studies examining MYCN, the altered expression of numerous other genes has now been characterized in neuroblastoma including those encoding for the high-affinity nerve growth factor receptor (TRK-A), multidrug resistance proteins (MDR1, MRP) and proteins regulating apoptosis (BCL-2, IGF-1R). Interestingly, rather than enhancing the malignant phenotype of neuroblastoma tumors, increased expression of TRK-A is strongly associated with a favorable prognosis for reasons which remain unclear. Although many questions remain, our increasingly sophisticated description of neuroblastoma at the molecular level has already allowed the development of clinical classification schema which stratify patients to treatment groups with high, standard, and lesser risk of disease recurrence based on the criteria summarized in Table I. The hope is that further insights into the molecular mechanisms of malignant transformation, differentiation, and apoptotic cell death in this tumor will lead to more effective therapies for children with poor prognosis forms of the disease.

II. CLINICAL PRESENTATION

A. Signs and Symptoms

Neuroblastoma originates in the adrenal medulla or the sympathetic ganglia and usually presents as a primary paraspinal or retroperitoneal mass. Common presenting signs and symptoms include an abdominal mass or bone pain secondary to metastases. Paraspinal neuroblastoma may invade through the neural foramina, resulting in spinal cord compression. Some patients may develop proptosis and periorbital ecchymosis from retrobulbar metastases or have anemia, hypertension, failure to thrive, or fever. Occasionally, the paraneoplastic

TABLE I
Neuroblastoma Classification Based on Risk of Relapse

	Low	Moderate	High
MYCN gene	Normal	Normal	Amplified
DNA content	Hyperdiploid	Near diploid	Near diploid
	Triploid	Near tetraploid	Near tetraploid
Karyotype			
1p deletion	Absent	Variable	Present
17q gain	Absent	Variable	Present
TRK-A level	High	Variable	Low
Age	Under 1 year	Over 1 year	Over 1 year
Clinical stage	1, 2, 4S	3, 4	3, 4

(Risk of relapse spans Low, Moderate, High columns)

syndrome of opsoclonus/myoclonus is present, often in patients with low-stage disease, which may be associated with permanent neurologic dysfunction. Rarely patients develop diarrhea secondary to secretion of vasoactive intestinal peptide by the tumor.

B. Diagnosis

Minimum criteria for the diagnosis of neuroblastoma should include a pathologic diagnosis made from tumor tissue or a bone marrow aspirate/biopsy containing tumor cells and increased levels of urine or serum catecholamines or metabolites (> 3 SD above the mean per mg/creatinine for age). The following additional investigations are recommended for staging before therapy is instituted: (1) meta-iodobenzylguanidine (MIBG) scan and/or technetium 99 bone scan with plain X rays of involved bones, (2) CT scan and/or magnetic resonance imaging (MRI) of the abdomen, and (3) chest X ray and, if chest involvement, CT or MRI scan of the chest.

C. Staging

Approximately two-thirds of patients with neuroblastoma will have metastases at the time of diagnosis. Common metastatic sites include bone marrow, bone, liver, and lymph nodes. An International Neuroblastoma Staging System has been proposed (Table II).

TABLE II
International Neuroblastoma Staging System

Stage 1: Localized tumor with complete gross excision, with or without microscopic residual disease; representative ipsilateral lymph nodes negative for tumor microscopically (nodes attached to and removed with the primary tumor may be positive)

Stage 2A: Localized tumor with incomplete gross excision; representative ipsilateral nonadherent lymph nodes negative for tumor microscopically

Stage 2B: Localized tumor with or without complete gross excision, with ipsilateral nonadherent lymph nodes positive for tumor. Enlarged contralateral lymph nodes negative microscopically

Stage 3: Unresectable unilateral tumor infiltrating across the midline, with or without regional lymph node involvement; or localized unilateral tumor with contralateral regional lymph node involvement; or midline tumor with bilateral extension by infiltration (unresectable) or by lymph node involvement. Tumors originating on one side and crossing the midline must infiltrate to or beyond the opposite side of the vertebral column

Stage 4: Any primary tumor with dissemination to distant lymph nodes, bone, bone marrow, liver, skin, and/or other organs (except as defined for stage 4S)

Stage 4S: Localized primary tumor (as defined for stage 1, 2A, or 2B), with dissemination limited to skin, liver, and/or bone marrow (limited to infants less than 1 year of age). Marrow involvement should be minimal (i.e., <10% of total nucleated cells identified as malignant by bone marrow biopsy or by bone marrow aspirate). More extensive bone marrow involvement would be considered to be stage IV disease. Results of the meta-iodobenzylguanidine scan (if performed) should be negative for disease in the bone marrow

III. TREATMENT

A. Conventional Therapy

1. Localized Resectable Neuroblastoma (Stage 1)

Adjuvant chemotherapy is not necessary in patients having a complete gross resection even with microscopic residual disease.

2. Localized Unresectable Neuroblastoma (Stage 2)

Following subtotal surgical resection patients require chemotherapy for 4 to 6 months. The most commonly used agents include cyclophosphamide, doxorubicin, cisplatin, and etoposide. Residual tumor may be resected at second-look surgery. Radiation may be utilized for residual disease following surgery.

3. Regional Neuroblastoma (Stage 3)

Complete surgical resection improves outcome and therefore should be attempted either at diagnosis or following reduction of the tumor with chemoradiotherapy. Chemotherapeutic agents used include combinations of vincristine, cyclophosphamide, doxorubicin, cisplatin, and etoposide. Patients older than 1 year with poor prognosis markers are candidates for high-dose chemotherapy with stem cell rescue.

4. Disseminated Neuroblastoma (Stage 4)

The outcome of patients with disseminated disease is dependent on age and other prognostic biologic markers. Surgery and radiation therapy may be used with chemotherapy, depending on the clinical presentation. In addition to the drugs noted earlier, ifosfamide and carboplatin have been found to be useful. Aggressive surgery is usually attempted following cytoreductive chemotherapy. Many patients may also benefit from radiation therapy. Matthay and co-workers compared high-dose conventional chemotherapy to purged autologous bone marrow transplantation. After the first three cycles of chemotherapy, patients were randomized to continue chemotherapy or to undergo transplantation. The 3-year event-free survival was significantly better in the autologous bone marrow transplantation arm (34%) when compared to the chemotherapy arm (22%). In a second randomization, patients received or did not receive 13-*cis*

retinoic acid for 6 months. Treatment with this differentiation agent significantly increased survival when it was administered after chemotherapy or transplantation (46% vs 29%). It is still unclear whether this represents a true increase in cure rate or a delay in relapse.

5. Stage 4S Neuroblastoma

Infants with stage 4S have a high rate of spontaneous regression and usually do not require chemotherapy. However, in certain situations such as massive hepatomegaly compromising other organs, a short course of chemotherapy is indicated.

B. Biologic Therapy

The poor prognosis of metastatic neuroblastoma has necessitated the evaluation of innovative therapeutic approaches. Because remissions can be achieved with conventional multimodal treatment, biologic therapy may be useful if applied at a time of minimal residual disease. Of all the pediatric malignancies, neuroblastoma has been at the forefront of testing various biologic approaches in an attempt to improve survival. Multiple phase I/II trials evaluating biologic agents in the treatment of neuroblastoma have been completed or are ongoing (outlined in Table III). These have included cytokines with or without adoptively transferred lymphokine activated killer cells (LAK), anti-G_{D2} monoclonal antibody based therapies, cytokine gene modified tumor vaccines, and dendritic cell-based vaccines.

TABLE III
Biologic Therapy for Neuroblastoma

IL-2
IL-2 + LAK
IL-2 post-ABMT
IFN-γ
Murine anti-G_{D2}
Murine–human chimeric anti-G_{D2}
IL-2 + anti-G_{D2}
M-CSF + anti-G_{D2}
^{131}I-labeled anti-G_{D2}
IL-2-transduced neuroblastoma cell vaccine
IFN-γ-transduced neuroblastoma cell vaccine
GM-CSF-transduced neuroblastoma cell vaccine
Dendritic cells pulsed with tumor lysates

Studies with interleukin-2 (IL-2) have demonstrated that this cytokine can be given in children with acceptable toxicity. Marked immune activation takes place but it is difficult to conclude from these phase I/II studies whether IL-2 therapy has an impact on improving survival. Interferon-γ (IFN-γ) has many immunomodulatory actions, including induction of MHC molecules, augmentation of cytotoxic activities of natural killer (NK) and T cells, and activation of macrophages. In one study, a transient increase in NK activity was seen and MHC class I expression was induced, but IFN-γ failed to induce clinical responses.

There has been increasing interest in using targeted immunotherapy against neuroblastoma in the form of antidisialoganglioside G_{D2} monoclonal antibodies. Various types of anti-G_{D2} antibodies have been developed (see Table III). These antibodies have been shown to effectively enhance the in vitro killing of neuroblastoma cells. Augmentation of lysis may occur by antibody-dependent cellular cytotoxicity, where the antibody bridges together Fc-bearing effector cells (NK cells, granulocytes, or macrophages) with the G_{D2} expressing neuroblastoma targets. Alternatively, antibody-coated tumor cells may be lysed by complement-mediated cytotoxicity. Anti-G_{D2} antibodies have been used as (a) single agents, (b) combination therapy with cytokines such as IL-2, granulocyte–macrophage colony-stimulating factor (GM-CSF), or macrophage colony-stimulating factor (M-CSF), and (c) a radiotherapeutic agent conjugated with ^{131}I. Side effects of anti-G_{D2} antibodies are urticaria, pruritis, hypertension, and severe pain during infusion predominantly in the abdomen and lower extremities requiring morphine. These trials to date have indicated that the anti-G_{D2} monoclonal antibody may be used successfully to treat patients with advanced neuroblastoma. It remains to be seen whether improved humanized antibodies, combination therapies with cytokines, or fusion proteins consisting of monoclonal antibody and cytokines, given in a minimal disease setting, will have a major impact in the survival of these patients.

Preclinical studies have demonstrated that murine tumor cells genetically modified to secrete cytokines locally are capable of generating potent antitumor responses against nontransduced wild-type tumor cells. Using this approach, cytokines can be secreted locally at high concentrations where they are needed most, without producing the toxicity associated with their systemic administration. These preclinical studies have prompted the initiation of clinical trials using genetically engineered tumor cell vaccines in neuroblastoma. In a dose-escalation study, autologous neuroblastoma cells transduced with an adenovirus–IL-2 were used to immunize 10 children with advanced neuroblastoma. Five patients had tumor responses (one complete tumor response, one partial response, and three with stable disease). Four of these five patients had coexisting antitumor cytotoxic activity in vitro against autologous tumor cells. These results show a promising correlation between preclinical observations and clinical outcome in this disease and support further exploration of vaccines against neuroblastoma. Because neuroblastoma continues to be a clinically significant problem, combining one or more of the described approaches with intensive chemoradiotherapy will be necessary for eradication of this aggressive tumor. It is hoped that applying novel immunobiologic treatments in the setting of minimal residual disease will improve the outcome of patients with advanced neuroblastoma.

IV. PROGNOSIS

Children with localized neuroblastoma and infants with advanced disease and favorable disease characteristics have a high likelihood of long-term, disease-free survival (70–90%). Older children with advanced-stage disease and unfavorable biologic markers, however, have a poor prognosis (10–40%).

There is no evidence from controlled studies that infant screening has an impact on neuroblastoma mortality. In the Quebec Neuroblastoma Screening Project, infants were screened at 3 weeks and 6 months of age. Screening resulted in an increased detection of early stage tumors that would have spontaneously regressed. Tumors detected by screening had almost exclusively biologically favorable properties associated with an excellent prognosis. However, screening did not reduce the incidence of advanced-stage neuroblastomas with unfavorable biological characteristics in older children.

See Also the Following Articles

Acute Lymphoblastic Leukemia in Children • Brain Tumors: Epidemiology and Molecular and Cellular Ab-

NORMALITIES • CYTOKINE GENE THERAPY • EWING'S SARCOMA (EWING'S FAMILY TUMORS) • PEDIATRIC CANCERS, MOLECULAR FEATURES

Bibliography

Cheung, N. K., Kushner, B. H., Cheung, I. Y., Kramer, K., Canete, A., Gerald, W., Bonilla, M. A., Finn, R., Yeh, S. J., and Larson, S. M. (1988). Anti-G(D2) antibody treatment of minimal residual stage 4 neuroblastoma diagnosed at more than 1 year of age. *J. Clin. Oncol.* **16,** 3053–3060.

Katsanis, E. (1997). Immunobiology and biologic therapy of neuroblastoma. *In* "Encyclopedia of Cancer," 1st Ed., pp. 1142–1154, Academic Press, San Diego.

Matthay, K. K., Villablanca, J. G., Seeger, R. C., Stram, D. O., Harris, R. E., Ramsay, N. K., Swift, P., Shimada, H., Black, C. T., Brodeur, G. M., Gerbing, R. B., and Reynolds, C. P. (1999). Treatment of high-risk neuroblastoma with intensive chemotherapy, radiotherapy, autologous bone marrow transplantation, and 13-cis-retinoic acid: Children's Cancer Group. *N. Engl. J. Med.* **341,** 1165–1173.

Nickerson, H. J., Matthay, K. K., Seeger, R. C., Brodeur, G. M., Shimada, H., Perez, C., Atkinson, J. B., Selch, M., Gerbing, R. B., Stram, D. O., and Lukens, J. (2000). Favorable biology and outcome of stage IV-S neuroblastoma with supportive care or minimal therapy: A Children's Cancer Group study. *J. Clin. Oncol.* **18,** 477–486.

Schmidt, M. L., Lukens, J. N., Seeger, R. C., Brodeur, G. M., Shimada, H., Gerbing, R. B., Stram, D. O., Perez, C., Haase, G. M., and Matthay, K. K. (2000). Biologic factors determine prognosis in infants with stage IV neuroblastoma: A prospective Children's Cancer Group study. *J. Clin. Oncol.* **18,** 1260–1268.

Seeger, R. C., Brodeur, G. M., Sather, H., Dalton, A., Siegel, S. E., Wong, K. Y., and Hammond, D. (1985). Association of multiple copies of the N-myc oncogene with rapid progression of neuroblastomas. *N. Engl. J. Med.* **313,** 1111–1116.

Shimada, H., Ambros, I. M., Dehner, L. P., Hata, J., Joshi, V. V., Roald, B., Stram, D. O., Gerbing, R. B., Lukens, J. N., Matthay, K. K., and Castleberry, R. P. (1999). The International Neuroblastoma Pathology Classification (the Shimada system). *Cancer* **86,** 364–372.

Woods, W. G., Tuchman, M., Robison, L. L., Bernstein, M., Leclerc, J. M., Brisson, L. C., Brossard, J., Hill, G., Shuster, J., Luepker, R., Byrne, T., Weitzman, S., Bunin, G., Lemieux, B., and Brodeur, G. M. (1997). Screening for neuroblastoma is ineffective in reducing the incidence of unfavourable advanced stage disease in older children. *Eur. J. Cancer* **33,** 2106–2112.

nm23 Metastasis Suppressor Gene

Patricia S. Steeg

National Cancer Institute, Bethesda, Maryland

GLOSSARY

awd *Drosophila* abnormal wing discs gene, for which mutation or lack of expression causes widespread developmental abnormalities postmetamorphosis.

metastasis suppressor gene A gene that, upon transfection into highly metastatic tumor cells, significantly reduces their *in vivo* metastatic potential.

nm23 Nonmetastatic cDNA clone No. 23, identified on the basis of its reduced expression in highly metastatic murine K-1753 melanoma cell lines, as compared to related, low metastatic potential cell lines.

nucleoside diphosphate kinase activity When the terminal phosphate is removed from a nucleotide triphosphate and transferred to a nucleoside diphosphate.

S uppressor genes for the tumor metastatic process have been identified. The *nm23* gene was identified on the basis of its reduced expression in highly metastatic murine melanoma cell lines. Transfection of *nm23* cDNA into highly metastatic breast carcinoma, melanoma, and other tumor cell lines significantly suppressed metastatic potential, without effects on tumorigenicity *in vivo*.

I. METASTASIS SUPPRESSOR GENES

The tumor metastatic process, in which cells spread from a primary tumor to distant sites of the body, is a significant contributor to cancer patient morbidity and mortality. Hallmarks of the tumor metastatic process include its complexity, requiring reversible adherence, motility, invasion, colonization, and angiogenesis; the chromosomal and phenotypic instability of metastatic tumor cells; and the redundant number of mechanisms by which a metastatic tumor cell can accomplish a given requirement (i.e., multiple proteases in invasion). In addition, it is not known whether part or most of the tumor metastatic process has been completed by the time of the patient's diagnosis and surgery, as micrometastases may exist undetected. Therefore, the proportion of the metastatic process that is open for therapeutic intervention is unknown.

Metastasis research typically uses genetically altered mice or the comparatively few tumor cell lines that have retained *in vivo* metastatic capability. For the latter, metastasis is measured by the injection of tumor cells into immunocompromised animals, either in an organ where a primary grows and seeds out metastases (spontaneous metastasis) or directly into the bloodstream whereby only the last portion of the metastatic cascade is measured (experimental metastasis). *In vitro* assays exist for many aspects of the metastatic process, including adherence, motility, protease production, invasion, colonization, and angiogenesis.

The development of therapeutic approaches to tumor metastasis will undoubtedly be fueled by the assembly of a molecular "map" of biochemical pathways. The existence of metastasis suppressor gene pathways was postulated from studies in which nonmetastatic and metastatic cells were fused, resulting in tumorigenic but nonmetastatic hybrids; more recently, transfection of chromosomes into metastatic cells reduced metastatic capacity but not tumorigenicity. A growing number of metastasis suppressor genes have been identified. Several, including E-cadherin, maspin, and the TIMPs (tissue inhibitor of metalloproteinase), have predictable mechanisms of action in adherence, proteolysis, and invasion. Others, including *nm23*, *kiss*, *KAI1*, and *BrMS1*, have unknown mechanisms of action and may identify new pathways important to metastasis.

II. THE NM23 FAMILY

The *nm23* gene was discovered using differential colony hybridization between low and high tumor metastatic potential K-1735 murine melanoma cell lines. Nm23 mRNA and protein levels were quantitatively higher in two low metastatic potential cell lines than five related, more highly metastatic cell lines. A correlation of reduced *nm23* expression and high tumor metastatic potential was observed in many but not all other model systems examined, consistent with the complexity and heterogeneity of the metastatic process. A family of highly conserved 17- to 18-kDa Nm23 proteins has been identified. Nm23 proteins localize to all subcellular compartments and are expressed by many cell types. Homologous proteins have been described as Awd in *Drosophila* and NDPK or Ndk in other organisms.

Several lines of investigation indicate a role for Nm23 in normal development and differentiation. Reduced expression or mutation of *Drosophila* awd resulted in defective differentiation of the presumptive epithelial cells in the imaginal discs postmetamorphosis, resulting in lethality. Transfection of *nm23* into rat PC12 phaeochromocytoma cells induced the extension of neurite processes (Fig. 1). Similarly, *nm23* transfection into human MDA-MB-435 breast carcinoma cells induced the formation of ascinus type structures, synthesis and basolateral secretion of basement membrane proteins, and synthesis of sialomucin upon culture in Matrigel, all consistent with mammary ductal differentiation. Both embryonic and metastatic cells move, invade, colonize, and reversibly adhere, with the former utilizing highly regulated cascades of sequential gene activation. The function of Nm23 in "normal" physiology may be in the acquisition or stabilization of the differentiated phenotype.

III. TRANSFECTION EXPERIMENTS

Most metastasis suppressor genes are confirmed by their reexpression in a metastatically competent tumor cell line, which, upon injection, exhibits suppressed metastatic potential without significant reductions in tumorigenicity. Data using spontaneous metastasis assays where cells were injected into an orthotopic location have provided the most convincing evidence. Table I summarizes the findings of nine transfection experiments reported for *nm23*, most of which utilized melanoma or breast carcinoma cell lines. A significant reduction in experimental or spon-

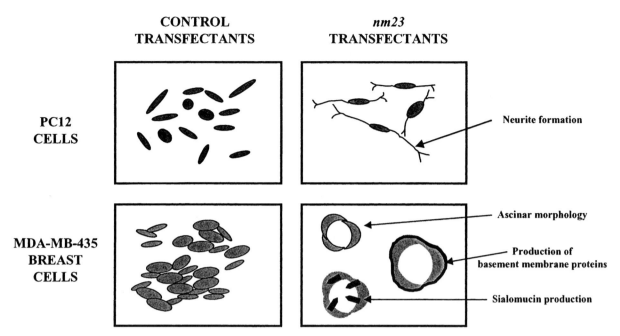

FIGURE 1 Transfection of *nm23* induces differentiation *in vitro*. Control and *nm23* transfectants of the PC12 phaeochromocytoma cell line and MDA-MB-435 human breast carcinoma cell line were analyzed for morphological and biochemical aspects of differentiation.

taneous metastatic potential was consistently reported, with no effect on tumorigenicity, confirming *nm23* as a metastasis suppressor gene. Most transfection experiments reported only partial reductions in metastatic potential, which is consistent with the heterogeneity of the process.

In vitro assays of the transfectants have pointed consistently to reduced motility, invasion, and colonization. The latter may be clinically relevant, as colonization of metastatic cells in a distant organ has not been completed in many cancer patients at the time of diagnosis and therapy and would therefore remain open for therapeutic intervention. In two studies, colonization of the highly metastatic control transfectants was stimulated by TGF-β, but not that of the *nm23* transfectants. This stimulation of colonization by a widely available cytokine is thought to be relevant to the outgrowth of cells in a foreign environment. Similarly, motility in Boyden chamber assays was significantly reduced in the *nm23* transfectants to a wide variety of chemoattractants, including serum and growth factors, suggesting that Nm23 blunts signal transduction responses downstream of specific receptors. Whenever tested, the proliferative capacity of control and *nm23* transfectants in tissue culture was comparable.

IV. BIOCHEMICAL ACTIVITIES

The biochemical pathway whereby Nm23 mediates tumor metastasis suppression or induction of differentiation is unknown. Biochemical and X-ray crystallography studies indicate the formation of homo- and heterooligomers by Nm23 family members, with a histidine containing active site capable of autophosphorylation. Nm23 has been reported to bind many proteins, including heat shock proteins, small and heterotrimeric G proteins, vimentin, and so on. It has an intrinsic nucleoside diphosphate kinase (NDPK) activity, which may regulate nucleotide pool concentrations, and some Nm23 family members have been proposed to bind or cut DNA. In *Drosophila*, the active site histidine is required for normal development. Nm23 belongs to a class of protein kinases poorly known in the cancer field, the histidine protein kinases. As shown in Fig. 2A, histidine kinases form the backbone of the "two-component" signal transduction pathway, in which bacteria, yeast, and plants respond to external environmental signals by autophosphorylation of a sensor protein on a histidine, and passage of the phosphate to an aspartate of a response regulator protein, possibly in two or more relays in yeast. In prokaryotes the activated response regulator typically functions as a transcription

TABLE I
Comparison of *nm23* Transfectants to Control Transfectants in Human Tumor Cell Lines[a]

Cell type	Cell line	In vivo effects		In vitro effects
		Primary tumor size	Incidence of metastases	
Breast	Human MDA-MB-435	Same	↓ 50–90%	↓ Soft agar ± TGF-β ↓ Motility ↑ Differentiation = Proliferation
	Human MDA-MB-435	↓ 13%	↓ 90–100%	Altered phospholipid metabolism
	Human MDA-MB-231	Same	↓ 45%	↓ Motility = Protease production = Proliferation
	Rat MTLn3	↑ 47%	↓ 48%	
Melanoma	Murine K-1735-TK	Same	↓ 52–96%	↓ Soft agar ± TGF-β = Proliferation
	Murine B16-FE7	Same	↓ 83%	= Proliferation
	Murine B16-F10		↓ 93%	↓ ICAM-1 ↓ Invasion
Colon	Rat Colon 26		↓ 94%	= Proliferation
Prostate	Human DU145			↓ Soft agar ↓ Invasion

[a] Reviewed in Hartsough and Steeg (2000).

factor, but in eukaryotes it feeds into traditional signal transduction pathways at the level of MAP kinase inactivation. Known Nm23 histidine protein kinase pathways are diagrammed in Fig. 2B and include its participation in prokaryotic "two-component" pathways, histidine–histidine transfers, histidine–aspartate transfers, and histidine–serine transfers of phosphate. Mutations to Nm23 amino acids, which disrupt histidine dependent phosphotransfers, concurrently disrupted the suppression of tumor cell motility upon transfection, suggesting that this general pathway may be relevant to its physiologic function.

V. TRANSLATIONAL DEVELOPMENT

A. Human Tumor Cohorts

Nm23 mRNA and protein levels have been determined in many human cancer types and correlated with indicators of metastatic propensity such as pa-
tient disease-free and overall survival, the presence of lymph node metastases, and tumor grade. The majority of studies in breast, hepatocellular, ovarian, gastric, and uterine cancers and melanoma have reported a significant correlation between reduced Nm23 expression and indicators of metastatic ability. These studies indicate that reduced Nm23 expression is relevant to human cancer progression; they do not indicate that Nm23 is an independent prognostic factor.

Studies in ovarian and esophageal cancer have suggested that reduced Nm23 expression also predicted a poor response to platinum-based chemotherapy. These conclusions were supported by transfection data in which *nm23* transfectants were preferentially sensitive to cisplatin *in vitro* and *in vivo*.

For most types of human cancer, Nm23 protein levels appear to be the most relevant predictor of metastatic potential, although allelic deletion (LOH) of *nm23*-H1 at 17q21 is frequent. Mutations in *nm23* are infrequently observed, with the exception of aggressive (stage IV) neuroblastoma.

A.

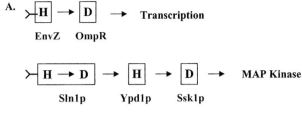

B.

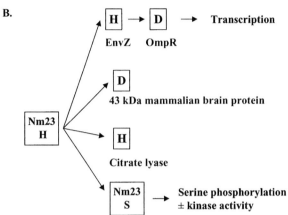

FIGURE 2 Histidine protein kinase pathways. Boxes represent proteins in signaling pathways, with the phosphorylated amino acid indicated within. (A) Prototypical "two-component" signal transduction pathways in *E. coli* (EnvZ-OmpR) and *S. cerevisea* (Sln1p-Ypd1p-Ssk1p). Binding of a ligand to a receptor initiates autophosphorylation on a histidine (H), which is passed to an aspartate (D) downstream. (B) Histidine protein kinase pathways in which Nm23 has been reported to function. Histidine autophosphorylated Nm23 can pass phosphate to "two-component" pathways, histidines or aspartates of other proteins, or to a serine (S) residue on Nm23.

B. Translational Hypothesis

Based on the observations that (a) many aggressive human tumors exhibit relatively low levels of Nm23 expression and (b) transfection of *nm23* significantly decreased tumor metastatic potential, it can be hypothesized that elevation of Nm23 expression in overt occult metastases may be of therapeutic benefit to the patient. Based on *in vitro* analyses of the transfectants, the differentiation status of the metastatic tumor cells, their colonization in foreign organs, and potentially their invasive/motile behavior in establishing secondary metastases could be impacted. The promoter region for various *nm23* family members has been reported, and characterization experiments are attempting to identify elements that could increase transcription.

See Also the Following Articles

AUTOCRINE AND PARACRINE GROWTH MECHANISMS IN CANCER PROGRESSION AND METASTASIS • MAP KINASE MODULES IN SIGNALING • P16 AND ARF • PTEN • RETINOBLASTOMA TUMOR SUPPRESSOR GENE • TP53 TUMOR SUPPRESSOR GENE • TUMOR SUPPRESSOR GENES: SPECIFIC CLASSES • WILMS TUMOR SUPPRESSOR WT1

Bibliography

Gervasi, F., D'Agnano, I., Vossio, S., Zupi, G., Sacchi, A., and Lombardi, D. (1996). *nm23* influences proliferation and differentiation of PC12 cells in response to nerve growth factor. *Cell Growth Diff.* **7,** 1689–1695.

Hartsough, M. T., and Steeg, P. S. (2000). Nm23/Nucleoside diphosphate kinase in human cancers. *J. Bioenerget. Biomembr.* **32,** 301–308.

Howlett, A. R., Petersen, O. W., Steeg, P. S., and Bissell, M. J. (1994). A novel function for Nm23: Overexpression in human breast carcinoma cells leads to the formation of basement membrane and growth arrest. *J. Natl. Cancer Inst.* **86,** 1838–1844.

Kantor, J. D., McCormick, B., Steeg, P. S., and Zetter, B. R. (1993). Inhibition of cell motility after *nm23* transfection of human and murine tumor cells. *Cancer Res.* **53,** 1971–1973.

Leone, A., Flatow, U., King, C. R., Sandeen, M. A., Margulies, I. M. K., Liotta, L. A., and Steeg, P. S. (1991). Reduced tumor incidence, metastatic potential, and cytokine responsiveness of *nm23*-transfected melanoma cells. *Cell* **65,** 25–35.

Lu, Q., Park, H., Egger, L., and Inouye, M. (1996). Nucleoside-diphosphate kinase-mediated signal transduction via histidyl-aspartyl phosphorelay systems in Escherichia coli. *J. Biol. Chem.* **271,** 32886–32893.

MacDonald, N., Freije, J., Stracke, M., Manrow, R., and Steeg, P. (1996). Site directed mutagenesis of *nm23*-H1: Mutation of proline 96 or serine 120 abrogates its motility inhibitory activity upon transfection into human breast carcinoma cells. *J. Biol. Chem.* **271,** 25107–25116.

Steeg, P. S., Bevilacqua, G., Kopper, L., Thorgeirsson, U. P., Talmadge, J. E., Liotta, L. A., and Sobel, M. E. (1988). Evidence for a novel gene associated with low tumor metastatic potential. *J. Natl. Cancer Inst.* **80,** 200–204.

Wagner, P. D., Steeg, P. S., and Vu, N.-D. (1997). Two-component kinase like activity of Nm23 correlates with its motility suppressing activity. *Proc. Natl. Acad. Sci. USA* **94,** 9000–9005.

Xu, J., Liu, L., Deng, F., Timmons, L., Hersperger, E., Steeg, P., Veron, M., and Shearn, A. (1996). Rescue of the awd mutant phenotype by expression of human Nm23/NDP kinase in Drosophila. *Dev. Biol.* **177,** 544–557.

Non-Hodgkin's Lymphoma and Multiple Myeloma: Incidence and Risk Factors

Leslie Bernstein
Wendy Cozen
Keck School of Medicine of the University of Southern California
The Norris Comprehensive Cancer Center

GLOSSARY

autoimmune disease A disease in which one or more elements are mistakenly recognized as foreign and are attacked by the body's own immune system. Examples are rheumatoid arthritis, in which the lining of the joints is attacked, and multiple sclerosis, in which the covering of the nerves is attacked.

cohort study An epidemiologic study in which subsets of a defined population are identified who may or may not be exposed, or may be exposed to different degrees (previously, now, or in the future) to a factor or factors hypothesized to influence the probability of developing a disease or experiencing another health outcome.

iatrogenic Resulting from a physician's or other health professional's professional activity.

immunophenotype The characterization of each immune cell according to certain protein markers on the surface of the cell. These markers determine how "old" a cell is and what kind of "job" it will have (for example, whether it will make antibodies, recognize foreign bacteria, or kill other infected cells).

immunosuppression A physiologic phenomenon in which one or several functions of the immune system are decreased or absent. The effect of immunosuppression is that certain types of tumors, mostly lymphomas, grow more easily and certain types of organisms, normally harmless, can cause serious or fatal disease, because the body's defenses are weak. Some reasons for immunosuppression include drugs administered to stop the immune system from rejecting a transplant, infection with HIV, pregnancy, tuberculosis, and malnutrition.

precursor cell A primitive, "young" cell that will mature into a more defined and specialized cell. These cells are sometimes called "blast" cells.

This article briefly covers the epidemiology of non-Hodgkin's lymphoma (NHL) and multiple myeloma (MM). Both of these hematologic malignancies exhibit unique epidemiologic patterns in terms of disease incidence, yet relatively little is known about the causes of these cancers.

I. NON-HODGKIN'S LYMPHOMA

Non-Hodgkin's lymphomas are a diverse collection of malignancies that originate in lymphoid cells. Because of their diversity, NHLs are difficult to study epidemiologically. NHLs differ in their morphologic presentation (large vs small cell, follicular vs diffuse cell, cleaved vs noncleaved cell, lymphocytic vs lymphoblastic vs histiocytic, B vs T cell vs non-B or T cell, degree of differentiation), immunological features, genetic characteristics, and prognosis. NHLs also differ according to the organ system that is affected. Because NHL is a malignancy of lymphoid tissue, one would expect that NHLs will occur only within the major lymphoid organs (the lymph nodes, spleen, thymus, and tonsils), but a substantial number of NHLs occur in other organ systems; these are termed extranodal NHLs. About one-third of these extranodal NHLs occur in the gastrointestinal tract, particularly in the stomach or small bowel.

A. Classification of NHL

A number of classification systems have been proposed for segregating NHLs into distinct subtypes. These systems have grouped NHLs according to the morphologic pattern of the cell, immunologic origin of the cell, histologic grade, and prognosis. Although most epidemiological studies do not present results separately for different types of non-Hodgkin's lymphoma, epidemiologists have tended to adopt the Working Formulation classification system for studies of incidence and survival. The Working Formulation bases the classification of NHLs on prognosis with three broad groups of tumors (low grade with the best prognosis, intermediate grade, and high grade with the poorest prognosis). A miscellaneous group includes mycosis fungoides. The major problem with this classification system is that these broad categories may not be etiologically distinct. The revised European–American Lymphoma (REAL) classification, published in 1994, was designed to classify tumors according to immunophenotype. In future epidemiologic studies, it will be important to provide information for subgroups of patients based on the REAL classification.

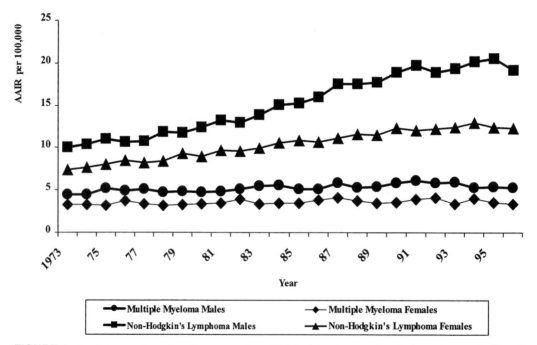

FIGURE 1   Trends in age-adjusted incidence rates of non-Hodgkin's lymphoma and multiple myeloma in the United States from 1973 to 1996. Data are for the nine original Surveillance, Epidemiology and End Results (SEER) cancer registries. Rates are standardized to the 1970 U.S. population

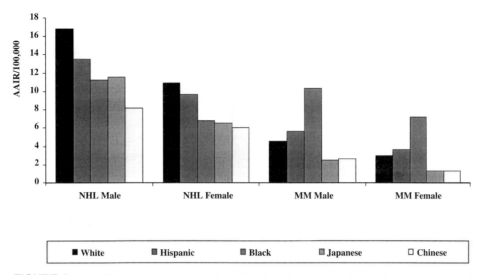

FIGURE 2 Age-adjusted incidence rates of non-Hodgkin's lymphoma and multiple myeloma by race/ethnicity and gender. Data are for Los Angeles County for the years 1972–1997 and were provided by the Cancer Surveillance Program of Los Angeles County. Incidence rates are standardized to the 1970 U.S. population.

B. Incidence

1. Adults

Incidence rates of adult-onset NHL have been increasing rapidly since the 1940s. In the United States, incidence has increased 3 to 5% per year since 1973 (Fig. 1). These increases in incidence are more striking for extranodal tumors than for tumors originating in the lymph nodes and are more marked among older persons than among younger persons. Although improved diagnostic methods can account for some of the early increases in incidence and infection with the human immunodeficiency virus (HIV) can account for some of the later increases in incidence, these two factors alone do not account for the majority of the increasing incidence of NHL.

NHL incidence rates are higher among men than among women [Fig. 1 shows data for nine Surveillance, Epidemiology and End Results (SEER) registries representing rates for the United States; Fig. 2 shows data for Los Angeles County, California]. In 1996, the incidence rates of NHL in U.S. males and females were 19.2 and 12.3, respectively, per 100,000 population (Fig. 1). Non-Hispanic whites have the highest incidence rates of NHL (Fig. 2).

The distribution of NHL subtypes varies around the world, suggesting that differences exist in the distribution of etiologic factors geographically or that individual responses to these etiologic factors differ geographically.

2. Children

While adults are more likely to be diagnosed with low or intermediate grade NHL, children are more likely to be diagnosed with high-grade tumors. NHL incidence rates for boys are two to three times higher than those for girls, and rates of white children are 30–40% higher than those of black children. Although the rates of NHL incidence have remained stable since the 1980s among children under age 15, those of older adolescents have increased. This increase in incidence is comparable to that seen among young adults.

C. Risk Factors for NHL

The risk factor relationships that might predispose an individual to develop NHL have been difficult to establish, most probably because NHLs represent such a heterogeneous group of malignancies. The only clearly established risk factors for NHL are immunosuppressed states due either to primary immunodeficiency conditions or to acquired immunodeficiency conditions such as occur in iatrogenic immunosuppression among organ transplant patients, Sjorgren's syndrome, and infection with HIV and other viruses. Other risk factors that have been studied in relation to the development of NHL include occupational exposure to pesticides and herbicides, occupational exposure to solvents and other chemicals, use of hair coloring products, dietary factors including intake of protein, fat, and alcohol, smoking, and exposure to ultraviolet light, radiation, and blood transfusions.

1. Primary and Acquired Immunosuppression

Patients with primary immunodeficiency diseases such as ataxia telangiectasia, common variable immunodeficiency, Wiskott–Aldrich syndrome, and severe combined immunodeficiency have a substantial risk of developing NHL, particularly as improvements in the health care of these patients increase their chances of survival with the primary immunodeficiency. Patients with chronic conditions involving immunological abnormalities, such as rheumatoid arthritis and Sjogren's syndrome, also have greater risk of NHL. As reported by Kinlen in 1992, among rheumatoid arthritis patients who are not treated with immunosuppressive therapy, the risk of NHL is 2.5 times that of the general population. Patients with other autoimmune diseases appear to develop NHL at related extranodal sites. Thus, those with Hashimoto's thyroiditis appear to be predisposed to develop primary thyroid lymphomas, and patients with celiac disease appear to have a high risk of NHLs of the intestinal tract.

Patients who are treated with immunosuppressive drugs such as azathioprine or cyclosporin are also at high risk of developing NHL. The NHL risk of organ transplant patients treated with immunosuppressive therapy ranges from 26 times to nearly 50 times that of the general population. Among patients treated for rheumatoid arthritis with these drugs, the risk is 10 times that expected in the general population.

2. Viral and Other Infections

Several types of viral infection are related to the increasing risk of NHL. The most well recognized of these is HIV, the retrovirus that causes the acquired immune deficiency syndrome (AIDS). NHL is the second most common malignancy associated with HIV infection. NHL affects all AIDS risk groups. HIV-related NHLs are primarily high-grade B-cell lymphomas and primary central nervous system lymphomas, although the AIDS case definition also in-

cludes intermediate-grade large cell NHL. Studies of the frequency of NHL as an AIDS-defining illness indicate that the rate of NHL diagnoses is increasing; the risk of NHL among HIV-infected patients is about 170 times that of the general population. Improvements in therapy for HIV that prolong survival and reduce the frequency of viral and bacterial infections actually may increase the frequency of NHL; as HIV patients live longer, they continue to be at high risk of developing NHL.

The Epstein–Barr virus (EBV) has also been implicated in the development of NHL, particularly in African Burkitt's lymphoma, a high-grade form of NHL. EBV is also associated with the development of NHL among patients with acquired or inherited immune suppression. It is possible that impaired immunosurveillance of EBV-infected cells leads to the development of NHL in these patients. Although it is possible that EBV plays a role in the development of NHL among persons who are not immunosuppressed, the evidence for this relationship is less clear.

Several studies have shown that patients diagnosed with B-cell NHL have a high prevalence of heptatitis C virus infection. Thus, it is possible that the hepatitis C virus may play a role in the development of B-cell lymphomas.

Human T-cell lymphotropic virus type I (HTLV-1) is known to cause NHL. Those individuals (particularly males) who were infected perinatally have the greatest NHL risk. Because of the restricted geographical distribution of HTLV-1 infection (primarily southernmost islands of Japan and certain areas in the Caribbean Islands), it is not a major contributor to the increasing rates of NHL worldwide.

As noted earlier, NHL frequently occurs at extranodal sites, particularly the gastrointestinal tract. NHLs that occur in the stomach have been associated with *Helicobacter pylori* infection, a bacterial infection that is strongly associated with risk of the more common adenocarcinomas of the stomach.

3. Agricultural and Occupational Exposures

The risk of NHL is slightly elevated among male farmers in the United States, which has raised concerns that pesticide exposure may increase the risk of NHL. Case-control studies conducted in Nebraska, Kansas, and New

Zealand have shown a greater risk of NHL among farmers who use a particular class of pesticides (phenoxy herbicides) with the level of increased risk directly related to the amount of exposure in the U.S. studies. However, risk of NHL has not been elevated among other exposed occupational groups, such as pesticide applicators. Furthermore, as reported by Blair *et al.* in 1992, no excess risk of death from NHL was found among farmers in a large meta-analysis of 23 studies. This lack of consistency across different exposure groups and outcomes detracts from the hypothesis that pesticide exposure is a cause of NHL. It is possible that pesticide exposure serves as a surrogate for another farm-related exposure, one that is more ubiquitous and could affect other segments of the population, such as oncogenic viruses carried by farm animals or ultraviolet (UV) radiation.

Other occupational exposures have been explored as possible risk factors for NHL, including exposure to benzene, chemical solvents, and work in the rubber manufacturing industry, plastics industry, and the logging or wood products industry. Some studies show increases in NHL risk with each of these exposures, but these associations are not observed in all studies. More research in this area is needed before any conclusions can be drawn regarding such exposures.

4. Lifestyle Factors

The lifestyle factor that has received the most attention in relation to NHL risk is the use of hair coloring products. Certain components of these products are mutagenic in the *Salmonella* test and carcinogenic in experimental animal tests. Early reports suggested a 50 to 100% increase in risk for NHL among women and men who used hair dyes. Later studies of this issue have not confirmed these findings. If exposure to these products through personal use was related to NHL risk, one would expect those exposed occupationally also to have an increased NHL risk, yet this is not the case. In 1995, LaVecchia *et al.* conducted a careful evaluation of the existing studies of occupational exposure to hair color products and found only a small (20%) increase in NHL risk.

Alcohol was initially investigated as a possible risk factor for NHL because it modulates the immune system and because alcohol abuse is associated with a greater infectious disease risk. Study results have not been consistent with the hypothesis that alcohol use

increases NHL risk, however. In fact, two carefully conducted epidemiological studies have shown that moderate alcohol consumption may reduce the risk of NHL among women. As with most factors suspected to affect NHL risk, no biological explanation has been identified to explain this observed relationship.

Some evidence suggests that cigarette smoking is related to the development of NHL, with a few, although not all, studies showing modest increases in risk.

Little has been published regarding dietary intake and NHL; two cohort studies have shown a relationship between the intake of certain meats and fats and the development of NHL.

5. Ultraviolet Radiation

UV radiation is temporarily immunosuppressive and thus may be associated with a greater risk of NHL. Several studies have noted that persons with a previous skin cancer have greater risk of NHL than those with no such history. Ecologic data from England and Wales that relate local NHL incidence rates to levels of solar UV exposure support a role for UV radiation in the development of NHL. However, a U.S. study of NHL mortality does not support this hypothesis.

6. Radiation

The effects of ionizing radiation on NHL risk have been evaluated among different groups of patients exposed to radiation treatments and among occupational groups exposed to radiation, such as atomic energy workers, uranium workers, and radiologists. Based on these studies, no convincing evidence exists for an increased risk of NHL associated with radiation exposure.

7. Blood Transfusions

Because blood products may contain viral or other infectious agents, as well as factors that might modulate the immune system, the effect of blood transfusions on NHL risk has been of concern. However, results of epidemiologic studies do not support a major role of transfusions in the development of NHL.

II. MULTIPLE MYELOMA

Multiple myeloma is a B-cell malignancy of plasma cells or their precursors that occurs among adults.

The most frequent site of occurrence of MM is the bone marrow, where plasma cells are produced.

A. Incidence

MM is a rare malignancy with about 12,000 new MM patients diagnosed annually in the United States. Incidence rates for men (5.3 per 100,000 men) are about 50% higher than those for women (3.4/100,000 women) (data for 1996 in Fig. 1). Blacks have the highest risk of this disease; in Los Angeles County, rates for blacks are about two times greater than those of whites and Hispanics and at least four times greater than those of Japanese and Chinese (Fig. 2). Despite this racial/ethnic difference in risk, MM does not appear to be related to socioeconomic status. MM incidence rates increase exponentially with age for both men and women, with peak incidence occurring in the sixth and seventh decades. Incidence rates for MM have remained relatively stable since the early 1970s (Fig. 1).

B. Risk Factors for MM

Relatively few epidemiologic studies of MM have been conducted due to the relative rarity of this malignancy. Risk factors that have been considered as possibly related to the development of MM are viral infection, immune suppression, radiation, occupational exposures, some lifestyle factors, and family history.

1. Viral Infection

After the identification of human herpes virus 8 (HHV8) as a possible cause of Kaposi's sarcoma, its role in the development of MM was examined. A 1997 study by Rettig *et al.* showing evidence of HHV8 infection in bone marrow cells from MM patients led to optimism that a viral cause of MM had been found. However, since this initial report was published, 14 additional studies have been conducted; none has been able to demonstrate any relationship between HHV8 and MM. No other viruses have been proposed as playing a role in the development of MM.

2. Chronic Antigenic Stimulation and Autoimmune Disease

MM cells are derived from antibody-producing cells (plasma cells or their precursors). Thus, it is possible that chronic antigenic stimulation (resulting from in-fections, vaccinations, allergies, or an autoimmune disease) might be a risk factor for MM. Studies of the effects of infections, vaccinations, or allergies on MM risk are difficult to conduct because of the variety of potential exposures, difficulties in ascertaining and defining these exposures, and the fact that allergies and infections affect large segments of the population. Although epidemiologic studies have not shown any consistent effect of infections or vaccinations on MM risk, several studies do report a positive association between MM and a history of allergies and autoimmune or inflammatory diseases. These results do not rule out the possibility that chronic B-cell stimulation to "self"-antigens may lead to the development of MM, but further studies are necessary to confirm these findings.

3. Radiation

Radiation exposure has also been considered in studies of MM. Although early studies reported an increased risk of MM among Japanese atomic bomb survivors, the most recent reanalysis of cases occurring between 1950 and 1987 showed no evidence of an excess risk associated with radiation exposure. This analysis by Preston *et al.* in 1994 was based on careful review of the case records and potential exposures to minimize misclassification. Based on this evidence, ionizing radiation (in large doses) is no longer considered to be a risk factor for MM. MM risk has been examined among persons with low-level occupational exposure to radiation, such as nuclear facility workers, X-ray technicians, and radium dial workers, with many studies showing a positive, although not definitive, relationship. It is difficult to draw conclusions from these studies because of differences in the accuracy of recording exposures, variations in the dose and duration of exposure across studies, and individual differences in the anatomic site exposed (e.g., direct exposure of the spine would be more detrimental than exposure to the pelvis because the bone marrow is less protected in the spine compared to the pelvis). If this association with occupational radiation exposure is real, it is puzzling why a low level exposure over a long period of time would cause MM when a very high exposure of short duration (atomic bomb) does not.

4. Agricultural and Occupational Exposures

Agricultural occupational exposures or farming has been the risk factor receiving the greatest attention in relation to MM risk, with more than 37 studies conducted thus far. In a meta-analysis of 32 of these studies, Khuder and Mutgi concluded that farming as an occupation was associated with a modest (23%) increased risk of MM; however, little progress has been made with respect to identification of the etiologic agent. Potential exposures associated with farming that might be associated with an increased risk of MM include pesticides, infection with animal viruses, antigenic stimulation, and organic dust exposure. A cohort study of Norwegian farmers showed a 50% increased risk of MM associated with pesticide purchase. However, in a study of Iowa farmers, no particular class of pesticide was associated with exposure, and men with the highest risk of MM had the fewest years on the job. Another study showed that pilots employed as aerial pesticide applicators had a lower risk of MM than other types of pilots. Only indirect evidence exists to support the animal virus hypothesis, an excess risk of MM among meat cutters. Thus, although a modest excess of MM among farmworkers has been confirmed in many studies, the etiologic agents have remained elusive.

Few studies have been conducted to evaluate other occupational exposures as risk factors for MM. Some studies have shown an increased MM risk among painters. Specific occupational exposures that have been studied include exposure to asbestos, pesticides, and benzene and other organic solvents. The most recent evidence suggests that there is no relationship between MM risk and either benzene or asbestos. Pesticide exposure unrelated to farming has been associated with an increased risk of MM in some studies, but not in others. Although several industrial and occupational exposures have been associated with an increased risk of MM in some studies (plastics, paints and solvents, diesel exhaust, and woodworking and carpentry), evidence for these effects is still limited.

5. Lifestyle Factors

Tobacco use, alcohol use, and obesity are not associated with an increased risk of MM. Because of concern that use of semipermanent and permanent hair dyes might be a risk factor for hematologic neoplasms, use of these products has been investigated in relation to MM risk. Neither personal use of hair dyes nor occupational exposure to these products appears to be related to increased risk.

6. Family History and Genetic Predisposition

The strong influence of race on MM risk and the reported clustering of MM in some families suggest that genetic factors may affect MM risk. Several case-control studies have reported a 3-5 fold increased risk of MM for persons with first-degree relatives diagnosed with MM and a 2-fold increased risk for persons with first degree relatives diagnosed with other hematologic malignancies. Genetic studies have focused mainly on HLA subtypes, although no specific antigen has been confirmed as predictive of risk.

See Also the Following Articles

ACUTE LYMPHOBLASTIC LEUKEMIA • CHRONIC LYMPHOCYTIC LEUKEMIA • HUMAN T-CELL LEUKEMIA/LYMPHOTROPIC VIRUS • MONOCLONAL ANTIBODIES: LEUKEMIA AND LYMPHOMA

Bibliography

Bentham, G. (1996). Association between incidence of non-Hodgkin's lymphoma and solar ultraviolet radiation in England and Wales. *Br. Med. J.* **312,** 1128–1131.

Bergsagel, D. E., Wong, O., Bergsagel, P. L., Alexanian, R., Anderson, K., Kyle, R. A., and Raabe, G. K. (1999). Benzene and multiple myeloma: Appraisal of the scientific evidence. *Blood* **94,** 1174–1182.

Blair, A., Hoar Zahm, S., Pearce, N. E., Heineman, E. F., and Fraumeni, J. F., Jr. (1992). Clues to cancer etiology from studies of farmers. *Scand. J. Work Environ. Health* **18,** 209–215.

Brown, L. M., Burmeister, L. F., Everett, G. D., and Blair, A. (1993). Pesticide exposures and multiple myeloma in Iowa men. *Cancer Causes Control* **4,** 153–156.

Brown, L. M., Linet, M. S., Greenberg, R. S., Silverman, D. T., Hayes, R. B., Sanson, G. M, Schwartz, A. G., Schoenberg, J. B., Pottern, L. M., and Fraumeni, J. F., Jr. (1999). Multiple myeloma and family history of cancer among blacks and whites in the U.S. *Cancer* **85,** 2385–2390.

Cantor, K. P., and Silberman, W. (1999). Mortality and among aerial pesticide applicators and flight instructors: Follow-up from 1965-1988. *Am. J. Industr. Med.* **36,** 239–247.

Devesa, S. S. (1991). Descriptive epidemiology of multiple myeloma. *In* "Epidemiology and Biology of Multiple Myeloma" (G. I. Obrams and M. Potter, eds.), pp. 3–12, Springer-Verlag, New York.

Eriksson, M. (1993). Rheumatoid arthritis as a risk factor for multiple myeloma: A case-control study. *Eur. J. Cancer* **29A,** 259–263.

Eriksson, M., and Hallberg, B. (1992). Familial occurrence of hematologic malignancies and other diseases in multiple myeloma: A case-control study. *Cancer Causes Control* **3,** 63–67.

Filipovich, A. H., Mathur, A., Kamat, D., and Shapiro, R. S. (1992). Primary immunodeficiencies: Genetic risk factors for lymphoma. *Cancer Res. (Suppl).* **52,** 5465s–5467s.

Franceschi, S., Dal Maso, L., and La Vecchia, C. (1999). Advances in the epidemiology of HIV-associated non-Hodgkin's lymphoma and other lymphoid neoplasms. *Int. J. Cancer* **83,** 481–485.

Freedman, D. M., Zahm, S. H., and Dosemeci, M. (1997). Residential and occupational exposure to sunlight and mortality from non-Hodgkin's lymphoma: Composite (threefold) case-control study. *Br. Med. J.* **314,** 1451–1455.

Grodstein, F., Hennekens, C. H., Colditz, G. A., Hunter, D. J, and Stampfer, M. J. (1994). A prospective study of permanent hair dye use and hematopoietic cancer. *J. Natl. Cancer Instit.* **86,** 1466–1470.

Harris, N. L., Jaffe, E. S., Stein, H., Banks, P. M., Chan, J. K., Cleary, M.L., Delsol, G., DeWolf-Peeters, C., Falini, B., and Gatter, K. C. (1994). A revised European-American classification of lymphoid neoplasms: A proposal from the International Lymphoma Study Group. *Blood* **84,** 1361–1392.

Herrinton, L. J., Weiss, N. S., and Olshan, A. F. (1996). Multiple myeloma. *In* "Cancer Epidemiology and Prevention" (D. Schottenfeld and J. F. Fraumeni, Jr., eds.), pp. 946–970. Oxford Univ. Press, New York

Holly, E. A., Lele, C., and Bracci, P. M. (1998). Hair-color products and risk for non-Hodgkin's lymphoma: A population-based study in the San Francisco Bay Area. *Am. J. Public Health* **88,** 1767–1773.

Johnson, E. S. (1990). Association between soft tissue sarcomas, malignant lymphomas, and phenoxy herbicides/chlorophenols: Evidence from occupational cohort studies. *Fundam. Appl. Toxicol.* **14,** 219–234.

Khuder, S. A., and Mutgi, A. B. (1997). Meta-analyses of multiple myeloma and farming. *Am. J. Indust. Med.* **32,** 510–516.

Kinlen, L. (1992). Immunosuppressive therapy and acquired immunological disorders. *Cancer Res. (Suppl.)* **52,** 5474s–5476s.

Kristensen, P., Andersen, A., Irgens, L. M., Laake, P., and Bye, A. S. (1996). Incidence and risk factors of cancer among men and women in Norwegian agriculture. *Scand. J. Work Environ. Health* **22,** 14–26.

LaVecchia, C., and Tavani, A. (1995). Epidemiological evidence on hair dyes and the risk of cancer in humans. *Eur. J. Cancer Prev.* **4,** 31–43.

Metayer, C., Johnson, E. S., and Rice, J. C. (1998). Nested case-control study of tumors of the hematopoietic and lymphatic systems among workers in the meat industry. *Am. J. Epidemiol.* **147,** 727–738

Nelson, R. A., Levine, A. M., and Bernstein, L. (1998). Blood transfusions and the risk of intermediate or high-grade non-Hodgkin's lymphoma. *J. Natl. Cancer Inst.* **90,** 1742–1743.

Non-Hodgkin's Lymphoma Pathologic Classification Project (1982). National Cancer Institute sponsored study of classifications of non-Hodgkin's lymphomas. *Cancer* **49,** 2112–2235.

Percy, C. L., Smith, M. A., Linet, M., Ries, L. A. G., and Friedman, D. L. (1999). Lymphomas and reticuloendothelial neoplasms. *In* "Cancer Incidence and Survival among Children and Adolescents: United States SEER Program 1975–1995" (L. A. G. Ries, M. A. Smith, J. G. Gurney, M. Linet, T. Tamra, J. L. Young, and G. R. Bunin, eds.), pp. 35–50, National Cancer Institute, SEER Program. NIH Pub. No. 99-4649, Bethesda, MD.

Preston, D. L., Kusumi, S., Tomonaga, M., Izumi, S., Ron, E., Kuramoto, A., Kamada, N., Dohy, H., Matsui, T., Nonaka, H., Thompson, D. E., Soda, M., and Mabuchi, K. (1994). Cancer incidence in atomic bomb survivors. III. Leukemia, lymphoma and multiple myeloma, 1950–1987. *Radiat. Res.* **137,** S68–S97.

Reidel, D. A. (1991). Epidemiologic studies of multiple myeloma: Occupation and radiation effects. In "Epidemiology and Biology of Multiple Myeloma" (G. I. Obrams and M. Potter, eds.), pp. 13–17, Springer-Verlag, New York.

Rettig, M. B., Ma, H. J., Vescio, R. A., Pold, M., Schiller, G., Belson, D., Savage, A., Nishikubo, C., Wu, C., Fraser, J., Said, J. M., and Berenson, J. R. (1997). Kaposi's sarcoma-associated herpesvirus infection of bone marrow dendritic cells from multiple myeloma patients. *Science* **276,** 1851–1854.

Scheer, P. A., and Mueller, N. E. (1996). Non-Hodgkin's lymphomas. *In* "Cancer Epidemiology and Prevention" (D. Schottenfeld and J. F. Fraumeni, Jr., eds.), pp. 920–945. Oxford Univ. Press, New York.

Tarte, K., Chang, Y., and Klein, B. (1999). Kaposi's sarcoma-associated herpesvirus and multiple myeloma: Lack of criteria for causality. *Blood* **93,** 3159–3163.

Zahm, S. H., Weisenburger, D. D., Babbitt, P. A., Saal, R. C., Vaught, J. B., and Blair, A. (1992). Use of hair coloring products and the risk of lymphoma, multiple myeloma, and chronic lymphocytic leukemia. *Am. J. Public Health* **83,** 990–997.

Zhang, S., Hunter, D. J., Rosner, B. A., Colditz, G. A., Fuchs, C. S., Speizer, F. E., and Willett, W. C. (1999). Dietary fat and protein in relation to risk of non-Hodgkin's lymphoma among women. *J. Natl. Cancer Inst.* **91,** 1751–1758.

Zuckerman, E., Zuckerman, T., Levine, A. M., Douer, D., Gutekunst, K., Mizokami, M., Qian, D. G., Velankar, M., Nathwani, B. N., and Fong, T. L. (1997). Hepatitis C virus infection in patients with B cell non-Hodgkin's lymphoma. *Ann. Intern. Med.* **127,** 423–428.

Nutritional Supplements and Diet as Chemoprevention Agents

Anna Giuliano
Susan Gapstur
Ellen Graver
Harinder Garewal
Arizona Cancer Center and
Southern Arizona VA Health Care System, Tucson

GLOSSARY

antioxidant nutrients Nutritional agents that have the capacity to neutralize damaging free radicals, thus inhibiting oxidative damage. Under the proper conditions, almost any chemical can play this role, but the term usually refers to agents such as β-carotene, vitamin E, or vitamin C.

cancer chemoprevention Use of selected chemicals to reduce cancer incidence.

intermediate end points Surrogate end point markers used as targets in prevention trials as substitutes for cancer incidence. At present, no intermediate end point has been definitively validated, but a large number are under study.

primary prevention A strategy in which intervention precedes the initiating event, e.g., the prevention of smoking by adolescents.

secondary prevention A strategy in which intervention occurs during the promotional stage of carcinogenesis, e.g., chemoprevention in cigarette smokers or asbestos workers.

tertiary prevention A strategy in which intervention targets end points such as preneoplastic lesions, i.e., late in the carcinogenesis pathway.

Encyclopedia of Cancer, Second Edition
Volume 3

Cancer chemoprevention consists of the use of selected chemicals, natural or synthetic, with the goal of reducing cancer incidence. Chemoprevention research involves analysis of multiple lines of evidence, often taking leads from epidemiologic, laboratory, and other preclinical information, performing initial clinical studies in humans culminating, whenever possible, in randomized, controlled clinical trials for confirmation. Simply inhibiting carcinogenesis is not enough; putative chemoprevention agents must also have properties that would allow their use in the population. Thus, they must be virtually free of harmful side effects, be readily available, and easily administered. Only under these conditions can widespread use be feasible so as to make a significant impact on cancer morbidity and mortality. Because they possess many of these properties, vitamins and related micronutrients have attracted a lot of attention in chemoprevention research (Table I). However, these same characteristics make it extremely difficult to conduct placebo-controlled, randomized clinical trials, many of which require long durations during which a "clean" placebo arm must be maintained in the face of ongoing publicity regarding "benefits." Results from epidemiologic studies have been remarkably consistent in showing an inverse association between fruit/vegetable consumption, intake of vitamins C, E, and A, folic acid, and with risk of many common cancers, e.g., lung, colon/rectum, stomach, esophagus, and cervix.

I. INTRODUCTION

Until recently, vitamin requirements have been determined based on their role in preventing deficiency syndromes, such as scurvy, beriberi, and pellagra, with biochemical studies emphasizing their coenzyme functions. However, recent research suggests that this basis for judging requirement is erroneous because vitamins have other significant health effects based on other properties, such as protection against oxidative-free radical damage (antioxidant role). Optimal nutrient health maintenance and chronic disease prevention rather than chemical deficiency prevention levels were defined (ORI).

Clinical trials provide a means for determining which of the numerous micronutrients present in the diet are active as cancer chemopreventive agents. Although it is widely accepted that the best way to prove clinical efficacy for any intervention is through a randomized, placebo-controlled, double-blind trial, conducted in subjects representative of the target population, with the appropriate disease end point, it is well recognized that such studies are often logistically, and practically, impossible. Disease end points, even for fairly common diseases, are still infrequent events in a generally healthy population, thereby necessitating that such trials involve many thousands of subjects and last decades. Maintenance of a blind for such prolonged periods can be a futile undertaking, especially when there are easily recognizable changes or side effects attributable to some agents, such as, for example, dermatologic and other effects associated with the retinoids or the yellow skin color resulting from high doses of β-carotene. Furthermore, in Western developed countries, particularly North America, acceptance by large segments of the population of the possible benefits in a variety of diseases, including cardiovascular disease and cataract prevention, in addition to cancer, of agents like β-carotene, vitamin E, and vitamin C, makes it problematic to conduct long-term trials involving placebo groups, especially in higher risk subjects eager to do everything to reduce their risk. Thus, direct evidence for efficacy based on perfectly designed studies is unlikely to be available for every agent and disease entity. Clinicians should become familiar with the available evidence supporting or refuting a chemopreventive role, along with an understanding of any side effects or toxicities attributable to these agents in order to advise patients appropriately.

This article reviews the main study design issues in planning and conducting cancer chemoprevention clinical trials, the rationale for use of vitamins as chemoprevention agents, and recent findings from published vitamin chemoprevention trials (Table I).

II. CANCER CHEMOPREVENTION TRIAL METHODOLOGY

Cancer prevention studies are designed to test hypotheses based on results from *in vitro*, animal, and

TABLE I
Antioxidant and Other Vitamin Cancer Prevention Studies

Senior author, year (location)	Organ	Subjects	Treatment	Results/end points
Stich, 1985 (Canada)	Oral cavity	Snuff users	Placebo vs β-carotene	Significant ($P < 0.001$) reduction in the frequency of buccal cell micronuclei in group I after 10 weeks
Stich, 1991 (India)	Oral cavity	Betel quid chewers with leukoplakia	Placebo vs β-carotene vs vitamin A and β-carotene	β-Carotene 14% complete regression; vitamins A and β-carotene: 27% complete repression; placebo: 3% complete repression
Stich, 1988 (India)	Oral cavity	Betel quid chewers with leukoplakia	Placebo vs vitamin A	After 6 months there was a greater leukoplakia remission rate ($P < 0.001$) and fewer newly developed leukoplakias ($P = 0.02$) in treatment vs placebo
Garewal, 1989 (United States)	Oral cavity	Leukoplakia	β-Carotene	71% regression
Garewal, 1994 (United States)	Oral cavity	Leukoplakia	β-Carotene	55% regression in a multicenter study
Benner, 1993 (United States)	Oral cavity	Leukoplakia	Vitamin E	46% regression overall; 65% in evaluable cases in multicenter study
Toma, 1992 (Italy)	Oral cavity	Leukoplakia	β-Carotene	44% regression
Malaker, 1991 (Canada)	Oral cavity	Leukoplakia	β-Carotene	50% regression
Zaridze, 1993 (Uzbekistan)	Oral cavity Esophagus	Leukoplakia Esophagitis	β-Carotene Vitamin E Vitamin A Riboflavin	Leukoplakia incidence decreased; nonsignificant effect on esophagitis
Munoz, 1987 (China)	Oral cavity	High-risk population	Placebo vs vitamin A and riboflavin and zinc	No significant difference in the prevalence of micronuclei after 13.5 months
Garewal, 1999 (United States)	Oral cavity prevention	Leukoplakia	Placebo vs β-carotene	β-Carotene activity in patients with oral leukoplakia was confirmed; responses produced were durable for 1 year
Mayne, (United States)	Oral cavity	Second primary prevention	Placebo vs β-carotene	Relative risk 0.69 in β-carotene arm (ns because of study size)
Pastorino, 1990 (Italy)	Lung	Stage I lung cancer	Placebo vs vitamin A	No difference between groups in recurrence, small decrease in occurrence of a second primary tumor
van Poppel, 1992 (Netherlands)	Lung	Heavy smokers	Placebo vs β-carotene	27% reduction in sputum micronuclei
ATBC Cancer Prevention Group, 1994 (Finland)	Lung	Heavy smokers	Placebo vs β-carotene and/or vitamin E	No decrease in cancer or heart disease, slight increase in lung cancer
Heimburger, 1988 (United States)	Lung	Smokers with sputum squamous metaplasia	Placebo vs folate and vitamin B_{12}	Significantly greater reduction of atypia in treatment compared to placebo group ($P < 0.02$)
Hennekens (United States)	Lung, all sites	Physicians	Placebo vs β-carotene ± aspirin	No effect on cardiovascular disease, lung cancer
Kok (Netherlands)	Lung	Heavy smokers	Placebo vs β-carotene	Ongoing study, sputum micronuclei
Kuller (United States)	Lung	Smokers	Placebo vs β-carotene	Ongoing study, sputum DNA analysis
McLarty (United States)	Lung	Asbestos workers	Placebo vs retinol and β-carotene	No effect on bronchial metaplasia and dysplasia
Musk, 1998 (Australia)	Lung	Crocodile workers	β-Carotene and retinol	Lack of any benefit from β-carotene; Lower rates of mesothelioma with retinol
Omenn, 1998 (United States)	Lung	Asbestos workers	Placebo vs β-carotene	No effect on lung cancer and retinol
Pastorino, 2000 (Italy)	Lung	Stage I nonsmall cell lung cancer	Placebo vs retinol N-acetylcysteine	No effect on head, neck, or lung cancer

continues

TABLE I *Continued*

Senior author, year (location)	Organ	Subjects	Treatment	Results/end points
Levshin (Russia)	Lung	Heavy smokers	Placebo vs stop smoking retinol, vitamin E	Ongoing study, risk of lung cancer after 10 years
Greenberg, 1990 (United States)	BCC/SCC	History BCC/SCC	Placebo vs β-carotene	Nonsignificant BCC/SCC recurrence
Luande (Tanzania)	BCC/SCC	Albinos or actinic keratosis	Placebo vs β-carotene	Ongoing study, lesion regression
Moon, 1997 (United States)	BCC/SCC	Actinic keratosis	Placebo vs retinol	Effective in prevention of SCC: no effect on BCC
Levine, 1977 (United States)	BCC/SCC	Multiple BCC/SCC	Placebo vs 13-*cis* retinoic acid, retinol	No effect in prevention of BCC/SCC
Clark, 1996 (United States)	BCC/SCC	Hx of BCC/SCC	Placebo vs selenium	No effect of BCC/SCC
Mobrahan (United States)	Colorectal	Healthy subjects; colon cancer/ adenoma	β-Carotene	Ongoing study, cell proliferation rate
Bonelli (Italy)	Colorectal	Adenomatous polyps	Placebo vs selenium and zinc and vitamins A, C, and E	Ongoing study, polyp recurrence after 5 years
De Gosse, 1989 (United States)	Colorectal	Familial adenomatous polyposis	Low fiber (Gp I) vs low fiber and vitamins C and E (Gp II) vs high fiber and vitamins C and E (Gp III)	Trend toward a reduced number of polyps in group III compared to groups I and II after 4 years of follow-up
Mckeowen-Eyswsen, 1988 (Canada)	Colorectal	Adenomatous polyps	Placebo vs vitamins C and E	No difference between treatment and control in polyp recurrence after 2 years
Bussey, 1982 (England)	Colorectal	Familial polyposis	Placebo vs vitamin C	(a) Significantly reduced polyp surface area at 9 months, (b) trend toward a treatment effect in polyp number, and (c) no difference in cell proliferation rate
Paganelli, 1992 (Italy)	Colorectal	Adenomatous polyps	Placebo vs vitamins A, C, and E	Significant ($P < 0.01$) decrease in rectal cell proliferation after 6 months vs no change in placebo group
Greenberg, 1994 (United States)	Colorectal	Adenomatous polyps	Placebo vs β-carotene vs vitamins C and E vs β-carotene and vitamins C and E	No effect on polyp recurrence after year 1 to year 4
Graves (United States)	Colorectal	Adenomatous polyps	Usual diet vs high fruit/vegetable	Ongoing study; polyp recurrence, cell proliferation rate
Schatzkin, Polyp Prevention Trial, 2000 (United States)	Colorectal	Adenomatous polyps	Usual diet vs low fat, high fruit/vegetable fiber	No effect of recurrence of colorectal adenomas
Alberts, 2000 (United States)	Colorectal	Adenomatous polyps	High vs low dietary wheat bran fiber supplement	No effect of recurrence of colorectal adenomas
Baron, 1999 (United States)	Colorectal	Colorectal Adenoma	Placebo vs calcium carbonate	Significant although moderate reduction in recurrence of colorectal adenomas
Alberts (United States)	Colorectal	Adenomatous polyps	Placebo vs selenium and/or celecoxib	Ongoing study; reduce risk of recurrence of colorectal adenomas
Rock (United States)	Cervix	CIN I, CIN II	Fruits and vegetables	Ongoing
Butterworth, 1992 (United States)	Uterine cervix	CIN I, CIN II	Vitamin C vs folate	No significant difference between groups

continues

TABLE I *Continued*

Senior author, year (location)	Organ	Subjects	Treatment	Results/end points
Butterworth, 1982 (United States)	Uterine cervix	OC users with mild–moderate dysplasia	Vitamin C vs folate	Significantly greater reduction of dysplasia in folate group compared to the vitamin C group ($P < 0.05$)
Berman (United States)	Uterine cervix	CIN I, CIN II	Placebo vs folate	Ongoing study, dysplasia regression
Romney, 1997 (United States)	Uterine cervix	CIN II	Placebo vs β-carotene	No effect on regression of CIN
Szarewski (United Kingdom)	Uterine cervix	CIN I	Placebo vs vitamin C, β-carotene, and vitamin E	Ongoing study. CIN I evolution and HPV infection after 1 year
Blot, 1993 (China)	Esophagus gastric	High-risk Chinese	β-carotene, vitamin E, selenium vs placebo vs other supplements	Reduction in gastric cancer incidence, mortality; reduction in overall mortality
Munoz, 1985 (China)	Esophageal	High-risk population	Placebo vs vitamin A, riboflavin, and zinc	No significant difference in prevalence of esophageal lesions after 13.5 months
Li, 1993 (China)	Esophageal	Esophageal dysplasia	Antioxidant arm: β-carotene, vitamin E, and selenium	16% lower death rate from esophageal cancer for those receiving antioxidants vs placebo after 6 years (nonsignificant)
Correa (Colombia)	Gastric	Intestinal metaplasia dysplasia	Anti-H, pylori plus β-carotene and vitamin C	Ongoing study, changes in precancerous lesions after 3 years
Munoz (Venezuela)	Gastric	Chronic atrophic gastritis, intestinal metaplasia, and dysplasia	Placebo vs vitamin C, β-carotene and vitamin E	Ongoing study, changes in precancerous lesions after 3 years
Reed (Europe)	Gastric	Chronic atrophic gastritis, intestinal metaplasia, and dysplasia	Placebo vs vitamin C	Ongoing study, precancerous lesions reversal
Clark 1998 (United States)	Prostate	Hx BCC/SCC	Placebo vs selenium	Significant reduction in prostate and total cancer incidence
NCI SELECT Trial (United States)	Prostate	Healthy subjects	Selenium, vitamin E	Ongoing study, incidence of prostate cancer
PIN Trial (United States)	Prostate	High-grade prostatic intraepithelial neoplasia	L-Selenomethionine	Ongoing study, incidence of prostate cancer

epidemiology studies. They can be classified into three broad categories: (1) primary prevention—where the intervention precedes the initiating event, such as an intervention to decrease the initiation of smoking among adolescents; (2) secondary prevention—where the intervention occurs during the promotional stage of carcinogenesis, such as chemoprevention trials among populations with elevated cancer risk, e.g., cigarette smokers, asbestos workers, and individuals with predisposing conditions like familial polyposis; and (3) tertiary prevention—where the intervention targets a preneoplastic lesion, or other indicators of cancer risk, such as trials designed to halt the progression of cervical dysplasia, esophageal dysplasia, colon polyps, or oral leukoplakia. Most of the completed and ongoing chemoprevention trials have as their goal the prevention of the first or primary tumor and fall into the category of secondary and tertiary prevention trials.

Once a putative chemopreventive agent has been selected for clinical trials, four main stages of experimentation generally occur. Phase I trials are conducted primarily to determine safety, establish acceptable dose schedules, and study metabolism and bioavailability. In contrast to standard oncologic anticancer drug development, the objective of chemoprevention dosing studies is not determination of a maximum tolerated dose, but rather the lowest or minimal effective dose that will produce an effect in order to minimize toxicity and promote compliance. Initial clinical investigations for treatment efficacy are then carried out in small-scale studies referred to as phase II trials. If the drug/nutrient continues to show promise, larger phase III trials are used to compare the new treatment with a standard treatment or placebo. Such phase III trials are considered the "gold standard" for clinical investigation. As mentioned earlier, however, there are many limitations and problems that frequently make such phase III trials impossible to conduct. Finally, phase IV trials or "postmarketing surveillance" describes ongoing data monitoring after the agent is in general use to look for continued efficacy and, more importantly, infrequent toxic effects that may only be detectable after widespread use.

Unlike pharmaceutical agents that are tested for their chemopreventive properties, the evaluation of vitamins and micronutrients has not usually proceeded through phases I and II prior to being tested in phase III trials. Most of the micronutrients of current interest, with the exception of higher doses of vitamin A and its synthetic analogs, have been previously demonstrated to be safe and tolerable across fairly large dose ranges and time periods. However, very few micronutrient pharmacokinetic and tissue distribution studies have been conducted thus far, often resulting in the need for best guess estimates in choosing doses and schedules for phase II and III clinical trials.

Doses of micronutrients for chemoprevention are usually several times the RDA; this is not surprising, as the RDA only provided guidance on nutrient intakes necessary to prevent symptoms of classic micronutrient deficiency syndromes (e.g., 60 mg vitamin C/day prevents scurvy) and do not consider sufficient levels for optimal health or disease prevention. Where experimental data were lacking, RDA estimates were based simply on the usual intake for that nutrient in the United States (e.g., vitamin E). The RDAs were based on data from younger-aged individuals, 25 to 50 years, and not on data derived from the population over age 50 who are at higher risk for cancer. New guidelines have been proposed that define the optimal and upper limits.

Similar to other cancer chemoprevention trials, micronutrient chemoprevention trials are often designed without adequate information on (1) where in the carcinogenesis continuum the nutrient is active (e.g., initiation, promotion, progression) and (2) the duration of treatment and the length of follow-up needed to demonstrate an effect. In general, doses are selected based on dietary intakes and serum micronutrient levels that appear to be protective in epidemiologic studies. Because many micronutrients are virtually without toxicity, one goal should be to use an adequately high dose to overcome variability in absorption among individuals. Doses have also been selected based on data from pharmacokinetic studies when such data are available. In some circumstances, however, low doses have been used for purposes such as "maintenance of a blind." For example, β-carotene produces a recognizable yellow skin coloration, the intensity of which depends on the dose and duration of use. Clearly such a strategy is open to criticism based on adequacy of the dose tested.

III. BIOMARKERS AS INTERMEDIATE END POINTS IN MICRONUTRIENT CHEMOPREVENTION TRIALS

The efficacy of any preventive agent is best supported by demonstrating a decrease in disease incidence that can be directly attributed to the agent under study. However, as discussed earlier, for most cancers, such trials would be prohibitively long, requiring impossibly large numbers of subjects. Thus, considerable attention is currently being devoted to developing possible intermediate or surrogate markers as end points in clinical trials. Although such markers have been available for heart and infectious disease trials for some time, it has only been in the last two decades that they have become a major focus for cancer etiology and prevention research.

Biologic intermediate markers fall into different broad categories, such as genomic markers (e.g., micronuclei, nuclear morphometry, oncogene mutations), proliferation-related markers (e.g., PCNA, thymidine-labeling index, polyamines, ornithine decarboxylase), or differentiation markers (e.g., keratinization, transglutaminase type 1). In addition to these biomarkers, there are clinical intermediate end points of which the most important are precancerous lesions (e.g., colorectal polyps, oral leukoplakia, or cervical dysplasia). Their recurrence, progression, or regression rates are all suitable intermediate end point targets for chemoprevention efforts. Current nutrient-based clinical trials often incorporate one or more of these markers in their design.

IV. OXIDANTS AND ANTIOXIDANT NUTRIENTS IN CANCER CHEMOPREVENTION

The role of oxidative damage in carcinogenesis is increasingly being appreciated. Oxygen species appear to play an important role in the promotion phase of carcinogenesis by affecting the regulation of cell growth and differentiation. Oxidants produced as a result of chronic inflammation, chemical exposure, radiation, and xenobiotic metabolism are known to cause sister chromatid exchanges and chromosomal abnormalities that result in mutation. In addition, oxidants have been shown to inhibit DNA repair and to cause immune dysfunction. Furthermore, oxidants amplify the expression of viral genes and cellular oncogenes in cultured cells. To prevent oxidant damage to tissues, cells are equipped with endogenous (e.g., superoxide dismutase, catalase, glutathione) and exogenous (e.g., vitamin C, β-carotene, vitamin E) antioxidant systems. The role of vitamin C, β-carotene, and vitamin E in inhibiting tumor promotion by quenching free radicals and oxidants is supported by animal and epidemiological studies, which have demonstrated a consistent inverse association between these antioxidant nutrients and the development of cancer at several sites. This group of vitamins and nutrients has consequently received the greatest attention in chemoprevention trials. Because most of the nutrient antioxidants and other essential nutrients are found in fruits and vegetables, these trials have been conducted with whole foods (fruits and vegetables) as well as with single nutrients and their combinations.

V. FRUIT AND VEGETABLE TRIALS

Much of the current knowledge regarding diet and cancer risk has been derived from epidemiologic studies conducted in many different countries and populations. From these studies, inverse associations between fruit and vegetable consumption and the risk of many cancers have been observed. A number of anticarcinogenic and antioxidant compounds have been identified in fruits and vegetables, each postulated to play a role in the carcinogenesis process. For example, the carotenoids (e.g., β-carotene), vitamin C, and folate are all found in high concentrations in fruits and vegetables. Because of the complexity of interactions of these compounds, the protective effect of fruits and vegetables on cancer may be multifactorial rather than attributable to one or two agents. Most dietary recommendations are therefore difficult to interpret and understand in terms of individual nutrients. Carefully designed studies exploring simple, interpretable dietary modifications that are affordable and accessible can provide valuable cancer prevention information for the general public.

Data from epidemiologic studies of diet and cancer risk suggest that a diet rich in fruits and vegetables is associated with a reduced risk of several cancers, particularly lung, oropharynx, stomach, and colon cancer. For the latter, the risk of precursor colorectal adenomatous polyps has also been associated with low fruit and vegetable consumption. Intervention trials utilizing polyps as an end point have gained popularity because of the prohibitive costs in conducting trials with colon cancer as the end point, as alluded to earlier. Two clinical trials have examined the effectiveness of fruits and vegetables and dietary fiber in the prevention of colorectal adenomas in subjects who previously had at least one adenoma removed prior to enrollment. In the Polyp Prevention Trial (PPT), 2079 subjects were followed for 4 years after randomization either to an intensive dietary counseling group aimed at changing their diet to one low in fat (< 20% calories as fat), high in fiber (18 g of dietary fiber per 1000 kcal) and fruits and vegetables (3.5 servings per 1000 kcal) or to a usual diet. In the Wheat Bran Fiber Trial, 1429 subjects were followed for 3 years after randomly assigning them to a supervised program of dietary supplementation with either high (13.5 g/day) or low (2 g/day) amounts of wheat bran fiber. The primary end point for both studies was the presence or absence of new adenomas measured at the follow-up colonoscopy. The results of these two trials suggest that adopting a diet that is low in fat and high in fiber, fruits, and vegetables or ingesting a daily wheat bran fiber supplement does not influence colorectal adenoma recurrence. However, there are several limitations that must be considered when interpreting the results of these studies. First, diet change occurred after the development of a polyp. Second, the diet change was implemented for a relatively short period of time. Third, the intervention occurred in the setting of the participant's usual dietary intake of foods previously shown to increase risk. Finally, the question of the validity of the end point remains unanswered, i.e., does failure to reduce adenoma recurrence mean no cancer preventive effect?

VI. β-CAROTENE / VITAMIN A CHEMOPREVENTION TRIALS

Retinoids and carotenoids, compounds related to vitamin A and β-carotene, respectively, received the attention of cancer prevention researchers due to observational epidemiological studies, laboratory and animal studies that demonstrated a protective effect of these compounds, and foods containing these compounds on the development of cancer, primarily, in epithelial tissues. As a result, β-carotene and vitamin A have been among the most commonly used nutrients in cancer chemoprevention trials.

Retinoids play an important role in cellular differentiation and proliferation, growth, and reproduction. Because malignancy is characterized by a loss of differentiation, retinoids have long been thought to play a role in the prevention of cancer. One of the effects of classic vitamin A deficiency is an increased risk of epithelial cancers. However, the toxicity of higher doses of vitamin A precludes its safe use as a chemopreventive agent. Supplemental doses in excess of about 25,000 IU/day must be used with caution and with regular safety monitoring and are thus unsuitable for primary cancer prevention. A large number of vitamin A analogs, synthetic retinoids,

have been produced with the goal of preserving activity and eliminating toxicity. Although the side effect profiles vary among synthetic retinoids, they unfortunately all still have significant toxicity that precludes extensive use in disease prevention. Nevertheless, the search for nontoxic retinoids continues. Furthermore, synthetic retinoids are compounds not normally found in significant amounts in the diet and are properly classified as pharmacological agents. Because these compounds are not nutrients, this article does not review those studies investigating synthetic retinoids.

In contrast to retinoids, β-carotene is essentially nontoxic and well suited for chemoprevention. Although β-carotene is best known as a precursor of vitamin A, data indicate that this carotenoid may have properties independent of its provitamin A activity, such as quenching of singlet oxygen, inhibition of lipid peroxidation, and modulation of the immune response. Data from prospective dietary studies, prospective serologic studies, and retrospective (case-control) epidemiologic studies suggest that dietary β-carotene reduces the risk for several different types of cancer. However, β-carotene is only one of a number of naturally occurring carotenoids found in pigmented fruits and vegetables. It therefore may only be a marker of other active carotenoids or it may work synergistically with other carotenoids or other compounds to prevent cancer. Data from animal studies suggest a protective role of other carotenoids (e.g., Iycopene, β-carotene) in the prevention of cancer. Although data from these studies are promising, β-carotene is the only carotenoid currently being investigated in cancer chemoprevention trials.

A. β-Carotene Chemoprevention Trials

Until the results of the ATBC trial were published, β-carotene was considered a safe compound in all subjects, even at very high doses. It had been used for several years in patients suffering from erythropoietic protoporphyria at doses of 180–300 mg/day without any serious toxicity symptoms. Because β-carotene is not itself a vitamin, being instead a provitamin A compound, RDAs have not been established. Based on balance studies, consumption of approximately

6 μg β-carotene is equivalent to 1 μg vitamin A. Conversion of β-carotene to vitamin A occurs primarily when preformed vitamin A in the diet is insufficient to meet requirements. Because most chemoprevention trials in developed countries are conducted in vitamin A-replete subjects, ingested β-carotene is presumed not to be metabolized to vitamin A to any great extent. Instead, β-carotene dosing in these populations results in significant increases in plasma and tissue levels of this carotenoid. Pharmacologic dosing studies suggest that 15–30 mg/day results in a 4- to 10-fold increase in plasma β-carotene. Less data are available on tissue level changes with supplementation, but increased levels have been found in buccal mucosal cells, cervix, and skin, which are well correlated with plasma levels.

Because of the extensive preclinical information supporting a role for β-carotene in cancer prevention, numerous chemoprevention trials have been conducted using this agent, either alone or in combination with other vitamins, such as vitamins A, E, or C. Targeted cancers include lung, oral cavity, nonmelanoma squamous cell skin cancer, esophageal, gastric, cervical, and colorectal cancers. Doses used range from 20 to 60 mg/day. Some studies, particularly those conducted in India and Uzbekistan, have used weekly or biweekly dosing in order to ensure adherence by providing the pills under supervised conditions. Although the weekly dose studies approximate the typical daily dose consumed over 7 days and because β-carotene absorption efficiency decreases with increasing single doses, the effective weekly dose is probably lower than the corresponding dose given daily. Targeted lesions include the cancers themselves or precursor lesions, such as oral leukoplakia, colonic adenomatous polyps, or bronchial metaplasia.

1. Oral Cavity Cancers

The ability of β-carotene to produce improvements in oral leukoplakia has been demonstrated in several trials, both in developing countries as well as in Western developed nations. In the United States, β-carotene supplementation produced sustained remissions in subjects with oral leukoplakia. β-Carotene, alone or in combination with small doses of vitamin A, produced clearing of leukoplakia in be-

tel quid chewers in India. In Uzbekistan, reductions in frequency of oral leukoplakia, as well as chronic esophagitis, were noted in populations supplemented with β-carotene versus placebo. Studies in Canada and the United States have used β-carotene alone or in combinations with vitamins E and C, with improvements in the lesion being documented.

Because of logistical and practical problems, studies using primary oral cancer as an end point are virtually impossible to carry out. An especially high-risk group of subjects are patients successfully treated (i.e., cured) for small primary head and neck cancer. These patients are known to be at substantial risk for developing a second primary lesion, often at rates of 2–4% per year, more so if they continue to use tobacco. Trials that attempted to reduce this risk using retinoids produced conflicting results. An initial, small study using high doses of 13-*cis* retinoic acid showed a substantial reduction in the incidence of second primary cancer, but a larger, randomized, placebo-controlled study from Europe that used etretinate, another synthetic retinoid active against oral leukoplakia, showed no effect. Both studies had substantial toxicity from the intervention agent, which led to premature discontinuation and/or dose reduction in a large number of subjects, particularly in the 13-*cis* retinoic acid trial. Thus, even in this very high-risk group, sustained use of these doses of retinoids was impossible to tolerate in many subjects, emphasizing the need to pay close attention to testing only those agents that will eventually be usable if the study proves to be positive, as otherwise the trial leads to unnecessary cost and clinically useless results. Studies of β-carotene to prevent a second malignancy are currently in progress.

2. Esophageal and Gastric Cancers

A large, prospective, placebo-controlled trial of vitamin supplementation in nearly 30,000 subjects was conducted in the Linxian province in China, a region with one of the highest rates of gastric and esophageal cancer in the world. A statistically significant reduction in gastric cancer incidence and mortality, as well as overall mortality, was found in the antioxidant arm, consisting of β-carotene, vitamin E, and selenium, when compared to placebo or other vitamin arms. Esophageal cancer was also reduced, but this did not reach statistical significance with the number of cases that occurred. Importantly, from a chronic disease prevention standpoint, substantial decreases were also found in cerebrovascular disease events (strokes) and cataracts. Results of trials, other high-risk areas such as Columbia, have reported end points including precursor lesions, such as chronic atrophic gastritis and gastric intestinal metaplasia. Statistically significant reductions in these were found with either β-carotene or vitamin C supplementation in a 6-year intervention study.

3. Nonmelanoma Squamous Cell Skin Cancer

Although preclinical epidemiology data in support of a protective role for β-carotene in this disease are limited, clinical trials were started based primarily on laboratory and animal data. A U. S. trial aimed at reducing the risk of recurrent skin cancers in patients previously diagnosed with multiple cancers did not find any protective effect of β-carotene after 3–4 years of follow-up. Trials in several other parts of the world are ongoing with either skin cancer or its precursor, actinic keratosis, being the end point.

4. Lung Cancer

Because of the incidence of the disease and strong epidemiologic data in support of a protective role for β-carotene, several studies have targeted lung cancer for chemoprevention with this agent. Once again, in addition to the cancer itself, other end points have included changes in micronuclei frequency, bronchial metaplasia index, and proliferation rate. Very high-risk populations, such as asbestos-exposed workers or heavy cigarette smokers, are participating in two ongoing trials in the United States. The results of a large intervention trial conducted in 29,000 heavy cigarette smokers in Finland have been reported. In that study, the intervention arms consisted of β-carotene, vitamin E, both, or placebo. No protective effect of either β-carotene or vitamin E was demonstrated after an average follow-up of about 6 years. In fact, a slight increase in lung cancer was noted, which, as the authors state, could have been by chance given the extensive prior information to the contrary.

It will be of considerable importance to reconcile the results of large clinical trials with that of observational epidemiologic information. Interestingly, in both the negative skin cancer and the Finland lung cancer studies mentioned earlier, a higher lung cancer incidence and mortality occurred in those subjects with the lowest quartiles of β-carotene levels at baseline compared with the highest group. These findings are consistent with previous epidemiologic data. Furthermore, analysis of the epidemiology studies that are based on plasma analyses suggests that the maximum protective benefit is probably obtained at plasma levels similar to the upper quartiles. Therefore, the benefit of supplementation may be limited to those subjects whose baseline levels are low. Such would be the case in the Linxian gastric and esophageal cancer trials, a population in which the median baseline levels were considerably lower than those in Western countries. Therefore, future trials may need to target subjects with low baseline levels, as any effect may be diluted and may not be detected in trials involving participants with starting levels that are already adequate. An alternative explanation, however, is that the protective effect associated with β-carotene in epidemiologic studies may simply reflect that β-carotene levels and intake are just a surrogate for some other protective entity in β-carotene -rich foods.

Another associated problem with studies such as the Finland trial is that they involve subjects with long histories of intense carcinogen exposure, groups that were selected in order to make the trials feasible by increasing the number of cancer end points. However, such a strategy will provide results applicable to a small minority of people who fall into those categories, whereas much of the epidemiology and other data are derived from broader cross sections of the population. Studies such as the Finland trial may indeed be negative, whereas trials in more representative subjects may indicate benefit. Negative results of another trial in asbestos-exposed smokers supplemental with vitamin A and β-carotene have similar implications in that a small increase in lung cancer was noted in the supplemented arm, thereby urging caution in the use of these agents in particularly high-risk groups. The Physicians Health Study found no effect on lung cancer of β-carotene supplementation.

B. Vitamin A Chemoprevention Trials

Unlike β-carotene, the prolonged use of moderate to high doses of vitamin A is associated with clinical toxicity. The following symptoms have been observed with sustained daily ingestion of greater than 15 mg (50,000 IU) vitamin A: headache, vomiting, alopecia, dryness of the mucous membranes, bone abnormalities, and liver damage. A daily dose of 15 mg/day is more than 10 times the RDA of 1 mg vitamin A/day for adult men (RDA for adult women is 0.8 mg/day). Large daily doses (>6 mg/day) also cause spontaneous abortions and birth defects in women during their first trimester of pregnancy. Because of the potential for vitamin A toxicity, vitamin A trials should not be conducted with women of reproductive age and should be limited to subjects with a very high cancer risk in whom close toxicity monitoring is feasible and justifiable. Thus, their eventual applicability will be very limited. Similar comments apply to the synthetic retinoids. Even at low doses these agents are toxic, and in two randomized, double-blind, placebo-controlled studies, such low doses of retinoids (13-*cis* retinoic acid) were ineffective for skin cancer prevention.

Vitamin A, alone or with β-carotene, can reverse oral leukoplakia. In fact, the highest complete reversal rates reported in oral precancerous lesion studies in very high-risk subjects were done in India using vitamin A alone or along with other nutrients. In the United States, several randomized, double-blind, controlled studies have examined the effect of retinol and isotretinoin supplementation on the incidence of nonmelanoma skin cancer in moderate and high-risk subjects. In one trial, daily supplementation with retinol was effective in preventing squamous cell carcinoma; however, in another trial, no beneficial effect from retinol or isotretinoin supplementation was observed in preventing either squamous cell carcinoma or basal cell carcinoma. In a European study, very high doses of vitamin A were ineffective for preventing recurrences and second primary cancers in subjects treated for stage I lung cancer. However, it did show a modest reduction in new cancer incidence. Using synthetic retinoids, similar trials in second primary prevention in lung and breast cancer have reported negative results. In fact, as with β-carotene trials, there is concern of an increase in incidence of lung cancer in 13-*cis* retinoic acid-treated subjects.

VII. VITAMIN C CANCER PREVENTION TRIALS

Results of many epidemiologic, animal, and laboratory studies have indicated an important role for vitamin C in disease prevention. Overall, epidemiologic studies suggest a consistent inverse association among vitamin C intake, serum ascorbate levels or fruit intake and risk of oral cavity, laryngeal, esophageal, lung, gastric, pancreatic, cervical, rectal, and breast cancer. However, vitamin C does not appear to be protective in the prevention of ovarian or prostate cancer.

Vitamin C is an essential nutrient that functions as a cofactor in collagen synthesis, cholesterol degradation, drug metabolism, iron absorption, and the immune system. This vitamin is perhaps best known for its role as a hydrophilic antioxidant, neutralizing superoxides, singlet oxygen, hydroxyl radicals, and hypochlorous acid. In addition to its function as a free radical scavenger, vitamin C has a sparing effect on vitamin E, where it participates in the reduction of the vitamin E radical to vitamin E. The role of vitamin C in cancer prevention is primarily thought to be due to its antioxidant properties. For example, vitamin C is thought to play a preventive role in gastric cancer through its ability to reduce nitrous acid and prevent formation of carcinogenic N-nitroso compounds in the human stomach.

The practice of ingesting moderately large quantities of vitamin C (1–2 g/day) does not result in toxicity, but when very high doses are used, they can result in gastrointestinal side effects, such as diarrhea. As the quantity of vitamin C ingested increases, the percentage absorption correspondingly decreases and the concentration of unmetabolized vitamin C increases. For example, with intakes of approximately 1500 mg/day, only 50% of the ingested vitamin C is absorbed. In one of the few pharmacokinetic studies conducted, 500 mg vitamin C daily increased the plasma vitamin C to the same levels attained with 1000 mg/day.

In a colorectal cancer prevention study of vitamin C, subjects with familial polyposis coli were recruited to participate in a randomized, placebo-controlled trial of 3000 mg vitamin C daily for 15–24 months.

A reduction in polyp number and surface area, as well as rectal cell proliferation rates, was assessed. Compared to the placebo group, a nonsignificant trend toward a reduced number of polyps and a significant reduction in polyp surface area ($P < 0.03$) was observed in the vitamin C treatment arm at 9 months. Overall, the mean cell proliferation rate was not different between the treatment and the placebo groups. Because of small subject numbers and the uncertainty of the relationship between the end points chosen and colorectal cancer, these findings must be interpreted with caution. As mentioned earlier, a gastric precancer trial in Columbia showed reduction by vitamin C treatment.

Currently, another phase III trial of vitamin C is being conducted in Europe to determine whether vitamin C (2000 mg/day) can reduce the progression of precancerous lesions of the stomach in 300 subjects with intestinal metaplasia and dysplasia, followed for 3 years. Because vitamin C supplementation in the United States is so widespread, conducting trials in Europe and Asia may be the only opportunity to test the efficacy of vitamin C in cancer prevention in controlled clinical trials.

VIII. ANTIOXIDANT COMBINATIONS

Each of the antioxidant nutrients, vitamin C, β-carotene, and vitamin E, function in different parts of the cell and tissues and on different types of oxidants (singlet oxygen vs hydroxyl radicals). Combined, these nutrients may work synergistically to provide maximal protection to cells and tissue that experience a high oxidant load. Therefore, the administration of antioxidant nutrient combinations should theoretically be most efficacious in reducing cancer risk.

Two intervention trials have been carried out to determine whether the protective effect of fruit and vegetable intake on risk of colon cancer can be attributed to an antioxidant nutrient effect. In one trial, 58 subjects with familial adenomatous polyps were randomized to receive placebo and low fiber, placebo plus vitamins E and C, or high fiber plus vitamins C and E. Subjects were followed for 4 years with polyp recurrence as the end point. The results provided no evidence for a protective effect of vitamins C and E alone on polyp recurrence, but an effect was observed in the high fiber plus vitamin intervention. Similarly, another trial found no apparent effect of a daily supplement of vitamins C and E on the incidence of polyps after 2 years among individuals with a history of adenomatous polyps. These findings are not consistent with the hypothesis of an antioxidant effect on reducing the risk of preneoplastic lesions of the colon.

Some of the other trials using a combination of antioxidant vitamins in oral cavity, gastric, esophageal and lung cancers have been mentioned earlier, while still others are ongoing in these sites and in cervical dysplasia.

IX. FOLATE CANCER PREVENTION TRIALS

A relative lack of folate has been implicated in human colorectal cancer, cervical cancer, and the preneoplastic lesions bronchial squamous metaplasia and dysplasia, cervical dysplasia, and chronic ulcerative colitis. Found in high concentrations in green leafy vegetables, folate is essential for the synthesis of purine nucleotides and thymidylate bases essential for the synthesis of DNA during cell replication and repair. Folate is also required for the synthesis of S-adenosylmethionine, the main donor of methyl groups in methylation reactions, such as the methylation of the DNA base cytosine.

Data from animal studies support a role for folate in cancer chemoprevention. Collectively, results of these studies have indicated that low tissue folate levels (1) increase the frequency of fragile sites on DNA, (2) increase the risk of DNA for attack by carcinogens and viruses, (3) increase the potential for chromosomal damage and oncogene expression, (4) decrease DNA repair, (5) decrease DNA methylation, and (6) increase tumor burden. Although an increase in cancer risk with low folate levels has been demonstrated in several animal and epidemiologic studies, relatively few cancer prevention intervention trials have been conducted to test the chemopreventive potential of folate.

Three folate intervention trials have been completed: one in lung cancer and two in cervical cancer.

In the lung cancer prevention trial, 73 smokers ($\geq$ 20 pack years) with bronchial squamous metaplasia completed a 4-month trial where subjects were randomized to daily folic acid (10 mg/day) plus vitamin B_{12} (500 μg/day) capsules or a placebo (lactose). A number of changes measuring the degree of atypia and metaplasia at baseline and the last sampling were determined. Folate/vitamin B_{12} supplementation was associated with a significant reduction ($P < 0.02$) in the prevalence of atypia but not of squamous metaplasia. Because of the use of a combined nutrient supplement, the effects of folate versus vitamin B_{12} on lesion regression cannot be ascertained.

The effect of folate supplementation alone was assessed in other trials involving the prevention of cervical cancer. In the first of these studies, 47 women with cervical intraepithelial neoplasia (CIN) I or II, who were current oral contraceptive users, were randomized to receive either a 10-mg folic acid supplement or a 10-mg vitamin C supplement (control) for 6 months. Subjects were followed monthly by pap smear and colposcopy. Cervical lesion progression/regression was assessed at the end of the 3-month period by biopsy. In this pilot trial, a significant increase in lesion severity ($P < 0.05$) among the control group compared to the treatment group was observed. In addition, women in the treatment group had *significant improvement* in megaloblastic scores compared with women in the control group. These promising results led to the establishment of a second, larger folic acid intervention trial for the prevention of cervical cancer. In this study, 199 women with CIN I or II on both a pap smear and by colposcopy were enrolled into a 6-month randomized, placebo-controlled trial. As in the first trial, subjects were randomized to receive either 10 mg folic acid daily or 10 mg vitamin C daily. Unlike the predecessor trial, no significant differences in lesion progression or regression rates were observed between the placebo and the treatment groups. The authors speculated that the unusually high rate of lesion regression in both the placebo-treated and the folic acid-supplemented groups might have contributed to the lack of significant differences. Alternatively, folic acid may not be effective in reversing mild/moderate cervical dysplastic lesions, but may be effective earlier in the carcinogenesis process, such as during early infection with the human papillomavirus. Given the promising data from epidemiologic and animal studies, more well-designed intervention trials utilizing folic acid are needed to delineate the cancer chemopreventive potential of folic acid.

X. SELENIUM TRIALS

Evidence from both observational epidemiologic studies and human intervention trials have suggested selenium's protective effects for a variety of cancer sites. Evidence is relatively strong for prostate cancer, moderately suggestive for lung and colorectal cancer, but not promising for skin and breast cancers. Two large-scale trials were conducted in China, in a region in which rates of liver cancer are very high and are inversely associated with population levels of serum selenium. In one trial, after 8 years of follow-up of 130,471 subjects, there was a 35% lower incidence of primary liver cancer in a selenium-supplemented township population compared to that of the unsupplemented population. After withdrawal of supplementation, liver cancer incidence began to rise, comparable to that of the control group. In the other Chinese trial, 2474 subjects with a first-degree relative with liver cancer were studied for 2 years. The incidence of liver cancer was reduced in subjects supplemented with selenium 200 μg/day as selenized yeast compared to those receiving placebo.

In the United States, the Nutritional Prevention of Cancer Trial, a placebo-controlled, randomized clinical trial, was designed to determine the effect of 200 μg/day of high-selenium yeast supplements on the incidence of cancer. Selenium treatment had no effect on the development of basal cell carcinoma or squamous cell carcinoma of the skin. However, results from secondary end point analyses supported the hypothesis that supplemental selenium was associated with significant reductions of total cancer incidence (all sites combined), lung, colorectal, and prostate cancer incidences and lung cancer mortality. In the United States, a large trial is planned to study the effects of selenium and celecoxib on reducing the recurrence of colon polyps.

Interpreting and generalizing the results of selenium studies must be done with caution for several reasons. First, selenium exposure varies substantially across populations. Second, selenium has a particularly narrow range between that which is recommended and that which is toxic. Third, there has been suggestive evidence that selenium might increase rather than reduce the risk for breast cancer. Therefore, before selenium can be advocated for cancer prevention, large-scale definitive trials must be completed. There are several such trials planned, which will investigate the cancer preventive effects for selenium. The SELECT trial is a randomized, placebo-controlled clinical trial designed to assess the independent and combined effects of selenium and vitamin E on the incidence of prostate cancer. Secondarily, the effects of selenium on total cancer and cancers of the lung and colon will be studied. This study plans to recruit 32,400 healthy men from up to 300 study centers across the United States and Canada. The PIN trial will compare the effects of oral L-selenomethionine and placebo administered under randomized, double-blind conditions on the incidence of prostate cancer among men diagnosed with high-grade prostatic intraepithelial neoplasia and who have not been found to have prostate cancer in two sequential prostatic biopsies.

XI. SUMMARY

This overview has attempted to summarize the emerging field of chemoprevention of cancer with vitamins. The emphasis has been on clinical trials, either completed or ongoing, designed to follow up on the leads from preclinical data. The accumulation of extensive epidemiologic data, suggesting a beneficial role for various vitamins in disease prevention, has been the main impetus for undertaking clinical intervention studies. As is evidenced by the large number of trials being attempted, this is an active area of chemoprevention research. Because most of these agents lack toxicity and are readily available, there is great interest in establishing their efficacy, as their eventual use, if proven beneficial, is very feasible. In fact, a large percentage of the population already consumes supplemental vitamins based on the notion that they may be beneficial. This widespread use poses a difficult problem for planning or executing clinical studies, particularly because most chemoprevention trials require several years of follow-up in large numbers of subjects in order to produce meaningful data. Although studies in high-risk groups, with a correspondingly high incidence of disease and end points, can be smaller and of shorter duration than general population trials, the lure of a nontoxic, possibly beneficial agent makes it especially difficult to conduct a placebo-controlled trial in such subjects. In fact, the very properties of these compounds that make them so attractive for chemoprevention, i.e., their easy availability and lack of toxicity, mitigates against the ability to successfully enroll patients and conduct a sufficiently conclusive trial. Nevertheless, several such trials have been initiated and will hopefully provide information in the near future on which one can base firmer recommendations as to their use as cancer preventive agents.

In addition to obtaining answers on efficacy, future clinical trials should take into account the notion of target levels, exceeding which may have no benefit. Because these agents lack toxicity, the tendency thus far has been to supplement all eligible participants. With this approach, possible benefits that are limited to those with low baseline levels, similar to the lowest quartiles found in epidemiologic studies, will not be confirmed. Thus, attempts to define such levels need to be pursued in order to design clinical trials aimed at supplementing only those individuals with the low levels associated with greatest risk.

See Also the Following Articles

Animal Models for Colon Cancer Chemoprevention • Antioxidants: Carcinogenic and Chemopreventive Properties • Cancer Risk Reduction (Diet/Smoking Cessation/Lifestyle Changes) • Chemoprevention, Principles of • Chemoprevention Trials • Molecular Epidemiology and Cancer Risk

Bibliography

Alberts, D. S., Martinez, M. E., Roe, D. J., Guillen-Rodriguez, J. M., Marshall, J. R., Van Leeuwen, J. B., Reid, M. E., Ritenbaugh, C., Vargas, P. A., Bhattacharyya, A. B., Earnest, D. L., and Sampliner, R. E. (2000). Lack of effect of high-fiber cereal supplement on the recurrence of colorectal adenomas. *N. Engl. J. Med.* **342,** 1156–1162.

Block, G., Patterson, B., and Subar, A. (1992). Fruit, vegetables and cancer prevention: A review of the epidemiological evidence. *Nutr. Cancer* **18,** 1–29.

Canfield, L. M., Krinsky, N. I., and Olson, J. A. (eds.) (1993). Carotenoids in human health. *Ann. N.Y. Acad. Sci.* **691.**

Clark, L. C., Combs, G. F., Jr., Turnbull, B. W., Slate, E. H., Chalker, D. K., Chow, J., Davis, L. S., Glover, R. A., Graham, G. F., Gross, E. G., Krongrad, A., Lesher, J. L., Park, K. H., Sanders, B. B., Smith, C. L., and Taylor, J. R. (1996). Effects of selenium supplementation for cancer prevention in patients with carcinoma of the skin. *J. Am. Med. Assoc.* **276,** 1957–1963.

Clark, L. C., Dalkin, B., Krongrad, A., Combs, G. F., Jr., Turnbull, B. W., Slate, E. H., Witherington, R., Herlong, J. H., Janosko, E., Carpenter, D., Borosso, C., Falk, S., and Rounder, J. (1998). Decreased incidence of prostate cancer with selenium supplementation: Results of a double-blind cancer prevention trial. *Br. J. Urol.* **81,** 730–734.

De Klerk, N. H., Musk, A. W., Ambrosini, G. L., Eccles, J. L., Hansen, J., Olsen, N., Watts, V. L., Lund, H. G., Pang, S. C., Beilby, J., and Hobbs, M. S. T. (1998). Vitamin A and cancer prevention II: Comparison of the effects of retinol and β-carotene. *Int. J. Cancer* **75,** 362–367.

Garewal, H. S. (1993). β-Carotene and vitamin E in oral cancer prevention. *J. Cell. Biochem. Suppl.* **17F,** 262–269.

Garewal, H. S., Katz, R. V., Meyskens, F., Pitcock, J., Morse, D., Friedman, S., Peng, Y., Pendrys, D. G., Mayne, S., Alberts, D., Kiersch, T., and Graver, E. (1999). β-Carotene produces sustained remissions in patients with oral leukoplakia. *Arch. Otolaryngol. Head Neck Surg.* **125,** 1305–1310.

Levine, N., Moon, T. E., Cartmel, B., Bangert, J. L., Rodney, S., Dong, Q., Peng, Y., and Alberts, D. S. (1997). Trial of retinal and isotretinoin in skin cancer prevention: A randomized, double-blind, controlled trial. *Cancer Epidemiol. Biomark. Prevent.* **6,** 957–961.

Moon, T. E., Levine, N., Cartmel, B., Bangert, J. L., Rodney, S., Dong, Q., Peng, Y., and Alberts, D. S. (1997). Effect of retinol in preventing squamous cell skin cancer in moderate-risk subjects: A randomized, double-blind, controlled trial. *Cancer Epidemiol. Biomark. Prevent.* **6,** 949–956.

Romney, S. L., Ho, G. Y. F., Palan, P. R., Basu, J., Kadish, A. S., Klein, S., Mikhail, M., Hagan, R. J., Chang, C. J., and Burk, R. D. (1997). Effects of β-carotene and other factors on outcome of cervical dysplasia and human papillomavirus infection. *Gynecol. Oncol.* **65,** 483–492.

Sauberlich, H. E., and Machlin, L. J. (eds.) (1992). Beyond deficiency: New views on the function and health effect of vitamins. *Ann. N.Y. Acad. Sci.* **669.**

Schatzkin, A., Lanza, E., Corle, D., Lance, P., Iber, F., Caan, B., Shike, M., Weissfeld, J., Burt, R., Cooper, M. R., Kikendall, J. W., and Cahill, J. (2000). Lack of effect of a low-fat, high-fiber diet on the recurrence of colorectal adenomas. *N. Engl. J. Med.* **342,** 1149–1155.

Van Zandwijk, N., Dalesio, O., Pastorino, U., De Vries, N., and Van Tinteren, H. (2000). EUROSCAN, a randomized trial of vitamin A and N-acetylcysteine in patients with head and neck cancer or lung cancer. *J. Natl. Cancer Inst.* **92,** 977–986.

Weisburger, J. H. (1991). Nutritional approach to cancer prevention with emphasis on vitamins, antioxidants and carotenoids. *Am. J. Clin. Nutr.* **53,** 226S–237S.

Ovarian Cancer: Diagnosis and Treatment

Robert F. Ozols

Fox Chase Cancer Center, Philadelphia, Pennsylvania

I. Epidemiology
II. Pathology
III. Diagnosis and Staging
IV. Screening
V. Management of Early Stage Ovarian Cancer
VI. Management of Advanced Stage Ovarian Cancer
VII. Germ Cell Tumors of the Ovary

GLOSSARY

borderline tumors of the ovary Epithelial ovarian tumors with cytologic abnormalities but without stromal invasion.

CA-125 An antigen associated with ovarian cancer, which is elevated in 80% of patients with advanced ovarian cancer.

hereditary breast–ovarian cancer Genetic syndrome, which accounts for 85 to 90% of hereditary ovarian cancers and is associated with mutations of the BRCA1 gene.

optimal cytoreduction Surgical removal of ovarian cancer metastases such that there is no residual tumor nodule greater than 1.0 cm in diameter.

second-look laparotomy A diagnostic laparotomy used to detect residual ovarian cancer in patients who have achieved a clinical complete remission following initial surgery followed by induction chemotherapy.

Ovarian cancer consists of a variety of neoplasms derived from different cell types within the ovary. These tumors have different clinical presentations, natural history, and prognosis and are approached with different therapeutic modalities. Epithelial tumors are derived from the surface epithelium cells of the ovary and constitute 90% of ovarian neoplasms. Most patients with epithelial ovarian cancer are diagnosed with widespread intraperitoneal disease and are treated by surgery together with combination chemotherapy. While most patients will respond to this therapeutic approach, the recurrence rate is high and the majority of patients with advanced stage disease are not cured by this standard approach. Germ cell tumors of the ovary are much less common; however, in contrast to epithelial tumors, most patients with germ cell tumors of the ovary are cured with chemotherapy and surgery.

I. EPIDEMIOLOGY

A. Incidence and Mortality

The age-specific incidence of ovarian cancer depends on the histologic type. Epithelial ovarian cancer is infrequent in women below age 40 with a peak rate of age 57 per 100,000 in the 70–74 age group. Almost 50% of patients are 65 years or older at the time of diagnosis. In contrast, germ cell tumors of the ovary occur primarily in the second and third decades of life. Overall, there has been little change in mortality in the last two decades from epithelial ovarian cancer, whereas for germ cell tumors of the ovary, which only account for 2 or 3% of all ovarian tumors in Western countries, there has been a significant improvement in survival due to the development of effective chemotherapy, and the majority of these young women are now cured by conservative surgery and chemotherapy.

B. Etiology

Epidemiology studies have identified endocrine, environmental, and genetic factors as important in ovarian carcinogenesis. Recognized risk factors include nulliparity, family history, early menarche, late menopause, white race, increasing age, and geographic factors (residence in North America and northern Europe).

C. Reproductive Factors

Compared to nulliparous women, women who were ever pregnant have a 30–60% decreased risk of ovarian cancer. There is an increasingly protective effect with multiple pregnancies. Breast feeding has also been associated with a decreased risk. Epidemiologic data also suggest an association between abnormalities in ovulation that reduce the likelihood of conception and a subsequent risk for ovarian cancer.

Oral contraceptive use also decreases ovarian cancer risk, which appears to be related to duration of use. A clear association between ovarian cancer risk and use of hormone replacement therapy has not been established. Meta-analysis of 21 epidemiologic studies has shown a slight increase in overall risk (relative risk 1.15). There also is an increased risk of ovarian cancer in women with a prior history of breast cancer, as well as a two- to fourfold increase risk for breast cancer in women with a history for ovarian cancer. Excessive gonadotrophin secretion [follicle-stimulating hormone (FSH) or luteinizing hormone (LH)] has been hypothesized to also play a role in ovarian oncogenesis. However, a unified model for the hormonal etiology of ovarian cancer has not been developed.

D. Genetic Factors

Family history is the single most important risk factor for ovarian cancer. A woman with a single family member affected by ovarian cancer has a 4–5% risk compared to the lifetime risk of 1.6% for the general population. Fewer than 10% of cases can be identified as hereditary ovarian cancer (at least two first-degree relatives affected). The hereditary breast–ovarian cancer (HBOC) syndrome accounts for 85–90% of all hereditary ovarian cancer cases currently identified. The majority of these cancers are associated with mutations of the BRCA1 locus. A second breast–ovarian cancer susceptibility gene, BRCA2, shares structural/functional similarities to BRCA1, which has been identified to be a tumor suppressor gene. BRCA1 functions as a transcription factor, which has a role in the regulation of differentiation, cell proliferation, and maintenance of genomic stability. The Ashkenazi Jewish population has a higher incidence of mutations in these genes, and it appears that a large fraction of all ovarian cancer cases in Ashkenazi Jews may be associated with germline mutations in either BRCA1 or BRCA2.

Epithelial ovarian cancer is also a component of the hereditary nonpolyposis colorectal syndrome (HNPCC). In this autosomal-dominant genetic syndrome, there is a predisposition to site-specific colorectal cancer and an increased predisposition for several other tumors, including stomach, endometrial, and ovarian cancer. Mutations in DNA mismatch repair genes predispose to HNPCC. Approximately 5–10% of HNPCC patients will develop ovarian cancer in one of three described germline mutations, with mutations in hMSH2 being most common.

Abnormalities of oncogenes and suppressor genes are also frequently found in ovarian cancer. Mutations of the p53 gene are frequent in ovarian cancer, although the prognostic significance of p53 expression remains to be fully determined. Abnormalities of the *c-myc, h-ras,* and *ki-ras* are also frequent in ovarian cancer but without established prognostic significance. Alterations in cell surface growth factor receptors and in downstream signal transduction pathways have also been identified to be abnormally functioning or dysregulated in ovarian cancer.

E. Environmental Factors

There is a higher incidence of ovarian cancer in industrialized Western countries. Epidemiologic studies have not identified specific risk factors to account for the geographic differences in ovarian cancer risk. There have also been conflicting reports regarding the association of the use of talcum powder and the development of ovarian cancer.

II. PATHOLOGY

Table I summarizes the classification of common epithelial tumors developed by the World Heath Organization and the International Federation of Gynecology and Obstetrics. The classification of these tumors is based on cell type, location, and degree of

malignancy (benign epithelial tumors, tumors of low malignant potential, and invasive carcinomas). Tumors of low malignant potential "borderline tumors" are characterized by atypical cell clusters in papillae with cellular stratification, nuclear atypia, and increased mitotic activity. The primary differentiation between these tumors and carcinomas is on an architectural basis of invasion.

Invasive epithelial carcinomas are classified by histologic type and grade (degree of cellular differentiation). Histologic grade is an important prognostic factor, particularly in patients with early stage tumors confined to the pelvis.

III. DIAGNOSIS AND STAGING

Vague abdominal discomfort and bloating are the most common symptoms of epithelial ovarian cancer. Urinary tract or gastrointestinal symptoms are also common. Patients can present with acute bowel obstruction or vaginal bleeding as well. Patients frequently have a palpable mass in the adnexa. Diagnostic ultrasound evaluation of such masses aids in the differentiation between benign and malignant tumors. Computed tomographic (CT) scans are useful in preoperatively evaluating the extent of disease in the presence of a pelvic mass. Measurement of serum CA-125 levels also aids in the differential diagnosis of epithelial ovarian cancers. Serum α-fetoprotein (AFP) and human chorionic gonadotrophin (HCG) are indicated in women with suspected germ cell tumors of the ovary. Serum CA-125 levels are elevated in 80% of women with advanced ovarian cancer. Staging of ovarian cancer is surgical (Table II) and disease spread occurs by direct extension to neighboring organs; lymphatic spread with involvement of pelvic lymph nodes (external iliac and obturator chains), as well as upper common iliac and periaortic lymph node chains; hematogenously to distant sites such as supraclavicular nodes; and peritoneal seeding of exfoliated tumor cells from the ovary, resulting in metastatic implants on parietal and visceral peritoneum.

The components of a comprehensive staging laparotomy are summarized in Table III. Complete surgical staging is necessary to determine whether additional therapy should be recommended.

TABLE I
World Health Organization Classification
of Malignant Ovarian Tumors

Common epithelial tumors
    Malignant serous tumors
    Malignant mucinous tumors
    Malignant endometrioid tumors
    Malignant mixed epithelial tumors
    Undifferentiated carcinoma
    Clear cell carcinoma
Sex cord-stromal tumors
    Granulosa-stromal cell tumors
    Thecoma-fibroma tumors
    Sertoli–Leydig cell tumors
Germ cell tumors
    Dysgerminoma
    Endodermal/sinus tumors
    Embryonal carcinoma
    Choriocarcinoma
    Teratomas

TABLE II
FIGO Stage Grouping for Primary Carcinoma of the Ovary

Stage	Description
Stage I	Growth limited to the ovaries
IA	Growth limited to one ovary; no ascites present containing malignant cells. No tumor on the external surface; capsule intact
IB	Growth limited to both ovaries; no ascites present containing malignant cells. No tumor on the external surfaces; capsules intact
IC[a]	Tumor either stage Ia or Ib, but with tumor on surface of one or both ovaries, with capsule ruptured, with ascites present containing malignant cells, or with positive peritoneal washings
Stage II	Growth involving one or both ovaries with pelvic extension
IIA	Extension and/or metastases to the uterus and/or tubes
IIB	Extension to other pelvic tissues
IIC[a]	Tumor either stage IIa or IIb, but with tumor on surface of one or both ovaries, with capsule(s) ruptured, with ascites present containing malignant cells, or with positive peritoneal washings
Stage III	Tumor involving one or both ovaries with histologically confirmed peritoneal implants outside the pelvis and/or positive retroperitoneal or inguinal nodes. Superficial liver metastases equal stage III. Tumor is limited to the true pelvis, but with histologically proven malignant extension to small bowel or omentum
IIIA	Tumor grossly limited to the true pelvis, with negative nodes, but with histologically confirmed microscopic seeding of abdominal peritoneal surfaces or histologic-proven extension to small bowel or mesentery
IIIB	Tumor of one or both ovaries with histologically confirmed implants, peritoneal metastases of abdominal peritoneal surfaces, nonexceeding 2 cm in diameter; nodes are negative
IIIC	Peritoneal metastasis beyond the pelvis >2 cm in diameter and/or positive retroperitoneal or inguinal nodes
Stage IV	Growth involving one or both ovaries with distant metastases. If pleural effusion is present, there must be positive cytology to allot a case to stage IV. Parenchymal liver metastasis equals stage IV

[a]To evaluate the impact on prognosis of the different criteria for allotting cases to stage IC or IIC, it would be of value to know if rupture of the capsule was spontaneous or was caused by the surgeon and if the source of malignant cells detected was peritoneal washings, or ascites.

IV. SCREENING

A successful screening program would decrease mortality and morbidity from cancer. For ovarian cancer, routine screening cannot be recommended because currently available screening techniques (ovarian palpation, transvaginal ultrasound, serum CA-125 determinations) are not sufficiently accurate. A laparotomy is required to diagnose ovarian cancer and consequently the positive predictive value (PPV) for screening is a primary consideration in the evaluation of any screening study. PPV is defined as the ratio of true-positive tests to true-positive plus false-positive tests. Several large ovarian cancer screening trials are currently in progress both in normal-risk individuals and in high-risk individuals. Prophylactic oophorectomies have been advocated in high-risk women with a strong family history associated with mutations in BRCA1 or BRCA2. These women remain, however, at risk for peritoneal carcinomatosis even after their ovaries are removed.

V. MANAGEMENT OF EARLY STAGE OVARIAN CANCER

Early stage ovarian cancer is defined as FIGO stages I–II (Table II). Based on clinical pathologic factors after comprehensive laparotomy, patients are categorized at either low risk or high risk for a recurrence of disease.

A. Low-Risk Ovarian Cancer

Patients with stage IA or IB disease with well or moderately well-differentiated tumors have a 5-year sur-

TABLE III

Factors Predisposing to Recurrence of Ovarian Cancer in Early Stage Ovarian Cancer

FIGO stage II

High-grade tumors

Clear cell histology

FIGO stage IC: Cyst rupture, tumor excrescences on surface of ovary, malignant ascites

vival rate of more than 90% without any adjuvant therapy. Consequently, these patients require no postoperative systemic or local treatment.

B. High-Risk Early Stage Ovarian Cancer

Table III summarizes factors associated with risk of recurrence >10% in patients with early stage ovarian cancer. Some factors, such as stage II disease, have a recurrence risk of 30–40%, whereas other factors may be substantially less. Due to the relatively small numbers of patients with early stage ovarian cancer, the specific risk for factors such as surgical rupture of the capsule remains to be defined. The appropriate treatment for patients with high-risk early stage ovarian cancer remains an area of controversy. In the United States, a series of clinical trials have evaluated different modalities of treatment and it is generally accepted that combination chemotherapy be administered after surgery. European studies have suggested no decrease in survival if immediate treatment is delayed until disease progression. These studies have led to a large multinational European trial in which patients with early stage ovarian cancer have been randomized to observation with treatment at the time of progression or to immediate therapy with the chemotherapeutic agent carboplatin. This study will accrue approximately 1000 patients and preliminary results are expected in 2001.

VI. MANAGEMENT OF ADVANCED STAGE OVARIAN CANCER

Standard treatment for patient with advanced stage (FIGO stages III–IV) ovarian cancer has been cytoreductive surgery, if feasible, followed by chemotherapy.

A. Surgical Cytoreduction

The goal of surgery is to remove all gross tumor. Such aggressive cytoreductive surgery or tumor debulking surgery has become accepted as an important part of initial surgery in the management of ovarian cancer patients. There has never been a prospective randomized trial, however, that has established a survival advantage for immediate cytoreductive surgery in pa-

tients with advanced stage ovarian cancer. Retrospective studies have demonstrated that optimally cytoreduced patients (no residual tumor nodule >1–2 cm in maximum diameter) have a median survival of 25–40 months, whereas patients who were suboptimally cytoreduced have a median survival of 10–18 months. It is estimated that 50–60% of all patients with advanced stage ovarian cancer can be optimally cytoreduced at the time of diagnosis. Two meta-analyses have provided somewhat conflicting results regarding the impact of cytoreductive surgery on survival. A large retrospective study from the Gynecologic Oncology Group (GOG) compared survival rates in women who underwent successful cytoreductive surgery compared to those patients with advanced stage disease who only had small volumes of disease in the upper abdomen and consequently did not require cytoreduction. Survival was worse for the group of patients who underwent successful cytoreduction compared to those patients with initial macroscopic disease <1 cm in the omentum or upper abdomen. Undefined biological factors responsible for bulk disease have a negative impact on survival despite the fact that resection is technically feasible.

The timing of cytoreductive surgery remains an area of clinical research. Chemotherapy may produce sufficient shrinkage of tumors to make more patients surgically resectable. Pending the outcome of prospective randomized trials incorporating neoadjuvant chemotherapy, the current recommendation is that advanced stage patients undergo an initial attempt at cytoreductive surgery at the time of diagnosis. Patients who have a long disease-free interval after initial surgery and chemotherapy may also benefit from secondary cytoreduction if their disease at relapse is localized and can be completely resected.

B. Chemotherapy

Epithelial ovarian cancer responds to a wide variety of chemotherapeutic agents. In the last two decades, numerous combinations of chemotherapy regimens have been studied, and a series of prospective randomized trials have led to the general acceptance of paclitaxel and a platinum compound as the standard of care. There is no evidence that more than six cycles of initial chemotherapy have meaningful clinical benefit. The most widely used regimen consists of carboplatin dosed to an area under the curve of 6–7.5 together with paclitaxel (175 mg/m^2 administered at a 3-h infusion). Major side effects of this chemotherapy consist of bone marrow suppression, alopecia, and peripheral neuropathy. Following six cycles of chemotherapy, the vast majority of patients with ovarian cancer achieve a clinical complete remission, which is defined as the absence of symptoms related to ovarian cancer, no evidence of disease on CT scans, no palpable disease on physical examination, and a normal serum CA-125 level.

While second-look laparotomies have been advocated by some investigators to determine if the patient has any residual disease, which is undetectable by noninvasive studies, there is no evidence to support the routine use of second-look laparotomies. Patients are frequently monitored after achieving a clinical complete remission by physical examinations and serum CA-125 levels.

The median time to progression following chemotherapy for patients with advanced ovarian cancer ranges from 18 to 22 months. The median survival for patients with advanced ovarian cancer ranges from 25 to 48 months, depending on prognostic factors at the time chemotherapy was administered. Shorter survivals are observed in patients with stage IV disease or with suboptimal residual disease following initial cytoreductive surgery. Clinical trials are in progress in patients with advanced ovarian cancer comparing carboplatin and paclitaxel with new combinations, which include agents such as topotecan, gemcitabine, and encapsulated doxorubicin. While some studies have suggested a benefit for high-dose chemotherapy together with peripheral stem cell support or the intraperitoneal administration of chemotherapeutic agents, these modalities of treatment remain experimental, as they have not been shown to be beneficial in prospective randomized trials compared to standard therapy.

1. Management of Recurrent Ovarian Cancer

Depending on the nature of the clinical recurrence and the length of the disease-free interval, patients who suffer disease recurrence are treated with secondary cytoreduction followed by chemotherapy or by chemotherapy alone. Patients with a prolonged disease-free interval to initial chemotherapy can frequently be successfully retreated with the same agents used to produce the initial remission. Once patients become resistant to paclitaxel and a platinum compound, there remain numerous chemotherapeutic options, including topotecan, gemcitabine, encapsulated doxorubicin, and oral etoposide. The goal of second-line chemotherapy in ovarian cancer is palliation. Many patients will have a prolonged survival following recurrence from initial therapy; however, cure no longer is a realistic possibility.

2. Borderline Tumors of the Ovary

Epithelial tumors of low malignant potential (also termed borderline malignant tumors) have a markedly superior prognosis than epithelial invasive carcinomas. They tend to occur in an earlier age group, are diagnosed more frequently at an earlier stage, and have less of a tendency to metastasize. Mortality rates, even in patients with advanced stage disease, are low. Borderline tumors are characterized by epithelial butting, multilayering of the epithelium, increased mitotic activity, and nuclear atypia; however, in contrast to carcinomas, they are not associated with stromal invasion. These tumors represent approximately 4–14% of all ovarian malignancies.

Management of patients with low malignant potential tumors consists primarily of surgical resection. Preservation of fertility can be routinely performed in young women. There is no evidence that adjuvant chemotherapy is beneficial. Survival for patients with early stage borderline tumors is greater than 95%, and even in patients with advanced stage disease, 5-year survival rates are greater than 75%.

3. Sex Cord-Stromal Tumors

Ovarian sex cord-stromal tumors represent approximately 5% of all ovarian cancers. These tumors can be associated with hormonal effects, including precocious puberty, amenorrhea, postmenopausal bleeding, or virilizing symptoms. Granulosa cell tumors are the most common of the sex cord-stromal tumors and frequently are associated with endometrial hyperplasia and endometrial carcinoma. Sertoli–Leydig cell tumors occur much less often than granulosa cell tumors but are the second most common sex cord-stromal tumor. The management is the same as for granulosa cell tumors. Surgery is a cornerstone of management for patients with sex cord-stromal tumors. Some investigators advocate the use of adjuvant chemotherapy in patients with advanced stage disease, although a survival benefit has not been established. Recurrent sex cord-stromal tumors are treated with surgical resection and often by additional chemotherapy. The natural history of granulosa cell tumors is characterized by late recurrences at times 10 and 20 years after initial resection. For those patients receiving chemotherapy, platinum-based regimens appear to have the most clinical benefit.

VII. GERM CELL TUMORS OF THE OVARY

Germ cell tumors of the ovary primarily affect young women of childbearing potential and account for 2–3% of all ovarian cancers in Western countries. Peak incidence is in the early 20's. These tumors are highly curable and fertility can be preserved in most patients.

A. Diagnosis

Abdominal pain, pelvic fullness, and urinary symptoms are common in germ cell tumors of the ovary. Patients frequently have a palpable adnexal mass, and serum levels of HCG and AFP are useful in the diagnosis of germ cell tumors. Most germ cell tumors are diagnosed with localized disease. However, the pattern of metastases appears to be similar to that of epithelial ovarian tumors, and patients can present with lymph node involvement, hepatic metastases, pulmonary involvement, and multiple peritoneal implants.

B. Surgical Management and Chemotherapy

Most patients can have fertility preserved; consequently, the initial surgical approach is of paramount importance and the extent of resection is dependent on operative findings. The contralateral ovary and the uterus can routinely be preserved. Bilateral oophorectomy is not routinely necessary because postoperative chemotherapy is curative and fertility can be preserved. Cytoreductive surgery is recommended, as for epithelial tumors of the ovary; however, even in the presence of widespread disease, the contralateral ovary and uterus can frequently be preserved. Current chemotherapy for germ cell tumors consists of the same three drug combination that has proven to be curative in testicular germ cell cancers (cisplatin, vinblastine, and bleomycin).

C. Management of Dysgerminomas

Dysgerminomas are the most common malignant germ cell tumor. While radiation is curative, it frequently is associated with infertility; consequently, most patients are now treated with surgery and, depending on clinical and pathologic findings, are treated with cisplatin-based chemotherapy instead of radiation.

D. Nondysgermanomatous Germ Cell Tumors

Immature teratomas are the second most common germ cell malignancy. These tumors contain elements resembling embryologically derived tissues and frequently contain mixed germ cells. Tumor markers AFP and HCG are negative in pure teratomas but can be elevated in mixed germ cell tumors containing elements of either choriocarcinoma or yolk sac tumors. Most of these tumors present with early stage disease. Surgery is conservative and postoperative chemotherapy is administered for all patients with grade 2 and grade 3 lesions.

Endodermal sinus (yolk sac) tumors are the third most frequent germ cell tumor of the ovary and are derived from the primitive yolk sac. These tumors secrete AFP. Embryonal carcinoma and nongestational choriocarcinoma are extremely rare. Embryonal carcinomas can secrete both AFP and HCG, whereas pure choriocarcinoma secretes only HCG. Treatment recommendations consist of unilateral oophorectomy or salpingo-oophorectomy, followed by platinum based chemotherapy as described.

What once was a highly lethal disease and at a minimum associated with significant surgical morbidity, including fertility, can now be routinely cured with conservative fertility-sparing surgery and combination chemotherapy.

See Also the Following Articles

ENDOMETRIAL CANCER • GERM CELL TUMORS • HEREDITARY RISK OF BREAST AND OVARIAN CANCER

Bibliography

Advanced Ovarian Cancer Trialists' Group (1991). Chemotherapy in advanced ovarian cancer: An overview of randomized clinical trials. *Br. Med. J.* **303,** 884–887.

Easton, D. F., Ford, D., and Bishop, D. T. (1995). Breast Cancer Linkage Consortium: Breast and ovarian cancer incidence in BRCA1-mutation carriers. *Am. J. Hum. Genet.* **56,** 265–271.

Greenlee, R. T., Murray, T., Bolden, S., and Wingo, P. A. (1999). Cancer statistics 2000. *Ca Cancer J. Clin.* **50,** 7–33.

Hoskins, W. J., McGuire, W. P., Brady, M. R., *et al.* (1994). The effect of diameter of largest residual disease on survival after primary cytoreductive surgery in patients with suboptimal residual epithelial ovarian carcinoma. *Am. J. Obstet. Gynecol.* **170,** 974–979.

McGuire, W. P., Hoskins, W. J., Brady, M. R., *et al.* (1996). Cyclophosphamide and cisplatin compared with paclitaxel and cisplatin in patients with stage III and stage IV ovarian cancer. *N. Engl. J. Med.* **334,** 1–6.

Narod, S. A., Risch, H., Moslehi, R., *et al.* (1998). Oral contraceptives and the risk of hereditary ovarian cancer. *N. Engl. J. Med.* **339,** 424–428.

NIH Consensus Development Panel on Ovarian Cancer (1995). Ovarian cancer: Screening, treatment and follow-up. *J. Am. Med. Assoc.* **273,** 491–497.

Ozols, R. F. (1997). Update of the NCCN ovarian cancer practice guidelines. *NCCN Proc.* **11,** 95–97.

Ozols, R. F., Schwartz, P., and Eiffel, P. (1997). Ovarian cancer, fallopian tube carcinoma, and peritoneal carcinoma. *In* "Principles and Practice of Oncology" (V. T. DeVita, S. A. Rosenberg, and S. Hellman, eds.), 5th Ed., pp. 1502–1534, Lippincott-Raven, New York.

Williams, S. D., Blessing, J. A., Slayton, *et al.* (1994). Ovarian germ cell tumors: Adjuvant trial of the Gynecologic Oncology Group. *J. Clin. Oncol.* **12.**

Young, R. C., Decker, D. G., Wharton, J. T., *et al.* (1983). Staging laparotomy in early ovarian cancer. *JAMA* **250,** 3072–3078.

Ovarian Cancer: Molecular and Cellular Abnormalities

Rajas Chodankar
Louis Dubeau
University of Southern California Keck School of Medicine

GLOSSARY

coelomic epithelium Mesothelial layer that lines all abdominal and pelvic surfaces, including the ovarian surface. This epithelium is the site of origin of ovarian epithelial tumors according to a favored theory.

cystadenoma Benign ovarian tumors characterized by fluid-filled cysts lined by neoplastic epithelium and surrounded by a thick fibrous capsule.

endometrioid Second most common subtype of ovarian epithelial tumors. At the morphological level, endometrioid ovarian carcinomas are identical to tumors arising in endometrium.

low malignant potential ovarian tumors Distinct subtype of ovarian tumors that shows morphological and biological characteristics that are intermediate between those of ovarian cystadenomas and carcinomas. These lesions are also referred to as borderline tumors or tumors of borderline malignancy.

mucinous Third most common subtype of ovarian epithelial tumors. At the morphological level, mucinous ovarian carcinomas are identical to tumors arising in endocervix.

Mullerian ducts Embryological structure that gives rise to fallopian tubes, uterus, cervix, and upper portion of the vagina. It has been suggested that ovarian epithelial tumors arise in remnants of mullerian ducts as opposed to coelomic epithelium.

serous Most common subtype of ovarian epithelial tumors. At the morphological level, serous ovarian carcinomas are identical to tumors arising in fallopian tubes.

O varian epithelial tumors are subdivided into distinct subgroups with marked differences in their malignant potential. They are identical, at least at the morphological level, to tumors arising in other parts of the female genital tract, such as the epithelium of fallopian tubes, endometrium, or endocervix. Familial predisposition accounts for approximately 10% of cases of ovarian carcinoma and is usually associated either with germline mutations in BRCA1/BRCA2 genes or with the Lynch II syndrome. Comparing the molecular genetic changes associated with benign, low malignant potential (LMP), and malignant ovarian epithelial tumors suggests that these different tumor subtypes may not be part of a disease continuum, but are instead distinct disease entities with different underlying molecular mechanisms. Furthermore, molecular studies of heterogeneous lesions with contiguous morphologically benign and malignant portions within the same tumor mass suggest that the morphologically benign portions are part of the malignant process, despite their morphological appearance. Identification of a precursor lesion to ovarian carcinoma, which would facilitate the development of screening strategies for populations at risk, is hampered by uncertainties about the exact cell of origin of these tumors within ovarian tissue.

Ovarian cancers are responsible for more deaths annually than cancers arising in any other organ of the female genital tract in the United States. This is a very heterogeneous group of tumors, as a number of different cell types give rise to various clinically important tumor subgroups within the ovary. This article focuses exclusively on tumors of epithelial origin, which are the most frequent ovarian neoplasms in adult women.

I. BIOLOGICAL AND MORPHOLOGICAL FEATURES OF OVARIAN EPITHELIAL TUMORS

Ovarian epithelial tumors are an attractive model to study cancer development because they are subdivided into distinct subgroups with marked differences in their malignant potential (Fig. 1). At one end of the spectrum are benign tumors called cystadenomas, which lack the ability to infiltrate into adjacent tissues and do not give rise to metastases. Ovarian tumors of low malignant potential are more complex

than cystadenomas at the morphological level and show some histopathological features normally associated with carcinomas, but have absent (or greatly reduced) invasive abilities. Malignant ovarian tumors, called carcinomas, can be further subdivided into those of low versus high histological grades. Such grades are a measure of degree of differentiation and are indicative of tumor biological aggressiveness.

Another characteristic of ovarian epithelial tumors is their tendency to differentiate into cell types seen in other organs of the female genital tract. Most ovarian epithelial tumors are reminiscent of the cells that line the fallopian tubes. Malignant tumors belonging to this subtype, called serous carcinomas, are indistinguishable from fallopian tube carcinomas. The second most common subtype of ovarian tumors, called endometrioid, has an appearance similar to endometrial tumors. A third subtype, called mucinous, resembles the mucous-secreting endocervical carcinomas. Other less common subtypes have also been described. This heterogeneity complicates the development of a unifying model of ovarian carcinogenesis, as it is not clear whether these different histological subtypes share a similar mechanism and, given current controversies regarding the normal cell type from which ovarian carcinomas originate (see later), it is still debatable whether they share a common cell of origin.

II. MOLECULAR DETERMINANTS OF OVARIAN EPITHELIAL TUMOR DEVELOPMENT

A. Genetic Predisposition to Ovarian Carcinoma

It is estimated that up to 10% of ovarian carcinomas occur in individuals with familial predisposition to this disease. Two different syndromes account for most of these cases. The first is the familial breast and ovarian cancer syndrome associated with inherited mutations in the BRCA1 and BRCA2 genes. Data suggest that tumors belonging to this group have distinct clinicopathological and molecular characteristics. Some features, however, are similar to those seen in sporadic ovarian cancers. For example, incessant ovulatory activity, which is an important risk factor for spo-

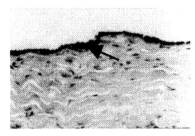

CYSTADENOMA
Fluid-filled cysts lined by usually a single layer of neoplastic epithelium (arrow) that lack invasive or metastatic abilities

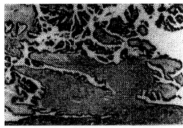

LOW MALIGNANT POTENTIAL
Compared to cystadenomas, the neoplastic cells have a more complex architecture. Compared to carcinomas, they have greatly reduced invasive abilities

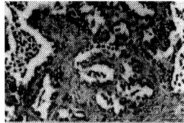

LOW GRADE CARCINOMA
Invasive and metastatic tumors that retain an ability to form differentiated structures such as glands

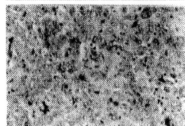

HIGH GRADE CARCINOMA
Invasive and metastatic tumors that tend to grow as solid sheets and do not organize into any recognizable structure

FIGURE 1 Classification of ovarian epithelial tumors based on their malignant potential.

radic cancers, also increases disease risk in patients with germline mutations in either one of these two genes. Molecular biological aspects of the BRCA1 and BRCA2 genes are reviewed elsewhere in this encyclopedia. The second group of familial ovarian cancers is associated with Lynch II syndrome, characterized by a predisposition to cancers of the colon, endometrium, and ovary. This syndrome is associated with inherited abnormalities in genes coding for mismatch repair enzymes.

Most familial ovarian carcinomas associated with inheritance of a BRCA1 mutation belong to the serous category, whereas those associated with the Lynch II syndrome belong to the endometrioid subtype. This ob-

servation suggests that these different subtypes of ovarian epithelial tumors may have different underlying mechanisms and underscores the difficulty of developing a general model of ovarian carcinoma development.

B. Molecular Genetic Changes Associated with Sporadic (Nonfamilial) Ovarian Carcinoma Development

1. Alterations Involving Oncogenes and Tumor Suppressor Genes

Genetic determinants of cancer development include two broad classes of genes; oncogenes and tumor suppressor genes. Oncogenes result from alterations in cellular protooncogenes, many of which are important components of signal transduction pathways. Alterations in tumor suppressor genes, in contrast to those affecting the dominantly acting oncogenes, are recessive. Common genetic mechanisms resulting in silencing of tumor suppressor genes include mutation, loss of heterozygosity, and double deletion. Although the exact function of most tumor suppressor genes is still unknown, they are often important regulators of cell cycle progression.

A number of abnormalities involving cellular protooncogenes, as well as tumor suppressor genes, have been reported in ovarian carcinomas since the early 1980s. Several chromosomes frequently harbor losses of heterozygosity in these tumors. Although our understanding of the specific signal transduction pathways that are altered in these tumors is still in its infancy, changes in a small number of such pathways are thought to be particularly relevant to ovarian cancer development and are the targets of experimental therapeutic protocols. A list of the most frequent molecular abnor-

malities thought to be associated in ovarian epithelial tumor development is provided in Table I.

2. Alterations in DNA Methylation

Alterations in the methylation of cytosine residues within genomic DNA, either focal or global, are another type of molecular change thought to play an important role in cancer development. Like those of most other cancer types, the genomes of ovarian epithelial tumors are characterized by a decrease in the total amount of methylated cytosine residues. Most of this decrease can be accounted for by demethylation of repetitive DNA sequences within centromeric and juxtacentromeric chromosomal regions. These changes are thought to lead to chromosomal instability and may play a role in the development of aneuploidy, which is a general hallmark of malignancy.

Much of the current interest in DNA methylation among cancer molecular biologists comes from the potential role of this epigenetic alteration in the silencing of tumor suppressor genes. Of particular importance to ovarian carcinogenesis is the fact that the

TABLE I

Most Common Molecular Abnormalities Reported in Sporadic (Nonfamilial) Ovarian Carcinomas

	Genes/chromosomes	Comment
Specific genes or signal transduction pathways affected	Her-2/neu	Tyrosine kinase receptor. Its overexpression is associated with poor prognosis of ovarian carcinomas. Its neutralization is the basis for current experimental therapeutic approaches
	K-ras	Mutations in the K-ras gene are frequent in mucinous ovarian tumors and in ovarian tumors of low malignant potential
	AKT-2	Member of subfamily of protein-serine/threonine kinases
	p53	Regulates the cell cycle and apoptosis
	PTEN	Phosphatase that inhibits cell death. Mutated in some endometrioid ovarian carcinomas
	NOEY2	Induces p21 and downregulates cyclin D1
	SPARC2	Encodes a calcium-binding matrix protein that contributes to cell adhesion
	Phosphatidyl inositol 3-kinase	The P110-α catalytic subunit is increased in ovarian carcinoma cells
	GM-CSF signaling	Agents targeting this pathway are currently being tested in clinical trials for ovarian carcinoma treatment
	Steroid and gonadotropin hormone receptor signaling	Ovarian epithelial tumors often express these hormone receptors and respond to their respective ligands *in vitro*
	Signaling through retinoic acid receptors	Retinoids inhibit the growth of ovarian carcinoma cell lines *in vitro*
	DOC-2	Binds GRB-2 upstream of Ras
Chromosomes with frequent losses of heterozygosity	3p, 6p, 6q, 7q, 9p, 11p, 11q, 13q, 17p, 17q, 19q, 22q, Xq	Multiple candidate tumor suppressor genes have been reported on these chromosomes, but their roles in ovarian tumorigenesis are still unclear

promoter region of the BRCA1 gene, which is associated with familial predisposition to ovarian carcinoma (see earlier discussion), is methylated in a significant proportion of sporadic ovarian epithelial tumors in which BRCA1 gene expression is downregulated. A potential role for DNA methylation in the silencing of other tumor suppressor genes, such as *p16/CDKN2*, has also been suggested.

3. Alterations Leading to Expression of Telomerase

Telomeres are tandemly repeated DNA sequences found at the end of all eukaryotic chromosomes. These sequences, which are essential for chromosomal DNA replication, become progressively shorter during each cell division. The majority of human malignant tumors, including ovarian carcinomas, maintain their telomeric lengths due to the expression of an enzyme called telomerase. Because this enzyme is either not expressed or expressed at very low levels in most normal somatic cells, it is an attractive target for chemotherapeutic drugs or gene therapy. It can also be useful as a cancer-specific marker. In that regard, data strongly suggest that testing for telomerase activity in peritoneal washings from patients treated for

ovarian cancer may constitute a sensitive mean of detecting minimal residual disease in such patients. It remains to be shown whether patients with no clinical evidence of residual disease but who test positive for telomerase in washings obtained from their peritoneal cavity are more likely to experience disease recurrences. This approach seems particularly appropriate to ovarian cancer management because these tumors tend to remain confined to the abdominal and pelvic cavities, even in advanced stages.

C. A Genetic Model for Ovarian Carcinoma Development

Important insights into the molecular determinants of ovarian carcinoma development can be obtained by comparing molecular changes associated with ovarian cystadenomas, ovarian tumors of low malignant potential, and different grades of ovarian carcinomas because these well-defined tumor subtypes represent a wide spectrum of changes associated with malignant transformation. The diagram shown in Fig. 2 is based on such comparison. The complexity of molecular genetic changes present in ovarian carcinomas clearly increases with increasing tumor histological grades,

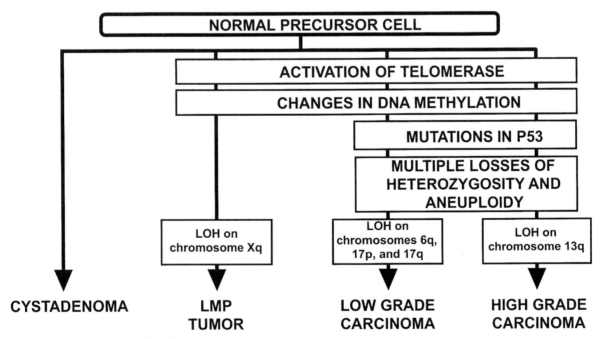

FIGURE 2 Molecular determinants of ovarian epithelial tumor development.

which can be regarded as a measure of their biological aggressiveness. However, as is apparent from Fig. 2, the grade of ovarian carcinomas is not only a function of the mere number of molecular genetic abnormalities present in a given tumor genome, as specific molecular abnormalities appear strongly associated with high histological grades. For example, losses of heterozygosity in certain chromosomal regions, such as 6q, 17p, and 17q, appear frequent in ovarian tumors of all histological grades, whereas losses in chromosome 13 are frequent only in those of high histological grades. It may be that the gene(s) targeted by losses of heterozygosity in chromosome 13 controls a different cellular pathway associated perhaps not with cell cycle regulation, but with differentiation or other determinants of tumor grade.

Another point illustrated in Fig. 2 is that although loss of heterozygosity, which is an important mechanism of inactivation of tumor suppressor genes in most human cancers, is frequent in ovarian carcinomas, this abnormality is rare in the biologically less aggressive ovarian epithelial tumors. Perhaps tumor suppressor gene inactivation, which is an important consequence of such losses, is not a feature of cystadenoma or low malignant potential tumor development. In support of this idea, mutations in the p53 gene, which are among the most frequent tumor suppressor gene alterations in cancer in general and are present in over 50% of ovarian carcinomas, are very rare in ovarian low malignant potential tumors and cystadenomas. Alterations in DNA methylation are associated with tumors of low malignant potential as well as carcinomas but not with cystadenomas, suggesting fundamental differences in the mechanisms underlying the development of these benign ovarian tumors. This conclusion is further strengthened by the fact that telomerase is usually not detected in cystadenomas, whereas it is expressed in most tumors of low malignant potential and carcinomas. Given that this enzyme is regarded as necessary for continuous cell growth, its absence in most cystadenomas suggests that these tumors may have a limited life span *in vivo*, an idea consistent with the observation that benign ovarian cysts frequently regress or remain unchanged in postmenopausal women.

The only exception to the rarity of losses of heterozygosity in LMP tumors is losses affecting the X chromosome, which are present in about 50% of the cases. The gene(s) targeted by such allelic losses in these tumors is still not known. The fact that the reduced allele invariably affects the inactive copy of the chromosome suggests that the targeted gene(s) escapes X chromosome inactivation. This suggestion is attractive because individuals born with a single X chromosome (Turner syndrome) show abnormal ovarian development (gonadal dysgenesis). Thus, the presence of the inactive X chromosome is necessary for normal ovarian development and it is conceivable that abnormalities in the same gene during adult life may lead to tumorigenesis. The X chromosome is also thought to be important for the establishment of *in vitro* immortality and has been implicated in the development of prostate cancer.

III. ARE OVARIAN CYSTADENOMAS, LOW MALIGNANT POTENTIAL TUMORS, AND CARCINOMAS PART OF A DISEASE CONTINUUM?

The question of whether ovarian cystadenomas, tumors of low malignant potential, and carcinomas represent distinct disease processes or are part of a single disease continuum is not only important for our understanding of ovarian tumor development, it is also relevant to the clinical management of cystadenomas and tumors of low malignant potential. Arguments in favor of a continuum come from morphological observations that areas histologically indistinguishable from typical ovarian cystadenomas are sometimes found contiguous to carcinomas. The most straightforward interpretation for these lesions, which are sometimes called cystadenocarcinomas, is that the histologically malignant areas arose from the preexisting morphologically benign areas. This interpretation implies that any molecular genetic change associated with carcinomas, but normally not present in solitary cystadenomas, should be confined to the histologically malignant portions of cystadenocarcinomas. However, losses of heterozygosity and p53 mutations, which are both frequent in carcinomas and absent or at least very rare in solitary cystadenomas, are usually concordant in all portions of ovarian cystadenocarcinomas, including the morphologically benign areas. Concordance for aneuploidy was likewise shown in different regions of cystadenocarcinomas using interphase cytogenetic approaches. Based on these observations, it seems clear that the histologically benign portions of cystadenocarcinomas are genetically different from typical (solitary) cystadenomas. This conclusion supports the idea that cystadenomas do not generally progress to malignancy unless they carry a genetic predisposition to such progression, such as, for example, a mutation in the p53 gene.

Another argument against the notion of a disease continuum is the presence of specific genetic abnormalities that are more frequent in tumors of low malignant potential than in low-grade carcinomas. Different authors reported on the high frequency of mutations in the k-*ras* gene in the former but not in the latter tumors. It is possible that mutations in this oncogene are associated primarily with mucinous differentiation, which is more common in tumors of low malignant potential than in carcinomas, as opposed to being associated with the low malignant potential phenotype itself. However, although interstitial allelic deletions within a small region of the X chromosome are frequent in tumors of low malignant potential, they are rare in low-grade carcinomas. It is unlikely that ovarian tumors of low malignant potential are precursors of low-grade carcinomas in the light of such observations. This conclusion is consistent with the clinicopathological behavior of these tumors. It is also consistent with the diagram shown in Fig. 2, which shows qualitative as opposed to purely quantitative differences among the various tumor subtypes, implying that each subtype develops through a distinct mechanism.

IV. PROSPECTS OF IDENTIFYING A PRECURSOR LESION FOR OVARIAN CARCINOMAS

Ovarian carcinomas account for the highest frequency of death from a gynecological cancer in the United States. This is not because they are more frequent than other gynecological cancers, as other such tumors, such as endometrial carcinomas, are more frequent, but because the ovaries are anatomically hidden and thus poorly accessible to physical examination. In addition, early ovarian cancers are usually asymptomatic. There is therefore much interest in developing novel strategies for early ovarian cancer detection. Levels of circulating CA125 have been used for several years as a marker of disease recurrence in treated patients. This antigen is often elevated in noncancerous conditions and its levels are often within normal limits in patients with early stage ovarian cancer. However, despite such suboptimal specificity and sensitivity, data suggest that testing for rising CA125 levels, when used in conjunction with radiological approaches, may be useful as a screening tool for the early detection of ovarian cancer in populations at risk. Another serum marker, lysophosphatidic acid, is also showing promise as a sensitive indicator of early ovarian carcinoma.

Screening protocols that have historically made the most impact on cancer incidence and mortality rates are those aimed not at the detection of early cancers, but at that of cancer precursor lesions. The use of PAP tests for the detection of cervical intraepithelial neoplasia, a precursor of cervical carcinoma, is an obvious example. One of the difficulties in defining a precursor lesion amenable to screening protocols for ovarian epithelial tumors is that the exact origin of these tumors is not clear. Thus, not only has a precursor lesion not been identified, but we are not even certain of where to look for such lesions. As pointed out earlier, ovarian epithelial tumors are similar to tumors arising in the fallopian tubes, endometrium, or endocervix. Two theories have been proposed to account for these morphological characteristics. The traditionally favored hypothesis stipulates that these tumors arise from the mesothelial cells that line the ovarian surface. This cell layer is often referred to as coelomic epithelium. According to this theory, this epithelium often invaginates into the ovarian cortex to create small mesothelial cysts that eventually lose their connection to the ovarian surface. It is hypothesized that the cells lining those cysts can differentiate, via a process called metaplasia, into fallopian tube, endometrial, or endocervical epithelium due to the hormone-rich ovarian milieu. The resulting metaplastic cells are predisposed to neoplastic transformation. Learning to control this metaplastic process would constitute an effective way of controlling ovarian cancer development if it indeed represented a necessary precursor step. If this hypothesis were true, ovarian carcinomas would be a rare example of a malignant tumor type that is better differentiated than its cell of origin. However, this theory has been challenged based on embryological and molecular genetic arguments, resulting in an alternative hypothesis, which suggests that ovarian epithelial tumors arise in embryological remnants of structures called mullerian ducts. Given that such ducts give rise to fallopian tubes, endometrium, and endocervix during embryological development, this theory readily accounts for the fact that ovarian tumors are similar to those arising in these various parts of the female genital tract. In addition, this hypothesis provides an explanation for the intriguing fact that tumors that are morphologically indistinguishable from ovarian epithelial tumors can arise outside the ovary. The development of such tumors, which are usually referred to as primary peritoneal tumors, has been observed in patients who have undergone prophylactic oophorectomies for familial predisposition to ovarian carcinoma. It is hoped that modern molecular techniques will facilitate the elucidation of the exact cell lineage of ovarian tumors and, in turn, lead to the identification of a precursor lesion amenable to screening strategies for ovarian carcinoma. This would undoubtedly have an important and immediate impact on the mortality and morbidity associated with this disease.

See Also the Following Articles

DNA Methylation and Cancer • Endometrial Cancer • Hereditary Risk of Breast Cancer and Ovarian Cancer • Telomeres and Telomerase

Bibliography

Dubeau, L. (1999). The cell of origin of ovarian epithelial tumors and the ovarian surface epithelium dogma: Does the emperor have no clothes? *Gynecol. Oncol.* **72,** 437–442.

Duggan, B., Wan, M., Yu, M., Roman, L., Muderspach, L., Delgadillo, E., Li, W.-Z., Martin, S., and Dubeau, L. (1998). Detection of ovarian cancer cells: Comparison of a telomerase assay and cytologic examination. *J. Natl. Cancer Inst.* **90,** 238–242.

Johannsson, O. T., Idvall, I., Anderson, C., Borg, A., Barkardottir, R. B., Egilsson, V., and Olsson, H. (1997). Tumour biological features of BRCA1-induced breast and ovarian cancer. *Eur. J. Cancer* **33,** 362–371.

Menon, U., and Jacobs, I. J. (2000). Recent developments in ovarian cancer screening. *Curr. Opin. Obstet. Gynecol.* **12,** 39–42.

Narod, S. A., Risch, H., Moslehi, R., Dorum, A., Neuhausen, S., Olsson, H., Provencher, D., Radice, P., Evans, G., Bishop, S., Brunet, J.-S., and Ponder, B. A. J. (1998). Oral contraceptives and the risk of hereditary ovarian cancer. *N. Engl. J. Med.* **339,** 424–428.

Qu, G., Dubeau, L., Narayan, A., Yu, M. C., and Ehrlich, M. (1999). Satellite DNA hypomethylation vs. overall genomic hypomethylation in ovarian epithelial tumors of different malignant potential. *Mutat. Res.* **423,** 91–101.

Rhei, E., Bogomolniy, F., Federici, M. G., Maresco, D. L., Offit, K., Robson, M. E., Saigo, P. E., and Boyd, J. (1998). Molecular genetic characterization of BRCA1- and BRCA2-linked hereditary ovarian cancers. *Cancer Res.* **58,** 3193–3196.

Rodriguez, M., and Dubeau, L. (2001). Ovarian tumor development: Insights from ovarian embryogenesis. *Eur. J. Gynaec. Oncol.*

Seidman, J. D., and Kurman, R. J. (1996). Subclassification of serous borderline tumors of the ovary into benign and malignant types: A clinicopathologic study of 65 advanced stage cases. *Am. J. Surg. Pathol.* **20,** 1331–1345.

Wolf, N. G., Abdul-Karim, F. W., Schork, N. J., and Schwartz, S. (1996). Origins of heterogeneous ovarian carcinomas: A molecular cytogenetic analysis of histologically benign, low malignant potential, and fully malignant components. *Am. J. Pathol.* **149,** 511–520.

Xu, Y., Shen, Z., Wiper, D. W., Wu, M., Morton, R. E., Elson, P., Kennedy, A. W., Belinson, J., Markman, M., and Casey, G. (1998). Lysophosphatidic acid as a potential biomarker for ovarian and other gynecological cancers. *J. Am. Med. Assoc.* **26,** 719–723.

Young, R. H., and Scully, R. E. (1992). Pathology of epithelial tumors. *Hematol. Oncol. Clin. North Am.* **6,** 739–760.

Zheng, J., Benedict, W. F., Xu, H.-J., Hu, S.-X., Kim, T. M., Velicesu, M., Wan, M., Cofer, K. F., and Dubeau, L. (1995). Genetic disparity between morphologically benign cysts contiguous to ovarian carcinomas and solitary cystadenomas. *J. Natl. Cancer Inst.* **87,** 1146–1153.

Pancreas and Periampullary Tumors

Harold O. Douglass, Jr.
Judy L. Smith
Hector R. Nava
John F. Gibbs
Roswell Park Cancer Institute

I. Exocrine Pancreas Tumors
II. Endocrine Pancreatic (Islet Cell) Tumors

Neoplasms of the pancreas include two very different groups of cancers: cancers of the exocrine pancreas, which are generally aggressive metastasizing early, and tumors of the endocrine pancreas, or islets of Langerhans, which generally have a more indolent course (Table I).

I. EXOCRINE PANCREAS TUMORS

A. Overview

Of the 28,000 to 30,000 patients in the United States who are diagnosed with cancers of the exocrine pancreas, 95% or more will die within a year of diagnosis and few will survive 5 years. While a long-term survival rate of close to 3% is a significant improvement compared to a survival rate of less than 1% two decades ago, for most patients the grim prognosis of this disease is unchanged. However, there has been a significant reduction in treatment-related mortality and morbidity, particularly in centers where large numbers of pancreatic cancer patients are treated. In these centers, the operative mortality for major pancreatic resection has fallen to less than 4%, compared to 20% operative mortalities not uncommonly reported a generation ago.

One area in which there has been considerable progress involves the genetic abnormalities of pancreatic cancer cells (Table II). Although K-ras is the most common abnormality, an early therapeutical trial with a K-ras vaccine did not provide significant benefit. Most genetic changes are found in only a small proportion of pancreatic cancers, with each cancer often expressing several different oncogenes and loss of tumor suppressor genes (Table III).

TABLE I
Most Common Malignant Tumors
of the Pancreas[a]

Exocrine pancreas
  Ductal adenocarcinoma
  Microadenocarcinoma
  Acinae cell adenocarcinoma
  Papillary adenocarcinoma
  Cystadenocarcinoma, including subtypes
  Avenous carcinoma
  Undifferentiated (anaplastic) adenocarcinoma
  Small cell carcinoma
  Squamous cell carcinoma
  Adenosquamous carcinoma
Endocrine pancreas
  Gastrinoma
  Insulinoma
  Glucogonoma
  Carcinoid
  VIPomas, Ppoma and other rare forms
  Nonspecific neuroendocrine carcinoma
Mixed endocrine and exocrine carcinoma
Pancreaticoblastoma (in children)

[a]More than 90% of pancreatic adenocarcinomas arise from the pancreatic ducts. Histologic examination reveals that exocrine tumors are often associated with an extensive fibroblastic response.

A continued research focus on the molecular genetics of pancreatic cancer may provide leads for prevention and early diagnosis trials.

B. Etiology

For the vast majority of pancreatic cancers, the etiology is unknown. Approximately 4% are thought to be familial (Table IV). Smokers are four times as likely to develop pancreatic cancer as nonsmokers. Coffee consumption, at one time thought to have a quantitative relationship to pancreatic cancer risk, and alcohol consumption are no longer considered etiologic factors, even though smoking, coffee, and alcohol consumption often occur in the same individual. The problem has been further confused by an association with chronic pancreatitis, but some of the pancreatitis found in cancer patients might be a result of the ductal obstruction caused by the previously undiagnosed enlarging neoplasm.

Nitrosoureas and azaserene have been utilized to induce pancreatic cancers in experimental animals, and historically pancreatic cancer has been more com-

TABLE II
Most Common Genetic Abnormalities of Exocrine
Pancreatic Cancers

Class	Gene	Location	Frequency
Oncogene	K-ras[a]	12p12	90+
	AKT2	19q13.1	<20
	MYB	6q24	~10
Suppressor	p16/RBI	9p21/13q24	90+
	P53	17p31	~75
	DPC4	18121	50–60
	BRCA2	13q13	<10
	All others	Various	<5

[a]With the exceptions of K-ras and p16, genetic changes in exocrine pancreatic cancer cells are found in a minority of the cancers (K-ras: Kirsten-ras oncogene; p16, also known as NST-1, is an inhibitor of cyclin/CdK-4).

mon among members of the American Chemical Society. Chemical carcinogens are likely agents in the multistep development of a diverse and genetically heterogeneous group of pancreatic cancers. This theory is compatible with the traditional concepts of chemical carcinogens in experimental animals.

More than one-third of pancreatic cancer patients become diabetic, whereas others become diabetic in the 2 years prior to cancer diagnosis. Despite this association, there is no evidence that diabetes mellitus is a premalignant condition. Nevertheless, in the absence of a family history of diabetes mellitus, the appearance of a new onset of diabetes should at least raise the question of a neoplastic process as part of the diagnostic evaluation.

C. Diagnosis

The pancreas is a retroperitoneal organ lying obliquely across the upper retroperitoneum. As a result, neoplasia develops insidiously, often giving rise to vague nonspecific symptoms (Table V). As the tumor pro-

TABLE III
Problems in the Molecular Biology
of Pancreatic Cancer

Multiple genetic changes in each tumor
May involve five or more genes
Most heterogeneous of cancers
Involves both oncogenes and tumor suppressor genes.

TABLE IV
Risk Factors for Pancreatic Cancer[a]

Familial syndromes: Genetic factors
    Familial pancreatic cancer
    Hereditary chronic pancreatitis
    Lynch II syndrome
    Familial atypical multiple mole melanoma
    Hippel–Landau Syndrome
    Neurofibromatosis, ataxia telangectasia syndrome
    Gardner's syndrome
Environmental factors
    Smoking
    Cocaine abuse
    ? chronic pancreatitis

[a]Whereas familial syndromes may be associated with 4% of pancreas cancers, environmental factors appear to have a major impact on carcinogenesis.

TABLE VI
Diagnostic Symptoms Suggesting Pancreas Cancer

Cancer of head of pancreas and uncinate process
    Asymptomatic jaundice
    Pain preceding jaundice
    Peptic ulcer syndrome in absence of peptic ulcer
Chronic cholecystitis syndrome
    Without cholelithiasis
    Postcholecystectomy
Cancer of body and tail of pancreas
    Unexplained weight loss
    Pain in upper abdomen, left paravertebral region, or both
    Diabetes mellitus of new onset in absence of family history
    Sudden worsening of long-standing diabetes

gresses, two clusters of symptoms separate cancers of the head and uncinate process vs cancers of the body and tail of the pancreas (Table VI). Pain is often the first symptom that brings the patient to medical attention (Table VII), whether associated with weight loss (cancer of the pancreatic body and tail) or jaundice (cancer of the head of the pancreas).

Because nearly two-thirds of pancreatic cancer patients have tumors arising in the head of the pancreas, with jaundice as the usual presenting symptom, the clinical and laboratory differential diagnosis of jaundice can expedite the correct diagnosis (Table VIII). Many patients with malignant biliary obstruction present for medical evaluation because a relative or friend has commented on the appearance of cutaneous or scleral jaundice, the patients themselves having noticed no change. This phenomenon is more common among men than among women.

D. Diagnostic Evaluation

1. Cancer of Ampulla of Vater and Head of the Pancreas

With the exception of the appearance of jaundice, the vague symptomatology of pancreatic cancer often results in a 3-month delay on the part of the patient before medical advice is sought. Another 3 months may be spent in biochemical and imaging studies before a diagnosis is finally made. Many patients are exposed to repeated costly studies during this interval. Evaluation of the benefits and limitation of the various diagnostic manipulations available (Table IX) has

TABLE V
Vague Symptomatology of Pancreatic Cancer[a]

Symptoms	Causes
Anorexia, nausea, vomiting	Pancreatic and biliary dysfunction and partial ductal obstruction
Weakness, fatigue, anemia	Bleeding into pancreatics, bile duct
Foul diarrhea, floating stools	Pancreatic insufficiency, ductal obstruction
Pain	Obstruction of pancreatic duct, perineural invasion
Anxiety, depression	Unknown

[a]Early pancreatic cancers are associated with nonspecific symptoms for which physiologic causes can be determined.

TABLE VII
Pain of Pancreatic Cancer Caused by Pancreatic and Bile Duct Obstruction or Perineural Invasion

Abdomen
    May occur anywhere, but commonly epigastric or left upper quadrant. Typically dull to boring, may be associated with nausea
    May suggest peptic ulcer disease but no ulcer found, does not usually respond to H-2 blockade
    May suggest gallbladder disease and Murphy sign may be present. Gallbladder palpable in minority of cases. May occur as a postcholecystectomy syndrome or in the absence of gallstones
Back
    Tends to be focused from T12 to L2, described as dull, aching, or boring, midline or off to one side, may respond to heating pad or NSAIDs, may not be improved or may be made worse by codeine or narcotics

TABLE VIII
Differential Diagnosis of Jaundice[a]

Hepatitis—patients look, feel "sick," weak; worse as bilirubin rises

Hemolysis—usually not severely jaundiced, may be anemic

Choledocholithiases: parasitic obstructions—pain colicky, stools tan to to yellow, bilirubin levels rise slowly, rare if biliary tract not previously manipulated; sclerosing—obstruction rarely complete until late, associated diseases (e.g., ulcerative colitis)

Cholestasis—usually drug related, subsides with medication withdrawal

Cancer—unless accompanied by dull constant pain, patients are asymptomatic with jaundice often identified by another person; bilirubin rises rapidly, often higher than 12 mg/dl; stools become clay colored; may have occult blood in stool

[a]The differential diagnosis of the causes of jaundice can often be determined on clinical grounds with a few readily available laboratory tests.

led to the formulation of a cost-effective and efficient approach to diagnosis. This approach can be effective in more than 90% of patients with pancreatic cancer (Table X). A review of the diagnostic evaluations performed in more than 400 patients with pancreatic cancer subsequently referred to Roswell Park revealed that large numbers of unnecessary studies and procedures had been performed before diagnosis, including an average of more than three computerized tomography (CT) scans. One helical CT scan, performed with a pancreatic protocol of continuous intravenous contrast infusion and 3-mm slices through the pancreas timed to provide visualization of both the superior mesenteric artery and the portal venous system, would have been sufficient and considerably less costly. The weakness of CT is its frequent failure to identify lymph node and peritoneal metastases.

Once a clinical diagnosis is established, treatment planning is based on the presence or absence of jaundice, cholangitis, and metastatic disease (Table XI). Figure 1 presents a simplified algorithm for the management of patients with cancer of the head of the pancreas and ampulla of vater. Patients with resectable disease do not benefit from preoperative endoscopic retrograde choloangiopancreatiography (ERCP). A study from Memorial Sloan-Kettering Cancer Center suggested that preoperative ERCP increases the risk of infection after surgery, as well as increasing the technical difficulty of the biliary-enteric anastomosis.

CT can often distinguish ampullary cancers from

TABLE IX
Diagnostic Testing in Pancreatic and Periampullary Cancer[a]

Ultrasound (US)
 First test: dilated ducts, mass, liver metastases, ascites
 Inexpensive

Computerized tomography (CT)
 Conventional
 10–15% false negative, not predictive for resectability unless metastases identified not seen on ultrasound, spiral CT will be required
 Should be omitted, spiral CT should be substituted

Spiral CT
 Pancreatic protocol of dual-phase imaging
  Arterial phase delineates pancreas
  Venous phase delineates liver metastases, may show venous obstruction and collateralization
 Helpful to determine resectability

Endoscopic retrograde cholangiopancreatography (ERCP)
 Allows stenting to relieve jaundice, but, if resectable, preoperative stenting may increase complications of Whipple procedure, including cholangitis and abscess
 Biopsies are positive 60% or more in large series but 20–40% in community practices
 Decreasing role as diagnostic tool for pancreas cancer
 May cause pancreatitis or cholangitis

Magnetic resonance imaging (MRI)
 No role as routine test
 T1 may visualize pancreas, T2 better for liver

Magnetic resonance cholangiopancreatography (MRCP)
 As accurate as ERCP to delineate obstruction
 Useful where ERCP unsuccessful
 In resectable patients, does not carry infectious risk of ERCP, but requires special technology

Positron emission tomography (PET)
 Uptake in some pancreatic tumors, not in normal pancreas
 Not useful in staging with regard to lymph nodes, resectability
 ? may rule out pancreatitis
 Currently experimental, no clinical role

Endoscopic ultrasonography (EUS)
 May differentiate pancreatitis vs cancer
 Useful to evaluate lymph nodes
 Allows biopsy of tumor, lymph nodes
 May be useful for performance of celiac nerve blocks
 Very operator dependent with long learning curve

Laparoscopy
 Detects peritoneal metastases not found with other methods
 Diagnostic value dependent on quality of prior imaging
 Cost effective as immediate preoperative procedure avoiding some laparotomies

Laparoscopic ultrasound
 Time-consuming
 Helpful in determining vascular invasion (16–20%) and occult liver metastases
 Results variable, dependent on quality of other preoperative studies. WIde variation (15–82%) in change of resectability determination, but most commonly 30–43% for head of pancreas, 43–75% for body and tail

[a]Benefits and limitations of the various diagnostic studies commonly utilized in pancreatic cancer patients.

TABLE X

Cost Effective and Expeditious Evaluation for the
Staging of Patients with Pancreas Cancer[a]

Stool examination: color, presence of occult blood

Liver function tests: bilirubin, alkaline phosphatase, AST

Ultrasound of upper abdomen
1. Dilated bile ducts, gallstones, stone in duct
2. Dilated bile ducts, no stones, or no gallbladder
3. Mass in pancreas
4. Liver metastases or ascites

Next step based on
1. Laparoscopic cholecystectomy, laparoscopic or endoscopic choledocholithotomy, examine abdomen for evidence of malignancy
2 and 3. *Spiral* computerized tomography
4. Ultrasound-guided liver biopsy or aspiration of ascites for cytology

---

[a]Numbered findings under ultrasound lead to "next step" using same numbers.

cancers of the pancreatic head. A dilated bile duct extending into the substance of the head of the pancreas toward the duodenum, often accompanied by a dilated pancreatic duct, can suggest the tumor is ampullary in origin. If there are no lymph node or other metastases, the prognosis of ampullary cancers is vastly superior to that of cancers of the head of the pancreas.

Upper gastrointestinal endoscopy can be utilized to differentiate ampullary, distal common bile duct, and pancreatic cancers. Endoscopy is also useful to provide biopsy confirmation of ampullary cancers.

TABLE XI

Treatment Planning for Pancreas and
Periampullary Cancer[a]

Jaundice, no metastases
   Symptoms of chlangitis, fever
   Temporary stent if resectable, no metastases
   Permanent biliary stent if nonresectable or metastases, followed by biopsy pancreas (CT guided)
   No symptoms of cholangitis
      Resectable, no metastases: proceed to laparoscopy or laparotomy
      Nonresectable: permanent biliary stent and biopsy
No jaundice
   Metastases: biopsy metastases
   Nonresectable: biopsy pancreas
   Resectable: proceed to laparoscopy or laparotomy

---

[a]Once a clinical diagnosis of pancreatic cancer has been established, treatment planning is based on the presence or absence of jaundice, cholangitis, and metastatic disease.

Magnetic resonance imaging (MRI) has not been shown to be superior to spiral CT, but magnetic resonance cholangiopancreatography (MRCP) may have a diagnostic role in pancreas cancer patients. MRCP is at least as accurate as ERCP in outlining the biliary tree. ERCP fails to visualize the bile duct in 10% or more of patients and the pancreatic duct is not seen in at least 20%.

ERCP offers the benefit of allowing palliation of obstructive jaundice but should be considered only when the cancer is unresectable. Jaundice should then be relieved by insertion of an expandable wire mesh permanent stent. Temporary stents should be reserved for patients with cholangitis and for those with histologically confirmed cancer for which neoadjuvant therapy is planned.

The role of a positron emission tomography (PET) scan in pancreatic cancer has not been established, but a single comparative study has suggested that PET scanning is more sensitive and specific than CT scanning.

2. Cancer of the Body and Tail of the Pancreas

Tumors of the body and tail of the pancreas can be more difficult to diagnose, but a significant proportion of patients present with one of four symptom complexes, either alone or in combination (Table VI). Unexplained weight loss, particularly if accompanied by epigastric or left paravertebral back pain, can suggest pancreatic cancer. Bowel dysfunction (constipation or, more commonly, floating loose stools with a foul odor) may accompany these symptoms. Another cluster of cancer patients are those suddenly found to be diabetic without a family history of diabetes mellitus, or those stable diabetics whose disease suddenly becomes much more difficult to control, particularly when accompanied by pain or weight loss. While abdominal ultrasound is an appropriate screening tool, the diagnosis is usually made by helical CT. For patients with symptoms suggesting peptic ulcer disease, gastrointestinal X rays or endoscopy are appropriate first steps (Fig. 2).

Spiral CT will delineate the extent of the primary tumor, identify enlarged, possibly metastatic lymph nodes, most liver metastases, and establish patency of the splenic and portal veins when a pancreatic protocol is utilized. While few of these cancers have been cured by surgical resection, patient survival and

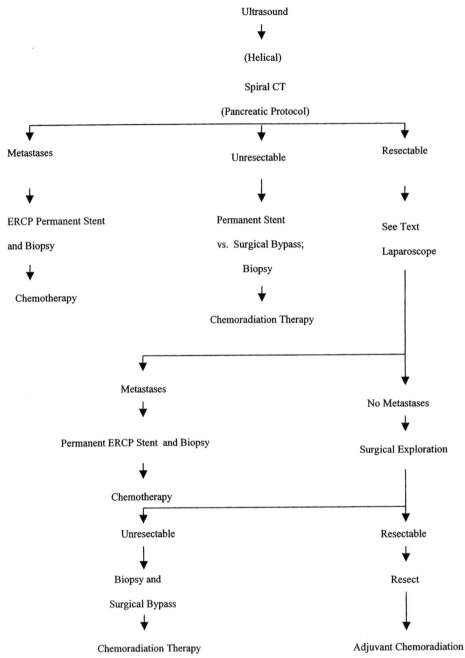

FIGURE 1 Algorithm for management of patients with the clinical diagnosis of cancer of the head of the pancreas.

quality of life are improved when resection is followed by postoperative radiation and chemotherapy.

E. Treatment

In the absence of liver or other distant metastases, portal vein obstruction, or other evidence of nonresectabil-ity on spiral CT scan, a growing body of evidence suggests that laparoscopy may segregate most of the truly resectable cancers from those that are unresectable or have peritoneal or small liver metastases. In this setting, laparoscopy would spare 10–30% of patients judged resectable by CT scan the several days of hospitalization that follow an open operation. Combined

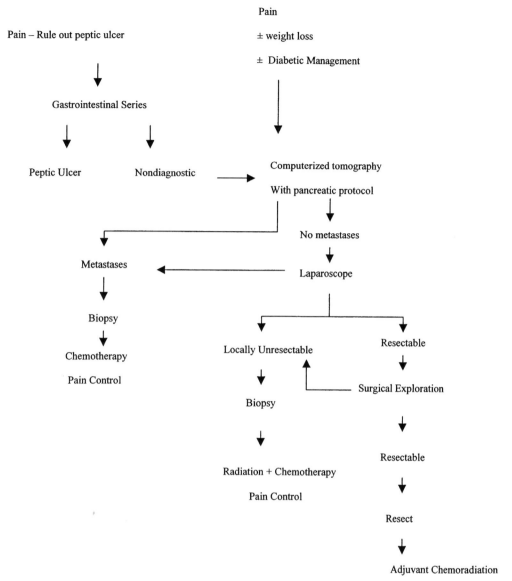

FIGURE 2 Algorithm for management of patients with suspected diagnosis of cancer of the body and tail of the pancreas.

with laparoscopic ultrasound, diagnostic laparoscopy is 90% accurate in predicting venous invasion. Patients with unresectable lesions can be biopsied laparoscopically. Those with jaundice can have "permanent" expanding stents placed by ERCP, whereas those with pain not responding to traditional narcotic and nonnarcotic therapies can be treated by celiac nerve blocks.

For patients with metastatic disease, gemcytabine is the first line of chemotherapy, providing response rates approaching 20%, but with better quality of life than treatment with 5-fluorouracil. Since the earliest

studies of the Gastrointestinal Tumor Study Group, the treatment of patients with locally unresectable but nonmetastatic pancreatic cancer has centered around combined radiation and chemotherapy (Table XII). Originally, patients received 40–60 Gy of radiation by split or double split course over 6–10 weeks combined with bolus injections of 5-fluorouracil on each of the first 3 days of each radiation course. More recently, most patients receive 50.4 Gy of radiation combined with continuous infusion 5-fluorouracil throughout the radiation therapy. Programs such as

TABLE XII
Overview of Treatment of Pancreatic Cancers

Disease status	Treatment
Metastases	Gemcytabine
	Fluorouracil or fluorourocil combinations
	Clinical trial
	Supportive care
Locally unresectable (no metastases)	Fluorouracil-based chemoradiation
	?gemcytabine and radiation therapy
	Clinical trial
Resected with positive margin	Same as locally unresectable
Resected	Postoperative fluorouracil-based chemoradiation
	Clinical trial

these provide median survivals of 10 months or more, with 40% of patients surviving 1 year compared to a median 4- to 6-month survival in patients treated with chemotherapy alone or who receive no antineoplastic treatment but supportive care alone. Patients with peritoneal or liver metastases generally live 3 months or less (Table XIII).

Currently, 60–70% of patients with ampullary cancers, 20% of patients with cancer of the pancreatic head, and fewer than 10% of patients with cancer of the uncinate, body of tail of the pancreas have resectable disease when first seen. While many of the ampullary cancers are resected, fewer than 10% of cancers of the head of the pancreas and 3% of cancers of the body and tail of the pancreas are actually resected. When a complete resection with tumor-free margins is followed by postoperative adjuvant radiation (40–50.4 Gy) and chemotherapy, approximately

TABLE XIII
Pathways of Metastases of Pancreatic Cancers

Pathway	Metastatic Site
Retroperitoneal lymph nodes	Supraclavicular nodes, lungs, bones
Peritoneum	Bowel, mesentery, ovaries, liver surface, ascites
Portal vein	Liver
Invasion of adjacent tissue	Portal vein, duodenum, stomach, spleen, retroperitoneum

20% of the pancreas cancer patients will survive 5 years, particularly if there are no lymph node metastases. Before adjuvant therapy was routinely applied, long-term survival after resection was only anecdotal.

Resection of carcinomas of the ampulla, head of the pancreas, and uncinate process must include, as a minimum, the head and part of the neck of the pancreas, the uncinate process, anterior, posterior, superior, and inferior peripancreatic lymph nodes, supra- and infrapyloric lymph nodes, lymph nodes surrounding the origin of the superior mesenteric artery, and the distal common bile duct and its lymph nodes. Because the gallbladder will not fill and is prone to stone formation once the distal bile duct is resected, the gallbladder is removed along with the lymph nodes at the triangle of Calot and the bile duct is divided at the level of the common hepatic duct.

The traditional pancreatoduodenectomy (Whipple) resection included removal of the gastric autrum and pylorus, but a recent modification of the procedure is applicable to many patients (the pyloruspreserving procedure) and allows for adequate lymphadenectomy without removing any gastric tissue. The long-term nutritional status of patients treated with pylorus preservation is superior to that of patients following a standard Whipple procedure, but the hospital stay is longer due to delayed pyloric function and gastric retention, a problem that may plague a few of these patients after discharge. Essentially, location and stage of the cancer (Table XIV), as well as surgeon preference, determine whether pylorus preservation will be performed.

Both resected and nonresected patients often have problems with bowel function, usually related to diarrhea with foul-odored floating stools, although an occasional patient will have constipation. Malnutrition can result. These problems are related to a failure to digest fats due to the lack of lipase in the small intestine, either as a result of obstruction of the pancreatic duct or from loss of pancreatic mass by resection. For most patients, 60–80,000 units of active lipase taken with meals (*not* before or after) will give relief. Unfortunately, lipase is a very fragile enzyme, rapidly deactivated by heat and acid. The lipase activity in many preparations or pancreatic enzymes is not constant. While many patients with pancreatic cancer are hypochlorhydric, a few have hyperacidic gastric

TABLE XIV
AJCC Staging of Cancer of the Exocrine Pancreas

Definitions							
T—Primary tumor		**N—Regional lymph nodes**		**M—Distant metastases**			
TX	Primary tumor cannot be assessed	Nx	Regional nodes cannot be assessed	Mx	Distant metastases cannot be assessed		
T0	No evidence of primary tumor	N0	No regional nodal metastases	M0	No distant metastases		
Tis	*In situ* carcinoma	N1	Regional nodal metastases	M1	Distant metastases		
T1	Confined to pancreas, ≤2 cm in size	pN1a	Single node metastasis				
T2	Confined to pancreas, ≥2 cm in size	pN1b	More than one node metastasis				
T3	Extends into duodenum, bile duct, or peripancreatic tissues						
T4	Extends to stomach, spleen, colon, or large vessels						

Stage grouping			
Stage 0	Tis	N0	M0
Stage I	I1, T2	N0	M0
Stage II	T3	N0	M0
Stage III	T1, T2, T3	N1	M0
Stage IVa	T4	any N	M0
Stage IVb	any T	any N	M1

secretions and may require an H-2-blocking agent so that the lipase activity is not lost.

In patients with end-stage pancreatic cancer, pain can be a major management problem. While usually responding to oral or transcutaneous narcotics, the pain is at times due to continued secretion by the residual functioning pancreas against the obstructing cancer. Because this function is prostaglandin mediated, nonsteroidal analgesics are often of value. When pain is not controllable with medication, celiac axis nerve block may be necessary and is sometimes effective for the duration of the patient's remaining life.

F. Newer Management Approaches

For patients with locally unresectable but non-metastatic disease, presurgical neoadjuvant chemoradiation has been administered in several centers (Table XV). Perhaps 20% of patients who were previously marginally nonresectable can be resected after neoadjuvant therapy, but often the additional resection and reanastomosis of the superior mesenteric and portal vein are required. A report from the MD An-

derson Cancer Center noted that histologic invasion of involved veins occurred in 71% of resected veins. Applying neoadjuvant therapy to potentially resectable patients has, thus far, not increased overall survival when compared to patients treated in a standard fashion (no neoadjuvant therapy), but a small percentage are saved from what would have been a nonbeneficial resection because of the appearance of evidence of liver metastases on the postneoadjuvant CT scan.

Biopsy (either laparoscopic or percutaneous CT guided) is essential before instituting neoadjuvant

TABLE XV
Neoadjuvant Therapy for Resectable Disease[a]

Experimental, most small phase II trials

Has not been found detrimental to resection

Few "locally unresectable" lesions converted to resectable (but many with vein resection)

No proven benefit over postoperative chemoradiation

[a]Summary of the experience of neoadjuvant chemoradiation therapy in patients with pancreatic cancer.

TABLE XVI
Metastatic Mimics of Pancreatic Cancer[a]

Metastases of breast, lung, ovarian cancers, and melanomas
Contiguous spread of cancer arising in body of stomach
Non-Hodgkins lymphomas

[a]Other sources of cancers found in patients thought to have primary pancreatic cancer but who did not.

therapy. At Roswell Park, of 100 patients referred for the management of pancreatic cancer with a pancreatic mass, 20 were found not to have cancer and were alive without treatment 5 years later. Another significant group were found to have other cancers (Table XVI).

G. Cystic Neoplasms

One of the largest groups of patients with cystic neoplasia of the pancreas was reported by the French Surgical Association. Misdiagnosis of these lesions as benign pseudocysts was not uncommon, reported in 15% of mucinous cystadenocarcinomas and 9% of benign mucinous cystadenomas. Resection was beneficial, with 63% of patients with mucinous cystadenocarcinomas surviving 5 years or more. Serous cystadenomas can occasionally be well characterized radiographically. A selected group of 26 patients with serous tumors were observed over 3 years, none of whom required surgical intervention.

II. ENDOCRINE PANCREATIC (ISLET CELL) TUMORS

A. Primary Tumor

Tumors of the pancreatic islet cells are made up of a diverse group of hormone-secreting and nonfunctional tumors (Table XVII) that are diagnosed because of the consequences of hypersecretion of a produced hormone (intractable hypoglycemia, migratory necrolytic erythema, diarrhea, multiple intractable peptic ulcers, etc.), pain, or the finding of an abdominal mass (including liver metastases). Computerized tomography of the upper abdomen with a pancreatic protocol is particularly useful in the patient population because the tumors are hypervascular compared to the surrounding tissues, thus larger lesions can be highlighted in the arterial phase. Fine needle aspiration biopsy confirms the pattern of small, often monotonous hyperchromatic cells indicative of a neuroendocrine tumor rather than a tumor of the exocrine pancreas. While the symptomatic history of the patient often suggests the type of tumor, further assays confirm the cell of origin (Table XVIII) and initial therapy, while planning for definitive therapy (Table XIX). Intraoperative ultrasound has been quite useful in localizing small nonpalpable tumors.

B. Recurrence

Growth of islet cell tumors is usually slow. The approach to patients who develop cancer recurrence

TABLE XVII
Islet Cell Tumors[a]

| Histology | Immunochemistry | | | | Notes |
	Cell of origin	Functional incidence	Proportion malignant	Proportion multiple	
Insulinoma	β	70%	10%	10%	50% ortreotide negative, 10% hyperplasia
Glucagonoma	α	15%	90%	Uncommon	Migratory necrolytic erythema
Gastrinoma	δ	10%	60%	75%	25% are MEN-1
VIP-oma	Stem	2%	50%	?	WDHA syndrome
Others	Stem	2%	80%	?	ACTH, serotonin, somatostatin, growth
PP-oma	PP	—	80%	Uncommon	"Nonfunctional," 15–30% of all islet cell cancer

[a]More common tumors of the endocrine pancreas. Histopathologic examination of a particular tumor often fails to distinguish cancers from benign tumors. Fifty percent of islet cell tumors secrete two or more hormones.

TABLE XVIII

Evaluation of Functioning Islet Cell Tumors and Initial
Management of Hormone Hypersecretion

Tumor	Work-up	Initial treatment
Insulinoma	Insulin/glucose ratio C-peptide 72-h fasting with insulin/glucose ratio	Stabilize glucose with diazoxide
Gastrinoma	Serum gastrin Secretin test	Hx antagonists or proton pump inhibitors
Glucagon	Glucagonoma	Octreotide
VIPoma	VIP	Correct electrolytes Octreotide

and those found to have metastatic disease at the time of initial diagnosis differs radically from the management of recurrent or metastatic disease of the exocrine pancreas and of most other cancers. Although the situation is uncommon, patients with totally resectable recurrent or metastatic disease should undergo reresection with curative intent.

For patients with recurrent or metastatic disease that is not surgically curable, concepts of optimum management are complicated by the generally slow rate of tumor progression. Asymptomatic patients may remain free of signs or symptoms of progressive disease for 1 to 3 years or more. Symptoms due to hormonal secretion may be readily managed medically

(e.g., H-2 blockade for gastrinoma, diazoxide for insulinoma, octreotide for glucagonoma, VIP-oma). While systemic chemotherapy with doxorubicin/streptozotocin combinations may cause tumor regression, its long-term effect on survival is difficult to measure. Thus, many asymptomatic patients are observed.

Symptomatic recurrences are managed according to the site of recurrence and the type of tumor (Table XX). The most common site of metastatic disease is the liver. Resection, chemoembolization, and radio frequency ablation are more effective than systemic chemotherapy, usually returning the patient to a relatively symptom-free status and, with repeated treatments as needed,

TABLE XIX

Definitive Treatment of Localized Islet Cell Tumors[a]

Tumor	If benign	If Malignant	Follow-up
Insulinoma[a]	Enucleation or local resection	Resection and lymph node dissection	Glucose, insulin, C-peptide, CT scan
Gastrinoma[b]	Local resection, duodenotomy with tumor enucleation	Resection and lymph node dissection	Gastrin, CT scan
Glucagonoma	Treat as malignant	Excision of tumor or distal pancreatectomy plus peripancreatic lymph node dissection	Glucagon, CT scan
VIPoma	Treat as malignant	Excision of tumor or Whipple procedure plus peripancreatic and regional lymph node dissection	Electrolyte imbalance, CT scan
Pancreatic polypeptidoma Somatostatinoma	Treat as malignant	Resection with peripancreatic lymph node dissection	CT scan

[a]Follow-up at 3 months, then markers are observed every 3 months for 1–2 years, every 6 months until 5 years, annually thereafter.
[b]Fifty percent of tumors are located in the duodenal wall and 25% in the pancreas. Other sites include regional lymph nodes (10%). Tumors in the pancreas tend to be sporadic (i.e., not MEN-1) and not multiple, but are often malignant.

TABLE XX
TABLE XX
Management of Locally Unresectable and Metastatic Islet Cell Cancer[a]

Symptom status	Recurrent or metastatic site	Management options
Asymptomatic	Any	Observe, markers and CT scans every 3–6 months
		? systemic chemotherapy
Symptomatic, hormonal only	Any	Gastrinoma—H-2 blockade
		Insulinoma—Diazoxide
		Glucagonoma, etc.—Octreotide
Pain or uncontrolled hormonal	Liver	Resectable: resect
		Unresectable: chemoembolization, radio frequency abalation, systemic chemotherapy
	Bone	Radiotherapy, biphosphonates
	Lung	Resection or systemic chemotherapy
	Pancreas	Resection or systemic chemotherapy

[a]Management of islet cell cancer recurrence depends on symptomatic status and site of recurrence. Often, combinations of management options are appropriate.

prolonging survival. Bone, particularly the spine, the next most common metastatic site, responds well to radiation therapy. Biphosphonates may be useful if bone pain recurs or if there are multiple sites of bone metastases. Lung metastases can be resected or treated with systemic chemotherapy.

Combined approaches can be quite rewarding. A patient who presents with a primary tumor and liver metastases may be well palliated by resection of the primary tumor and resection or radio frequency ablation of the liver lesions. In a symptomatic patient, the resection of multiple small liver metastases can often be useful. Similarly, a patient with bone and liver metastases may be benefited by radiation therapy to the osseous lesion and chemoembolization of the liver. For systemic chemotherapy, five drugs with varying degrees of activity against islet cell tumors have been used, usually in two drug combinations. Most effective has been the combination of doxorubicin and streptozotocin, but 5-fluorouracil, imidazole-carboxamide, and cyclophosphamide also have some activity.

C. MEN-1

Parathyroid hyperplasia, pituitary adenoma, and islet cell tumors (usually multiple) together comprise the multiple endocrine neoplasia syndrome, type 1 (MEN-1), an autosomal dominant inherited defect due to loss of heterozygosity at 11q13 of the human genome (Table XXI). Of patients with gastrinomas, 25% have MEN-1 tumors. Gastrinomas and other islet cell tumors are usually malignant, with gastrinomas being the most common tumors in MEN-1 patients. Despite the multiplicity of tumors that occur, these patients frequently have a long survival, generally dying of a peptic ulcer or renal complications of their disease. Management of their pancreatic tumors is the same as for patients with sporadic pancreatic endocrine tumors, but usually after the parathyroidectomy has been performed for hypercalcemia.

TABLE XXI
MEN-1 and Islet Cell Tumors[a]

MEN-1	Penetrance (%)
Parathyroid hyperplasia	90
Pituitary adenoma	65
Islet cell tumor (usually multiple)	75
Gastrinoma	40
Glucagonoma	10
Vipoma	2
Somatostatinoma	2
Others (growth hormone releasing, ACTH secreting, etc.)	

[a]Although MEN-1 is associated with loss of heterozygosity at 11q13, each kindred has its own distinct mutation.

See Also the Following Articles

ENDOCRINE TUMORS • PANCREATIC CANCER: CELLULAR AND MOLECULAR MECHANISMS

Bibliography

Douglass, H. O., Jr., Kim, S. Y., and Merepol, N. J. (1997). Neoplasms of the exocrine pancreas. *In* "Cancer Medicine" (J. F. Holland, R. C. Bast, Jr., D. L. Morton, E. Frei, III, D. W. Kufe, and R. R. Weichselbaum, eds.), 4th Ed., pp. 1989–2017. Williams & Wilkins, Baltimore MD.

Hilgers, W., and Kern, S. E. (1999). Molecular genetic basis of pancreatic adenocarcinoma. *Genes Chromosomes Cancer* **26,** 1–12.

Neuroendocrine Tumors Guidelines Panel (1999). NCCN practice guidelines for neuroendocrine tumors. *Oncology* **13**(Suppl. 11A), 297–344.

Pancreatic Cancer Practice Guidelines Panel (1997). NCCN practice guidelines for pancreatic cancer. *Oncology* **11**(Suppl. 11A), 41–56.

Tan, H. P., Smith, J., and Garberoglio, C. A. (1996). Pancreatic adenocarcinoma: An update. *J. Am. Coll. Surg.* **183,** 165–184.

Vinik, A. I., and Perry, R. R. (1997). Neoplasms of the gastroenteropancreatic endocrine system. *In* "Cancer Medicine" (J. F. Holland, R. C. Bast, Jr., and D. L. Morton, eds.), 4th Ed., pp. 1605–1639. Williams & Wilkins, Baltimore, MD

Pancreatic Cancer: Cellular and Molecular Mechanisms

Raul Urrutia
Abigail A. Conley
Volker Ellenrieder
Joanna Kaczynski
Eugene P. DiMagno
Mayo Clinic, Rochester, Minnesota

GLOSSARY

cell cycle A series of events that an eukaryotic cell follows in order to divide. It is usually represented by a circular diagram beginning at interphase, a step in the cycle used by the cell to prepare for division, and mitosis, or actual cell division. In addition, several subdivisions of interphase and mitosis are diagrammed within this cycle to indicate the occurrence of distinct cellular events.

oncogene A gene which, when expressed, increases the potential of an eukaryotic cell to transform into a tumor cell.

signaling proteins Proteins that are selectively activated in the cell to transduce a signal emanating from a particular receptor. Cells contain a large repertoire of proteins that participate in distinct signaling cascades for growth factors, hormones, neurotransmitters, and so on and mediate specific cellular functions.

transcription factors Proteins that, in conjunction with RNA polymerases, are responsible for the synthesis of RNA from a DNA template.

tumor suppressor A gene which, when expressed, prevents the transformation of a normal eukaryotic cell into a tumor cell.

I n the United States, pancreatic cancer is diagnosed in 28,000 patients every year. Of those, 26,000 will die. This disease currently ranks fifth as a cause of death by cancer in the United States and has one of the poorest prognoses among the human neoplasias. Indeed, pancreatic cancer has an overall 5-year survival rate of only 3%, largely due to its particularly aggressive nature. Although the etiology of pancreatic cancer is poorly understood, increasing evidence indicates that alterations in the molecular pathways that regulate cell proliferation and differentiation are often associated with this disease. Such changes can result in abnormalities in growth factor-mediated signaling cascades, cell cycle control, and transcriptional regulation. Recent developments in these areas of research are providing a theoretical framework for the development of models of pancreatic cancer initiation and development.

I. INTRODUCTION: ABNORMAL CELL PROLIFERATION AND DIFFERENTIATION CHARACTERIZE PANCREATIC CANCER

The pancreas is a gland with both endocrine and exocrine functions. The endocrine portion of the pancreas consists of the islets of Langerhans, which are small spherical structures containing cells that secrete the hormones insulin, glucagon, somatostatin, and pancreatic polypeptide. The exocrine pancreas is a tubuloacinar gland composed of two major cell populations: acinar cells, which secrete digestive enzymes, and ductal cells, which line the ducts and carry secretions into the duodenum.

The most common type of pancreatic cancer is adenocarcinoma arising from the exocrine epithelial cells of the duct. Benign and malignant endocrine or exocrine pancreatic tumors also occur, but adenocarcinoma of the pancreas accounts for 90% of all pancreatic tumors and is the most feared neoplastic disease of this organ. The majority develop in the head of the pancreas, where cancerous growth frequently obstructs the common bile duct and leads to the classic symptom of painless jaundice. Dramatic weight loss, nausea, and vomiting can also herald the disease. Pancreatic adenocarcinomas are particularly aggressive and unless complete surgical resection is possible, they are usually diagnosed too late for therapy to be effective. Therefore, efforts to understand the molecular mechanisms underlying the development of pancreatic cancer may lead to preventive and treatment strategies to improve the prognosis of this disease. Toward this end, many investigators throughout the world are directing their research toward the understanding of the molecular mechanisms underlying the regulation of cell proliferation and differentiation in pancreatic cells because these phenomena are the landmarks of neoplastic transformation. From these studies, a better understanding of the pathobiology of pancreatic cancer is emerging that should provide a theoretical framework useful for designing diagnostic as well as therapeutic approaches to fight this disease.

II. CELL TO NUCLEUS SIGNALING REGULATES CELL PROLIFERATION AND DIFFERENTIATION

Cell proliferation and differentiation are the culmination of multiple cellular processes, including the initiation of intracellular signaling pathways and activation of transcription factors. In the pancreas, a variety of extracellular matrix proteins and cytokines that modulate cell differentiation and growth by interacting directly with cell surface receptors have been described (Fig. 1). Among these substances are growth factors, including extracellular growth factor (EGF), transforming growth factor α (TGFα), TGFβ, IGF I, IGF II, and hepatocyte growth factor (HGF), and hormones such as glucocorticoids, thyroxin, cholecystokinin, and bombesin. Mutations in some of these growth factors and hormones and their receptors are frequently found in pancreatic cancer and are considered to play an essential role in pancreatic carcinogenesis.

A. EGFR: A Model for Tyrosine Kinase Receptor

Epidermal growth factor and transforming growth factor α are the best studied members of a growing family of EGF-like ligands. At least 13 other EGF-like ligands have been described, including amphiregulin, heparin-binding EGF-like growth factor, and betacellulin. Early studies indicated that both EGF and TGFα regulate normal pancreatic cell growth. It has also been revealed that EGF, TGFα, amphiregulin, and heparin-binding EGF-like growth factor are potent

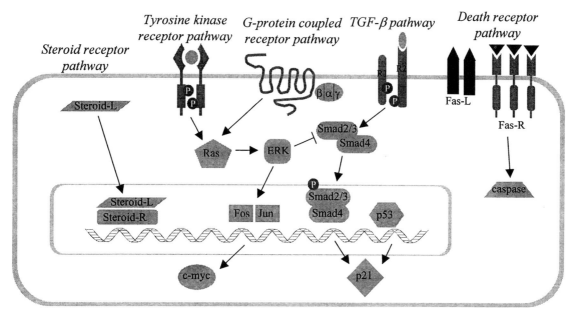

FIGURE 1 Summary of the growth regulatory pathways in the pancreatic cancer cell. Control of proliferation, cell cycle progression, and apoptosis results from the interplay between extracellular signaling and transcriptional regulation. The receptors (R) that recognize extracellular signals are grouped into general structural families, which are coupled with distinct sets of intracellular signaling molecules or ligands (L). Tyrosine kinase receptors, serine/threonine kinase receptors, G protein-coupled receptors, and Fas are transmembrane receptors located on the cell surface, whereas steroid hormone receptors are zinc finger proteins, which act as transcriptional regulators in the nucleus.

inducers of malignant transformation and proliferation in cultured pancreatic cancer cells. These growth factors interact with cell surface receptors called receptor tyrosine kinases (RTKs). In mammals, the EGF receptor (EGFR) family of RTKs consists of four closely related transmembrane glycoproteins: the ErbB1 receptor (also called EGFR), ErbB2 (also called c-Neu), ErbB3, and ErbB4 receptor. In each case, EGF, or a related growth factor, binds to the extracellular domain of the receptor, stimulating tyrosine kinase activity in the cytoplasmic domain. This results in tyrosine phosphorylation of the receptor itself (autophosphorylation) and of other cytoplasmic proteins. Phosphorylation of these molecules alters their activity and/or ability to interact with other proteins. Thus, a cascade of altered protein interactions, or signal transduction events, is initiated.

Overexpression of an EGFR is a common feature in pancreatic cancer tissues and cell lines and has often been described in association with increased levels of EGFR ligands, such as EGF and TGFα. Such dual overexpression has been shown to stimulate pancreatic cell growth in both autocrine and paracrine man-

ners, is frequently found in advanced clinical stage tumors, and is associated with enhanced tumor aggressiveness. Of greatest interest in pancreatic carcinogenesis, however, is the c-ErbB-2 protooncogene. It is not expressed in normal pancreas but there is accumulating evidence regarding the incidence of c-ErbB-2 expression in invasive ductal adenocarcinomas and in intraductal mucin-hypersecreting neoplasms of the pancreas. Statistical analysis has revealed that higher levels of c-ErbB-2 expression correlate with lesser degrees of differentiation in the tumor. In summary, data suggest that the family of EGF receptors and ligands is involved in the pathogenesis of pancreatic cancer, leading to a more malignant phenotype.

B. Other Tyrosine Kinase Receptor Proteins Expressed in Pancreatic Cancer

Hepatocyte growth factor is a peptide that binds and activates the tyrosine kinase receptor c-Met, a well-characterized protooncogene. In a variety of epithelial cells, c-Met activation results in increased cell proliferation. HGF and its receptor are detectable at low levels in the normal exocrine pancreas but are often overexpressed in pancreatic cancer. Immunohistochemical studies detect HGF mainly in stromal cells, whereas distribution of c-Met is diffuse. *In vitro*, HGF stimulates the motility of cancer cells, typically accompanied by increased cellular adhesion, suggesting a role for HGF and its receptor in the metastatic spread of pancreatic cancer.

Insulin-like growth factor I, keratinocyte growth factor, platelet-derived growth factor, and acidic and basic fibroblast growth factors can induce cell proliferation in a variety of mammalian cell populations and furthermore have been shown to be overexpressed in pancreatic tumors. Overexpression of fibroblast growth factor, for example, correlates with advanced tumor stages and shorter patient survival. In conclusion, increasing evidence supports a role for HGF and other ligands of tyrosine receptor proteins in the aggressive behavior of pancreatic cancer.

C. Ras-Mediated Signaling

One of the most frequent genetic alterations in human cancer is the constitutive activation of the Ras signaling pathway. The Ras family consists of three functional genes: H-ras, K-ras, and N-ras. Ras proteins are located at the inner leaflet of the plasma membrane where they transduce signals emanating from a variety of extracellular receptors, such as RTKs and G protein-coupled receptors (Fig. 1). Therefore, Ras proteins play a central role in the regulation of cell proliferation and differentiation. Activated Ras has many targets and affects various signaling pathways, one of the best characterized being the Raf-MEK-ERK cascade. One of the most prominent effects resulting from the activation of this cascade is the phosphorylation and activation of several transcription factors, including c-Myc, NF-IL6, Elk-1, ATF-2, and c-Jun.

Ras is active when bound to GTP and inactive when bound to GDP, its inactivation being regulated by GTPase-activating proteins (GAPs). Some mutations render Ras insensitive to the inhibitory effects of GAPs, locking it into an active GTP-bound state and leading to constitutive activation of the downstream signaling pathways. The incidence of mutated Ras genes varies widely and depends on tumor types.

Mutations of the K-ras oncogene are found in 85–95% of pancreatic adenocarcinomas. K-ras mutations have also been described in cystadenocarcinomas, cystadenomas, and intraductal papillary mucinous tumors of the pancreas. In almost all cases, the mutations are exclusively located in codon 12 of the K-ras gene. These mutations appear to arise very early in the development of pancreatic cancer, suggesting that the K-ras oncogene is involved in the initiation of neoplastic transformation of epithelial cells. Ongoing studies are investigating the value of K-ras mutations as a molecular marker for malignancy and may prove helpful in distinguishing chronic pancreatitis from early pancreatic cancer.

D. The TGFβ Family and Its Serine/Threonine Kinase Receptors

The transforming growth factor β family consists of three highly homologous genes: TGFβ1, TGFβ2, and TGFβ3. Among them, they exert pleiotropic effects on growth and differentiation in various cell types, as well as affecting immunosuppression and the formation of the extracellular matrix. Signaling is initiated when TGFβ binds to its specific type II receptor (TGFβR-II), an event that induces phosphorylation of the TGFβ type I receptor (TGFβR-I). The activated TGFβR-I then phosphorylates Smad2 or Smad3, enabling their association with Smad4 and subsequent translocation into the nucleus (Fig. 1). When in the nucleus, Smad4 can associate with DNA-binding proteins, such as Fast-1, and regulate transcription.

The TGFβ signaling pathway can function as a tumor suppressor pathway, leading to antiproliferation and apoptosis. Escape from growth regulation by TGFβ is seen in many different human cancers, and resistance to TGFβ-induced growth control has also been demonstrated in many cell lines derived from different epithelial tumors, such as breast cancer, colon cancer, and pancreatic cancer. Multiple mechanisms account for the loss or attenuation of TGFβ-induced growth regulation in epithelial cancer cells. These include a decrease in expression of the TGFβ receptors, mutations of the type II receptor, and mutations of downstream Smad4 signaling protein. Genetic alterations of other proteins within the TGFβ pathway, e.g., Smad2, are also likely.

Interestingly, observations suggest that TGFβ may also act as a strong promoter of cancer progression, leading to a more malignant phenotype. In this role, TGFβ has been shown to induce angiogenesis and tumor cell migration in more advanced tumor stages and to suppress immunosurveillance. Overexpression of TGFβ and its type II receptor has been found in the majority of human pancreatic cancers and, in some studies, shown to correlate with decreased patient survival. A biphasic effect of TGFβ has also been described in some experimental models, e.g., in transgenic mice containing keratinocyte-targeted expression of TGFβ, it initially suppressed the formation of chemically induced skin tumors but later enhanced malignant progression. In conclusion, TGFβ appears to play a dual role in tumorigenesis, acting early as a tumor suppressor but promoting tumor progression in later tumor stages.

E. Steroid Hormones in the Pancreas

Steroid hormones do not require cell surface receptors, as they are lipid soluble and can traverse the plasma membrane. Steroid receptors are zinc finger transcription factors that directly regulate gene expression when bound to the steroid (Fig. 1). Adrenal corticoids, particularly glucocorticoids, stimulate acinar pancreatic cell differentiation *in vivo*, in cultured embryonic pancreas, and in pancreatic cell lines. Glucocorticoids can also arrest cell proliferation in exocrine pancreatic cells. Although the glucocorticoid receptor was shown to be present in 60% of 20 pancreatic tumors, the relationship between adrenal steroids and pancreatic cancer remains unclear. Androgen and estrogen receptors are also expressed in pancreas, but their roles in normal pancreatic cell proliferation and differentiation, let alone during neoplastic transformation, remain to be defined.

F. Gastrointestinal Hormones in Pancreatic Cells and Pancreatic Cancer

Most of the gastrointestinal (GI) hormones, which exert their effect on pancreatic cells, bind to and activate distinct G protein-coupled receptors. Activation of these receptors initiates signaling via distinct sets of intracellular factors, including kinases, phosphatases, and calcium. Evidence strongly suggests that G protein-coupled receptor signaling is linked to activation of the MAP kinase pathway. Peptides such as cholecystokinin (CCK), gastrin, bombesin, and secretin are mitogenic for pancreatic cell lines, whereas somatostatin has an antiproliferative effect on these cells. The effects of CCK on pancreatic cell growth have been extensively characterized using experimental models of pancreatic carcinogenesis. This hormone, acting *via* the CCK_A receptor, stimulates the growth of carcinogen-induced preneoplastic lesions in rat. The CCK_A receptor also mediates cell proliferation in response to CCK in transformed pancreatic cell lines. Based on the effects of CCK on pancreatic cell growth, CCK antagonists have been tested for the treatment of pancreatic cancer but without promising results.

Because of the known antiproliferative actions of somatostatin on pancreatic cell lines, its long-acting analog, octreoctide, has been tested for the treatment of human pancreatic cancer and found to increase the survival rate of patients with unresectable and resected tumors. To our knowledge, no significant data are available on the therapeutic effects of other GI hormones in human clinical trials for pancreatic cancer.

G. Apoptosis Signaling in Pancreatic Cancer

Apoptosis, or physiologic cell death, is an evolutionarily conserved cellular process by which multicellular organisms eliminate unnecessary cells during embryonic development, tissue remodeling, immune regulation, and tumor regression. Many intracellular and extracellular signals stimulate apoptosis, and although these signals may initially engage different pathways, the effector phase of apoptosis is generally conserved and relies on the activation of a family of proteolytic enzymes called caspases. Caspase activation leads to cleavage of cellular proteins, resulting in a regulated disassembly of the cell.

One mechanism of triggering apoptosis is mediated by death receptors, which transmit apoptotic signals initiated by specific death ligands. Death receptors are characterized by a conserved intracellular death domain and include tumor necrosis factor receptor-1 (TNFR), Fas, and TNF-related apoptosis induction ligand receptor (TRAIL). The Fas death receptor, for example, is expressed on all normal cells. When Fas binds the Fas–ligand, the receptor oligomerizes, allowing the death domains to interact with the adaptor protein FADD (Fas associated protein with death domain). This results in activation of procaspase 8, leading to apoptosis. The Fas–ligand is expressed by circulating T cells and is an efficient tool for the immunological elimination of suspect cells. However, certain immune-privileged sites, such as the testis and cornea, have also been shown to express Fas–ligand, allowing them to "counterattack" and prevent activation of their own apoptotic pathways. It has been found that some pancreatic cancer cells can also escape Fas-mediated apoptosis in this manner.

Apoptosis can additionally be triggered by intracellular signals, such as mitochondrial damage, resulting in the activation of Bcl-2 protein family members, which are found associated with various organelles. Pro- and antiapoptotic Bcl-2 family members can heterodimerize and modulate each other's functions, suggesting that their relative concentrations determine whether a cell undergoes apoptosis in response to intracellular damage. It has been reported that the cellular content of Bcl-2 protein, an inhibitor of apoptosis, negatively correlates with the sensitivity to the cytotoxic effects of the drug gemcitabine, a nucleotide analog used in the treatment of unresectable pancreatic cancer in conjunction with radiation therapy. The higher the level of Bcl-2, the higher the dose of gemcitabine is needed to induce apoptosis. By measuring the level of Bcl-2 expression in tumors, it may be possible to predict which patients will respond to gemcitabine treatment. Therefore, the apoptotic molecules that a pancreatic tumor expresses are important for determining whether the tumor cells are susceptible to cell death and present potential targets for therapeutic intervention.

III. THE CELL CYCLE AS A GENERAL MODEL FOR EUKARYOTIC CELL DIVISION: ALTERATIONS IN PANCREATIC CANCER

A. The Cell Cycle and Its Regulation

Mitotic cell division can be described in terms of the cell cycle, a progression of four tightly regulated phases. Most spectacular of these is mitosis, or M phase, during which nuclear and ultimately cellular divisions occur. Nonetheless, in most mammalian cells this phase constitutes only a small fraction of the total cell cycle. The remainder (interphase) is subdivided into three phases (G_1, S, and G_2) during which the events that commit the cell to division occur (Fig. 2A). In higher eukaryotes, the cell cycle is regulated by the activities of two families of proteins: cyclins and cyclin-dependent kinases (Cdks). Cdks are a family of at least seven serine/threonine kinases that require cyclins for their full activation. Because the activities of distinct Cdk–cyclin pairs are required during the different stages of the cell cycle, their rates of expression and degradation are limiting steps for correct cell cycle progression. Generally, the levels of Cdks remain fairly constant throughout the cell cycle and it is the level of cyclins that can be modulated by mitogenic stimuli. Posttranslational modifications of cyclin–Cdk complexes by cyclin-activated kinase (CAK) may also play a significant regulatory role.

B. The Restriction Point and Retinoblastoma Protein

Detailed biochemical analyses of the cell cycle have led to a better understanding of the mitogenic signals involved in its regulation. It has been found that mitogenic growth factor stimulation is required only during the first two-thirds of G_1. Then the "restriction point" (R point) is reached. At this important juncture, the fate of the cell is decided; if it has received sufficient mitogenic signaling, it advances past the R point and through the remainder of G_1, i.e., it is committed to division. In contrast, a cell that has received suboptimal mitogenic stimulation is unable to complete G_1 and returns to quiescence. Whether the cell is able to advance through the R point is mediated in large part by the activity of the retinoblastoma protein (Rb). Unphosphorylated Rb suppresses growth by binding to transcription factors and preventing their activity. When phosphorylated, Rb is rendered inactive and transcription factors necessary for S phase progression, such as E2F, are liberated.

Phosphorylation of Rb is accomplished by a combination of cyclin D–Cdk4, cyclin D–Cdk6, and cyclin E–Cdk2 activities (Fig. 2B). Cyclin D1 synthesis in particular has been shown to be directly induced

A

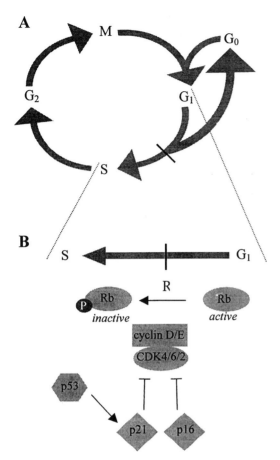

B

FIGURE 2 (A) Diagram of a typical eukaryotic cell cycle. The cell cycle starts at G_1, which is also the point of entry of quiescent cells. Cells then pass into S phase, when new DNA is synthesized and the cell's genome is duplicated. Once this has occurred, the cells move into G_2 and finally into mitosis (M), when cellular and nuclear division occurs. The resulting daughter cells may continue to proliferate, in which case they will remain in cell cycle or their growth may be arrested whereupon they return to the quiescent state also known as G_0. (B) Regulation of the R point. Growth regulatory molecules induce cells to transit through different phases of the cell cycle. Complexes of distinct cyclin and cyclin-dependent kinases (Cdks) positively regulate these cell cycle transitions (see text). The R point is an important G_1 checkpoint. The phosphorylation state of the Rb protein determines whether a cell traverses the R point and becomes committed to division. Cyclins D and E, in a complex with CDK 4, 6, or 2, phosphorylate the Rb protein. In contrast, Cdk inhibitor molecules (CKIs), such as p21 and p16, interfere with the function of these complexes and therefore are known to negatively regulate the cell cycle.

by mitogenic stimulation. The negative regulation of cyclin–Cdk complexes is generally enforced by cyclin–Cdk inhibitors (CKIs) belonging to one of two major families. In the first of these families are proteins structurally related to the p16 Ink4a polypep-

tide, e.g., p15Ink4b, p18Ink4c, and p19Ink4d; the second family includes the proteins p21 (Waf1), p27 (Kip1), and p57 (Kip2). Members of the latter family can bind to, and inactivate, many different cyclin–Cdk complexes, including those responsible for Rb phosphorylation (Fig. 2B).

p21/Waf1 has been shown to lie downstream of Smad4/DPC4, a locus inactivated in the majority of pancreatic carcinomas. The deletion of Smad4 functions in transformed pancreatic cells releases the brake on the cell cycle, leading to unregulated growth. The Ink4 family of proteins prevents Cdks 4 and 6 from associating with cyclin D (Fig. 2B), leading to G_1 arrest. Mutation, deletion, or methylation of p16Ink4a is common in many tumors and occurs with a frequency of nearly 100% in pancreatic carcinomas.

C. Mutations in p53 Facilitate Escape from Apoptosis

In addition to death receptor-mediated cell death, apoptosis may result from genomic DNA damage. DNA damage can trigger the expression of tumor suppressor p53, a transcription factor with a twofold function. First, p53 induces expression of the p21/Waf1 Cdk inhibitor, causing cell cycle arrest and (Fig. 2B), providing an opportunity for the damage to be repaired. If that repair process is inadequate, p53 initiates apoptotic pathways, leading to cell death. p53 is the most common mutation found in all cancers, and mutations have been reported in up to 70% of all primary pancreatic adenocarcinomas.

IV. TRANSCRIPTION FACTORS IN NORMAL AND NEOPLASTIC PANCREATIC CELL POPULATIONS

A. Regulation of Transcription

Transcription factors are nuclear proteins that regulate gene expression by recognizing conserved promoter DNA elements. Transcription factors are classified into different families based on the structure of the nucleic acid-binding motifs that are conserved within each group (e.g., helix–turn–helix, helix–loop–helix, leucine zippers, and zinc fingers domains).

Members of these families of proteins have been shown to regulate cell homeostasis, proliferation, and differentiation in a variety of cell types. In addition, mutations in transcription factor genes have been found in some tumors, suggesting an association with neoplastic transformation.

B. Role of Transcription Factors in Cancer

One transcription factor involved in pancreatic cancer is the DPC4 (deleted in pancreatic cancer) gene, which encodes the protein Smad4, a member of the TGFβ responsive transcription factor family described earlier (see Sections II and III). Other examples of TGFβ responsive transcription factors are the TIEG1 and TIEG2 proteins (TGFβ inducible early genes 1 and 2), which are Sp1-like, zinc finger transcription factors highly expressed in the normal adult pancreas. They bind and repress transcription at GC-rich promoters found in the regulatory regions of many genes involved in cell growth regulation. Overexpression of TIEG1 has been shown to cause apoptosis of pancreatic cancer cells, and TIEG2 overexpression has been shown to be antiproliferative in the epithelial Chinese hamster ovary cell line. However, the precise role of TIEG proteins in regulating pancreatic cell growth *in vivo* remains to be determined.

The activities of growth stimulatory transcription factors are generally downregulated in normal pancreatic cells. Nonetheless, transformed pancreatic cells frequently harbor mutated versions of upstream regulatory proteins (e.g., K-ras) that can lead to the inappropriate activation of these transcription factors. For example, activation of transcription factor Tcf (T-cell factor) has been shown in some pancreatic cancer cell lines. Tcf is the downstream effector of the APC/E-cadherin/β-catenin signaling pathway, first described in the molecular pathogenesis of colon cancer. Analogous to the colon cancer model, some pancreatic cell lines have been shown to exhibit mutations in β-catenin, leading to constitutive activation of Tcf. Tcf is involved in the transcriptional activation of genes involved in promoting cell growth, such as c-Myc.

Members of the Id family of proteins are homologous to the basic helix–loop–helix (bHLH) transcription factors, which bind and activate promoters of genes involved in differentiation. Id proteins, however, lack a DNA-binding domain and antagonize the function of bHLH transcription factors by forming Id–bHLH heterodimers. Overexpression of Id-1 and Id-2 has been demonstrated in pancreatic cancer cells. Furthermore, Id-1 and Id-2 overexpression has been detected in dysplastic papillary ductal cells found in chronic pancreatitis. Id expression may be a marker of enhanced proliferative potential in both pancreatic cancer and dysplastic ductal cells. Taken together, these data show that transcription factors involved in the regulation of normal cell proliferation and differentiation also play important roles in the molecular mechanisms underlying the development of pancreatic cancer.

V. CONCLUDING REMARKS

This article outlined the cellular and molecular mechanisms of cell proliferation and differentiation with a particular emphasis on the relationship of these phenomena to pancreatic cancer. It also described the results of experiments that have expanded our understanding of growth factor-mediated processes, cell cycle regulation, and transcriptional control, which are among the most promising areas in this field of research. The emerging concept, similar to other cancer models, is that alterations in the cellular pathways regulating normal cell growth are associated with the development of pancreatic cancer. By addressing how this disease arises on a molecular level, researchers can develop both precise diagnostic tools for its early detection and therapies that will specifically target the mutated protein or pathway. We are optimistic that the rapid translation of knowledge from the bench to the bedside will prove beneficial in this endeavor.

See Also the Following Articles

Bcl-2 Family Proteins and the Dysregulation of Programmed Cell Death • Cell Cycle Control • Pancreas and Periampullary Tumors • Ras Proteins • Retinoblastoma Tumor Suppressor Gene • Steroid Hormones and Hormone Receptors • TGFβ Receptor Signaling Mechanisms • Tumor Necrosis Factors

Bibliography

Go, V. W., DiMagno, E., Gardner, J. D., Lebenthal, E., Reber, H. A., and Scheele, G. A. (1994). "The Pancreas, Biology, Pathobiology, and Disease." Raven Press, New York.

Gold, L. I. (1999). The role for transforming growth factor-beta (TGF-beta) in human cancer. *Crit. Rev. Oncol.* **10**(4), 303–360.

Lundberg, A. S., and Weinberg, R. A. (1999). Control of the cell cycle and apoptosis. *Eur. J. Cancer* **35,** 531–539.

Mendelsohn, J., Howley, P. M., Istrael, M. A., and Liotta, L. A. (1995). "The Molecular Basis of Cancer." Saunders, Philadelphia.

Reber, H. A. (1998). "Pancreatic Cancer: Pathogenesis, Diagnosis and Treatment." Humana Press, Totowa, NJ.

Sakorafas, G. H., Tsiotou, A. G., and Tsiotos, G. G. (2000). Molecular biology of pancreatic cancer; oncogenes, tumour suppressor genes, growth factors, and their receptors from a clinical perspective. *Cancer Treat. Rev.* **26,** 29–52.

Papillomaviruses

Karl Münger
Harvard Medical School

GLOSSARY

apoptosis A genetically hard-wired suicide program that is built into cells that can be triggered by developmental cues or by signs of abnormal cell functions such as conflicting growth signals that a cell might receive in response to an oncogenic event.

pap smear The Papanicolaou smear is a procedure where cells derived from a cervical smear are microscopically evaluated for cytological abnormalities. This procedure has dramatically decreased the incidence and mortality of cervical cancer.

posttranslational modifications In many proteins, certain amino acids are subject to modification by a number of chemical reactions, including phosphorylation, acetylation, and ubiquitination. These reversible enzymatic reactions alter the biochemical and functional activities of a protein.

tumor suppressors Negative cellular regulatory nodes of very limited redundancy. A loss of function mutations has a dramatic impact on multiple regulatory pathways, causing dysregulation of fundamentally important cellular functions, including proliferation, differentiation, and/or cell death, thereby contributing to carcinogenesis.

S ome high-risk human papillomaviruses (HPVs) are highly associated with cervical cancer and other squamous cell carcinoma. The development of cancer is not part of the normal life cycle of these viruses but represents the outcome of a terminal accident where the viral genome becomes integrated into the host genome. High-risk HPVs encode two oncoproteins, E6 and E7, which play important roles in the normal life cycle of these viruses. It is of paramount importance that papillomaviruses be able to establish a cellular milieu that allows for the synthesis of viral genomes in cells that would have normally withdrawn from the cell division cycle and cannot support DNA synthesis.

E6 and E7 proteins play eminent roles in subverting the host cell to allow for viral replication by targeting important negative cellular regulatory proteins, among them the p53 and retinoblastoma tumor suppressors, respectively. Uncontrolled expression of E6 and E7 proteins, which is consistently observed after viral integration, contributes to the establishment of the malignant state, and continued expression of E6 and E7 is necessary for the maintenance of cellular transformation. In addition, high-risk HPV E7 and E6 induce genomic instability and allow for the propagation of cells with aberrant genomes, respectively. Hence there is strong evidence for a mechanistic contribution of the integrated viral sequences to carcinogenesis.

I. PAPILLOMAVIRUSES

Papillomaviruses are DNA viruses with a pronounced tropism for epithelial cells that have been detected in a wide range of animal species, from birds to humans. In addition to their tissue tropism, these viruses also are highly species specific and there is little evidence for transmission of the virus from one species to another. Papillomaviruses have small, circular double-stranded DNA genomes of approximately 8000 bp in size, with a very simple genomic organization. A schematic outline of the HPV-16 genome is represented in Fig. 1A. Only one of the two strands is transcribed. The major open reading frames are overlapping and encoded in all three possible reading frames. Papillomaviruses have approximately 10 open reading frames: 8 of them are designated as "early" and 2 of them as "late." The early and late open reading frames are identified by the prefix E and L, respectively, and a numeral. The lowest number distinguishes the longest open reading frame. Early viral genes encode viral replication proteins, whereas late genes encode the viral capsid proteins. During expression of the early genes, there are complex patterns of splicing, and mRNAs are expressed that contain coding information derived from more than one open reading frame. In addition to the early and late coding sequence, which takes up approximately 7000 bp of genomic information, there is an additional portion of the genome that does not specify major open reading frames but contains regulatory DNA elements, including the origin of viral DNA replication and binding sites for viral and cellular transcription factors. This region has been designated the long control region (LCR) (Fig. 1A).

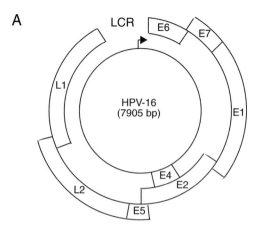

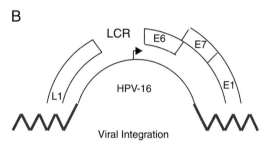

FIGURE 1 (A) Schematic map of the genome of the high-risk HPV-16. LCR denotes the long control region, which harbors various sequence elements important for the regulation of viral replication and transcription. The major early promoter that drives expression of the E6/E7 genes is indicated by an arrow. Only one strand of the double-stranded circular DNA genome is transcribed; open reading frames are encoded in all three different open reading frames. The early (E) genes each have functions relevant to the replication of the virus, and the two late (L) genes encode the viral capsid proteins. (B) Integration of the viral genome into the host chromosome is a hallmark of malignant progression. Integration generally retains expression of the E6 and E7 genes and frequently disrupts expression of the E2 gene. Because E2 encodes a transcriptional repressor for the E6/E7 promoter, disruption of E2 function is thought to lead to a high level, dysregulated expression of E6 and E7.

II. REGULATION OF VIRAL REPLICATION AND GENE EXPRESSION

Like other viruses, papillomaviruses are obligatory intracellular parasites with a single-minded purpose to survive and replicate in their host cell. Because of their limited coding potential, they heavily rely on host cellular replication factors for synthesizing their genomes. This is a particularly challenging feat given that these viruses replicate in the skin. Papillomaviruses initially infect basal cells, undifferentiated proliferating cells in the deepest layer of the skin. Some human papillomavirus particles interact with integrin structures that specifically decorate such cells. Viral replication is tightly coupled to the process of cellular differentiation. Amplification of viral genomes, as well as late gene expression and the ensuing generation of infectious particles, is confined to the differentiated layers of the skin. Papillomaviruses are nonlytic viruses, and the newly produced particles are shed together with the uppermost dead layers of the skin. The fact that differentiated cells normally have permanently withdrawn from the cell replication cycle and thus are unfit to act as replication factories for the virus is a major obstacle that has to be overcome. Hence a major theme of papillomavirus replication is the necessity of these viruses to encode proteins that can subvert the differentiated host cells and trick them into maintaining a "replication-competent milieu." The strategies that these papillomaviruses have developed to attain this goal are central to the understanding of the process of HPV-associated carcinogenesis.

Two viral genes, E1 and E2, play direct roles in viral replication. E1 is an origin binding protein with helicase activity and represents the core replication protein. It can physically interact with the E2 DNA-binding protein, and E2 is an important auxiliary factor for E1 binding to the origin of replication and, thus, for viral replication. The E2 protein is also the major viral transcriptional regulator. It is a DNA-binding protein that interacts with specific sequence elements in the LCR and in other portions of the genome. Like many transcription factors, the E2 protein is a functional dimer. Each monomer consists of an amino-terminal transcriptional activation domain, followed by a flexible hinge and a carboxyl-terminal DNA-binding domain. Many papillomaviruses encode multiple E2 species with different transcriptional activities. The bovine papillomavirus type 1, BPV1, for example, encodes a full-length E2 protein that acts as a transcriptional activator, as well as two repressor forms. One is generated by initiation at an in-ternal methionine residue and encodes a carboxyl-terminal DNA-binding domain. A second repressor form is generated by a splicing event where a portion of the E8 open reading frame is fused to the E2 DNA-binding domain. Other papillomavirus types also have the capacity to encode multiple, functionally distinct E2 transcription factors. In addition, the viral transcriptional program is also modulated by cellular factors. Of particular importance are differentiation-specific proteins that regulate the early to late switch in viral gene expression. In addition to transcription, some of these proteins regulate splicing and/or mRNA stability. Relatively little is known about the identity of such factors, as it has been impossible for many years to readily grow papillomaviruses in tissue culture systems. Recent advances, however, have finally yielded such systems and these questions can now be addressed.

III. ASSOCIATION OF HUMAN PAPILLOMAVIRUSES WITH HUMAN CANCERS

Approximately 100 different HPVs have been identified and new virus types are regularly added to this list. Most humans, at one time or another, have been infected with some HPV. How then can a conclusive etiologic link of HPV infection with the genesis of human tumors be established? There are multiple answers to this question, including the ability of many HPVs to transform cells in tissue culture and to cause lesions in transgenic mouse models. Regardless, most HPVs cause benign hyperplastic skin lesions or warts in their natural hosts. The majority of these lesions have a negligible propensity for malignant progression; thus, HPVs associated with such lesions are commonly referred to as "low-risk" HPVs. This is in contrast to "high-risk" HPVs that cause lesions that have a certain potential for carcinogenic progression. Regardless, even for a tumor caused by a high-risk HPV, the overall potential to undergo malignant progression is still quite low and often occurs only in the presence of certain risk factors, such as decreased immune functions or after a long latency period after other genomic alterations in the host cell DNA have occurred. According to some estimations, a woman infected with a high-risk HPV has a less than 1 in 30 lifetime risk of developing cervical cancer.

The major HPV-associated malignancies, including anogenital tract cancers, represent nonproductive HPV infections. Carcinogenic progression is the result of an "accident" that has a deleterious effect on viral replication. Despite the production of viral proteins, no infectious virus is produced in these lesions (Fig. 1B). The following is a list of a number of human cancers that have been associated with HPV infections. The viral DNA sequences are retained and continue to be expressed in these tumors, and there is ample evidence from experimental systems that support an oncogenic role for these viruses.

A. Epidermodysplasia Verruciformis and Nonmelanoma Skin Cancers

A rare skin disease, epidermodysplasia verruciformis (EV), provided the first evidence that implicated HPVs in the genesis of human tumors. This lifelong ailment typically begins in early childhood and its symptoms are reddish, flat, wart-like cutaneous lesions. Approximately 20 different HPV types are associated with this disease. Some of these lesions show a propensity for carcinogenic progression, and a sizable portion of EV patients develop skin cancers later in life. Lesions caused by infections with HPV-5 and HPV-8 are most highly predisposed to progress to malignant tumors. The viral genomes remain transcriptionally active in the carcinomas, and hence it is likely that some virally encoded functions directly contribute to carcinogenic progression. Despite extensive studies, the virally encoded oncogenic functions and their cellular targets have not yet been conclusively identified.

The carcinogenic progression of EV lesions often occurs specifically in those areas of the body that are most exposed to sunlight, and a possible cocarcinogenic function of UV radiation has been postulated. In addition, there are other risk factors, including a possible genetic predisposition and impaired cell-mediated immunity. Another hint that problems with immune surveillance contribute to progression of EV lesions was provided by epidemiological studies that have revealed increased incidence rates for EV in immune-suppressed patients after organ transplanta-

tion or as a consequence of HIV infection. A growing list of HPV-5- and HPV-8-related HPV types are identified in nonmelanoma skin cancers from both immune-suppressed and immune-competent patients, and the possible etiologic role of these viruses is evaluated.

B. Squamous Cell Carcinoma of the Upper Respiratory Tract and the Oral Cavity

Epidemiologic studies have indicated that approximately 25% of oral carcinomas are HPV positive. Oropharyngeal carcinomas are particularly highly associated with HPVs. The spectrum of HPVs detected in these cancers is quite similar to those in anogenital tract cancers, even though there are studies that have suggested specific HPV variants may be associated with oral cancers. Similarly, some tonsilar cancers harbor HPVs that are similar or identical to high-risk HPVs typically associated with anogenital tract cancers. HPV-positive oral cancers can occur in younger patients that lack some of the main risk factors for the development of this disease, such as tobacco and alcohol abuse. Benign oral papillomas and oral focal epithelial hyperplasias have been connected to infections with low risk HPVs.

C. Squamous Cell Carcinomas of the Anogenital Tract

Approximately 30 different HPVs preferentially infect the mucosal epithelium anogenital tract. HPVs associated with such anogenital tract lesions are classified into low risk and high risk groups.

Low-risk HPVs (HPV-6 and HPV-11) are mostly associated with genital warts or condyloma acuminata. Approximately 90% of these lesions are low-risk HPV positive, and HPV-6 and HPV-11 were directly cloned from such tumors. They only very rarely progress to malignancy, although on occasion they can become locally invasive and form the giant condylomas described by Buschke and Löwenstein.

In contrast, high-risk HPVs cause squamous intraepithelial lesions (SIL). Even though the majority of SILs regress spontaneously, they can progress to cervical carcinomas. The first high-risk HPV sequences were directly cloned from cervical carcinoma.

In the majority of all cases, there is no viral replication in the cancers. The HPV sequences are integrated in the host genome, and in many cases, only fragments of the viral genomes are retained. However, the integrated sequences remain transcriptionally active and virus-specific mRNAs are detected. Large-scale screening studies demonstrated that the vast majority of cervical cancers are high-risk HPV positive. With the availability of ever more sensitive methods, the proportion of HPV-positive cervical carcinoma asymptotically approaches 100%.

Malignant progression often occurs after a prolonged latency period, supporting the notion that additional cellular changes need to occur before malignant progression ensues. This long latency period, however, also allows for a window of opportunity to recognize these potentially premalignant lesions before they progress to invasive carcinoma. The most commonly used technique is a cytological examination of cervical cells, the Papanicolaou smear ("Pap smear"). Widespread use of this simple procedure has dramatically decreased the incidence rate of cervical cancer in many countries, and it is possibly the most impressive illustration of the value of early detection in cancer prevention. In countries where pap smears are not routinely performed, cervical cancer is the leading cause of cancer death in young women. Annually, there are nearly 500,000 new cases of cervical cancer worldwide, and in the United States alone, there are 13,500 new cervical carcinoma cases diagnosed per year, causing the death of almost 5000 women.

It has long been suggested that cervical carcinoma is a venereal disease. In keeping with this notion, early onset of sexual activity and multiple sexual partners have now been firmly established as the most prominent major risk factors for the development of SIL and cervical cancer.

In males, infections with high-risk HPVs can cause penile intraepithelial neoplasia (PIN), a male counterpart of SIL. Although rarer than SIL, these are precancerous lesions that can progress to penile carcinoma. There is a good correlation between the incidence rates of cervical and penile carcinoma in many parts of the world.

In addition, several other squamous cell carcinomas that arise in the anogenital tract, including vulvar, perianal, and penile carcinomas, are also etiologically linked to high-risk HPVs.

IV. HUMAN PAPILLOMAVIRUS ONCOGENES AND INITIATION OF CARCINOGENESIS

One of the most consistent hallmarks of carcinogenic progression is the physical integration of the HPV genome into the host cell DNA (Fig. 1B). Integration does not occur at preferred chromosomal locations but frequently involves common fragile sites in the human genome. There is, however, a remarkable conservation of the pattern of integration with respect to the viral genome. The LCR region, as well as the E6 and E7 open reading frames, is consistently retained, whereas expression of the E2 transcriptional regulator is frequently abrogated as a result of integration. In high-risk HPVs, the E2 protein functions as a transcriptional repressor of the promoter that drives expression of the E6 and E7 genes. Abrogation of E2 expression critically dysregulates expression of the remaining viral genes, E6 and E7. The importance of this integration event and the continued expression of E6 and E7 for the induction and maintenance of the transformed state are supported by numerous experimental findings. First of all, both E6 and E7 have oncogenic functions in tissue culture cells and transgenic mouse models. Expression of E6 and E7 in primary human genital epithelial cells, for example, causes their immortalization and induces histopathological abnormalities that are reminiscent of high-grade precancerous SILs.

Continued expression of high-risk HPV sequences is necessary for the maintenance of the transformed state. When expression of E6 and E7 is inhibited by antisense or ribozyme technologies or by reexpression of the E2 open reading frame in cervical cancer cell lines that have been cultured for several decades and have undergone a large spectrum of additional genomic alterations, they undergo growth arrest, replicative senescence, or apoptosis.

The E5 gene may also be important for the initial induction of the transformed state. E5 encodes a small protein that localizes to intracellular membranes, particularly to the Golgi apparatus. It is thought to target cellular growth factor receptor molecules, including EGF and PDGF receptors, leading to their increased activation. Even though it is not expressed in cervical cancers, it is possible that HPV E5 proteins contribute to HPV transformation and tumorigenesis by providing a cell with an initial mitogenic stimulus.

The following discussion, however, is focused on the E6 and E7 proteins. For the sake of simplicity, only the main cellular targets are discussed. The E6 and E7 open reading frames encode small proteins of approximately 150 and 100 amino acid residues, respectively. There are no closely related cellular homologues. Both proteins contain related cysteine-rich zinc-binding motives. They do not appear to be sequence specific DNA-binding proteins and do not have any known enzymatic activities.

The transforming activities of these proteins are a reflection of the viral replication strategy that ensures long-term survival and replication in a tissue that turns over very rapidly and where most cells do not support DNA synthesis. This dictates that HPVs need to encode functions that can subvert the normal programs of cellular proliferation, differentiation, senescence, and cell death (Fig. 2). During the normal productive viral life cycle, these functions are regulated by a complex interplay of viral and cellular factors and they cause only minor disruptions of cellular functions, which are clinically manifested as warts. When this regulatory balance is distorted, however, and no viral particles are produced, the replication strategy of a high-risk HPV becomes a serious predicament for the cell that can lead to cancer and the demise of the host.

A. HPV E6 and E7 Proteins and Their Cellular Targets

The E7 protein shares limited sequence similarity to oncoproteins encoded by other small DNA tumor viruses, including the large tumor antigens (T Ag) of many polyomaviruses and the adenovirus E1A oncoproteins. A portion of the conserved sequence represents the interaction domain with the retinoblastoma susceptibility gene product pRB. The pRB protein is the prototypical and first-cloned member of a class of molecules called tumor suppressors. These are functional counterparts to cellular protooncogenes and contribute to carcinogenesis when they are inactivated. Aberration at the retinoblastoma locus is the rate limiting and most clearly discernible mutation that leads to the development of retinoblastoma, a relatively rare childhood eye tumor. The finding that viral oncoproteins, including high-risk HPV E7, can interact with and functionally inactivate the tumor suppressor pRB led to a novel concept of viral replication and human carcinogenesis that has been described as "suppressing the suppressors." The HPV E7 oncoprotein not only physically interacts with pRB, but also has the unique ability to interfere with the intracellular stability of pRB. As a consequence, pRB-regulated control circuits are functionally compromised. Multiple cellular functions are regulated by pRB, including cellular proliferation, differentiation, and apoptosis. Molecularly best understood is the growth inhibitory function of pRB, limiting the ability of a cell to enter DNA synthesis (S phase). Prior

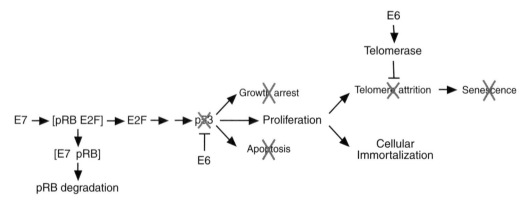

FIGURE 2 Cellular targets of the E6 and E7 proteins. Interfering with their functions is necessary for the ability of the high-risk HPVs to replicate their genomes in cells that would not normally support DNA synthesis, and for prolonged survival of HPVs within their infected host cells. After viral integration, when E6 and E7 genes are expressed at high levels, inactivation of these cellular targets contributes to cellular transformation. See text for details.

to S-phase entry, the intracellular pRB pool is hypophosphorylated. This form is able to interact with members of the E2F family of transcription factors, important regulators of factors that are necessary for DNA replication and cell division. The pRB protein contains a transcriptional repressor domain, which converts the bound E2F molecules into transcriptional repressors. Upon S-phase entry, a class of protein kinases, the cyclin-dependent kinases (cdks), are activated to drive progression through the cell division cycle. The pRB protein is phosphorylated by the very first cdk complex that is activated as a prelude to S-phase entry. Phosphorylated forms of pRB are no longer able to form complexes with E2F. Devoid of its transcriptional repressor subunit, E2F complexes act as transcriptional activators and increase expression of their target genes. Because high-risk HPV E7 proteins bind to and destabilize hypophosphorylated pRB, the overall steady-state levels of pRB are much lower, and much of the remaining hypophosphorylated pRB is bound to E7 and not to E2F. As a consequence, an important cellular regulatory node that limits DNA synthesis is functionally subverted (Fig. 2).

However, cells can normally sense if this regulatory circuit is compromised, and the tumor suppressor p53 plays an important role in this process. Upon activation by such cues, this normally short lived protein is stabilized and undergoes posttranslational modifications. The p53 protein acts as a DNA-binding transcription factor and induces the expression of cellular target genes that signal either growth arrest or apoptosis (Fig. 2).

Such an outcome is not desirable during a viral infection, and high-risk HPVs, like other small DNA tumor viruses, have evolved to corrupt this surveillance function. The unique strategy developed by high-risk HPVs is to mark p53 for rapid proteolytic degradation. The high-risk HPV E6 proteins bind to the ubiquitin ligase E6-AP and reprograms it to recognize p53 (Fig. 2). Ubiquitin ligases are specificity factors of enzymatic cascades that mark proteins for degradation by posttranslational modification with ubiquitin peptide tags. Proteins decorated with multiple ubiquitin tags are disposed of by a molecular degradation machine, the proteasome. Hence, by inducing the degradation of p53, high risk HPV E6 proteins deflect the normal cellular response to pRB inactivation. In combination, the functional inactivation of

pRB and p53 by the E7 and E6 oncoproteins allows a cell to undergo and support DNA replication in an uncontrolled manner.

However, most normal cells cannot undergo an indefinite number of cell division, as the termini of the chromosomes, the telomeres, shorten with every cell division. The telomeric sequences consist of short repetitive sequences, and once they have been eroded to a critical length, this is signaled to the cell and they undergo replicative senescence, an irreversible withdrawal from cell division. However, the stem cell population in an organism can undergo many more rounds of cell divisions than normal somatic cells. Such cells maintain the length of their telomeres through the activity of a specific enzyme, telomerase.

For an HPV to remain within its host cell for extended periods of time, it has to ensure that the infected cell does not undergo replicative senescence. It has been demonstrated that high-risk HPV E6 proteins can activate cellular telomerase expression and activity (Fig. 2). Therefore, high-risk HPV E6/E7 expressing cells by inactivating pRB and p53 can divide for extended periods of time, overcome the normal limitation of replicative senescence by activating telomerase activity, and become immortal. This is consistent with the finding that the ectopic expression of E6 and E7 induces the immortalization of many diverse primary cell types, including genital tract derived epithelial cells (Fig. 2).

It is interesting to note that the cellular pathways targeted by the E6 and E7 oncoproteins are rendered dysfunctional in the vast majority of cancers. The p53 and pRB pathways are inactivated by some mutational event in most human tumors and many cancers also exhibit telomerase activity.

V. HUMAN PAPILLOMAVIRUS E6 AND E7 AND MALIGNANT PROGRESSION

Immortalization is thought to represent an important aspect of cellular transformation. Regardless, high-risk HPV immortalized cells are not transformed, they remain density arrested and do not readily form tumors in nude mice. Similarly, primary lesions induced by the expression of high-risk HPV sequences in animal models are mostly benign and only slowly progress to malignancy. This is reminiscent of high-risk HPV-induced lesions that undergo carcinogenic progression relatively rarely and often only years after the initial infection event. Hence it is clear that additional cellular abnormalities need to be accumulated before malignant progression occurs. A frequent event during carcinogenic progression appears to be loss of genetic information on the short arm of chromosome 3 (3p21), a locus that contains the FHIT tumor suppressor gene and also appears abnormal in many other tumor types.

Normal cells highly effectively maintain the integrity of their genomes and accumulate mutations at an exceedingly low rate. Expression of E6 and E7 directly contributes to the loss of genomic integrity of a cell (Fig. 3). It has already been mentioned that p53 plays a major role as a cellular surveillance factor that recognizes DNA damage and limits the propagation of mutated genomes by inducing growth arrest or cell death. Hence, the impairment of this function by high-risk HPV E6 oncoprotein allows propagation of mutations, increasing the potential that abnormal cells are accumulated. High-risk HPV E7 oncoproteins induce genomic instability by increasing the incidence of mitotic aberrations by interfering with the regulation of mitotic spindle pole body (centrosome) synthesis (Fig. 3). In normal cells, centrosome synthesis is tightly coupled to cell division. It occurs once and only once per cell division to ensure the formation of two mitotic spindle poles and the symmetrical distribution of chromosomes during cell division. Pathologist have recognized many years ago that cervical cancers are characterized by the presence of abnormal, asymmetrical mitoses that contain more than two poles. This greatly enhances the potential for chromosomes to be partitioned unequally during mitosis. Daughter cells that are formed after such aberrant mitoses will contain abnormal chromosome sets; they will be aneuploid. Aneuploidy is the most frequent manifestation of genomic instability in tumors overall, and cervical cancers are frequently aneuploid. The E7 protein can rapidly induce abnormal centrosome numbers, which leads to a marked increase in abnormal mitoses and an increased potential to develop aneuploidy. Together with decreased cellular surveillance as a consequence of E6-mediated p53 inactivation, this increases the possibility that abnor-

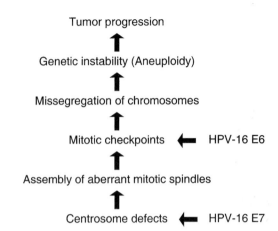

FIGURE 3 High-risk HPV E7 and E6 oncoproteins can induce and perpetuate genomic instability, respectively. See text for details.

mal cells with an increased growth potential can develop and malignant progression can ensue.

VI. CLINICAL INTERVENTION

Although there have been impressive advances in deciphering the molecular mechanisms of HPV-induced carcinogenesis, the impact on developing novel mechanism based means of intervention has been disappointingly scant. HPVs encode only a single known enzymatic function, the E1 helicase, which is a possible target for the discovery of specific antiviral compounds. The oncogenic activities of E6 and E7 are mediated through cellular systems, the ubiquitin ligase E6-AP in the case of E6 and possibly a presently unknown factor targeted by E7 that induces the degradation of pRB. Although these molecules may be targeted, functional inhibition of these cellular factors may have dire consequences for uninfected cells. It has also been proposed that the interactions of E6 with E6-AP or E7 with pRB might be targeted. This appears a promising approach, as structural information is now available on some of the proteins involved. However, it has proven difficult to target molecular interfaces of protein–protein interactions with small molecule inhibitors and most of these attempts have been rather disappointing. Given the dramatic antiproliferative effects that have been noted upon reexpression of E2 in cervical cancer cell lines, this might be an interesting avenue to explore.

A large effort has been focused on the development of vaccine approaches. Empty viral shells, "virus like particles," can be produced in large amounts and are currently tested for efficacy as protective vaccines. Given the heterogeneity of HPVs, a useful vaccine formulation will need to cover multiple different HPV types and has to be administered prior to the onset of sexual activity. Other strategies that are currently evaluated are postexposure therapeutic vaccines often directed against the HPV E7 oncoprotein. These vaccines will have to be matched to the HPV type causing the lesion, and advanced low cost HPV-typing strategies are currently being developed.

Large-scale use of the pap smear as a relatively inexpensive and easy screening method has had a dramatic impact on the incidence and mortality of cervical cancer. More sophisticated implementations of basic pap-smear technology will be implemented that allow for more consistent sampling of the cells and automated processing and reading of the specimen. These innovations may be coupled with low-cost HPV-typing methods, which may further increase the sensitivity and specificity of this test.

See Also the Following Articles

DNA Tumor Viruses: Adenovirus • Epstein-Barr Virus and Associated Malignancies • Hepatitis B Viruses • Hepatitis C Virus • HIV (Human Immunodeficiency Virus) • Human T-Cell Leukemia/Lymphotropic Virus • Retroviruses

Bibliography

De Villiers, E. M., Ruhland, A., and Sekaric, P. (1999). Human papillomaviruses in non-melanoma skin cancer. *Semin. Cancer Biol.* **9,** 413.

Howley, P. M. (1996). Papillomavirinae: The viruses and their replication. *In* "Fundamental Virology" (B. N. Fields, D. M. Knipe, and P. M. Howley, eds.), p. 947. Lippincott-Raven, Philadelphia.

Huibregtse, J. M., and Beaudenon, S. L. (1996). Mechanism of HPV E6 proteins in cellular transformation. *Semin. Cancer Biol.* **7,** 317.

Lowy, D. R., and Schiller, J. T. (1999). Papillomaviruses: Prophylactic vaccine prospects. *Biochim. Biophys. Acta* **1423,** M1.

Münger, K., and Hesselmeyer, K. (1999). The molecular pathogenesis of cervical cancer: the role of of human papillomaviruses. *In* "Molecular Pathology of Early Cancer" (S. Srivastava, D. E. Henson, and A. Gazdar, eds.), p. 97. IOS Press, Amsterdam.

Stoler, M. H. (2000). Advances in cervical screening technology. *Mod. Pathol.* **13,** 275.

Stubenrauch, F., and Laimins, L. A. (1999). Human papillomavirus life cycle: Active and latent phases. *Semin. Cancer Biol.* **9,** 379.

Zur Hausen, H. (1999). Immortalization of human cells and their malignant conversion by high risk human papillomavirus genotypes. *Semin. Cancer Biol.* **9,** 405.

Zwerschke, W., and Jansen-Dürr, P. (2000). Cell transformation by the E7 oncoprotein of human papillomavirus type 16: Interactions with nuclear and cytoplasmic target proteins. *Adv. Cancer Res.* **78,** 1.

PAX3–FKHR and PAX7–FKHR Gene Fusions in Alveolar Rhabdomyosarcoma

Frederic G. Barr

University of Pennsylvania School of Medicine

GLOSSARY

amplification An aberrant increase in the number of copies of a chromosomal region presenting as multiple extrachromosomal elements or a tandem array integrated into a chromosome.

chromosomal translocation A structural chromosome alteration consisting of an exchange of segments between two or more chromosomes.

c-met The cellular gene encoding the receptor for the growth and motility factor hepatocyte growth factor.

DNA-binding domain The functional domain of a transcription factor responsible for recognition and interaction with specific DNA target sequences.

fork head A conserved DNA-binding motif characteristic of a family of transcription factors.

paired box A conserved DNA-binding motif characteristic of a family of transcription factors.

rhabdomyosarcoma A family of cancers occurring in soft tissue sites, related to the striated muscle lineage, and usually occurring in children and young adults.

splotch A murine strain with heritable mutations of the Pax-3 gene, characterized by neural tube, neural crest, and peripheral muscle abnormalities.

transcriptional activation domain The functional domain of a transcription factor responsible for interacting with the transcriptional machinery to effect a change in the transcriptional rate.

Alveolar rhabdomyosarcoma (ARMS), a myogenic pediatric soft tissue tumor, is associated with chromosomal translocations joining chromosome 13 with chromosome 2, or less frequently with chromosome 1. These translocations juxtapose the FKHR gene on chromosome 13 with the PAX3 or PAX7 genes on chromosomes 2 and 1, respectively. These genetic events generate PAX3–FKHR or PAX7–FKHR fusion genes that are expressed as chimeric transcripts and ultimately chimeric proteins. The wild-type genes encode transcription factors, and the resulting chimeric proteins are novel transcriptional regulators whose expression and subcellular localization are also influenced by the translocation event. These genetic changes result in high nuclear expression of potent transcription factors that are postulated to deregulate the expression of PAX3 and PAX7 target genes to induce oncogenic changes in the myogenic lineage.

I. PATHOLOGIC, CLINICAL, AND CYTOGENETIC FEATURES OF RHABDOMYOSARCOMA

Rhabdomyosarcoma (RMS) is a family of soft tissue tumors that are related to the skeletal muscle lineage and generally present in the pediatric population. Using histopathologic criteria, RMS can be divided into two principle subtypes, alveolar (ARMS) and embryonal (ERMS). These two histopathologic entities are associated with distinct clinical behaviors. ERMS occurs mainly in children less than 10 years old; presents in the head and neck, genitourinary tract, and retroperitoneum; and is associated with a favorable prognosis. In contrast, ARMS presents more often in adolescents and young adults, often occurs in the extremities and trunk, and is associated with an unfavorable prognosis. Diagnosis of these two forms of RMS is often complicated by a paucity of features of striated muscle differentiation, the subtle histologic criteria for distinguishing RMS subtypes, and the tendency for RMS and other pediatric solid tumors to present as collections of poorly differentiated cells.

Although no consistent structural chromosomal changes have been found in ERMS, cytogenetic studies have identified nonrandom chromosomal translocations in ARMS. The most prevalent finding is a translocation involving chromosomes 2 and 13, t(2;13)(q35-37;q14), that was detected in 70% of published ARMS cases. A variant translocation, t(1;13)(p36;q14), has been observed in a smaller subset of ARMS cases. The 2;13 and 1;13 translocations have not been associated with any other tumor type and appear to be specific markers for ARMS.

II. PAX3–FKHR FUSION GENERATED BY 2;13 TRANSLOCATION

PAX3 is the chromosome 2 locus rearranged by the 2;13 translocation (Fig. 1). This gene encodes a member of the paired box transcription factor family and is expressed in skeletal muscle progenitors. The PAX3 gene product contains an N-terminal DNA binding domain containing paired box and homeobox motifs and a C-terminal transcriptional activation domain. The PAX3 gene consists of nine exons dispersed over 100 kb; exons 2, 3, and 4 encode the paired box, whereas the homeobox is encoded by exons 5 and 6 and the transactivation domain is encoded by exons 6, 7, and 8. The 2;13 translocation breakpoints disrupt the 18-kb intron separating exons 7 and 8, and thus maintain the integrity of the N-terminal DNA-binding domain and separate it from an essential part of the transactivation domain.

The chromosome 13 locus rearranged by the 2;13 translocation is FKHR (Fig. 1), which encodes a widely expressed member of the fork head transcription factor family. The FKHR gene product is organized with an N-terminal DNA-binding domain containing a fork head or winged helix motif and a C-terminal transcriptional activation domain. FKHR consists of three exons spanning 140 kb; the fork head domain is encoded by portions of exons 1 and 2 and the transcriptional activation domain is encoded by the C-terminal portion of exon 2. The 2;13 translocation breakpoints occur within the 130 kb intron between FKHR exons 1 and 2; this intron provides a large target for rearrangements and allows disruption of the fork head DNA-binding domain while main-

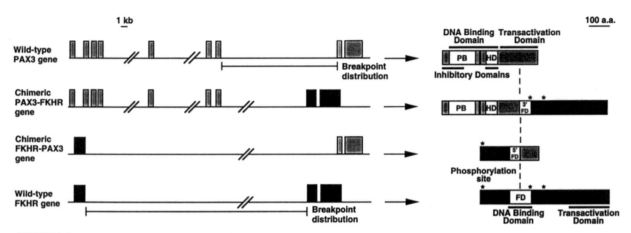

FIGURE 1 Chimeric genes and products generated by the 2;13 translocation in ARMS. On the left, exons of the wild-type and fusion genes are shown as boxes above each map and the translocation breakpoint distributions are shown as line segments below the map of the wild-type genes. On the right, protein products of the wild-type and chimeric genes are shown; the paired box, octapeptide, homeobox, and fork head domain are indicated as open boxes, and transcriptional domains are shown as solid bars. Sites phosphorylated by Akt are indicated by stars. The vertical dash line indicates the translocation fusion point.

taining the integrity of the C-terminal FKHR transactivation domain.

The 2;13 translocation results in juxtaposition of the PAX3 and FKHR genes and generation of chimeric genes at the translocation breakpoints (Fig. 1). The chimeric genes are expressed as chimeric transcripts that are translated into chimeric proteins. Although both reciprocal chimeric genes, PAX3–FKHR and FKHR–PAX3, are often present, the higher and more consistent expression of the former supports that PAX3–FKHR is the product involved in ARMS pathogenesis. The transcriptional product of the PAX3–FKHR chimeric gene is a 7.2-kb transcript in which the 5' PAX3 and 3' FKHR coding sequences are fused in-frame to generate a 2508 nucleotide open reading frame encoding an 836 amino acid fusion protein. The FKHR breakpoint occurs within the fork head DNA-binding domain, whereas the PAX3 breakpoint occurs distal to the PAX3 DNA-binding domain. Therefore, this fusion protein contains an intact PAX3 DNA binding domain, the C-terminal half of the fork head domain, and the C-terminal FKHR region. A similar fusion cannot be created by any other combination of PAX3 and FKHR exons because of incompatible reading frames or loss of needed functional domains. These findings support the premise that rearrangements of PAX3 intron 7 and FKHR intron 2 are selected due to functional constraints related to the genomic organization of PAX3 and FKHR.

III. PAX7–FKHR FUSION GENERATED BY 1;13 TRANSLOCATION

In the variant 1;13 translocation, the disrupted locus on chromosome 1 is PAX7, which encodes another member of the paired box-containing transcription factor family. The PAX3 and PAX7 genes have very similar genomic organization, homologous coding sequence, and overlapping expression patterns. Similar to the 2;13 translocation, the chromosome 13 breakpoints occur in FKHR intron 2, and the chromosome 1 breakpoints occur in PAX7 intron 7, which spans 30 kb. The PAX7–FKHR chimeric gene generated by this variant translocation is expressed as a chimeric transcript consisting of 5' PAX7 and 3' FKHR regions, which is nearly identical in structure and organization to the PAX3–FKHR product of the 2;13 translocation.

IV. TRANSCRIPTIONAL PROPERTIES OF PAX3–FKHR AND PAX7–FKHR FUSION PROTEINS

In fusion proteins, the PAX3 or PAX7 DNA binding domain is intact and provides the DNA-binding specificity for the fusion transcription factor. The PAX3–FKHR and PAX7–FKHR proteins are capable of recognizing PAX3/PAX7 DNA-binding sites and regulating the expression of genes containing these sites. When compared to the transcriptional activity of wild-type PAX proteins, PAX3–FKHR and PAX7–FKHR fusion proteins have enhanced transcriptional activity. In studies with model target genes, whereas the wild-type PAX3 and PAX7 proteins induced low or undetectable levels of transcriptional activation, the PAX3–FKHR and PAX7–FKHR fusion proteins induced up to 10- to 100-fold more activity. This difference in transcriptional activity cannot be directly attributed to simple differences between the C-terminal transcriptional regulatory domains. When isolated and analyzed in association with heterologous DNA-binding domains, the PAX3, PAX7, and FKHR activation domains have comparable transactivation activities. However, these activation domains appear to interact differently with transcriptional inhibitory domains in the N-terminal portions of the PAX3 and PAX7 proteins (Fig. 1). These N-terminal PAX3/PAX7 inhibitory domains effectively inhibit the activity of the C-terminal PAX3 or PAX7 activation domain, but have a very modest effect on the C-terminal FKHR activation domain. Therefore, the translocations create potent transcriptional activators by introducing a C-terminal transactivation domain that is relatively insensitive to the negative modulatory effects of the N-terminal PAX3 and PAX7 domains.

V. EXPRESSION OF PAX3–FKHR AND PAX7–FKHR FUSION PRODUCTS IN ALVEOLAR RHABDOMYOSARCOMA

ARMS tumor cells have developed strategies for overexpressing the PAX3–FKHR and PAX7–FKHR fusion products. At both the RNA and protein level, there is a severalfold greater expression of PAX3–FKHR relative to wild-type PAX3 in 2;13 translocation-containing ARMS cases. Similarly, the PAX7–FKHR fusion is expressed at higher levels than wild-type PAX7 in 1;13 translocation-containing ARMS cases. Therefore, overexpression of PAX3–FKHR and PAX7–FKHR relative to wild-type PAX3 and PAX7 is characteristic of ARMS tumors and is postulated to generate a level of fusion product above a critical

threshold for oncogenic activity. Despite the common feature of fusion gene overepression in the two ARMS fusion subtypes, there is a striking difference in the mechanism of fusion gene overexpression between these two fusion subtypes. In PAX7–FKHR-expressing tumors, the fusion gene is present in increased copy number due to *in vivo* amplification of the genomic region containing the fusion gene. In contrast, the PAX3–FKHR fusion gene is rarely amplified, but instead is overexpressed due to a copy number-independent increase in transcriptional rate. These findings indicate significant biological differences in the regulation of expression of these fusion genes.

VI. SUBCELLULAR LOCALIZATION OF WILD-TYPE AND FUSION PROTEINS

The localization of FKHR and the related proteins AFX and FKHRL1 can be regulated by a signal transduction pathway involving phosphatidylinositol-3 kinase and Akt. This pathway is activated by extracellular signals, including insulin and insulin-like growth factors. There are three phosphorylation motifs in FKHR: one proximal to the 2;13 translocation fusion points and two distal to the fusion points (Fig. 1). When phosphorylated by Akt at these sites, the wild-type FKHR protein shuttles from the nucleus into the cytoplasm, thereby inactivating FKHR transcriptional function. Although two of the three phosphorylation sites are present in the PAX3–FKHR fusion protein, this protein is not transported into the nucleus in the presence of active Akt. Therefore, the translocation event has released the C-terminal FKHR domains from this control pathway and resulted in a constitutive nuclear localization of the fusion protein.

VII. PHENOTYPIC CONSEQUENCES OF PAX–FKHR FUSIONS

Expression, transcriptional, and subcellular localization studies indicate that the 2;13 translocation results in a "gain of function" from several biological perspectives. These findings are consistent with the hypothesis that the fusion activates the oncogenic potential of PAX3 by exaggerating its function in the myogenic lineage. PAX3 function has been investigated in the *splotch* murine strain in which the murine Pax3 gene is mutated. In homozygously mutated *splotch* mice, the limb musculature is absent, whereas the axial musculature is reduced but relatively normal. The limb musculature defect appears to result from the inability of myogenic precursors to successfully migrate from the somites into the limb buds and is associated with the reduced expression of the c-met receptor in myogenic progenitors. Based on the known role of c-met in cell motility and growth signaling in combination with evidence that c-met is a transcriptional target of the PAX3 protein, the migration problem has been proposed to at least partly result from the defective regulation of c-met expression by the mutant PAX3 transcription factor.

The cellular activity of PAX3–FKHR has been examined in several model cell culture systems. A role for PAX3–FKHR in the control of cell growth is indicated by the finding of transforming activity in chicken embryo fibroblasts and immortalized murine fibroblasts. A complex impact on myogenic differentiation is revealed by one study in which PAX3–FKHR inhibited myogenic differentiation of C2C12 myoblasts or MyoD-expressing 10T1/2 cells, and a second study in which PAX3–FKHR stimulated myogenic expression in murine fibroblasts. Finally, a role for PAX3–FKHR in the maintenance of ARMS cellular viability is revealed by the finding of cell death following the inhibition of endogenous PAX3–FKHR expression with an antisense oligonucleotide directed against the PAX3 translational start site. These various phenotypic studies indicate that PAX3–FKHR can influence cellular growth, differentiation, and apoptosis and thus may exert an oncogenic effect through multiple pathways that exaggerate the normal role of the wild-type PAX3 protein.

VIII. MOLECULAR DIAGNOSTIC ASSESSMENT OF PAX3–FKHR AND PAX7–FKHR FUSIONS

The 2;13 and 1;13 translocations can be detected in clinical material by a variety of molecular assays. In Southern blot assays, the junction generated by the translocation is detected as a novel restriction fragment hybridizing to adjacent probes. However, the clinical utility of Southern blot assays is complicated by the occurrence of breaks within large introns and the requirement for DNA amounts often exceeding that available from small biopsies. These problems can be circumvented by polymerase chain reaction (PCR) and fluorescence *in situ* hybridization (FISH) assays. PCR assays detect juxtaposition of two genes with oligonucleotide primers specific for each gene. Although the variability in genomic breakpoints complicates design of a genomic DNA-based assay, the breakpoint variability is confined to single introns so that consistent chimeric transcripts are formed that can be detected with RT-PCR assays. In FISH assays, simultaneous hybridization of probes corresponding to the two loci followed by fluorescence detection of hybridization in tumor nuclei demonstrates colocalization of the loci by translocation. Alternatively, probes flanking or spanning the breakpoint site of one locus can be labeled and shown to separate due to translocation.

The frequencies of PAX3–FKHR and PAX7–FKHR fusions in ARMS are approximately 70 and 10%, respectively. In addition, approximately 20% of cases of histologically diagnosed ARMS tumors do not express PAX3–FKHR or PAX7–FKHR fusions. Although these negative results may be explained by variable application of histopathologic criteria or suboptimal samples, the possibilities of variant fusions or other genetic events that can substitute for the fusions should also be considered. In contrast, the majority of ERMS cases do not contain either fusion. PAX3–FKHR and PAX7–FKHR fusions are detected in approximately 5% of histologically diagnosed ERMS tumors; these fusion-positive cases may represent subtle histologic presentations of the ARMS subtype. Despite the small subset of cases in which histologic and genetic classifications do not overlap, these findings confirm that these gene fusions are generally sensitive and specific markers of the ARMS category.

Comparison of clinical characteristics between tumors with PAX3–FKHR and PAX7–FKHR fusions demonstrates differences in presentation and tumor behavior. Tumors with the PAX7–FKHR fusion occur more often in younger patients and in extremity sites than tumors with the PAX3–FKHR fusion. Furthermore, patients with PAX7–FKHR tumors generally have a better outcome that those with PAX3–FKHR tumors. These findings indicate that genetic heterogeneity can at least partly explain the clinical heterogeneity within the ARMS category.

IX. CONCLUSIONS

The 2;13 and 1;13 chromosomal translocations are specific and consistent features of ARMS, a cancer of the myogenic lineage. These translocations juxtapose the transcription factor-encoding genes PAX3 or PAX7 with FKHR to generate PAX3–FKHR and PAX7–FKHR chimeric genes. These genetic events deregulate biological activity by several biological mechanisms, including increasing PAX3/PAX7 DNA-binding site-dependent transcriptional function, increasing expression from PAX3 and PAX7 promoters, and abolishing regulation of FKHR-dependent subcellular localization by the Akt signaling pathway. These findings indicate that the chromosomal changes in these tumors result in high levels of nuclear chimeric transcription factors that inappropriately activate transcription of genes with PAX3 and PAX7 DNA-binding sites to induce tumorigenic behavior. Much of the biological and clinical data indicate important similarities between the PAX3–FKHR and the PAX7–FKHR fusions and thus point to a common fundamental mechanism in the pathogenesis of ARMS. However, several biological and clinical findings indicate differences between the two fusions that highlight the heterogeneity within this tumor category and distinctions between two highly related members of the paired box family.

See Also the Following Articles

ALL-1 • EWS/ETS Fusion Genes • Pediatric Cancers, Molecular Features • RUNX/CBF Transcription Factors • TLS-CHOP

Bibliography

Barr, F. G., Chatten, J., D'Cruz, C. M., Wilson, A. E., Nauta, L. E., Nycum, L. M., Biegel, J. A., and Womer, R. B. (1995). Molecular assays for chromosomal translocations in the diagnosis of pediatric soft tissue sarcomas. *JAMA* **273,** 553–557.

Bennicelli, J. L., Edwards, R. H., and Barr, F. G. (1996). Mechanism for transcriptional gain of function resulting from chromosomal translocation in alveolar rhabdomyosarcoma. *Proc. Natl. Acad. Sci. USA* **93,** 5455–5459.

Bernasconi, M., Remppis, A., Fredericks, W. J., Rauscher, F. J., III, and Schafer, B. W. (1996). Induction of apoptosis in rhabdomyosarcoma cells through down-regulation of PAX proteins. *Proc. Natl. Acad. Sci. USA* **93,** 13164–13169.

Davis, R. J., and Barr, F. G. (1997) Fusion genes resulting from alternative chromosomal translocations are overexpressed by gene-specific mechanisms in alveolar rhabdomyosarcoma. *Proc. Natl. Acad. Sci. USA* **94,** 8047–8051.

Davis, R. J., D'Cruz, C. M., Lovell, M. A., Biegel, J. A., and Barr, F. G. (1994). Fusion of PAX7 to FKHR by the variant t(1;13)(p36;q14) translocation in alveolar rhabdomyosarcoma. *Cancer Res.* **54,** 2869–2872.

del Peso, L., Gonzalez, V. M., Hernandez, R., Barr, F. G., and Nunez, G. (1999). Regulation of the forkhead transcription factor FKHR, but not the PAX3-FKHR fusion protein, by the serine/threonine kinase Akt. *Oncogene* **18,** 7328–7333.

Epstein, J. A., Lam, P., Jepeal, L., Maas, R. L., and Shapiro, D. N. (1995). Pax3 inhibits myogenic differentiation of cultured myoblast cells. *J. Biol. Chem.* **270,** 11719–11722.

Epstein, J. A., Shapiro, D. N., Cheng, J., Lam, P. Y., and Maas, R. L. (1996). Pax3 modulates expression of the c-Met receptor during limb muscle development. *Proc. Natl. Acad. Sci. USA* **93,** 4213–4218.

Galili, N., Davis, R. J., Fredericks, W. J., Mukhopadhyay, S., Rauscher, F. J., Emanuel, B. S., Rovera, G., and Barr, F. G. (1993). Fusion of a fork head domain gene to PAX3 in the solid tumour alveolar rhabdomyosarcoma. *Nature Genet.* **5,** 230–235.

Kelly, K. M., Womer, R. B., Sorensen, P. H., Xiong, Q. B., and Barr, F. G. (1997). Common and variant gene fusions predict distinct clinical phenotypes in rhabdomyosarcoma. *J. Clin. Oncol.* **15,** 1831–1836.

Khan, J., Bittner, M. L., Saal, L. H., Teichmann, U., Azorsa, D. O., Gooden, G. C., Pavan, W. J., Trent, J. M., and Meltzer, P. S. (1999). cDNA microarrays detect activation of a myogenic transcription program by the PAX3-FKHR fusion oncogene. *Proc. Natl. Acad. Sci. USA* **96,** 13264–13269.

Scheidler, S., Fredericks, W. J., Rauscher, F. J., Barr, F. G., and Vogt, P. K. (1996). The hybrid PAX3-FKHR fusion protein of alveolar rhabdomyosarcoma transforms fibroblasts in culture. *Proc. Natl. Acad. Sci. USA* **93,** 9805–9809.

Pediatric Cancers, Molecular Features

Gian Paolo Tonini

National Institute for Cancer Research, Genoa, Italy

GLOSSARY

allele One of the several alternate forms of a gene occupying a given locus on the chromosome.

allelic loss or **loss of heterozygosity** Absence of one of the two alleles in tumor DNA as compared to nontumor DNA of the same patient.

amplification The production of additional copies of a gene.

expressed sequence tag A short (100–300 bp) partial cDNA sequence.

gene A segment of DNA involved in producing a polypeptide chain: it includes exons, coding regions, which are maintained in the RNA (mRNA), and introns, nucleotide sequences that are spliced out of the mRNA.

kilobase One thousand base pairs of DNA or 1000 base of RNA.

locus The position of a chromosome where a gene resides.

oncogene The activated counterpart of a protooncogene. An oncogene is a gene whose product may transform a normal cell into a malignant one; it may also participate in tumor progression.

restriction length fragment polymorphism A genetic variation in individual members of populations resulting from mutation affecting restriction enzyme sites.

smaller region of overlapping The minimal deleted chromosome region found in a large series of tumors.

tumor suppressor gene or **antioncogene** A gene whose functional product diminishes the likelihood of transformation of normal cell into malignant one.

Tumors occurring in childhood usually arise from embryonal tissues: retinoblastoma originates from primitive retinal cells, Wilms' tumor from metanephric blastemic cells that normally form the components of the nephron, and neuroblastoma from the neural crest cells that normally differentiate into ganglionic and adrenal cells. The embryonal origin of these tumors suggests that mutational events occur in an early stage of cellular differentiation or that a mutated gene could be inherited from the parents. Although pediatric cancers occur with low frequency compared to adult cancer, they have a great medical and social impact. Some of them, such as tumors of the central nervous system (CNS) and neuroblastoma, present a very low survival rate and high cost for patient treatment and care. Biological knowledge of pediatric cancers has advanced greatly in the last decade, and several genetic abnormalities have been identified and found to be associated with tumor progression. A deep knowledge of the molecular defects present in pediatric tumors helps in the definition of high-risk patients classified according to the molecular and genetics abnormalities found in tumor cells. This article is an overview on the most recent molecular and genetics defects discovered in the most common cancers of pediatric age. It focuses on protooncogenes that are activated in the tumor and on suppressor genes that are lost; furthermore, it shows how some of these molecular defects are employed as prognostic markers and how they may help the clinician in the treatment of cancer. Finally, the employment of DNA microarray analysis to find new genes abnormally expressed in these tumors is described briefly.

I. PEDIATRIC CANCERS: ETIOLOGY AND DISEASE-ASSOCIATED GENE

The etiology of pediatric cancer remains elusive. Among childhood cancers, retinoblatsoma is the prototype used to understand the heredity and genetics of pediatric tumors. Patients with retinoblastoma show leucoria at one or both eyes; diagnosis is via ophthalmoscopic examination. About 10% of the new cases of retinoblastoma have a familial history, among the remaining 90% of sporadic tumors, 20–30% are bilateral, indicating that they are inherited. Finally, among unilateral tumors, it is estimated that 10% are heritable. Retinoblastoma is inherited as an autosomal dominant trait; the majority of cases are diagnosed before 5 years of age. The *RB* gene has been mapped at 13q14.1-q14.2. The gene contains 27 exons transcribing for a 4.7-kb mRNA detectable in many tissues and several tumors but not in retinoblastoma cells. The *RB* gene encodes a nuclear phosphoprotein with a negative regulator function of cellular proliferation (Table I).

Wilms' tumor or nephroblastoma usually onsets as an asymptomatic mass with pain and microscopic or

TABLE I

Oncosuppressor Genes in Pediatric Tumors[a]

Neoplasm	Gene	Chromosomal locus	Protein	Function
Retinoblastoma	*RB1*	13q14	110 kDa	Modulator factor
Wilms' tumor	*WT1*	11p13	45 kDa	Transcription factor
	WT2	11p15.5		
	WT3[b]	?		
Neuroblastoma	*NB1*[b]	1p36	?	?
	NB2[b]	1p32		
Rabdomyosarcoma	*RMS1*[c]	11p15	?	?
Astrocytoma	?	17q	?	?
Medulloblastoma	*MB*[d]	17p	?	?
Neurofibromatosis type 1	*NF1*	17q11.2	327 kDa	Activator *Ras* gene
Neurofibromatosis type 2	*NF2*	22q12.2	66 kDa	Membrane–cytoskeleton protein
Multiple endocrine neoplasia type 1	*MEN1*	11q13	?	?
Multiple endocrine neoplasia type 2	*MEN2*[d]	10q11.2	?	?

[a]Some of the suppressor genes, such as *RB1*, have been cloned and sequenced, whereas for unknown genes, the locus has been identified by linkage analysis or LOH.

[b]*WT3*, *NB1*, and *NB2* genes are not yet cloned.

[c]*RMS1* is only a suggestion for the acronym of the rhabdomyosarcoma gene, which is not yet isolated.

[d]*MB* and *MEN2* are the loci for medulloblastoma and multiple endocrine neoplasia type 2, respectively.

gross hematuria. Familial cases of Wilms' tumor are estimated in about 1% of all cases; Wilms trait is inherited as an autosomal-dominant disease with a variable penetrance. In inherited cases, a bilateral tumor occurs in about 20% of patients, whereas in sporadic cases, only 3% are bilateral. The Wilms' tumor gene (*WT1*) was identified using a combination of the physical map of the 11p13 region and a panel of irradiated somatic cell hybrids. The *WT1* gene includes 10 exons and transcribes 4 mRNAs; the gene product is a zinc finger protein, which is involved in the control of cellular proliferation and differentiation. Another gene, *PAX2*, seems to be involved in the pathogenesis of this tumor. *PAX2* has been found highly expressed in the epithelial cells of Wilms' tumor. *PAX2* gene is active during the transition from mesenchyme to epithelium in the early stages of kidney development. Both genes, *WT1* and *PAX2*, could be deregulated in early embryogenesis; the abnormal function of *WT1* and *PAX2* changes the normal pathway of cells committed to form the nephron. Furthermore, it is likely that other genes take part in the genesis of Wilms' tumor. Deletion at 11p15 has been observed in about 10–15% of cases. This chromosome region contains the *WT2* gene, a second gene associated with Wilms' tumor. Finally, more than 50% of Wilms' tumors do not show loss of heterozygosity (LOH) at neither 11p13 nor 11p15, suggesting that another putative oncosoppressor gene, called *WT3*, is involved in Wilms' tumor growth (Table I). In an extended review, Sharpe and Franco summarized the etiology of Wilms' tumor. Maternal exposure to progestins significantly increases the risk of multifocal Wilms' tumor in the offspring. Moreover, several studies have pointed out the role of the oral contraceptives taken during the first trimester of pregnancy. A very strong association was found between maternal exposure to pesticides in agriculture work before the birth of the child and Wilms' tumor. Finally, maternal use of alcoholic beverages during pregnancy was found to be associated with an increased risk of nephroblastoma. No clear association has been reported between paternal occupational exposure to a hydrocarbon-related substance and Wilms' tumor in offspring. In conclusion, additional studies are required to establish an univocal association between parental exposure to drugs or chemical agents and Wilms' tumor.

Rhabdomyosarcoma is a tumor that originates from primitive mesenchymal cells and can arise anywhere in the body. Rhabdomyosarcoma may appear as a mass lesion without a history of temporally associated trauma. In embryonal rhabdomyosarcoma, a role of the putative *RMS1* oncosuppressor gene located at 11p15.5, a region very close to Wilms' locus has been suggested. Furthermore, the *MYOD1* gene appears to be involved in tumor growth and development. It is noteworthy that most of the embryonal rhabdomyosarcomas show LOH at 11p15 where the *MYOD1* gene is located. Evidence also suggests a role of insulin growth factor-2 (*IGF2*), a gene located at 11p15.5. Normally, the *IFG2* gene is monoallically expressed in muscle tissue, whereas more than two copies of the *IGF2* active alleles have been present in about 80% of rhabdomyosarcomas. Indeed, Scrable and colleagues showed an isodisomy for chromosome 11p in tumor cells of both familial and sporadic rhabdomyosarcoma. In alveolar rhabdomyosarcomas, the translocation t(2;13)(q35;q14) resulting in a fusion of the *PAX3* gene on chromosome 2, with the *FKHR* gene on chromosome 13, has been observed (Fig. 1). The chimeric gene *PAX3–FKHR* is expressed in rhabdomyosarcoma, whereas *PAX3* is expressed only in embryonic neuroepithelium and *FKHR* is ubiquitous. The translocation t(1;13)(p36;q14) has been also observed in rhabdomyosarcomas. This rearrangement fuses the *PAX7* gene with *FKHR*, producing a new chimeric transcript *PAX7–FKHR*. It is interesting to note that both *PAX3* and *PAX7* genes are involved in tissue development; in particular, the product of the *PAX3* gene is a DNA-binding protein expressed in the early stages of neurogenesis.

Neuroblastoma is a tumor of the sympathetic tissue that arises from neural crest cells. Normally, these cells are committed to differentiate into ganglionic and adrenal cells. Patients with neuroblastoma ususally show an addominal massa at onset. About 50% of infants and 70% of older children present a disseminated disease. The presence of more than one NB putative gene has been suggested by the observation of a nonrandom deletion occurring in several chromosomal regions; however, no one NB gene has been isolated. Chromosome 1p36 is lost in more than

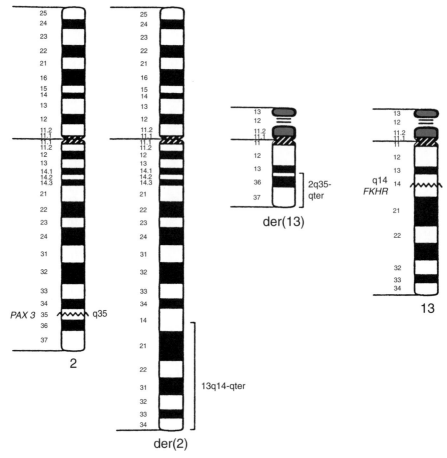

FIGURE 1 Chromosomal translocation t(2;13)(q35;q14) observed in rhabdomyosarcoma juxtaposes the *PAX3* gene located on chromosome 2q35 to the *FKHR* gene at 13q14. Ideograms of normal chromosomes 2 and 13, along with the localizations of *PAX3* and *FKHR*. Tumor-specific der(2) and der(13) chromosomes are indicated. [Reprinted with permission from D. N. Shapiro (1995). "Rhabdomyosarcoma," *In* "Molecular Genetics of Cancer," edited by J. K. Cowell, Bios Scientific Publications, UK.]

50% of tumors (Fig. 2); moreover, nonrandom deletion at 9p, 11q, 14q regions has also been detected with a relatively high frequency. Studies of the deleted mapping region of chromosome 1p have shown a shortest region of overlapping (SRO) deletion at 1p36; this region harbors the following genes: *TP73* (1p36.33-p36.32), a homologue of *TP53* involved in apotosis; *PAX7* (1p36.2-p36.12) a gene associated with rhabdomyosarcoma; *FGR* (1p36.2-p36.1), an oncogene; *DAN* (1p36.13-p36.11), a gene aberrant in some neuroblastomas; *HMG17* (1p36.1), a nonhistone chromosomal protein; *HMG2* (1p36.1), a heparan sulfate proteoglycan involved in basement membrane architecture and probably important for

the metastatic process; and *MEMO1* (1p36.1), a methylation modifier gene for class I HLA. Linkage analysis has been used to identify the neuroblastoma gene in familial cases; because the frequency of familial neuroblastoma is about 1% of all cases, one of the major problems is the collection of large pedigrees. Experimental data show that the chromosome 1p36 region is not associated with disease transmission, suggesting that neuroblastoma has a great genetic heterogeneity.

About 20% of neuroblastomas show amplification of *MYCN*, a gene of the MYC family. The *MYCN* gene is located on chromosome 2p24 and can be amplified in a range from 10 to more that 700 copies; the ampli-

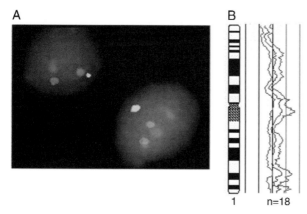

FIGURE 2 Chromosome 1p36 deletion observed in primary neuroblastoma by fluorescence *in situ* hybridization (FISH) and comparative genomic hybridization (CGH) analysis. (A) FISH on two interphase nuclei shows the presence of two red signals corresponding to the centromer of chromosome 1 and only one green signal corresponding to the presence of one end of chromosome 1p. (B) CGH shows a shift toward the red, indicating loss of genetic material at subtelomeric chromosome region 1p36. Normal and tumor DNA are labeled with red and green fluorochromes, respectively, and then matched the mixture hybridized to a normal karyotype preparation. An excess of red signal corresponds to a loss of tumor DNA and an excess of green signal to a gain of tumor DNA. (Left) the ideogram of chromosome 1 is represented; in the middle it shows the 95%-confidence curves of fluorochromes, 18 chromosomes 1 were analysed. Analysis performed with a Eclipse 800 Nikon microscope and CytoVision system.

con structure shows a head-to-tail tandem arrangement. The *MYCN*-amplified gene has been found in both the homogeneously staining region (HSR) and in double minute (DMs) structures of neuroblastoma cells. The *MYCN* gene is involved in neuroblastoma cell differentiation. Well-known experiments show that all-*trans* retinoic acid is able to revert the malignant neuroblastoma phenotype *in vitro*, inducing the maturation of neuroblastoma cells with a concomitant significantly decrease of *MYCN* expression. More recently, chromosome 17q gain has been observed in more than 60% of neuroblastomas. This region contains important genes, such as *HOXB* (17q21-q22), a homeo box B cluster; *NGFR* (17q21-q22), the nerve growth factor receptor involved in neuroblastoma cell differentiation; *SHCL1* (17q21-q22), which encodes for a protein containing a Scr homology; *NEU* (17q21.1), a neuro/glioblastoma-derived oncogene homologue, *MAPT* (17q21.1), a microtubule-associated protein tau; *NM23* (17q21.3), a gene associated with metastatic processes; *TNF1* (17q22-q23), a tu-

mor necrosis factor; and *TIMP2* (17q25), the tissue inhibitor of metalloproteinase-2 that is also involved in metastatic processes. Finally, this region also contains the *Survivin* gene (17q25); patients who show high *Survivin* expression in neuroblastoma cells have a poor outcome. The etiology of neuroblastoma is poorly understood. An overview of the literature reports very few case-control studies to determine the association among environmental factors, drugs, carcinogens, magnetic fields, radioactives, and the risk of neuroblastoma. Some studies provide evidence for a risk of neuroblastoma in children of mothers who used drugs during pregnancy.

A weak evidence of the association between hormonal treatment during pregnancy and neuroblastoma in the neonate has also been reported. Interestingly, a significant high association was observed in mothers with vaginal infection during pregnancy. The role of paternal hormone consumption and occupational exposure has also been considered in the etiology of neuroblastoma, but clear-cut results have not been reported. Finally, case-control studies show inconclusive results about parental exposure to electromagnetic fields and the risk of neuroblastoma in the offspring.

Hepatoblastoma in children occurs with low frequency; usually it is concomitant with Beckwith–Wiedemann (BW) syndrome; furthermore, in about 50% of patients with BW syndrome, Wilms' tumor can also be observed. Indeed, BW syndrome, which displays gigantism in the neonate, is caused by a nonrandom mutation occurring at chromosome 11p15.5 region, a locus for Wilms' tumor. Most hepatoblastomas show fetal or embryonal cells, whereas mixed hepatoblastomas contain mesenchymal tissue with epithelial elements. The beta-catenin plays an important role in the development of hepatoblastoma. Beta-catenin is an adherens junction protein. Adherens junction proteins are critical for the establishment and maintenance of epithelial layers because they mediate (i) adhesion between cells, (ii) communication signals with neighboring cells, and (iii) anchorage for the actin cytoskeleton. Moreover, adherent junction proteins regulate normal cell growth and may also function in the transmission of the contact inhibition signal.

Among tumors of the central nervous system, astrocytoma and medulloblastoma, are the most common

CNS cancers that occur during childhood. These tumors may cause neurologic dysfunction by infiltrating or compressing the normal CNS structure. An association between the occurrence of CNS tumors and several heritable syndrome, such as neurofibromatosis type 1, has been observed. Indeed, the loss of chromosome 17q, which includes the *NF1* locus, has been observed in astrocytoma. *TP53* is rarely observed mutated in this neoplasm, suggesting that *TP53* is not involved in the tumorigenesis of astrocytoma. On the contrary, isochromosome 17q is frequently present in medulloblastoma; furthermore, the tumor also shows deletion of chromosome 17p13.1-p12; in this region, the following genes are located: *ROX* gene (17p13.3), a member of the helix-loop-helix (HLH) protein family, which has been isolated from human fetal brain; *TP53* (17p13.1); and *MDB* (17p13.1-p12), a locus that frequently shows LOH in medulloblastoma.

Neurofibromatosis type 1 (NF1) and type 2 (NF2) and multiple endocrine neoplasia (MEN1 and MEN2) represent a group of pediatric syndromes occurring at a very low frequency. NF1 is inherited in an autosomal-dominant manner. Although the full sequence of the *NF1* gene is unknown, mutations and deletions have been identified in the exon regions of the gene. *NF1* is located on chromosome 17q11. MEN1 and MEN2 include tumors that arise in more than one endocrine gland. MEN1 shows frequent LOH at 11q13, and MEN2 displays chromosome 10q11.2 abnormalities. These regions should contain an oncosuppressor gene (Table I).

II. LOSS OF ONCOSUPPRESSOR GENES AND ROLE OF ONCOGENES

Cytogenetic analysis of cancer cells shows several chromosomal abnormalities, such as deletions, translocations, HSRs, and DMs. Nonrandom chromosome deletions observed in pediatric cancers suggest that a loss of oncosuppressor genes is involved in tumor development and progression. *In vitro* experiments show that injection of the lost chromosome in tumor cells induces the revertion of the malignant phenotype to a normal one. Because most of pediatric tumors show nonrandom chromosome deletion, it is

reasonable to think that pediatric cancers arise as a result of loss of an oncosuppressor gene (Fig. 3). This hypothesis is also supported by the following points.

1. The *RB* gene was the first oncosuppressor gene found closely associated with retinoblastoma. The *RB* gene can be partially or completely lost or inactivated by mutation in one or both alleles.
2. The loss of *WT1* seems responsible for tumorigenesis in Wilms' tumor; however, some Wilms' tumors show deletion of *WT2*, but about 50% of them have neither *WT1* nor *WT2* damage, suggesting that a third gene called *WT3* may be affected (Table I).
3. The chromosome 1p36 deletion is often observed in neuroblastoma cells, indicating that the loss of a *NB* oncosuppressor gene located in this region is responsible for this tumor.
4. Introduction of chromosome 1 into neuroblastoma cells results in the reversion of a malignant phenotype.

Furthermore, another group of genes, called oncogenes, actively participate in the cancer growth. These genes are the activated (activation may be caused by mutation, rearrangement, or amplification) counterpart of the protooncogene that normally controls cell growth and differentiation. In Wilms' tumor, the acquisition of a double dosage of *IFG2* should be important for tumor initiation and progression. In neuroblastoma, *MYCN* gene amplification is strictly associated with tumor progression. In the same tumor, the duplication of chromosome 17q, frequently found in advanced stages, indicates the presence of another putative oncogene strongly involved in the progression and aggressiveness of neuroblastoma cells. All of these findings show that both oncosuppressor genes and oncogenes contribute to the pathogenesis of pediatric cancers. Indeed, in some pediatric cancers, such as neuroblastoma, tumors show both the loss of oncosuppressor genes and the activation of protooncogenes.

Cytogenetic and molecular analysis of neuroblastoma show that aggressive metastatic tumor cells have a chromosome 1p36 deletion, 17q gain, and *MYCN* amplification. These mutations seem to occur in a

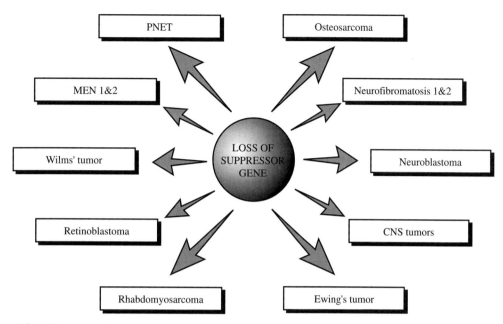

FIGURE 3 Loss of oncosuppressor genes are responsible for most of the pediatric cancers. The figure suggests that loss of oncosuppressor genes takes part in the tumorigenesis of the major pediatric cancers. PNET, peripheral neuroectodermal tumor; MEN 1&2, multiple endocrine neoplasia types 1 and 2; CNS, central nervous system.

time-specific manner: chromosome 17q gain, 1p36 deletion, and *MYCN* amplification. Furthermore, activation of the following genes—*MYB*, *RAS*, *SRC*, *TRKA*, *TRKB*, and *TRKC*—and the deletion of chromosome 9p, 14q can also be present in this tumor and they probably participate in the initiation and/or progression of neuroblastoma.

III. TWO-HIT MODEL IN PEDIATRIC CANCERS

The two-hit model predicts that cancer is caused by a double mutation occurring in germline cells and/or somatic cells. A gene mutation can occur by deletion, point mutation, viral insertion, and gene translocation. In familial retinoblastoma, loss and/or inactivation of *RB* alleles represses the gene function. In hereditary retinoblastoma, the first mutation occurs in the germinal cells and is present in all the cells of the body; the second mutation may occur in the germ cells or may occur in somatic ones, in the latter case, the second somatic mutation is present only in tumor cells. This type of retinoblastoma in which a muta-

tion is somatic usually arises later, in the second or third year of life. The two-hit hypothesis has also been proposed for Wilms' tumor and neuroblastoma. Wilms' tumor and neuroblastoma show a subset of patients with a familial history, they account for about 1 and 2% of all cases, respectively; moreover, neuroblastoma shows a group of patients with a multifocal tumor. Both familial and multifocal neuroblastoma suggest the presence of a mutation in the germline cells.

Most of the children affected by cancer have a fatal exitus as a consequence of tumor dissemination. Genes that are related to the metastatic process are poorly known; one of them is *NM23*. As mentioned earlier, the *NM23* gene is assigned to chromosome 17q21.3; the product of the *NM23* gene is a nucleoside diphosphate kinase. The reduced expression of *NM23* is associated with metastasis and it looks like an oncosuppressor metastatic gene. A somatic *NM23* allelic deletion could explain the low expression of the gene observed in cells from adult breast cancer, renal cancer, colorectal cancer, and lung carcinomas. However, *NM23* expression is increased in aggressive disseminated neuroblastoma.

IV. SEARCH FOR NEW GENES OF PEDIATRIC CANCERS BY NEW TECHNOLOGIES

The search for the tumor-associated gene has greatly improved in the last decade. Publication of the human genome sequence in *Nature* (2001) will help in the identification of disease-associated gene, including cancer. Furthermore, the development of nanotechnology, which allows one to spot more than 20,000 genes on a 1-cm^2 surface, and permits the simultaneous analysis of different classes of genes, including cell cycle-related genes, oncogenes, oncosuppressor genes, genes related to signal transduction, apoptosis, and angiogenesis. This section focuses on the application of these new technologies to pediatric cancers.

A cytogenetic–molecular combined technique called comparative genomic hybridization (CGH) has been employed to bypass the inability of several solid tumors to have mitosis *in vitro*, which enables karyotype analysis. CGH finds chromosome loss, imbalance translocation, and chromosome gain by the hybridization of a normal cell karyotype with tumoral DNA. This technique is very useful as a first line of genomic analysis because (a) it does not need chromosome preparation of tumor cells and (b) only a small amount of tumor DNA is necessary for the study. CGH has been employed in the study of chromosome

abnormality of neuroblastoma, rhabdomyosarcoma, and tumors of the CNS (Figs. 2 and 4).

DNA microarray technology permits the simultaneous analysis of thousands of sequences of DNA for genomic research and diagnostics applications. The DNA chip can be built in the laboratory spotting short DNA sequences on a glass support or it is available from companies that assembly DNA chips with known genes and/or an expressed sequence tag. The variation of gene expression may be detected by DNA microarray in a typical gene expression profile experiment. RNAs from control cells and tumor cells are labeled with a green dye and a red dye, respectively; then the two labeled RNAs are then mixed and hybridize to their complementary sequences on the chip. To measure the relative abundance of the hybridized RNA, the array is excited by a laser. If RNAs from tumor cells are in abundance, the spot will be red, whereas if RNAs from control cells are in abundance, it will be green. If sample and control bind equally, the spot will be yellow, whereas if neither binds, it will appear black. Software assigns a unique value to each pixel of the fluorescent image and a database is being built up to evaluate the difference in the expression of the different genes. Khan and co-workers used the cDNA microarray technology to identify new genes expressed in alveolar rhabdomyosarcoma. RNAs from alveolar rhabdomyosarcoma cell lines that have shown the *PAX3–FKHR* gene due to the translocation t(2;13) (q35;q14-qter) were spotted on glass slide microarray-containing 1238 cDNAs. Thirty-seven out of 1238 genes were found more consistently expressed and only 3/37 were previously reported to be expressed in the alveolar rhabdomyosarcoma. Furthermore, microarray analysis showed that the genes *TOP2A*, *MYCL1*, *MYBL2*, and *MYCN* were consistently overexpressed. DNA microarray technology will be applied in the future for further studies of pediatric tumors; the study of the gene expression profile of pediatric cancer will help better understand the mutations that lead to the development of these tumors.

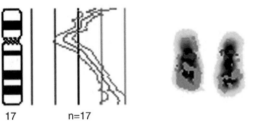

FIGURE 4 Representaive analysis of chromosome 17 by CGH. The figure shows a duplication of chromosome 17q observed in a primary neuroblastoma. Normal and tumor DNA are labeled with red and green fluorochromes, respectively, and then matched. The mixture is hybridized to a normal karyotype preparation. An excess of red signal corresponds to a loss of tumor DNA, and an excess of green signal corresponds to a gain of tumor DNA. (Left) the ideogram of chromosome 17 is represented; (center) the 95% confidence curves of fluorochromes; and (right) the digitized fluorescence image of chromosome 17 captured by fluorescent light microscope and processed by appropriate software. Analysis was performed with a Eclipse 800 Nikon microscope and CytoVision system.

Acknowledgments

This work was partially supported by Associazione Italiana per la Lotta al Neuroblastoma. I am grateful to Miss Annalisa Damonte for her assistance in the editing of the manuscript.

See Also the Following Articles

Bibliography

Dennis, C., Gallengher, R., and Campbell, P. (eds.) (2001). The human genome. *Nature* **409,** 813–958.

Khan, J., Bittner, M. L., Saal, L. H., Teichmann, U., Azorsa, D. O., Gooden, G. C., Pavan, W. J., Trent, J. M., and Meltzer, P. S. (1999). cDNA microarrays detect activation of a myogenic transcription program by the PAX3-FKHR fusion oncogene. *Proc. Natl. Acad. Sci. USA* **96,** 13264–13269.

Knudson, A. G., Jr. (1971). Mutation and cancer: statistical study of retinoblastoma. *Proc. Natl. Acad. Sci. USA* **68,** 820–823.

Knudson, A. G., and Strong, L. C. (1972). Mutation and cancer: Neuroblastoma and pheochromocytoma. *Am. J. Hum. Genet.* **24,** 514–532.

Maris, J. M., and Matthay, K. K. (1999). Molecular biology of neuroblastoma. *J. Clin. Oncol.* **17,** 2264–2279.

Scrable, H., Cavenee, W., Ghavimi, F., Lovell, M., Morgan, K., and Sapienza, C. (1989). A model for embryonal rhabdomyosarcoma tumorigenesis that involves genome imprinting. *Proc. Nat. Acad. Sci. USA* **86,** 7480–7484.

Scrable, H., Witte, D., Shimada, H., Seemayer, T., Wang-Wuu, S., Soukup, S., Koufus, A., Houghton, P., Lampkin, B., and Cavanee, W. (1989). Molecular differential pathology of rhabdomyosarcoma. *Genes Chromosom. Cancer* **1,** 23–25.

Shapiro, D. N. Rhabdomyosarcoma. (1995). *In* "Molecular Genetics of Cancer" (J. K. Cowell, ed.). Bios Scientific, UK.

Sharpe, C. R., and Franco, E. L. (1995). Etiology of Wilms' tumor. *Epidemiol. Rev.* **17,** 415–432.

Tonini, G. P. (1997). Pediatric solid tumors: Molecular genetics. *In* "Encyclopedia of Cancer" (J. R. Bertino, ed.), pp. 1212–1239. Academic Press, San Diego.

PET Imaging and Cancer

Jerry M. Collins

U.S. Food and Drug Administration, Rockville, Maryland

GLOSSARY

fluorodeoxyglucose (FDG) A modified sugar that is transported into the cell and phosphorylated by the same pathways as glucose. When the fluorine atom is ^{18}F, FDG is the most commonly used PET probe in oncology.

pharmacodynamics The effect of a drug in the body. Informally, "what the drug does to the body."

pharmacokinetics Absorption, distribution, metabolism, and excretion of a drug or probe in the body. Informally, "what the body does to the drug."

positron The positively charged equivalent of an electron. When emitted from the nucleus, the positron travels a few millimeters in the body until it reacts with an electron, an-

nihilating both particles and releasing a pair of photons that can be visualized by a PET scanner.

I. OVERVIEW OF POSITRON EMISSION TOMOGRAPHY (PET) AND CANCER

Most imaging modalities provide anatomic information. Images from positron emission tomography provide functional assessments of tumor status, rather than structural data. There are two general application categories for PET in oncology: diagnosis/staging/prognosis or as a guide for the selection of therapy and assessment of therapeutic impact.

PET is a relatively noninvasive technique, but it does require the intravenous injection of a radiolabeled tracer. External imaging is conducted in devices that resemble computerized tomography (CT) scanners. PET images provide tremendous sensitivity (picomolar quantities), but spatial resolution (2–5 mm) is less impressive than with magnetic resonance imaging. The need for complex equipment and technical support has generally limited PET facilities to major medical centers.

^{18}F-Fluorodeoxyglucose (FDG) has led the way for getting PET imaging into oncologic practice, with emphasis on the detection and staging of tumors. The diagnostic/prognostic utility of PET has been more fully developed than the emerging area of therapeutic assessment. Indeed, sufficient value has been demonstrated that government agencies and insurance payers now reimburse costs for specific diagnostic situations.

Applications related to the selection and assessment of therapy could encompass drug development, as well as customizing of patient- and tumor-specific treatment. However, a wide range of versatile probes needs development in order to explore the broad set of targets for therapy. For some imaging targets (e.g., enzymes, receptors, transporters), individual tumors can be phenotyped *prior* to initiation of treatment to obtain information that can optimize the match between drugs and the specific tumor to be treated. During treatment, the goal of imaging is to provide accelerated therapeutic assessment, rather than waiting until overt failure.

Functional imaging evaluates processes occurring at the cellular or tissue/organ level: physiological, molecular, or biochemical. Focus on targets at these levels is part of a general shift in the paradigm of cancer diagnosis and treatment. Traditional selection of therapy for tumors in individual patients has relied on prognostic factors such as the histopathology or tumor type. Once therapy has been selected, it is generally continued until there is an obvious failure to control tumor growth. By emphasizing targets, functional imaging with PET has the potential to improve both selection and subsequent evaluations of therapy.

II. CELLULAR AND MOLECULAR TARGETS FOR PET IMAGING

There are many similarities between the development (or selection) of therapeutic agents and functional probes. Both approaches attempt to exploit differences between some process within the target to be imaged or treated (i.e., the tumor) and the surrounding normal tissue. Currently, emphasis is being placed on information obtained from exhaustive molecular characterization of human tissue biopsies. Noninvasive functional imaging *in situ* can be highly complementary to laboratory studies of biopsies *ex vivo*.

For both therapeutics and imaging probes, another very practical characteristic is that the development process is a pipeline that stretches over several years. Once a target for screening of new therapeutics has been identified, it also becomes a target to be considered for imaging. Even if developed from the same screening approach, the ideal probe molecule may be the same as the optimal therapeutic.

One way to classify PET probes is shown in Table I. The first two categories, energy metabolism and DNA synthesis, are very general approaches to the determination of tumor functional status. Even though our contemporary emphasis is on the precise molecular classification of tumors, it is still quite desirable to have these "universal" probes as a check on the relevance of our hypotheses, as well as for the situations in which an appropriate, target-specific probe is simply not available.

A much more target-specific approach is represented by the last three categories of probes: transporters, receptors, and enzymes. Programs for probes of drug uptake into the cell and efflux from the cell are in early stages of development, but build on a tradition of monitoring PET probes of the transporters for amino acid entry into the cell. This approach is further stimulated by the results of the Human Genome Project, which has confirmed that the genes coding for transporters are one of the most abundant classes.

The final two categories, receptors and enzymes, are well established as drug targets and are also the cornerstones of contemporary therapeutic development programs in the areas of cell signaling and reg-

TABLE I
Categories of PET Imaging Targets

General energy metabolism (FDG)
DNA synthesis/cellular proliferation
Transporters: drug entry/efflux
Receptors: signaling/regulation
Enzymes: many tumor targets

ulation. According to our paradigm for probe development, receptors and enzymes are, therefore, also potential targets for functional imaging. Although the imaging of these targets remains in the pilot stage for oncology, the feasibility for monitoring *in situ* receptor occupancy and enzyme activity has been solidly established in neuropharmacology.

Thus, in the current situation, one of our major challenges for oncologic imaging is the development of new probes. FDG is the only functional imaging probe readily available at all PET facilities. Exploratory trials have been reported for a variety of other potential probes, but a concerted effort is required to prioritize targets and probe development projects.

III. UTILITY OF PET FOR DIAGNOSIS

The pivotal question for diagnosis is whether a mass is malignant or benign. In typical scenarios, the "suspicious" mass may be discovered initially by anatomic imaging. If the mass is observed following surgery or radiotherapy, it could be the result of incomplete treatment or it may be scar tissue or swelling of normal tissue. In the context of follow-up for prior successful therapy, the concern would be whether the mass represents a recurrence of tumor.

Ever since Warburg hypothesized in the 1920s that the energy metabolism of tumors is different than normal tissues, the energetics of glucose has been a parameter for the evaluation of cancer. For the scenarios described earlier, it is reasonable to expect that viable tumor cells would have glucose uptake that was considerably greater than an area of scar tissue or swelling.

Glucose enters cells via carrier proteins in the GLUT family, is phosphorylated, and undergoes complex metabolism. A modified sugar, 2-deoxyglucose, is transported into the cell and phosphorylated by the same pathways, but further metabolism is blocked. The phosphorylated species cannot cross the cell membrane, so it is trapped inside the cell, which is desirable for imaging. Further, the addition of ^{18}F to 2-deoxyglucose creates a molecule (FDG) that does not perturb the transport and metabolism and is more convenient as a probe for PET imaging.

In the literature for PET applied to cancer, the overwhelming majority of articles are related to the use of FDG. As a practical matter, FDG is readily available at all PET facilities, either via production from an on-site cyclotron or from a regional supplier of nuclear medicine products. FDG has proven to be versatile in many diagnostic situations. Government agencies and insurance companies have chosen to provide selective reimbursement of FDG-PET imaging for well-defined clinical settings. For example, FDG-PET to determine if a single pulmonary nodule is benign or malignant is commonly reimbursed. A negative scan spares the patient the morbidity of an invasive procedure to biopsy the nodule and saves the payer the cost of the biopsy procedure. In addition, some unnecessary surgical procedures are avoided for cases in which the biopsy is indeterminate, but the mass is found to be benign. The current expansion of PET facilities is driven in part by this availability of reimbursement for selected diagnostic procedures and the expectation for coverage extension as more controlled clinical trials are completed.

There are certain clinical situations in which FDG is not completely successful, either because of a very low-grade tumor or because of an unusually high FDG uptake in surrounding normal tissue. As experience with other probes matures, e.g., the thymidine analogs and labeled hormones discussed later, these tools may complement FDG in diagnostic settings.

IV. ASSESSMENT OF DRUG DELIVERY VIA PET

PET imaging can be viewed as an extension of pharmacokinetics (PK) and pharmacodynamics (PD). The ultimate goal of PK is drug delivery to the target. One of the major opportunities for PET imaging is the ability to assess the delivery of drugs to tumors, particularly the impact of modulators of delivery. Development programs for probes of drug uptake into the cell and efflux from the cell are in early stages of development, but build on a tradition of monitoring PET probes of the transporters for amino acid entry into the cell.

Efflux pumps can mediate resistance to anticancer drugs. As the drug approaches its target, the tumor has mechanisms for pumping it out. Thus, concentrations at the target are very low, making them ineffective and actually promoting the development of further resistance mechanisms. There are a number of efforts underway to develop modulators that block these transport systems

Our traditional PK tools of plasma and urine sampling are unable to assess either baseline or modulated drug delivery to specific tumors. In fact, because the delivery of drugs to tissues is generally a reversible process, PK parameters, such as the area under the curve, will be unaffected by the presence or absence of a functioning efflux pump at a target site in a tumor.

PET imaging is a tool that can focus directly on drug delivery at the target of interest. While delivery of a drug to the tumor does not guarantee successful therapy, if the drug never gets to the target or gets pushed away as soon as it arrives, it certainly will not be effective. The earlier that we discover the problem, the sooner that we can implement strategies for attempting to modulate this PK issue or the sooner we can consider alternative therapy.

V. ASSESSMENT OF TARGET RESPONSE VIA PET

The ability to image the response of the target of drug action is fundamental to the advances in the individualization of therapy, as well as enhancements in drug development. These concepts are illustrated by the following two examples.

A. Estrogen Receptor Binding

For hormone-sensitive tumors such as breast cancer, the contemporary approach to disease management is based on characterization of the hormone receptors in biopsies from individual tumors. The ability to noninvasively monitor receptors is a natural extension of the existing practice.

The overall approach is illustrated in Fig. 1. ^{18}F-fluoroestradiol (FES) is injected into a patient with a large metastasis of breast cancer in the pleural space, which is known to have estrogen receptors. Prior to therapy, ^{18}F-FES binds avidly to the receptors on the tumor. Therapy with tamoxifen is initiated, with the intent of occupying estrogen receptors and blocking the uptake of other estrogenic substances. As demonstrated in the PET images, localization at the tumor site of ^{18}F-FES has markedly diminished after 7 days of tamoxifen therapy. Although these images do not constitute an index of clinical value, they verify that the specific therapy for this particular tumor is acting as intended.

B. Tumor Cell Proliferation Probed with Thymidine Analogs

In the laboratory, tritiated thymidine (dThd) has been used for decades to monitor DNA synthesis/cellular proliferation in cell culture and animals. Positron-labeled ^{11}C-dThd can be utilized for PET imaging. The "proof of concept" for PET-dThd for therapeutic assessment is shown in Fig. 2 for a patient with pri-

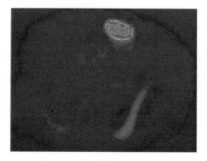

FIGURE 1 Patient with estrogen receptor positive metastases of breast cancer in the pleural space. 18F-Fluoroestradiol is the probe. (Left) The PET image obtained prior to therapy, clearly showing uptake by the tumor (oval at top). (Right) The same image slice after 7 days of tamoxifen therapy. [Reprinted from Dehdashti, F., *et al.* (1999). Positron emission tomographic assessment of "metabolic flare" to predict response of metastatic breast cancer to antiestrogen therapy. *Eur. J. Nucl. Med.* **26**, 51–56.] See color insert in Volume 1.

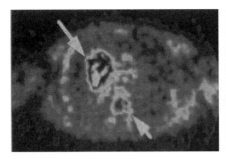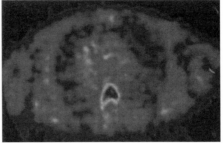

FIGURE 2 Patient with primary lung cancer, evaluated with ^{11}C-dThd as the probe. (Left) PET image prior to therapy. Note extensive uptake of ^{11}C-dThd both in the tumor (large arrow) and in the vertebral space (smaller arrow). (Right) Patient is evaluated on day 6, after a dose of cisplatin on day 1 and etoposide on days 1–3. The tumor is still present anatomically, but has stopped taking up ^{11}C-dThd for DNA synthesis/cell proliferation. [Reprinted by permission of the Society of Nuclear Medicine from: Shields, A. F., et al. (1998). Carbon-11-thymidine and FDG to measure therapy response. *J. Nucl. Med.* **39**, 1757–1762.] See color insert in Volume 1.

mary lung cancer. Prior to therapy, there is extensive uptake of ^{11}C-dThd both in tumor and in vertebral space. After a standard regimen of cisplatin on day 1 and etoposide on days 1–3, the patient was reevaluated on day 6. The tumor is still present anatomically, but has stopped taking up ^{11}C-dThd for DNA synthesis/cellular proliferation.

Although this initial demonstration of the principle has been gratifying, there are major weaknesses that will restrict any further attempts for practical imaging studies with this ^{11}C-dThd as a probe. Rapid catabolism of dThd in humans creates a large background signal of labeled molecules, and ^{11}C-dThd itself is available for labeling of DNA for only a few minutes.

An extensive search has been underway to find an analog of dThd that has minimal catabolism, but retains the favorable anabolic (DNA-labeling) properties of dThd itself. The 20-min half-life of ^{11}C causes a number of logistic difficulties in the preparation and administration of the dose, as well as the timing of images that can be reliably obtained. Thus, labeling of various dThd derivatives with ^{18}F with a half-life of 110 min is being actively pursued in clinical studies. For the set of gene therapy protocols that utilize HSV-thymidine kinase as either a suicide gene or as a reporter gene, various fluorinated or iodinated dThd analogs are being tested to provide an assessment of whether expression was successful.

Delineation of the differences between information obtained via PET with dThd analogs versus PET-FDG

will be a key aspect of further clinical investigations. Anecdotal experiences with inflammatory lesions suggest situations that favor dThd analogs. In this report, the qualitative information obtained from PET-dThd was similar to PET-FDG in the same patients, but the quantitative assessment with dThd seemed more closely related to clinical outcome. However, bone lesions would be easier to follow with FDG. When compared with CT, PET-dThd images obtained before and after therapy provided a more accurate assessment of tumor response.

VI. CONCLUDING PERSPECTIVES

Although FDG is the most advanced probe for PET imaging in oncologic practice, its precise role is still undergoing determination. In order to extend the success of FDG to other applications, more emphasis is required for target/probe definition and development. This task will require broad collaboration among synthetic chemists, pharmacologists, and clinicians from both nuclear medicine and oncology.

When embarking on new drug development or trying to optimize therapy for an individual patient, there are three questions to address: (1) Did this treatment impact its presumed target? (2) Do we know the best dose? (3) What is the preferred interval between doses? These questions can sometimes be answered with clinical observations, but the explorations are very inefficient in the absence of a window into the fine structure of the targets. As demonstrated by many studies in psychopharmacology, PET imaging can provide a unique tool to help us answer all three of these questions.

As the focus shifts toward PET evaluation of the impact of the drug on the target, it is important to classify this type of imaging information properly, namely, as a biomarker. In the spectrum of events from biomarkers to surrogate end points to clinical outcome measures, there are opportunities for new contributions and improvements at all levels. Biomarkers should be useful early in development to guide the selection of dose and dose interval. When the focus moves forward toward marketing approval of therapeutics, the criteria are based on clinical benefit. Biomarkers (such as PET probes) by themselves do not determine quality of life or increased survival. Controlled clinical trials can evaluate biomarkers to determine if they are candidates to become surrogate end points for clinical benefit, but this is a much larger and somewhat different undertaking than the development of biomarkers.

See Also the Following Articles

BRAIN CANCER AND MAGNETIC RESONANCE SPECTROSCOPY • MAGNETIC RESONANCE SPECTROSCOPY AND MAGNETIC RESO-NANCE IMAGING, INTRODUCTION • MAGNETIC RESONANCE SPECTROSCOPY OF CANCER: CLINICAL OVERVIEW • MAGNETIC RESONANCE STUDIES OF TUMORS: EXPERIMENTAL MODELS • METABOLIC DIAGNOSIS OF PROSTATE CANCER BY MAGNETIC RESONANCE SPECTROSCOPY

Bibliography

Christman, D., Crawford, E. J., Friedkin, M., and Wolf, A. P. (1972). Detection of DNA synthesis in intact organisms with positron-emitting [methyl-^{11}C]thymidine. *Proc. Natl. Acad. Sci. USA* **69,** 988–992.

Dehdashti, F., Flanagan, F. L., Mortimer, J. E., *et al.* (1999). Positron emission tomography assessment of "metabolic flare" to predict response of metastatic breast cancer to antiestrogen therapy. *Eur. J. Nucl. Med.* **26,** 51–56.

Delbeke, D. (1999). Oncological applications of FDG PET imaging. *J. Nucl. Med.* **40,** 1706–1715.

Fowler, J. S., Volkow, N. D., Wang, G.-J., and Dewey, S. L. (1999). PET and drug research and development. *J. Nucl. Med.* **40,** 1154–1163.

Mortimer, J. E., Dehdashti, F., Siegel, B. A., *et al.* (1996). Positron emission tomography with 2-[18F]fluoro-2-deoxy-D-glucose and 16alpha-[18F]fluoro-17beta-estradiol in breast cancer: Correlation with estrogen receptor status and response to systemic therapy. *Clin. Cancer Res.* **2,** 933–939.

Sadelain, M., and Blasberg, R. G. (1999). Imaging transgene expression for gene therapy. *J. Clin. Pharmacol.* **39,** 34S–39S.

Shields, A. F., Mankoff, D. A., Link, J. M., *et al.* (1998). Carbon-11-thyjmidine and FDG to measure therapy response. *J. Nucl. Med.* **39,** 1757–1762.

p53 Gene Therapy

N. Saadatmandi
Sidney Kimmel Cancer Center

D. R. Wilson
Introgen Therapeutics, Inc.

R. A. Gjerset
Sidney Kimmel Cancer Center

GLOSSARY

adenovirus type 5 A human DNA virus that has provided the basis of gene therapy vectors presently in clinical use.

chemotherapy A form of therapy that employs chemicals to achieve growth arrest or cell death of cancer cells.

gene therapy A therapeutic modality in which genes are transferred to a cell in order to alter the properties of the cell. Gene therapy is often accomplished by incorporating the gene of interest into a virus (vector) and then using the natural cellular entry mechanisms of the virus to achieve gene transfer. Tumor suppressor gene therapy transfers normal ("wild-type") forms of tumor suppressor genes such as p53 into the cancer cell to achieve growth arrest or cell death.

nude mouse A strain of laboratory mice often used for preclinical studies of human cancer. Nude mice do not reject human cells as most mice do and can therefore be used to study the response of human tumor cells (usually implanted under the skin of the mouse) to various treatments prior to testing these treatments in clinical trials in humans.

oncogene A gene that promotes the growth and survival of tumor cells. Oncogenes may derive from normal cellular genes and acquire altered growth promoting activity through mutation or deregulated (excessive) expression.

p53 A tumor suppressor gene encoding a cellular protein capable of inducing growth arrest and death of abnormal cells, including cancer cells. The p53 gene is often lost in cancer cells due to gene deletion or mutation.

phase I clinical trial The first step in clinical testing of a new treatment. A phase I trial is a controlled, clinical research study of the safety based on a small number of patients and conducted over the period of about a year.

phase II clinical trial The second step in clinical testing of a new treatment. A phase II trial is a controlled, clinical research study of the efficacy of a new treatment based on several hundred patient volunteers, generally conducted over a period of about 2 years.

phase III clinical trial The final step in clinical testing of a new treatment A controlled, clinical research study of the efficacy of a new treatment based on a larger group of patient volunteers, generally conducted over a period of about 3 years in order to assess the long-term benefit.

transgenic mouse A genetically engineered mouse carrying a known gene alteration. Such animals provide a means to evaluate the role of specific genes in normal development and in specific diseases such as cancer.

tumor suppressor A gene that inhibits the growth and survival of cancer cells. Tumor suppressors are normal cellular genes but are frequently found to be missing in cancer cells.

wild type Genetic term designating the normal form of the gene.

The p53 tumor suppressor protein is a 53-kDa transcription factor that plays a key role in inducing cell cycle arrest and DNA damage-induced programmed cell death (apoptosis) in tumor cells. The highly conserved sequence of p53, and the finding that it is frequently lost or mutated in most types of cancer, suggests a central role of p53 in the process controlling tumorigenesis. Since the early 1990s, p53 has been the focus of a large body of research, which has led to an expanded and refined understanding of cancer on the one hand, and provided us, on the other hand with new therapeutic strategies to cancer treatment. p53 gene therapy is presently being tested for therapeutic efficacy in clinical trials of several cancers, including those of the head and neck, prostate, breast, and lung.

I. LOSS OF p53 AND THE PATHOGENESIS OF CANCER

Initially, p53 was identified as an SV40 T antigen-binding protein in cells transformed with the simian virus 40 (SV40) tumor virus. This observation, together with the frequent overexpression of p53 in murine and human tumor cells, led initially to the erroneous classification of p53 as an oncogene. Some early cellular transformation experiments corroborated this notion by showing that p53 gene transfer could promote transformation and immortalization of murine fibroblasts in cell culture. However, it was later discovered that it was the mutated form of p53

that had been used in these cellular transformation assays. Wild-type p53 had no ongenic activity and was instead a potent tumor suppressor that was profoundly growth suppressive in tumor cells and inhibitory to cellular transformation. The accumulation of p53 protein that was often observed in tumor cells resulted from mutations that conferred enhanced stability to the protein and increased its half-life from minutes for the wild-type protein to several hours for the mutant protein, but neither the stabilized form of the mutant protein nor T antigen-bound wild-type p53 could carry out wild-type p53 functions.

Various lines of evidence suggest that an important component of the tumor suppressor function of wild-type p53 involves DNA damage recognition and induction of apoptosis. Following DNA damage recognition, p53 is stabilized and activated as a transcription factor, which in turn leads to the expression of p53 target genes involved in apoptosis. Endogenous DNA damage may be a fundamental feature of the cancer cell, arising as a consequence of genome instability, a hallmark of cancer. Because this endogenous damage could serve as a trigger for p53-mediated apoptosis, the loss of p53, through gene deletion or mutation, would provide a survival advantage for the cancer cell by enabling escape from apoptosis. Such a model is consistent with studies in transgenic mice predisposed to mammary tumors, where loss of p53 was correlated with increased genome instability and aneuploidy.

II. LOSS OF p53 AND THERAPY RESISTANCE

While loss of p53-mediated DNA damage-induced apoptosis would favor the outgrowth of genomically unstable cancer cells, it also promotes resistance to a variety of anticancer agents that act, at least in part, through the induction of DNA damage. For example, hematopoietic cells from p53-null transgenic mice, as well as E1A-transformed fibroblasts from p53-null transgenic mice, were found to be much more resistant to DNA-damaging treatments than were the corresponding cells from normal mice. Furthermore, the growth inhibitory properties of a large panel of anticancer agents were seen to correlate with the p53 status of the tumor cells. In general, tumor cells that expressed wild-type p53 were more responsive to most of these agents than tumor cells with mutated or deleted p53. An exception to this general observation was found with the class of agents known as antimitotics, which target the mitotic apparatus rather than DNA.

These observations are particularly important in light of the fact that resistance to conventional chemotherapeutic drugs is still a major obstacle to the successful treatment of cancer and is likely to account for treatment failure in about half of all cancers. To the extent that loss of wild-type p53 function contributes to drug resistance, it may be possible, using p53 gene replacement strategies as described later, to reverse or alleviate drug resistance, enabling us to fully exploit the potential of standard chemotherapies. A variety of gene transfer approaches are being developed for clinical application of gene therapy, including viral and nonviral approaches. This article focuses on approaches that use adenovirus, chosen for its unparalleled gene transfer efficiency to a wide range of tissue types and for its relative safety and minimal toxicity.

III. GENE REPLACEMENT STRATEGIES INVOLVING ADENOVIRUS

The first representative of the adenovirus family was isolated in the early 1950s from the adenoids of individuals suffering from upper respiratory tract infections. More than 100 different species of adenovirus have now been identified, and they are associated with a range of illnesses of varying severity depending on type. However, one of the most studied of these virus species, human adenovirus type 5, primarily causes mild cold-like symptoms and is not associated with serious pathogenicity. For this reason, adenovirus type 5 has attracted interest as a vector for cancer gene therapy.

Adenoviruses are characterized by a capsid consisting of several well-defined structural proteins, including the main structural proteins termed hexon (surrounded by six other capsid proteins), penton (surrounded by five other capsid proteins), and fiber (which mediates attachment to the target cell). The assembled capsid is icosahedral in shape (20 faces)

and measures about 900 Å in diameter. Adenoviral genomes are linear, double-stranded DNA molecules. A great deal has been learned about their genome structure and the functions of the various viral gene products, and genetically engineered versions of adenovirus suitable for gene transfer applications have been generated. The vectors based on adenovirus type 5 presently in use in both preclinical and clinical studies lack specific genes required for virus replication. Although these viruses are still able to enter their target cell, delivering the human gene of interest, they are unable to replicate their DNA and produce progeny, and therefore are disabled with regard to pathogenicity.

In addition to their lack of serious pathogenicity and their high efficiency of gene transfer, adenoviruses are attractive for therapeutic applications because of their broad host cell specificity. Furthermore, adenoviruses are relatively easy to prepare in high titer on an industrial scale. Long-term transgene expression is not anticipated with adenovirus, as the vectors are impaired for replication in the target cell, and the vector DNA does not integrate into the host cell genome. While transient expression could constitute a disadvantage for certain gene therapy applications, it is not a limitation for cancer gene therapy, where the end point of therapy is cell death. Another potential limitation of adenovirus, namely its immunogenicity, has not been a limitation for application in clinical trials of cancer patients to date (see later).

IV. PRECLINICAL APPLICATIONS OF p53 ADENOVIRUS

Numerous *in vitro* studies carried out on tumor cells in culture have demonstrated that the restoration of p53 activity in tumor cells is growth suppressive in itself, and this suppression is enhanced in the presence of any of a wide variety of chemotherapeutic drugs, including cisplatin, doxorubicin (Adriamycin), and 5-fluorouracil. In some cases, the suppressive effect of the combination of p53 gene replacement and chemotherapeutic drug treatment is greater than the sum of the suppressive effects of each agent used singly, suggestive of mechanistic synergy, and is consistent with the DNA damage-dependent mechanism by which p53 is believed to act. One example of this is shown in Fig. 1, where the T47D breast cancer cell line was treated with p53 adenovirus under conditions where approximately 70% of the culture expressed wild-type p53, with the DNA-damaging chemotherapeutic drug, cisplatin, alone, or with a combination of the two. Six days posttreatment, the viability of cells treated with the individual agents had dropped to about 70% of that of the control cells. However, when cells were treated with a combination of p53 adenovirus and cisplatin, the viability of the cells dropped to 10% of that of the control cells, a value less than would be expected based on merely additive effects. These effects are not seen in normal cells, possibly because wild-type p53 has a very short half-life in normal cells. Taken together, *in vitro* results support the clinical application of p53 gene therapy to suppress tumor growth and enhance tumor responsiveness to chemotherapy.

Subcutaneous tumor models in nude mice have been used to demonstrate the *in vivo* efficacy of p53 adenovirus for the treatment of a variety of human tumors, including breast cancer, lung cancer, colon cancer, and head and neck cancer. In these studies, p53 adenovirus administered intratumorally or regionally to preestablished tumors resulted in a marked reduction in tumor growth, which was further reduced when treatment was combined with chemotherapy. Figure 2 shows the results of a study carried out to test

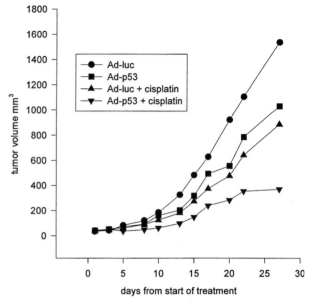

FIGURE 2 Suppression of established subcutaneous tumors of FaDu head and neck cancer cells in nude mice by various treatments. Cisplatin-treated animals received cisplatin on days 1 and 15. Virus-treated animals received either Ad5CMV-*p53* (Adp53) or Adluc (control) on days 3, 6, and 8 and again on days 17, 20, and 22.

the efficacy of a combination of p53 adenovirus plus cisplatin for the treatment of head and neck cancer. Cisplatin is an effective and commonly used chemotherapeutic for head and neck cancer, but therapy often fails due to acquired resistance. Nude mice were implanted with Fadu head and neck tumor cells and tumors were allowed to develop to a size of about 40 mm^3. Animals were then randomized into treatment groups of 10 animals each and treatment was administered (the first day of treatment was designated day 1). All groups received adenovirus [p53 adenovirus or luciferase adenovirus (control)] on days 3, 6, and 8 and again on days 17, 20, and 22. Two groups received cisplatin on days 1 and 15 by intraperitoneal injection. Tumor size was monitored at 2- to 3-day intervals. As shown in Fig. 2, both p53 adenovirus and cisplatin had a suppressive effect when used as single agent treatments. However, the combination of p53 adenovirus and cisplatin resulted in a highly significant suppression of tumor growth relative to that seen in each of the other three treatment groups [$p < 0.01$ by a nonparametric (Omnibus) analysis]. Treatments were well tolerated by the animals, as judged by weight measurements and histo-

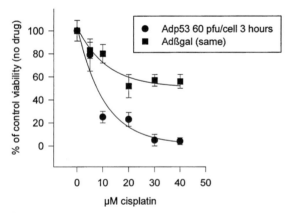

FIGURE 1 Viability of T47D breast cancer cells *in vitro* 6 days following treatment with Adp53 or Adβgal (control) and 5 days following a 1-h treatment with the indicated doses of cisplatin. Each curve is normalized to its own zero (virus only, no cisplatin), which for Ad5CMV-*p53* (Adp53)-treated cells was 60% of Adβgal-treated cells.

logical analyses. These results suggest that the clinical application of p53 adenovirus to the treatment of head and neck cancer may be very effective in suppressing tumor growth and in enhancing responsiveness to cisplatin. Similar results have been observed using subcutaneous models for a variety of other human cancers, indicating that p53 gene therapy has broad clinical application as a tumor suppressor and therapy sensitizer.

V. CLINICAL APPLICATIONS OF THE p53 ADENOVIRUS, Ad5CMV-p53 (INGN 201)

A. Clinical Targets for Local/Regional Vector Administration

Many of the preclinical studies that have been done with the p53 adenoviral vector have involved direct intratumoral administration into a subcutaneous tumor in a nude mouse model. The reason for this is to maximize the exposure of the target tumor cells to the vector. The current generation adenoviral vector used for delivery of the p53 gene relies on normal adenoviral tropism in order to infect cells. Because many cell types in addition to the target tumor cells can be infected by the vector, injection into the circulation would serve to reduce the amount of vector that actually reaches these tumor cells due to the effects of dilution and uptake by nontarget cells. Thus, in most of the clinical studies currently ongoing with the p53 adenovirus Ad5CMV-p53, delivery of the vector to the target tumor cells is accomplished by a direct administration into a patient's tumor or into the region where a tumor is localized.

The selection of clinical targets for this type of administration has therefore focused on those cancers that would benefit from an improvement in local or regional control of tumor growth. Head and neck cancer is an excellent example of such a disease. The vast majority of patients who die from head and neck cancer die from disease in a very localized region. Intratumoral administration in this disease is also straightforward, as most of the lesions can be readily accessed for vector injection. Other tumor types that are amenable to this type of approach include brain can-

cer, locally advanced prostate cancer, ovarian cancer, bladder cancer, and nonmetastatic stages of non-small cell lung cancer. Metastatic lesions that cause significant patient morbidity and that can be needle accessed can also be treated in order to potentially provide patients with symptomatic improvement and possibly increased survival.

Initial phase I studies with the p53 adenovirus Ad5CMV-p53 have been conducted in two tumor types: non-small cell lung cancer (NSCLC) and head and neck cancer (SCCHN). In each study the vector was administered by direct intratumoral injection into patients with advanced disease. These phase I studies were primarily designed to determine the safety of the vector and to verify that it was able to infect and be expressed in the target tumor tissue. Each study included a dose escalation between patient cohorts; once the vector was demonstrated to be safe in patients at one dose level, the next cohort of patients was treated at a higher dose. Dose levels ranged from 10^6 to 10^{11} plaque forming units (pfu)/injection. Patients were treated by different schedules of administration in the two studies. In the non-small cell lung cancer study, patients received a single injection of the vector once a month; this administration could then be repeated monthly as long as there was no progression of the patient's cancer. In the head and neck cancer study, patients received six injections over a 2-week period. The six-injection regimen could also be repeated monthly as long as the disease did not progress. The two treatment regimens were each well tolerated by the patients; the major side effects resulting from administration of Ad5CMV-p53 were transient fever and chills and injection site pain, and, in the head and neck cancer study, injection site bleeding. There was no dose-limiting toxicity found in either study. Some patients received injections for up to 6–7 months, the cut-offs for treatment that had been predefined for each study. These results demonstrated that Ad5CMV-p53 administered by intratumoral injection had an excellent safety profile in patients with advanced cancers.

Each of these phase I studies demonstrated that Ad5CMV-p53 successfully transduced target tumor cells and resulted in the expression of the p53 transgene. Although patients on the trials generally had an increase in antiadenoviral antibody titer following treatment, this did not appear to abrogate transduction, as investigators demonstrated both transduction and transgene expression in biopsy material recovered from patients with elevated antibody titers. Results of these studies indicate that multiple cycles of intratumoral injection are reasonable, from both safety and transduction standpoints, to provide for longer-term patient treatment.

Additional phase I trials have been completed for locally advanced prostate cancer and are ongoing in additional cancers, indications that are amenable to local/regional treatment approaches, including bladder, brain (glioblastoma multiforme), breast, ovarian, and bronchoalveolar carcinoma, a type of non-small cell lung cancer. These studies are utilizing different routes of vector administration, which include transrectal ultrasound-guided (TRUS), transperineal injection into the prostate, intravesical (bladder) instillation, direct injection into chest wall lesions, intraperitoneal administration, and bronchial lavage. As with the initial phase I studies, end points for these studies are primarily safety and demonstration of transduction/expression by the various routes of administration.

B. Demonstration of Clinical Activity of Ad5CMV-p53 in Phase I and Phase II Clinical Trials

Although the primary goal of the phase I studies in NSCLC and SCCHN was to evaluate the safety of Ad5CMV-p53, measurements of the treated lesions were made before treatment and at various times following treatment in order to determine whether there was objective evidence of clinical activity. Several of the tumors injected in the phase I studies underwent shrinkage or elimination in response to the administration of Ad5CMV-p53. On the head and neck cancer study, 2 of 33 patients had a partial response, i.e., a greater than 50% reduction in tumor size, in their treated tumors, and 1 patient had a complete response, or elimination, of the treated lesion. These responses occurred in both p53$^{\text{wild-type}}$ and p53^{mutant} SCCHN tumors, indicating that the vector can have activity regardless of the endogenous p53 status. Of the 52 patients treated on the non-small cell lung cancer study, 4 had a greater than 50% decrease in the treated lesion in response to vector injection. Many other patients on the two

trials had disease stabilization that lasted for 2–14 months.

Based on the promising results of the phase I study, phase II studies in patients with recurrent or refractory SCCHN were initiated. The largest of the phase II studies examined the effect of schedule on clinical activity and safety. Two schedules of administration were tested; a daily × 3 injection and the six injections over 2 weeks that had been used in the initial phase I trial. Each regimen was repeated monthly until disease progressed or patients became otherwise ineligible. Preliminary results have been reported for 106 of the patients treated on the trial. The vector was well tolerated with side effects similar to those seen in the phase I trial. Of the 167 lesions that were treated and evaluable for response, there were 6 and 11 that underwent complete and partial responses, respectively. As had been true in the phase I study, responses were found in both p53$^{\text{wild-type}}$ and p53^{mutant} tumors. An additional 82 lesions displayed a minor response or had disease stabilization for 3–7+ months. There was a trend toward an improved survival in patients receiving the more intensive six-dose regimen. Phase III studies have now been initiated to determine whether administration of the vector leads to clinical benefit in patients with refractory SCCHN.

C. Combination of p53 Gene Therapy with Conventional Cancer Treatment

Each of the initial phase I studies in SCCHN and NSCLC included a second treatment arm in which a conventional cancer treatment was tested in combination with p53 gene therapy. Combination approaches are generally used for cancer treatment in order to improve the therapeutic benefit to the patient. In the non-small cell lung cancer study, patients on the second treatment arm received Ad5CMV-p53 following a pretreatment with cisplatin. This combination had been found in preclinical studies with models of non-small cell lung cancer to lead to increased antitumor effects over either agent alone. As in the arm where patients received only Ad5CMV-p53, there was a dose escalation of the vector between cohorts of patients in order to determine the safety of the combination approach. Results showed that there was no increase in toxicity due to combination treatment. This study has paved the way for further clinical studies in which the p53 adenovirus will be combined with commonly used chemotherapeutic agents to test its ability to improve therapeutic benefit.

The second arm of the phase I head and neck cancer study involved patients whose tumors could be resected, although not as a curative procedure. Surgery, particularly in combination with radiotherapy, is a standard treatment for newly diagnosed head and neck cancer. As in the arm where patients received only Ad5CMV-p53, there was a dose escalation of the vector between cohorts of patients in order to determine whether vector administration could be safely combined with surgery. Results of the study showed that vector administration had no impact on wound healing and suggested that additional trials should be conducted to further explore the benefits of this approach.

A phase II program is ongoing in patients with NSCLC in which Ad5CMV-p53 is being administered in combination with external beam radiation for patients with localized, inoperable NSCLC who are not eligible for chemotherapy. Patients receive three doses of Ad5CMV-p53 during a 6-week course of radiotherapy. The study is examining the safety of the combination treatment and uses radiographic imaging and biopsy analysis to assess clinical activity. Preliminary results for the first 17 patients established an acceptable safety profile for the combination approach. Eleven of the 17 patients had complete or partial responses of the injected tumors. Of these, 9 also had no evidence of viable tumor cells in the biopsy specimen taken from the injected lesion. These results have formed the basis for an additional, larger clinical trial that is designed to assess the clinical activity of Ad5CMV-p53 in combination with both chemotherapy and radiotherapy in newly diagnosed NSCLC patients.

The status of the various trials that have been conducted or that are ongoing with Ad5CMV-p53 is indicated in Table I. Ad5CMV-p53 in being developed by Introgen Therapeutics and Aventis Pharma.

D. Directions for the Future

The apparent safety of Ad5CMV-p53 in combination with standard cancer treatments such as surgery, radiotherapy, and chemotherapy supports its testing in combination approaches for many types of cancer where improved local/regional control will provide patient benefit. As has been seen in preclinical studies, the vector may act as a chemosensitizing or radiosensitizing agent that will increase the antitumor effects of these standard approaches. As an adjuvant to surgery, Ad5CMV-p53 may act to eliminate microscopic disease that is left behind during a surgical resection. For patients who have disease that is resistant to standard

TABLE I
Development Status of Ad5CMV-p53 (INGN 201)

Indication	Development phase	Combination study?	Status[a]
Squamous cell carcinoma of the head and neck (SCCHN)	Phase III	Yes, with chemotherapy	Ongoing
SCCHN	Phase III	No	Ongoing
Breast cancer[b]	Phase II	Yes, with chemotherapy	Ongoing
SCCHN	Phase II	No	Completed
Non-small cell lung cancer (NSCLC)	Phase II	Yes, with radiotherapy	Completed
Prostate cancer	Phase I	Yes, with surgery	Completed
Brain cancer[b]	Phase I	Yes, with surgery	Ongoing
Ovarian cancer[b]	Phase I	No	Ongoing
Bladder cancer[b]	Phase I	No	Ongoing
Breast cancer[b]	Phase I	Yes, with chemotherapy	Closed
Bronchoalveolar carcinoma[b]	Phase I	No	Ongoing
NSCLC	Phase I	Yes, with chemotherapy	Completed
SCCHN	Phase I	Yes, with surgery	Completed

[a]As of March 2002.
[b]Conducted in conjunction with the National Cancer Institute.

approaches, it may act as a stand-alone agent whose antitumor effects provide patient benefit.

These approaches are being incorporated into the larger clinical trials that are designed to demonstrate the clinical benefit and safety necessary for approval of the product by the Food and Drug Administration and other worldwide regulatory authorities. These pivotal programs, usually designated as phase III trials, are typically randomized, controlled studies where treatments that are standard for a particular type of cancer are used as the control arm for the study. For one of the phase III studies planned for Ad5CMV-*p53*, the experimental arm will be the vector administered as a single agent to refractory SCCHN patients who have failed multiple conventional treatments. The primary end point that will be evaluated will be patient survival. In another phase III study in patients with recurrent, but not refractory, SCCHN, the experimental arm will be Ad5CMV-*p53* tested in combination with 5-fluorouracil and cisplatin, agents that are commonly used to treat this disease. The primary end point for this study will be the time that it takes the tumor to progress. These studies are designed to form the basis for the first product approval for Ad5CMV-*p53*. Additional pivotal programs in other cancer types or with additional combinations may expand the indications for which Ad5CMV-*p53* will ultimately be used in standard clinical practice.

See Also the Following Articles

Adeno-Associated Virus • Cell Cycle Checkpoints • Cellular Responses to DNA Damage • Head and Neck Cancer • Targeted Vectors for Cancer Gene Therapy

Bibliography

Clayman, G. L., el-Naggar, A. K., Lippma, S. M., *et al.* (1998). Adenovirus-mediated p53 gene transfer in patients with advanced recurrent head and neck squamous cell carcinoma. *J. Clin. Oncol.* **16**, 2221–2232.

Donehower, L. A., Godley, L. A., Alsaz, C. M., *et al.* (1995). Deficiency of p53 accelerates mammary tumorigenesis in Wnt-1 transgenic mice and promotes chromosomal instability. *Genes Dev.* **9**, 882–895.

Gjerset, R. A., Turla, S. T., Sobol, R. E., *et al.* (1995). Use of wild-type p53 to achieve complete treatment sensitization of tumor cells expressing endogenous mutant p53. *Mol. Carcinog.* **14**, 275–285.

Goodwin, W. J., Esser, D., Clayman, G. L., *et al.* (1999). Randomized phase II study of intratumoral injection of two dosing schedules using a replication-deficient adenovirus carrying the p53 gene (Ad5CMV-p53) in patients with recurrent/refractory head and neck cancer. *J. Clin. Oncol.* **18**, 1717A.

Kubba, S., Adak, S., Schiller, J., *et al.* (2000). Phase I trial of adenovirus p53 in bronchioloalveolar cell lung carcinoma (BAC) administered by bronchoalveolar lavage. *J. Clin. Oncol.* **19**, 1904A.

Lang, F. F., Fuller, G. N., Prados, M., *et al.* (2000). Preliminary results of a phase I clinical trial of adenovirus-mediated p53 gene therapy for recurrent gliomas: Biological studies. *J. Clin. Oncol.* **19**, 1785A.

Levine, A. J. (1993). The tumor suppressor genes. *Annu. Rev. Biochem.* **62**, 623–651.

Logothetis, C. J., Hossan, E., Evans, R., *et al.* (1999). Ad5CMV-p53 intraprostatic gene therapy preceeding radical prostatectomy (RP): An *in vivo* model for targeted therapy development. *J. Clin. Oncol.* **18**, 1203A.

Lotem, J., and Sachs, L. (1993). Hematopoietic cells from mice deficient in wild-type p53 are more resistant to induction of apoptosis by some agents. *Blood* **82**, 1092–1096.

Lowe, S. W., Ruley, H. E., Jacks, T., and Houseman, D. E. *et al.* (1993). p53-dependent apoptosis modulates the cytotoxicity of anticancer agents. *Cell* **74**, 957–967.

Nemunaitis, J., Swisher, S. G., Timmons, T., *et al.* (2000). Adenovirus-mediated p53 gene transfer in sequence with cisplatin to tumors of patients with non-small-cell lung cancer. *J. Clin. Oncol.* **18**, 609–622.

Nguyen, D. M., Spitz, F. R. Yen, N., *et al.* (1996). Gene therapy for lung cancer: Enhancement of tumor suppression by a combination of sequential systemic cisplatin and adenovirus-mediated p53 gene transfer. *J. Thorac. Cardiovasc. Surg.* **112**, 1372–1376.

O'Connor, P. M., Jackman, J., Bae, L., *et al.* (1997). Characterization of the p53 tumor suppressor pathway in cell lines of the National Cancer Institute anticancer drug screen and correlations with the growth-inhibitory potency of 123 anticancer agents. *Cancer Res.* **57**, 4285–4300.

Pagliaro, L. C. (2000). Gene therapy for bladder cancer. *World J. Urol.* **18**, 148–151.

Sweeney, P., and Pisters, L. L. (2000). Ad5CMVp53 gene therapy for locally advanced prostate cancer—where do we stand? *World J. Urol.* **18**, 121–124.

Swisher, S., Roth, J. A., Nemunaitus, J., *et al.* (2000). A phase II trial of adenoviral-mediated p53 gene transfer (RPR/INGN 201) in conjunction with radiation therapy in patients with localized non-small cell lung cancer (NSCLC). *J. Clin. Oncol.* **19**, 1807A.

Swisher, S. G., Roth, J. A., Komacki, R., *et al.* (1999). Adenovirus-mediated p53 gene transfer in advanced non-small-cell lung cancer. *J. Natl. Cancer Inst.* **91**, 763–771.

Wolf, J. K., Bodurka-Bevers, D., Gano, J., *et al.* (2000). A phase I trial of Adp53 for ovarian cancer patients: Correlation with p53 and anti-adenovirus AB status. *J. Clin. Oncol.* **19**, 1510A.

P-glycoprotein as a General Antiapoptotic Protein

Astrid A. Ruefli
Mark J. Smyth
Ricky W. Johnstone
The Peter MacCallum Cancer Institute, East Melbourne, Australia

GLOSSARY

apoptosis A mechanism of cell death characterized morphologically by DNA fragmentation and the formation of membrane blebs.

caspases A highly conserved family of cysteine proteases essential to the execution of some forms of apoptosis.

death receptors Include the tumor necrosis (TNF) superfamily of molecules, such as the Fas receptor and TNF receptor, which, upon binding of their ligand, initiate apoptosis through recruitment and activation of caspases.

death-inducing signal complex Includes a death receptor, adaptor molecule, and initiator caspase, which form at the cell surface upon ligation of a death receptor and its ligand.

Chemotherapy is a common and effective treatment for many types of neoplasms, particularly systemic and metastatic disease. However, a major impediment to successful treatment has been a phenomenon known as multidrug resistance (MDR). Typically, MDR tumor cells are able to survive clinical doses of a broad range of chemotherapeutic agents. Some tumors are inherently resistant to the majority of chemotherapeutic compounds (intrinsic resistance), whereas others exhibit MDR after initial exposure to one chemotherapeutic agent (acquired resistance). A hallmark of MDR is the expression of the *MDR1* gene product, P-glycoprotein (P-gp). Indeed, P-gp is expressed in many types of cancers, and the clinical success of chemotherapeutic treatment often correlates inversely with the level of P-gp expression. P-gp is a 170- to 180-kDa cell surface transporter protein and has historically been thought to confer resistance to chemotoxins by actively effluxing them from the cell. In fact, significant evidence in both *in vitro* and *in vivo* models supports this hypothesis. While there is little doubt that P-gp plays an important role as an efflux pump, new evidence is mounting to suggest that P-gp may also act as a general antiapoptotic protein to increase the threshold for cell death. Effectively, P-gp may protect cells at two levels by (1) decreasing the amount of toxins that accumulate in the cell and (2) providing a block in the mechanisms of cell death induced by toxins and cellular stress. Understanding how P-gp can regulate cell death could lead to novel therapies for the treatment of MDR tumors.

I. INTRODUCTION: HISTORICAL PERSPECTIVE OF P-GLYCOPROTEIN AND MULTIDRUG RESISTANCE

The human genome contains two highly homologous P-gp genes, *MDR1* and *MDR2*, which are adjacent to one another on the long arm of chromosome 7. In mice, there are three P-gp genes: *mdr1a*, *mdr1b*, and *mdr2*. P-gp is a member of the ATP-binding cassette (ABC) transporter family of proteins, which includes the related multidrug resistance related protein MRP, the cystic fibrosis transmembrane conductance regulator (CFTR), and the yeast mating factor transporter STE6.

P-gp was first implicated in multidrug resistance in experiments that utilized MDR tumor cell lines. Numerous tissue culture experiments have convincingly shown that P-gp is responsible for drug efflux. P-gp can confer resistance to many structurally and functionally diverse compounds, including alkaloid compounds, bacterial and fungal antibiotics, such as anthracyclines, actinomycin D, etoposide, paclitaxel, and vinca alkaloids. Since it was first discovered that P-gp was largely responsible for decreased drug accumulation in MDR cells, much work has focused on defining the mechanism of action of this protein. For many years the model for drug resistance conferred by

P-gp has been a relatively simple one. Cytotoxic drugs are actively effluxed out of P-gp-expressing cells against a concentration gradient, thereby reducing intracellular drug accumulation and inhibiting drug-mediated cell death.

However, despite the volume of work dedicated to elucidating the exact mechanisms of P-gp-mediated drug efflux, just how P-gp manages to remove and protect cells from such a broad range of structurally diverse compounds is still not fully understood. While it is clear that P-gp can function as a very efficient efflux pump, the recently described role of P-gp in regulating apoptosis may also serve to impinge on the cytotoxic action of many different types of chemotherapeutic agents.

II. EXPRESSION OF P-GLYCOPROTEIN IN NORMAL TISSUES

A role for P-gp-like molecules in removing toxic substances from cells is highly conserved throughout evolution, and it was demonstrated that the *Lactococcus lactis* antibiotic resistance protein, LmrA, could functionally complement P-gp in mammalian cells to induce MDR. However, examination of the tissue expression of P-gp indicates that there may be more to P-gp function than simply protection from exotoxins. P-gp is expressed in relatively high and homogeneous levels in normal tissues, such as the brush border of renal proximal tubule epithelium, the luminal surface of biliary hepatocytes, small and large intestinal mucosal cells, and pancreatic ductules. P-gp is also expressed at the blood–brain barrier and the blood–testis barrier. In fact, expression of P-gp in these tissues led to the hypothesis that P-gp functions physiologically to protect vital organs from toxins. This was subsequently confirmed in *mdr1a/1b* knockout mice, which had profound defects in drug distribution. However, P-gp is also expressed in the adrenal gland, on hemopoietic stem cells, natural killer (NK) cells, antigen-presenting dendritic cells (DC), and T and B lymphocytes. Whereas *mdr1a/1b* knockout mice display a seemingly complete immune cell repertoire, an exhaustive study of the capacity of these mice to mount an efficient immune response against pathogens or tumors, and the relative susceptibility of these mice to autoimmunity, has not been reported to date. Interestingly, MDR1 P-gp is also expressed in a stage-specific manner in the placenta and has restricted expression in the developing embryo, a time when orchestrated cell division and death are essential to normal development. While expression of P-gp on blood–tissue barriers and on epithelial cells of the gastrointestinal or urinary system is consistent with a toxin removal role, the selective expression on these other cell types led some researchers to propose additional functions for P-gp. To date, P-gp has been implicated in chloride channel activity, phospholipid transport, cholesterol esterification, secretion of interleukins, and migration of DC. Perhaps the most relevant "alternative" function of P-gp in multidrug resistance is its putative role as a general antiapoptotic protein.

III. CHEMOTHERAPY AND APOPTOSIS

Once a chemotherapeutic agent enters a cell, whether by passive diffusion or facilitated entry via a pore or carrier, it must first bind to its target, such as DNA or microtubules, before it can exhibit an effect on cell viability. Most active drugs interfere with cellular metabolism (methotrexate and 5-fluorouracil), mitosis (vincristine, etoposide), or DNA replication (doxorubicin, cisplatin). Although chemotherapeutic drugs vary greatly in structure and cellular targets, many initiate a highly organized and distinct process known as programmed cell death or apoptosis to quickly and efficiently kill the target cell. All living cells inherently possess the machinery to induce apoptosis. Apoptotic death is initiated by the cell when it senses that its environment or physical state has been compromised. Defined by a specific morphology, an apoptotic cell discretely packages its DNA and organelles into small bodies, DNA is fragmented, and all evidence of death is eliminated, thus avoiding any inflammatory response.

A. Death Receptor and Mitochondria-Mediated Cell Death

Central to the execution of apoptosis is a family of cysteine proteases known as caspases. Constitutively present in the cytosol of most cells, caspases are involved in at least two pathways leading to apoptosis (Fig. 1). The best defined pathway involves ligation of death receptors, typically members of the tumor necrosis factor (TNF) superfamily, such as Fas and TNF receptor (TNFR), at the cell surface. Adapter molecules, such as Fas-associated death domain (FADD) or TNF receptor-associated death domain (TRADD), and initiator caspases, such as caspase 8, are recruited and bind to the receptor to form a complex referred to as the death-inducing signal complex (DISC). Upon formation of the DISC, caspase 8 is autocatalyzed and the active form is released and can subsequently activate effector caspases (i.e., caspase 3) or can cleave and activate the proapoptotic Bcl-2 family member, Bid.

The second, less well-defined caspase-dependent pathway involves the disruption of the mitochondrial transmembrane potential ($\Delta\Psi_m$) and the release of mitochondrial proteins such as cytochrome c. Cytochrome c cooperates with dATP and adapter protein Apaf-1 to induce the activation of caspase 9, which can cleave and activate caspase 3. Importantly, release of mitochondrial cytochrome c is inhibited by antiapoptotic members of the Bcl-2 family, such as Bcl-2 and Bcl-X$_L$, and is promoted by proapoptotic members, such as Bid, Bax, and Bak.

B. Caspase-Independent Cell Death

In addition to caspase-dependent apoptosis, there is now sufficient evidence to suggest that apoptosis can occur in the absence of active caspases. Caspase-independent cell death has been shown to be induced by perforin and granzyme B, anti-CD2, the protein kinase C inhibitor staurosporine, proapoptotic Bcl-2 family member Bax, and the hybrid polar compound, HMBA. In the absence of caspase activation, cytoplasmic events related to apoptosis, such as cell shrinkage, cytoplasmic condensation, and loss of mitochondrial membrane integrity and exposure of phosphatidylserine, are still induced by these stimuli (Fig. 2). Therefore, although many drugs induce caspase activation, the caspase pathway is not always necessary for a drug to induce apoptosis. Different drugs have different "relative dependence" on caspase activation. Caspase-independent cell death is often

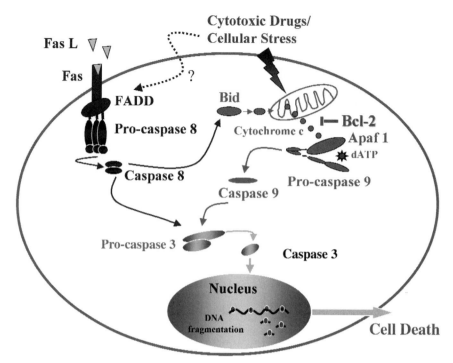

FIGURE 1 Caspase-dependent cell death pathways. Apoptosis can be triggered by receptor-mediated death stimuli (blue pathway) (i.e., Fas ligand), which bind and cross-link the death receptor (Fas). This stimulates the binding of adaptor proteins such as FADD, which recruit activator caspases (i.e., caspase 8). Formation of this death-inducing signal complex (DISC) allows cleavage and activation of the activator caspase, which can then cleave and activate the downstream effector caspase, such as caspase 3 (yellow). The effector caspase then cleaves cellular substrates to induce the morphological changes associated with programmed cell death, such as DNA fragmentation and membrane blebbing. A separate pathway (green) is triggered via an "intrinsic" apoptotic stimuli (i.e., cellular stress) and involves the release of cytochrome c from the mitochondria. Cytochrome c in synergy with ATP allows a conformational change of Apaf-1 (a caspase coactivator) to occur, which in turn binds the activator caspase (caspase 9). Caspase 9 autoactivates and can cleave and activate effector caspases, thereby feeding into the receptor-mediated pathway. Cleavage of BID by caspase 8 serves to link these two pathways following DISC formation. The activation of the thus far undefined "intrinsic" apoptotic stimuli may be trigged by chemotherapeutic drugs, and the release of cytochrome c can be regulated by Bcl-2 and related family members.

inhibited by Bcl-2, suggesting that a loss of mitochondrial function is central to this death process.

C. Apoptosis Induced by Chemotherapeutic Drugs

The mechanisms by which chemotherapeutic drugs induce apoptosis are still a topic of much debate. Cytotoxic drugs, particularly those commonly used in the chemotherapy of leukemias, have been reported to upregulate Fas ligand (FasL) expression and are therefore thought to activate the death receptor pathway. However, reports using cells depleted of functional caspase 8 appear to refute activation of death-receptor mediated apoptosis as a primary function of chemotherapeutic drugs. Work by our group and others has shown that chemotoxins can induce mitochondrial membrane depolarization and release of cytochrome c, thereby activating the mitochondria-mediated death pathway to eliminate tumor cells in the absence of activation of upstream caspases such as caspase 8. In response to the DNA damage induced by some chemotherapeutic drugs, the p53 tumor suppressor protein is upregulated and activated. p53 can transcriptionally activate Bax, which in turn can induce mitochondrial membrane depolarization and ultimately cell death. It should be noted, however, that in the absence of functional p53, many drugs, including those that target DNA, are still active.

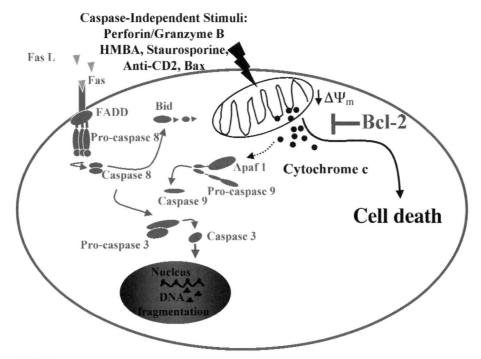

FIGURE 2 Caspase-independent cell death pathway. Stimuli such as perforin and granzyme B, staurosporine, HMBA, anti-CD2, and Bax can induce cell death in the absence of caspase activation (purple pathway). These stimuli disrupt mitochondrial membrane potential, induce the release of cytochrome c, and lead to cell death via an uncharacterized mechanism. Although these stimuli can induce activation of caspases, particularly caspases 9 and 3, active caspases are not necessary for the execution of cell death. Antiapoptotic Bcl-2 family members can inhibit this form of cell death.

Clearly, the biochemical processes leading to apoptosis are quite complex and indeed far from being completely characterized. One can imagine that if a vital step in an apoptotic pathway is inhibited, a neoplastic or virally infected cell may effectively evade cell death. In fact, there are many examples of exactly that. For example, proteins such as viral and cellular FLIP (FLICE-like inhibitory protein) can bind the DISC and prevent recruitment and activation of caspase 8, whereas the cow pox virus Crm A (cytokine response modifier A) blocks activation of caspases 8 and 3.

IV. REGULATION OF APOPTOSIS BY P-GLYCOPROTEIN

Studies have shown that P-gp confers resistance to apoptosis mediated by a range of different stimuli, including FasL and TNF, that require caspase activation to induce cell death. Moreover, activation of some caspases is inhibited by the expression of functional

P-gp, and antagonistic antibodies to P-gp can reverse this inhibition. Interestingly, these P-gp-expressing cells are sensitive to caspase-independent forms of cell death, suggesting that P-gp may have a role in inhibiting *specific* forms of cell death. The fact that Fas ligand mediates apoptosis by binding to a membrane-bound receptor indicates that resistance to death receptor-mediated apoptosis is not due to P-gp physically extruding drugs or peptides out of the cell. Rather, P-gp may be hindering subsequent interactions during ligation of death receptors, or it may be inhibiting caspase-dependent apoptosis via one or more of a multitude of putative mechanisms.

A. Inhibition of Caspase Activation by P-glycoprotein

A series of studies have shown that *MDR1* P-gp confers resistance to apoptosis induced by a range of chemotherapeutic drugs, Fas ligation, binding of TNF to the TNF receptor, serum starvation, and UV irradiation. As discussed earlier, these stimuli induce cell death by activating the common cell death cascade mediated by caspases. Biochemical analyses have shown that upon Fas ligation, functional P-gp can inhibit the activation of downstream caspases such as caspases 8 and 3. This inhibitory effect can be completely reversed by the addition of anti-P-gp monoclonal antibodies or a pharmacological inhibitor of P-gp function, verapamil. However, P-gp-expressing cells are not resistant to all death stimuli, as P-gp^{+ve} and parental P-gp^{-ve} cell lines are equally sensitive to death induced by the chemotherapeutic agent HMBA, pore-forming proteins such as perforin or pneumolysin, sublytic doses of perforin and the cytotoxic leukocyte cell granule protein, granzyme B, and NK cells. It is interesting to note that while expression of P-gp inhibits activation of caspases 3 and 8 during receptor-mediated cell death, P-gp has no apparent effect on the cleavage and activation of caspase 9 during HMBA-mediated apoptosis, suggesting that P-gp may only affect certain caspases. Moreover, as perforin and granzyme B and the chemotoxin HMBA can kill cells in the absence of caspase activation, it seems likely that P-gp may inhibit caspase-dependent but not caspase-independent cell death. A caveat to this hypothesis are the studies discussed later showing that P-gp can confer resistance to cell lysis induced by activated complement. It is currently not clear how P-gp may specifically inhibit complement-mediated pore formation, yet not the functionally related proteins perforin and pneumolysin. Nevertheless, there is now a growing body of evidence that P-gp can protect cells against a range of different cell death stimuli.

These observations call for new models to explain how P-gp might affect cell death induced by such disparate apoptotic stimuli. Although no hard experimental evidence exists to define the method of apoptosis inhibition by P-gp, the following two hypotheses can be suggested.

1. P-gp Inhibits Formation of a Death-Inducing Signaling Complex

Ligation of cell surface death receptor molecules such as Fas or TNF receptor results in DISC formation following the recruitment of adaptor proteins (FADD, TRADD) and a proximal caspase (caspase 8), which is then autoactivated to trigger the caspase cascade. It is possible that the expression of a large molecule

such as P-gp may perturb plasma membrane content and context and could thereby interfere with DISC formation (Fig. 3). However, unpublished observations have shown that P-gp does not interfere with formation of the DISC, but rather inhibits the autocatalysis of caspase 8.

2. P-gp Inhibits Caspase Activation by Altering Intracellular pH (pH$_i$)

Expression of P-gp correlates with an increase in pH$_i$, which has been proposed to result in decreased free drug concentrations due to altered transmembrane partitioning or intracellular sequestration. Apoptosis is often preceded by intracellular acidification, and the induction of apoptotic events such as DNA laddering can be inhibited by increasing pH$_i$. Cells that are normally sensitive to apoptosis by Fas cross-linking or serum starvation can be made resistant to these caspase-dependent death stimuli by elevating pH$_i$. Thus, it is possible that the expression of P-gp alters pH$_i$, thereby placing the cell in a state of caspase inactivity, rendering P-gp^{+ve} cells relatively resistant to multiple forms of caspase-dependent cell death stimuli (Fig. 3). The addition of P-gp inhibitors such as verapamil to cells transfected with *MDR1* correlates with reduced pH$_i$ and increased sensitivity to apoptotic stimuli. It is interesting to note that mutation of the ABC transporter, CFTR, results in an increase in pH$_i$ and cellular resistance to apoptosis in cystic fibrosis.

B. Inhibition of Complement-Mediated Cell Death by P-glycoprotein

Studies performed by Weisburg and colleagues have demonstrated that P-gp mediates resistance to activated complement-induced cell lysis. Elevated pH$_i$ and decreased membrane potential (V_m) have been proposed as the mode by which P-gp inhibits complement-mediated cytotoxicity. P-gp^{-ve} cells with artificially elevated pH$_i$ were found to exhibit similar resistance to activated complement-mediated cell death as P-gp^{+ve} cells, and the degree of intracellular alkalinization correlated with an increased resistance to complement. Specifically, the changes in pH$_i$ inhibited formation of a functional membrane attack complex (MAC) on the surface of the target cell.

It is unclear why complement-mediated pore for-

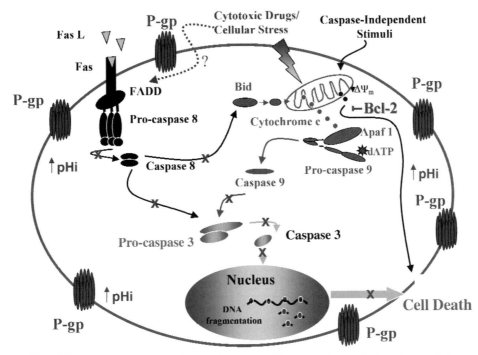

FIGURE 3 Regulation of apoptosis by P-gp. Expression of functional P-gp results in an increase in intracellular pH (pH_i) and inhibition of caspase 8 and caspase 3 activation. The activation of caspases and the release of cytochrome c from the mitochondria may be optimal in an acidic cytosolic environment. It is therefore possible that both apoptosis pathways are affected by a P-gp-mediated increase in pH_i as indicated by red crosses. Expression of P-gp may also disrupt formation of the DISC (Fas receptor, FADD, and caspase 8) at the cell surface by an as yet unidentified mechanism. See color insert in Volume 1.

mation is apparently affected by P-gp expression, whereas structurally similar proteins such as perforin, streptolysin, and pneumolysin are unaffected. However, it is possible that while proteins such as complement, perforin, and bacterial toxins are structurally similar and can all induce cell membrane pores, their biomolecular properties are distinct and may therefore be differentially modulated by molecular events such as altered pH_i, V_m, or lipid membrane composition and conformation mediated by functional P-gp. That activated complement does not synergize with GzB to induce target cell apoptosis, while perforin, pneumolysin, and streptolysin can all perform this function highlights the functional differences that exist among these structurally related proteins.

C. Other P-gp-Related Phenomena That May Affect Apoptosis

Expression of functional P-gp has been shown to correlate with a significant decrease in the inner leaflet associated sphingomyelin (SM) pool and inhibition of TNF-induced ceramide production and apoptosis. Ceramide is generated by the cleavage of the SM precursor by acidic sphingomyelinase (aSMase) or neutral sphingomyelinase (nSMase). Apoptotic stimuli such as TNF, Fas ligand, and ionizing radiation have been shown to mediate rapid ceramide production, which in some instances correlates with the induction of apoptosis. Therefore, P-gp-mediated movement of SM out of the inner leaflet of the plasma membrane may result in a decrease in ceramide production by reducing the availability of SM to be acted on by either aSMase or nSMase. However, the fundamental role of ceramide in apoptosis induction is controversial. This therefore places some doubt on the physiological importance of P-gp-mediated ceramide regulation in the cell death pathway. As with the two hypotheses stated earlier, this is still a theoretical model and precise experimental systems need to be devised to formally demonstrate its importance.

V. SUMMARY/CONCLUSIONS

A physiological role for P-gp in effluxing toxins from cells has been well established, and expression of P-gp on the apical membranes of the gut, on liver cells, kidney tubules, and at the blood–brain barriers is consistent with this role. However, there is no obvious requirement for P-gp expression on pluripotent hemopoietic stem cells and immune cells such as NK cells and other lymphocytes. It is possible that P-gp may serve to protect immune cells against stress-induced apoptosis or bystander lysis mediated by triggering either Fas or TNF death pathways in the hostile site of inflammation.

The possibility that P-gp can regulate apoptosis is supported by the fact that other ABC transporters have been implicated in programmed cell death. For example, loss of the cystic fibrosis transmembrane regulator (CFTR) correlates with cellular resistance to apoptosis and is associated with a decrease in pH_i. In contrast, P-gp expression has been associated with an increase in intracellular pH. Considering that CFTR and P-gp have complementary expression, regulated expression of these proteins may determine the relative sensitivity of a given cell to various death stimuli.

Although significant evidence in tissue culture experiments suggests that P-gp may indeed play an important role in the regulation of cell death, *in vivo* experiments to support these findings have yet to be reported. Experiments utilizing *mdr1a/mdr1b* gene knockout mice will help define a physiological role for P-gp in the regulation of apoptosis.

Results suggest that a more effective way to treat P-gp-expressing MDR tumors may hinge on the selection of drugs that are less reliant on caspase activation. These drugs would be capable of rapidly inducing caspase-independent apoptosis via mitochondrial membrane disruption and would not require activation of caspases central to the receptor-mediated cell death pathway. Future drug design for the most effective treatment of P-gp-expressing MDR tumors could therefore focus on agents that meet two criteria: (i) they cannot be effluxed by P-gp and (ii) they do not rely on the activation of caspases to induce cell death. Thus, the development of chemotherapeutic reagents that function to perturb the mitochondrial membrane, mediate the release of cytochrome c, and induce caspase-independent cell death may lead to improved outcomes in the treatment of multidrug-resistant tumors.

See Also the Following Articles

CASPASES IN PROGRAMMED CELL DEATH • MULTIDRUG RESISTANCE I • MULTIDRUG RESISTANCE II • STEM CELL TRANSPLANTATION • TUMOR NECROSIS FACTORS

Bibliography

Ambudkar, S. V., Dey, S., Hrycyna, C. A., Rmachandra, M., Pastan, I., and Gottesman, M. M. (1999). Biochemical, cellular, and pharmacological aspects of the multidrug transporter. *Annu. Rev. Pharmacol. Toxicol.* **39**, 361.

Bezombes, C., Maestre, N., Laurent, G., Levade, T., Bettaieb, A., and Jaffrezou, J. P. (1998). Restoration of TNF-alpha-induced ceramide generation and apoptosis in resistant human leukemia KG1a cells by the P-glycoprotein blocker PSC833. *FASEB J.* **12**, 101–109.

Budihardjo, I., Oliver, H., Lutter, M., Lou, X., and Wang, X. (1999). Biochemical pathways of caspase activation during apoptosis. *Annu. Rev. Cell Dev. Biol.* **15**, 269.

Gottesman, M. M., and Pastan, I. (1993). Biochemistry of multidrug resistance mediated by the multidrug transporter. *Annu. Rev. Biochem.* **62**, 385.

Gottlieb, R. A., Nordberg, J., Skowronski, E., and Babior, B. M. (1996). Apoptosis induced in Jurkat cells by several agents is preceded by intracellular acidification. *Proc. Natl. Acad. Sci. USA* **93**, 654.

Hannun, Y. (1997). Apoptosis and the dilemma of cancer chemotherapy. *Blood* **89**, 1845.

Hofmann, K., and Dixit, V. M. (1998). Ceramide in apoptosis-does it really matter? *Trends Biochem. Sci.* **23**, 374.

Johnstone, R. W., Cretney, E., and Smyth, M. J. (1999). P-glycoprotein protects leukemia cells against caspase-dependent, but not caspase-independent, cell death. *Blood* **93**, 1075.

Johnstone, R. W., Ruefli, A. A., and Smyth, M. J. (2000). Multiple physiological functions for multidrug transporter P-glycoprotein. *Trends Biochem. Sci.* **25**, 1.

Krammer, P. H. (1999). CD95 (APO-1/Fas)-mediated apoptosis: Live and let die. *Adv. Immunol.* **71**, 163.

Los, M., Herr, I., Friesen, C., Fulda, S., Schulze-Osthoff, K., and Debatin, K.-M. (1997). Cross resistance of CD95- and drug-induced apoptosis as a consequence of deficient activation of caspases. *Blood* **90**, 3118.

Newton, K., and Strasser, A. (2000). Ionizing radiation and chemotherapeutic drugs induce apoptosis in lymphocytes in the absence of Fas or FADD/MORT1 signaling: Implications for cancer therapy. *J. Exp. Med.* **191**, 195.

Robinson, L. J., Roberts, W. K., Ling, T. T., Lamming, D., Sternberg, S. S., and Roepe, P. D. (1997). Human MDR1 protein overexpression delays the apoptotic cascade in Chinese hamster ovary fibroblasts. *Biochemistry* **36,** 11169.

Ruefli, A. A., Smyth, M. J., and Johnstone, R. W. (2000). HMBA induces activation of a caspase-independent cell death pathway to overcome P-glycoprotein-mediated drug resistance. *Blood* **95,** 2378.

Smyth, M. J., Krasovskis, E., Sutton, V. R., and Johnstone, R. W. (1998). The drug efflux protein, P-glycoprotein, additionally protects drug-resistant cells from multiple forms of caspase-dependent apoptosis. *Proc. Natl. Acad. Sci. USA* **95,** 7024.

Trezise, A. E., Romano, P. R., Gill, D. R., Hyde, S. C., Sepulveda, F. V., Buchwald, M., and Higgins, C. F. (1992). The multidrug resistance and cystic fibrosis genes have complementary patterns of epithelial expression. *EMBO J.* **12,** 4291.

van Veen, H. W., Callaghan, R., Soceneantu, L., Sardini, A., Konings, W. N., and Higgins, C. F. (1998). A bacterial antibiotic-resistance gene that complements the human multidrug resistance P-glycoprotein. *Nature* **391,** 291.

Weisburg, J. H., Roepe, P. D., Dzekunovm, S., and Scheinberg, D. A. (1999). Intracellular pH and multidrug resistance regulate complement-mediated cytotoxicity of nucleated human cells. *J. Biol. Chem.* **274,** 10877.

Photodynamic Therapy: Basic Principles and Applications to Skin Cancer

Sol Kimel
Genady Kostenich
Arie Orenstein

Sheba Medical Center, Tel Hashomer, Israel

GLOSSARY

autofluorescence Fluorescence arising from molecules occurring naturally in normal or diseased tissue.

fluorescence Reemission of light by a molecule upon absorption of a light photon, with the wavelength of the emitted light being greater than that of the absorbed light.

light-emitting diode A type of nonlaser light source in the form of small emitting elements, which may be arranged as a one or two-dimensional array for PDT treatments.

Nd:YAG laser A type of laser emitting near-infrared light used to cut or ablate tissue by conversion of the light into heat upon absorption by the tissue.

optical fiber A means of efficiently transmitting light energy over a distance, used in PDT to deliver light from a laser to the tissue.

photodynamic The biological effect of light activation of a photosensitizer, usually in the presence of oxygen.

photodynamic therapy (PDT) A treatment modality exploiting the use of light-activated drugs (photosensitizers).

photosensitizer A molecule (drug) that can absorb light and be transformed to a biologically active excited state.

singlet oxygen ($^1O_2$) An excited state of oxygen generated by energy transfer from an excited photosensitizer molecule.

I. INTRODUCTION

Photodynamic therapy (PDT), also termed photochemotherapy (PCT), is a novel modality for the treatment of cancer (see Fig. 1). It is based on systemic

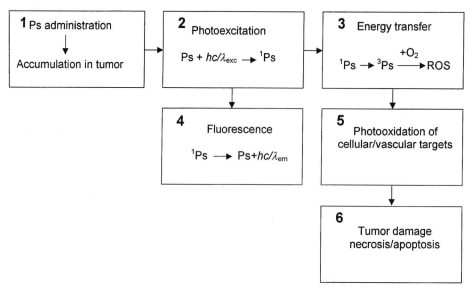

FIGURE 1   Schematic representation of PDT. Administration of photosensitizer (Ps) in conjunction with biological (frames 1, 6), photophysical (frames 2, 3, 4), and photochemical (frame 5) mechanisms leads to tumor reduction (frame 6).

or topical administration of a photosensitizer, which over time becomes preferentially retained in tumor tissue for reasons that are still not completely understood. When the ratio of photosensitizer accumulation in tumor and surrounding normal tissue (tumor to tissue ratio, TTR) is optimal, the tumor area is exposed to an appropriate light dose at a wavelength λ_{exc} selected to coincide with an absorption peak of the photosensitizer. Photoexcitation of a sensitizer molecule (to an excited state ^{1}Ps), followed by triplet formation (^{3}Ps) and subsequent energy transfer to ambient oxygen in tissue, leads to the generation of short-lived reactive oxygen species (ROS), including singlet molecular oxygen, $^1O_2$. These species are cytotoxic and elicit necrosis or apoptosis in tumor tissue when the tolerance threshold for PDT is exceeded. This may occur directly by cell inactivation ("cellular mechanism") and/or indirectly by destruction of the microcirculation that supplies blood to the tumor, inflicting lethal damage to cancerous cells ("vascular mechanism").

The necessary ingredients for PDT then are photosensitizer, oxygen, and light. This explains the advantage of PCT over regular chemotherapy. The photosensitizer is chosen to be nontoxic in the absence of light, and the process of preferential accumulation in tumors (which may last from hours to days) has few deleterious side effects. Moreover, there is threefold selectivity in PDT:

i. biological—sensitizer molecules are taken up preferentially in tumor cells (TTR>1)
ii. photophysical—irradiation is restricted to the tumor area
iii. photochemical—ROS are short-lived and only affect neighboring biomolecules.

The synthesis, in the early sixties, of the tumor-localizing hematoporphyrin derivative (HpD) preparation marks the beginning of modern PDT. Starting with the pioneering studies of Dougherty and coworkers in 1976, hundreds of articles have reported on the chemical constituents of HpD and of the commercial porphyrin preparations Photofrin or Photosan (manufactured, respectively, in Canada and in Germany), which are enriched in tumor-localizing components possessing more potent photodynamic activity. However, the intense research efforts expended in analyzing the complex mixtures HpD and Photofrin (Porfimer) have not led to a satisfactory understanding of their composition and degree of aggregation, nor of their mode(s) of action in PDT. After 1995, Photofrin (Fig. 2A) has received regulatory approval in various countries for PDT of selected neoplastic diseases. This has brought about an increase in the number of PDT-treated patients worldwide from a few hundred to a few thousand per year.

II. SELECTED PHOTOSENSITIZING AGENTS

Among the limitations of Photofrin we mention: (i) partially known heterogeneous composition; (ii) weak absorption of light in the therapeutic spectral region;

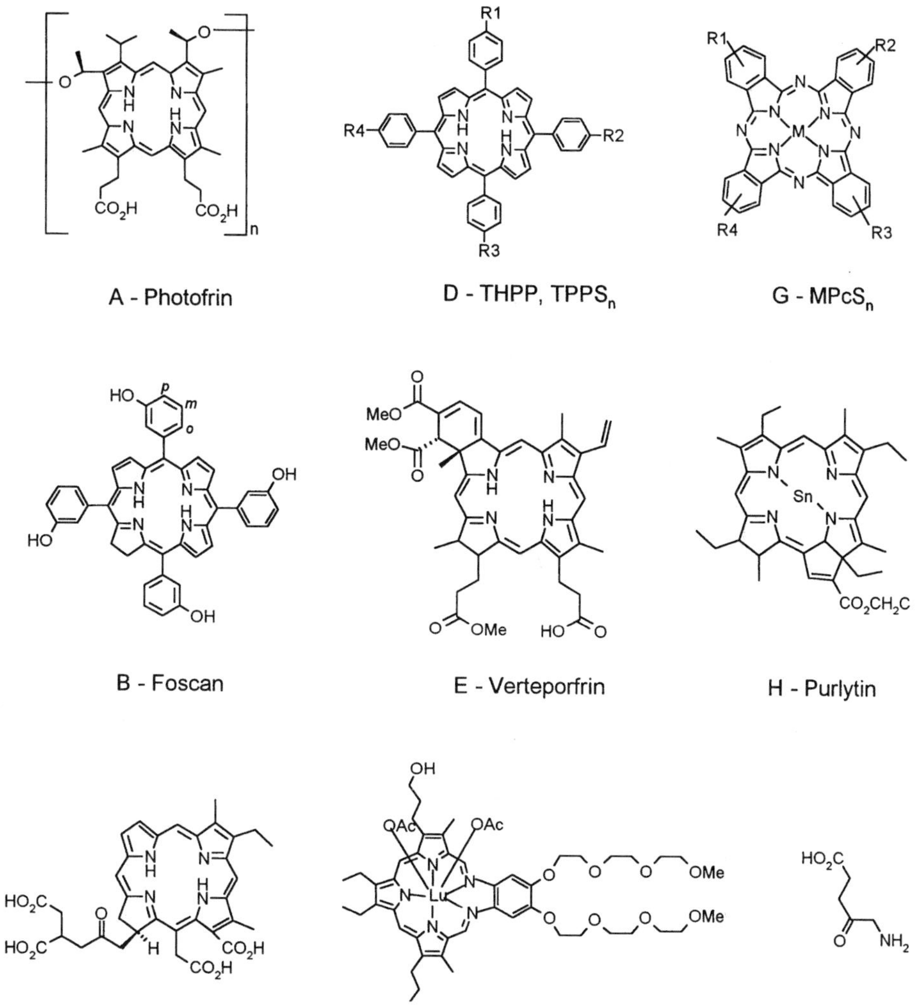

FIGURE 2 Chemical structures of several second-generation photosensitizers. Structure A: Photofrin, where n = 2 to 4. Structure B: meso-tetra(m-hydroxyphenyl) chlorin, m-THPC, where o, m, and p denote, respectively, ortho, meta, and para positions in the phenyl rings. Structure C: mono-L-aspartyl chlorin e_6. Structure D: hydroxylated or sulfonated tetraphenyl porphines, THPP or $TPPS_n$, where R_n=OH or SO_3^- and R_{4-n}=H. Structure E: benzoporphyrin derivative mono acid, BPD-MA. Structure F: Lutetium texaphyrin or Lutrin. Structure G: sulfonated metallo-phthalocyanines, $MPcS_n$, where M=Al, Zn; S=SO_3^-, and n = 0, 1, 2, 3, 4. In structure G, the substituents R=SO_3^- are located on positions 4 or 5 (counting from an N atom). CASPc is a mixed chloroaluminum sulfonated phthalocyanine, with n = 3, 4. Structure H: tin ethyl etiopurpurin. Structure K: 5-aminolevulinic acid, ALA.

(iii) poor preferential uptake/retention in tumor tissue (TTR<2); and (iv) long-lasting generalized cutaneous phototoxicity. Second-generation photosensitizers for improved PDT protocols are under development in many laboratories and are in various phases of pre-clinical and clinical trials. Such photosensitizers should be chemically pure nontoxic compounds, characterized by strong absorption in the red and near-infrared spectral region, 630–800 nm, and possess photophysical properties conducive for generating ROS. Ideally, they should display advantageous tumor-localizing features (TTR>3) and be rapidly cleared from healthy tissue and plasma.

A few dozen porphyrin analogs are currently being evaluated for their PDT potential, some of them in phase II/III clinical trials. These include *meso*-tetra (*m*-hydroxyphenyl)chlorin, *m*-THPC (Foscan, Fig. 2B), mono-L-aspartyl chlorin e_6 (NPe$_6$, Fig. 2C), hydroxy-lated and sulfonated tetraphenyl porphines, THPP and TPPS$_n$ (Fig. 2D), benzoporphyrin derivative mono acid, BPD-MA (Verteporfin, Fig. 2E), Lu-texaphyrin (Lutex, Fig. 2F), sulfonated metallo-phthalocyanines, MPcS$_n$ (M=Al, Zn; S=SO$_3^-$, Fig. 2G), e.g., chloro-aluminum sulfonated phthalocyanine (CASPc), tin ethyl etiopurpurin (Purlytin, Fig. 2H), and the prodrug 5-aminolevulinic acid, ALA (Levulan, Fig. 2K), a precursor of endogenous protoporphyrin IX.

ALA is part of the natural heme biosynthetic pathway in mammalian cells. The initial step in this synthesis is formation of ALA by ALA synthase, and the final step is the incorporation of ferric ion into the tetrapyrrole ring of protoporphyrin IX (Pp-IX) by ferrochelatase. The rate of synthesis is regulated by negative feedback heme control of the ALA synthase activity. Supplying cells with exogenous ALA (Fig. 2K) bypasses this control, leading to overproduction of endogenous porphyrins. Because of the limited ferrochelatase capacity, exogenous ALA mainly produces highly photoactive Pp-IX.

In cancerous cells, ALA-induced Pp-IX may be overexpressed because of the disturbed activity of some enzymes in the heme biosynthetic pathway. The systemic administration of ALA (intravenous, intraperitoneal, or oral) leads to increased Pp-IX concentration in blood and internal organs. Malignant tumors in particular show a higher accumulation of ALA-induced Pp-IX than adjacent normal tissues. In contrast to slow-acting Photofrin, selective Pp-IX accumulation can be achieved 1–3 h after ALA administration, followed by a decrease of the Pp-IX concentration to the normal level within 24 h. TTR of Pp-IX depends on tumor type/location and varies from 1.4 (carcinoma of esophagus) to 5 (skin squamous cell carcinoma). ALA induces Pp-IX also when applied topically (or by inhalation and instillation). ALA molecules can penetrate through skin layers and produce Pp-IX intracellularly in tumor depth.

These second-generation photosensitizers differ significantly in their photophysical properties and pharmacokinetics and, consequently, in PDT efficacy. For a given photosensitizer, the therapeutic effect of PDT is mainly dependent on three parameters: photosensitizer dose, light dose, and interval between drug administration and photoirradiation. Many PDT trials using systemic and topically applied photosensitizers have been performed for different types of cancers. However, no standard clinical protocol is available for each photosensitizer and each morphological type of tumor.

The following sections review general properties for the major classes of sensitizers. Their advantages are discussed in comparison with Photofrin. This is illustrated by a discussion of structure–activity relationships (SAR) for AlPcS$_n$.

III. PHOTOPHYSICAL AND PHOTOBIOLOGICAL PROPERTIES

A. Spectral Considerations

"Molecular design" has been successful in optimizing sensitizers with desired spectral properties. By judicious modification of the chemical structure of the tetrapyrrole macrocycle common to most photosensitizers (e.g., hydrogenation, insertion of double bonds, addition of ring moieties, peripheral substitution, and metal–ion coordination), spectral characteristics can be changed to order in a predetermined fashion.

1. Intensities

The large range of absorbance values associated with various photosensitizers, as exemplified in Fig. 3, presents interesting challenges for light dosimetry. Often, clinical comparisons do not take this into account. Photoactivity based on drug dosages should be nor-

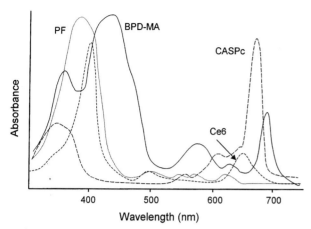

FIGURE 3 Absorption spectra of photosensitizers in the visible region. Note the large differences in the absorbance of Photofrin (PF at 630 nm), chlorin (Ce6 at 650 nm), BPD (at 690 nm), and CASPc (at 675 nm).

malized for absorbance to obtain inherent efficacy values. On a practical level, high absorption of "therapeutic light" (in the red spectral region) allows using smaller drug dosages with concomitant lower general toxicity.

2. Spectral Ranges

A characteristic spectrum shows a strong absorbance in the blue spectral region (Soret band, around 400 nm) and several weak absorbances in the red spectral region (Q bands, between 600 and 800 nm) (Fig. 3). By chemical modification of structure, Q bands can be intensified and shifted further into the red and near-infrared region to allow deeper tissue penetration of therapeutic light. However, occasionally it is advantageous to use a sensitizer with a less red-shifted Q band to avoid PDT damage to deeper lying, healthy tissue.

B. Biodistribution and Pharmacokinetics

This remains the single most important open question in PDT. Extensive research is being carried out to correlate biological characteristics, such as TTR, with chemical structure, but the mechanisms remain largely unknown. In the "cellular mechanism," sensitizer molecules administered intravenously have to pass through endothelial cells and vascular membrane structures, and diffuse through interstitial spaces be-

fore entering tumor cells. In the "vascular mechanism" too, the route to endothelial cell uptake and destruction is arduous. We mention here four approaches to the better understanding, on the molecular level, of uptake and retention of sensitizers in various biological compartments:

1. Hydro/lipo/amphiphilicity

Cellular internalization of sensitizers by passive diffusion seems to correlate with lipophilicity. For hydrophilic and ionic compounds, endocytosis becomes the dominant mode of cellular uptake. This has been studied systematically for a series of increasingly sulfonated tetraphenyl porphines, $TPPS_n$ (Fig. 2D), and metallo-phthalocyanines, $MPcS_n$ (Fig. 2G). Uptake *in vitro* correlates positively with lipophilicity, whereas uptake *in vivo* may show a negative correlation.

2. Conjugation to Tumor-Specific Delivery Systems

Binding of sensitizers to lipoproteins and monoclonal antibodies or encapsulation in liposomes has been used to improve *in vivo* tumor uptake (TTR) and PDT efficacy. Peripheral substitution in *m*-THPC (Fig. 2B) with high molecular weight polyethyleneglycol chains (PEG-*m*-THPC) influences the TTR and the "drug–light time window."

3. Tissue–pH-Dependent Uptake

Because of metabolic acidosis, the average pH of tumor tissue is about one unit lower (pH 6.4) than in normal tissue (pH 7.4). Porphyrins exist in a dynamic ionic equilibrium of various species, ranging from dicationic, through neutral to dianionic, depending on the pH of the microenvironment. In extracellular tumor space, at pH 6.4, neutral molecules can cross a cell membrane by diffusion, but in the intracellular medium at pH 7.4 they are transformed into ionic species and become "trapped." Anionic species tend to localize in lysosomes and cationic ones in mitochondria.

4. Stereochemical Factors

Amphiphilic compounds, such as $TPPS_{2a}$ (sulfonated on two adjacent phenyl rings, Fig. 2D) or $AlPcS_{2a}$ (sulfonated on two adjacent phthalic subunits, Fig. 2G), where $R_1=R_2=SO_3^-$ and $R_3=R_4=H$, or

BPD (Fig. 2E), are taken up to a greater extent and show higher biological activity than S_{2o}-type sensitizers (sulfonated on opposite subunits, where $R_1 = R_3 = SO_3^-$ and $R_2 = R_4 = H$). This is presumably because amphiphilic compounds can enter cells by several complementary uptake mechanisms.

The high PDT efficacy of amphiphilic S_{2a}-type compared to otherwise similar S_{2o}-type porphines and phthalocyanines (Figs. 2D,G), and also the high PDT efficacy of meta-THPC versus the nonactive isomeric species ortho-THPC and para-THPC (Fig. 2B), has led to a study of common geometrical features of active photosensitizers. Structural modeling of these and related compounds showed that a pair of oxygen atoms (originating in SO_3^-, COO^-, or OH substituents), separated by a "critical" distance of 1.2 nm, confer increased photodynamic efficacy to a sensitizer. The more difficult question as to what receptor molecule in a target cell is responsible for the preferential binding of a sensitizer molecule remains to be resolved; tubulin and calmodulin have been suggested.

C. Structure–Activity Relationships

SAR for AlPcS$_n$

Comparing photophysical and chemical properties of a series of structurally related photosensitizers in solution provides important information on their potential photodynamic applications. The monomeric (photoactive) form is favored for preparations consisting of mixtures of various regioisomers (e.g., substituted on different locations in a phthalic subunit, Fig. 2G) or of compounds sulfonated to a different degree ($n = 0$, 1, 2, 3, or 4). Although pure compounds are generally preferred as pharmaceuticals, mixed isomeric preparations may be favored as photodynamic agents compared to isomerically pure compounds. Mixed preparations are likely to be more efficient drugs for PDT. They contain a higher monomer fraction, exhibit better uptake characteristics, and can attack a variety of intracellular target molecules. This may be the reason for the relatively high PDT efficacy of the "impure" commercial porphyrin preparations HpD, Photofrin, and Photosan or commercial mixed AlPcS$_n$ preparations CASPc and Photosens.

IV. PHOTODYNAMIC THERAPY OF SKIN CANCERS

Cancer registries have reported an increase in the past decade of the incidence rates of BCC and SCC, the more common types of nonmelanoma skin cancer. Conventional treatments include surgical excision, cryotherapy, curettage, electrodesiccation, ionizing radiation, and topical chemotherapy. PDT presents a novel alternative that is noninvasive, is well tolerated by patients, and can be repeated without cumulative toxicity. PDT is the treatment of choice for patients with large or multicentric lesions, especially on facial areas where cosmetic considerations are important. Also, PDT is preferred for patients under anticoagulant therapy and for patients with contraindications for multifactorial health risks that prohibit surgical intervention. This section reviews therapeutic results for several types of nonmelanoma skin cancers.

A. Basal Cell Carcinoma

HpD- or Photofrin-based PDT was applied to many patients bearing BCC. Clinical protocols included 1–5 mg/kg intravenous (iv) drug administration, a 24- to 48-h drug–light interval, and photoirradiation using lasers (630 nm) or noncoherent (600–700 nm) light sources. In most studies, complete response (CR) was achieved in 90–100% of tumors after 70–280 J/cm^2 irradiation at 630 nm, with a follow-up of 20–43 months. The main disadvantage of HpD- or Photofrin-based PDT is increased skin photosensitivity persisting 6–8 weeks after drug administration.

Currently, some experimental photosensitizers, e.g., BPD, NPe6, m-THPC, and AlPcS$_n$, are under active investigation for PDT of skin cancer; BPD and NPe6 are reported to cause less skin photosensitivity than Photofrin.

Topical ALA-mediated PDT is now used extensively for the local treatment of various skin cancers, including BCC. It can be applied to patients with multiple tumors without causing general phototoxicity. In a typical clinical protocol, an oil-in-water emulsion (dermatological cream, lotion or ointment) of 20% ALA is applied to a skin lesion for 3–16 h, followed by photoirradiation using laser (630 nm) or nonlaser light sources. The duration of ALA exposure influences the Pp-IX concentration and distribution in tumor. A prolonged application time increases the depth of ALA penetration and homogeneity of Pp-IX distribution but decreases selectivity of the treatment.

The results of ALA-PDT depended significantly on the tumor depth. For superficial BCC (sBCC), CR ranged from 80 to100%, with a follow-up of 3–36 months. For nodular BCC (nBCC), CR varied from 70%, for tumors with depth <2 mm, to 40% for tumors with depth >2 mm, at a mean follow-up period of 10 months.

B. Squamous Cell Carcinoma

Bowen's disease (*in situ* intraepidermal squamous cell carcinoma) is sensitive to PDT. Excellent results, with CR close to 100%, were achieved using systemic administration of HpD and laser irradiation. A high CR rate (90–100%) was also demonstrated using a protocol for topical ALA-PDT, with a follow-up from 7 to 22 months. A comparative randomized study showed that topical ALA-PDT is more efficient than cryotherapy in the treatment of Bowen's disease: 100% CR was achieved after one to two PDT sessions, compared with 90% CR after one to three cryotherapy sessions (1 year follow-up).

SCC (superficial and nodular) lesions were treated using systemic HpD/Photofrin administration followed by laser irradiation. Depending on the light dose, CR varied from 40 to 77%, as confirmed by histology; with a follow-up at 48 months. For topical ALA-PDT, the CR rate depended on tumor thickness. Superficial tumors showed a high response to treatment (CR 80–90%), as opposed to poor response for nodular ulcerated SCC (CR 30%); follow-up was 24–36 months.

C. Other Tumors

PDT of mycosis fungoides (MF) has been demonstrated with HpD (systemic administration) and ALA (topical application). MF is a form of cutaneous T-cell lymphoma, a malignancy of T-helper cells, which initially appears in the skin. The advanced stage of the disease involves the entire lymphoreticular system, the lymph nodes, and internal organs. In comparison to BCC lesions, MF showed an erratic therapeutic response. Clinical and histological remission was achieved in early plaque stage MF after a number of PDT sessions. Advanced tumor stage MF responded poorly to PDT (CR 30–60%). In addition, patients should be treated as needed for systemic involvement of the disease.

Kaposi's sarcoma (KS) was treated mainly by systemic HpD-PDT. The response varied from partial to complete depending on the treatment parameters. HpD-PDT may be used as a palliative for skin metastases of breast cancer (BC). The treatment showed good short-term results; however, recurrence is frequent, especially in thick and extensive lesions. Topical ALA-PDT of KS and BC is not effective because of the limited penetration of ALA into the tumor depth.

V. FLUORESCENCE DETECTION, TREATMENT MONITORING, AND CONTROL

Porphyrin-type photosensitizers fluoresce red light at λ_{em} when illuminated with ultraviolet-blue light. This property is used for tumor detection, if a photosensitizer has accumulated selectively in the tumor (Fig. 1). Fluorescence via endoscopic observation can significantly enhance the early diagnosis of many (pre)cancerous lesions of the aerodigestive and gastrointestinal tracts, and of urothelial and gynecologic abnormalities. The photodynamic diagnosis (PDD) method of tumor detection is now in progress in several clinical trials. Integrated imaging and light emitting systems include fiber optic components delivering diagnostic (blue) light for fluorescence excitation and therapeutic (red) light for treatment.

During photoirradiation, the fluorescence decreases due to photobleaching of the photosensitizer, i.e., photodestruction caused by ROS. Modification of Pp-IX molecules is accompanied by the reduction of a double bond and formation of chlorin-type photoproducts [compare the macrocycle of porphyrin (Fig. 2A) with that of chlorin (Fig. 2B)], which are characterized by fluorescence at 680 nm (Fig. 4). Photobleaching

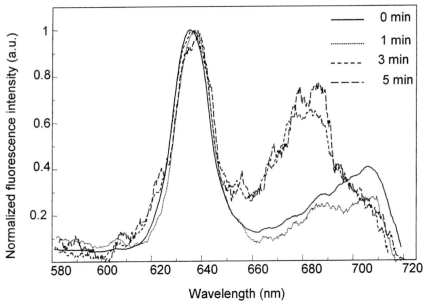

FIGURE 4 Photodegradation of ALA-mediated Pp-IX. Note that after 3 and 5 min irradiation, chlorin-type photoproducts are formed that fluoresce at 680 nm.

kinetics may be influenced by the tumor size and thickness and can provide additional information for PDD. For example, after topical application of ALA, different patterns of Pp-IX photobleaching were observed in superficial and nodular skin lesions. Superficial lesions exhibited a fast decrease of fluorescence intensity, whereas in thick lesions (nodular BCC, MF, and KS), fluorescence decreased at a slower rate and reappeared after a period of time (Fig. 5). The phenomenon of fluorescence recovery probably reflects

continued Pp-IX production in the deeply located areas of the tumor and diffusion of Pp-IX to the surface of the lesion (either from living or from damaged cells). In such cases an additional photoirradiation procedure can be performed. Thus, fluorescence monitoring, when included in the clinical PDT protocol, may be helpful for light dose optimization and treatment control.

In conclusion, the past decade has seen an evolution of PDT from an experimental technique to a fully fledged clinical modality for the treatment of a variety of neoplasms.

See Also the Following Articles

Molecular Aspects of Radiation Biology • Photodynamic Therapy: Clinical Applications • Skin Cancer (Non-Melanoma)

Bibliography

Boyle, R. W., and Dolphin, D. (1996). Structure and biodistribution relationships of photodynamic sensitizers. *Photochem. Photobiol.* **64,** 469–485.

Fisher, A. M. R., Murphree, A. L., and Gomer, C. J. (1995). Clinical and preclinical photodynamic therapy. *Lasers Surg. Med.* **17,** 2–31.

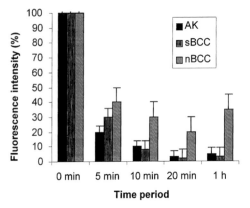

FIGURE 5 Fluorescence monitoring of ALA-mediated Pp-IX in patients bearing actinic keratosis (AK) and superficial (sBCC) and nodular BCC (nBCC).

Henderson, B. W., and Dougherty, T. J. (eds.) (1992). "Photodynamic Therapy: Basic Principles and Clinical Applications," pp. 1–444. Dekker, New York.

Jori, G. (1996). Tumour photosensitizers: Approaches to enhance the selectivity and efficiency of photodynamic therapy. *J. Photochem. Photobiol. B Biol.* **36,** 87–93.

Ochsner, M. (1997). Photophysical and photobiological processes in the photodynamic therapy of tumours. *J. Photochem. Photobiol. B Biol.* **39,** 1–18.

Orenstein, A., Kostenich, G., and Malik, Z. (1997). The kinetics of protoporphyrin fluorescence during ALA-PDT in human malignant skin tumors. *Cancer Lett.* **120,** 229–234.

Peng, Q., Warloe, T., Berg, K., Moan, J., Kongshaug, M., Gierscksky, K. E., and Nesland, J. M. (1997). 5-Aminolevulinic acid-based photodynamic therapy: Clinical research and future challenges. *Cancer* **79,** 2282–2308.

Winkelman, J. W., Arad, D., and Kimel, S. (1993). Stereochemical factors in the transport and binding of photosensitizers in biological systems and in photodynamic therapy. *J. Photochem. Photobiol. B Biol.* **18,** 181–189.

Photodynamic Therapy: Clinical Applications

Brian C. Wilson

Ontario Cancer Institute/University of Toronto and
Photonics Research Ontario

I. Introduction
II. Clinical Techniques
III. Specific Clinical Applications
IV. Photodynamic Diagnostics
V. Summary

GLOSSARY

autofluorescence Fluorescence arising from molecules occurring naturally in normal or diseased tissue.

fluorescence Reemission of light by a molecule upon absorption of a light photon, with the wavelength of the emitted light being greater than that of the absorbed light.

light-emitting diode A type of nonlaser light source in the form of small emitting elements, which may be arranged as a one or two-dimensional array for PDT treatments.

Nd:YAG laser A type of laser emitting near-infrared light used to cut or ablate tissue by conversion of the light into heat upon absorption by the tissue.

optical fiber A means of efficiently transmitting light energy over a distance, used in PDT to deliver light from a laser to the tissue.

photodynamic The biological effect of light activation of a photosensitizer, usually in the presence of oxygen.

photodynamic therapy (PDT) A treatment modality exploiting the use of light-activated drugs (photosensitizers).

photosensitizer A molecule (drug) that can absorb light and be transformed to a biologically active excited state.

singlet oxygen ($^1O_2$) An excited state of oxygen generated by energy transfer from an excited photosensitizer molecule.

The primary application of light-activated drugs (photodynamic therapy: PDT) in oncology is for local destruction of solid tumors. After outlining the technical approaches to this treatment, the status of its use in specific sites is reviewed. The general advantages and current limitations are summarized and the roles of tumor detection and localization are also described. This article complements the companion article "Photodynamic Therapy: Basic Principles and Applications to Skin Cancer" by Kimel, Kosterich, and Orenstein.

I. INTRODUCTION

The basic aspects of photodynamic therapy and application to skin cancer treatment have been described in the previous article in this volume. The focus here is on the wider clinical applications in oncology. Beyond this, the concept of light-activated drugs is also being explored for nononcologic clinical applications, exploiting the different mechanisms of action. For example, vascularly targeted PDT is being developed for the treatment of macular degeneration in which choroidal neovasculature leads to blindness. A second example is the treatment of rheumatoid arthritis, in which both tissue destruction and induced immune response are involved. In cardiology, PDT is being evaluated for the prevention of restenosis following angioplasty, based on selective reduction of smooth muscle cell proliferation, whereas in gynecology it may be useful for selective endometrial ablation. Applied *ex vivo*, it is under evaluation for viral purging of blood products.

In oncology, the primary application of PDT is in the destruction of solid tumors. The tumor sites where clinical trials have been reported (Table I) include (i) lesions located in easily accessible sites such as skin and oral cavity, (ii) lesions in hollow organs that can

be treated endoscopically, as in the bronchus, gastrointestinal tract, urinary bladder, and female reproductive tract, (iii) deep-seated lesions within solid organs that can be treated either by interstitial light delivery or at the time of surgical resection, and (iv) diffuse lesions of the thoracic cavity and peritoneum.

Depending on the tumor site and stage, the clinical intent may be palliative, curative, or prophylactic. Palliative examples are opening of obstructing bronchial or esophageal lesions and treatment of cutaneous metastases of breast cancer. Curative intent is seen in dysplasias and early stage tumors of several sites, including lung, esophagus, skin, and bladder. For prophylaxis, PDT has been used to eradicate metaplastic esophageal mucosa (Barrett's disease) and in actinic keratosis of the skin.

Although an estimated 10,000 cancer patients have been treated with PDT since its first clinical use in the late 1970s, most have been outside randomized trials, often upon failure of standard modalities. Hence, there are relatively few completed prospectively randomized Phase III trials. The technique it-

TABLE I
Reported Solid Tumor Sites of PDT Clinical Trials (Roughly in Decreasing Order
of Number of Patients), Clinical Intent, and Tumor Type

Site	Intent	Tumor type
Skin	Cure or palliation Palliation	Basal cell carcinoma, squamous cell carcinoma, Bowen's disease, nonpigmented melanoma, cutaneous metastases of breast cancer, Kaposi's sarcoma
Lung	Cure Palliation Reduction presurgery	Dysplasia, CIS, early stage (non-small cell)[a] Obstructing,[a] mesothelioma Obstructing
Esophagus	Prophylaxis Cure[a] Palliation	Barrett's disease Dysplasia, CIS, noninvasive early stage Obstructing[a]
Bladder	Cure or palliation[a]	Superficial transitional cell carcinoma
Head and neck	Cure Palliation	Leukoplakia, field cancerization Recurrent or metastatic
Brain	Extend survival Cure Palliation	Malignant glial: primary or recurrent Pituitary adenoma Intracranial metastasis
Gynecological	Palliation Cure	Diffuse peritoneal spread of ovarian cancer Vulvar/vaginal dysplasia[a]
Stomach	Cure	Early gastric adenocarcinoma[a]
Colorectal	Palliation or reduction presurgery	Obstructing adenocarcinoma
Eye	Cure	Choiroidal, iris, or ciliary body melanoma

[a]Existing governmental approvals in the United States, Canada, Japan, and/or Europe (all with Photofrin).

self also continues to evolve, with new light sources, light delivery technologies, and new photosensitizers entering clinical trials. In some cases, this has radically changed the treatment so that the results are not necessarily comparable with earlier data. Hence, we will not attempt to be exhaustive here, but rather will illustrate key concepts and point to future developments.

II. CLINICAL TECHNIQUES

This section briefly describes the main technical features of PDT as applied to solid tumor therapy.

A. Photosensitizers

The majority of clinical studies of PDT have used a purified version of hematoporphyrin derivative (HpD), developed originally as a fluorescent tumor-localizing agent. All governmental approvals for PDT in solid tumor therapy to date have used a commercial version of this drug (Photofrin, Axcan, Canada). Although it is quite effective, Photofrin has limitations in that it causes general skin photosensitivity over several weeks and has only a low light absorption at the longer red/near-infrared wavelengths where light penetration in tissue is greatest. Photofrin is usually administered intravenously as an aqueous solution, typically at around 2 mg per kg body weight, and is activated at 630 nm. The uptake in tumor and the tumor-to-host tissue ratio (typically <3:1) is highest at 1–2 days postadministration.

Second-generation photosensitizers, as listed in Table II, offer several advantages, namely improved light absorption at long wavelengths, reduced skin photosensitivity, better tumor selectivity in some cases, higher photodynamic efficiency, and well-defined pharmacokinetics (being single chemical species). An alternative approach is aminolevulinic acid (ALA), the administration of which leads to an increased endogenous generation of the protoporphyrin

TABLE II
PDT Agents in Clinical Trials for Solid Tumor Therapy and Main (Long) Activation Wavelength[a]

Photosensitizer (trade name)	Wavelength (nm)	Specific clinically relevant characteristic
HpD hemato<u>porphyrin</u> derivative (Photofrin or Photosan)	630	Water soluble Complex mixture of many porphyrins
PpIX 5-aminolevulinic acid-induced proto<u>porphyrin</u> IX, (Levulan)	630	Selective synthesis in different tissue compartments Topical or systemic application
mTHPC meso-tetra(m-hydroxyphenyl)<u>chlorin</u> (Foscan)	650	Low drug and light dose Requires delivery vehicle
SnET$_2$ tin ethyl etiopurpurin (<u>chlorin</u>) (Purlytin)	660	Mild but extended photosensitivity Requires delivery vehicle
Npe6 mono-L-aspartyl <u>chlorin</u> e6	660	Minimal long-term skin photosensitivity Water soluble
ZnPC Zinc(II) <u>phthalocyanine</u>	670	Mild skin photosensitivity Liposomal delivery
BPD-MA Benzo<u>porphyrin</u> derivative-monoacid ring A (Verteporfin)	690	Mild skin photosensitivity Liposomal delivery Primarily nononcologic applications
Lutetium <u>texaphrin</u> (Lutrin)	730	Rapid clearance Water soluble High tumor-to-skin selectivity

[a]The chemical class is underlined.

photosensitizer PpIX. ALA may be given topically (e.g., for skin lesions) or orally. It does show excellent tumor selectivity in some sites, but is less potent than some of the other second-generation drugs (partly due to its high rate of photobleaching), and its longest activation wavelength is still only around 630 nm.

B. Light Sources

The light sources used for PDT must have adequate power delivered to the lesion at the wavelength ap-propriate to the specific photosensitizer used. The power required depends on the lesion surface area or volume. For example, to treat a 5-cm-diameter lesion using surface irradiation to a typical energy density (fluence) of 100 Joules · cm^{-2} in a treatment time of 15 min requires 2.2 W of delivered power (19.6 cm^2 × 100 J · cm^{-2}/900 s). Similarly, interstitial irradia-tion (see Fig. 1) using four 3-cm-long diffusing fibers delivering 100 J · cm^{-1} in 15 min requires 1.3 W (12 cm × 100 J · cm^{-1}/900 s). Presently, three main tech-nologies are available: lasers, high-brightness lamps

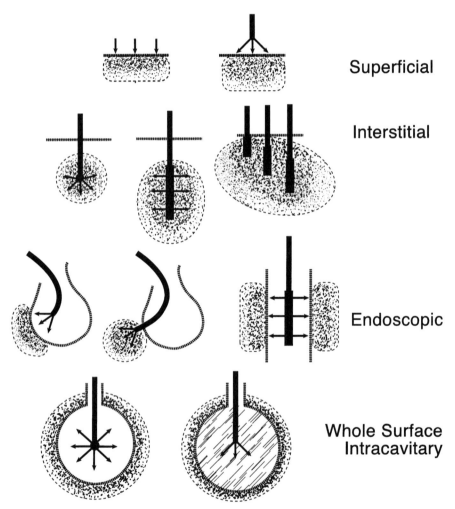

Superficial

Interstitial

Endoscopic

Whole Surface Intracavitary

FIGURE 1 Light irradiation techniques used in solid tumor PDT showing the methods for differ-ent tumor forms and sites using optical fiber-based light delivery. Intraluminal and interstitial cases show the use of cylindrical diffusing fibers (see also Fig. 2, top) or point diffusers. A point diffuser is also seen in the intracavitary case (left), with the alternative (right) being to fill the cavity with a light-scatter-ing liquid. Stippled regions indicate schematically the light distributions within the tissue, which de-crease exponentially with distance from the irradiated tissue surface or interstitial source.

with wavelength filtering, and light-emitting diode (LED) arrays, the main characteristics of which are listed in Table III. These technologies continue to evolve, and it is also likely that new sources, particularly pulsed lasers, will be introduced.

C. Light Delivery Devices

A critical part of PDT treatment is delivering the light efficiently and accurately to the target lesion. Figure 1 shows the variety of "geometries" that can be used, including (i) surface irradiation of accessible tissues (skin, oral cavity, surgical resection cavities); (ii) interstitial irradiation with point- or cylindrically diffusing tipped optical fibers inserted into the tumor, with the fiber length and spacing (typically 5–10 mm) being selected to cover the tumor volume; and (iii) intraluminal irradiation, either endoscopic or intraoperative. Whole surface treatments, as in the esophagus, bladder, body cavities, or intraoperative resection cavities, normally utilize a means to distribute the light uniformly, either by a diffusing-tip fiber or by a light-scattering liquid filling the cavity or within an extendable balloon (Fig. 2, bottom). For endoscopy, the light applicator may be placed directly or via the endoscope instrument channel (Fig. 2, top).

D. PDT Dosimetry

Successful PDT treatment requires achieving an adequate level of singlet oxygen ($^1O_2$) generation throughout the tumor volume. This depends on the light distribution, the photosensitizer uptake and distribution, and the local tissue oxygen concentration, each of which can vary significantly from patient to patient and even from lesion to lesion in the same patient. Hence, ideally, some form of monitoring or "dosimetry" should be used to tailor the treatment for individual patients. This is technically very challenging and, while methods are under development, these have not yet entered routine clinical use. Hence, PDT trials have been carried out largely according to empirically determined administered photosensitizer and light "doses." This makes comparisons between trials uncertain and likely contributes to treatment failures and unacceptable toxicities found in some studies.

III. SPECIFIC CLINICAL APPLICATIONS

A. Skin

Compared to other lesion sites, these treatments are technically straightforward. Optical fiber delivery is generally not required, except for interstitial irradiation of thicker nodular lesions. Skin lesions have been one of the main sites for topical ALA-PDT, but other second-generation photosensitizers have also been investigated. The clinical response rates can be comparable to standard therapies, there is generally excellent cosmesis, lesions can be retreated if they recur, and prior surgical, radiotherapy, and chemotherapy failures may be treated successfully. PDT is particularly attractive for widespread lesions, as in basal cell nevus syndrome. Melanoma remains a problem because of the poor light penetration in these pigmented lesions, but may be treatable with longer wavelength photosensitizers.

TABLE III
Clinical Light Sources for Solid Tumor PDT

Source type	Main advantages	Main limitations
Laser	Coupling to single optical fibers for interstitial or endoscopic use Well-defined wavelength	High cost Single wavelength per laser or complex tunable laser required
Filtered lamp	Low cost High total power for surface irradiation Wavelength selectable over wide range	Cannot be used with single optical fibers
LED array	Low cost High power over both large and small areas	Rigid structure Limited wavelengths available

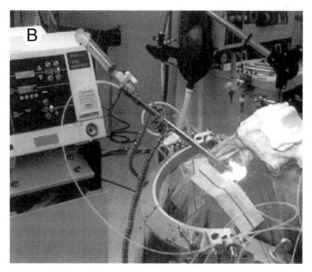

FIGURE 2 Examples of clinical treatments in progress. (Top) Cylindrical diffuser fiber being placed within the instrument channel of an endoscope for intraluminal irradiation (here, esophageal). Courtesy of Dr. Norman Marcon. (Bottom) Irradiation of the resection cavity using an inflatable balloon device filled with a light-scattering liquid following surgical resection of a brain tumor. The laser source is seen on the left, with optical fibers carrying the light to the treatment applicator. Courtesy of Dr. Paul Muller.

B. Lung

For bronchial tumors, PDT is delivered endoscopically. Photofrin-PDT is effective in the palliation of obstructing, inoperable lesions. (Note: Historically, clinical trials have used different variants of HpD-based photosensitizers. Here these will be referred to simply as "Photofrin-PDT," although not all trials used this specific commercial formulation.) In patients who are not candidates for surgery and radiotherapy, PDT has been compared with conventional endoscopic Nd:YAG laser debulking. The response rate in the PDT group at 1 month was approximately double that of the thermal ablation group, with similar adverse reaction rates. In other studies, PDT plus external beam radiotherapy gave a 70% complete luminal reopening in obstructing bronchial tumors versus 10% in radiation-only controls, with double the time to local recurrence and more frequent long-term responses. PDT has also been used preoperatively to reduce the extent of surgical resection or to make patients suitable for surgery.

Photofrin-PDT has been approved in some jurisdictions as a stand-alone treatment for early stage bronchial lesions. Complete response rates of over 90% have been achieved for superficial lesions less than 1 cm in diameter, although this fell to less than 40% for lesions greater than 2 cm. Overall, a 5-year disease-free survival of 68% has been reported, with follow-up periods as long as 176 months. Toilet bronchoscopy is performed to remove the necrotic debris a day or two after treatment, at which time a second light application can be given for any residual tumor. In these patients, PDT preserves lung function, can be repeated if there is local recurrence or second primaries, and does not preclude subsequent surgery. It remains to be seen if the response rates can be increased in the larger and nodular lesions with newer photosensitizers.

C. Gastrointestinal Tract (GI)

The esophagus has been the main focus for PDT studies in the GI tract. As in the bronchus, both curative and palliative applications have been developed, in addition to prophylaxis of premalignant disease.

Multicenter randomized trials comparing Photofrin-PDT with Nd:YAG thermal laser ablation for the palliation of obstructing esophageal cancer have shown equivalent improvement in dysphagia between the two groups, but the PDT response was longer lasting (32% versus 20% of patients at 1 month), with more complete responses (9 versus 2) and required fewer procedures. A drawback remains the relatively high cost of the drug compared with thermal laser ablation or stenting.

Studies with curative intent for early stage, noninvasive esophageal cancer (squamous cell and adenocarcinoma) have been reported with both Photofrin and mTHPC. For example, with the latter, 30 of 36 tumors showed no recurrence after disease-free survival intervals of 3–35 months using red light activation. Reduced responses were seen with T_1 and T_2 lesions, but long-term (>5 year) disease-free survivors were noted in the early stage group. The use of less penetrating green light reduced the perforation rate in these patients.

There has been considerable interest in the use of PDT to eliminate metaplasic mucosa of Barrett's esophagus, where the risk of dysplasia and subsequent cancer is very high. In a comparison with Nd:YAG laser ablation, up to 80% of Photofrin-PDT-treated Barrett's segments showed reepithelialization by normal squamous mucosa in all 100 patients, with complete destruction of metaplasia in 43 cases and elimination of dysplasia in 79% of the noncancer patients. A limitation was the relatively high rate of stricture due to damage to the submucosa/muscularis. This was improved by using a balloon to center the diffusing fiber in the esophagus. Studies with oral ALA have also shown high rates of complete elimination of Barrett's, where ALA-induced PpIX synthesis is largely confined to the mucosal layer.

In gastric cancer, there have been a number of studies, particularly in Japan, with response rates above 60% for stage I–III adenocarcinomas. PDT with pulsed laser activation has been found effective in treating early gastric lesions, with complete responses seen in 75% of patients. In colorectal disease, PDT has been found effective in palliating obstructing lesions, although this experience is limited.

D. Bladder

The first governmental approval for PDT (1993 in Canada) was for refractory superficial transitional cell carcinoma of the bladder, where Photofrin-PDT was given by whole bladder irradiation and compared with observation only. At 1 year the recurrence rates were 39 and 81%, respectively, with corresponding median times to recurrence of 394 versus 91 days. However, there was a high incidence of long-term bladder contracture with PDT, which might be reduced by fractionating the treatment, by using photosensitizers with higher tumor selectivity, and/or by improved light dosimetry. Focal irradiation of lesions, with or without whole bladder treatment, is also an option.

E. Head and Neck

There are several studies of PDT in recurrent head and neck tumors, including intraoperative application following resection, which shows evidence of low local recurrence rates. However, the value of PDT for debulking of larger tumors is controversial and care has to be taken near major blood vessels. For early stage lesions, Biel has reported excellent results with Photofrin-PDT, mainly in lesions of the larynx and nasal cavity/pharynx, using surface or, for larger lesions, interstitial irradiation. Complete responses were seen in all cases, with low recurrence rates during the follow-up period (average 3 years, maximum > 5 years).

There is also potential in the treatment of oral cancers/dysplasias by PDT, including field cancerization and leukoplakia. Superficial lesions have showed excellent responses using ALA, with deeper effect using mTHPC. PDT is particularly attractive for these patients because, with appropriate selection of photosensitizer and careful dosimetry, it involves minimal morbidity and gives good functional preservation.

F. Brain

The main application of PDT in neurooncology has been as an adjuvant to surgery for supratentorial malignant glial tumors, providing a further degree of tumor kill immediately following maximal resection.

Uniform illumination of the resection cavity has commonly been achieved by an inflatable balloon applicator (Fig. 2, bottom). Photofrin-PDT has demonstrated individual long-term survivors, extension of median survival or time to recurrence, and increased survival time with high light doses. Consequently, randomized trials are in progress to confirm this last finding prospectively in recurrent gliomas and to determine survival time with primary gliomas when intraoperative PDT is added to surgery, radiotherapy, and chemotherapy. PDT has been given preoperatively and in nonresectable patients by interstitial irradiation with diffusing fibers placed by hand or stereotactically. This has been used for deep-seated, unresectable gliomas and also to destroy focal metastatic lesions in the brain, although definitive systematic trials have not been reported to date. Photofrin-PDT has been investigated as a surgical adjuvant in refractory recurrent pituitary adenomas and, in a small series of patients, follow-up to 30 months showed no progression or recurrence of disease.

An important, and possibly unique, aspect of PDT in brain tumors is the very high tumor-to-normal tissue uptake ratio of photosensitizer ($>10:1$ for Photofrin) due to the exclusion of drug by the normal intact blood–brain barrier. However, the normal brain is nevertheless extremely sensitive to PDT, as confirmed in animal models with Photofrin and several second-generation drugs. An exception is ALA, where white matter does not synthesize PpIX, although this has yet to be confirmed clinically.

G. Gynecology

Limited studies of PDT for endometrial carcinoma and dysplasia/carcinoma *in situ* of the vulva, vagina, and the perianum have been reported, with mixed responses, but including some complete remissions. The most recent study was with topical ALA in vulvar intraepithelial neoplasia (VIN, grades 1–3), which demonstrated complete responses in VIN-1 and monofocal and bifocal VIN-2 and VIN-3. However, multifocal VIN with pigmented and hyperkeratinic lesions was difficult to treat, at least with this photosensitizer and route of administration.

H. Intrathoracic and Intraperitoneal

Photofrin-PDT has been investigated as a surgical adjuvant for pleural cancers, particularly mesothelioma, distributing the light by filling the thoracic cavity with a light-scattering liquid after resection. An overall median survival of 12 months was reported (>3 years for stages I and II), suggesting that PDT was effective in reducing residual disease.

Analogously, dose-ranging studies have been performed following debulking surgery of intraperitoneal tumors in patients with ovarian cancer, peritoneal studding from sarcoma, or gastrointestinal carcinomatosis. A combination of green and red light was used, depending on the required depth of treatment. The procedure required multiple irradiation fields throughout the cavity wall and passage of the intestines through a special light box in order to ensure complete treatment. Thirty of 39 patients were reported alive (9 disease free) at a median follow-up of nearly 2 years.

I. Other

Early in its clinical development, PDT was used in ocular tumors, particularly choroidal, iris, or ciliary body melanomas, where the objective was tumor destruction with preservation of the eye. However, the tumor control rates were disappointing, probably due to an inadequate depth of treatment. This application could be reexamined with longer wavelength photosensitizers.

PDT has been proposed as an alternative to prostatectomy where disease is confined to the capsule. This poses significant technical problems in achieving uniform and complete light delivery throughout the gland and will require development of treatment planning, fiber placement, and monitoring techniques analogous to brachytherapy. Preclinical studies in dog models have shown that this should be possible.

Finally, PDT has been investigated as a means of selectively purging tumor cells in autologous bone marrow transplants for leukemia and lymphoma. Various photosensitizers have been tested preclinically: Merocyanine 540, Photofrin, BPD, ALA, phthalocyanines, and rhodamine derivatives. The procedure involves extracorporeal mixing of the photosensitizer with the marrow and subsequent irradiation. It has been possible to achieve up to 8 logs of tumor cell kill with preservation of 50% of pluripotent hematopoetic progenitor cells in human marrow; consequently, clinical trials have been initiated.

IV. PHOTODYNAMIC DIAGNOSTICS

The focus of this article has been on the therapeutic uses of light-activated drugs. However, there are important complementary roles in tumor detection and localization, as reviewed by Wagnieres and colleagues, exploiting the fact that many photosensitizers are also fluorescent, i.e., emit longer wavelength light upon activation by shorter wavelength light. This fluorescence can be measured using a contact fiber-optic probe or an imaging device. Typically, the latter incorporates two wavelength channels: one to image the drug fluorescence and one to account for the background (auto)fluorescence from the tissue itself. Clinical and preclinical studies have examined the best photosensitizer and the optimal drug and time intervals to give maximum tumor selectivity and definition. These likely vary with tumor site and stage. ALA has been a particular focus for diagnostics, with topical or intravesical administration. In some cases, it may be more effective not to use a drug, and autofluorescence endoscopy is now commercially available in the lung. Fluorescence diagnostics can be used independently of whether PDT is subsequently performed, and in this case, subtherapeutic photosensitizer doses can be employed. Non-PDT agents are also being explored that are optimized for their diagnostic rather than therapeutic characteristics. In conjunction with PDT, fluorescence can be used both to delineate the lesion to be treated and to monitor the treatment through the bleaching (loss of fluorescence) of the drug with light exposure.

V. SUMMARY

A number of advantages and limitations of PDT have been highlighted in the main clinical applications. At its current stage of development, PDT has some distinct generic advantages compared with other therapeutic options, but also some limitations, as listed in Table IV. Some limitations are fundamental to the technique, whereas others reflect only the stage of development. In the immediate future, additional government approvals can be anticipated, both for Photofrin and second-generation photosensitizers. Nononcologic applications will be increasingly significant. This technique is at the transition from being an experimental to an established modality. In oncology, it is not likely to lead to a new clinical specialty as such, because its use is heavily dependent on subspeciality expertise, as in surgery and endoscopy.

TABLE IV
Advantages and Current Limitations of PDT for Solid Tumors

Advantages	Limitations
Minimally invasive procedure: well tolerated with rapid recovery	Restricted light penetration and hence depth or volume of lesion[a]
Curative for early stage lesions	General skin photosensitization with some drugs
Applicable to many tumor sites	Dose optimization complex and site and photosensitizer specific[a]
Not contraindicated before or after other treatments (surgery, radiotherapy, chemotherapy)	Requires both drugs and devices: complex regulatory approvals
May be repeated without known limit	Technology (drugs and devices) still evolving
Few significant side effects and nonmutagenic/carcinogenic	
Good normal tissue healing/cosmesis	
Relatively inexpensive	

[a]Intrinsic: i.e., not likely to be overcome by foreseeable technical advances

Nevertheless, the fact that it is highly complementary to established oncological modalities should facilitate its adoption into multidisciplinary clinical practice.

See Also the Following Articles

BLADDER CANCER: EPIDEMIOLOGY • BRAIN AND CENTRAL NERVOUS SYSTEM CANCER • GASTRIC CANCER • PHOTODYNAMIC THERAPY: BASIC PRINCIPLES AND APPLICATIONS TO SKIN CANCER

Bibliography

Buskard, N. A., and Wilson, B. C. (eds.) (1994). The use of photodynamic therapy in cancer. *Semin. Oncol.* **21**(6), Suppl. 15.

Dougherty, T. J. (ed.) (1996). Photodynamic therapy. *J. Clin. Laser Med. Surg.* **14,** 219–348.

Dougherty, T. J., Gomer, C. J., Henderson, B. W., Jori, G., Kessel, D., Korbelik, M., Moan, J., and Peng, Q. (1998). Photodynamic therapy. *J. Natl. Cancer Inst.* **90,** 889–905.

Fisher, A. M. R., Murphree, A. L., and Gomer, C. J. (1996). Clinical and preclinical photodynamic therapy. *In* "Laser Surgery and Medicine" (C. A. Puliafito, ed.), pp. 339–368. Wiley-Liss, New York.

Marcus, S. L., Sobel, R. S., Golub, A. L., Carroll, R. L., Lundahl, S., and Shulman, D. G. (1996). Photodynamic therapy (PDT) and photodiagnosis (PD) using endogenous photosensitization induced by 5-aminolevulinic acid (ALA): Current clinical and developmental status. *J. Clin. Laser Surg. Med.* **14,** 59–66.

Wagnieres, G. A., Star, W. M., and Wilson, B. C. (1998). In vivo fluorescence spectroscopy and imaging for oncological applications. *Photochem. Photobiol.* **68,** 603–632.

Prostate Cancer

Donald L. Trump
University of Pittsburgh Medical Center

GLOSSARY

Gleason grade A numeric score used to predict the biologic aggressiveness of a tumor; correlates with prognosis and extent of disease.

PSA Prostate-specific antigen.

In 2001, it was estimated that prostate cancer would be the most commonly diagnosed cancer in the United States, and approximately 180,400 new cases would be diagnosed. Prostate cancer is second only to lung cancer as a cause of cancer mortality in men, and in 2001, at least 31,900 men died from this disease. Among males, no cancer is more prevalent than prostate cancer; it is second only to heart disease as a cause of death in adults, and accounts for one-fifth of the cancer deaths in men over the age of 75. One of every eight men in the 60- to 79-year age group will be diagnosed with prostate cancer; by comparison, one in 15 women of the same age will be diagnosed with breast cancer. Prostate cancer is a major cause of mortality, morbidity, and health care expenditure.

I. RISK FACTORS

Age is the greatest risk factor for the development of prostate cancer. The incidence of prostate cancer increases exponentially with age, reaching an apparent peak in the eighth decade of life. The underlying biologic cause of this increased incidence is not clear. A simplistic explanation is that with greater age there is greater opportunity for cumulative genomic damage that could lead to cancer. While this is true, this begs the question as to why prostate cancer is so much more related to increasing age than other cancers.

Other identified risk factors for the development of prostate cancer include family history and race. Men with a first-degree relative (father or brother) with prostate cancer have a twofold increase in the risk of developing the disease, and the risk increases with the number of involved relatives. The risk of prostate cancer is also increased in men with a first-degree female relative with breast or ovarian carcinoma. Linkage analysis suggests that alterations at the BRCA1 site may be associated with prostate, ovarian, and breast cancer in some families. In terms of candidate prostate cancer genes, data are incomplete: 75–80% of prostate cancer specimens have a normal karyotype. Careful family and detailed linkage studies indicate that familial aggregation of this disease occurs in one-quarter of men (two first degree relatives); however, linkage studies revealing a susceptibility inherited with a Mendelian pattern seems to account for only 9% of prostate cancer. Genes located on chromosome 1q 24-25 and 1q 42.2-43, 1p36, the HPC1, as well as the X chromosome (Xq 27-28) and chromosome 17 (17p) have been implicated in the development of prostate cancers. While other loci including myc and erb 2/neu proto-oncogenes have been implicated, data supporting a causative or primary genetic role for these loci are lacking. Alterations in loci on chromosomes 8, 10, and 16 have also been identified as potential markers for the development of prostate cancer.

The racial distribution of prostate cancer also offers clues to the causes of prostate cancer. Autopsy studies reveal that blacks, whites, and Asians have essentially the same prevalence of "clinically silent" or latent prostatic carcinoma. Blacks, however, have a higher rate of clinically significant prostate cancer compared with whites and Asians. There is evidence that Asian immigrants to the United States have increasing risk in successive generations; this risk gradually approaches that seen in African-Americans and whites in the United States. This suggests that environmental factors play a role in the progression from latent to clinically significant prostate cancer. There are several hypotheses for these observations, including variations in quantity and quality of dietary fat intake and alterations in vitamin A or vitamin D intake/production. Androgens are *clearly* important in prostate cancer. Men who are hypogonadal rarely, if ever, develop prostate cancer. There are data indicating that certain polymorphisms in both androgen re-

ception structure and the androgen metabolizing enzyme, 5 alpha reductase, confer increased risk of prostate cancer. Certain polymorphisms in these moieties can enhance androgen effects on target cells, and this may contribute to enhanced prostate cancer risk. Studies by Modugno and colleagues suggest a role of polymorphism in androgen, estrogen, and vitamin D receptors, supporting a polygenic etiology of prostate cancer.

II. SCREENING FOR PROSTATE CANCER

There are several issues concerning screening for prostate cancer. Two fundamental components of a successful screening strategy are the ability to identify significant cases and the ability to administer effective therapy. Despite multiple studies, current diagnosis and therapy of prostate cancer remain controversial in these two aspects. The measurement of the serum content of prostate-specific antigen (PSA) provides an early indicator of the presence of prostatic disease, but not necessarily prostate cancer. PSA levels reflect abnormalities in the prostate—benign hypertrophy, infection, infarction, or cancer. Until recently it was unclear whether men who are diagnosed with prostatic malignancy using a PSA-based strategy have clinically significant disease that will result in morbidity and mortality. Data from the Physician's Health Study in 1999 indicate that an elevated PSA level on a single blood draw is predictive of clinically significant prostate cancer with a low false-positive rate. This argues strongly that PSA-based screening will be unlikely to overdetect indolent cancers. A more difficult problem to address is the fact that the definitive therapies for prostate cancer have not been shown to improve unequivocally quality of life or overall survival. Identifying a patient with prostate cancer may lead to significant diagnostic and therapeutic morbidity and cost for the patient and family. Treatment decisions are difficult to avoid once the diagnosis is made. Thus, prior to obtaining a screening serum PSA level, a frank and open discussion about the use of the information and the consequences of the various options is needed. The specific clinical parameters of each individual must be considered. For a man with a life expectancy of less than ten years, even the most ardent therapist is hard pressed to suggest an advantage to diagnosing and subsequently treating prostate cancer.

III. DIAGNOSIS OF PROSTATE CANCER

Prostate cancer has a long and variable natural history, and patients may present with any of several manifestations of the disease. These range from the patient who presents with symptoms of bladder outlet obstruction and a normal PSA in whom cancer is discovered as an incidental finding at transurethral resection of the prostate, to the patient who presents with debilitating bone pain secondary to metastatic disease. In all cases, the diagnosis of prostate cancer should be established by biopsy. A typical scenario is the patient who presents with an elevated PSA, with or without a palpable abnormality of the prostate on digital rectal examination. These patients usually undergo transrectal ultrasound guided biopsy of the prostate. If treatment is considered, the importance of this biopsy cannot be overstated, particularly since there are benign conditions that can result in a mild to moderate elevation in the serum PSA. Furthermore, histologic examination of the biopsy in cases of malignancy yields prognostic information that can have a significant impact on the future management of the disease. Once the diagnosis of prostate cancer has been established, at least a limited staging evaluation is indicated. This should include a bone scan, if the risk of metastatic disease is deemed high, and routine laboratory studies. There are data indicating that a bone scan is unnecessary for asymptomatic patients with PSA of less than 20 ng/ml. More intensive staging procedures, such as computed tomography or magnetic resonance imaging, are reserved for special situations and do not impact routinely on clinical decisions.

The clinical stage of prostate cancer is based on extent of disease determined by these data. Histologic description of the biopsy specimen also offers important prognostic information. While relatively simple staging descriptions have been used for years, the best available system is that based on the tumor-node-metastasis (TNM) analysis (see Table I).

TABLE I

Tumor-Node-Metastasis (TNM) Staging System

Clinical findings	TNM
Diagnosed incidentally at TURP[a]	T1
<5% of tissue involved	T1a
>5% of tissue involved	T1b
Diagnosed by needle biopsy, elevated PSA only	T1c
Palpable nodule	T2
<half of a lobe	T2a
>half of a lobe, not both	T2b
Both lobes	T2c
Tumor penetrates capsule	T3
Unilateral	T3a
Bilateral	T3b
Seminal vesicle invasion	T3c
Tumor fixed or invades adjacent structures	T4
Bladder, neck, sphincter, rectum	T4a
Levator muscles or fixed to pelvic sidewall	T4b
Regional nodes (true pelvis)	N
One node <2 cm	N1
One node >2 cm, <5 cm; multiple nodes	N2
Any node >5 cm	N3
Metastases	M1
Nonregional nodes	M1a
Bone	M1b
Other	M1c

[a]Transurethral resection of prostate.

Another important prognostic factor is the histologic appearance of the tumor; this is particularly important in early-stage lesions. The information derived from the histologic evaluation includes the extent of involvement of the resected specimen and the extent of differentiation of the tumor. This latter characteristic is best described in terms of the Gleason grade. The Gleason grade or Gleason score ranges from 2 to 10. Gleason scores (1 through 5) are assigned to the *two* most prevalent histologic patterns seen in the prostate specimen. A well-differentiated tumor is scored as 1 or 2, while a poorly differentiated tumor receives a 4 or 5 score. These two scores are added together and expressed as a total Gleason score or sum; for example, $4 + 3 = 7$. This grade is useful in predicting the biologic aggressiveness of a tumor and correlates with prognosis and extent of disease. In 1997 Partin and colleagues reported an extensive retrospective data set and prospectively validated this analysis, which substantiates the importance of Gleason score, clinical stage, and PSA in predicting pathologic stage of prostate cancer.

IV. MANAGEMENT OF THE PATIENT WITH PROSTATE CANCER

Once a histologic diagnosis and clinical stage have been established, patients and their physicians face several major decisions. These decisions are complicated by the variable natural history of this disease and the paucity of randomized prospective trials to guide therapeutic decisions. The decisions to be made differ widely based on the extent of the disease. In general, patients can be grouped into three categories: (1) those with organ-confined disease, (2) those with regionally advanced disease, and (3) those with metastatic disease.

A. Organ-Confined Disease

This category consists of patients with localized prostate cancer (T_{1-2c}, N_0, M_0). There is controversy regarding the management of patients in this broad category. These patients range from those with well-differentiated, incidentally detected tumors involving less than 5% of the gland (T_{1a}), to those with diffuse palpable tumor involving both lobes (T_{2c}). These tumors have widely variable natural histories, but the unifying characteristic is that they are potentially curable by definitive therapy. Whether such therapy has an impact on overall survival, particularly for the population of men with T_{1a} and T_{1b} is not known. Thus there is significant debate as to how these patients should be managed.

Consideration of the natural history of prostate cancer is crucial. The average survival for patients with organ-confined disease who are not treated is several years. The two definitive therapeutic modalities that have been used to treat this disease are radical prostatectomy and irradiation. There are several techniques for administering irradiation—external beam irradiation administered via an increasing number of techniques that allow increase in dose intensity of irradiation.

After surgical treatment for T_1 and T_2 prostate cancer, the cancer-specific survival rate is 90–94% at 10 years and 82–90% at 15 years. If the PSA level is considered as an indicator of disease progression, the reported nonprogression rate for the above group is 69–83% at five years and 47–77% at 10 years. Before comparing outcomes with irradiation and prostatectomy, it is critical to realize that surgical series usually include younger men and report results by pathologic stage. By contrast, irradiation series generally are composed of older men and results are reported as the clinical stage, which notoriously underestimates the local and regional extent of tumor. There are no satisfactory trials that compare surgery and irradiation, and few data evaluating surgery plus other modalities. Careful studies have been carried out in localized prostate cancer using combinations of external beam radiation and systemic androgen deprivation with goserelin (a gonadotropin-releasing hormone agonist [GnRH]). Bolla and colleagues studied 415 patients with T_3-T_4 prostate cancer, randomly assigned to irradiation vs radiation and goserelin. The survival rate in the combined therapy arm was 79% at 5 years vs 62% in the radiation-only group. Eighty-five percent of the surviving patients were free of disease at five years. When comparing these data with those for surgery, it should be noted that the Bolla study included patients with T_3 and T_4 prostate cancer, which are not included in most surgical series. Studies by the Radiation Therapy Oncology Group (RTOG) also clearly indicate improved local control and delay in time to PSA progression when irradiation is combined with androgen deprivation. These studies have not demonstrated improved survival, perhaps due to relatively short follow-up.

Surgery and irradiation have complications, which may have a significant impact on quality of life. The major complications of these approaches are listed in Table II. Radiation proctitis and cystitis are seen in a significant percentage of men receiving external beam radiotherapy and infrequently become chronic. For radical prostatectomy, impotence and incontinence are the complications with the most significant impact on quality of life. In addition, this procedure may be associated with significant blood loss and carries a 0.1–2% risk of perioperative mortality. A survey of Medicare patients in 1990 who had undergone radical prostatectomy revealed that the vast majority were impotent and that over 40% had some problems with continence. Nearly one-fourth of the patients reported that they required further therapy for recurrent cancer. This survey suggests that the published estimates for the efficacy and complication

TABLE II
Complications of Prostate Cancer Treatments

Treatment	Complications
External beam radiotherapy	Acute cystitis, proctitis
	Urinary retention, 30–50%
	Chronic prostitis, cystitis, 4–7%
	Impotence, 40–60%
Radical prostatectomy	Blood loss, 1–2 units
	Impotence, 40–60%
	Incontinence, 5–15%
	Anastomotic stricture, 1–25%
	Thromboembolism, 1–12%
	Mortality, 0.1–2%

rates of this procedure may be overly optimistic. There are no satisfactory trials comparing prostatectomy with radiation. At this time there is little compelling evidence to support irradiation or prostatectomy as superior.

The debate regarding radical prostatectomy compared to radiotherapy takes on particular significance in men with competing morbidities—particularly when there are data suggesting that no treatment at all is an acceptable approach for some men. There are published series that suggest that the survival of men with localized prostate cancer who are not treated is comparable to that of men who undergo radical prostatectomy; however, methodologic problems, including the lack of statistical power, limit the conclusions to be drawn from these trials.

Observation-only is an option for some men with organ-confined prostate cancer. This is especially true in men with other illnesses and reduced life expectancy. Several studies have shown that most men with small tumors and well- or moderately differentiated cancer will have long survival without major interventions. A pooled analysis of more than 800 men with localized disease identified tumor grade as the major factor in predicting disease-specific and metastasis-free survival. The 10-year disease-specific survival rate is 87% for men with histologic grade 1 and 2 tumors (Gleason < 7) and 34% for men with grade 3 (Gleason > 7) tumors. This disease-specific survival for men with well- and moderately differentiated tumors compares favorably with the reported survival for both radical prostatectomy and external beam radiotherapy.

One development in the therapy of localized prostate cancer is the use of ultrasound-guided cryoablation of the prostate. A preliminary report on this technique showed that 82% of the 55 men who underwent the procedure had no residual disease at three months of follow-up. The procedure is associated with significantly shortened hospital stays and overall morbidity when compared with prostatectomy. However, it has been studied in a relatively small number of men, and short- and long-term efficacy is unknown. Currently, cryoablation for localized prostate cancer is an experimental procedure.

Clinical decision-making in men with organ-confined disease is largely an issue of how many and which risks patients are willing to tolerate. With observation alone, there is the risk of developing widespread metastatic disease, while each of the therapeutic modalities carries significant risk of side effects. The risk of developing metastatic disease must be weighed against the comorbid conditions that may limit that life expectancy and raise the risk associated with therapy. An open and frank discussion of these risks with each individual patient is required.

B. Regionally Advanced Disease

These patients have cancer that is no longer confined to the prostate gland but has spread to the soft tissue structures of the pelvis (T_3, N_0-T_X, N_{1-3}). Patients with clinical T_3 tumors have five-year survival rates of 64–72% following radical prostatectomy, external beam radiotherapy, or hormonal therapy, and ten-year survival rates of 29–47%. Recognizing the increased risk for local recurrence and development of progressive disease, most investigators do not feel that patients in this broad disease category are curable by either radical prostatectomy or external beam radiotherapy alone. In general, however, these patients do appear to have the potential for prolonged survival, with median survival greater than five years in most studies no matter what therapy is given.

Intuitively, pathologic stage T_3 disease (microscopic penetration of the prostatic capsule or invasion of the seminal vesicles) should have a better prognosis than clinical stage T_3 disease (palpable involvement of the seminal vesicles). Unfortunately, the data to support this assumption are lacking. Patients with T_3 prostate cancer have been treated with radical prostatectomy, with or without additional (adjunctive) irradiation or hormonal therapy, definitive radiotherapy, immediate hormonal therapy, or observation with hormonal therapy on progression. Adjuvant radiotherapy has been the primary modality of treatment for patients with extracapsular spread after prostatectomy (pathologic stage C disease). In most studies, the five-year survival rates range from 60 to 75% regardless of therapy. Thus, there are no convincing data to support any of these approaches.

Regional nodal involvement (N_1) is associated with a worse prognosis. Median survival has been reported to be as low as 39.5 months. In this small study (44 patients), radical prostatectomy, adjuvant hormonal, and radiotherapy seemed indistinguishable with regard to survival. However, in a large consecutive series of 120 patients with D1 disease, the five-year prostate cancer-specific survival rate was 61% in a group followed with expectant management alone. The group at the Mayo Clinic has argued that the high risk of recurrence in N_1 patients justifies adjuvant hormonal therapy. This group has reviewed data from 631 patients who underwent pelvic node dissection and were found to have D_1 disease. Of these patients, 251 went on to radical prostatectomy and orchiectomy, 97 received radiation and orchiectomy, and 60 underwent only orchiectomy. Prostate cancer-specific survival was markedly improved in the prostatectomy patients at five and ten years when compared with the orchiectomy-alone patients (5 year: 90% vs 66%; 10 year: 78% vs 39%). As with many prostate cancer studies, however, these are retrospective data; unknown, unrecognized, or unstated selection bias leading to treatment decisions prevent firm conclusions from such data.

C. Adjunctive Androgen Deprivation

Considerable data have emerged since 1996 regarding the use of androgen deprivation therapies (ADT) (usually luteinizing hormone-releasing hormone analogues [GnRHa] ± antiandrogen) in conjunction with irradiation and surgery for localized disease. Already referred to are the data of Bolla et al., which demonstrate a substantial survival advantage for patients

with T_3-T_4 primary tumors treated with irradiation plus LHRHa compared to irradiation alone. In 2001 the RTOG was conducting trials of T_3, T_4 and T_1, T_2 tumors, evaluating peri-irradiation as well as prolonged androgen deprivation compared to irradiation alone. Freedom from local progression and freedom from PSA progression occur significantly more often when irradiation is accompanied by ADT in RTOG studies. In a multi-institutional randomized trial, Messing et al. found an improved survival rate in men with N + disease following prostatectomy if ADT is employed. D'Amico and colleagues noted improved survival when irradiation was combined with TAD in a retrospective, case-control study. Taken together, these data suggest that adjunctive ADT improves survival in certain subsets of patients. While considerably more work is required to clearly define the role of "early" ADT, these observations call into question the long-held dictum that ADT does *not* effect survival in prostate cancer. No data examining the role of ADT as sole therapy for clinically localized prostate cancer are available. Studies demonstrating superiority of ADT plus irradiation vs irradiation alone raise the question of the role of ADT alone in men with localized disease—especially, perhaps, men with competing causes of morbidity/mortality.

D. Metastatic Disease

Approximately 30% of patients diagnosed with prostate cancer have metastatic disease at presentation. An additional 30%, who initially present with organ-confined or regionally advanced disease, manifest evidence of metastasis at some point in the course of their disease. Metastatic prostate cancer is a significant cause of morbidity and mortality.

Hormonal therapy of patients with metastatic prostate cancer is one of the most effective therapies available for the treatment of disseminated malignancy. Based on the Nobel Prize-winning work of Huggins and Hodges in the 1940s, ADT had been used with great palliative benefit in patients with disseminated prostate cancer. Response rates of 80 to 90% are reported with each of the currently available therapies, which include estrogens, orchiectomy, and the GnRHa. Diethylstilbestrol (DES) is the primary estrogen used in the therapy of prostate cancer. This agent is clearly effective in treating metastatic prostate cancer, with response rates comparable to orchiectomy. Unfortunately, even in low-dose regimens, this agent is associated with a significant incidence of cardiovascular side effects, including cardiovascular death.

Orchiectomy is the "gold standard" for ADT, particularly for men at risk for early complications as indicated by extensive bony involvement, obstructive uropathy, or tumor threatening cord compression. Surgical castration results in a rapid, 95% reduction in circulating testosterone and is not associated with the cardiovascular complications of DES. By comparison, the most widely available GnRHa analogues that are GnRH agonists require 2 to 3 weeks to produce castrate levels of circulating testosterone. Nonetheless, these GnRHa analogues are effective therapy for prostate cancer. The major limitations to their use are compliance and cost. The currently available analogues require injections either monthly or every three or four months; the cost of these injections is approximately $400 and $1,400, respectively. Once per year injectable formulations are available, and a GnRH antagonist that rapidly reduces testosterone without the initial increase in testosterone is also under development. In a cost comparison analysis with the GnRHa analogues, orchiectomy is clearly more cost effective. In addition, GnRHa initially induces an increase in circulating levels of testosterone, which may result in tumor flare. This surge in testosterone can cause a significant exacerbation of bone pain, increased urinary obstruction, and potentially significant spinal cord compression in some patients. The effects of this flare can be controlled using antiandrogens such as flutamide, bicalutamide, or nilutamide or the newly developed GnRH antagonist.

The antiandrogens have been combined with the GnRHa analogues or orchiectomy in a strategy known as total androgen deprivation (TAD). This therapeutic approach seeks to improve outcome by total abrogation of androgen-stimulated growth of prostate cancer by reducing the circulating testosterone level and blocking receptor binding by any remaining testosterone. In uncontrolled studies, response rates as high as 97% with two-year survival rates of 89% were reported. There are currently three antiandrogens in use in the United States: flutamide (Eulexin), bicalu-

tamide (Casodex), and nilutamide (Nilandron). Numerous trials have explored TAD with either orchiectomy or GnRHa plus antiandrogens compared to orchiectomy or GnRHa alone. Flutamide was studied in a randomized controlled trial in which previously untreated patients with metastatic prostate cancer were randomized to receive the GnRHa analogue leuprolide (Lupron®, daily subcutaneous injection) with or without flutamide. This trial enrolled more than 600 patients and demonstrated a statistically significant benefit for the combination therapy in terms of both progression-free survival and overall survival. In a subset analysis, these differences were particularly marked in the patients with good performance status and minimal disease. In contrast, a European study of 571 patients randomized to goserelin with or without flutamide showed no advantage for the combination in terms of response rate, time to progression, or overall survival. Thus, the efficacy of this combination remains controversial. Meta-analyses reveal either no or limited benefit of TAD compared to testicular androgen suppression. An important U.S. trial randomized 1200 men to orchiectomy alone or orchiectomy plus flutamide. No benefit of TAD was seen in this trial. Benefits of TAD—if any—seem to be limited to TAD employing LHRHa plus antiandrogen. This may reflect the benefits of antiandrogen antagonism of the initial androgen surge that accompanies initiation of LHRHa or conceivably antiandrogens offsetting a small, but perhaps important, frequency of failure of LHRHa to completely suppress testicular androgen secretion. In my practice, I feel that orchiectomy alone is a highly effective form of androgen suppression. If LHRHa are employed I routinely initiate antiandrogens simultaneously and continue antiandrogens for at least 6–10 months. The major drawbacks to total androgen blockade are the costs and the side effects of antiandrogens. Flutamide is associated with diarrhea and both flutamide and bicalutamide cause occasional cases of hepatic toxicity. Nilutamide causes hepatic toxicity as well as reduction in night vision.

Preliminary preclinical and limited clinical data suggest that intermittent androgen deprivation (IAD) may have merit in prostate cancer treatment. In androgen-independent animal tumor models, IAD appears to delay the emergence of androgen-independent tumor growth. In a number of pilot clinical trials IAD appears to be better tolerated than continuous androgen suppression and may be associated with a delay in development of androgen-independent disease progression. In 2001, a large randomized national trial comparing IAD to continuous androgen deprivation was under way. If IAD is equivalent or superior to continuous therapy in terms of disease control, it will clearly be the preferred approach, since suppressed libido, hot flashes, and loss of bone mineralization should be less frequent with IAD.

Despite the success of androgen deprivation therapy as measured by "response," palliation of symptoms, improvement in bone scan, and reduced PSA, the median duration of response for men with metastatic prostate cancer is approximately 18–24 months, no matter what therapy they receive. Eventually, in all men, cells emerge that are able to grow despite androgen deprivation. Median survival, once this hormone-"independent" state is established, is approximately one year. It is these patients who are destined to die of their prostate cancer. To date, no therapy has been shown to improve overall survival in the setting of hormone-insensitive disease. With the increased use of PSA levels to monitor the status of disease in men with prostate cancer, evidence of tumor activity despite androgen deprivation is able to be ascertained earlier than symptomatic recurrence, radiographic, or physical exam would reveal. By defining survival from the date of increasing PSA, survival in the "androgen-insensitive" phase of disease may appear to be increasing—although this is an artifact of earlier definition of androgen independent.

Studies have indicated that the first intervention in patients with androgen independent prostate cancer should be withdrawal of antiandrogens in those who are taking them. Declines in PSA and decreases in the size of soft tissue masses have been documented following cessation of therapy with flutamide and bicalutamide as well as progestational agents. These responses occur primarily in men treated for a prolonged period with total androgen blockade and are usually short-lived (6–9 months), but some patients may have extended periods of disease regression.

Secondary hormonal therapy has been used for many years in the treatment of men with androgen-independent disease. Unfortunately, unlike breast cancer, a prior response to hormonal therapy does not predict for response to secondary hormonal therapy in prostate cancer. Numerous agents including glucocorticoids, progestational agents, adrenal steroid synthesis inhibitors (e.g., ketoconazole) have been tested. Objective responses (primarily reduction in PSA) occur in 15–20% of patients and are typically of short duration. Appetite stimulation has been demonstrated as a side effect of progestational agent, megestrol acetate. Such agents may address the cachexia often seen in these patients but have limited benefit in treating prostate cancer.

Two secondary "hormonal approaches" merit special mention.

a. Several randomized trials have employed glucocorticoids alone as the standard therapy for androgen-independent prostate cancer. These studies consistently reveal a 15–20% frequency of 50% or greater decrease in PSA, a similar rate of pain reduction, and an improved sense of well-being. These data suggest that relatively low dose glucocorticoids provide real, albeit relatively infrequent, and temporary benefit in men with androgen independent prostate cancer.

b. PC-SPES: This agent is a commercially available combination of eight Chinese herbs. The active component or components in PC-SPES are unclear, but preclinical studies and clinical trials indicate that PC-SPES suppresses the growth of prostate cancer cells *in vitro*, reduces PSA levels in men with no prior hormonal therapy, and, most intriguingly, results in subjective improvement and <50% decrease in PSA in approximately 50% of men with androgen independent prostate cancer. This activity of PC-SPES is dependent, at least in part, on the fact that PC-SPES contains phytoestrogen compounds that suppress testicular androgen synthesis and likely have direct antiproliferative effects against prostate cancer. The toxicity of PC-SPES is the toxicity of estrogen: thromboembolic disease, fluid retention, congestive heart failure.

Cytotoxic chemotherapy has been studied extensively in men with hormone-refractory prostate cancer. Despite numerous studies, there is no evidence that cytotoxic therapy provides survival benefit. This has led some investigators to question whether any patient with prostate cancer should receive cytotoxic chemotherapy. Two carefully conducted randomized trials have evaluated the role of mitoxantrone and glucocorticoids. Both studies revealed a significant improvement in palliation of bone pain and greater reduction in serum PSA in those who received the combination compared to the arm receiving only glucocorticoids. Mitoxantrone has been approved by the U.S. Food and Drug Administration for use in metastatic prostate cancer. While no impact in survival has been seen with mitoxantrone therapy, these studies do indicate that limited, but real, palliative benefit is achieved with a very safe and well-tolerated cytotoxic therapy.

Several other studies show that taxanes (paclitaxel or docetaxel) with or without estramustine have antitumor effects in men with androgen independent prostate cancer. Ketoconazole plus doxorubicin alternating with vinblastine plus estramustine also has clear antitumor effects. While "effective" systemic cytotoxic therapy for androgen-independent prostate cancer remains to be defined, considerable data suggest that we have entered an era in the care of prostate cancer patients in which the use of cytotoxic therapy will be increasingly employed.

V. SUPPORTIVE CARE OF THE PATIENT WITH PROSTATE CANCER

Prostate cancer is a significant cause of morbidity in men, even in those destined to die of other causes. The major cause of morbidity in advanced prostate cancer is bone metastases. These metastases often involve critical structures such as the vertebral bodies and weight-bearing bones, as well as the marrow cavity itself. These patients are at risk for cord compression, major fractures, and bony pain.

A. Spinal Cord Compression

Spinal cord compression is a true oncologic emergency and occurs in 10–15% of patients with prostate cancer. The key to the management of this complication is early recognition. Most patients develop back pain prior to the onset of neurologic symptoms; any evidence of neurologic impairment consistent with either nerve root or cord compression is an in-

dication for careful evaluation. Motor abnormalities are usually the initial neurologic manifestation, sensory loss is less common. Once motor or sphincter function is impaired, improvement is relatively uncommon. Approximately 50% of patients who are paraparetic at presentation are able to ambulate at discharge, but patients who present with frank paraplegia rarely regain ambulatory function. A high index of suspicion of spinal cord compression must be maintained. High-dose intravenous corticosteroid therapy (dexamethasone 6 mg q 6 hours) should be instituted in cases of suspected cord compression. Contrast enhanced magnetic resonance imaging or computed tomographic (CT) myelography are the diagnostic tools of choice in assessing this condition. The thoracic spine is the most commonly involved site, and multiple levels of compression are not unusual. Once the diagnosis has been established, therapy is directed at relieving the pressure on the cord exerted by the tumor mass either with external beam radiotherapy or with surgery. Currently, there is no evidence that surgery yields superior results when compared with radiotherapy alone in terms of preservation or recovery of neurologic function.

B. Bone Metastases

1. Impending Fracture

The management of bony metastases in patients with advanced prostate cancer presents a major challenge. Not only can these metastases result in cord compression, as noted above, but also they are a significant cause of morbidity and contribute to mortality, particularly when they involve the long bones. Pathologic fracture involving the proximal femur has an even more ominous prognosis than traumatic fractures do in the healthy elderly. Pathologic fractures are relatively rare in men with prostate cancer despite the high rate of bone involvement. This is likely due to the propensity for these metastases to be osteoblastic rather than osteolytic. The development of pain on weight bearing is often the first sign of an impending fracture and should be investigated promptly in patients with known metastatic disease. External beam radiotherapy and prophylactic orthopedic procedures will often prevent the development of debilitating fractures and preserve function. Once a pathologic fracture has developed, the outlook for regaining function is markedly decreased, and an aggressive approach to preventing fractures is clearly waranted.

2. Pain

Pain due to bone metastases is a vexing clinical problem; it is common and effective management is often difficult. Pain may be a major cause of functional limitation and suffering. Several surveys have indicated that patients are extremely fearful of cancer pain and that our current approaches to pain management are marked by an underutilization of appropriate medication. Narcotic analgesics are the mainstay of the management of cancer pain. Sustained-release morphine preparations with shorter acting opioids for breakthrough pain are effective in most patients. Elderly patients are reported to have a higher risk of cognitive impairment with narcotics, but they can be used safely in this population. In the case of bony metastases, narcotics are often supplemented with nonsteroidal anti-inflammatory drugs to good advantage. These agents are associated with side effects including gastric erosions and bleeding and must be used with care in an elderly population.

External beam radiotherapy frequently should be used in the management of painful bone metastases. Irradiation has the advantage of often providing rapid and complete relief of pain. However, it is not unusual for patients to develop multiple areas of involvement, with new areas of bony pain occurring during a course of radiotherapy. This often results in expansion or addition to previously existing radiotherapy ports with a resultant exposure of significant amounts of marrow to the toxicity of radiotherapy. This may contribute to the anemia associated with marrow infiltration by prostate cancer, thus having a significant negative impact on quality of life.

Newer approaches to the management of painful bone metastases include the use of bisphosphonates and radio-labeled compounds that are incorporated into bone. These include radioisotopes of strontium, samarium, and rhenium. These agents are preferentially taken up in bone and appear to have significant activity in terms of ameliorating bone pain; up to 70 to 80% of patients report decreased pain. The bisphosphonates may be useful in prostate cancer in-

volving the bone. These agents inhibit osteoclast activity and erosion of bone. Several bisphosphonates have undergone clinical trials to assess their effect on bone pain, with encouraging results. Bisphosphonates decrease indices of bone resorption that are above normal in 50 to 80% of cancer patients. Data indicate that these drugs may also inhibit the adhesion of tumor cells to bone, thereby preventing or delaying the development of new bony metastases. The precise role of bisphosphonates in men with prostate cancer is uncertain. In patients with either breast cancer or multiple myeloma initiation of bisphosphonates early in the evolution of metastatic disease is associated with reduced skeletal morbidity and even improved survival. Some have argued that the primarily osteoblastic nature of bone metastases in patients with prostate cancer means that bisphosphonates will have a limited role. However, osteolysis does accompany even markedly osteoblastic bone metastases. The role of bisphosphonates in men with this disease remains to be determined.

See Also the Following Articles

BLADDER CANCER • GASTRIC CANCER • GENETIC PREDISPOSITION TO PROSTATE CANCER • HORMONAL CARCINOGENESIS • HORMONE RESISTANCE IN PROSTATE CANCER • METABOLIC DIAGNOSIS OF PROSTATE CANCER BY MAGNETIC RESONANCE SPECTROSCOPY • RENAL CELL CANCER • TESTICULAR CANCER • THYROID CANCER

Bibliography

Bolla, M. (1997). Improved survival in patients with locally advanced prostate cancer treated with radiotherapy and goserelin. *N. Engl. J. Med.* **337,** 295–300.

Edwards, S. M., *et al.* (1999). Androgen receptor polymorphisms: Association with prostate cancer risk, relapse and overall survival. *Int. J. Cancer* **84**(5), 458–465.

Greenlee, R. T., Murray, T., Bolden, S., *et al.* (2000). Cancer statistics 2000. *CA Cancer J. Clin.* **50**(1).

Kantoff, P. W., *et al.* (1999). Hydrocortisone with or without mitoxantrone in men with hormone-refractory prostate cancer: Results of the cancer and leukemia group B9182 study. *J. Clin. Onc.* **17**(8), 2506–2513.

Messing, E. M., *et al.* (1999). Immediate hormonal therapy compared with observation after radical prostatectomy and pelvic lymphadenectomy in men with node positive prostate cancer. *N. Engl. J. Med.* **341,** 781–788.

Partin, A. W., Kattan, M. W., Suboney, E. N. P., *et al.* (1997). Combination of PSA clinical stage and Gleason score to predict pathological stage in men with localized prostate cancer: A multi-institutional update. *JAMA* **277**(18), 1445–1451.

Smith, D. C., Bahnson, R. R., and Trump, D. L. (1995). Secondary hormonal manipulation (prostate cancer). *In* "Comprehensive Textbook of Genitourinary Oncology" (Vogelzang, N. J, *et al.*, Eds.). Williams & Wilkins, Baltimore.

Tannock, I. F., *et al.* (1996). Chemotherapy with mitoxantrone plus prednisone or prednisone alone for symptomatic hormone resistant prostate cancer: A Canadian randomized trial with palliative endpoints. *J. Clin. Oncol.* **14,** 1756–1764.

Protein Kinase Inhibitors

Alexander Levitzki
The Hebrew University of Jerusalem

GLOSSARY

kinase domain Approximately a 300 amino acid portion of a tyrosine kinase, containing all the catalytic mechanisms required for phosphate transfer. It contains 12 recognizable conserved subdomains.

protein tyrosine kinases An enzyme that catalyzes the transfer phosphate from ATP to the phenolic hydroxyl of a tyrosine side chain.

receptor tyrosine kinase A large membrane-spanning molecule that contains an extracellular ligand-binding domain connected by a membrane-spanning chain to an intracellular tyrosine kinase domain.

$\mathbf{D}$uring the course of a decade beginning in the mid-1980s, aberrant signal transduction pathways were discovered to be the source of cancer and these pathways quickly became a primary target for drug design. By the mid-1990s it had also become apparent that both receptor tyrosine kinases (RPTKs) and cellular protein tyrosine kinases (CPTKs) play a key role in aberrant signal transduction pathways. Persistent autocrine stimulation, overexpression, and mutations of protein tyrosine kinases (PTKs) are the molecular hallmarks responsible for the transformed phenotype of many cancer cells. For example, in many epithelial cancers, epidermal growth factor (EGF) receptors are overexpressed concomitantly to the expression of EGFR ligands such as transforming growth factor (TGF)-α and EGF, thus establishing robust autocrine signaling. Similarly, robust autocrine cytokine signaling is the hallmark of many hematopoetic malignancies . Truncations such as the deletion of exon 2 to 7 in the EGFR and chromosomal translocations, which lead to chimeric proteins such as Bcr-Abl and Tel-PDGFR, produce persistently active PTKs. These and other mutations that were recognized during the 1980s changed our understanding of the cancer process. The scientific community began to recognize the pivotal role of PTKs in the initiation and progression of cancer and therefore to consider them as targets for novel drugs. At about the same time it was recognized that, a subset of serine kinases activated by PTKs carry out some of the aberrant actions of PTKs, thus themselves becoming potential targets. Within a decade of first demonstrating the feasibility of generating PTK inhibitors as potential antitumor agents in 1988, pharmaceutical companies, nonprofit organizations, and academic laboratories were investing vast sums of money toward the development of novel protein kinase inhibitors.

I. PROTEIN KINASES AS TARGETS FOR DRUGS: A SHIFT IN PARADIGM

Since the early 1980s, the molecular bases of numerous diseases have been discovered. These diseases are often derived from aberrations found in either intracellular or intercellular signaling pathways. This is particularly true for proliferative diseases such as cancers, atherosclerosis, restenosis, and psoriasis and of inflammatory conditions such as sepsis, rheumatoid arthritis, autoimmune diseases, and tissue rejection. Protein kinases, both protein tyrosine kinases and a small subset of the few hundred serine/threonine (Ser/Thr) kinases, are the key signaling elements involved in these pathophysiological conditions . In the human genome, 409 Ser/Thr kinases, 59 RPTKs, and 32 nonreceptor PTKs are identifiable. Following the discovery by Tony Hunter in 1979 that the viral oncoprotein (cancer-producing protein) v-Src was a protein tyrosine kinase, it quickly became apparent that the majority of human oncoproteins are PTKs. In the early 1980s, many RPTKs as well as cellular PTKs were defined and shown to be involved in cancer. This realization led to a landmark study, which showed for the first time that low molecular weight tyrosine phosphorylation inhibitors ("tyrphostins") can be systematically designed and synthesized. Findings from Levitzki's pioneering studies between 1988 and 1991 showed that a certain class of tyrphostins effectively inhibits EGFR kinase and the growth of cancer cells that overexpress EGF receptors in cell culture as well as *in vivo*. These early studies refuted the prevailing dogma that the high level of conservation among the various kinases in the kinase domain precluded the identification of small molecules that selectively inhibit specific kinases or sets of kinases. As a result of these early studies, many academic laboratories as well as pharmaceutical companies embarked on projects aimed at developing selective PTK inhibitors for clinical use. During the 1990s a number of PTK inhibitors were shown to be effective as antitumor agents. The most significant leap came in 1996 when it was demonstrated that tyrphostin AG 490 eradicates Janus kinase 2 (Jak2, a nonreceptor tyrosine kinase)-driven recurrent human pre-B acute lymphoblastic leukemia in mice. Pathologically enhanced activities of PTKs are also a hallmark of such nonmalignant proliferative diseases as restenosis, psoriasis, and pulmonary fibrosis. It is therefore likely that PTK inhibitors will be used as antiproliferative agents against such conditions.

Over the past decade, success in developing PTK inhibitors (tyrphostins) has led to a reevaluation of the possibility of designing selective Ser/Thr kinase. Efforts have been focused around those Ser/Thr kinases that play a role in the signaling networks of PTKs that are obviously involved in signal transduction and are thus themselves potential targets for drug development. Figure 1 depicts a portion of the signaling network of PTKs and identifies those serine protein kinases that can be targeted for drug development. Table I is a summary of PTKs and Ser kinases whose aberrant activities have been correlated with pathophysiological conditions. Table I also identifies protein kinase inhibitors currently being developed that target protein kinases found to play a pivotal role in specific cancers. Some of the protein kinase inhibitors presently being developed may become universal components in numerous anticancer cocktails. For example, vascular endothelial factor receptor (VEGFR)/Flk-1 kinase inhibitors could be useful in treating many types of cancer because this receptor

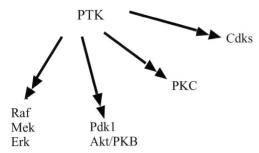

FIGURE 1 Serine kinases as targets for drug design. The serine kinases depicted are turned on by oncogenic signals emanating from PTKs, as well as from mitogenic G protein coupled receptors.

mediates neovascularization (angiogenesis) essential for the progression of all cancers. Because Src kinase mediates the expression of VEGF and is involved in the oncogenic phenotype, Src kinase inhibitors may also become universal components of many anticancer cocktails. Similarly, Cdk and Mek inhibitors may also become universal anticancer agents due to their involvement in all proliferative processes. Flavopiridol, a Cdk inhibitor, inhibits *vivo cell* growth in lymphoid,

myeloid, colon, and prostate cancers, demonstrating wide ranging potential against a variety of tumors.

II. CML, BCR-ABL AND STI 571

One well-known oncogenic PTK is Bcr-Abl, which results from the reciprocal chromosomal translocation [(9:22) (q34;q11)] between the c-ABL protooncogene on chromosome 9 and the breakpoint cluster (BCR) region gene on chromosome 22 (Philadelphia chromosome). This PTK is associated with 95% of chronic myelogenous leukemia (CML) cases. CML is a myeloproliferative disorder typically characterized by clonal expansion of hematopoietic progenitor cells and granulocyte lineage cells.

The BCR/ABL fusion gene codes for a novel protein Bcr-Abl actually come in three principal forms: P190, P210, and P230. They all possess persistent tyrosine kinase activity, altered substrate specificity, and altered cellular localization as compared to the normal Abl protein. Strong correlations found between

TABLE I
Protein Kinase Inhibitors in Development

Kinase inhibitor	Target	Diseases involved	Comments
STI 571/CGP57148B	Bcr-Abl	CML	Excellent efficacy in the clinic
(Gleevec)	c-Kit	Gastrointestinal cancer	Excellent efficacy in the clinic
ZD 1839 (Iressa)	EGFR	NSCL cancer	Clinical response
CP 358,774	EGFR	NSCL cancer	Clinical response
AG 1478/CDDP	(2-7)EGFR	Glioma multiforme	Phase I
SU 5416	VEGFR-2/KDR/Flk-1	Cancers	Phase II, stopped
ZD 4190			
CGP79787			
CP564959			
SU 6668	PDGFR/FGFR/VEGFR-2	Cancers	Phase II
AGL 2043	PDGFR, TEL-PDGFR	Restenosis	In development
		CMML	
AG 490	Jak-2	Leukemias, multiple myloma, breast cancer	In development
Flavopiridol (L868275)	Cdks (cell cycle)	Prostate, colon cancers, lymphomas	In development
CGP 60474	Cdks (cell cycle)	Cancers	In development
CGP 41251	Protein kinase C	Cancers	In development
PD 184352	MEK	Cancers	In development
ZM 33672	Raf	Cancers	In development
L-779,450	Raf	Cancers	In development

certain PTKs and specific diseases made it extremely important to test the hypothesis that selective tyrosine phosphorylation inhibitors could make effective anticancer agents. Indeed, by the early 1990s, Bcr-Abl inhibitors AG 957 and AG 1112 were shown to induce the terminal differentiation or death of Ph$^+$ cells but these agents never got as far as clinical trials. The compound CGP57148B/STI571, discovered by Novartis in 1996, is a high-affinity competitive inhibitor of the adenosine triphosphate (ATP)-binding cleft of Abl kinase. STI 571 is highly effective in inducing the programmed cell death of Ph$^+$ cells both *in vitro* and *in vivo*. Clinical trials begun in 1998 have shown excellent results on patients. The success of STI 571 validates the approach of "signal transduction therapy" and is likely to accelerate efforts to develop drugs from protein kinase inhibitors. CML is special in the sense that during the chronic phase of the disease, the oncogenic state of the Ph$^+$ cells exclusively depends on the single oncoproteins, namely the fusion protein Bcr-Abl. In the acute stage, other chromosomal aberrations occur so that Bcr-Abl kinase inhibition becomes less successful as a sole modality. Nonetheless, STI 571 will doubtlessly remain an essential part of treatment for all CML cases.

III. SELECTIVITY AND TOXICITY OF PROTEIN TYROSINE KINASES (PTK) INHIBITORS

Initially, the idea of generating selective protein kinase inhibitors was met with skepticism. This was due to the concern that the high degree of conservation among the various kinases in the kinase domain would have toxic effects. However, early studies already found that tyrphostins can selectively inhibit EGFR 1000-fold more effectively than insulin receptors and Ser/Thr protein kinases. Another issue connected with this question is whether we should develop "ATP mimics," which bind to the ATP pocket, or "substrate mimics" designed to bind to the substrate pocket. Most of the agents currently being developed are ATP mimics as these are easier to design and synthesize. Success in this area stems from the fact that despite the high degree of sequence and structural homology between the ATP-binding pockets of various kinases, subtle differences between

the kinases are sufficient to generate small molecules that can distinguish between these binding sites. This is exemplified by the binding of the crystal structure of the Src kinase family inhibitor PP1 to the Src family kinase Hck. Structural analysis shows why PP1 binds well to Hck and not to the kinase domain of cAMP-dependent protein kinase (PKA,1999). Interestingly, STI 571 binds with high affinity not only to Bcr-Abl, but also to PDGFR and Kit receptor kinase. This is why STI 571 shows efficacy in the clinic against a subset of gastrointestinal cancers in which Kit plays a key role. Despite the fact that STI 571 binds with high affinity to the binding pocket of three different PTKs, only mild side effects have been observed in patients. From this we may deduce that we should be developing inhibitors that target a narrow set of PTKs rather than uniselective protein kinase inhibitors.

Figure 2 depicts the active site of Hck, a member of the Src family kinases. The structure of the active site of the enzyme cooccupied by AppNHp (black) and by the ATP mimic PP1(dotted) has been solved. This structure, as well as similar structures, of other PTKs in complex with inhibitors, assist in the design and synthesis of more selective and potent compounds. Current efforts are directed toward the generation of inhibitors that "cover" areas in the substrate-binding domain.

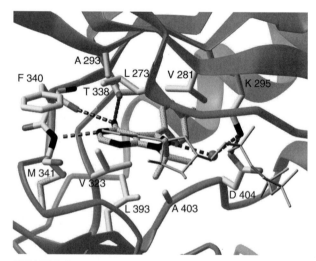

FIGURE 2 The ATP-binding site of Src kinase Hck. The ATP analog APPNHP (black) is depicted in parallel to PP1, the Src kinase inhibitor (dotted). The lower right-hand-side shows the substrate binding domain. Current efforts are directed toward the generation of inhibitors that "cover" areas in the substrate-binding domain.

IV. INDUCTION OF APOPTOSIS

Induction of apoptosis in tumor cells is a most appealing therapeutic treatment for cancer. If apoptosis could be induced in cancer cells, the prospect of eradicating malignant tumors would improve considerably. We would be able to induce apoptosis in noncycling cancer cells as well as in cycling cancer cells. Tumor progression by definition always involves escape from apoptotic stimuli, but this is not necessarily followed by rapid proliferation. The antiapoptotic shield is composed of overexpressing antiapoptotic proteins such as Bcl-2 or the nullification of response to proapoptotic stimuli, e.g., through the Fas system and persistent activation of Akt/PKB. Some PTKs, such as the truncated EGF receptor $\Delta(2\text{-}7)$ EGFR, Src, or Jak-2, have already been found to transmit strong antiapoptotic signals in a significant number of tumors (Table II). PTK inhibitors that target these kinases are expected to develop into essential components of many anticancer cocktails and should therefore become prime targets for drug development. Similarly, the enhanced activity of Akt/PKB is a hallmark of many aggressive forms of cancers (Table II). Persistent activation of Akt/PKB in tumors can result from the enhanced activation of the PI-3' kinase pathway as a consequence of enhanced PTK activity, but it is frequently a result of PTEN deletion, with PTEN (phosphatase and tensin homolog on chromosome 10, a tumor suppressor) being the negative regulator of PKB. PKB/Akt delivers strong antiapoptotic and proliferative signals in a significant number of cancers, making it also a primary target for drug development. The obvious challenge is to develop agents that are capable of discriminating between PKB/Akt and its closely related enzyme PKA (cAMP dependent protein kinase, protein kinase A). Some progress has been been made in this direction, but we still do not have any agents ready for clinical development.

V. COMBINATION THERAPY

Several studies have shown that tyrosine kinase inhibitors synergize with cytotoxic drugs, Fas ligand and IL-12, to induce cell death. These findings suggest that blockades of PTK pathways sensitize target cells to proapoptotic stimuli and to immune system actions against cancer cells. Cisplatin synergizes with the EGFR kinase inhibitor AG 1478 (Table II) to induce massive apoptosis of glioma cells, which are otherwise resistant to both these compounds. Similarly, the Jak-2 kinase inhibitor AG 490 synergizes with the anti-Fas antibody and with interleukin-12 to induce death in multiple myeloma cells. In both instances, the combinations proved effective *in vivo*. This combinatorial approach is likely to gain popularity in the future.

VI. PTK INHIBITORS FOR NONCANCER INDICATIONS

The enhanced activity of PTKs is a hallmark of many other diseases besides cancer. Atherosclerosis and its accelerated form restenosis, which occurs after balloon angioplasty and bypass surgery, are activated by platelet-derived growth factor (PDGF). The growth factor released from injured endothelium and aggregating platelets induces the migration of smooth muscle cells from the blood vessel environment to the lumen, where they proliferate and generate the neointima, which cloggs the blood vessel. It has therefore been argued that selective PGDF receptor kinase tyrphostins could

TABLE II
The Antiapoptotic Action of Protein Kinases

Protein kinase	Target	Consequence	Lead inhibiting agent
Src	PI-3' kinase	Activation of PKB/Akt	PP1
	Stat 3 tyrosine phosphorylation	Expression of Bcl-X_L, onset of aerobic glycolysis	AGL 2132
(Δ2-7)EGFR	Stat 3	Expression of BclX$_L$	AG 1478
Jak-2	Stat 3	Expression of BclX$_L$	AF 490
Akt/PKB	P21^{cip}	Retention in the cytoplasm freeing Bcl-X_L, Bcl-2	PTR101
	BAD		

become effective agents against restenosis following balloon angioplasty. By 1998 it had been discovered that PDGFR kinase inhibitors delivered to injury sites during balloon procedures inhibited balloon-induced injury in the femoral and heart blood vessels of experimental pigs. These kinase inhibitors are currently in clinical development (Table II).

Enhanced activity of the EGF receptor kinase appears to play an important role in psoriasis and papilloma. In both cases, one finds that the diseased cells express about 10-fold higher level of the receptor as well as the ligands that stimulate it, EGF and TGF-α. The autocrinic stimulation that results from these molecular aberrations is an important factor in the proliferative phenotype of psoriasis and papilloma. Indeed, EGFR kinase-directed tyrphostins were shown to induce the growth arrest of human psoriatic cells and HPV 16-transformed human keratinocytes. Interestingly, these inhibitors induce terminal differentiation of HPV 16-immortalized keratinocytes. The arrest of papilloma growth may also be viewed as a prophilactic regimen, as papilloma can develop into cervical cancer over a period of years. The HPV 16/18 genome is found in >90% of all cervical cancer biopsies. Thus the use of PTK inhibitors should be carefully considered as a means of treating these conditions. Other conditions, such as pulmonary fibrosis and postoperative development of kelloid scars, are also candidates for tyrphostin treatment. Preliminary data from the Levitzki laboratory certainly point in this direction.

VII. SERINE KINASE INHIBITORS

Since the early 1990s, attempts have been made to develop protein kinase C inhibitors into anticancer agents, but these endeavors have met with little success. This slow development may be a consequence of the multiple PKC forms currently in existence, coupled with a lack of precise knowledge regarding the exact role of PKC isozymes in human disease. However, the identification of cyclin-dependent kinases and Erks as central elements in the signaling of oncogenic pathways was responsible for promoting these targets for drug development. Cdk inhibitors, as well as Raf and Mek inhibitors are currently under clinical development (Table I). Cdk inhibitors currently being developed are ATP mimics that display significant selectiv-

ity toward Cdks. These findings strengthen the assertion that despite high degrees of homology between the kinase domains of serine kinases, the small structural differences between the kinase pocket are sufficient to allow the development of selective inhibitors.

VIII. DESIGN OF PROTEIN KINASE INHIBITORS

A fair amount of scaffolds have been developed as ATP mimics so that most of the protein kinase inhibitors are ATP competitive. In fact, most of the agents currently in clinical development are ATP competitive inhibitors. The exceptions are Mek inhibitors, which are not competitive with either the ATP or the substrate because they are allosteric inhibitors. Random screening followed by optimization remains the main avenue for discovering inhibitors. The availability of several three-dimensional protein kinase structures, often with inhibitors or APPNHP (adenylyl-imido-diphosphate), facilitates the design of novel inhibitors to the kinase whose structure is solved, as well as related ones. Detailed knowledge of ATP-binding pockets in the various kinases will facilitate a thorough understanding of the differences between such pockets in the various different kinases. Such knowledge could help facilitate the design of novel inhibitors.

See Also the Following Articles

BCR-ABL • CHRONIC MYELOGENOUS LEUKEMIA • INTEGRIN RECEPTOR SIGNALING PATHWAYS • MAP KINASE MODULES IN SIGNALING • PAPILLOMAVIRUSES • PYRUVATE KINASES • SIGNAL TRANSDUCTION MECHANISMS INITIATED BY RECEPTOR TYROSINE KINASES

Bibliography

Drucker, B., and Lydon, N. B. (2000). Lessons learned from the development of an Abl tyrosine kinase inhibitor for chronic myelogenous leukemia. *J. Clin. Invest.* **105,** 1.

Gibbs, J. B. (2000). Mechanism-based target identification and drug discovery in cancer research. *Science* **287,** 1969–1973.

Levitzki, A. (2000). Protein tyrosine kinase inhibitors as therapeutic agents. *Top. Curr. Chem.* **211.**

Levitzki, A., and Gazit, A. (1995). Tyrosine kinase inhibition: An approach to drug development. *Science* **267,** 1782–1788.

Schindler, T., Sicheri, F., Rico, A., Gazit, A., Levitski, A., and Kuriyan, J. (1999). Crystal structure of Hck in complex with Src family-selective tyrosine kinase inhibitor. *Mol. Cell* **3,** 633–648.

Proton Beam Radiation Therapy

Jay S. Loeffler
Alfred R. Smith

Harvard Medical School and Massachusetts General Hospital

I. Introduction
II. Physical Characteristics of Protons
III. Proton Beam Radiation Treatment: Historical Note
IV. Clinical Results
V. Design of Clinical Trials Using Proton Beams
VI. Conclusions and Future Directions

GLOSSARY

conformal radiation therapy A form of radiation therapy that utilizes multiple external beams and beam-shaping/delivery methods to concentrate the high dose volume to the tumor volume while not exceeding the tolerance dose to critical normal tissues and organs. A new form of conformal therapy, used for both photons and protons, is a method of planning and delivering radiation beams called "intensity-molulated" radiation therapy, whereby multiple beams of radiation, generally nonuniform in cross section, are designed and delivered such that the resultant total dose distribution is uniformly high in the tumor/target volume and much lower and nonuniform in normal tissues and organs.

dose distribution The spatial (geometric) distribution of radiation dose in the patient. Dose distributions are usually characterized by isodose contours that connect points of equal dose. For example, in two dimensions, the 90% isodose contour would be a line drawn through all of the dose points that are 90% of the maximum dose point. In three dimensions, the collection of all such 90% points would describe a 90% surface. In practice, the dose prescription specifies the particular isodose contour or surface that should circumscribe or surround the tumor/target. For example, a prescription of 75 Gy means that the entire tumor/target should receive at least 75 Gy and, in three dimensions, the 75-Gy surface should surround the tumor/target.

fractionation A method whereby a total dose prescription is delivered in multiple segments (fractions). For example, a particular treatment prescription of 70 Gy in 35 fractions means that a total dose of 70 Gy is to be delivered in 35 fractions of 2 Gy each. In the usual case, treatments are delivered in 5 fractions per week so a treatment course of 35 fractions would require 7 weeks of treatment.

local control A measure of treatment outcome. In radiation therapy, the aim is to treat and "control" the localized solid tumor. A tumor is controlled if its growth is halted (tumor cells cease to replicate); in most cases this is accompanied by a decrease in size or complete removal of the tumor. The typical time period of assessing local control is 5 years (a tumor controlled for 5 years is unlikely to reoccur) and an analysis of a clinical trial might lead to a statement such as "local control of 95% was achieved with a median follow-up of 5 years."

particle accelerator An accelerator such as a cyclotron or synchrotron is used to produce intense beams of high-energy particles such as protons and helium ions (the nuclei of helium atoms) used in particle therapy. Cyclotrons use magnetic fields to produce particle motion in circular orbits while accelerating the particles by electric fields. The energy of the particles increases with each orbit and the orbits gradually increase in size with increasing energy until the particles reach the desired energy and are extracted. The extracted beam of particles is transported to the desired treatment room where it undergoes additional modifications for use in a specific patient's treatment.

photon (X ray) A bundle of electromagnetic energy that has no mass and travels at the speed of light. Photons are referred to interchangeably as γ rays (when emitted from an isotope such as cobalt-60) or X rays (when produced by the interactions of accelerated electrons with a metallic target). Beams of photons account for the major part of external beam radiation therapy.

proton The nucleus of the hydrogen atom. Beams of protons that have been accelerated to high energies in accelerators, such as cyclotrons, can penetrate the body to treat deep-seated tumors.

quality of life (QOL) A measure of the effect of treatment on the QOL a patient experiences. Patients may be locally controlled and experience a lengthy period of disease-free survival and yet be unable to maintain a reasonable level of their personal, social, or professional life because of the late effects of treatment. For example, patients with prostate cancer may be "cured" of their tumor, but experience rectal complications, impotence, or inability to control urination. Inclusion of quality of life measures in treatment outcome analyses is an attempt to study the broader issues of cancer treatment. QOL measures are frequently patient reported rather than physician reported.

radiation (absorbed) dose A measure of the energy per unit mass delivered to tissue by ionizing radiation. The unit of absorbed dose is the Gray (Gy) which is equal to 1 joule per kilogram (a dose of 1 Gy equals 1 joule of energy deposited in 1 kg of tissue).

radiation therapy A treatment modality that uses ionizing radiation to kill tumor cells. It is frequently used in conjunction with surgery and chemotherapy. External beam radiation therapy (discussed in this article) utilizes high-energy beams from an external source that penetrates the body and deposits cell-killing energy in the tumor.

recurrence/disease-free survival A measure of treatment outcome. Recurrence-free survival is the time a patient or cohort of patients (in which case it is the median time) survives with no evidence of the recurrence of primary disease. Disease-free survival is the length of time a patient or cohort of patients survives with no evidence or primary or metastatic disease.

treatment-related morbidity/late effects Negative outcomes of treatment evidenced by functional, structural, or cosmetic effects. These effects can be of a low grade and transitional nature, life-threatening, or fatal and include very long-term effects, such as cancer induction due to the radiation treatment. The aim of good treatment is to maximize local control and survival and to minimize treatment-related morbidity.

This article describes the properties of therapeutic proton beams and summarizes important clinical results and future directions of proton therapy. Radiation therapy, used alone or in conjunction with surgery and/or chemotherapy, is an important cancer treatment modality. However, it is estimated that between 20 and 80% of patients treated for locally advanced epithelial or mesenchymal tumors will die secondary to the failure of standard photon therapy and/or surgery to achieve local control of the disease. Furthermore, these aggressive local therapies are themselves often associated with significant acute and late morbidity. There are other tumors, particularly pediatric tumors, for which local control is often satisfactory, but treatment-related late effects are high because healthy tissues and organs receive substantial amounts of radiation when conventional photon therapy is employed.

I. INTRODUCTION

During the past decade there has been increasing interest in developing techniques that produce extremely conformal radiation dose distributions that confine the high-dose region to the tumor/target volume and respect the radiation tolerance of critical normal tissues and organs. Such techniques may permit the delivery of higher doses of radiation to the tumor, resulting in an increase in local control and disease-free survival without a corresponding increase in treatment-related morbidity. New developments that have been implemented include three-dimensional treatment planning using CT (computerized tomography) and MR (magnetic resonance) imaging, stereotactic and image-based patient positioning, advanced treatment delivery techniques, such as intensity modulation, and hospital-based proton therapy facilities. This article focuses on proton radiation therapy because it offers substantial advantages, discussed later, over conventional treatment with high-energy photons. These advantages are a consequence of the laws of physics and are independent of the methods of treatment planning, patient positioning, and treatment delivery, which, in practice, are essentially the same (or can be made to be the same for purposes of comparison) for photon and proton therapy.

II. PHYSICAL CHARACTERISTICS OF PROTONS

The advantages of proton radiation therapy, compared to photon (γ or X-ray) therapy, are due mainly to the superiority of proton physical dose distributions in specific treatment conditions rather than in any inherent differences in the biological effects of the two modalities. Protons and photons are ionizing radiations that basically use the same mechanisms to kill tumor cells, i.e., through a transfer of energy (from the photon or proton to the cell) that results in damage to the cellular DNA and subsequent cell death. In general, the radiation tolerance of normal tissues and organs is dependent on both the level of radiation dose and the volume irradiated. A decrease in either or both of these parameters will result in a decrease in treatment-related morbidity or an opportunity to increase the tumor dose without exceeding the radiation tolerance limits of critical normal structures. In practice, relative to photons, protons deposit a greater fraction of their cell-killing ionization within the tumor volume and less in normal tissues and organs, and thus have the potential for a greater therapeutic gain, e.g., increased tumor control and/or decreased treatment-related morbidity.

Protons, the nuclei of hydrogen atoms, are accelerated to high energies [70–230 million electron volts (MeV)] in accelerators, such as cyclotrons or synchrotrons, and then extracted and transported to

treatment rooms using a series of focusing and bending magnets. Before entering a patient in the treatment room, the proton beam undergoes a series of modifications (spreading and shaping) that cause the peak dose distribution in a particular patient to conform to the prescribed tumor/target volume.

A proton loses its energy in tissue through multiple interactions with electrons in the atoms of cells, although a small fraction of energy is transferred to tissue through collisions with the nuclei of atoms. The energy loss per unit path length is relatively small and constant until near the end of the proton range where the residual energy is lost over a short distance, resulting in a steep rise in the absorbed dose (energy absorbed per unit mass). This portion of the particle track, where energy is rapidly lost over a short distance, is known as the Bragg peak (see the curve in Fig. 1). In physical terms, the magnitude of the transfer of energy to tissue is inversely proportional to the square of the proton velocity. The initial low-dose region in the depth–dose curve, before the Bragg peak, is referred to as the plateau of the dose distribution and is about 30% of the Bragg peak maximum dose.

The Bragg peak is too narrow to treat any but the smallest of tumors. For irradiation of larger tumors, the beam energy is modulated to widen the volume over which the high dose is deposited. This is accomplished

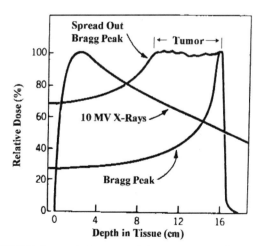

FIGURE 1 Depth dose curves (relative percentage dose vs depth in tissue) for an unmodulated proton beam (Bragg peak), a modulated proton peak (spread out Bragg peak or SOBP), and 10-MV photons. The SOBP has been modulated to treat a tumor that extends from approximately 9 to 16 cm in depth.

by superimposing several Bragg peaks of descending energies (ranges) and weights to create a region of uniform dose over the depth of the target; these extended regions of uniform dose are called "spread-out Bragg peaks" (SOBP). The depth–dose curves for a 160-MeV unmodulated proton beam (Bragg peak) and a modulated SOBP are shown in Fig. 1. For comparison, Fig. 1 also shows the depth–dose curve for 10-MV X rays, a beam commonly used to treat deep-seated tumors. For illustration, a tumor is indicated in the region between 9 and 16 cm in depth. The proton dose distribution is characterized by a relatively low-dose region in normal tissue proximal to the tumor, a uniform, high-dose region in the tumor, and zero dose beyond the tumor. The photon dose distribution is characterized by a maximum dose in normal tissue proximal to the tumor, a lower and nonuniform dose in the tumor, and a significant dose to normal tissues and organs beyond the tumor.

The physical and clinical superiority of a single proton beam dose distribution, compared to that for photons, is illustrated for the treatment of medulloblas-toma in Fig. 2 where a single posterior beam of either photons (X rays) or protons is used for the irradiation of the spinal axis in the treatment of medulloblastoma. Medulloblastoma is a pediatric malignancy that occurs in the posterior fossa and can spread through the CSF (cerebrospinal fluid) to seed in the brain and the spinal axis. This requires radiation treatment to the cranial contents, as well as the spinal axis. As a result, these patients frequently experience hearing, neurologic, neuropsychologic, endocrine, musculoskeletal, cardiac, and fertility deficits due to the combined chemotherapy and radiation treatment. Figure 2 illustrates the dramatic reduction in the volume of normal tissue irradiated in the thorax (heart, lung, and esophagus), abdomen (stomach, small bowel, pancreas, and liver), and pelvis (ovaries, bladder, and bowel) seen with protons. Also, in the treatment of the whole brain and posterior fossa boost (not shown in Fig. 2), the dose to the middle ear (cochlear) can be reduced by 50% using proton techniques. Therefore, there will be decreased nausea, vomiting, esophagitis, cardiac and pulmonary damage, ovarian failure, and loss of

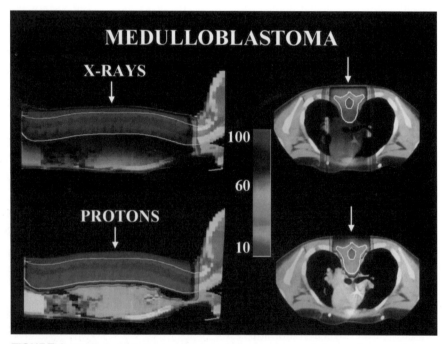

FIGURE 2 Comparison of photon and proton single posterior portals for spinal axis irradiation in the treatment of medulloblastoma. The photon plan results in the irradiation of normal tissues and organs in the thorax, abdomen, and pelvis. For protons, there is no dose beyond the bony spine, which is uniformly irradiated to prevent irregular bone growth. The color scale is a percentage of prescription dose. See color insert in Volume 1.

hearing for proton treatments as compared to conventional photon treatments.

In the usual clinical situation, more than one radiation beam is used in both photon and proton treatments. Several individual beams are aimed at the tumor from different directions with a resultant uniform dose in the tumor/target and a more distributed dose to normal tissues and organs outside the target. However, when comparing photon and proton multibeam treatments, the advantage shown for protons using single beams is present for each and every beam and the proton dose distribution will be more conformal. Compared to photons, the proton treatment will deliver about one-half the dose to normal tissues and organs (on the average—clinical sites will vary) resulting in the opportunity for tumor dose escalation using proton beams or fewer treatment-related complications for equal tumor doses.

These concepts are illustrated in the treatment of rectal carcinoma as shown in Fig. 3, which shows dose distributions for X rays (left) and protons (right). For both X rays and protons, a three-field technique (posterior, right, and left lateral) has been used. Cur-

rent treatment of patients with stages II and III rectal carcinoma includes surgical resection, pelvic radiation, and infusional 5-fluorouracil. There is significant treatment-related morbidity from this regimen due to the irradiation of large volumes of normal bowel and bladder with conventional X-ray radiation techniques. Commonly described complications include dysfunction of large and small bowel, including diarrhea, rectal urgency, reduced fecal control, bleeding and bowel obstruction. Proton treatment results in reduced radiation to the intestinal tract (except for the rectum), urinary bladder, uterus, and most of the prostate or vagina. Therefore, proton radiation therapy will significantly reduce acute and late radiation toxicity, reduce bowel, urinary, and sexual dysfunction, and, as a result, quality of life. It is also expected that the reduction in irradiated volumes of normal tissues/organs will result in better treatment compliance and/or increased intensity of multimodality (radiation and chemotherapy) treatment.

In general, one cannot overcome the physical disadvantage of photons relative to protons by the use of multiple beams, complex beam arrangements, or highly

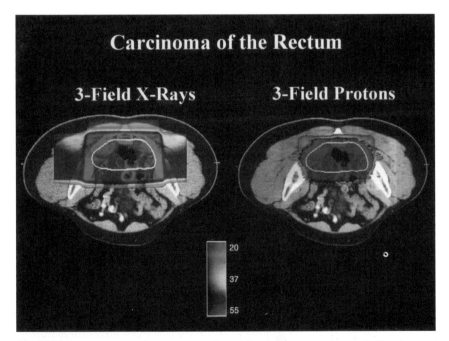

FIGURE 3 A treatment plan comparison for rectal carcinoma using photons (left) and protons (right). Both plans use three treatment fields (posterior, right, and left laterals). The photon plan irradiates a larger volume of normal tissues/organs in the abdomen and pelvis. The color scale is total dose (Gray). See color insert in Volume 1.

sophisticated beam delivery techniques. In modern proton therapy facilities, which have isocentric gantries, pencil beam scanning, and modern treatment control systems, proton therapy capabilities are equivalent to those for state-of-the-art conformal therapy using photons with respect to numbers of beams, beam directions, and complex delivery techniques. Therefore, the most advanced photon techniques, such as intensity-modulated therapy, can also be used for protons and their physical advantages over photons are retained.

The reduced irradiated volume of normal tissues and organs in proton therapy may also be important in the acute tolerance to combined treatment with chemotherapy and radiation. The expected reduction in side effects with proton radiation should result in fewer interruptions in treatment and enhanced treatment intensity in multimodality treatments. Improved treatment intensity may ultimately result in higher cure rates. It is also expected that the quality of life (personal, social, and professional) for radiation therapy patients will be improved with proton therapy due to decreases in treatment-related morbidity.

III. PROTON BEAM RADIATION TREATMENT: HISTORICAL NOTE

In 1946, Robert Wilson proposed that proton beams would provide superior dose distributions and should be considered for the treatment of cancer as a replacement for photons. Initial efforts were directed at intracranial targets that utilized single-dose protocols. The first treatments using proton or helium ion beams (helium ions and ions of heavier atoms such as carbon have dose distributions similar to those for protons) were at the University of California at Berkeley (1955), University of Uppsala, Sweden (1957), Massachusetts General Hospital (1961), Physics Research Institute, Dubna, Russia (1964), and the Institute for Experimental and Theoretical Physics, Moscow (1969). As of January 2002, approximately 31,000 patients have received part or all of their radiation treatment by proton beams. Today there are 20 proton treatment centers worldwide, with as many more centers planned to be built in the near future.

The proton treatment program at the Massachusetts General Hospital (MGH) began in 1961, led by the neurosurgical group of W. Sweet and R. Kjellberg using the 160-MeV cyclotron in the Department of Physics at Harvard University. Their targets were principally pituitary adenomas, arteriovenous malformations, and other benign intracranial neoplasms and were treated by single-dose radiotherapy. In January 1974, the Department of Radiation Oncology began a program of fractionated proton treatment for cancers. This clinical research program, funded by the National Cancer Institute from 1974 until the present time, represents an active collaboration between the Harvard Cyclotron Laboratory (HCL), the Massachusetts Eye and Ear Infirmary (MEEI), the Harvard Medical School, and the MGH. Because of the limitations of HCL (low beam energy, limited capacity, and fixed horizontal treatment beams), only a few clinical sites have been studied. Clinical results from the MGH/MEEI/HCL program and from other proton therapy programs are discussed in the following section.

IV. CLINICAL RESULTS

A. Carcinoma of the Prostate

Investigators at the MGH completed a phase III trial comparing 67.2 Gy of photons versus 75.6 CGE using a conformal perineal proton boost. From 1982 through 1992, 202 patients with T3–T4 prostate cancer received 50.4 Gy by four-field photons. Patients then received either 25.2 CGE with conformal protons or a 16.8-Gy photon boost. No differences were found in overall survival, total recurrence-free survival or local recurrence-free survival in the two groups. The local recurrence-free survival at 7 years for patients with poorly differentiated (Gleason 9 and 10) tumors was 85% on the proton arm and 37% on the photon arm. Grade 1 and 2 rectal bleeding was higher in the proton arm (32% versus 12%), as was urethral stricture (19% versus 8%). In conclusion, dose escalation to 75.6 CGE by a conformal proton boost led to increased late radiation sequelae, but not to increased total survival in any subgroup. However, there was an improved local recurrence-free survival in patients with poorly differentiated tumors.

Based on these results, a new clinical trial, PROG 95-09, was initiated. Participants in the trial were from MGH and Loma Linda University (LLU) Medical Center. PROG 95-09 is a randomized phase III trial employing conformal photons with a proton boost in early stage prostate cancer. The study was proposed because a long-term follow-up of T1–T2-irradiated patients demonstrated biochemical disease-free survival rates of 50, 35, and 20%, respectively, for well, moderate, and poorly differentiated tumors. This study randomized patients to two different proton boost dose levels with patients receiving a total dose of either 79.2 Gy versus 70.2 Gy. Patients deemed to be a low risk for local failure (PSA <4 ng/ml) and patients with a high risk for distant disease (PSA >15 ng/ml and/or positive lymph nodes) are not likely to benefit from this dose escalation and thus were excluded. This randomized trial, designed to detect a 20% increase in freedom from local failure and biochemical relapse at 5 years, is now closed with 390 patients entered and is undergoing analysis.

Results of the Loma Linda experience in early stage prostate cancer have been published. Three hundred and nineteen men with T1–T2b tumors were treated with 74-75 CGE protons or combined protons and photons. The overall 5-year biochemical disease-free survival rate was 88%. No severe treatment-related morbidity was observed.

B. Uveal Melanoma

As of October 1998, a total of 2586 patients have been treated for uveal melanoma at the MGH with protons in collaboration with the MEEI. Patients were treated with 70 CGE in five fractions over 7–9 days. The 5-year actuarial local control rate is 96% for all sites within the globe with a 80% survival. The probability of eye retention at 5 years was estimated to be 90% for the entire group and 97, 93, and 78% for patients with small, intermediate, and large tumors, respectively. Independent risk factors for enucleation were involvement of the ciliary body, a tumor height more than 8 mm, and distance between the posterior tumor edge and the fovea. These results compare fa-

vorably with local control rates of 89% reported by Courdi with protons in Nice, France.

Because some patients have experienced deteriorating vision following doses of 70 CGE, a randomized trial of 50 versus 70 CGE for small and intermediate sized lesions, located within 6 mm of the optic disc or macula, was initiated. This dose reduction study was completed in June 1994 with accrual of 188 patients. Interim analysis based on patients followed through September 1997 (a median follow-up of 60 months) suggested no reduction in either local control or survival. No marked improvement in visual outcome or complications has been observed. However, visual field analysis does show a smaller mean defect in the patients randomized to 50 CGE.

A study has been completed comparing ^{125}I plaques to helium ions by the group at the University of California, San Francisco (UCSF), and Lawrence Berkeley Laboratories (LBL). Patients with melanomas less than 10 mm in height and less then 15 mm in diameter were randomized by the UCSF/LBL group to receive either 70 CGE in five treatments with helium ions or 70 Gy to the tumor apex with ^{125}I plaque brachytherapy. Local control was 100% in those patients treated with helium ions versus 87% in those patients treated with ^{125}I plaques.

C. Sarcomas of the Skull Base and Cervical Spine

Treatment of a patient with a sarcoma of the skull base is challenging because of the very large number of critical structures penetrating the skull base and the proximity of these tumors to the brain stem and optic pathways. These factors have limited the success of conventional photon radiation therapy and surgery. Results of the MGH series have been analyzed by Munzenrider and Liebsch. One hundred and sixty-nine patients with chordoma and 165 patients with chondrosarcoma were treated with protons between 1975 and 1998. The 5-year actuarial local control rates for skull base chondrosarcomas were 98 and 73% for chordoma patients. For cervical spine patients, local control rates were 54 and 48% for chondrosarcoma and chordoma patients, respectively. The LLU proton experience for skull base tumors showed

5-year actuarial local control rates of 75% for chondrosarcoma and 59% for chordoma. The MGH results compare favorably with the experience (median dose 50 Gy) from the Princess Margaret Hospital with only 2 of 28 patients being free of progressive disease with a median follow-up of 5 years.

D. Optic Pathway Glioma

Seven patients with optic pathway glioma were treated at LLU between 1992 and 1997. Tumor volumes ranged between 3.9 and 127 cm^3. At a median follow-up time of 37 months, all patients were locally controlled. A reduction in tumor volume was seen in three patients and tumor volumes remained stable in four patients. Visual acuity remained stable in patients who presented with useful vision. Proton radiation therapy was shown to reduce the dose to the contralateral optic nerve by 47% compared to three-dimensional photon techniques.

E. Astrocytoma

Between 1993 and 1998, 48 patients were treated for nonresectable grade II and III intracranial tumors at the Center for Proton Therapy in d'Orsay, France. Mean tumor doses ranged from 63 to 67 Gy at 1.8 Gy per fraction. With a median follow-up time of 18 months, local control was 97% (33/34) and 43% (6/14) for nonparenchymal and parenchymal lesions, respectively.

Twenty-four patients with the diagnosis of glioblastoma multiforme were treated to 90 CGE with twice-daily protons at the MGH. Median survival time was 20 months from date of surgery and 18.6 months from the start of radiation treatment. Actuarial survival at 2 and 3 years was 34, and 18%, respectively. Sixteen of the 23 patients were judged to have had tumor progression. Of these 16, 15 had progression in tissues that received 60–70 CGE (or less). In only 1 patient was there evidence of failure within the 90 CGE volume. This is the only patient who had a biopsy only with no resection. All patients developed new areas of gadolinium enhancement during the follow-up period. Pathological material was examined in 15 patients. Radiation necrosis only was demonstrated in 7 patients. The survival rate for this group of 23 patients is comparable to that of the best brachytherapy or radiosurgery series. However, there was a trend toward larger and less accessible tumors in this patient population. This regimen has achieved an apparent high frequency of tumor eradication in the 90 CGE volume, although toxicity has been significant.

F. Benign Meningioma

Between 1981 and 1996, 46 patients with incompletely resected or recurrent benign meningioma were treated at the HCL with a combined proton/photon technique. The median dose to the tumor volume was 59.0 CGE. Overall survival at 5 and 10 years was 93 and 77%, respectively, and recurrence-free survival at 5 and 10 years was 100 and 88%. Three patients developed local tumor recurrence at 61, 95, and 125 months, although no patient died from recurrent disease. Complications included focal brain stem necrosis in 2 patients and grade 3 memory loss in another patient. In 4 patients who developed ophthalmologic toxicity, the maximum dose to the optic structures was 58.4, 59.2, 59.3, and 63.0 CGE. Unilateral sensineural hearing loss developed in 2 patients and endocrinopathy in 11 patients.

Nineteen patients with inextirpable skull-base meningiomas were treated at the Svedberg Laboratory in Uppsala with 24 Gy in four fractions. With a minimum follow-up time of 36 months, no patients have experienced disease progression.

G. Paranasal Sinus Carcinoma

Between 1991 and 1996, 32 patients with carcinomas of the paranasal sinuses were treated on an accelerated dose proton/photon protocol. The stage distribution was T3 in 2 cases and T4 in 30 cases and all were N$_0$ and M$_0$. Four patients had had a gross total resection while the others had had only a biopsy (7) or subtotal resection (19). The median observation period is 2.7 years. Actuarial disease-specific survival at 3 years was 62%. There have been 10 deaths: 3 with intercurrent disease and 7 with metastatic tumor. Three patients developed local failure. The 3-year actuarial local control rate was 89%. Late toxicity has included temporal lobe necrosis in three patients, although all have regressed with steroid treatment. Three patients have required surgical soft tissue repair. These local control results appear to constitute a substantial gain over conventional surgery and photon treatment techniques.

H. Hepatocellular Carcinoma

Matsuzaki and colleagues at Tsukuba University, Japan, have reported impressive long-term control and survival results in patients with primary hepatocellular carcinoma treated with proton radiation therapy. The dose per fraction was 4 Gy, and the mean total dose was 72 Gy. The 7-year local control and survival results in this series of 122 patients were reported as 94 and 27%. Proton therapy did not cause clinically symptomatic changes in liver function. The only notable change observed was a transient increase in liver transaminases.

I. Lung Cancer

Between 1994 and 1998, 37 patients with medically inoperable stage I–IIIa lung cancer were treated at Loma Linda with conformal photons and protons. Patients received either photons and protons or protons alone to 73.8 CGE over 5 weeks. Patients with poor lung function received 51 CGE in 10 fractions over 2 weeks to the gross tumor volume. With a median follow-up time of 14 months, disease-free survival at 2 years was 63% for all patients and 86% for stage I patients.

J. Proton Radiosurgery

Between 1961 and 1993, 2987 patients were treated with single fraction proton therapy (proton radiosurgery). This effort was led by the late Dr. Raymond Kjellberg, a neurosurgeon at the MGH. The majority of patients were treated for inoperable arteriovenous malformations and pituitary adenomas. Beginning in 1991, a second proton radiosurgery technique was developed using a patient positioning system capable of stereotactic alignment for radiosurgery. This system was developed because of the inherent restrictions of the fixed horizontal beam at the HCL and was based on target coordinates obtained directly from CT, MRI, or angiography. Early results with arteriovenous malformations, acoustic neuromas, and brain metastases are comparable with those produced by other stereotactic technologies (gamma knife, linear accelerator).

V. DESIGN OF CLINICAL TRIALS USING PROTON BEAMS

The fixed horizontal, 160-MeV HCL proton beam, with an effective treatment depth of 16 cm, constrained the number of sites that could effectively be treated. For this reason, past efforts have focused on intracranial targets, skull-based tumors, head/neck tumors, eye tumors, and prostatic carcinoma. The very positive results from the limited studies carried out at the HCL, and the limitations of the HCL, led to the development of a hospital-based proton therapy facility on the MGH main campus. This new facility, the Northeast Proton Therapy Center (NPTC), which opened in the fall of 2001, has the capacity to treat over 1000 patients per year. The NPTC, jointly funded by the National Cancer Institute and the MGH, has a more energetic beam (230 MeV) capable of treating to depths of 32 cm, an isocentric gantry delivery system, and state-of-the-art patient positioners and safety/control systems. These improvements will increase the numbers of patients that can be treated and will facilitate treatment at a number of new sites, including lung, rectum, and liver. In addition, a major effort will be placed in developing protocols for the treatment of pediatric malignancies.

The reduction in normal tissue irradiation with protons has significant implications for combined radiation and chemotherapy protocols. Even when modest doses of radiation are prescribed, as in the case of rectal carcinoma, proton radiation should improve tolerance to the combined regimen. This should result in fewer dose-limiting toxicities, as well as improved treatment intensity and treatment compliance. This may allow for higher chemotherapy doses and ultimately lead to higher cancer control rates.

VI. CONCLUSIONS AND FUTURE DIRECTIONS

The history of radiation oncology has demonstrated that major improvements in local control have occurred because of improved dose distributions that concentrate the high-dose region to the tumor/target volume and respect the radiation tolerance of critical tissues and organs. Proton radiation therapy represents one of the most precise and sophisticated treatment delivery systems in radiation oncology. Proton therapy will also utilize some of the same improvements that have developed in conformal photon therapy (intensity modulation, rotational delivery, multileaf collimation, stereotactic localization) to further improve the dose distribution of protons. Such improvements will allow for continued escalation in tumor doses while minimizing the dose to normal, nontarget tissues. With the recent installation of a high-energy (230 MeV) hospital-based proton therapy facility at the Northeast Proton Therapy Center at the MGH and the existing facility at LLU Medical Center, the technology exists for continuing clinical research in proton radiation therapy. Efforts for the next 10 years will include (1) comparisons of intensity modulated protons and photons, (2) assessment of the gains in treatment intensity in combined modality therapy with protons, and (3) assessment of the impact of proton therapy in improving cure rates in pediatric cancer and reducing late effects.

Acknowledgment

This work was supported in part by Grant CA21239 from the National Cancer Institute.

See Also the Following Articles

BRACHYTHERAPY • DOSIMETRY AND TREATMENT PLANNING FOR THREE-DIMENSIONAL RADIATION THERAPY • LATE EFFECTS OF RADIATION THERAPY • PHOTODYNAMIC THERAPY: CLINICAL APPLICATIONS • RADIATION RESISTANCE • RADIOBIOLOGY, PRINCIPLES OF • TOTAL BODY IRRADIATION

Bibliography

Amin-Hanjani, S. Ogilvy, C. S., Candia, G. J., Lyons, S., and Chapman, P. H. (1998). Stereotactic radiosurgery for cavernous malformations. *Neurosurgery* **42**, 1229–1236.

Bush, D. A., Slater, J. D., Bonnet, R., *et al.* (1999). Proton-beam radiotherapy for early-stage lung cancer. *Chest* **116**, 1313–1319.

Catton, C., O'Sullivan, B., Bell, R., *et al.* (1996). Chordoma: long-term follow-up after radical photon irradiation. *Radiother. Oncol.* **41**, 67–70.

Char, D. H., Quivey, J. M., Castro, J. R., Kroll, S., and Phillips, T. (1993). Helium ions versus iodine 125 brachytherapy in the management of uveal melanoma. A prospective, randomized, dynamically balanced trial. *Ophthalmology* **100**, 1547–1554.

Courdi, A., Caujolle, J. P., Grange, J. D., *et al.* (1999). Results of proton therapy of uveal melanomas treated in Nice. *Int. J. Radiat. Oncol. Biol. Phys.* **45**, 5–11.

Fitzek, M. M., Thornton, A. F., Rabinov, J. D., *et al.* (1999). Accelerated fractionated proton/photon irradiation to 90 cobalt gray equivalent for glioblastoma multiforme: Results of a phase II prospective trial. *J. Neurosurg.* **91**, 251–260.

Fuss, M., Hug, E., Schaefe, R. A., *et al.* (1999). Proton radiation therapy (PRT) for pediatric optic pathway gliomas: Comparison with 3D planned conventional photons and a standard photon technique. *Int. J. Radiat. Oncol. Biol. Phys.* **45**, 1117–1126.

Gudjonsson, O., Blomquist, E., Nyberg, G., *et al.* (1999). Stereotactic irradiation of skull base meningiomas with high energy protons. *Acta Neurochir.(Wien.)* **141**, 933–940.

Habrand, J. L., Haie-Meder, C., Rey, A., *et al.* (1999). Radiotherapy using a combination of photons and protons for locally aggressive intracranial tumors: Preliminary results of protocol CPO 94- C1. *Cancer Radiother.* **3**, 480–488.

Harsh, G., Loeffler, J. S., Thornton, A., Smith, A., Bussiere, M., and Chapman, P. H. (1999). Stereotactic proton radiosurgery. *Neurosurg. Clin. North Am.* **10**, 243–256.

Hug, E. B., Loredo, L. N., Slater, J. D., *et al.* (1999). Proton radiation therapy for chordomas and chondrosarcomas of the skull base. *J. Neurosurg.* **91**, 432–439.

Matsuzaki, Y., Osuga, T., Chiba, T., *et al.* (1995). New, effective treatment using proton irradiation for unresectable hepatocellular carcinoma. *Intern. Med.* **34**, 302–304.

Mirabell, R. A., Lomax, A., and Russo, M. (1997). Potential role of proton therapy in the treatment of pediatric medulloblastoma/primitive neuroectodermal tumors: Spinal theca irradiation. *Int. J. Radiat. Oncol. Biol. Phys.* **38**, 805–811.

Munzenrider, J. E. (1999). Proton therapy for uveal melanomas and other eye lesions. *Strahlenther. Onkol.* **175**(Suppl. 2), 68–73.

Munzenrider, J. E., and Liebsch, N. J. (1999). Proton therapy for tumors of the skull base. *Strahlenther. Onkol.* **175**(Suppl. 2), 57–63.

Raju, M. R. (1995). Proton radiobiology, radiosurgery and radiotherapy. *Int. J. Radiat. Biol. Phys.* **67**, 237–259.

Shipley, W. U., Verhey, L. J., Munzenrider, J. E., *et al.* (1995). Advanced prostate cancer: The results of a randomized comparative trial of high dose irradiation boosting with conformal protons compared with conventional dose irradiation using photons alone. *Int. J. Radiat. Oncol. Biol. Phys.* **32**, 3–12.

Sisterson, J. (2002). Particles Newsletter 29 (J. Sisterson, ed.), p. 15, Northeast Proton Therapy Center, Massachusetts General Hospital, Boston, MA.

Slater, J. D., Rossi, C. J. J., Yonemoto, L. T., *et al.* (1999). Conformal proton therapy for early-stage prostate cancer. *Urology* **53**, 978–984.

Thornton, A. F., Fitzek, M. M., Varvarres, M., *et al.* (1998). Accelerated, hyperfractionated proton/photon irradiation for advanced paranasal sinus cancer: Results of a prospective phase I-II study. *Int. J. Radiat. Oncol. Biol. Phys.* (Abstract) **42**, 222.

Tsuji, H., Okumura, T., Maruhashi, A., *et al.* (1995). Dose-volume histogram analysis of patients with hepatocellular carcinoma regarding changes in liver function after proton therapy. [Japanese]. *Nippon Igaku Hoshasen Gakkai Zasshi* **55**, 322–328.

Wilson, R. R. (1946). Radiological use of fast protons. *Radiology* **47**, 487–491.

p16 and ARF: Crossroads of Tumorigenesis

Wendell G. Yarbrough
Yue Xiong

University of North Carolina at Chapel Hill

The p16^{INK4a} locus on human chromosome 9p21 is homozygously deleted or mutated at a remarkably high frequency in many established cell lines derived from various types of human cancers. It is now clear that such high frequency of alteration, second only to that of p53 locus, stems from its unique genomic structure that encodes a hidden second tumor suppressor gene, ARF, allowing this one locus to activate the two major human tumor suppressors; p53 and retinoblastoma (Fig. 1). The ARF gene is expressed from a separate promoter with a distinct first exon (exon 1β). The AUG codon within the exon 1β of ARF predicts a protein completely unrelated to p16 via an unprecedented mechanism of translation in an alternative reading frame (Fig. 2A). This article briefly examines evidence supporting tumor suppression activities of p16 and ARF and the molecular mechanism underlying their function.

I. TUMOR SUPPRESSION BY p16 AND ARF

A. p16 as the Major Tumor Suppressor of the ARF-INK4a Locus: The Champion

1. Frequent Mutations of p16 in Human Tumors

The strongest evidence implicating p16 in tumor suppression comes from mutational analyses of the p16 gene in familial cancers, in particular familial melanoma. Additionally, familial mutations affecting p16 have been associated with pancreatic cancer and head and neck squamous cell cancer. Analyses of familial mutations within the p16 gene have found that these mutations segregate with the tumor and that the encoded p16 proteins are nonfunctional, offering strong evidence that p16 is the mutational target at 9p21. These data would ordinarily be taken unquestionably

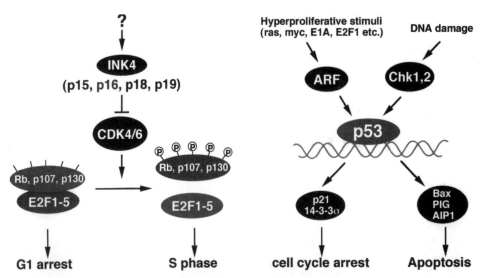

FIGURE 1 Schematic illustration of the Rb and p53 tumor suppression pathways. Under- or hypophos-phorylated pocket proteins (Rb, p107, and p130) bind to and repress the transcription of E2F target genes. During G1 progression, pocket proteins are phosphorylated by CDK4/6-cyclin Ds and CDK2/cyclin Es, releasing the repression of E2F responsive genes to permit S-phase entry. The activity of CDK4 and CDK6 is inhibited by binding with an INK4 protein. Following DNA damage or oncogenic stimulation, p53 is activated and functions as a sequence-specific transcription factor to express genes involved in either cell cycle arrest or apoptosis.

as confirmation of tumor suppressor qualities, but due to the fact that many of these mutations also alter ARF amino acid sequence, closer examination is required. In an attempt to differentiate the individual contributions of ARF and p16 to tumor suppression, this article focus on mutations or genetic alterations that uniquely alter either p16 or ARF.

While there are many examples of tumor-associated point mutations that exclusively alter only p16, there are fewer mutations reported that only change ARF coding sequence and, to date, there are no described point mutations within the critical exon 1β that uniquely encode ARF. Many examples of mutations that alter p16 without affecting the ARF amino acid sequence occur in familial melanoma cohorts. One of these mutations, P48L, is of particular interest because it occurs in exon 1α of p16 and therefore does not alter the ARF nucleotide or amino acid sequence. Substantiating the role of this exon 1α mutation in tumorigenesis, P48L encodes a defective p16 protein. Analyses of several other p16-specific mutations (N71S, P81L, R87P, and H98P) reveal altered biological and biochemical activities of the mutant

protein, suggesting that the alteration of p16, not ARF, predisposes to melanoma in these kindreds. Although there are less extensive data, somatic mutations that alter p16, but not ARF, have been described in multiple tumor types (astorcytoma, HNSCC, and thyroid cancer). Functional testing of the mutant p16 proteins derived from these tumors confirms that the p16 mutants do not function normally, suggesting that the role of p16 in tumor suppression is not limited to melanoma, but likely encompasses a large array of different tumor types. These data further suggest that p16 is a critical mutational target of the INK4a/ARF locus during human tumor development.

Deletion of the entire ARF-INK4a gene locus is the most common means of inactivation of p16, but many human tumors are associated with loss of p16 protein expression without gene mutations or deletions. The mechanism of p16 inactivation in these cases is attributable to transcriptional silencing of the p16 gene. Methylation of a specific element (CpG island) within the p16-specific exon1α promoter extending into exon 1α itself mechanistically explains the transcriptional block and lack of p16 expression

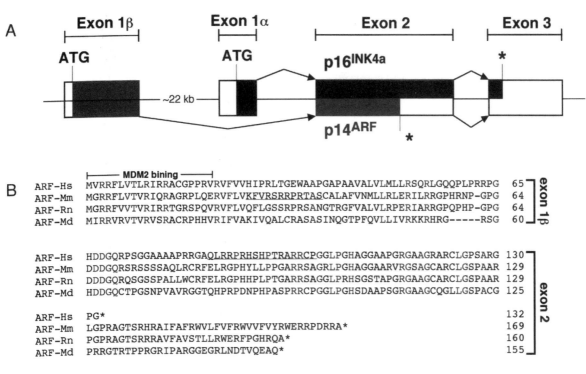

B

ARF-Hs	MVRRFLVTLRIRRACGPPRVRVFVVHIPRLTGEWAAPGAPAAVALVLMLLRSQRLGQQPLPRRPG	65	
ARF-Mm	MGRRFLVTVRIQRAGRPLQERVFLVKFVRSRRPRTASCALAFVNMLLRLERILRRGPHRNP-GPG	64	
ARF-Rn	MGRRFVVTVRIRRTGRSPQVRVFLVQFLGSSRPRSANGTRGFVALVLRPERIARRGPQPHP-GPG	64	
ARF-Md	MIRRVRVTVRVSRACRPHHVRIFVAKIVQALCRASASINQGTPFQVLLIVRKKRHRG-----RSG	60	

MDM2 binning (above ARF-Hs, spanning exon 1β region)

exon 1β

ARF-Hs	HDDGQRPSGGAAAAPRRGAQLRRPRHSHPTRARRCPGGLPGHAGGAAPGRGAAGRARCLGPSARG	130
ARF-Mm	DDDGQRSRSSSSAQLRCRFELRGPHYLLPPGARRSAGRLPGHAGGAARVRGSAGCARCLGSPAAR	129
ARF-Rn	DDDGQRQSGSSPALLWCRFELRGPHHPLPTGARRSAGGLPRHSGSTAPGRGAAGCARCLGSPAAR	129
ARF-Md	HDDGQCTPGSNPVAVRGGTQHPRPDNPHPASPRRCPGGLPGHSDAAPSGRGAAGCQGLLGSPACG	125

ARF-Hs	PG*	132
ARF-Mm	LGPRAGTSRHRAIFAFRWVLFVFRWVVFVYRWERRPDRRA*	169
ARF-Rn	PGPRAGTSRRRAVFAVSTLLRWERFPGHRQA*	160
ARF-Md	PRRGTRTPPRGRIPARGGEGRLNDTVQEAQ*	155

exon 2

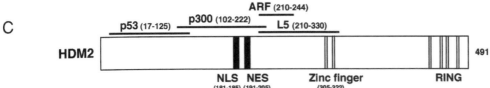

C

FIGURE 2 Genomic structure of ARF-INK4a locus and sequence comparison of ARF proteins. (A) Schematic representation of the human ARF-INK4a locus. (B) Sequence comparison of ARF proteins from different species: human (Hs, *Homo sapiens*), mouse (Mm, *Mus musculus*), rat (Rn, *Rattus norvegicus*), and a grey opossum (Md, *Monodelplus domestica*). (C) Schematic representation of the HDM2 protein. Various functional motifs are indicated below and regions for binding with p53, p300, ribosomal protein L5, and ARF are indicated above. Each vertical line represents a cysteine or histidine residue in the zinc or RING finger.

that is observed in a portion of all common human cancer types. Notably, this epigenetic mechanism of altering p16 activity is very prevalent in tumors that lack deletions or point mutations, such as colon carcinomas, and may account for inactivation of p16 that is more prevalent than previously expected. Analyses of p16 and ARF proteins in neoplastic keratinocytes that lacked deletions of the ARF-p16 locus revealed frequent lack of p16 expression with maintenance of ARF expression supposedly through specific methylation of the p16 promoter. Because p16 and ARF have separate promoters, methylation of the exon 1α promoter CpG island specifically downregu-

lates p16 without altering ARF. This epigenetic mechanism of specific p16 inactivation further supports the role of p16 in tumor suppression.

B. ARF as the Major Tumor Suppressor of the ARF-INK4a Locus: The Challenger

1. ARF-Specific Mutation Is Not Frequent in Human Tumors

There is no report thus far of human tumor-associated point mutations within the critical region of ARF encoded by exon 1β. An explanation of this lack of point mutations within exon1β of ARF could relate to an extended or dual MDM2-binding site within exon 1β of ARF that cannot be destroyed by a single point mutation. Despite the absence of point mutations within exon 1β, specific deletions of this exon have been described. Mapping of 9p21 deletions within a large cohort of T-cell leukemias found that the smallest common deletion targeted ARF sequences rather than p16. In addition to ARF-specific genomic deletions, promoter methylation has also been reported as a mechanism to repress ARF expression without altering p16. As with the p16 promoter, the ARF promoter has been found to contain a CpG island that, when methylated, prevents ARF expression independent of INK4a. Such epigenetic alteration may explain the absence of ARF protein in tumors despite the existence of a normal gene.

Although less common than mutations that exclusively alter p16, examples of human tumor-associated mutations of exon 2 that alter ARF amino acid sequences, with or without alteration of p16, are described. Because the peptide encoded by exon 1β of ARF is sufficient for p53 activation, it was originally assumed that exon 2-encoded sequences may not be necessary for ARF activity, an assumption that has recently been challenged. Discovery of a nucleolus localization signal (NoLS) in the exon2-encoded C-terminal domain of human, but not mouse, ARF (see later) provided more sensitive functional analyses of human tumor-associated exon 2 mutations. Tumor-derived mutations in the exon 2, including mutations that do not alter p16 function, resulted in ARF delocalization and partial loss of ARF-induced stabilization and activation of p53. These data suggest that mutations that alter only ARF may predispose to tumor formation.

2. ARF Single- and ARF-p16 Double-Deficient Mice Have Similar Phenotypes

Characterization of a knockout mouse targeting only exon 1β provided strong genetic evidence supporting ARF as a bona fide tumor suppressor and directly challenged the role of p16 in tumorigenesis and cellular senescence in mice. Phenotypically, ARF$^{-/-}$ mice develop spontaneous and carcinogen-induced tumors similar to mice lacking both p16 and ARF. The tumor spectrum of ARF null mice, like that of p16-ARF double null mice, was dominated by sarcomas and lym-

phomas and, like p16$^{-/-}$/ARF$^{-/-}$ cells, cultures of ARF$^{-/-}$ MEFs grew to a higher density than wild-type MEFs, did not undergo a detectable senescent crisis, and could be transformed by oncogenic ras alone. Hence, as determined by the incidence and spectrum of tumor development, by the loss of cell senescence control, and by the cellular response to oncogenic ras, expression ARF deficiency is very similar, if not the same, as loss of both ARF and p16 in mice.

To unambiguously determine the individual contribution of p16 and ARF to tumor formation in the mouse, characterization of a p16 knockout mouse that does not affect ARF is needed. Preliminary results from such mice have been presented, suggesting that by 20 weeks of age, the pure p16$^{-/-}$ mice do not develop tumors. MEF cells derived from p16$^{-/-}$ mice retain normal senescence phenotype and are resistant to ras-mediated transformation. Although longer examination of p16$^{-/-}$ mice is needed to determine if a tumor phenotype exists, these preliminary studies suggest that ARF in mice plays at least an earlier if not a more prominent role than p16 in tumor suppression.

3. p53-Independent Function of ARF

Predictably, if all tumor suppressor activity of ARF were dependent solely on functional p53, the tumor phenotype of p53$^{-/-}$ mice would be more severe and encompass the ARF$^{-/-}$ tumor phenotype. However, comparison of tumor formation in p53$^{-/-}$ and ARF$^{-/-}$ mice reveals distinct differences, suggesting that for tumor formation, loss of p53 and ARF are similar but not equivalent. A substantial percentage of ARF$^{-/-}$ mice spontaneously develop carcinomas and neurogenic tumors that are rarely seen in p53$^{-/-}$ mice, suggesting that ARF may have functions unrelated to p53. More direct genetic evidence supporting a p53-independent function of ARF in tumor suppression has been provided by the finding that ARF-MDM2-p53 triple knockout mice develop a wider range of tumors than observed in p53-MDM2 double knockout mice. Likewise, mice lacking p53 and ARF develop oncogene-induced lymphoma earlier than mice lacking either p53 or ARF alone, and cells derived from these ARF and p53 double null lymphomas grow faster than lymphoma cells derived from ARF or p53 single null lymphomas. The exact mechanism of p53-independent activity of ARF remains controver-

TABLE I
Evidence Supporting p16 and ARF as Tumor Suppressors

	Human data	Mouse data
p16	Familial mutations that alter p16 (not ARF) segregate with cancer predisposition	Mice expressing mutant CDK4 that cannot be inhibited by p16 develop spontaneous tumors
	Tumor-associated somatic mutations affect p16 sequence and activity without altering ARF	Mice lacking both p16 and ARF develop tumors earlier than mice lacking only ARF
	Specific p16 promoter methylation occurs in many somatic tumor types	
	CDK4 mutant unresponsive to p16 is associated with familial melanoma	
ARF	The smallest common area of 9p21 deletion in gliomas and T-cell leukemias includes ARF encoding exon 1β but not p16 encoding sequences	Mice lacking ARF, but retaining p16, develop spontaneous and carcinogen-induced tumors
	Tumor-associated somatic mutations alter the ability of ARF to stabilize p53 but do not alter p16 function	Mouse cells lacking ARF can be transformed by a single oncogene and do not senesce

sial because it has been shown to be inhibited by MDM2 and to rely on functional Rb under separate experimental conditions.

Multiple lines of evidence from analyses of both human and mice data suggest that both ARF and p16 act in prevention of tumorigenesis (Table I). The function of p16 and ARF as activators of retinoblastoma and p53 offers a firm biological foundation supporting both as tumor suppressors. In general, human data are more supportive of p16 as the major tumor suppressor of the ARF-INK4a locus, whereas murine data strongly support ARF as the major tumor suppressor of the locus. It appears that p16 plays an equally critical role in suppressing tumor growth as ARF in humans; however, in mice, p16 may either have a subtler tumor suppressor activity or its activity may be compensated by redundancy within the INK4 family.

II. BIOCHEMICAL MECHANISMS OF p16 AND ARF

A. p16^{INK4a}, the Initial Inhibitor of the ARF-INK4a Locus

Ectopic expression of individual INK4 genes, including p16, induces a G1 cell cycle arrest in cells with wild-type Rb function, but not in cells where the Rb function is compromised, leading to the notion that

Rb is the major target of the growth suppressive activity of INK4 during G1 progression. A consequential interpretation is that during G1 progression, the principal targets of INK4 proteins are cyclin D-dependent kinases, CDK4 or CDK6, whose primary substrate is Rb. Genetic evidence supporting this notion comes from the finding that loss of p18^{INK4c}, like loss of one allele of Rb, leads to the development of intermediate lobe pituitary adenomas. The puzzle—why activation of phosphorylation of the other two pocket proteins, p107 and p130, in the absence of Rb had no obvious effects on G1 progression—has been clarified by the realization that the three pocket proteins exert their growth suppressive effect through two distinct mechanism and that both mechanisms are required to effect a G1 arrest. While Rb mainly binds to E2Fs1-3 and recruits histone deacetylase (HDAC) to repress E2F responsive promoters, p107 and p130 exclusively bind to E2Fs4 and 5 and recruit HDAC to antagonize the E2Fs1-3-mediated transactivation. MEFs retaining the wild-type function of Rb, but lacking the combination of p107 and p130, or E2F4 and E2F5, like Rb-deficient cells, are resistant to p16-mediated G1 arrest. Hence, the notion of a linear p16-Rb pathway is more appropriately defined as INK4-pocket protein pathways.

The biochemical mechanism of p16-mediated CDK4/6 inhibition is well understood now and is relatively simple. p16 and its three related INK4 proteins consist of four to five ankyrin repeats. In the majority of cells examined, p16 binds to CDK4 and/or CDK6 to form a binary complex, thereby preventing the binding and activation of CDK4/6 by D-type cyclins. This is consistent with the crystal structural analysis of p16^{INK4a}-CDK4 and p19^{INK4d}-CDK6 complexes showing that INK4 binds close to the ATP-binding site of the catalytic cleft in CDK4 or CDK6, inducing structural changes that distort the binding of ATP and D-cyclins proteins.

B. ARF: Invader of the p16 Locus

Thus far, the ARF gene has been identified in only four mammalian organisms (Fig. 2B). ARF does not share significant sequence similarity with any proteins currently deposited within the protein database and contains no obvious sequence motifs, providing little clue to its biochemical properties. One distinct property common to ARF proteins from different species is their unusually high contents of basic charged residues. As a result, the isoelectric point (pI) of human (12.4), mouse (12.1), rat (12.3), and opossum (11.9) ARF proteins is remarkably high. A single INK4 gene, p13^{CDKN2X}, has been reported in the Southern platyfish (*Xiphophorus maculatus*) genome and has been linked to hereditary susceptibility to UV-induced melanomas. The fish INK4 gene contains an intron at the same position as other mammalian INK4 genes and is equally related to the four mammalian INK4 genes, indicating that the fish INK4 gene may have evolved from a common ancestor, which gave rise to the four mammalian INK4 genes after two gene duplication events. A 5′ RACE (rapid amplification of cDNA ends) using primers with the second exon of p13^{CDK2NX} failed to identify products representative of an ARF. Conceptual translation of exon 2 of the platyfish INK4, as well as that of mammalian INK4b, INK4c, and INK4d genes, yields only a short alternative open reading frame bearing no significant similarity to either human or mouse ARF and lacking the conserved ARF C-terminal domain. These observations, together with the early origin of the anykrin motif during evolution (as early as the origin of bacteria), suggest that the ARF gene might have been a late invader of the p16 locus. The MDM2 gene, the major target of ARF, has been identified in frog, zebrafish (database accession AAB64176), and ascidian (database accession AV382318) and appears

to have evolved earlier than ARF. Further still, the *Drosophila melanogaster* genome contains a single p53 gene, but not MDM2 or ARF (or INK4). It therefore appears that the ARF-MDM2-p53 pathway evolved by the sequential addition of upstream regulators, first the control of p53 by MDM2 and then MDM2 by ARF during evolution. One possibility is that the puzzling genomic arrangement of the ARF-INK4a locus was evolved by the insertion of a MDM2-binding domain into the existing p16 locus that conferred on cells the ability to couple the MDM2-p53 and INK4-Rb pathways through coordinated regulation of the chromatin structure at the locus and thus transcription of both genes.

The ARF gene has undergone relatively rapid evolutionary sequence drift. Human ARF, for example, shares only 49 and 44% amino acid sequence identity with its mouse and opossum homologues, respectively. As a comparison, the human p16 protein is 63% identical to both mouse and opossum p16. Such a high degree of sequence divergence indicates that the ARF gene was not highly constrained during evolution, suggesting that ARF function was not initially evolved to perform functions important for cell survival or organismal development. Many established cell lines sustain homozygous deletion of the ARF-INK4a locus, and mice lacking ARF spontaneously develop tumors early in their life, but exhibit no obvious developmental defects.

C. ARF Binds to MDM2

Three lines of genetic evidence link the function of ARF to p53 pathway. Tumors that arise from ARF/INK4a-deficient mice lack p53 mutation/deletion; ectopic expression of ARF inhibits S-phase entry in wild type MEFs, but not in several established fibroblast cell lines lacking p53 function; and ARF inhibits cellular transformation only in the presence of functional p53. The finding that ARF binds MDM2 and stabilizes p53 was pivotal in advancing understanding of the molecular mechanism of ARF activity.

MDM2-binding activity resides entirely within the N-terminal domain of ARF encoded by the exon 1β. A synthetic peptide corresponding to the first 15 amino acids of human or mouse ARF binds tightly to MDM2 or HDM2. The N-terminal 15 residues of

ARF represent one of two highly conserved regions in ARF and contains 7 identical and 4 similar residues among the four mammalian ARF proteins (Fig. 2B). Mouse ARF contains a second MDM2-binding site, between residues 15 to 40, albeit with lower affinity than peptides 1–15. The mouse ARF sequence 15 to 40 is, however, not conserved in ARF from other species and contains only 3 identical and 3 similar residues (Fig. 2B). Hence, mouse and human ARF proteins were structurally distinct in their interactions with MDM2/HDM2. It has yet to be determined if the two MDM2-binding sites in mouse ARF allosterically cooperate with each other to increase the murine ARF-MDM2-binding affinity. ARF, however, binds to a central domain of MDM2, between amino acids 210 and 244 in HDM2, separate from the p53-binding domain located at the N-terminal region of HDM2. The binding of ARF and p53 to separate regions in MDM2 is supported by the assembly of ternary ARF-MDM2-p53 complex. The central region of MDM2 contains several functional domains, including NLS, NES, a L5 ribosomal binding site, and a zinc finger (Fig. 2C), whose activities could potentially be affected by ARF binding.

D. ARF Localizes to the Nucleolus

ARF protein normally localizes to the nucleolus, a property that appears to be important for its function (see later). Two distinct nucleolus localization signals (NoLS) were found in ARF, and again there are topographical differences between human and mouse ARF proteins. While deletion of mouse ARF residues 26–37 (underlined in Fig. 2B) results in altered nucleolar localization, human ARF[85-101] (underlined in Fig. 2B) within the exon 2-encoded C-terminal domain is necessary to localize to the nucleolus. Neither mARF[26-37] nor hARF[85-101] is conserved in other species. A second NoLS was found overlapping with the MDM2-binding site, raising the possibility that subnuclear distribution of the ARF-MDM2 complex could conceivably be affected by proteins that can bind to MDM2 and be assembled into an ARF-MDM2 complex.

E. ARF Function in p53 Stabilization

MDM2-mediated p53 degradation occurs in the cytoplasm. Regardless of whether nuclear p53 is shuttled from the nucleus to the cytoplasm by MDM2, exits independently, or exits dependent on MDM2-mediated ubiquitination, blocking p53 nuclear export or separating the MDM2-p53 complex would similarly cause p53 stabilization (Fig. 3A). ARF inhibits MDM2-mediated p53 degradation, at least in part, by blocking the nuclear export of p53 and MDM2. Presently, there are three competing models concerning the molecular mechanism by which ARF inhibits MDM2-mediated p53 nuclear export.

1. Nucleolar Sequestration

The nucleolar sequestration model proposes that ARF sequesters MDM2 in the nucleolus, releasing p53 from MDM2 inhibition (Fig. 3B). This model is based mainly on two observations. First, a portion of MDM2 protein was localized into nucleoli in HeLa cells cotransfected with plasmids expressing MDM2 and mouse ARF, in MEFs microinjected with plasmids encoding mouse ARF, and in aging MEFs where both MDM2 and ARF protein levels are elevated. Second, a mouse ARF mutant that was defective in nucleolar localization, yet retaining MDM2-binding activity, was unable to mobilize MDM2 into the nucleolus and had a decreased ability to stabilize p53. The nucleolar sequestration model has been presented in two different versions. The first simply proposes that ARF relocalizes MDM2 from the nucleoplasm to the nucleolus, enabling p53 to accumulate in the nucleoplasm free from MDM2 inhibition. A more intricate version, rooted in the idea of MDM2-dependent p53 export, postulates that the normal nuclear export of MDM2 and MDM2-p53 complexes travels through the nucleolus and ARF tethers crossing MDM2 in the nucleolus, thereby blocking its export as well as that of p53.

2. ARF-MDM2-p53 Ternary Complex

In the second model, ARF binds to and is relocalized by MDM2 from the nucleolus to the nucleoplasm. Coexpression of all three proteins revealed that ARF colocalizes with MDM2 and p53 into discreet nuclear bodies located in the nucleoplasm (Fig. 3C). This model is supported by the findings that ARF, MDM2, and p53 can form ternary complexes and that blocking nuclear export by the CRM-1 inhibitor leptomycin B analogously induces relocalization of both MDM2 and p53 to nuclear bodies. Deletion of the

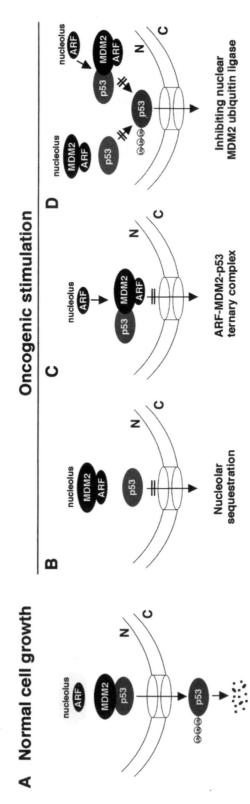

FIGURE 3 Models of ARF-mediated MDM2 inhibition and p53 activation. (A) During normal cell growth, ARF remains in the nucleolus and MDM2 binds to p53 and targets p53 for a ubiquitin-mediated degradation in the cytoplasm. (B) ARF sequesters MDM2 in the nucleolus. (C) ARF is moved from the nucleolus by MDM2, forming a ternary complex with MDM2 and p53 that localize in nuclear bodies. (D) ARF inhibits the ubiquitin ligase activity of MDM2.

exon 1β-encoded MDM2-binding domain or mutations in the nuclear/nucleolar localization signals in exon 2 of ARF abrogated the ability of ARF to form nuclear bodies and reduced the activity of ARF to stabilize p53, providing a correlative link between nuclear body formation and ARF-mediated p53 stabilization. When ARF is coexpressed with p53 in the absence of MDM2, neither the nucleolar localization of ARF nor the nucleoplasmic distribution of p53 is changed, consistent with the observations that thus far ARF is known to activate p53 only through inhibiting MDM2. Ectopic expression of E2F1, an activator of ARF gene expression, resulted in an accumulation of ARF in the nucleoplasm in normal cells or in cells with MDM2 gene amplification, but exclusively in the nucleolus in p53-deficient cells that express undetectable levels of MDM2, providing physiological evidence for the ability of MDM2 to alter ARF localization and induce nuclear body formation in the presence of ARF and p53.

3. *Inhibiting p53 Nuclear Ubiquitination*

The third model proposes that MDM2 binds to and targets p53 for ubiquitination in the nucleus and that ubiquitination of p53 facilitates, and may be required for, nuclear export and subsequent cytoplasmic p53 degradation. Because binding with ARF inhibits the ubiquitin ligase activity of MDM2, it may prevent p53 nuclear export by blocking the MDM2-mediated nuclear ubiquitination of p53 (Fig. 3D). This model is largely supported by experiments in which MDM2 and p53-GFP were coexpressed, resulting in p53-GFP cytoplasmic accumulation or even nuclear exclusion in some cells, an observation that was interpreted as evidence for a MDM2-mediated p53 nuclear export. Relocalization of p53-GFP is abrogated by a mutation in the RING finger domain of MDM2 that inactivated its ubiquitin ligase activity or by a temperature-sensitive mutation in the E1 ubiquitin-activating enzyme. Supporting this model, inhibition of nuclear export by LMP treatment resulted in a notable accumulation of ubiquitinated p53 in the nuclear fraction relative to the cytoplasm, and mutations in the C-terminal p53 NES blocked p53 nuclear export but not ubiquitination, suggesting that p53 ubiquitination may occur in the nucleus prior to translocation to the cytoplasm. This model is compatible with either nucleolar sequestration or the nuclear body model; separating MDM2 from p53 or the binding of ARF to p53-bound MDM2 would inhibit p53 ubiquitination by MDM2 and thereby block p53 nuclear export. If proven true, this model presents a novel function of ubiquitination, apart from proteolytic degradation, in regulating protein trafficking. It also represents an attractive mechanism for ARF function; coupling inhibition of p53 ubiquitination with a block of p53 nuclear export, which could further potentiate p53 activity in the nucleus than either action alone.

III. REGULATION OF p16 AND ARF

A. Upstream Regulators of p16

The existence of unique first exons and separate promoters for p16 and ARF allows differential regulation of these tumor suppressors despite the fact that they share coding sequence (summarized in Fig. 4). Recognition of the importance of p16 and elucidation of its biochemical functions occurred years before the discovery of ARF, yet little information on upstream regulators of p16 exists. Embryonic cells do not express detectable levels of p16, and mice nullizygous for ARF and p16 develop normally, implying that p16 function is not essential for normal developmental. However, MEFs are placed in tissue culture, the expression of p16 (as well as p15^{INK4b}) is rapidly activated and increases as the cells continue to age until their growth arrests at the senescence checkpoint. The mechanism underlying p16 accumulation during cell aging remains unclear. JunB, an immediate early transcription factor, has been implicated in the activation of p16 gene expression during cell senescence.

Two negative p16 regulators, Rb and Bmi-1, have been reported. Many human tumor cell lines lacking Rb function express abnormally high levels of p16. This apparent paradox—loss of one growth suppressor accompanied by the overproduction of another—was rationalized by the realization that Rb is the cardinal target of p16 in causing a G1 cell cycle arrest and was explained by the finding that Rb suppresses the p16 promoter. The activity of the TATA-less human p16 promoter is significantly higher in cells lacking Rb function than that seen in cells expressing Rb

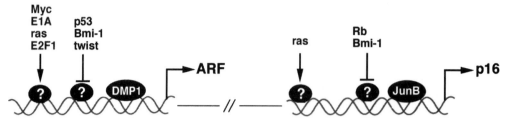

FIGURE 4   Upstream regulation of p16 and ARF genes. Schematic summary of transcriptional regulation of ARF and p16 genes. Genes that activate and repress the expression of ARF or p16 are distinguished by green and red colors, respectively. Although a number of genes have been linked to the regulation of p16 and ARF gene expression, only DMP1 and JunB have been shown to directly bind ARF and p16 promoters, respectively.

and can be repressed by the coexpression of Rb. Rb-mediated repression of the human p16 promoter does not appear to involve E2F1 suggesting that another Rb-regulated factor(s) is involved in controlling p16 expression. Intriguingly, the mouse p16 promoter shares little similarity to the human p16 promoter. In accordance, inactivation of Rb function in mouse cells, by either SV40 T antigen expression or mutation in the Rb locus, does not increase the levels of p16 mRNA and protein. The physiologic significance of this negative feedback regulation of p16 by Rb in human cells remains to be elucidated. It is tempting to consider that this difference may be part of an overall difference between mouse and human cells in their tumorigenic response to the inactivation of the INK4-Rb pathway.

The oncogene Bmi-1, a member of the mammalian Polycomb group of transcription repressors, was initially isolated by virtue of its ability to cooperate with c-Myc in lymphomagenesis. Mice lacking Bmi-1 exhibit severe neurological and lymphoid cell proliferation defects, which can be rescued by crossing with p16-ARF deficient mice, indicating that p16 and/or ARF is a critical *in vivo* target for Bmi-1. Supporting this notion, Bmi-1$^{-/-}$ MEFs have increased expression of both p16 and ARF, resulting in a reduced proliferation rate and premature entry into senescence. Conversely, ectopic expression of Bmi-1 inhibits p16 and ARF expression, although direct binding of Bmi-1 to either the p16 or ARF promoter remains to be demonstrated. Expression of Bmi-1 prior to Myc expression blocks ARF induction and inhibits myc-induced apoptosis. These results suggest that ARF likely plays a more prominent role in suppressing

Bmi-1/Myc-induced tumors, leaving the role of p16 uncertain at present.

B. Upstream Regulators of ARF

1. ARF Repressors

Three negative regulators of ARF expression, p53, Bmi-1, and Twist, have been described. Just as Rb inhibits p16 expression, ARF levels are downregulated by p53 and elevated in cells lacking p53 function, creating a negative feedback loop in which p53 inactivation by MDM2 allows for increased ARF protein levels with the subsequent activation of p53 and repression of ARF. The ARF promoter, also TATA-less, can be significantly repressed by p53, but does not contain a recognizable p53-binding site, suggesting that p53 represses the ARF promoter through binding with additional factors such as TBP components of the TFIID complex.

In addition to Bmi-1, Twist, a basic helix–loop–helix (bHLH) transcription factor first identified in *Drosophila* as a protein involved in establishing dorsoventral polarity, also reduces ARF expression. The Twist-ARF connection was suggested by the isolation of Twist in a genetic screen for genes whose ectopic expression can effectively block Myc-induced, p53-dependent apoptosis and was strengthened by the finding that ectopic Twist expression can release p53-mediated growth arrest. ARF mRNA levels are high in MEFs expressing both E1A and Ha-Ras^{V12} and were substantially reduced by the ectopic expression of Twist, leading to the proposal that downregulation of ARF may be a potential mechanism by which

Twist affects p53 function. As in the case of Bmi-1, direct binding of the ARF promoter and repression by Twist have yet to be demonstrated.

2. Many Oncogenes Activate ARF Expression

ARF expression can be activated by various hyperproliferative oncogenes, including E2F1, oncogenic Ras, E1A, Myc, and v-Abl, leading to the concept that ARF mediates a oncogene checkpoint pathway. For years, the apparently discordant observations that oncogenes simultaneously increase tumor development yet also inhibit tumor formation by increasing p53 and inducing apoptosis have puzzled investigators searching for a mechanism. The apoptotic response to oncogenes is thought to be a major cellular defense against tumor formation and depends on functional p53, but the exact mechanism by which oncogenes activate p53 was unknown. Both myc and E1A trigger apoptosis in cultured fibroblasts deprived of serum survival factors, and this apoptotic response is attenuated by the inactivation of ARF. *In vivo*, Rb deficiency can trigger apoptosis in developing mouse lens cells, but this effect of Rb was attenuated by the disruption of both p16 and ARF genes. Because p16 is believed to be nonfunctional in the absence of Rb, the reduction of apoptosis in $Rb^{-/-}/p16^{-/-}/ARF^{-/-}$ triple deficient cells can be most likely attributed to the loss of ARF function. In accordance with the notion that a Rb⊣ E2F1 → ARF → p53 pathway induces apoptosis in response to hyperproliferative oncogenic stimulation, E2F1 loss of function suppresses p53-dependent apoptosis observed in Rb-deficient cells *in vivo*. Taken together, these results suggest a biological role for the activation of ARF expression by proliferative oncogenic stimulation, namely, stabilization of p53 and induction of a p53-dependent apoptosis. Two critical issues concerning ARF-mediated apoptosis in response to oncogenic insults remain to be addressed. First, a direct demonstration that ARF loss of function, like E2F1 deficiency, suppresses apoptosis and rescues/delays embryonic lethality of Rb null mouse has not been provided and remains to be a critical test for a role of ARF in mediating E2F1-induced, p53-dependent apoptosis. Second, given that the ARF promoter does not contain a discernible myc-binding site, direct regulation of ARF gene expression by other oncogenes, especially myc and ras, remains to be determined. DMP1, a myb-like transcription factor, is the only factor that has been shown to bind and transactivate the ARF promoter, and ectopic expression of DMP1 inhibits DNA synthesis in wild type but not in ARF null MEFs. DMP1 deficiency reduces the accumulation of ARF during the *in vitro* passage of MEFs or in response to Ras^{V12} expression and partially bypasses the senescence checkpoint, despite retention of functional p53. DMP1-deficient mice develop spontaneous tumors at a very low incidence and are tumor prone following carcinogen treatment. Taken together, these results support the idea that ARF expression is modulated by DMP1 *in vivo* and is partially compromised in animals lacking DMP1 function. The activation of ARF gene expression by hyperproliferative oncogenes, however, does not appear to be dependent on DMP1.

IV. CONCLUSION

Arguably, the study of p16 and ARF since the mid-1990s represents one of the most exciting and rewarding areas in cancer research. These studies have significantly deepened our understanding of p53 and Rb tumor suppression pathways, both mechanistically and physiologically, and of the interaction between tumor suppressors and oncogenes. Studies on ARF and p16 have also provided inceptive insights into the molecular mechanisms of cellular senescence and immortalization. There is every reason to believe that more new discoveries, and possibly some surprises, especially regarding the physiological role of INK4 genes and molecular mechanisms of ARF function, are yet to come.

Acknowledgments

W.G.Y. is supported in part by a grant from the National Institutes of Health (KO8-CA72968) and Y.X. is a Pew Scholar in Biomedical Science and a recipient of the United States Department of Defense Breast Cancer Research Career Development Award. This study was supported by NIH Grants CA65572 and CA68377 to Y.X.

See Also the Following Articles

Bibliography

Arap, W., Knudsen, E. S., Wang, J. Y. J., Cavenee, W. K., and Huang, H.-J. S. (1997). Point mutations can inactivate *in vitro* and *in vivo* activities of p16$^{INK4a/CDKN2A}$ in human glioma. *Oncogene* **14**, 603–609.

Bates, S., Phillips, A. C., Clark, P., Stott, F., Peters, G., Ludwig, R., and Vousden, K. H. (1998). p14^{ARF} links the tumor suppressors RB and p53. *Nature* **395**, 124–125.

Boyd, S. D., Tsai, K. Y., and Jacks, T. (2000). An intact HDM2 RING-finger domain is required for nuclear exclusion of p53. *Nature Cell Biol.* **2**, 563–568.

Brotherton, D. H., Dhanaraj, V., Wick, S., Brizuela, L., Domaille, P. J., Volyanik, E., Xu, X., Parisin, E., Smith, B. O., Archer, S. J., Serrano, M., Brenner, S. L., Blundell, T. L., and Laue, E. D. (1998). Crystal structure of the complex of the cyclin D-dependent kinase Cdk6 bound to the cell cycle inhibitor p19^{INK4d}. *Nature* **395**, 244–250.

Bruce, J. L., Hurford, R. K., Classon, M., Koh, J., and Dyson, N. (2000). Requirement for cell cycle arrest by p16^{INK4a}. *Mol. Cell* **6**, 737–742.

Carnero, A., Hudson, J. D., Price, C. M., and Beach, D. H. (2000). p16^{INK4a} and p19^{ARF} act overlapping pathways in cellular immortalization. *Nature Cell Biol.* **2**, 148–155.

Castellano, M., Pollock, P. M., Walters, M. K., Sparrow, L. E., Down, L. M., Gabrielli, B. G., Parsons, P. G., and Hayward, N. K. (1997). CDKN2A/p16 is inactivated in most melanoma cell lines. *Cancer Res.* **57**, 4868–4875.

Chao, H. H. A., Buchmann, A. M., and DeCaprio, J. A. (2000). Loss of p19^{ARF} eliminates the requirement for the pRB-binding motif in simian virus 40 large T antigen-mediated transformation. *Mol. Cell Biol.* **20**, 7624–7633.

Chen, J., Marechal, V., and Levine, A. J. (1993). Mapping of the p53 and mdm-2 interaction domains. *Mol. Cell Biol.* **13**, 4107–4114.

Chin, L., Pomerantz, J., Polsky, D., Jacobson, M., Cohen, C., Cordon-Cardo, C., Horner, J. W., and DePinho, R. A. (1997). Cooperative effects of INK4a and ras in melanoma susceptibility in vivo. *Genes Dev.* **11**, 2822–2834.

de Stanchina, E., McCurrach, M. E., Zindy, F., Shieh, S.-Y., Ferbeyre, G., Samuelson, A. V., Prives, C., Roussel, M. F., Sherr, C. J., and Lowe, S. W. (1998). E1A signaling to p53 involves the p19^{ARF} tumor suppressor. *Genes Dev.* **12**, 2434–2442.

Donehower, L. A., Harvey, M., Slagle, B. L., McArthur, M. J., Montgomery, C. A., Butel, J. S., and Bradley, A. (1992). Mice deficient for p53 are developmentally normal but susceptible to spontaneous tumors. *Nature* **356**, 215–221.

Fargnoli, M. C., Chimenti, S., Keller, G., Soyer, H. P., Dal Pozzo, V., Hofler, H., and Peris, K. (1998). CDKN2a/p16INK4a mutations and lack of p19ARF involvement in familial melanoma kindreds. *J. Invest. Dematol.* **111**, 1202–1206.

Foulkes, W. D., Flanders, T. Y., Pollock, P. M., and Hayward, N. K. (1997). The CDK2A (p16) gene and human cancer. *Mol. Med.* **3**, 5–20.

Freedman, D. A., and Levine, A. J. (1998). Nuclear export is required for degradation of endogenous p53 by MDM2 and human papillomavirus E6. *Mol. Cell Biol.* **18**, 7288–7293.

Gardie, B., Cayuela, J.-M., Martini, S., and Sigaux, F. (1998). Genomic alterations of the p19ARF encoding exons in T-cell acute lymphoblastic leukemia. *Blood* **91**, 1016–1020.

Gaubatz, S., Lindeman, G., Ishida, S., Jakoi, L., Nevins, J., Kinvinston, D. M., and Rempel, R. R. (2000). E2F4 and E2F5 play an essential role in pocket protein-mediated G1 control. *Mol. Cell* **6**, 729–735.

Geyer, R. K., Yu, Z. K., and Maki, C. G. (2000). The MDM2 RING-finger domain is required to promote p53 nuclear export. *Nature Cell Biol.* **2**, 569–573.

Goldstein, A. M., Fraser, M. C., Struewing, J. P., Hussussian, C. J., Ranade, K., Zametkin, D. P., Fontaine, L. S., Organic, S. M., Dracopoli, N. C., Clark, W. H., and Tucker, M. A. (1995) Increased risk of pancreatic cancer in melanoma-prone kindreds with p16INK4 mutations. *N. Engl. J. Med.* **333**, 970–974.

Grossman, S. R., Perez, M., Kung, A. L., Joseph, M., Mansur, C., Xiao, Z. X., Kumar, S., Howley, P. M., and Livingston, D. M. (1998). p300/MDM2 complexes participate in MDM2-mediated p53 degradation. *Mol. Cell* **2**, 405–415.

Gruis, N. A., Velden, van der., Sandkuiji, L. A., Prins, D. E., Weaver-Feldhaus, J., Kamb, A., Berman, W., and Frants, P. R. (1995). Homozygotes of human CDKN2 (p16) germline mutation in Dutch familial melanoma kindreds. *Nature Genet.* **10**, 351–353.

Guan, K.-L., Jenkins, C. W., Li, Y., Nichols, M. A., Wu, X., O'Keefe, C. L., Matera, A. G., and Xiong, Y. (1994). Growth suppression by p18, a p16$^{INK4/MTS1}$- and p14$^{INK4B/MTS2}$-related CDK6 inhibitor, correlates with wild-type pRb function. *Genes Dev.* **8**, 2939–2952.

Hara, E., Smith, R., Parry, D., Tahara, H., Stone, S., and Peters, G. (1996). Regulation of p16CDKN2 expression and its implications for cell immortalization and senescence. *Mol. Cell Biol.* **16**, 859–867.

Harvey, M., McArthur, M. J., Montgomery, C. S., Butel, A., Bradley, A., and Donehower, L. A. (1993). Spontaneous and carcinogen-induced tumorigenesis in p53-deficient mice. *Nature Genet.* **5**, 225–229.

Herman, J. G., Merlo, A., Mao, L., Lapidus, R. G., Issa, J. P. J., Davidson, N. E., Sidransky, D., and Baylin, S. B. (1995).

Inactivation of the CDKN2/p16/MTS1 gene is frequently associated with aberrant DNA methylation in all common human cancers. *Cancer Res.* **55,** 4525–4530.

Honda, R., and Yasuda, H. (1999). Association of p19[ARF] with MDM2 inhibits ubiquitin ligase activity of MDM2 for tumor suppressor p53. *EMBO J.* **18,** 22–27.

Inoue, K., Roussel, M. F., and Sherr, C. J. (1999). Induction of ARF tumor suppressor gene expression and cell cycle arrest by transcription factor DMP1. *Proc. Natl. Acad. Sci. USA* **96,** 3993–3998.

Inoue, K. Wen, R., Rehg, J. E., Adachi, M., Cleveland, J. L., Roussel, M. F., and Sherr, C. J. (2000). Disruption of the ARF transcriptional activator DMP1 facilitates cell immortalization, Ras transformation and tumorigenesis. *Gene Dev.* **14,** 1797–1809.

Jacobs, J. J., Kieboom, K., Marino, S., DePinho, R. A., and van Louhuizen, M. (1999). The oncogene and Polycomb-group gene bmi-1 regulates cell proliferation and senescence through the ink4a locus. *Nature* **397,** 164–168.

Jacobs, J. J., Scheijen, B., Voncken, J. W., Kieboom, K., Berns, A., and van Lohuizen, M. (1999). Bmi-1 collaborates with c-myc in tumorigenesis by inhibiting c-Myc-induced apoptosis via INK4a/ARF. *Genes Dev.* **13,** 2678–2690.

James, M. C., and Peters, G. (2000). Alternative product of the p16/CKDN2A locus connects the Rb and p53 tumor suppressors. *Prog. Cell Cycle Res.* **4,** 71–81.

Jeffrey, P. D., Tong,, L., and Pavletich, N. P. (2000). Structural basis of inhibition of CDK-cyclin complexes by INK4 inhibitors. *Genes Dev.* **14,** 3115–3125.

Kamb, A., Gruis, N. A., Weaver-Feldhaus, J., Liu, Q., Harshman, K., Tavitgian, S. V., Stockert, E., Day, R. S., Johnson, B. E., and Skolnick, M. H. (1994). A cell cycle regulator potentially involved in genesis of many tumor types. *Science* **264,** 436–440.

Kamb, A., Shattuck-Eidens, D., Eeles, R., Liu, Q., Gruis, N. A., Ding, W., Hussey, C., Tran, T., Miki, Y., Weaver-Feldhaus, J., McClure, M., Aitken, J. F., Anderson, D. E., Bergman, W., Frants, R., Goldgar, D. E., Green, A., MacLennan, R., Martin, N. G., Meyer, L. J., Youl, P., Zone, J. J., Skolnick, M. H., and Cannon-Albright, L. A. (1994). Analysis of the p16 gene (CDKN2) as a candidate for the chromosome 9p melanoma susceptibility locus. *Nature Genet.* **8,** 22–26.

Kamijo, T., van de Kamp, E., Chong, M. J., Zindy, F., Diehl, J. A., Sherr, C. J., and McKinnon, P. J. (1999). Loss of the ARF tumor suppressor reverses premature replicative arrest but not radiation hypersensitivity arising from disabled atm function. *Cancer Res.* **59,** 2464–2469.

Kamijo, T., Weber, J. D., Zambetti, G., Zindy, F., Roussel, M., and Sherr, C. J. (1998). Functional and physical interaction of the ARF tumor suppressor with p53 and MDM2. *Proc. Natl. Acad. Sci. USA* **95,** 8292–8297.

Kamijo, T., Zindy, F., Roussel, M. F., Quelle, D. E., Downing, J. R., Ashmun, R. A., Grosveld, G., and Sherr, C. J. (1997). Tumor suppression at the mouse INK4a locus mediated by the alternative reading frame product p19[ARF]. *Cell* **91,** 649–659.

Kazianis, S., Morizot, D. C., Colletta, L. D., Johnston, D. A., Woolcock, B., Vielkind, J. R., and Nairn, R. S. (1999). Comparative structure and characterization of a CDKN2 gene in a *Xiphophorus* fish melanoma model. *Oncogene* **18,** 5088–5099.

Koh, J., Enders, G. H., Dynlacht, B. D., and Harlow, E. (1995). Tumor-derived p16 alleles encoding proteins defective in cell-cycle inhibition. *Nature* **375,** 506–510.

Kussie, P. H., Gorina, S., Marechal, V., Elenbaas, B., Moreau, J., Levine, A. J., and Pavletich, N. P. (1996). Structure of the MDM2 oncoprotein bound to the p53 tumor suppressor transactivation domain. *Science* **274,** 948–953.

Lain, S., Midgley, C., Sparks, A., Lane, E. B., and Lane, D. (1999). An inhibitor of nuclear export activates the p53 response and induces the localization of HDM2 and p53 to U1A-positive nuclear bodies associated with the PODs. *Exp. Cell Res.* **248,** 457–472.

Li, Y., Nichols, M. A., Shay, J. W., and Xiong, Y. (1994). Transcriptional repression of the D-type cyclin-dependent kinases inhibitor p16 by the retinoblastoma susceptibility gene product, pRb. *Cancer Res.* **54,** 6078–6082.

Lukas, J., Parry, D., Aagaard, L., Mann, D. J., Bartkova, J., Strauss, M., Peters, G., and Bartek, J. (1995). Retinoblastoma-protein-dependent cell cycle inhibition by the tumor suppressor p16. *Nature* **375,** 503–506.

Marechal, V., Elenbaas, B., Piette, J., Nicolas, J.-C., and Levine, A. J. (1994). The ribosomal protein L5 is associated with mdm-2 and mdm2-p53 complexes. *Mol. Cell Biol.* **14,** 7414–7420.

Marechal, V., Elenbaas, B., Taneyhill, L., Piette, J., Mechali, M., Nicolas, J. C., Levine, A. J., and Moreau, J. (1997). Conservation of structural domains and biochemical activities of the MDM2 protein from *Xenopus laevis*. *Oncogene* **14,** 1427–1433.

Medema, R. H., Herrera, R. E., Lam, F., and Weinberg, R. A. (1995). Growth suppression by p16[INK4] requires functional retinoblastoma protein. *Proc. Natl. Acad. Sci. USA* **92,** 6289–6293.

Midgley, C. A., Desterro, J. M, Saville, M. K., Howard, S., Sparks, A., Hay, R. T., and Lane, D. P. (2000). An N-terminal p14[ARF] peptide blocks Mdm2-dependent ubiquitination in vitro and can activate p53 in vivo. *Oncogene* **19,** 2312–2323.

Munro, J., Stott, F. J., Vousden, K. H., Peters, G., and Parkinson, E. K. (1999). Role of the alternative INK4A proteins in human keratinocyte senescence: Evidence for the specific inactivation of p16[INK4A] upon immortalization. *Cancer Res.* **59,** 2516–2521.

Nairn, R. S., Kazianis, S., McEntire, B. B., Coletta, L. D., Walter, R. B., and Morizot, D. C. (1996). A CDKN2-like polymorphism in *Xiphophorus* LG V is associated with UV-B-induced melanoma formation in platyfish-swordtail hybrid. *Proc. Natl. Acad. Sci. USA* **93,** 13042–13047.

Nobori, T., Mlura, K., Wu, D. J., Lois, A., Takabayashi, K., and Carson, D. A. (1994). Deletion of the cyclin-dependent kinase-4 inhibitor gene in multiple human cancers. *Nature* **368**, 753–756.

Palmero, I., Pantoja, C., and Serrano, M. (1998). p19^{ARF} links the tumor suppressor p53 and Ras. *Nature* **395**, 125–126.

Parry, D., Bates, S., Mann, D. J., and Peters, G. (1995). Lack of cyclin D-Cdk complexes in Rb-negative cells correlates with high levels of p16$^{INK4/MTS1}$ tumour suppressor gene product. *EMBO J.* **14**, 503–511.

Parry, D., and Peters, G. (1996). Temperature-sensitive mutants of p16^{CDK2N} associated with familial melanoma. *Mol. Cell Biol.* **16**, 3844–3852.

Passegue, E., and Wagner, E. F. (2000). JunB suppresses cell proliferation by transcriptional activation of p16INK4a expression. *EMBO J.* **19**, 2969–2979.

Pomerantz, J., Schreiber-Agus, N., Liegeois, N. J., Silverman, A., Alland, L., Chin, L., Potes, J., Chen, K., Orlow, I., and DePinho, R. A. (1998). The INK4a tumor suppressor gene product, p19^{Arf}, interacts with MDM2 and neutralizes MDM2's inhibition of p53. *Cell* **92**, 713–723.

Quelle, D. E., Zindy, F., Ashmun, R., and Sherr, C. J. (1995). Alternative reading frames of the INK4a tumor suppressor gene encode two unrelated proteins capable of inducing cell cycle arrest. *Cell* **83**, 993–1000.

Radfar, A., Unnikrishnan, I., Lee, H.-W., DePinho, R. A., and Rosenberg, N. (1998). p19^{ARF} induces p53-dependent apoptosis during Abelson virus-mediated pre-B cell transformation. *Proc. Natl. Acad. Sci. USA* **95**, 13194–13199.

Ranade, K., Hussussian, C. J., Sikorski, R. S., Varmus, H. E., Goldstein, A. M., Tucker, M. A., Serrano, M., Hannon, G. J., Beach, D., and Dracopoli, N. C. (1995). Mutations associated with familial melanoma impair p16^{INK4} function. *Nature Genet.* **10**, 114–116.

Reymond, A., and Brent, R. (1995). p16 proteins from melanoma-prone families are deficient in binding to Cdk4. *Oncogene* **11**, 1173–1178.

Rizos, H., Darmanian, A. P., Mann, G. J., and Kefford, R. F. (2000). Two arginine rich domain in the p14^{ARF} tumor suppressor mediate nucleolar localization. *Oncogene* **19**, 2978–2985.

Robertson, K. D., and Jones, P. A. (1998). The human ARF cell cycle regulatory gene promoter is a CpG island which can be silenced by DNA methylation and down-regulated by wild-type p53. *Mol. Cell Biol.* **18**, 6457–6471.

Roth, J., Dobbelstein, M., Freedman, D. A., Shenk, T., and Levine, A. J. (1998). Nucleocytoplasmic shuttling of the hdm2 oncoprotein regulates the levels of the p53 protein via a pathway used by the human immunodeficiency virus rev protein. *EMBO J.* **17**, 554–564.

Ruas, M., and Peters, G. (1998). The p16$^{INK4a/CDK2A}$ tumor suppressor and its relatives. *Biochim. Biophys. Acta* **1378**, F115–F177.

Rubin, G. M., *et al.* (2000). Comparative genomics of the eukaryotes. *Science* **287**, 2204–2215.

Russo, A. A., Tong, L., Lee, J.-O., Jerrrey, P. D., and Pavletich, N. P. (1998). Structural basis for inhibition of the cyclin-dependent kinase Cdk6 by the tumor suppressor p16^{INK4a}. *Nature* **395**, 237–243.

Serrano, M., Gomez-Lahoz, E., DePinho, R. A., Beach, D., and Bar-Sagi, D. (1995). Inhibition of ras-induced proliferation and cellular transformation by p16^{INK4}. *Science* **267**, 249–252.

Serrano, M., Hannon, G. J., and Beach, D. (1993). A new regulatory motif in cell cycle control causing specific inhibition of cyclin D/CDK4. *Nature* **366**, 704–707.

Serrano, M., Lee, H.-W., Chin, L., Cordon-Cardos, C., Beach, D., and DePinho, R. A. (1996). Role of the INK4a locus in tumor suppression and cell mortality. *Cell* **85**, 27–37.

Serrano, M., Lin, A. W., McCurrach, M. E., Beach, D., and Lowe, S. W. (1997). Oncogenic ras provokes premature cell senescence associated with accumulation of p53 and p16^{INK4a}. *Cell* **88**, 593–602.

Serrano, M., and Massague, J. (2000). Networks of tumor suppressors. *EMBO Reports* **1**, 115–119.

Sharpless, N. E, and DePinho, R. A. (1999). The INK4A/ARF locus and its two gene products. *Curr. Opin. Genet. Dev.* **9**, 22–30.

Sherr, C. J. (1998). Tumor surveillance via the ARF-p53 pathway. *Genes Dev.* **12**, 2984–2991.

Stommel, J. M., Marchenko, N. D., Jimenez, G. S., Moll, U. M., Hope, T. J., and Wahl, G. M. (1999). A leucine-rich nuclear export signal in the p53 tetramerization domain: Regulation of subcellular localization and p53 activity by NES masking. *EMBO J.* **18**, 1660–1672.

Stone, S., Jiang, P., Dayananth, P., Tavtigian, S. V., Katcher, H., Parry, D., Peters, G., and Kamb, A. (1995). Complex structure and regulation of the p16(MTS1) locus. *Cancer Res.* **55**, 2988–2994.

Stott, F. J., Bates, S., James, M. C., McConnell, B. B., Starborg, M., Brookes, S., Palmero, I., Ryan, K., Hara, E., Vousden, K. H., and Peters, G. (1998). The alternative product from the human CDK2A locus, p14^{ARF}, participates in a regulatory feedback loop with p53 and MDM2. *EMBO J.* **17**, 5001–5014.

Tao, W., and Levine, A. J. (1999). Nucleocytoplasmic shuttling of oncoprotein Hdm2 is required for Hdm2-mediated degradation of p53. *Proc. Natl. Acad. Sci. USA* **96**, 3077–3080.

Tao, W., and Levine, A. J. (1999). p19^{ARF} stabilizes p53 by blocking nucleo-cytoplasmic shuttling of Mdm2. *Proc. Natl. Acad. Sci. USA* **96**, 6937–6941.

Tung, W. S., Shevlin, D. W., Bartsch, D., Norton, J. A., Wells, S. A., and Goodfellow, P. J. (1996). Infrequent CDKN2 mutation inhuman differentiated thyroid cancers. *Mol. Carcinog.* **15**, 5–10.

Ueki, K., Rubio, M.-P., Ramesh, V., Correa, K. M., Rutter, J. I., von Deimling, A., Buckler, A. J., Gusella, J. F., and Louis, D. N. (1994). MTS1/CDKN2 gene mutations are rare in primary human astrocytomas with allelic loss of chromosome 9p. *Hum. Mol. Genet.* **3**, 1841–1845.

Weber, J. D., Jeffers, J. R., Rehg, J. E., Randle, D. H., Lozano, G., Roussel, M. F., Sherr, C. J., and Zambetti, G. P. (2000). p53-independent functions of the p19[ARF] tumor suppressor. *Genes Dev.* **14,** 2358–2365.

Weber, J. D., Kuo, M.-L., Bothner, B., Digiammarino, E. L., Kriwacki, R. W., Roussel, M. F., and Sherr, C. J. (2000). Cooperative signals governing ARF-MDM2 interaction and nucleolar localization of the complex. *Mol. Cell Biol.* **20,** 2517–2528.

Weber, J. D., Taylor, L. J., Roussel, M. F., Sherr, C. J., and Bar-Sagi, D. (1999). Nucleolar Arf sequesters Mdm2 and activates p53. *Nature. Cell Biol.* **1,** 20–26.

Whelan, A. J., Bartsch, D., and Goodfellow, P. J. (1995). Brief report: A familial syndrome of pancreatic cancer and melanoma with a mutation in the CDKN2 tumor-suppressor gene. *N. Engl. J. Med.* **333,** 975–977.

Wolfel, T., Hauer, M., Schneider, J., Serrano, M., Wolfel, C., Klehmann-Hieb, E., De Plaen, E., Hankeln, T., Buschenfelde, M., and Beach, D. (1995). A p16[INK4a]-insensitive CDK4 mutant targeted by cytolytic T lymphocytes in a human melanoma. *Science* **269,** 1281–1284.

Xiong, Y., Zhang, H., and Beach, D. (1993). Subunit rearrangement of cyclin-dependent kinases is associated with cellular transformation. *Genes Dev.* **7,** 1572–1583.

Yarbrough, W. G., Aprelikova, O., Pei, H., Olshan, A. F., and Liu, E. T. (1996). Familial tumor syndrome associated with a germline nonfunctional p16[INK4a] allele. *J. Natl. Cancer Inst.* **88,** 1489–1491.

Yarbrough, W. G., Buckmire, R. A., Bessho, M., and Liu, E. T. (1999). Biologic and biochemical analysis of p16 (INK4a) mutations from primary tumors. *J. Natl. Cancer Inst.* **91,** 1569–1574.

Yu, Z. K., Geyer, R. K., and Maki, C. G. (2000). MDM2-dependent ubiquitination of nuclear and cytoplasmic p53. *Oncogene* **19,** 5892–5897.

Zhang, B., and Peng, Z.-Y (1996). Defective folding of mutant p16[INK4a] proteins encoded by tumor-derived alleles. *J. Biol. Chem.* **271,** 28734–28737.

Zhang, Y., and Xiong, Y. (1999). Mutation in human ARF exon 2 disrupt its nucleolar localization and impair its ability to block nuclear export of MDM2 and p53. *Mol. Cell* **3,** 579–591.

Zhang, Y., Xiong, Y., and Yarbrough, W. G. (1998). ARF promotes MDM2 degradation and stabilizes p53: ARF-INK4a locus deletion impairs both the Rb and p53 tumor suppression pathways. *Cell* **92,** 725–734.

Zindy, F., Eischen, C. M., Randle, D. H., Kamijo, T., Cleveland, J. L., Sherr, C. J., and Roussel, M. F. (1998). Myc signaling via the ARF tumor suppressor regulates p53-dependent apoptosis and immortalization. *Genes Dev.* **12,** 2424–2433.

Zindy, F., Quelle, D. E., Roussel, M. F., and Sherr, C. J. (1997). Expression of the p16[INK4a] tumor suppressor versus other INK4 family members during mouse development and aging. *Oncogene* **15,** 203–211.

PTEN

Frank B. Furnari
H.-J. Su Huang
Webster K. Cavenee
University of California–San Diego

GLOSSARY

anoikis Apoptosis triggered by cell detachment.

apoptosis Programmed cell death.

C2 domain Calcium-binding domains found in a large family of proteins and originally described for protein kinase C.

PDZ-binding domain A short peptide sequence that usually localizes to the C-terminal tail of proteins that binds PDZ domain proteins. PDZ domains consist of ~90 amino acid residues and were originally found in three structurally related proteins: PSD-95/SAP90, DLG, and ZO1.

phosphatase Enzyme that catalyzes the removal of a phosphate molecule from its substrate.

phosphoinositide 3-kinase Kinase that catalyzes the addition of phosphate to the 3 position of phosphatidylinositol.

pleckstrin homology Modular protein domains with phosphoinositide selective binding.

PTEN Phosphatase and tensin homology.

tumor suppressor A gene whose function is to control cell growth.

The ability of protein phosphatases to counteract the growth-promoting activity of kinases has suggested for some time their possible roles as tumor suppressors. This expectation was confirmed by identification of the *PTEN* gene (phosphatase and tensin homology), also known as *MMAC1* (mutated in multiple advanced cancers) and *TEP1* (TGF-β-regulated and epithelial cell-enriched phosphatase). *PTEN*, which localizes to chromosome 10q23.3, is mutated in a number of cancers, including glioma, prostate, endometrium, and melanoma, and in the cancer-predisposition syndromes, Cowden disease, Bannayan–Zonana syndrome, and Lhermitte–Duclos disease. The protein product of the *PTEN* gene contains a central domain with the invariant signature motif HCXXGXXRS/T, which defines the protein tyrosine phosphatase supergene family, and an amino-terminal domain with extensive homology to tensin and auxilin (cytoplasmic proteins involved in interactions with actin filaments at focal adhesions and uncoating of clathrin-coated vesicles, respectively). As such, PTEN protein has been shown to possess both protein phosphatase and 3′ phosphoinositol phosphatase activities from its single catalytic domain. Analysis of PTEN mutants has shown that the 3′ phosphoinositol phosphatase activity is essential to mediate a G1 cell cycle block and may also cause an apoptotic response. In contrast, PTEN protein phosphatase activity appears to be required for the regulation of *in vitro* cell migration through focal adhesion kinase (FAK) and the SH2 domain-containing adapter protein Shc.

I. STRUCTURE/FUNCTION

A. Domains

The *PTEN* tumor suppressor gene encodes a 403 amino acid protein with a relative molecular mass of 47,000 D. Two major transcripts of approximately 2 and 5 kb plus several other minor transcripts are detected in a wide variety of cell lines. PTEN protein is detected predominately in the cytoplasm of most cells, with the exception of a nuclear form found in neurons. Sequence analysis of PTEN shows extensive NH2-terminal homology to tensin (Fig.1), a protein that binds to actin and participates in the assembly of signaling complexes at focal adhesions, auxilin, a protein involved in synaptic vesicle transport, as well as a central domain with perfect homology to protein tyrosine phosphatases (Fig. 1). Within this domain is the invariant signature motif HCXXGXXRS/T, which defines the PTPase (protein tyrosine phosphatase) supergene family (Fig. 1). The cysteine residue within this catalytic domain is essential for catalysis, and the arginine residue plays an essential role in binding to the phosphoryl group of the targeted substrate. This gene family can be subdivided into classic PTP and dual specificity families. The former are selective for phosphotyrosine residues and the latter, as their name implies, typically dephosphorylate phosphotyrosine, phosphoserine, and/or phosphothreonine. Overlapping the catalytic domain is a stretch of sequence similar to the cytoskelatal proteins tensin and auxilin.

In addition to its catalytic domain, PTEN has a potential binding site for PDZ domain proteins at its COOH terminus (Fig. 1). PDZ proteins have been shown to direct the assembly of multiprotein complexes at membrane/cytoskeletal interfaces. This PTEN PDZ-binding site has been shown by yeast two-hybrid experiments to interact with hDLG (disc-large) and hMAST205 and that modification of this binding site by threonine phosphorylation disrupts these interactions while promoting an interaction with unidentified 90- and 120-kDa proteins. The role that these PDZ domain-binding proteins play in modulating PTEN function is currently unknown.

B. Crystal Structure

The crystal structure of PTEN has been solved to 2.1 Å. It has been determined that the COOH end of PTEN, roughly amino acids 186–351 (Fig. 1), has a structure similar to the C2 domain that mediates the Ca^{2+}-dependent membrane recruitment of several signaling proteins, such as phospholipase Cδ1 (PLCδ1), phosphoinositide 3-kinase (PI3K), and protein kinase C (PKC). The C2 domains of these signaling proteins bind Ca^{2+}, that mediates and regulates their association with membranes. In contrast, the PTEN C2 domain lacks residues that bind Ca^{2+} and is thus unlikely to be regulated by Ca^{2+}. Instead, a cluster of basic residues and hydrophobic side chains found within this region, on the same face and in close proximity to the catalytic site, is consistent with a possible role in membrane association. As such, this C2 domain has affinity for lipid vesicles *in vitro*, and mutation of this domain can disrupt PTEN vesicle association, leading to an inhibition of its tumor suppressive function without affecting its catalytic activities. These results indicate that proper cellular location of PTEN is essential for function.

II. PTEN SUBSTRATES

A. PTEN Regulates PI3K Signaling by Targeting PtdIns(3,4,5)P₃

Despite sequence similarity to other protein phosphatases it was surprising to find that PTEN preferred a very select type of peptide substrate, that which was highly negatively charged (poly(Glu_4-$pTyr_1$). This

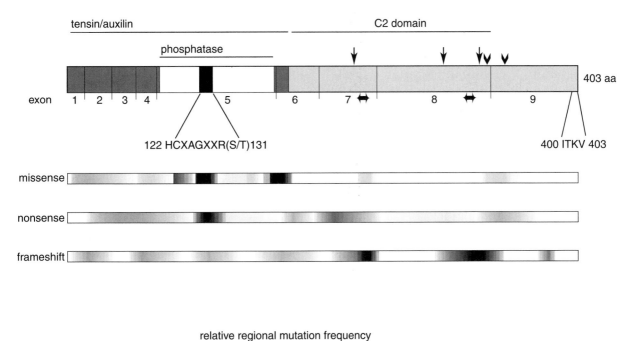

FIGURE 1 Structure of the PTEN tumor suppressor protein and mutation spectra. (Top) PTEN is divided into an NH₂-terminal phosphatase domain embedded within a region containing homology to tensin and auxilin and a COOH-terminal membrane-targeting C2 domain. The tyrosine phosphatase catalytic core signature sequence is indicated as residues 122–131. The PDZ-binding site for PDZ domain-containing proteins is indicated as residues 400–403. Double-headed arrows at codons 265–267 and 321–323 indicate poly(A)₆ regions frequently mutated in endometrial cancer. Arrows at tyrosine residues 240 and 315 and arrowheads at serine residues 338 and 355 indicate potential phosphorylation sites. (Bottom) PTEN mutation spectra are shown according to mutation type and frequency along the protein. Relative mutation frequency is shown as a gradient of white (low or no mutations reported) to black (frequently mutated).

observation suggested that PTEN prefers acidic substrates. A class of molecules that fulfill this criteria are the phosphoinositides. In accordance with this, PTEN has been shown to efficiently dephosphorylate one of the products of activated PI3K, the lipid second messenger phosphatidylinositol (3,4,5)-trisphosphate [PtdIns(3,4,5)P₃] (Fig. 2), and also inositol (1,3,4,5)-tetrakisphosphate. This activity was specific for the 3′ phosphoinositol position, producing PtdIns(4,5)P₂ and inositol (1,4,5)P₃.

Among the downstream targets of PI3K activation is the Akt (also known as protein kinase B; PKB) (Fig. 2) family of serine/threonine kinases consisting of Akt-1, -2, and -3. Akt proteins contain at their NH2 terminus conserved protein–lipid interaction domains found in a wide variety of proteins known as pleckstrin homology (PH) domains. The PH domain of Akt can bind with high affinity to PtdIns(3,4,5)P₃,

which results in the translocation of Akt from the cytosol to the plasma membrane and a conformational change in the enzyme exposing its activation loop. This loop is then phosphorylated on Thr-308 by PDK1, another PI3K-dependent serine/threonine kinase, and on Ser-473 by an as of yet unidentified distinct kinase, PDK2. There is some speculation that PDK2 might be a modified form of PDK1 or perhaps ILK (integrin-linked kinase), which has been shown to phosphorylate Akt on Ser-473 *in vitro*, the activity of which is blocked by PTEN expression.

When activated, Akt modulates the activity of a variety of downstream proteins. The majority of these phosphorylation events render the target molecules inactive. Substrates include GSK3β, p70^S6K, the Bcl-2 family member Bad, pro-caspase 9, 4E-BP1, IKKα, and members of the Forkhead family of transcription factors (Fig. 2).

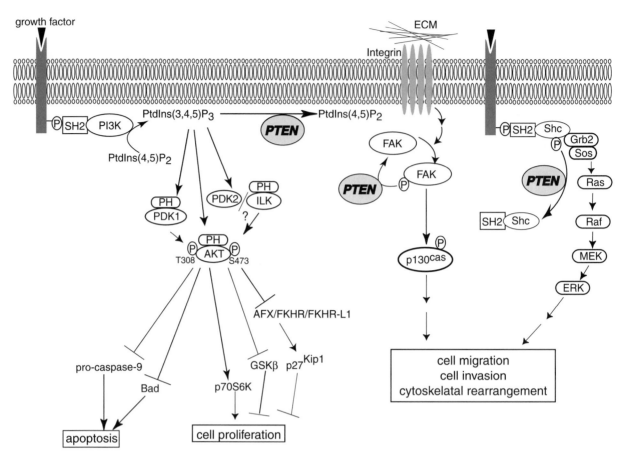

FIGURE 2   Growth and cell migration pathways regulated by PTEN. Activation of PI3K through growth factor receptor signaling leads to the production of the second messenger phospholipid, PtdIns(3,4,5)P₃. This lipid recruits the PH domain-containing serine/threonine kinases Akt, PDK1, and PDK2 (ILK) to the cell membrane, resulting in activation of Akt. Downstream targets of activated Akt are procaspase-9 and Bad, leading to protection from cell death, and p70S6K, GSKβ, and Forkhead transcription factors (AFX, FKHR, and FKHR-L1), resulting in the promotion of cell proliferation. PTEN impinges on the PI3K/Akt pathway by directly dephosphorylating PtdIns(3,4,5)P₃. ECM binding to integrin leads to activation of FAK. Once activated through phosphorylation, FAK associates with and activates p130cas through phosphorylation. This in turn leads to cytoskeletal rearrangement and cell migration. When activated by receptor signaling, the Shc/MAP kinase pathway also contributes to the cell migratory phenotype. PTEN impinges on these two pathways by directly dephosphorylating FAK and Shc. Protein phosphorylation is indicated by circled "P."

The ability to evade cell death is a critical event in cancer progression, and thus the PI3K/Akt pathway has been shown to provide a survival signal in response to growth factors, cytokines, UV irradiation, CD95/Fas, and the extracellular matrix. Of these substrates, Akt is likely to send antiapoptotic signals by phosphorylating Bad and procaspase 9 (Fig. 2). This antiapoptotic role of Akt suggests that PTEN loss might influence cell survival. In fact, in certain PTEN null tumor cells, reexpression of PTEN induces apoptosis or a form of cell death induced upon cell detachment known as anoikis.

In contrast, by phosphorylating and thus inhibiting GSK3β, Akt may regulate cell proliferation, as activity of this kinase has been shown to promote cyclin D proteolysis (Fig. 2). By inactivating GSK3β, Akt may promote cell cycle progression through the accumulation of cyclin D. However, an increase in the cyclin-dependent kinase inhibitor p27Kip1 and a concomitant decrease in Rb phosphorylation and Cdk2 kinase activity have been observed after restoring PTEN expression in PTEN-deficient glioblastoma cells (Fig. 2). This increase in p27Kip1 levels has been directly linked to the transcriptional activation of the p27^Kip1 promoter by FKHR-related transcription factors, the activities of which are blocked by Akt-dependent phosphorylation (Fig. 2). These results suggest that upregulation of p27^{Kip1} levels might lead to a decrease in activity in the G1 cell cycle kinases required for S phase entry (Fig. 2). PTEN has also been shown to inhibit hypoxia- and IGF-1-mediated induction of HIF-1 (hypoxia induced factor), a factor shown to upregulate genes important for angiogenesis (i.e., VEGF and COX-1).

Thus, PTEN can regulate the PI3K/Akt pathway, leading to apoptosis and cell cycle arrest, or downregulate genes required for angiogenesis. These disparate mechanisms appear to be cell type specific, mainly promoting cell death in carcinoma cell lines such as prostate and breast and cell cycle arrest in glioblastoma cells. A possible reason for this difference may be a divergent expression of downstream targets of Akt or additional alterations in cell death pathways that may abrogate PTEN-induced apoptosis. The cell type specificity of PTEN angiogenic regulation remains to be tested.

B. PTEN Regulates Cell Spreading and Migration by Targeting FAK

PTEN dephosphorylates phosphoprotein substrates as well as phospholipids. Overexpression of PTEN inhibits glioma cell migration and adhesion on the extracellular matrix (ECM) proteins fibronectin and vitronectin through its ability to dephosphorylate tyrosine-phosphorylated FAK *in vitro* and *in vivo*. This has led to the notion that PTEN regulates focal adhesion structure, cell spreading, and cell motility (Fig. 2). Because PI3K activity has been found in association with FAK, these effects of PTEN could still result from antagonism of the PI3K pathway. Against this possibility is the finding that a PTEN mutant, G129E, which lacks lipid phosphatase activity and the ability to arrest cells in G1 or promote apoptosis, still retained the capacity to inhibit cell spreading and motility mediated by the dephosphorylation of FAK. Thus, from these experiments and the fact that the G129E mutant appears in a number of Cowden disease kindreds, it would appear that the lipid phosphatase activity of PTEN is essential for growth regulation, whereas its protein phosphatase activity is required for the regulation of

cell migration. Whether PTEN protein phosphatase activity contributes in any way towards tumor formation or tumor spectrum is still under investigation.

C. PTEN Specifically Dephosphorylates the SH2-Containing Adapter Protein, Shc

PTEN can inhibit both integrin- and growth factor-mediated activation of the MAP kinases, Erk1 and 2. This inhibition appears to be at the level of Shc phosphorylation, as EGF receptor phosphorylation is unaffected, yet Ras activity is inhibited by the expression of PTEN. Furthermore, Shc was shown to be directly dephosphorylated on tyrosine by PTEN (Fig. 2). Activation of MAP kinase has been shown to stimulate cell migration by phosphorylating myosin light chain kinase. These results suggest that PTEN can regulate two aspects of cell motility through two different substrates: (1) through the Shc and MAP kinase pathway, PTEN may regulate random migration; and (2) through FAK, PTEN may regulate directional persistent cell motility involving actin cytoskeletal organization and focal contacts.

III. PTEN MUTATIONS

A. Cancer Predisposition Syndromes in Humans

Germline *PTEN* point mutations are associated with the hamartomatous polyposis syndromes: Cowden disease (CD) and Bannayan-Zonana syndrome (BZS). A hallmark of these syndromes is the appearance of hamartomas, benign tumors in which differentiation is normal, but cell architecture is highly disorganized, a phenotype suggestive of a breakdown in normal physiological cell migration. Data suggest that these two syndromes primarily reflect phenotypic variation of a single disease. Phenotypic characteristics can include trichilemmomas, macrocephaly, mental retardation, and hamartomas of the skin, breast, thyroid, endometrium, gastrointestinal tract, and central nervous system. Breast cancers typically develop in 25–50% of affected women and thyroid cancer in 3–10% of affected individuals. Lhermitte–Duclos disease, which is associated with Cowden disease, is characterized by cerebellar dysplastic gangliocytoma. In addition to the germline mutation carried by pedigrees, deletion of the remaining wild-type *PTEN* allele is detected in tumors. This would suggest that: (1) haploinsufficiency at the *PTEN* locus is sufficient to cause the developmental defects and hamartomas seen in affected individuals and (2) loss of the remaining *PTEN* allele is an early event leading to increased susceptibility of tumor development.

B. Sporadic Cancers: Late Mutation

The region on chromosome 10q harboring the *PTEN* gene is hemizygously deleted in many human cancers, with a frequency approaching 60–80% in prostate cancer, endometrial carcinoma, and glioblastomas. The gene is inactivated by multiple mechanisms, including homozygous deletions, in tumors with hemizygous deletions, frameshifts causing protein truncations or missense mutations severely impair protein function (see Fig. 1 for mutation spectra).

In glioma, *PTEN* mutations occur in approximately 44% of high-grade tumors, whereas mutations are rare in lower grade astrocytic tumors. *PTEN* mutations are found in 12–15% of primary prostate tumors and in 60% of metastatic prostate cancer. Thus, similar to glioma, *PTEN* loss in prostate cancer is associated with a more aggressive tumor.

C. Sporadic Cancer: Early Mutation

PTEN is the most frequently mutated gene in endometrial cancers of endometriod histology with a frequency of 33–55%. These mutations occur in early well-differentiated lesions as well as in very advanced and invasive tumors, suggesting that *PTEN* inactivation, in contrast to glioblastomas and prostate cancers, may be involved in the initiation of endometrial tumorigenesis. One striking feature of the mutation spectrum of *PTEN* in endometrial cancer is the high frequency of mutations found in microsatellite instability-positive tumors (78–86%) compared to microsatellite instability-negative tumors (30%). Two hot spot regions for this instability in *PTEN* are found at poly(A)$_6$ stretches between codons 265–267 and codons 321–323 (Fig. 1).

Occasional *PTEN* mutations are found in head and neck and thyroid cancers, but not in other tumors associated with 10q abnormalities, which include meningioma and lung cancer, thus raising the possibility of other tumor suppressor genes in this region of chromosome 10.

D. Germline Mutations in Mice

Three separate reports of mice harboring a disruption of the *PTEN* gene have supported the conclusion that *PTEN* indeed functions as a tumor suppressor and plays a role in embryonic development. These studies were performed using different deletions in the *PTEN* gene and mice with different genetic backgrounds and thus have yielded some variations in phenotype, such as the timing of embryonic lethality in homozygous knockout mice and the spectrum of lesions in heterozygous mice. One study reported (deleting exons 4–5) hyperplastic–dysplastic changes in the prostate, skin, and colon similar to those seen in CD and BZS patients. In another study (deletion of exon 5), multiple neoplasms were reported in prostate, thyroid, gastrointestinal tract, and endometrium. A third study reported (deletion of exons 3–5) that heterozygous mice are predisposed to developing T-cell lymphoma or leukemia, teratocarcinoma, and microscopic hamartomas of the colon and were highly susceptible to radiation-induced thymic lymphomas. In addition, cells derived from the aforementioned PTEN-deficient mouse embryos contained elevated levels of PtdIns(3,4,5)P$_3$ and demonstrated decreased sensitivity to apoptosis, supporting the previous findings that this second messenger molecule is a substrate of PTEN and that PTEN is a negative regulator of cell survival.

IV. PTEN GENETICS IN OTHER ORGANISMS

The PTEN protein contains remarkable structural similarities across species. In the worm *Caenorhabditis elegans*, the DAF-18 gene is the homologue of *PTEN*, which functions in the insulin receptor pathway playing a role in aging regulation. Under certain conditions, *C. elegans* enter an arrested developmental condition known as the dauer state. Genetic analysis of this pathway has led to the characterization of worms that are defective in dauer formation (daf). Among the first characterized mutations were the daf-2 allele, which turns out to be a member of the insulin receptor family, and AGE-1, which codes for a PI3K homologue. Disruption of AGE-1 causes dauer formation, which is rescued by the disruption of DAF-18. Thus loss of PTEN function can rescue loss of the PI3K phenotype.

The *Drosophila PTEN* gene (*dPTEN*) has also been identified and its function in fly eye development has been explored. While deletion of *dPTEN* leads to an increase in eye cell size, overexpression arrests cell cycle progression in mitosis in proliferating eye cells while promoting apoptosis in differentiating cells. Thus, similar to the results seen in human cancers, the phenotype elicited by *dPTEN* may be cell type specific.

The *PTEN* homologue has been identified in both fission and budding yeast. However, when it is disrupted by homologous recombination, no discernible phenotypic abnormalities have been detected, perhaps suggesting that yeast express redundant phosphatases.

V. SUMMARY AND FUTURE PROSPECTS

Since the identification of *PTEN* as a putative tumor suppressor gene, several lines of evidence have confirmed its role in cancer development both *in vitro* and *in vivo*. This gene has been shown to regulate a variety of phenotypes such as cell proliferation, cell survival, and potentially angiogenesis through downregulation of the Akt pathway by direct dephosphorylation of PtdIns(3,4,5)P$_3$; and regulation of cell migration and invasion through dephosphorylation of FAK and Shc.

However, many aspects of PTEN biology remain unclear. To date, there is little information regarding the regulation of PTEN aside from the fact that PTEN mRNA levels are modulated by TGFβ stimulation. It is likely that other mechanisms, such as subcellular location and modification by phosphorylation, play a role in PTEN function. In addition, because the PTEN/PI3K/Akt pathway is emerging as a critical pathway often perturbed in cancer development, further characterization of other physiological PTEN substrates or mechanisms of tumor growth inhibition will aid in designing pharmacological agents directed against components of this pathway.

See Also the Following Articles

LUNG CANCER: MOLECULAR AND CELLULAR ABNORMALITIES • MELANOMA: MOLECULAR AND CELLULAR ABNORMALITIES • NM23 METASTASIS SUPPRESSOR GENE • P16 AND ARF: CROSSROADS OF TUMORIGENESIS • TUMOR SUPPRESSOR GENES: SPECIFIC CLASSES

Bibliography

Adey, N. B., Huang, L., Ormonde, P. A., Baumgard, M. L., Pero, R., Byreddy, D. V., Tavtigian, S. V., and Bartel, P. L. (2000). Threonine phosphorylation of the MMAC1/PTEN PDZ binding domain both inhibits and stimulates PDZ binding. *Cancer Res.* **60,** 35–37.

Ali, I. U., Schriml, L. M., and Dean, M. (1999). Mutational spectra of PTEN/MMAC1 gene: A tumor suppressor with lipid phosphatase activity. *J. Natl. Cancer Inst.* **91,** 1922–1932.

Cantley, L. C., and Neel, B. G. (1999). New insights into tumor suppression: PTEN suppresses tumor formation by restraining the phosphoinositide 3-kinase/AKT pathway. *Proc. Natl. Acad. Sci. USA* **96,** 4240–4245.

Cheney, I. W., Neuteboom, S. T., Vaillancourt, M. T., Ramachandra, M., and Bookstein, R. (1999). Adenovirus-mediated gene transfer of MMAC1/PTEN to glioblastoma cells inhibits S phase entry by the recruitment of p27Kip1 into cyclin E/CDK2 complexes. *Cancer Res.* **59,** 2318–2323.

Davies, M. A., Lu, Y., Sano, T., Fang, X., Tang, P., LaPushin, R., Koul, D., Bookstein, R., Stokoe, D., Yung, W. K., Mills, G. B., and Steck, P. A. (1998). Adenoviral transgene expression of MMAC/PTEN in human glioma cells inhibits Akt activation and induces anoikis. *Cancer Res.* **58,** 5285–5290.

Di Cristofano, A., Pesce, B., Cordon-Cardo, C., and Pandolfi, P. P. (1998). Pten is essential for embryonic development and tumour suppression. *Nature Genet.* **19,** 348–355.

Furnari, F. B., Huang, H. J., and Cavenee, W. K. (1998). The phosphoinositol phosphatase activity of PTEN mediates a serum-sensitive G1 growth arrest in glioma cells. *Cancer Res.* **58,** 5002–5008.

Gu, J., Tamura, M., Pankov, R., Danen, E. H., Takino, T., Matsumoto, K., and Yamada, K. M. (1999). Shc and FAK differentially regulate cell motility and directionality modulated by PTEN. *J. Cell Biol.* **146,** 389–403.

Gu, J., Tamura, M., and Yamada, K. M. (1998). Tumor suppressor PTEN inhibits integrin- and growth factor-mediated mitogen-activated protein (MAP) kinase signaling pathways. *J. Cell Biol.* **143,** 1375–1383.

Huang, H., Potter, C. J., Tao, W., Li, D. M., Brogiolo, W., Hafen, E., Sun, H., and Xu, T. (1999). PTEN affects cell size, cell proliferation and apoptosis during *Drosophila* eye development. *Development* **126**, 5365–5372.

Lee, J. O., Yang, H., Georgescu, M. M., Di Cristofano, A., Maehama, T., Shi, Y., Dixon, J. E., Pandolfi, P., and Pavletich, N. P. (1999). Crystal structure of the PTEN tumor suppressor: Implications for its phosphoinositide phosphatase activity and membrane association. *Cell* **99**, 323–334.

Li, D. M., and Sun, H. (1997a). TEP1, encoded by a candidate tumor suppressor locus, is a novel protein tyrosine phosphatase regulated by transforming growth factor beta. *Cancer Res.* **57**, 2124–2129.

Li, J., Yen, C., Liaw, D., Podsypanina, K., Bose, S., Wang, S. I., Puc, J., Miliaresis, C., Rodgers, L., McCombie, R., Bigner, S. H., Giovanella, B. C., Ittmann, M., Tycko, B., Hibshoosh, H., Wigler, M. H., and Parsons, R. (1997b). PTEN, a putative protein tyrosine phosphatase gene mutated in human brain, breast, and prostate cancer. *Science* **275**, 1943–1947.

Li, L., Ernsting, B. R., Wishart, M. J., Lohse, D. L., and Dixon, J. E. (1997c). A family of putative tumor suppressors is structurally and functionally conserved in humans and yeast. *J. Biol. Chem.* **272**, 29403–29406.

Maehama, T., and Dixon, J. E. (1998). The tumor suppressor, PTEN/MMAC1, dephosphorylates the lipid second messenger, phosphatidylinositol, 3,4,5-triphosphate. *J. Biol. Chem.* **273**, 13375–13378.

Medema, R. H., Kops, G. J. P. L., Bos, J. L., and Burgering, B. M. T. (2000). AFX-like Forkhead transcription factors mediate cell-cycle regulation by Ras and PKB through p27kip1. *Nature* **404**, 782–787.

Myers, M. P., Stolarov, J. P., Eng, C., Li, J., Wang, S. I., Wigler, M. H., Parsons, R., and Tonks, N. K. (1997). P-TEN, the tumor suppressor from human chromosome 10q23, is a dual-specificity phosphatase. *Proc. Natl. Acad. Sci. USA* **94**, 9052–9057.

Ogg, S., and Ruvkun, G. (1998). The *C. elegans* PTEN homolog, DAF-18, acts in the insulin receptor-like metabolic signaling pathway. *Mol. Cell* **2**, 887–893.

Persad, S., Attwell, S., Gray, V., Delcommenne, M., Troussard, A., Sanghera, J., and Dedhar, S. (2000). Inhibition of integrin-linked kinase (ILK) suppresses activation of protein kinase B/Akt and induces cell cycle arrest and apoptosis of PTEN-mutant prostate cancer cells. *Proc. Natl. Acad. Sci. USA* **97**, 3207–3212.

Podsypanina, K., Ellenson, L. H., Nemes, A., Gu, J., Tamura, M., Yamada, K. M., Cordon-Cardo, C., Catoretti, G., Fisher, P. E., and Parsons, R. (1999). Mutation of Pten/Mmac1 in mice causes neoplasia in multiple organ systems. *Proc. Natl. Acad. Sci. USA* **96**, 1563–1568.

Sano, T., Lin, H., Chen, X., Langford, L. A., Koul, D., Bondy, M. L., Hess, K. R., Myers, J. N., Hong, Y. K., Yung, W. K., and Steck, P. A. (1999). Differential expression of MMAC/PTEN in glioblastoma multiforme: Relationship to localization and prognosis. *Cancer Res.* **59**, 1820–1824.

Stambolic, V., Suzuki, A., de la Pompa, J. L., Brothers, G. M., Mirtsos, C., Sasaki, T., Ruland, J., Penninger, J. M., Siderovski, D. P., and Mak, T. W. (1998). Negative regulation of PKB/Akt-dependent cell survival by the tumor suppressor PTEN. *Cell* **95**, 29–39.

Steck, P. A., Pershouse, M. A., Jasser, S. A., Yung, W. K., Lin, H., Ligon, A. H., Langford, L. A., Baumgard, M. L., Hattier, T., Davis, T., Frye, C., Hu, R., Swedlund, B., Teng, D. H., and Tavtigian, S. V. (1997). Identification of a candidate tumour suppressor gene, MMAC1, at chromosome 10q23.3 that is mutated in multiple advanced cancers. *Nature Genet.* **15**, 356–362.

Suzuki, A., de la Pompa, J. L., Stambolic, V., Elia, A. J., Sasaki, T., del Barco Barrantes, I., Ho, A., Wakeham, A., Itie, A., Khoo, W., Fukumoto, M., and Mak, T. W. (1998). High cancer susceptibility and embryonic lethality associated with mutation of the PTEN tumor suppressor gene in mice. *Curr. Biol.* **8**, 1169–1178.

Tamura, M., Gu, J., Matsumoto, K., Aota, S., Parsons, R., and Yamada, K. M. (1998). Inhibition of cell migration, spreading, and focal adhesions by tumor suppressor PTEN. *Science* **280**, 1614–1617.

Zundel, W., Schindler, C., Haas-Kogan, D., Koong, A., Kaper, F., Chen, E., Gottschalk, A. R., Ryan, H. E., Johnson, R. S., Jefferson, A. B., Stokoe, D., and Giaccia, A. J. (2000). Loss of PTEN facilitates HIF-1 mediated gene expression. *Genes Dev.* **14**, 391–396.

Purine Antimetabolites

Kenneth R. Hande

Vanderbilt University School of Medicine

I. GUANINE ANALOGS

Since the early 1950s, 6-mercaptopurine (6-MP) has been used as therapy for children with acute lymphoblastic leukemia (ALL). Azathioprine, a prodrug of 6-MP, is widely employed as an immunosuppressant. 6-Thioguanine (6-TG) is occasionally used for therapy of acute leukemias. These three drugs are closely related in structure (Fig. 1), metabolism, mechanism of action, and toxicity. Their key pharmacologic features are summarized in Table I.

A. Mechanism of Action

6-Mercaptopurine is a structural analog of guanine (Fig. 1). 6-MP undergoes extensive metabolism after dosing. Three major competing transformation routes are present: one anabolic and two catabolic. 6-MP is activated intracellularly by hypoxanthine-guanine phosphoribosyl transferase (HGPRT) to form 6-thioinosine monophosphate (TIMP). TIMP can inhibit *de novo* purine synthesis. Sequential metabolism of TIMP to thioguanine triphosphates occurs. Incorporation of 6-thioguanine triphosphate (6-TGTP) into DNA causes miscoding during DNA replication and triggers programmed cell death by a process involving the mismatch repair pathway.

Thioguanine is converted to 6-thioguanylic acid (TGMP) by HGPRT. TGMP is subsequently incorporated into RNA and DNA in its deoxytriphosphate form. Incorporation of fraudulent nucleotides leads to defective DNA replication, triggering apoptosis.

Azathioprine is rapidly cleaved by nonenzymatic mechanisms to 6-mercaptopurine and methyl-4-nitro-5-imidazole derivatives (Fig. 2). While incorporation of false nucleotides into DNA is the probable mechanism for cytotoxicity, the mechanism by which azathioprine and mercaptopurine modify immune response is less well understood. The thioimidazole metabolites may contribute to the immunosuppressive effects of azathioprine. Azathioprine inhibits

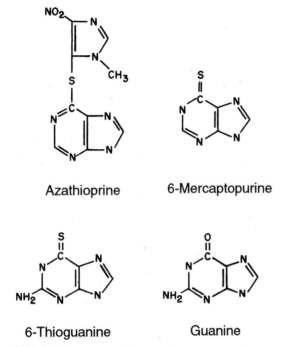

FIGURE 1   Structures of the naturally occurring purine guanine and related antineoplastic agents 6-mercaptopurine, 6-thioguanine, and azathioprine.

the intestinal wall into the portal circulation and metabolized by xanthine oxidase in the intestine and liver. Even at high 6-MP doses (500 mg/m^2), xanthine oxidase is not saturated and no improvement in bioavailability is seen. The concomitant use of allopurinol (an inhibitor of xanthine oxidase) significantly increases 6-MP bioavailability. Concomitant use of methotrexate, a weak inhibitor of xanthine oxidase, results in a small, clinically insignificant increase in 6-MP bioavailability. Food intake and oral antibiotic use can reduce the absorption of 6-MP.

6-MP also undergoes S-methylation by the enzyme thiopurine methyltransferase (TPMT) to yield inactive 6-methyl mercaptopurine. Patient-to-patient variation in TPMT activity results in significant changes in 6-MP metabolism and drug toxicity. Interindividual TPMT activity is controlled by a common genetic polymorphism. The frequency distribution of TPMT activity in large population studies is trimodal. One in 300 subjects has very low enzyme activity; 11% of the population has intermediate activity and the rest have high enzyme activity. A single genetic locus with two alleles (one for low and

T lymphocyte activity to a greater extent than B lymphocytes. It interferes with the synthesis of some cytokines, such as interleukin-2.

B. Clinical Pharmacology

1. 6-Mercaptopurine

6-Mercaptopurine is commercially available in 50-mg tablets. About 2 h following oral administration, peak plasma 6-MP concentrations of 0.3–1.8 μM are seen with commonly used doses. In human leukemic cell culture models, concentrations of 1–10 μM are cytotoxic. The 6-MP half-life is 50–100 min. The volume of distribution exceeds that of total body water (0.9 liter/kg). There is minimal drug penetration into the cerebral spinal fluid (CSF). Oral absorption of 6-MP is incomplete and highly variable. Bioavailability averages 16% (range 5–37%). Clearance occurs through two metabolic routes. 6-MP is oxidized to the inactive metabolite, 6-thiouric acid, by xanthine oxidase (Fig. 2). The low bioavailability of 6-MP is due to a large first pass effect as the drug is absorbed through

TABLE I
Key Features of Guanine Analogs 6-MP, 6-TG, and Azathioprine

Mechanism of action	Incorporation of fraudulent nucleotides into DNA
Metabolism	Activation: conversion to thiopurine nucleotides
	Catabolism: to 6-thiouric acid by xanthine oxidase (except 6-TG)
	Catabolism: to 6-methylthiopurine by thiopurine methyltransferase (TPMT)
Pharmacokinetics	Poor and variable oral bioavailability
Elimination	Metabolism (primarily hepatic)
Drug interactions	Allopurinol decreases 6-mercaptopurine and azathioprine elimination and concomitant use requires dose reduction (75%)
Toxicity	Myelosuppression
	Mild gastrointestinal (nausea, vomiting)
	Rare hepatotoxicity
Precautions	Dose reductions with allopurinol (except 6-TG)
	Increased toxicity in individuals with genetic deficiency of TPMT (genetic screening possible)

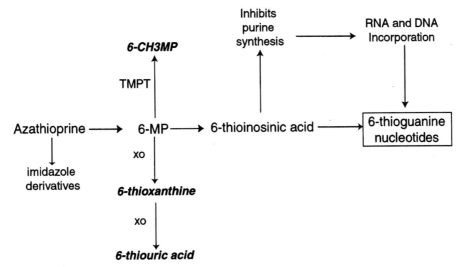

FIGURE 2 Mechanism of activation and catabolism of azathioprine and 6-mercaptopurine. Active metabolites are indicated in the box. Inactive (or less active) metabolites are indicated by bold italic print. XO, xanthine oxidase; TPMT, thiopurine methyltransferase.

one for high activity) is responsible for the trimodal distribution. Patients with low TPMT activity are more susceptible to 6-MP- and 6-TG-induced myelosuppression. Patients with absent TMPT require a 10- to 15-fold reduction in 6-MP dosage. A reciprocal relationship between TPMT activity and the formation of 6-thiopurine nucleotides has been demonstrated. TPMT wild-type patients tolerate 75 mg/m^2 per day of 6-MP during most of their scheduled therapy (84%), whereas heterozygous patients require a dose reduction 35% of the time. All TPMT-deficient patients require dose reductions. The TPMT gene has now been cloned.

2. Thioguanine

6-TG is available as 40-mg tablets for oral use. Like 6-MP, the absorption of 6-TG is variable and incomplete (mean bioavailability is 30% with a range of 14–46%). Plasma concentrations of 0.03–5 μM are seen 2–4 h after ingestion; the median drug half-life is 90 min but wide variability is reported. Thioguanine is not a substrate for xanthine oxidase, but is converted to 6-thioinosine (an inactive metabolite) by the action of the enzyme, guanase. Inhibitors of xanthine oxidase, such as allopurinol, do not interfere with 6-TG metabolism. Methylation of thioguanine, via thiopurine methyltransferase (TPMT) to an inac-

tive metabolite, is more extensive than that of 6-MP. No data are available regarding toxicity among TPMT-deficient patients, but increased toxicity could be expected.

3. Azathioprine

Azathioprine is rapidly degraded by nonenzymatic mechanisms to 6-mercaptopurine. The metabolic pathways thereafter are identical to 6-MP. Plasma concentrations of 6-MP exceed those of azathioprine within an hour of drug administration. Renal function impairment does not alter the plasma kinetics of either azathioprine or 6-MP. As expected, azathioprine toxicity is dependent on the TPMT genotype.

C. Toxicity

1. 6-Mercaptopurine

Myelosuppression is the dose-limiting toxicity of 6-MP, occurring 1–4 weeks following the onset of therapy and is reversible when the drug is discontinued. Platelets, granulocytes, and erythrocytes are all affected. Weekly monitoring of blood counts during the first 2 months of therapy is recommended. 6-MP is also an immunosuppressant and will inhibit allograft rejection and immunity to infectious agents. Approximately 25% of treated patients experience nausea, vomiting, and anorexia. Gastrointestinal side effects are more common in adults than in children. Hepatotoxicity is infrequent, usually mild and reversible with a clinical picture consistent with cholestatic jaundice. Increased transaminase levels are noted in roughly 15% of patients. Frank hepatic necrosis can occur. An increased incidence of myelodysplasia and AML following 6-MP therapy has been reported in children who have low TPMT activity. Similarly, an increased risk of brain tumors has been found following cranial irradiation and 6-MP therapy, again primarily in patients with absent TPMT.

2. Thioguanine

As with 6-MP, the primary toxicity of 6-TG is myelosuppression. Blood counts should be frequently monitored, as there may be delayed toxicity. Thioguanine produces gastrointestinal toxicities similar to 6-MP but less frequently. Jaundice and hepatic veno-occlusive disease have been reported.

3. Azathioprine

Adverse effects from azathioprine are similar to those seen with 6-MP, including leukopenia, diarrhea, nausea, and abnormal liver function tests and skin rashes. Frequent monitoring of the CBC is warranted throughout therapy (weekly during the first 8 weeks of therapy). A hypersensitivity reaction generally characterized by fever, severe nausea, diarrhea, and vomiting has been reported. Chronic immunosuppressive therapy, including the use of azathioprine, results in an increased frequency of secondary infections and an increased risk of malignant tumors. AML associated with karyotypic changes of 7q-/-7 has been reported. The risk of cancer development increases with longer duration of azathioprine use [<5 years the relative risk (RR) = 1.3; 5–10 years use RR = 2.0; >10 years RR = 4.4]. Toxicity from azathioprine, primarily myelosuppression and gastrointestinal intolerance, requires dose adjustment or discontinuation of treatment in up to 40% of patients. Patients heterozygous for mutant TPMT are at high risk for toxicity and dose modification. Molecular testing may be a cost-effective way of identifying the 12% of the population at high risk for toxicity.

D. Use and Drug Interactions

6-Mercaptopurine is a regular component of maintenance therapy of ALL. It has little role in the therapy of solid tumors or myeloid leukemias. While dosage reductions have been suggested for patients with hepatic and renal function impairment, there is no good data justifying such dose adjustments. Thioguanine is used as a second-line agent for AML. Azathioprine is used as an immunosuppressant in preventing the rejection of organ transplants and in the therapy of illnesses believed autoimmune in character (lupus, rheumatoid arthritis, ulcerative colitis, etc). Doses should be adjusted to the minimal needed to prevent organ rejection and control disease. The intravenous drug should be used only in patients unable to tolerate oral therapy. In patients with TMPT mutations, therapy with lower doses of all three guanine analogs should be considered. Allopurinol inhibits the catabolism of 6-MP and azathioprine. Oral doses of these drugs should be reduced by at least 75% in patients also receiving allopurinol. Methotrexate causes a modest increase in 6-MP bioavailability but not to an extent significant enough to warrant dosage reduction.

II. ADENOSINE ANALOGS

Adenosine deaminase (ADA) catalyzes the deamination of adenosine to inosine and deoxyadenosine to deoxyinosine. Lack of ADA results in the accumulation of deoxyadenosine, a compound cytotoxic to lymphocytes, and severely impairs cellular immunity. The effect of deoxyadenosine on lymphocytes prompted investigators to evaluate adenosine analogs in the treatment of lymphocytic malignancies. Adenosine analogs with documented clinical utility are fludarabine, pentostatin, and cladribine (2'-chlorodeoxyadenosine) (Fig. 3).

A. Fludarabine (Key Features in Table II)

1. Mechanism of Action

After iv administration, fludarabine is rapidly dephosphorylated in plasma to the nucleoside 2-fluoro-ara-A (Fig. 4). This compound enters cells via carrier-

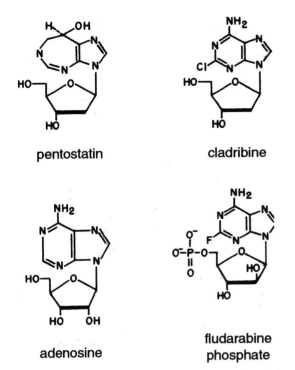

FIGURE 3 Structures of adenosine and adenosine analogs fludarabine (9-α-arabinofuranosyl-2-fluoroadenosine monophosphate; F-ara-AMP), pentostatin (2-deoxycoformycin), and cladribine (2-chlorodeoxyadenosine).

interference with normal DNA repair. The most suggestive evidence suggests that fludarabine triggers apoptosis during the DNA repair process.

2. Clinical Pharmacology

Following iv administration, fludarabine undergoes rapid (2–4 min) conversion to 2-F-ara-A. Peak plasma F-ara-A concentrations of 0.3–1.0 mg/liter are achieved after doses of 80–250 mg fludarabine. Wide variations in terminal drug half-life (7–33 h) and AUC are found. 2-F-ara-A is excreted primarily in the urine (30–60%). There is a significant decrease in 2-F-ara-A clearance in patients with renal failure (Cl = 51.82 ± 6.70 ml/min/m^2) compared to patients with normal kidney function (Cl = 73.53 ± 3.79 ml/min/m^2). Dose reductions are recommended for patients with renal dysfunction. Oral bioavailability is 55–75%, and oral formulations for commercial use are being developed.

3. Toxicity

Fludarabine toxicities are primarily myelosuppression and immunosuppression. Reversible leukopenia and

mediated transport and is phosphorylated to its active form, F-ara-ATP. F-ara-ATP inhibits several intracellular enzymes important in DNA replication, including DNA polymerase, ribonucleotide reductase, DNA primase, and DNA ligase I. In addition, F-ara-ATP is incorporated into DNA. Excision of a 3′-terminal F-ara-AMP in DNA does not easily occur, and the presence of this false nucleotide leads to apoptosis. The amount of fludarabine incorporated into DNA is linearly correlated with cytotoxicity. While the effects of fludarabine on DNA synthesis account for its activity in dividing cells, fludarabine is also cytotoxic in diseases with low growth fractions such as CLL and indolent lymphomas. While the specific mechanism(s) by which fludarabine induces cell death among quiescent cells is under investigation, proposed mechanisms of action include the ability of fludarabine to inhibit RNA polymerases by incorporation into RNA, depletion of nicotinamide adenine dinucleotide (NAD) with a resultant decrease in cellular energy stores, and

TABLE II
Key Features of Fludarabine

Mechanism of action	Incorporation into DNA as a false nucleotide
	Inhibition of DNA polymerase, DNA primase, and DNA ligase
	DNA chain termination
Metabolism	Rapid dephosphorylation in plasma to 2-fluoro-ara A
	Activation of F-ara-A to F-ara-ATP within cells
Pharmacokinetics	Rapid dephosphorylation to 2-F-ara A
	$T_{1/2}$ 2-F-ara-A = 6–30 h
Elimination	Primarily renal excretion of 2-F-ara-A
Drug interactions	Increases cytotoxicity of cytarabine and cisplatin
Toxicity	Myelosuppression
	Immunosuppression
	Neurotoxicity at high doses
	Rare: intestinal pneumonitis and hemolytic anemia
Precautions	Dose reduction for patients with renal failure

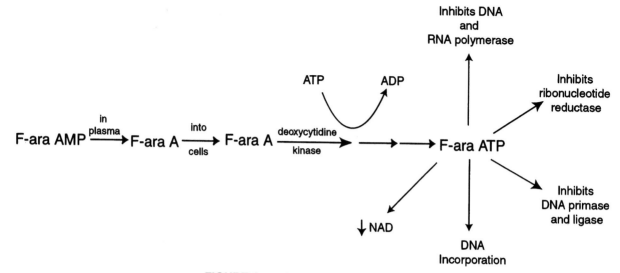

FIGURE 4 Mechanism of action of fludarabine.

thrombocytopenia occur with a median time to nadir of 13 days (range: 3 to 25 days) and 16 days (range: 2 to 32 days), respectively. At standard doses (25 mg/m^2/day for 5 days), 20–50% of patients have neutrophil nadirs less than 1000/mm^3. Up to 25% of patients treated with fludarabine will have a febrile episode. Many will be fevers of unknown origin, but one-third will have a serious infection documented. Platelet nadirs of less than 50–100,000/mm^3 are seen in 20%. Fludarabine is immunosuppressive. Therapy is associated with an increased risk of opportunistic infections. CD4 and CD8 T-lymphocytic subpopulations decrease to levels of 150–200/mm^3 after three courses of therapy. The most frequent infectious complications are respiratory. Infections with cryptococcus, listeria monocytogenes, pneumocystis carinii, CMV, herpes simplex virus, varicella zoster, and mycobacterium, organisms associated with T-cell dysfunction, are seen. Previous therapy, advanced disease, and neutropenia are risk factors. The use of prednisone with fludarabine has been reported to increase infectious complications. Other reported fludarabine toxicities include mild nausea and vomiting, peripheral sensorimotor neuropathy, hemolytic anemia, and pulmonary and hepatocellular toxicity. Mild, reversible neurotoxicity is seen with increased frequency and severity with older age.

4. Clinical Use

Fludarabine is active against a variety of low-grade lymphoproliferative malignancies, including CLL, hairy cell leukemia, Waldenstrom's macroglobulinemia, and non-Hodgkin's lymphoma. Response rates from 32 to 57% have been reported among patients with refractory previously treated CLL and in 70% of untreated patients. A median survival of 63 months has been reported. Approximately 50% of patients with indolent, non-Hodgkin's lymphoma respond to fludarabine. Response rates for intermediate and high-grade non-Hodgkin's lymphoma are significantly lower (0–10%).

5. Drug Interactions

Fludarabine is synergistic with at least two antineoplastic agents: cytosine arabinoside and cisplatin. Fludarabine increases intracellular accumulation of ara-C. Increased incorporation of ara-CTP into DNA occurs through the modulation of dNTP pools by fludarabine. Fludarabine increases the cytotoxicity of cisplatin by inhibiting the repair of cisplatin-induced DNA strand breaks.

B. Pentostatin (Deoxycoformycin)

Pentostatin or 2′-deoxycoformycin (dCF) was identified as a potent ADA inhibitor and subsequently tested as therapy for lymphocytic leukemias. No activity was noted in patients with acute leukemias, but pentostatin was found useful in the therapy of hairy cell leukemia and some indolent lymphomas.

1. Mechanism of Action

The specific mechanism for pentostatin cytotoxicity is unknown but is believed due to the accumulation of deoxyadenosine and dATP following ADA inhibition. Abnormally high levels of deoxyadenosine triphosphate (dATP), which accumulate with ADA inhibition, exert a negative feedback on ribonucleotide reductase, resulting in an imbalance in deoxynucleotide pools. This imbalance inhibits DNA synthesis and alters DNA replication and repair.

2. Clinical Pharmacology

When diluted with 5% dextrose in water, the stability of pentostatin may be compromised (at pH values less than 5). Plasma levels of pentostatin 1 h after administration exceed the ADA inhibitory concentration by approximately 10^6, supporting the recommendation for an intermittent infusion schedule. Pentostatin has a large volume of distribution but little protein binding. It has a terminal elimination half-life of 2.6–15 h. Only a small amount of pentostatin is metabolized. Plasma clearance averages 68 ml/min/m^2 and correlates with creatinine clearance. For patients with impaired renal function, the drug half-life is prolonged and dose reductions are indicated. Pentostatin is not bioavailable by the oral route. Pentostatin crosses the blood–brain barrier with CSF concentrations 10–13% of serum drug concentrations.

3. Toxicity

At doses used for hairy cell leukemia (4 mg/m^2 biweekly), side effects include neutropenia (70% of patients), mild to moderate lethargy, and rash. Renal toxicity, seen in early studies, has been minimized with the use of lower drug doses and adequate hydration. Neurotoxicity is seen at higher drug doses. Patients with poor performance status or impaired renal function have a higher incidence of life-threatening toxicity. Nausea and vomiting, seen in 40–70% of patients, may be delayed (12–72 h after administration). Elevation in transaminase concentrations occurs fol-

lowing drug administration but will usually return to normal. Keratoconjunctivitis has been reported.

4. Clinical Use

In clinical trials, pentostatin produces responses in more than 90% of patients with hairy cell leukemia, even those refractory to splenectomy and interferon-α therapy. Because of its activity in hairy cell leukemia, pentostatin has also been evaluated in a number of other closely related disorders. Further trials are needed to determine the usefulness of pentostatin in these disorders.

C. Cladribine or 2-Chlorodeoxyadenosine (Leustatin)

1. Mechanism of Action

The important pharmacologic features of cladribine are noted in Table III. Substitution of chlorine at the two position of deoxyadenosine produces 2-chlorodeoxyadenosine or cladribine (2-CdA) (Fig. 3), which is relatively resistant to enzymatic deamination by adenosine deaminase. Intracellular transport of 2-CdA occurs via nucleoside delivery mechanisms. Cladribine is a prodrug and needs intracellular phosphorylation to be active. The 5′-triphosphate metabolite (2-chloro-2′-deoxyadenosine 5′triphosphate, 2-CdATP) accumulates in cells rich in deoxycytidine

TABLE III
Key Features of Cladribine (2-Chlorodeoxadenosine)

Mechanism of action	Activation to 2-CdATP, which is incorporated into DNA, producing DNA strand breaks
	2-CdATP inhibits ribonucleotide reductase
	Triggers apoptosis by activating caspaces
Metabolism	Activation of 2-CdATP within cells
Pharmacokinetics	Significant variability in cladribine plasma AUC
	40–50% oral bioavailability
	50% urinary excretion
Drug interactions	Increases toxicity of cytarabine
Toxicity	Myelosuppression
	Fever
	Immunosuppression
	Renal failure at high doses

kinase (Fig. 5). This compound is incorporated into DNA and produces DNA strand breaks and inhibition of DNA synthesis. High intracellular concentrations of 2-CdATP also inhibit DNA polymerases and ribonucleotide reductase, causing an imbalance in deoxyribonucleotide triphosphate pools with subsequent impairment of DNA synthesis and repair. The mechanism for triggering apoptosis in nondividing cells is not clear. Cysteine proteases, referred to as caspaces, are active in apoptosis. Caspaces activate endonucleases, causing cleavage of genomic DNA. 2CdATP may interact with cytochrome C and protease activating factor-1 (PAF-1) to initiate the caspace cascade leading to DNA degradation, even in the absence of cell division. Apoptosis appears triggered by the phosphorylation of 2CdA followed by expression of Fas and Fas-L and activation of caspaces 8 and 3.

2. Clinical Pharmacology

Following a 2-h infusion of 0.12 mg/kg cladribine, peak serum concentrations of nearly 50 μg/ml are seen. A linear dose–concentration relationship is present up to doses of 2.5 mg/m²/h. The drug is weakly bound to plasma proteins (20%). Renal clearance accounts for 50% of total drug clearance with 20–30% of drug excreted as unchanged cladribine within the first 24 h. Little information is available regarding dose adjustments for renal or hepatic insufficiency.

However, given the high renal drug clearance, caution should be taken in using cladribine in patients with renal failure. Cladribine nucleotides are retained in leukemic cells with an intracellular half-life of 9–30 h. The long intracellular half-life supports the use of intermittent drug administration. The bioavailability of subcutaneously administer cladribine is excellent (100%). The AUC achieved is similar to that of continuous iv infusion. Oral bioavailability averages 50%. Significant patient-to-patient variability (± 28%) exists in the AUC achieved following the administration of drug by any method.

3. Toxicity

A common cladribine dosage has been a continuous 7-day infusion of 0.1 mg/kg/day. Severe (grades 3–4) neutropenia and lymphopenia occur in half of treated patients. Neutrophil counts decrease 1–2 weeks after starting therapy and persist for 3–4 weeks. Fever (T >100°F) is seen in two-thirds of patients mostly during the period of neutropenia. In many patients, no infection is documented. Twenty percent of patients develop grade 3–4 thrombocytopenia. Infections occur in 15–40% of patients, often opportunistic infections, such as *Candida* or *Aspergillis*. Reducing the dose of 2CdA from 0.7 to 0.5 mg/kg/cycle decreases the frequency of grade 3 myelosuppression from 33 to 8% and the infection rate from 30 to 7%.

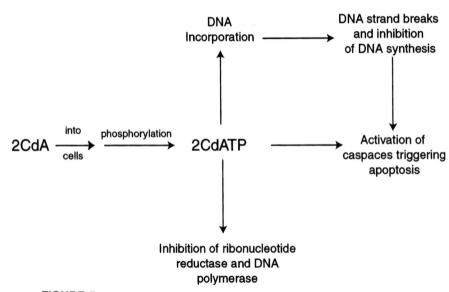

FIGURE 5 Mechanism of action of cladribine (2-chlorodeoxyadenosine or 2 CdA).

No change in lymphoma response rate has been noted with this dose reduction. Toxicities other than myelosuppression and infections are rare, but autoimmune hemolytic anemia, eosinophilia, nausea, and fatigue have been reported with high-dose 2CdA therapy (5–10 times the recommended dose). Renal failure has been reported.

4. Clinical Use

The spectrum of 2CdA activity appears similar to fludarabine. Cladribine is effective in CLL, hairy cell leukemia, low-grade non-Hodgkin's lymphomas, cutaneous T-cell lymphoma, Waldenstrom's macroglobulinemia, and blast phase CML. Cladribine has been tested in the therapy of the nonhematologic disorders, multiple sclerosis, and rheumatoid arthritis.

5. Drug Interactions

A drug–drug interaction between cladribine and cytarabine has been reported. Pretreatment of patients with cladribine increases the intracellular accumulation of ara-CTP, the active metabolite of cytarabine by 40%. Other pyrimidine analogs, such as gemcitabine, may be similarly affected.

III. ALLOPURINOL

Allopurinol has no antineoplastic activity. However, it is frequently used in patients with malignant disease to prevent hyperuricemia and uric acid nephropathy.

A. Mechanism of Action

Allopurinol and its major metabolic product, oxipurinol, are analogs of hypoxanthine and xanthine, respectively. Both inhibit the enzyme xanthine oxidase and block the conversion of hypoxanthine and xanthine to uric acid. Allopurinol reduces serum uric acid concentrations not only by inhibiting xanthine oxidase, but also by decreasing the rate of *de novo* purine biosynthesis. However, the effect of allopurinol on *de novo* purine synthesis is negligible in treatment of the tumor lysis syndrome where the release of preformed purines from DNA occurs.

B. Clinical Pharmacology

Allopurinol is well absorbed orally (80% of an administered dose). The half-life of the drug is short (30 to 100 min) with rapid conversion of allopurinol to oxipurinol. After oral administration of 300 mg of allopurinol, plasma oxipurinol concentrations of 10–40 μM are achieved within 1 to 3 h. Steady-state oxipurinol plasma concentrations (100 μM) are in excess of these needed to inhibit xanthine oxidase (25 μM). Linear absorption is noted up to doses of 900 mg. The volume of distribution of both allopurinol and oxipurinol is roughly that of total body water with little binding of either drug to plasma proteins. Oxipurinol clearance is closely tied to creatinine clearance. Patients with renal failure have delayed oxipurinol excretion and require a dose reduction to prevent drug accumulation. Elderly patients have reduced oxipurinol clearance due to a age-dependent reduction in creatinine clearance.

C. Toxicity

Allopurinol therapy is well tolerated in most patients, producing few side effects. Skin rash is seen in 2% of patients. A severe, potentially life-threatening hypersensitivity syndrome resulting from allopurinol use has been reported. Patients have fever (87% of reported cases), eosinophilia (73%), skin rash (including toxic epidermal necrolysis), renal dysfunction, and hepatic failure (68%). Death has been reported in 21% of published cases. This hypersensitivity syndrome usually appears 2 to 4 weeks after the initiation of 300 to 400 mg per day allopurinol. Over 80% of patients developing this syndrome have underlying renal failure. Steady-state concentrations of oxipurinol are elevated in this situation and may play a role in the development of the toxicity syndrome.

D. Uses of Allopurinol in Oncology

With rapid tumor lysis following cancer treatment, there is a sudden, temporary rise in uric acid serum due to cell destruction with the release of purines from DNA. The marked increase in urinary uric acid excretion may lead to renal failure due to the precipitation of urate crystals in the distal renal tubules where concentration and acidification are maximal. If marked tumor lysis and hyperuricemia are expected from chemotherapy (generally following therapy of ALL and lymphomas), optimal management consists of lowering serum uric concentrations before initiating treatment. If rapid antineoplastic treatment is required, significant oxipurinol blood levels can be achieved within 30 min of an iv allopurinol infusion and within 2 to 4 h of oral allopurinol administration. Doses of 300 to 400 mg/m^2/day allopurinol should be given for 2 to 3 days, with subsequent doses reduced to 300 to 400 mg/day. These doses prevent marked increases in uric acid excretion after chemotherapy, although clinically significant tumor lysis is still seen in 5% of patients with high-grade lymphomas and laboratory abnormalities in 40%.

E. Drug Interactions

Xanthine oxidase catalyzes the conversion of both azathioprine and 6-mercaptopurine to the inactive metabolite, 6-thiouric acid. Concomitant administration of allopurinol with either of these two agents results in increased 6-MP plasma concentrations and increased toxicity.

See Also the Following Articles

Acute Lymphoblastic Leukemia in Children • Chemotherapy: Synergism and Antagonism • Folate Antagonists • Hypoxia and Drug Resistance • Pyrimidine Antimetabolites • Resistance to Inhibitors of Dihydrofolate Reductase

Bibliography

Adkins, J. C., Peters, D. H., and Markham, A. (1997). Fludarabine: An update of its pharmacology and use in the treatment of haematological malignancies. *Drugs* **53,** 1005–1037.

Anaissie, E. J., Kontoyiannis, D. P., O'Brien, S. *et al.* (1998). Infections in patients with chronic lymphocytic leukemia treated with fludarabine. *Ann. Intern Med.* **129,** 559–566.

Begleiter, A., Liliemark, O., Plunkett, W., and Reed, J. C. (1996). Why do drugs work in CLL? *Leukemia Lymphoma* **22**(S2), 1–11.

Beutler, E., Carrera, C. J., Carson, D. A., and Piro, L. D. (1988). 2-Chlorodeoxyadenosine: An effective new agent for the treatment of chronic lymphocytic leukemia. *Blood* **72,** 1069–1073.

Beutler, E., Piro, L. D., Saven, A., *et al.* (1991). 2-Chlorodeoxyadenosine (2-CdA): A potent chemotherapeutic and immunosuppressive nucleoside. *Leukemia Lymphoma* **5,** 1–8.

Black, A. J., McLeod, H. L., Capell, H. A., *et al.* (1995). Thiopurine methyltransferase genotype predicts therapy-limiting severe toxicity from azathioprine. *Ann. Intern. Med.* **129,** 716–718.

Calabresi, P., and DeConti, R. C. (1966). Use of allopurinol for prevention and control of hyperuricemia in patients with neoplastic disease. *N. Engl. J. Med.* **274,** 481–486.

Chan, C. L. C., Erdmen, G. R., Gruber, S. A., et al. (1990). Azathioprine metabolism: Pharmacokinetics of 6-mercaptopurine, 6-thiouric acid and 6-thioguanine nucleotides in renal transplant patients. *J. Clin. Pharm.* **30,** 358–363.

Chao, Q., Cottam, H. B., Leoni, L. M., *et al.* (1998). Induction of an apoptotic program in cell free extracts by 2-chloro-2′deoxyadenosine 5′ triphosphate and cytochrome C. *Proc. Natl. Acad. Sci. USA* **95,** 9567–9571.

Cheson, B. D. (1995). Infectious and immunosuppressive complications of purine analog therapy. *J. Clin. Oncol.* **13,** 2431–2448.

Cheson, B. D., Foss, F. M., Vena, D. A., *et al.* (1994). Neurotoxicity of purine analogs: A review. *J. Clin. Oncol.* **12,** 2216–2228.

Collins, J. M., Riccardi, R., Zimm, S., *et al.* (1983). Variable bioavailability of oral mercaptopurine: Is maintenance chemotherapy in acute lymphoblastic leukemia being optimally delivered? *N. Eng. J. Med.* **308,** 1005–1009.

Fallavollita, A., Sorensen, J. M., Vena, D. A., *et al.* (1997). Treatment of refractory chronic lymphocytic leukemia with fludarabine phosphate via the group C protocol mechanism of the National Cancer Institute: Five-year follow-up report. *J. Clin. Oncol.* **15,** 458–465.

Fidias, P., Chabner, B., and Grossbard, M. L. (1996). Purine analogs for the treatment of low-grade lymphoproliferative disorders. *Oncologist* **1,** 125–139.

Hande, K. R., Chabner, B. A., and Reed, E. (1978). Allopurinol kinetics. *Clin. Pharmacol. Ther.* **23,** 598–605.

Hande, K. R., Noone, R. M., and Stone, W. J. (1984). Severe allopurinol toxicity; description and guidelines for prevention in patients with renal insufficiency. *Am. J. Med.* **76,** 47–56.

Kane, B. J., Kuhn, J. G., and Roush, M. K. (1992). Pentostatin: An adenosine deaminase inhibitor for the treatment of hairy cell leukemia. *Ann. Pharmacother.* **26,** 939–946.

Klohs, W. D., and Kraker, A. J. (1992). Pentostatin: Future directions. *Pharmacol. Rev.* **44,** 459–477.

Lennard, L. (1992). The clinical pharmacology of 6-mercaptopurine. *Eur. J. Clin. Pharmacol.* **43,** 329–339.

LePage, G. A., and Whitecar, J. P. (1971). Pharmacology of 6-thioguanine in man. *Cancer Res.* **31,** 1627–1631.

Liliemark, J. (1997). The clinical pharmacokinetics of cladribine. *Clin. Pharmacokinet.* **32,** 120–131.

McLeod, H. L., Krynetski, E. Y., Relling, M. V., and Evans, W. E. (2000). Genetic polymorphism of thiopurine methyltransferase and its clinical relevance for childhood acute lymphoblastic leukemia. *Leukemia* **14,** 567–572.

Plunkett, W., and Gandhi, V. (1996). Pharmacology of purine nucleoside analogs. *Hematol. Cell Ther.* **38,** 567–574.

Relling, M. V., Hancock, M. L., Rivera, G. K., *et al.* (1999). Mercaptopurine therapy intolerance and heterozygosity at the thiopurine 5-methyltransferase gene locus. *J. Natl. Cancer Inst.* **91,** 2001–2008.

Swann, P. F., Waters, T. R., Moulton, D. C., *et al.* (1996). Role of postreplicative DNA mismatch repair in the cytotoxic action of thioguanine. *Science* **273,** 1109–1111.

Yates, C. R., Krynetski, E. Y., Loennechen, T., *et al.* (1997) Molecular diagnosis of thiopurine 5-methyltransferase deficiency: Genetic basis for azathioprine and mercaptopurine intolerance. *Ann. Intern. Med.* **126,** 608–614.

Pyrimidine Antimetabolites

Amanda Psyrri
Giuseppe Pizzorno
Yale University School of Medicine

GLOSSARY

alopecia Absence or loss of hair, particularly from the head.

antimetabolites A molecule structurally similar to a metabolite that can oppose or replace the activity of the natural metabolite. Many anticancer drugs and antibiotics act as antimetabolites.

circadian Biological function characterized by a 24-h cycle.

dysphagia Inability or difficulty in swallowing.

ischemia Insufficiency of blood supply to a given organ or tissue.

myelosuppression Inhibition of bone marrow functions.

nucleoside A glycoside formed by a purine or pyrimidine base linked to ribose (pentose sugar). Deoxynucleoside when linked to deoxyribose.

polymerases Enzymes that catalyze the polymerization of ribo- and deoxynucleotides to form nucleic acids.

proctitis Inflammation of rectum and anus.

purine Heterocyclic nitrogen molecule, parent compound of DNA and RNA bases: adenine and guanine.

pyrimidine Heterocyclic nitrogen-containing molecule, parent compound of DNA and RNA bases: cytosine, thymine, and uracil.

thrombocytopenia Atypical decrease in the number of blood platelets.

I. INTRODUCTION

One of the main features of cancer cells is uncontrolled cell proliferation. Interest in the development of purine and pyrimidine analogs as antineoplastic agents followed the observation that nucleic acids play a crucial role in cellular growth. Elucidation of the biochemical pathways leading to the synthesis nucleic acid allowed the development of several analogs structurally similar to the natural substrates or to critical intermediates in these pathways.

The main mechanism of action of these drugs includes the competition with normal metabolites for the catalytic or regulatory site of key enzymes or the substitution for a metabolite that is normally incorporated into DNA or RNA. The majority of the antimetabolites interfere with nucleic acid synthesis, which takes place during the S phase of the cell cycle (S-phase specific). Therefore, these drugs are able to kill rapidly proliferating cells but have little effect on slowly cycling or resting cells.

This article discusses the clinically most useful pyrimidine analogs: fluorouracil (5-FU), cytosine arabinoside (Ara-C), and gemcitabine (dFdC).

II. FLUOROURACIL

A. Structure and Mechanism of Action

5-FU (Fig. 1) is an analog of the pyrimidine base uracil with a fluorine atom substituted at the carbon −5 position (C-5) of the pyrimidine ring in place of hydrogen. The fluorine atom resembles that of hydrogen in dimension (similar Van der Waals radii) and allows the molecule to mimic uracil biochemically. The development of this agent by Dushinsky and Heidelberger was based on the observation that preneo-

plastic rat liver and hepatomas incorporated uracil more actively than the normal liver tissue.

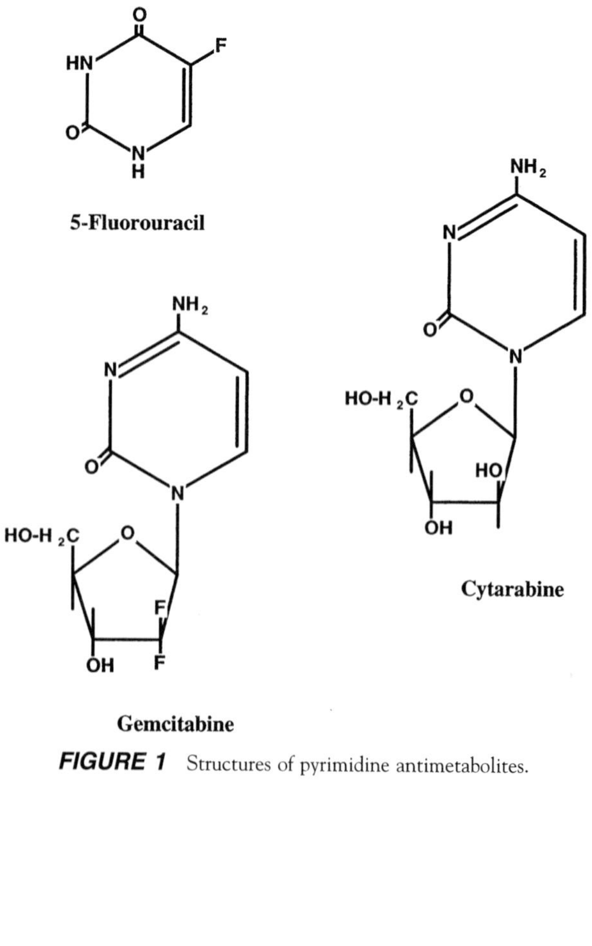

Two primary mechanisms are responsible for the antiproliferative activity of 5-FU: (1) inhibition of thymidylate synthase (TS) activity and (2) incorporation of 5-FU nucleotides into RNA. The inhibition of TS follows the activation of 5-FU to fluorodeoxyuridine monophosphate (FdUMP). The transfer of a methyl group to the 5 position of deoxyuridylate (dUMP) to obtain thymidine occurs through the formation of a ternary covalent complex of TS with dUMP and the folate cofactor 5,10-methylenetetrahydrofolate serving as a methyl donor. The presence of FdUMP results in the formation of a more stable ternary complex, leading to a sustained enzyme inhibition and reduction in the formation of thymidine monophosphate, which is the precursor of thymidine triphosphate (dTTP), one of the four deoxyribonucleotides required for DNA synthesis and repair.

5-FU is incorporated into both RNA and DNA. The incorporation of 5-FU ribonucleotides into RNA leads to alterations in RNA processing and translation, whereas the incorporation of fluorinated deoxyribonucleotides into DNA results in the inhibition of DNA synthesis and function.

dUTP (the substrate that accumulates behind the blocked TS reaction) is also misincorporated into DNA, resulting in the inhibition of DNA synthesis and function. The misincorporation of dUTP and the fluorinated deaxyribonucletide triphosphate into DNA would initiate the excision-repair process. However, in the presence of a reduced dTTP pool, required for DNA repair, this altered process may lead to the formation of DNA strand breaks.

B. Mechanisms of Resistance

An initial partial or complete response of tumors to 5-FU is generally followed by the eventual regrowth of the tumor, despite sustained, or even increased, dosages of the drug. The mechanisms of resistance to the cytotoxic effects of 5-FU are outlined in Table I.

From those mechanisms, only an inadequate size of the folate pools has been associated with clinical resistance to 5-FU and its derivatives. The addition of exogenous folate in the form of leucovorin to increase the formation of the ternary complex has enhanced the responsiveness to 5-FU in clinical trials. Prelimi-

FIGURE 1 Structures of pyrimidine antimetabolites.

TABLE I
Mechanisms of Resistance to 5-FU

Decreased activity of anabolic enzymes

Increased activity of catabolic enzymes

Overexpression of TS (gene amplification, transcriptional and translational mechanisms)

Alterations in binding affinity of TS for FdUMP

Decreased intracellular folate levels

Decreased incorporation into DNA and RNA

Increased DNA repair mechanisms

Increased salvage of physiologic nucleosides

Decreased availability of ribose/deoxyribose donors

nary clinical data also suggest that overexpression of TS in tumor biopsies predicts for resistance to 5-FU-based regimens.

C. Administration

5-FU is generally administered parenterally because of unpredictable absorption and erratic bioavailability after oral administration. The most common dosage schedules are a monthly course of five daily doses given as an iv bolus of 400 to 600 mg/m^2 or the same dosage given as a single bolus on a weekly basis. The limiting toxicities of these regimens is myelosuppression or mucositis.

Higher doses of 5-FU (1000–2000 mg/m^2/day) are required to achieve therapeutic effects when continuous infusion is employed. With this route, mucositis and hand and foot syndrome are the dose-limiting toxicities, whereas myelosuppression is minimal. Studies have shown that this regimen is superior to the bolus when 5-FU is given as a single agent. This treatment requires a 48-h infusion at weekly intervals, which results in both improved response and survival. Prolonged infusion of 5-FU for up to 12 weeks at 300 mg/m^2/day also produced a better response than the bolus regimen. The most prominent toxicity associated with this regimen is a reversible hand and foot syndrome.

D. Clinical Pharmacology

5-FU distributes into the extracellular space and readily enters the cerebrospinal fluid (CSF). The rate of plasma clearance is first order, with a half-life of 10 to 20 min. Clearance, however, may decrease rapidly when dosage exceeds 800 mg/m^2 due to saturation of the catabolic reactions.

Intraarterial infusion of 5-FU has been used to treat patients with isolated liver metastases. Hepatic FU concentrations considerably higher than those tolerated systemically can be achieved. Cholestatic jaundice is the dose-limiting toxicity for this route of administration.

The primary clearance mode of 5-FU is via catabolism along the degradative pathway of uracil. The initial rate-limiting step is its reduction by dihydrouracil dehydrogenase (DPD), which occurs primarily in the liver. Inherited deficiency of this enzyme leads to profound drug toxicity in conventional doses of the drug.

Marked circadian variations in the metabolism of 5-FU have been detected and related to a 24-h cyclic variations in DPD activity. Investigators have tried to employ these differences in the design of clinical trials. The circadian administration of 5-FU appears to increase the maximum tolerated dose.

E. Biochemical Modulation of Therapy

A number of agents have been combined with 5-FU in an attempt to increase the cytotoxicity of 5-FU through biochemical modulation. A major focus in this area has been enhancing the efficiency with which the covalent complex of FdUMP with the folate cofactor and thymidylate synthase is formed by supplementation with the reduced folate cofactor.

To stabilize the covalent complex, large doses of leucovorin (d-L-N-5-formyl tetrahydrofolate) have been employed to saturate the target enzyme with L-5,10-methylene-tetrahydrofolate via conversion of the L-isomer of leucovorin to 5-methyltetrahydrofolate.

With this combination, the dose of 5-FU should be reduced by 20%. A wide range of clinical trials have shown an increased response rate to 5-FU therapy in colorectal cancer when in the presence of leucovorin, although this regimen did not translate into a survival advantage. Diarrhea and mucositis are the limiting toxicities.

Adjuvant therapy trials in colorectal cancer have indicated a benefit in terms of disease-free survival and overall survival for node-positive patients treated with 5-FU combined with the immunomodulator levamisole compared with patients receiving no additional therapy or levamisole alone. In contrast, 5-FU/levamisole was not superior to 5-FU alone in advanced colorectal cancer. No clear mechanistic explanation for the basis of these therapeutic effects can be given. Adjuvant therapy with 5-FU and levamisole has been associated with neurotoxicity and hepatic toxicity.

Modulation of 5-FU therapy with methotrexate has been widely documented to increase the cytotoxicity of 5-FU both in cell cultures and in animal models. By inhibiting purine synthesis and increasing cellular pools of 5-phosphoribosyl-1-pyrophosphate (PRPP), which reacts directly with 5-FU to form fluorouridylate, methotrexate enhances the activation of 5-FU when given prior to but not following 5-FU in clinical trials.

The interferons have also been evaluated as a means to recruit host defense mechanisms during 5-FU therapy. The enhanced effect of 5-FU, generated by interferon-α, has been attributed to the activation of macrophages in a species-specific manner. Interferon-γ suppresses the 5-FU-mediated elevation in TS activity and protein expression. Both interferon-α and -γ increase the accumulation of FdUMP in cancer cells. Limited clinical studies have been reported using interferon-α in combination with 5-FU. Although an initial response rate of 76% has been reported in colorectal cancer, major increases in the incidence of both mucositis and granulocytopenia required dose reductions of both 5-FU and interferon; subsequent confirmatory studies yielded response rates of only 26 to 35%.

5-Ethynyluracil is an irreversible inhibitor of dihydropyrimidine dehydrogenase, which is the initial enzyme in the catabolism of 5-FU. Because more than 80% of an initial dose of 5-FU is degraded through this mechanism, the inhibition of DPD activity results in an increased exposure to the fluoropyrimidine. In animal models, ethynyluracil, combined with 5-FU, was found to improve the efficacy and therapeutic index of fluoropyrimidines. Due to inhibition of 5-FU catabolism, a 100% oral bioavailability is achieved when 5-FU is coadministered with ethynyluracil. A substantial decrease in FU dosage is necessary to avoid severe host toxicity. In phase I and II studies, diarrhea was the dose-limiting toxicity, whereas hand and foot syndrome and myelosuppression were uncommon.

F. Therapeutic Uses

5-FU therapy has shown to induce partial responses in 10–30% of patients with metastatic carcinomas of the breast and the gastrointestinal tract. It also exerts clinical activity against carcinomas of the head and neck, ovary, urinary bladder, cervix, prostate, and pancreas.

Higher response rates are seen when 5-FU is used in combination with other antineoplastic agents, such as cyclophosphamide and methotrexate (CMF) or cyclophosphamide and adriamycin (CAF) in breast cancer, cisplatin (ovary and head and neck cancer), and leucovorin (colorectal cancer).

G. Clinical Toxicity

The main toxic effects of 5-FU are exerted in rapidly proliferating tissues, primarily the bone marrow and the gastrointestinal tract. 5-FU host toxicity is dose, schedule, and route dependent.

Myelosuppression is the dose-limiting toxicity for bolus iv infusion. The nadir of leukopenia is usually between days 9 and 14 after the first administration of the drug. Anemia and thrombocytopenia also may occur. Myelosuppression is less intense for continuous infusion.

The gastrointestinal toxicity can be life-threatening. Enteric ulcerations may occur at any level and result in clinical symptoms of dysphagia, watery diarrhea, and proctitis. Octreotide has been used with some success in patients who develop 5-FU-associated diarrhea. Mucositis and diarrhea are the dose-limiting toxicities for continuous infusion.

Dermatological toxicity occurs with CI and rapid infusion 5-FU. Alopecia, nail changes, increased pigmentation, and atrophy of the skin may occur. Palmar–plantar erythrodysesthesia ("hand–foot" syndrome) is more commonly observed with continuous iv therapy. Oral pyridoxine may be used to treat this toxicity.

5-FU may cause acute neurologic symptoms, including somnolence, cerebellar ataxia, confusion, seizures, and upper motor signs. Severe neurotoxic reactions have been observed in patients with DPD deficiency after receiving 5-FU.

5-FU may produce cardiac toxicity manifested by chest pain, changes in electrocardiogram, and serum enzyme elevations. Some of these episodes have occurred in patients with a prior history of ischemic heart disease or chest irradiation. Coronary vasospasm might be the mechanism of cardiotoxicity.

H. Oral Prodrugs of 5-FU

To allow the oral administration of 5-FU with a consistent bioavailability and to provide long-term delivery of the drug without the use of surgically implanted infusion pumps, 5-FU has been coadministered with inhibitors of its catabolism (ethynyluracil) or by developing orally stable prodrugs that can be readily converted to 5-FU. Several agents have been recently introduced in the clinic or are at different stages of development.

Tegafur (Ftorafur), a 1-(2-tetrahydrofuranyl) derivative of 5-FU, is metabolized to free 5-FU in liver by both cytochrome P450 and cytoplasmic activation. Initial clinical trials indicate that this agent is equally effective to 5-FU at a comparable dose.

UTF, a new formulation of Tegafur, is a combination of Ftorafur with uracil in a molar ratio of 1:4. The competition of uracil at the level of the catabolic enzymes inhibits the degradation of 5-FU that is released from Ftorafur. Double-blind, randomized clinical trials of Tegafur and UTF in patients with breast and gastric cancers have resulted in better response rates for UFT with no difference in the frequency or severity of adverse effects between the two formulations.

S-1 is a combination of tegafur, 5-chloro-2,4-dihydroxypyridine (CDHP), and oxonic acid with a fixed molar ratio of 1:0.4:1. CDHP is an inhibitor of DPD, therefore reducing FU degradation, and oxonic acid decreases the activity of orotidylate pyrophosphorylase that activates FU to FUMP. By mostly inhibiting orotidylate pyrophosphorylase in the gastrointestinal tract, oxonic acid has been shown to reduce diarrhea associated with fluoropyrimidine therapy. A significant activity with a 46% response rate was observed in patients with gastric cancer with limited gastrointestinal toxicity.

Capecitabine, recently introduced on the market as Xeloda, is an orally administered fluoropyrimidine carbamate prodrug of FU. A liver carboxyesterase hydrolyses the N-pentyl carbamate chain to form 5-deoxy-5-fluorocytidine, which is deaminated to 5-deoxy-5-fluorouridine (5-DFUR) by cytidine deaminase, and finally thymidine phosphorylase hydrolyses 5-DFUR to produce FU. The higher phosphorolytic activity expressed in tumor tissue compared to the surrounding normal tissue provides a selective activation and improved therapeutic index.

Toxicities are similar to a continuous 5-FU infusion with diarrhea, mucositis, and hand and foot syndrome. The maximum tolerated dose of 1657 mg/m²/day for 14 days generates peak plasma levels, 2 h after administration, comparable to a CI of 300 mg/m²/day of 5-FU.

Capecitabine has been approved for the treatment of metastatic breast cancer resistant to both paclitaxel and anthracyclin containing chemotherapy. A randomized phase II study in colorectal cancer indicated a 21–24% response rate whether capecitabine was administered alone or in combination with leucovorin. Capecitabine may be effective even in patients who do not respond to 5-FU.

III. CYTARABINE

A. Metabolism and Mechanism of Action

Ara-C (Fig. 1) is an analog of deoxycitidine that differs from the physiologic deoxyribonucleosides by the presence of a β–OH group in the 2′ position of the sugar. Ara-C requires intracellular activation to the nucleotide metabolite ara-CTP. The conversion to Ara-CMP is catalyzed by deoxycitidine kinase. Ara-CMP subsequently reacts with the appropriate nucleotide kinases to form AraCDP and AraCTP.

Ara-C and Ara-CMP are subject to degradation by two inactivating enzymes, cytidine deaminase and dCMP deaminase, respectively, to form two inactive metabolites: arabinosyluracil (Ara-U) and Ara-UMP. The balance between intracellular activation and degradation is critical in determining the cytotoxicity of Ara-C.

The most important mechanism of action is incorporation into DNA by the metabolite Ara-CTP. Once incorporated into DNA, tumor cells are not able to excise the nucleotide. Thus, template function and chain elongation are inhibited. Other mechanisms that contribute to Ara-C cytotoxicity include inhibition of

(1) DNA synthesis via inhibition of DNA polymerase-α, (2) DNA repair through inhibition of DNA polymerase-β, (3) ribonucleotide reductase, and (4) membrane glycoprotein and glycolipid synthesis.

At noncytotoxic concentrations, Ara-C may cause human promyeloblast cell lines to differentiate. Due to the differentiation effects, low-dose Ara-C has been used with modest success in the treatment of patients with myelodysplastic syndromes.

B. Mechanisms of Resistance

The mechanisms of resistance to the cytotoxic effects of cytarabine are outlined in Table II. All of these mechanisms have been implicated as causing clinical Ara-C resistance in patients with leukemia. To date there is no agreement as to the specific changes responsible for resistance in human leukemia.

C. Clinical Pharmacology

The presence of high concentrations of cytidine deaminase in gastrointestinal epithelium and the liver prevents its oral use. After parenteral administration, Ara-C rapidly disappears from plasma, with a plasma half-life of 7 to 20 min mostly due to deamination.

Ara-C is usually administered every 8–12 h for 5–7 days. This interval may be determined by the requirement to maintain intracellular concentrations of Ara-CTP at cytotoxic levels for at least one cell cycle. The mean duration of cell cycle for acute myelocytic leukemia cells is 1 to 2 days. Ara-C is also given by continuous infusion for 7 days to circumvent the rapid metabolism and the short half-life.

Ara-C crosses into the central nervous system and the CSF, with levels reaching 20–40% of serum levels after 2 h of continuous infusion. It may be given

TABLE II
Mechanisms of Resistance to Ara-C

Decrease in anabolic enzymes (deoxycitidine kinase)

Increase in catabolic enzymes (cytidine deaminase, dCMP deaminase)

Decrease in Ara-C membrane transport

Increase in competing physiologic nucleotides, CTP through an increase in CTP synthetase.

---

intrathecally for the treatment of meningeal leukemia or peritoneal carcinomatosis.

High-dose Ara-C (2 to 3 g/m^2 every 12 h for six doses) has greater efficacy in patients with acute myelocytic leukemia but results in additional toxicities. Low-dose Ara-C (20 mg/m^2 for 7–21 days) has been used in elderly patients with myelodysplastic syndrome. The response has been disappointing, with only 20% of the patients achieving a clinical remission.

D. Therapeutic Uses

Cytarabine is indicated for remission induction in patients with acute myelocytic leukemia. It is more effective when it is combined with anthracyclines. Low-dose Ara-C is used in the treatment of chronic myelogenous leukemia in combination with interferon-α.

It is also active against acute lymphocytic leukemia and may be used for the treatment of relapses of acute lymphocytic leukemia in both children and adults. In combination with other agents, Ara-C is used in the treatment of non-Hodgkin lymphomas. Ara-C is not particularly useful in the treatment of solid tumors.

E. Clinical Toxicity

Toxicity depends on drug concentration and duration of exposure. Myelosuppression, with leukopenia and thrombocytopenia, and gastrointestinal epithelial toxicity are the main toxic side effects of standard dose Ara-C.

High-dose Ara-C has the same side effects on gastrointestinal epithelium and bone marrow but has additional toxicities. Pulmonary toxicity, manifested by irreversible noncardiogenic pulmonary edema (~10% of the patients) and a high incidence of *Streptococcus viridans* pneumonia, has been reported. Cerebral and cerebellar dysfunction, manifested by slurred speech, ataxia, confusion, and coma, occurs in 20% of patients receiving 3 g/m^2 for 12 doses and in two-thirds of patients receiving 4.5 g/m^2 for 12 doses. Patients older than age 40, those with renal dysfunction, and those with elevated alkaline phosphatase activity in the serum are especially sensitive to this toxicity. Ara-C given intrathecally may rarely cause fever and seizures, which occur within 24 h of administration.

IV. GEMCITABINE

A. Metabolism and Mechanism of Action

Gemcitabine (Fig. 1) is a deoxycytidine analog with two fluorine atoms in the 2' position of the sugar moiety. This drug maintains many of the characteristics of Ara-C in that it has the same pathway of activation (deoxycytidine kinase) and inactivation (by deamination), inhibits DNA synthesis, and exerts its cytotoxicity through incorporation into DNA. Phase I clinical trials have shown that gemcitabine has a very rapid half-life (8 min) because of deamination over a wide range of doses.

Gemcitabine, however, differs from Ara-C in some aspects: it does not cause DNA chain termination as effectively as Ara-C, but once incorporated, it is more difficult to excise from DNA.

dFdCDP directly inhibits ribonucleotide reductase. Additionally, dFdCTP retards the degradation of gemcitabine via the inhibition of dCMP deaminase. Kinetics studies suggest that the cytotoxic activity of gemcitabine is not limited in the S phase of the cell cycle. Gemcitabine exerts its cytotoxic effects possibly through apoptosis and differentiation.

B. Therapeutic Uses

Gemcitabine was approved by the FDA in 1996 as a first-line treatment for patients with locally advanced or metastatic pancreatic cancer. A phase III multicenter randomized trial has shown a clinical benefit response (CBR) in 24% of patients treated with gemcitabine versus 5% in the group treated with 5-FU and a 1-year survival of 18% for patients on gemcitabine compared to 2% for patients treated with 5-FU. In patients previously treated with 5-FU the CBR was 27%.

In non-small cell lung cancer, a 20–26% response rate put gemcitabine in line with other neoplastic drugs used as single agents, including cisplatin. Moderate activity was seen in bladder cancer.

C. Clinical Toxicity

The dose-limiting toxicity has been mild to moderate myelosuppression. Nonhematological toxicity includes gastrointestinal (nausea, vomiting, elevation in liver function tests), dermatological (skin rash, pruritus, alopecia), and flu-like symptoms. Hemolytic uremic syndrome has rarely been reported.

See Also the Following Articles

CELL CYCLE CHECKPOINTS • FOLATE ANTAGONISTS • HYPOXIA AND DRUG RESISTANCE • PURINE ANTIMETABOLITES • RESISTANCE TO DNA DAMAGING AGENTS • RESISTANCE TO INHIBITORS OF DIHYDROFOLATE REDUCTASE

Bibliography

Advanced Colorectal Cancer Meta-Analysis Project (1992). Modulation of fluorouracil by leucovorin in patients with advanced colorectal cancer: Evidence in terms of response rate. *J. Clin. Oncol.* **10**, 896–903.

Baccanari, D. P., Davis, S. T., Knick, V. C., and Spector, T. (1993). 5-Ethynyluracil (776C85): A potent modulator of the pharmacokinetics and antitumor efficacy of 5-fluorouracil. *Proc. Natl. Acad. Sci. USA* **90**, 11064–11068.

Baker, S. D., Khor, S. P., Adjei, A. A., Doucette, M., Spector, T., Donehower, R. C., Grochow, L. B., Sartorius, S. E., Noe, D. A., Hohneker, J. A., and Rowinsky, E. K. (1996). Pharmacokinetics, oral bioavailability and safety study of fluorouracil in patients treated with 776C85, an inactivator of dihydropyrimidine dehydrogenase. *J. Clin. Oncol.* **14**, 3085–3096.

Burris, H. A., Moore, M. J., Andersen, J., Green, M. R., Rothenberg, M. L., Modiano, M. R., Cripps, M. C., Portenoy, R. K., Storniolo, A. M., Tarassoff, P., Nelson, R., Dorr, F. A., Stephens, C. D., and Von Hoff, D. D. (1997). Improvements in survival and clinical benefit with gemcitabine as first line therapy for patients with advanced pancreas cancer: A randomized trial. *J. Clin. Oncol.* **15**, 2403.

Cassidy, J. (1999). Potential of Xeloda in colorectal cancer and other solid tumors. *Oncology* **57**, 27–32.

Chu, E., Koeller, D. M., Johnston, P. G., Zinn, S., and Allegra, C. J. (1992). Regulation of thymidylate synthase in human colon cancer cells treated with 5-fluorouracil and interferon-γ. *Mol. Pharmacol.* **43**, 527–533.

Diasio, R. B., and Harris, B. E. (1989). Clinical pharmacology of 5-fluorouracil. *Clin. Pharmacokinet.* **16**, 215–237.

Duschinsky, R., Pleven, E., and Heidelberger, C. (1957). The synthesis of 5-fluoropyrimidines. *J. Am. Chem. Soc.* **79**, 4559.

Erlichman, C., Fine, S., Wong, A., and Elhakim T. (1988). A randomized trial of fluorouracil and folinic acid in patients with metastatic colorectal carcinoma. *J. Clin. Oncol.* **6**, 469–475.

Grem, J. L. (1990). Levamisole as a therapeutic agent for colorectal carcinoma. *Cancer Cells* **2**, 131–137.

Johnston, P. G., Lenz, H. J., Leichman, C. G., Danenberg, K. D., Allegra, C. J., Danenberg, P. V., and Leichman, L. (1995). Thymidylate synthase protein and gene expression predicts for response to 5 fluorouracil/leucovorin chemotherapy in patients with colorectal and gastric cancer. *Cancer Res.* **55**, 1407–1412.

Laurie, J. A., Moertel, C. G., Fleming, T. R., Wieand, H. S., Leigh, J. E., Rubin, J., McCormack, G. W., Gerstner, J. B., Krook, J. E., Malliard, J., Twito, D. I., Morton, R. F., Tschetter, L. K., and Barlow, J. F. (1989). Surgical adjuvant therapy of large-bowel carcinoma: An evaluation of levamisole and the combination of levamisole and fluorouracil. *J. Clin. Oncol.* **7**, 1447–1458.

Lokich, J., Ahlgren, J., Gullo, J., Philips, J., and Fryer, J. (1989). A prospective randomized comparison of continuous infusion fluorouracil with a conventional bolus schedule in metastatic colorectal carcinoma: A Mid-Atlantic Oncology Program study. *J. Clin. Oncol.* **7**, 425–432.

Major, P. P., Egan, E. M., Beardsley, G. P., Minden, M. D., and Kufe, D. W. (1981). Lethality of human myeloblasts correlates with the incorporation of arabinofuranosylcytosine into DNA. *J. Biol. Chem.* **78**, 3235–3239.

Marsh, J. C., Bertino, J. R., Katz, K. H., Davis, C. A., Durivage, H. J., and Rome, L. S. (1991). The influence of drug interval on the effect of methotrexate and fluorouracil in the treatment of advanced colorectal cancer. *J. Clin. Oncol.* **9**, 371–380.

Santi, D. V., McHenry, C. S., and Sommer H. (1974). Mechanism of interaction of thymidylate synthetase with 5-fluorodeoxyuridylate. *Biochemistry* **13**, 471–481.

Seifert, P., Baker, L., Reed, M. L., and Vaitkevicius, V. K. (1975). Comparison of continuously infused 5-fluorouracil with bolus injection in treatment of patients with colorectal adenocarcinoma. *Cancer* **36**, 123–128.

Shah, A., MacDonald, W., Goldie, J., Gudauskas, G., and Brisebois, B. (1985). 5-Fluorouracil infusion in advanced colorectal cancer: A comparison of three dose schedules. *Cancer Treat. Rep.* **69**, 739–742.

Ullman, B., Lee, M., Martin, D. W., Jr., and Santi, D. V. (1978). Cytotoxicity of 5-fluoro-2′-deoxyuridine: Requirement for reduced folate cofactors and antagonism by methotrexate. *Proc. Natl. Acad. Sci. USA* **75**, 980–983.

Valeriote, F. (1982). Cellular aspects of the action of cytosine arabinoside. *Med. Pediatr. Oncol.* **10**(S1), 5–26.

Wadler, S., Schwartz, E. L., Goldman, M., Lyver, A., Rader, M., Zimmerman, M., Itri, L., Weinberg, V., and Wiernik, P. H. (1989). Fluorouracil and recombinant α-2a-interferon: An active regimen against advanced colorectal carcinoma. *J. Clin. Oncol.* **7**, 1769–1775.

Pyruvate Kinases

Paschal A. Oude Weernink
Gerard E. J. Staal
Gert Rijksen
University Hospital, Utrecht, The Netherlands

GLOSSARY

allosteric enzyme An enzyme whose catalytic activity is modulated through the noncovalent binding of a specific metabolite at a site on the protein, other than the catalytic site.

isozymes Multiple forms of a given enzyme that occur within a single species of organism. Isozymes differ in amino acid composition and thus in their physicochemical properties, but they catalyze the same reaction.

phosphorylation Covalent attachment, catalyzed by a protein kinase, of a phosphate group to, for instance, a regulatory enzyme, thereby modulating the biological function of this enzyme.

Pyruvate kinase is an important regulatory enzyme of glycolysis and catalyzes the formation of pyruvate. Four isozymes are present in mammalian tissues, the M1 (or M)-, M2 (or K)-, L-, and R-types, which differ in their regulatory behavior. Type M2 is the main isozyme in fetal tissues and is progressively replaced by tissue-specific isozymes with special functions during differentiation. Neoplasia of various tissues is associated with high activities of pyruvate kinase and reexpression of the type M2 isozyme. In human brain tumors this isozymic shift from the M1-type toward the M2-type is closely associated with the histological grading and growth rate of the tumor. As pyruvate kinase type M2 has unique regulatory properties, the expression of this particular isozyme contributes to the altered regulation of carbohydrate metabolism in pro-liferating tumor cells. Its presence provides the cell with metabolic advantages, by supplying the cell with sufficient precursors for several metabolic pathways.

I. INTRODUCTION

Besides unrestrained growth, decreased growth factor requirements, invasive and metastatic capacity, loss of differentiated traits, changed morphology, and altered chromosomal composition, cancer cells are character-ized by changes in their metabolism. The biochemi-cal profile of tumors is marked by a prevalence of cer-tain anabolic pathways over catabolic pathways. This reorganization of metabolic routes is regulated by an elaborate network of control mechanisms. Probably the most important requisite is the expression of iso-forms of key enzymes, with altered regulatory proper-ties. The study of these tumor-associated isozymes can provide more insight into the biochemistry of tumor cells. In addition, isozyme patterns have proved to be valuable diagnostic and prognostic indices.

Glycolysis is one of the metabolic processes that is favored in tumor cells. Glucose catabolism not only represents the principal source of energy production, but also supplies the tumor cell with metabolites that are used in various biosynthetic pathways. Therefore, glycolysis takes a central position in the metabolism of the tumor cell. Pyruvate kinase (EC 2.7.1.40) is an important key enzyme in the regulation of glucose utilization. It catalyzes one of the last steps of glycol-ysis, the formation of pyruvate and ATP from phos-phoenolpyruvate and ADP. Besides ADP, pyruvate ki-nase can also use other nucleotide diphosphates like CDP, GDP, and UDP as substrates. The altered ex-pression of pyruvate kinase isozymes in tumor cells is an example of the specific and ordered isozyme distri-bution in cancer, and it is believed to be necessary to support the unrestrained growth of tumor cells.

II. REGULATION OF THE GLYCOLYTIC PATHWAY IN CANCER CELLS

A. Aerobic Glycolysis in Proliferating Cells

For decades investigators have tried to find properties of cancer cells that are consistently different from

properties of normal cells. Well known is the original observation of Otto Warburg in 1926 that a high rate of aerobic glycolysis is a hallmark of malignant cells. Warburg measured the oxygen consumption and rates of aerobic and anaerobic glycolysis of tumors of ani-mal and human origin. He observed that, whereas slices of both normal tissues and tumors rapidly pro-duced lactate from glucose or glycogen in the absence of oxygen (anaerobic glycolysis), virtually only the tumor slices showed an ability to produce lactate from glucose in the presence of oxygen (aerobic glycolysis). So, tumor cells seem to be characterized by the ab-sence of the Pasteur effect, the inhibition of glycoly-sis by oxygen. The Pasteur effect is a mechanism for adjusting the consumption of glucose in the presence of oxygen to the energy needs of the cell. The con-cept of aerobic glycolysis means that the pyruvate production from glucose exceeds the capacity of the tricarboxylic acid cycle and mitochondrial respira-tion, but it also implies that the tumor cell harvests only 2 moles of ATP per mole of glucose instead of the maximum energy yield of 38 moles of ATP.

The original observation of Warburg was confirmed in numerous studies. It was demonstrated for instance that well-differentiated, slowly growing Morris hep-atoma cells show a low aerobic glycolysis whereas the fast growing, poorly differentiated cells have a high glycolysis. It has now become clear, however, that an elevated aerobic glycolysis is not unique to tumor cells, but also takes place in normal proliferating cells and even in quiescent cells of retina and renal medulla and in myeloid cells of the bone marrow. This sug-gests that the phenomenon of aerobic glycolysis is merely a function of the increased cellular proliferation in tumors rather than a characteristic of cancer cells.

B. The Molecular Correlation Concept of Weber

Weber has postulated the existence of an ordered and specific pattern of enzymatic imbalance in tumors re-sulting in biological advantages to the tumor cells. He investigated a series of transplantable Morris he-patomas with varying growth rates and focused on the concentrations of specific key enzymes. Criteria for the identification of key enzymes are, inter alia, that they catalyze nonequilibrium reactions, are restricted to a synthetic or to a catabolic pathway, and are the first or the last enzyme in a reaction sequence. Furthermore, key enzymes possess regulatory properties and will determine the flux through the pathway.

Weber observed that in parallel with the malignancy of the different tumors, the activities and concentrations of certain enzymes were increased and those of the opposing enzymes were decreased. More than 40 enzymes representing a variety of metabolic pathways were found to correlate with growth rate (progression-linked alterations). The overall trend was an increase of the activities of anabolic pathways and a diminution of the activities of the corresponding catabolic pathways. The specific metabolic demands of rapidly multiplying tumor cells include an increased need for nucleotide biosynthesis for RNA and DNA production. Furthermore, there is an increased need for glycolytic intermediates, especially phosphorylated hexoses and trioses for the synthesis of nucleotides and amino acids. Although these biochemical alterations are linked to the rate of tumor growth, such linkage does not indicate that the high activity of a particular enzyme had a role in the initial process of transformation; rather, it may be part of the metabolic adaptation required by the tumor to sustain its high growth rate.

In summary, tumor cells can regulate the fluxes through their metabolic pathways by alterations in activities of the regulatory key enzymes. A mechanism by which this regulation can be achieved is the differential expression of isozymes.

C. Isozymes

After the discovery by Markert and Möller in 1959 that enzymes can exist in multimolecular forms, it became evident that alteration in gene expression in neoplasia may be manifested (among other things) by a change in isozyme distribution. Isozymes are different molecular forms of proteins with the same enzymatic specificity and arise as a result of the presence of more than one structural gene or messenger RNA. Isozymes may be affected in a different way by regulatory mechanisms such as feedback and substrate inhibition, allosteric and hormonal control, subcellular localization, posttranslational modification, and turnover rate.

In 1963 Schapira *et al.* were the first to report an alteration in the isozyme composition of aldolase in hepatic carcinomas, in which the adult liver type (B)

was replaced by the fetal liver type (A). Nowadays more than 20 examples of enzymes are known, being representatives of diverse metabolic pathways, of which the fetal isozyme is preferentially expressed in tumors. These changes have been interpreted as representing an altered regulation of gene expression, reflecting a reactivation of the fetal genes and a repression of the adult genes. An excellent model system for comparative studies of isozyme composition in cancer is offered by the already mentioned Morris hepatomas. These comprise a spectrum of chemically induced, transplantable rat neoplasms, which exhibit a wide range of growth rates, degrees of differentiation, and retention of liver functions. Using the Morris hepatoma system, it was shown that the extent of the reappearance of the fetal type of some of these enzymes correlated with the proliferative capacity of the tumor cells.

The expression of fetal enzymes in tumors may confer distinct selective advantages to these cells, supporting the neoplastic transformation. Interestingly, the resurgence of the same fetal isozymes has also been demonstrated in regenerating tissues, stressing the importance of these proteins for cell proliferation. Studies on isozyme changes in tumors have mainly been focused on the glycolytic enzymes, as the glycolytic pathway takes a central position in the metabolism of the tumor cell.

D. The Glycolytic Pathway and Glutaminolysis

Glucose is one of the most important metabolic fuels for malignant tumors and other rapidly dividing cells. The linkage between aerobic glycolysis and proliferation of malignantly transformed cells has been discussed earlier (Section II.A).

Glycolysis takes place in two stages (Fig. 1). In the first, glucose is transformed into 2 molecules of glyceraldehyde 3-phosphate with the investment of 2 molecules of ATP. In the second stage glyceraldehyde 3-phosphate is converted in a series of steps to pyruvate/lactate, resulting in the generation of 2 molecules of ATP per molecule of glyceraldehyde-3-phosphate. Thus, a net of 2 molecules of ATP is generated in the conversion of glucose to pyruvate. Besides the production of energy, the degradation of glucose also provides the tumor cell with metabolic

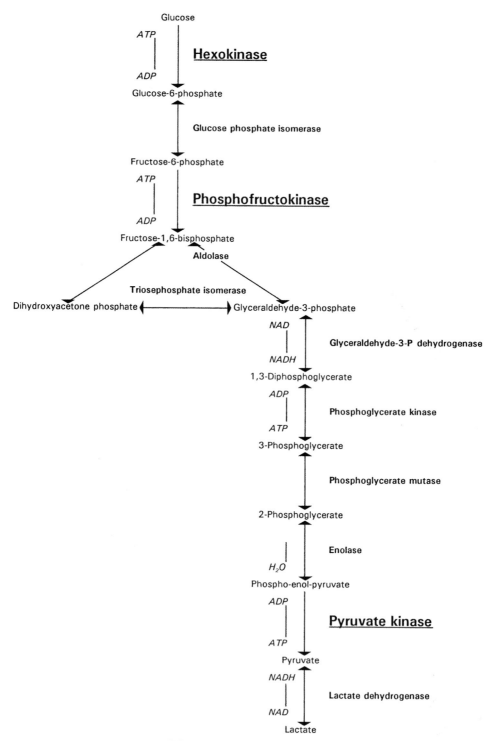

FIGURE 1 The glycolytic pathway.

intermediates that are used as precursors in various biosynthetic pathways (e.g., 3-phosphoglycerate for serine synthesis; glyceraldehyde 3-phosphate for phospholipid, triglyceride, and sphingomyelin synthesis; and glucose 6-phosphate for the formation of ribose 5-phosphate).

A substantial body of experimental evidence indicates that the amino acid glutamine is also a major respiratory fuel for rapidly growing cells. In the presence of oxygen glutamine provides energy by aerobic oxidation using a part of the tricarboxylic acid cycle, and it is eventually converted to pyruvate. This glutaminolytic pathway leads to the production of 5 moles ATP and 1 mole GTP per mole glutamine. It may be noted that glutamine is the most abundant amino acid in blood plasma and in optimal culture media.

The relative importance of glycolysis and glutaminolysis is dependent on both nutrient and oxygen supply and intracellular demands for energy and metabolites. In cultures of HeLa cells it has been demonstrated that, even when high concentrations of glucose were present, half of the energy needs of the cell was provided by glutaminolysis. Under these culture conditions 80% of the glucose was converted to lactate. Also in other fast growing cells, such as undifferentiated HL60 cells and human hair follicles, only 10% of the total glucose utilized was oxidized to CO_2, while up to 35% of the glutamine uptake was oxidized. At limited glucose levels in the culture medium, in HeLa cells more than 90% of the energy was delivered by glutaminolysis, and all lactate formed was derived from glutamine. Under these conditions, carbohydrate-derived carbons were detectable only in nucleotides, amino acids, and macromolecules like RNA, DNA, phospholipids, proteins, and complex carbohydrates. Obviously, when the supply of glucose is reduced, proliferating cells have to rearrange their glycolytic metabolism in order to maintain intermediates at a sufficient level to allow the important anabolic pathways to continue. It may be clear that these adjustments can only take place if the enzymes controlling the glycolytic flux undergo alterations with regard to their regulatory properties. The molecular correlation concept of Weber and the expression of fetal isozymes in tumors have already indicated the importance of the key enzymes in the metabolism of tumor cells.

Hexokinase, phosphofructokinase, and pyruvate kinase have been recognized as the regulatory enzymes of glycolysis. It is supposed that the special features of their isozymes are responsible for the altered control of glycolysis in tumor cells. Indeed, besides overexpression of these key enzymes in tumor cells, changes in isozyme composition are reported in a series of tumors. For hexokinase both an altered expression of isozymes and an altered subcellular localization have been demonstrated. Increased hexokinase activity and preferential expression of the fetal hexokinase type II have been reported in gliomas and in carcinomas of the uterus and of the thyroid gland. In addition, alterations in hexokinase compartmentation have been observed in rapidly growing hepatomas. There is an increase of the enzyme fraction associated with the outer surface of the mitochondrial membrane. As the bound enzyme is less inhibited by its product glucose 6-phosphate than the cytosolic form and can directly benefit from the ATP produced by the mitochondrial respiration, the presence of this enzyme will allow a higher rate of glucose conversion in tumor cells.

Phosphofructokinase is an enzyme of central importance to the regulation of glycolysis and is subject to multiple control by many allosteric regulators. Positive effectors are fructose 2,6-bisphosphate, fructose 1,6-bisphosphate, and AMP, whereas citrate, phosphoenolpyruvate, and ATP act as negative effectors. Three different subunits are expressed in mammalian tissues (types L, M, and C), which undergo random tetramerization. Studies of various human cancers and cultured cell lines have shown that human phosphofructokinase exhibits comparable changes in subunit composition, with an increase in expression of the L-type. In human gliomas this shift toward L-type phosphofructokinase was accompanied by alterations in the kinetic and regulatory properties of the enzyme. Notable were a decreased sensitivity of phosphofructokinase from gliomas to inhibition by citrate and an increased sensitivity to activation by fructose 2,6-biphosphate. In addition, in gliomas the L-type subunit can be phosphorylated by a cyclic AMP-dependent protein kinase; phosphorylation is not seen in normal human brain. However, the influence of the altered phosphofructokinase isozyme expression in tumors on the rate of glycolysis has yet to be elucidated.

It has been suggested by Eigenbrodt *et al.* that the third glycolytic key enzyme, pyruvate kinase, plays a crucial and double role in the regulation of glycolysis in cancer cells. Expression of the fetal isozyme of pyruvate kinase would represent a mechanism that allows inhibition of the enzyme at low glucose concentrations. This is supposed to block lactate production from glucose and to result in a damming up of the essential glycolytic intermediates. At the same time energy requirements would be met by glutaminolysis. At high glucose concentrations pyruvate kinase is fully reactivated, and its very high activity in tumor cells allows an unhindered glycolytic flux.

III. GENETIC SYSTEM OF PYRUVATE KINASES

Isozymes of pyruvate kinase were first demonstrated in 1965 by Tanaka *et al.* Four distinct forms are recognized in mammalian tissues, which are named L (liver), R (red blood cells), M (muscle), and K (kidney). The M and K isozymes are nowadays usually designated as M1 and M2, respectively. The isozymes are generally isolated as tetrameric proteins ranging between 200 and 250 kDa. Besides the four homotetramers, hybrid isozymes have been demonstrated in many tissues, especially from rat organs. L–M2 hybrids have been found in kidney and intestinal extracts and M1–M2 hybrids in many other tissues.

The dominant isozyme in fetal tissue is type M2 (K), which is progressively replaced by tissue-specific isozymes with special functions during differentiation. In adult organisms type L is present in gluconeogenic tissues: it is predominant in liver and is a minor type in kidney and intestine. The R type is restricted to erythrocytes and hematopoietic tissues. M1 (M) is the main type in differentiated tissues with high glycolytic activity, such as skeletal muscle, heart, and brain. Type M2 is widely distributed in adult tissues. It is a minor isozyme in liver but the major one in kidney, spleen, lung, and leukocytes. Furthermore, the M2 isozyme is expressed in neoplasia and in undifferentiated or proliferating tissues.

Studies on the physicochemical, kinetic, and immunological behavior as well as the amino acid compositions and peptide maps of limited-proteolysis products indicated a relationship between L- and R-type pyruvate kinase on the one hand and between M1- and M2-type pyruvate kinase on the other. Comparing the L-type found in liver with the R-type present in erythrocytes, differences are found with respect to molecular weight, kinetics, ability to be phosphorylated, and electrophoretic behavior. However, the two isozymes have very similar immunological properties. An antiserum raised in rabbits against pure human L-type pyruvate kinase does not discriminate between the liver and the erythrocyte enzyme. Studies on pyruvate kinase isozymes from patients with hereditary erythrocyte pyruvate kinase deficiency, and on mutant mice with low levels of this enzyme in erythrocytes, suggested that the L-type isozyme is encoded by the same gene as the R-type, as the liver isozyme was also affected in these cases. *In vitro* translation of isolated mRNA fractions from liver and erythrocytes demonstrated that two different mRNAs encode for the L- and R-type pyruvate kinases. It was shown that the two types of mRNAs are transcribed from a single L-type pyruvate kinase gene by use of two different, tissue-specific promoters. The human L-type pyruvate kinase gene is mapped to band q21 of chromosome 1.

Structural and immunological studies have suggested that the M1 isozyme of pyruvate kinase has a primary structure very similar, but not identical, to that of the M2 isozyme. The M2 subunit from rat has been reported to be 1000 to 2000 daltons larger than the M1 subunit, and the two isozymes have different isoelectric points. Genetic evidence suggested that the two isozymes are derived from the same gene. The question whether the M1- and M2-type isozymes of pyruvate kinase are synthesized by a common mRNA has been examined by isolating total RNA from rat skeletal muscle (M1-type) and AH-130 Yoshida ascites hepatoma cells (M2-type) and then translating the preparations in a rabbit reticulocyte lysate system. It appeared that the two isozymes were translated from two different mRNAs. A definitive answer was given by the determination of the complete nucleotide sequences for both M1- and M2-type pyruvate kinase from rat by sequencing the cDNAs (complementary DNAs). The derived amino acid sequences turned out to be identical except for one region of 45 residues. It was concluded that alternative RNA splicing of the same primary transcript from the M-type gene produces the M1- and M2-type isozymes of pyruvate kinase.

In summary, two structural genes, the L-type gene (coding for the L and R isozymes) and the M-type gene (coding for the M1 and M2 isozymes), and four different messenger RNAs control the synthesis of pyruvate kinase isozymes. The organization of the pyruvate kinase genes is schematically depicted in Fig. 2.

IV. PYRUVATE KINASE IN HUMAN TUMORS

It is not surprising that malignant cells, which usually exhibit a high rate of glycolysis, possess a high pyruvate kinase activity. In most tumors an increase in

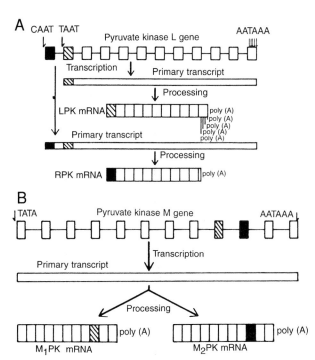

FIGURE 2 Schematic representation of transcription of the pyruvate kinase L and M genes. In the pyruvate kinase type L gene (A), the exons specific for type L and R are indicated by hatched and solid boxes, respectively. In the pyruvate kinase type M gene (B), the exons specific for type M1 and M2 are indicated by hatched and solid boxes, respectively. The common exons are shown by open boxes. CAAT, CAT box; TATA, TATA box; AATAAA, polyadenylation signal; LPK, L-type pyruvate kinase; RPK, R-type pyruvate kinase; M1PK, M1-type pyruvate kinase; M2PK, M2-type pyruvate kinase. From T. Noguchi *et al.* (1986). *J. Biol. Chem.* **261**, 13807, T. Noguchi *et al.* (1987). *J. Biol. Chem.* **262**, 14366.

specific enzyme activity is observed when compared with the corresponding normal tissue. This increase in pyruvate kinase activity tends to correlate with the malignancy of the tumor. In some cases the activity of pyruvate kinase allows one to distinguish between metastatic and nonmetastatic tumor cells. However, tumors residing in tissues that are known to be glycolytically very active, like brain, muscle, and retina, show decreased pyruvate kinase activities.

Besides the elevated pyruvate kinase activity, neoplasia is frequently associated with a change in pyruvate kinase isozyme expression. Pyruvate kinase type M2 is the main isozyme in fetal tissues and is therefore designated as the fetal type or prototype of the pyruvate kinase isozymes. In the late period of gestation, tissue-specific changes in the isozyme pattern occur, the M1-type becoming the major form in skeletal muscle, heart, and brain, and the L-type becoming predominant in liver. The pyruvate kinase isozyme patterns of undifferentiated, highly malignant tumors, regardless of their cell origin, tend to resemble one another and the pattern of fetal tissues more than that of the corresponding normal adult tissues. The isozyme patterns are shifted in favor of the prototype pattern (M2-type) and against the differentiated pattern (L- or M1-type), whereas well- or highly differentiated tumors tend to resemble their cells of origin more than other tumors. This phenomenon has been nicely shown in a series of Morris transplantable hepatomas. Highly differentiated tumors have isozyme patterns not necessarily different from those of normal liver. Well-differentiated tumors show a marked decrease in the activity of the L-type isozyme, whereas poorly differentiated tumors have little L isozyme and show a manyfold increase in M2 isozyme-specific activity.

The preferential expression of pyruvate kinase type M2 has now been demonstrated in tumors of various organs. The phenomenon is observed in tumors of the brain, breast, thyroid gland, and liver, and in cases of retinoblastoma, leiomyosarcoma, and rhabdomyosarcoma. A dramatic shift in pyruvate kinase isozyme expression is found in human neuroectodermal tumors, and this altered isozyme pattern is used as an helpful tool in diagnosis and prognosis of brain tumors.

In fetal brain, both M1 and M2 subunits are synthesized simultaneously. These subunits randomly tetramerize to form the $M1_4$, $M1_3M2$, $M1_2M_2$, $M1M2_3$, and $M2_4$ enzyme molecules. During development of the brain, the synthesis of M2 subunits is obviously repressed and the synthesis of M1 subunits favored. In the newborn, both type $M1_4$ and $M2_4$ are present, but $M1_4$ is already predominant. Adult brain contains mainly $M1_4$ and only minor amounts $M2_4$ and $M2_3M1$, indicating that the M1-type subunit is predominantly expressed.

Meningiomas and malignant gliomas are characterized by the absence of the original $M1_4$ enzyme, and the $M2_4$ enzyme and the hybrid M23M1 are predominant. The isozyme composition of a tissue can easily be assessed electrophoretically, as the isozymes have different electrophoretic mobilities. With this technique it is possible to separate both the $M1_4$ and the $M2_4$ enzymes, as well as intermediate hybrids. In addition, a biochemical assay is available for quick diagnosis. Pyruvate kinase type M2 is strongly and completely inhibited by the amino acid alanine, whereas the activity of type M1 is not affected. The residual enzyme activity of an extract, measured in the presence of alanine, precisely represents the proportion of M1-type subunits in the tissue.

In astrocytomas, oligodendrogliomas, and glioblastomas, which are localized in the cerebral hemispheres of adult patients, the pyruvate kinase isozyme shift from the M1- to M2-type correlates well with histological grading of the tumors. Figure 3 shows the electrophoretic pattern of examples of some representa-tive tumors. Well-differentiated astrocytomas are characterized by the presence of both $M1_4$ and $M2_4$ and the hybrid $M2_3M1$. On the other hand, in highly malignant glioblastomas the isozyme shift is more severe, and only $M2_4$ and $M2_3M1$ are observed. Results of the alanine inhibition assay, performed on tumors with different histological classification, are in agreement with the electrophoresis. Well-differentiated grade I and II astrocytomas exhibit relatively high residual enzyme activities in the presence of alanine (moderate shift toward the M2-type), whereas anaplastic astrocytomas of grades III and IV and also poorly differentiated glioblastomas have low residual activities (severe shift) (Fig. 4).

In gliomas there also exists a correlation between pyruvate kinase isozyme composition and growth rate of the tumor, as expressed in postoperative survival of the patients. The survival in a series of 84 patients after complete or subtotal resection of the tumors is depicted in Fig. 5. The gliomas are subdivided into four groups, according to the residual pyruvate kinase activity in the presence of alanine. The diagram shows

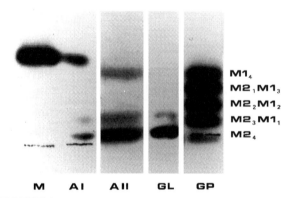

FIGURE 3 Electrophoretic patterns of pyruvate kinase from tumors with different histological classifications and grading. Lane AI, grade I astrocytoma; AII, grade II astrocytoma; GL, glioblastoma. Lanes marked M (muscle) and GP (glandula pinealis) serve as references.

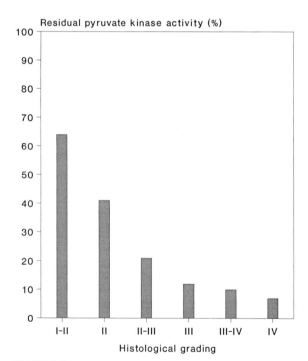

FIGURE 4 Correlation between residual pyruvate kinase activity in the presence of alanine, representing the percentage of pyruvate kinase type M1, and grading of human astrocytomas.

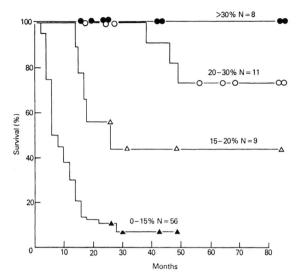

FIGURE 5 Postoperative survival of adult patients with glioma ($n = 84$) related to the residual activity (%) of pyruvate kinase in the presence of alanine. Tumors are divided into four groups according to the residual activity.

a strong positive correlation between the M1/M2 ratio of pyruvate kinase and survival. Thus, in brain tumors the pyruvate kinase isozyme shift appears to have important diagnostic and prognostic value. As the isozyme composition of a tissue specimen can be reliably and rapidly assessed (within 15 minutes) with the alanine inhibition method, this assay has found application in the treatment of human gliomas. The pyruvate kinase isozyme ratio is used for intraoperative grading of hemispheric gliomas of adults and also in the demarcation of the resection of these tumors.

Further refinement in the detection of pyruvate kinase isozyme expression has been achieved by applying isozyme-specific antibodies. Despite the strong structural homology of the isozymes, antibodies discriminating between the M1- and M2-type pyruvate kinases have been produced. These antibodies have proved to be useful for immunohistochemical demonstration of isozyme expression at single cell level. In specimens of brain, monoclonal antibodies against M2-type pyruvate kinase show reactivity with neurons and astrocytes, but not with other types of glial cells such as oligodendrocytes and microglia. In addition, Kupffer cells in liver, connective tissue cells, and vascular smooth muscle cells are M2-type positive, whereas hepatocytes and striated muscle cells in both

skeletal muscle and heart are negative. In contrast to nonmalignant counterparts, strong immunoreactivity was found in a rhabdomyosarcoma, in a carcinoma of the pancreas, and in a neurofibroma. These studies indicate that the antibodies are able to identify the individual cell types where transformation is actually accompanied by an altered pyruvate kinase gene expression. These are the cell types in which the appearance of pyruvate kinase type M2 is expected to function optimally as an oncodevelopmental marker.

V. REGULATION OF PYRUVATE KINASE ACTIVITY

Pyruvate kinases belong to the group of allosteric enzymes. The enzyme activity can be modulated by substrate concentration, various metabolic intermediates, and additionally by phosphorylation. Although the general scheme of regulation for the different isozymes appears to be the same, essential differences, for instance, in substrate affinity, yield four isozymes with individual kinetic characteristics. Their properties are in alignment with the specific metabolic demands of the tissues in which they are expressed.

A. Allosteric Modulation

Tanaka *et al.* were the first to demonstrate that the L-type pyruvate kinase is under allosteric control. The enzyme exhibits cooperativity with respect to phosphoenolpyruvate (PEP) and is activated by fructose 1,6-bisphosphate (FDP), which shifts the kinetics from sigmoidal to hyperbolic. The enzymatic activity of the L-type can be modulated to a great extent. The enzyme is allosterically inhibited by ATP and alanine, the inhibitory effect of which can be counteracted by the addition of FDP, inorganic phosphate (P_i), and glucose 1,6-bisphosphate. The presence of L-type pyruvate kinase in gluconeogenic tissues with their complex carbohydrate metabolism accounts for the extensive regulation of this isozyme. In the liver, the rates of the antagonistic pathways of glycolysis and gluconeogenesis are strictly regulated to maintain blood glucose homeostasis. As a key enzyme, pyruvate kinase accomplishes an essential role in this tuning; the activity of pyruvate kinase type L is modulated by substrate supply, metabolic intermediates, and hormones. Pyruvate kinase of erythrocytes (type R) resembles the L-type but is, unlike the hepatic isozyme, not under hormonal and dietary control.

Pyruvate kinase type M2 shows a slight cooperative interaction between the binding sites for phosphoenolpyruvate. The M2 isozyme is inhibited by a series of amino acids. Activity curves obtained in the presence of the allosteric inhibitor alanine are sigmoidal and resemble the normal activity curves obtained with the L-type enzyme, whereas FDP induces hyperbolic curves. In the absence of effectors, pyruvate kinase type M1 exhibits Michaelis–Menten kinetics with regard to PEP. It has a higher affinity for PEP (K_m 0.08 mM) as compared with pyruvate kinase type M2 (K_m 0.4 mM). The M1-type is inhibited only by phenylalanine, but it can also be restimulated by FDP.

Both the M1 and the M2 isozyme appear to be subject to qualitatively similar modes of allosteric regulation, and these interactions can be described with a simple two-state model of allosterism (as proposed by Monod, Wyman, and Changeux): the enzyme exists in R (active) and T (inactive) states, the distribution of which is governed by an equilibrium. These two states exhibit different affinities for substrate and effectors. In this model the M1 and the M2 isozymes probably have different allosteric constants in the absence of effectors, the M2 isozyme favoring the T form and the M1 isozyme being stabilized in the R form. Consequently, the M1 enzyme shows a hyperbolic saturation curve for PEP while the M2 enzyme shows a sigmoidal curve, resulting in a lower affinity for its substrate.

As mentioned before, the M1- and M2-type isozymes differ only in a region of 45 amino acids. The remaining part of the molecule, including the active sites, are identical. The region of difference was shown to be present in the domain responsible for intersubunit contact, which supports the idea of a different cooperativity between the subunits leading to a different allosteric constant.

B. Phosphorylation

Genetic alterations resulting in either enhanced or diminished turnover and expression of isozymes can be considered as relatively long-term mechanisms that allow sustained or permanent changes in the flux through a metabolic pathway. However, cells require additional short-term regulatory mechanisms to react immediately to external (growth factors, hormones) or internal stimuli (changes in concentrations of ions or metabolites). Besides allosteric modulation, reversible phosphorylation of enzymes and other proteins is a mechanism by which this can be adequately accomplished.

Glucagon activates gluconeogenesis in the liver by increasing the intracellular concentration of cAMP. One of the effects of glucagon administration is a rapid decrease in pyruvate kinase activity, which can be counteracted by insulin. Ljungström et al. were the first to demonstrate that rat liver pyruvate kinase can be phosphorylated by ATP in a reaction catalyzed by a cAMP-dependent protein kinase. The phosphorylation of L-type pyruvate kinase causes important changes in the kinetics of the enzyme: decreased affinity for PEP and increased inhibition by the allosteric inhibitors ATP and alanine. These kinetic modifications are expected to play an important physiological role in the dynamic balance between glycolysis and glyconeogenesis by blocking the pyruvate kinase reaction when gluconeogenesis is the predominant pathway.

Much less is known about the possible contribution of phosphorylation to the regulation of the M1- and M2-type kinases. Phosphorylation of type M1 has never been reported. Phosphorylation of pyruvate kinase type M2 from chicken liver catalyzed by a cAMP-independent protein kinase was initially observed in 1977 by Eigenbrodt et al. and has subsequently been demonstrated in isolated chicken hepatocytes, in rat pancreatic islet cells, in rat medullary thyroid carcinomas, and in human gliomas. Furthermore, transformation of chicken embryo cells by Rous sarcoma virus results in phosphorylation of pyruvate kinase type M2 on a tyrosine residue. However, phosphorylation on tyrosine residues seems to be restricted to cells transformed by the Rous sarcoma virus, as in all other cases only phosphorylations on serine and threonine residues can be detected. Both types of phosphorylation of pyruvate kinase type M2 result in inactivation of the enzyme.

Comparing the phosphorylation of pyruvate kinase types M2 and L, it is remarkable that in both cases phosphorylation can be completely inhibited by fructose, 1,6-biphosphate, a positive effector of both isozymes. However, there are some fundamental differences between M2- and L-type phosphorylation. In contrast to the L-type phosphorylation, the phosphorylation of the M2-type is independent of the presence of cyclic AMP. Furthermore, the phosphorylation site of the L-type (Ser-12 at the N-terminal end of the molecule) is not present in the M2-type, so the latter must be phosphorylated at an entirely other, yet undefined, phosphorylation site.

C. Quaternary Structure

Although pyruvate kinase is generally isolated as a tetrameric protein, monomers and dimers of pyruvate kinase type M2 have been described. The dimer and tetramer forms are interconvertible, and the equilibrium is governed by various metabolites: the dimeric state is stabilized by the amino acids alanine, phenylalanine, and cysteine. An important regulator of the dimer–tetramer interconversion appears to be fructose 1,6-bisphosphate, which stabilizes the enzyme in its tetrameric conformation. Removal of fructose 1,6-bisphosphate from an enzyme preparation *in vitro* results in dissociation of the $M2_4$ enzyme into $M2_2$ dimers, which exhibit a lower affinity for the substrate phosphoenolpyruvate. Catalytically inactive M2-type monomers are also formed. This monomer, and not the tetramer, has been shown to be the major cytosolic binding protein for the thyroid hormone 3,3′,5-triiodo-L-thyronine (T_3). Indeed, the monomeric and dimeric configurations of pyruvate kinase type M2 are stabilized by thyroid hormones. *In vivo*, the formation of T_3-binding monomers is regulated by glucose via fructose 1,6-bisphosphate. Lowering the glucose concentration in the culture medium leads to a rapid increase in the concentration of cellular M2-type monomers and hence in the cytosolic thyroid hormone binding activity. In addition, T_3 seems to be involved in the regulation of the synthesis of the M2 subunits during liver regeneration.

Although pyruvate kinase type M1 remains a stable tetramer even in the absence of fructose 1,6-bisphosphate, the M1-type monomer has also been identified as a thyroid hormone-binding protein. In addition, T_3-binding properties have been proposed for pyruvate kinase type R from human erythrocytes.

VI. DISCUSSION AND CONCLUDING REMARKS

One of the most remarkable enzymological features of malignant tumors is the similarity of some isozyme patterns to those in fetal organs. Pyruvate kinase is one of the enzymes involved in this phenomenon. Pyruvate kinase type M2 is the main isozyme in fetal tissues and is also predominant in neoplastic transformations of many tissues.

The isozyme shift is studied in various human and rat tumors and is well described in human brain tumors. Pyruvate kinase type M1 is the characteristic adult brain isozyme. In neuroectodermal tumors an isozyme shift of pyruvate kinase occurs from the M1-toward the M2-type, which is related to the degree of differentiation and the growth rate of the tumors. This shift may be due not only to true changes in isozyme composition of a homogeneous cell population, but also to alterations in cell populations comprising the tumor. Pyruvate kinase type M2 is the main isozyme in both differentiated astrocytes and astrocytomas. Thus, the prevalence of the M2 isozyme in astrocytomas is likely to be interpreted merely as a proliferation and condensation of cells that originally contain the M2-type. In oligodendrogliomas, on the other hand, expression of the M2 isozyme appears to be associated with tumorigenesis, as in normal oligodendrocytes no M2-type enzyme could be observed.

Little is known about the mechanisms that control this change in pyruvate kinase gene expression, resulting in the induction of the M2 isozyme in tumor cells. Some data suggest that nuclear proteins act as desuppressors of M2 gene expression in hepatomas. It is also interesting that an increased expression of the M2-type is observed histologically in normal brain adjacent to a glioma, since this increase may be due to the effect of a humoral factor derived from the tumor cells.

A probable rationale for the expression of pyruvate kinase type M2 in tumors is that the presence of this particular isozyme endows the tumor cells with selective metabolic advantages enabling them to proliferate. This view is supported by the presence of pyruvate kinase type M2 in nonmalignant cells with pronounced proliferative character, such as fibroblasts, spermatids, and lymphocytes. Indeed, M1- and

M2-type pyruvate kinases have different kinetic properties. The M2 isozyme has a lower affinity for its substrate phosphoenolpyruvate and is more strongly inhibited by amino acids like alanine. The presence of an isozyme with lower affinity for its substrate in cells characterized by a high glycolytic activity may seem paradoxical. However, this enzyme characteristic assures that phosphoenolpyruvate and other glycolytic intermediates upstream of pyruvate kinase are maintained at a higher steady-state level. This accumulation of metabolites provides the cell with precursors for DNA and protein synthesis, while at the same time the net glycolytic flux is not necessarily diminished.

A second property of the M2 isozyme that might benefit the metabolism of the tumor cell is its ability to become phosphorylated. This provides an additional way to quickly modulate the enzyme activity. It has been shown that phosphorylation of pyruvate kinase type M2 results in a decreased substrate affinity and an increased inhibition by allosteric inhibitors. Thus, phosphorylation of the M2 isozyme would further amplify its specific kinetic features. Alternatively, phosphorylation is implicated as a regulator of turnover of several proteins and may either decrease or increase the susceptibility to proteolysis. For pyruvate kinase type L it has been shown that phosphorylation selectively influences protein processing. The importance of proteolytic modification of the M2 isozyme to its regulation remains to be elucidated.

The effects of fructose 1,6-bisphosphate on pyruvate kinase type M2 are threefold: (1) fructose 1,6-bisphosphate is an allosteric activator of the catalytic activity, (2) it induces tetramerization of M2-type subunits, and (3) it inhibits phosphorylation of the enzyme. There is experimental evidence that the latter two effects are linked and that fructose 1,6-bisphosphate prevents phosphorylation of pyruvate kinase type M2 by freezing the enzyme in its tetrameric conformation. Only lowering the concentration of fructose 1,6-bisphosphate would allow the formation of monomers and dimers, thereby permitting phosphorylation of the subunits. Indeed, analysis of a glioma extract with a heterogeneous pyruvate kinase isozyme composition revealed that phosphorylated enzyme molecules are exclusively present in the $M2_2$ dimer fraction. No phosphorylated subunits are found in the monomeric and tetrameric fractions. In the same sample and under identical conditions (in the absence of fructose 1,6-bisphosphate), pyruvate kinase type M1 maintains its tetrameric conformation and is not phosphorylated.

The M1 and M2 isozymes are produced from the same gene by alternative splicing, and the difference in primary structure between the enzymes resides in a region of only 45 amino acids. This region has been shown to be responsible for subunit interaction and does not contain either sequences belonging to catalytic sites or a phosphorylation site. The isozyme-specific region seems to be important for the greater stability of the tetrameric configuration of the M1-type enzyme. The $M1_2M2_2$ hybrid enzyme is also regained as a tetramer in the absence of fructose 1,6-bisphosphate. Obviously, the presence of two M1-type subunits suffices to stabilize the tetrameric molecule. The homology between the M1- and M2-types and the inability of the M1-type to dimerize or to become phosphorylated argue for the proposition that phosphorylation of M2-type pyruvate kinase is allowed after dissociation of the tetramer into its dimers and concomitant conformational changes along the enzyme.

Pyruvate kinase type M2 is the predominant form in all types of malignancies, regardless of the isozyme composition of the cells from which the malignancies are derived. As the M2 isozyme is also predominant or increased in actively proliferating cells and tissues, this isozyme may be important to sustain the proliferative character of tumor cells. Glycolysis is not only a catabolic mechanism for purpose of energy production; it also provides tumor cells with metabolites, which are channeled into various anabolic pathways for the biosynthesis of DNA, proteins, and other macromolecules. Although on average glucose uptake of brain tumors is not significantly different as compared with normal cerebral cortex, there may be qualitative differences in glucose utilization between normal and malignant cells. Tumor cells will have an increased need of glycolytic intermediates to support their biosynthetic processes. Indeed, in proliferating cells the levels of these intermediates were found to be enhanced.

During tumor growth, the blood supply to many tumors becomes insufficient and inadequate, resulting in the development of oxygen-depleted areas in malignancies which coincides with nutrient and energy deprivation. There is ample evidence that the substrate supply and not the metabolic demand of the tumor cells limits the glucose uptake. Thus, tumor cells may be confronted with very low glucose concentrations. Under these conditions the level of fructose 1,6-bisphosphate will be reduced as well. As a consequence, tetrameric pyruvate kinase type M2 will dissociate to form less active dimers which can become phosphorylated. Because of the specific kinetic properties of the M2 isozyme and presumably the additional effects of its phosphorylation, accumulation of intermediates will occur, including fructose 1,6-bisphosphate. The rising fructose 1,6-bisphosphate concentration will cause tetramerization of pyruvate kinase which is accompanied by dephosphorylation and reactivation of the enzyme. One may expect that these regulatory mechanisms of M2-type pyruvate kinase act in concert to maintain the upstream metabolites at a constant and satisfactory level. This implicates that phosphorylation of the enzyme occurs only temporarily and is not a long-term effect.

The expression of pyruvate kinase type M2 in tumors is a good example of shifting isozyme patterns in neoplasia. The presence of this isozyme is supposed to support the characteristic biochemistry of proliferating tumor cells. In tumors residing in tissues that predominantly express M1-type pyruvate kinase, the extent of the appearance of the M2-type isozyme can be exploited for diagnostic purposes. The next goal must be to understand the mechanisms that govern the alterations in isozyme patterns in transformed cells.

See Also the Following Articles

Kinase-Regulated Signal Transduction Pathways • MAP Kinase Modules in Signaling • Protein Kinase Inhibitors

Bibliography

Eigenbrodt, E., Fister, P., and Reinacher, M. (1985). New perspectives on carbohydrate metabolism in tumor cells. *In* "Regulation of Carbohydrate Metabolism" (R. Beitner, ed.), Vol. 2, p. 141. CRC Press, Boca Raton, Florida.

Eigenbrodt, E., Reinacher, M., Scheefers-Borchel, U., Scheefers, H., and Friis, R. (1992). Double role for pyruvate kinase type M2 in the expansion of phosphometabolite pools found in tumor cells. *Crit. Rev. Oncog.* **3,** 297.

Imamura, K., Noguchi, T., and Tanaka, T. (1986). Regulation of isozyme patterns of pyruvate kinase in normal and neoplastic tissues. *In* "Markers of Human Neuroectodermal Tumors" (G. E. J. Staal and C. W. M. van Veelen, eds.), p. 191, CRC Press, Boca Raton, Florida.

Medina, M. A., Sánchez-Jiménez, F., Márquez, J., Quesada, A. R., and Núñez de Castro, I. (1992). Relevance of glutamine metabolism to tumor cell growth. *Mol. Cell Biochem.* **113,** 1.

Newsholme, E. A., and Board, M. (1991). Application of metabolic-control logic to fuel utilization and its significance in tumor cells. *Adv. Enzyme Regul.* **31,** 225.

Staal, G. E. J., and Rijksen, G. (1990). Pyruvate kinase in selected human tumors. *In* "Biochemical and Molecular Aspects of Selected Cancers" (T. G. Pretlow and T. P. Pretlow, eds.), Vol. 1, p. 313. Academic Press, Orlando, Florida.

Van Veelen, C. W. M., and Staal, G. E. J. (1986). Pyruvate kinase and human brain tumors. *In* "Markers of Human Neuroectodermal Tumors" (G. E. J. Staal and C. W. M. van Veelen, eds.), p. 63. CRC Press, Boca Raton, Florida.

ISBN 0-12-227558-6